List of Elements with Their Symbols and Atom[ic]

Element	Symbol	Atomic Number	Atomic Mass	Element	Symbol	Atomic Number	Atomic Mass
Actinium	Ac	89	227.03[a]	Molybdenum	Mo	42	
Aluminum	Al	13	26.98	Neodymium	Nd	60	
Americium	Am	95	243.06[a]	Neon	Ne	10	
Antimony	Sb	51	121.76	Neptunium	Np	93	
Argon	Ar	18	39.95	Nickel	Ni	28	
Arsenic	As	33	74.92	Niobium	Nb	41	
Astatine	At	85	209.99[a]	Nitrogen	N	7	14.
Barium	Ba	56	137.33	Nobelium	No	102	259.1
Berkelium	Bk	97	247.07[a]	Osmium	Os	76	190.23
Beryllium	Be	4	9.012	Oxygen	O	8	16.00
Bismuth	Bi	83	208.98	Palladium	Pd	46	106.42
Bohrium	Bh	107	264.12[a]	Phosphorus	P	15	30.97
Boron	B	5	10.81	Platinum	Pt	78	195.08
Bromine	Br	35	79.90	Plutonium	Pu	94	244.06[a]
Cadmium	Cd	48	112.41	Polonium	Po	84	208.98[a]
Calcium	Ca	20	40.08	Potassium	K	19	39.10
Californium	Cf	98	251.08[a]	Praseodymium	Pr	59	140.91
Carbon	C	6	12.01	Promethium	Pm	61	145[a]
Cerium	Ce	58	140.12	Protactinium	Pa	91	231.04
Cesium	Cs	55	132.91	Radium	Ra	88	226.03[a]
Chlorine	Cl	17	35.45	Radon	Rn	86	222.02[a]
Chromium	Cr	24	52.00	Rhenium	Re	75	186.21
Cobalt	Co	27	58.93	Rhodium	Rh	45	102.91
Copper	Cu	29	63.55	Roentgenium	Rg	111	272[a]
Curium	Cm	96	247.07[a]	Rubidium	Rb	37	85.47
Darmstadtium	Ds	110	271[a]	Ruthenium	Ru	44	101.07
Dubnium	Db	105	262.11[a]	Rutherfordium	Rf	104	261.11[a]
Dysprosium	Dy	66	162.50	Samarium	Sm	62	150.36
Einsteinium	Es	99	252.08[a]	Scandium	Sc	21	44.96
Erbium	Er	68	167.26	Seaborgium	Sg	106	266.12[a]
Europium	Eu	63	151.96	Selenium	Se	34	78.96
Fermium	Fm	100	257.10[a]	Silicon	Si	14	28.09
Fluorine	F	9	19.00	Silver	Ag	47	107.87
Francium	Fr	87	223.02[a]	Sodium	Na	11	22.99
Gadolinium	Gd	64	157.25	Strontium	Sr	38	87.62
Gallium	Ga	31	69.72	Sulfur	S	16	32.07
Germanium	Ge	32	72.64	Tantalum	Ta	73	180.95
Gold	Au	79	196.97	Technetium	Tc	43	98[a]
Hafnium	Hf	72	178.49	Tellurium	Te	52	127.60
Hassium	Hs	108	269.13[a]	Terbium	Tb	65	158.93
Helium	He	2	4.003	Thallium	Tl	81	204.38
Holmium	Ho	67	164.93	Thorium	Th	90	232.04
Hydrogen	H	1	1.008	Thulium	Tm	69	168.93
Indium	In	49	114.82	Tin	Sn	50	118.71
Iodine	I	53	126.90	Titanium	Ti	22	47.87
Iridium	Ir	77	192.22	Tungsten	W	74	183.84
Iron	Fe	26	55.85	Uranium	U	92	238.03
Krypton	Kr	36	83.80	Vanadium	V	23	50.94
Lanthanum	La	57	138.91	Xenon	Xe	54	131.293
Lawrencium	Lr	103	262.11[a]	Ytterbium	Yb	70	173.05
Lead	Pb	82	207.2	Yttrium	Y	39	88.91
Lithium	Li	3	6.941	Zinc	Zn	30	65.38
Lutetium	Lu	71	174.97	Zirconium	Zr	40	91.22
Magnesium	Mg	12	24.31	*[b]		112	277[a]
Manganese	Mn	25	54.94	*[b]		113	284[a]
Meitnerium	Mt	109	268.14[a]	*[b]		114	289[a]
Mendelevium	Md	101	258.10[a]	*[b]		115	288[a]
Mercury	Hg	80	200.59	*[b]		116	292[a]

[a]Mass of longest-lived or most important isotope.
[b]The names of these elements have not yet been decided.

General College Chemistry
Chemistry 400

A Custom Edition for Cosumnes River College

Taken from:
Chemistry: A Molecular Approach, Second Edition
by Nivaldo J. Tro

Selected Solutions Manual
to accompany *Chemistry: A Molecular Approach,* Second Edition
by Kathleen Thrush Shaginaw and Mary Beth Kramer

Cover Art: Courtesy of Photodisc/Getty Images.

Taken from:

Chemistry: A Molecular Approach, Second Edition
by Nivaldo J. Tro
Copyright © 2011, 2008 by Pearson Education, Inc.
Published by Prentice Hall
Upper Saddle River, New Jersey 07458

Selected Solutions Manual to accompany *Chemistry: A Molecular Approach*, Second Edition
by Kathleen Thrush Shaginaw and Mary Beth Kramer
Copyright © 2011, 2008 by Pearson Education, Inc.
Published by Prentice Hall

Pearson Learning Solutions, 501 Boylston Street, Suite 900, Boston, MA 02116
A Pearson Education Company
www.pearsoned.com

Printed in the United States of America

2 3 4 5 6 7 8 9 10 V092 16 15 14 13 12 11

000200010270778414

SW

ISBN 10: 1-256-31742-X
ISBN 13: 978-1-256-31742-5

5 Gases **178**

6 Thermochemistry **230**

7   The Quantum-Mechanical Model of the Atom   276

8   Periodic Properties of the Elements   314

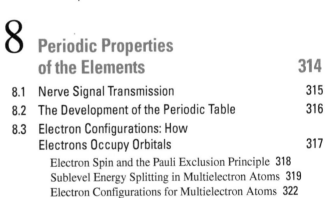

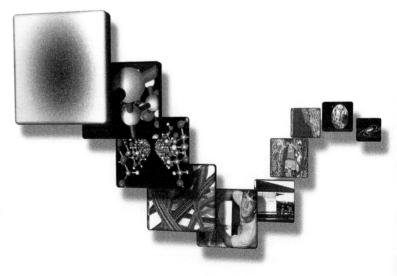

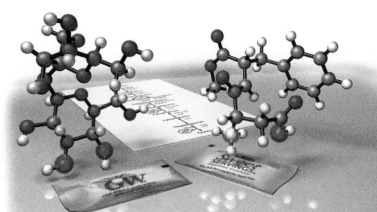

Preface

To the Student

As you begin this course, I invite you to think about your reasons for enrolling in it. Why are you taking general chemistry? More generally, why are you pursuing a college education? If you are like most college students taking general chemistry, part of your answer is probably that this course is required for your major and that you are pursuing a college education so you can get a good job some day. While these are good reasons, I would like to suggest a better one. I think the primary reason for your education is to prepare you to *live a good life*. You should understand chemistry—not for what it can *get* you—but for what it can *do* to you. Understanding chemistry, I believe, is an important source of happiness and fulfillment. Let me explain.

Understanding chemistry helps you to live life to its fullest for two basic reasons. The first is *intrinsic*: through an understanding of chemistry, you gain a powerful appreciation for just how rich and extraordinary the world really is. The second reason is *extrinsic*: understanding chemistry makes you a more informed citizen—it allows you to engage with many of the issues of our day. In other words, understanding chemistry makes *you* a deeper and richer person and makes your country and the world a better place to live. These reasons have been the foundation of education from the very beginnings of civilization.

How does chemistry help prepare you for a rich life and conscientious citizenship? Let me explain with two examples. My first one comes from the very first page of Chapter 1 of this book. There, I ask the following question: What is the most important idea in all of scientific knowledge? My answer to that question is this: **the behavior of matter is determined by the properties of molecules and atoms**. That simple statement is the reason I love chemistry. We humans have been able to study the substances that compose the world around us and explain their behavior by reference to particles so small that they can hardly be imagined. If you have never realized the remarkable sensitivity of the world we *can* see to the world we *cannot*, you have missed out on a fundamental truth about our universe. To have never encountered this truth is like never having read a play by Shakespeare or seen a sculpture by Michelangelo—or, for that matter, like never having discovered that the world is round. It robs you of an amazing and unforgettable experience of the world and the human ability to understand it.

My second example demonstrates how science literacy helps you to be a better citizen. Although I am largely sympathetic to the environmental movement, a lack of science literacy within some sectors of that movement, and the resulting antienvironmental backlash, creates confusion that impedes real progress and opens the door to what could be misinformed policies. For example, I have heard conservative pundits say that volcanoes emit more carbon dioxide—the most significant greenhouse gas—than does petroleum combustion. I have also heard a liberal environmentalist say that we have to stop using hairspray because it is causing holes in the ozone layer that will lead to global warming. Well, the claim about volcanoes emitting more carbon dioxide than petroleum combustion can be refuted by the basic tools you will learn to use in Chapter 4 of this book. We can easily show that volcanoes emit only 1/50th as much carbon dioxide as petroleum combustion. As for hairspray depleting the ozone layer and thereby leading to global warming: the chlorofluorocarbons that deplete ozone have been banned from hairspray since 1978, and ozone depletion has nothing to do with global warming anyway. People with special interests or axes to grind can conveniently distort the truth before an ill-informed public, which is why we all need to be knowledgeable.

So this is why I think you should take this course. Not just to satisfy the requirement for your major, and not just to get a good job some day, but to help you to lead a fuller life and to make the world a little better for everyone. I wish you the best as you embark on the journey to understand the world around you at the molecular level. The rewards are well worth the effort.

To the Professor

First and foremost, thanks to all of you who adopted this book in its first edition. You helped to make this book the most successful first edition general chemistry book in many years. I am grateful beyond words. Second, I have listened carefully to your feedback on the first edition. The changes you see in the second edition are the direct result of your input, as well as my own experience in using the book in my general chemistry courses. If you have acted as a reviewer, or have contacted me directly, you are likely to see your suggestions reflected in the changes I have made. Thirdly, revising the first edition has been incredibly satisfying for me. When writing the first edition, I could never see the book as a whole—now, I can. That global vision has allowed me to fine-tune the coverage to maximize the clarity and optimize the sequence of the presentation. My hope is that the second edition is clearer, cleaner, and crisper than the first edition.

In spite of the changes I just mentioned, the goal of the book remains the same: *to present a rigorous and accessible treatment of general chemistry in the context of relevance.* Teaching general chemistry would be much easier if all of our students had exactly the same level of preparation and ability. But alas, that is not the case. Even though I teach at a relatively selective institution, my courses are populated with students with a range of backgrounds and abilities in chemistry. The challenge of successful teaching, in my opinion, is therefore figuring out how to instruct and challenge the best students while not losing those with lesser backgrounds and abilities. My strategy has always been to set the bar relatively high, while at the same time providing the motivation and support necessary to reach the high bar. That is exactly the philosophy of this book. We do not have to compromise away rigor in order

to make chemistry accessible to our students. In this book, I have worked hard to combine rigor with accessibility—to create a book that does not dilute the content, yet can be used and understood by any student willing to put in the necessary effort.

Chemistry: A Molecular Approach is first and foremost a *student-oriented book.* My main goal is to motivate students and get them to achieve at the highest possible level. As we all know, many students take general chemistry because it is a requirement; they do not see the connection between chemistry and their lives or their intended careers. *Chemistry: A Molecular Approach* strives to make those connections consistently and effectively. Unlike other books, which often teach chemistry as something that happens only in the laboratory or in industry, this book teaches chemistry in the context of relevance. It shows students *why* chemistry is important to them, to their future careers, and to their world.

Chemistry: A Molecular Approach is secondly a *pedagogically driven book.* In seeking to develop problem-solving skills, a consistent approach (Sort, Strategize, Solve, and Check) is applied, usually in a two- or three-column format. In the two-column format, the left column shows the student how to analyze the problem and devise a solution strategy. It also lists the steps of the solution, explaining the rationale for each one, while the right column shows the implementation of each step. In the three-column format, the left column outlines the general procedure for solving an important category of problems that is then applied to two side-by-side examples. This strategy allows students to see both the general pattern and the slightly different ways in which the procedure may be applied in differing contexts. The aim is to help students understand both the *concept of the problem* (through the formulation of an explicit conceptual plan for each problem) and the *solution to the problem.*

Chemistry: A Molecular Approach is thirdly a *visual book.* Wherever possible, images are used to deepen the student's insight into chemistry. In developing chemical principles, multipart images help to show the connection between everyday processes visible to the unaided eye and what atoms and molecules are actually doing. Many of these images have three parts: macroscopic, molecular, and symbolic. This combination helps students to see the relationships between the formulas they write down on paper (symbolic), the world they see around them (macroscopic), and the atoms and molecules that compose that world (molecular). In addition, most figures are designed to teach rather than just to illustrate. They are rich with annotations and labels intended to help the student grasp the most important processes and the principles that underlie them. The resulting images are rich with information, but also uncommonly clear and quickly understood.

Chemistry: A Molecular Approach is fourthly a *"big picture" book.* At the beginning of each chapter, a short paragraph helps students to see the key relationships between the different topics they are learning. Through focused and concise narrative, I strive to make the basic ideas of every chapter clear to the student. Interim summaries are provided at selected spots in the narrative, making it easier to grasp (and review) the main points of important discussions. And to make sure that students never lose sight of the forest for the trees, each chapter includes

several *Conceptual Connections,* which ask them to think about concepts and solve problems without doing any math. I want students to learn the concepts, not just plug numbers into equations to churn out the right answer.

Chemistry: A Molecular Approach is lastly a book that delivers the depth of coverage faculty want. We do not have to cut corners and water down the material in order to get our students interested. We simply have to meet them where they are, challenge them to the highest level of achievement, and then support them with enough pedagogy to allow them to succeed.

I hope that this book supports you in your vocation of teaching students chemistry. I am increasingly convinced of the importance of our task. Please feel free to email me with any questions or comments about the book.

Nivaldo J. Tro
tro@westmont.edu

What's New in This Edition?

The book has been extensively revised, and contains more small changes than can be detailed here. I have detailed the most significant changes to the book and its supplements below.

- I have added approximately 250 new end-of-chapter problems, most of these in the cumulative and challenge categories. As a result, the book now has about 20% more cumulative problems and about 50% more challenge problems. I have also added eight new in-chapter conceptual connection questions designed to reinforce conceptual understanding.

- I have worked with designers at Pearson to create a new design that increases readability, clarity, and visual appeal. You will find the text itself easier to read, even though the new font does not take up additional space. You will also find the two- and three-column in-text examples easier to navigate and work through. I think the result is cleaner, crisper presentation of the material.

- In Chapter 18 (Electrochemistry), I have changed the way I present the calculation of cell potentials from $E°_{cell} = E°_{oxidation} + E°_{reduction}$ to $E°_{cell} = E°_{cathode} - E°_{anode}$, where $E°_{oxidation}$ is $E°_{cathode}$ and $E°_{reduction}$ is simply $-E°_{anode}$. Although the two methods are numerically and mathematically equivalent, several of my reviewers and adopters have convinced me that the second method is conceptually superior because the driving force of an electrochemical cell really is a *difference*, not a sum. As an analogy, consider skiing down a mountain and calculating the vertical feet that you have descended. You naturally would take the *difference* between your starting elevation and your final elevation. You would *not* take the sum of the starting elevation plus the negative of your final elevation. Both ways give the same answer, but the difference method is a more conceptually accurate way to think of the problem.

- I have added a section on thermal energy transfer to Chapter 6 (Thermochemistry). The addition of this material (in Section 6.4), as well as the corresponding new example and conceptual connection, gives students a better foundation for understanding calorimetry.

- I have moved coverage of Coulomb's law from Chapter 9 (Chemical Bonding I: Lewis Theory) to Chapter 8 (Periodic Properties of the Elements). The earlier introduction of Coulomb's law in Section 8.3 allows me to better explain key concepts in Chapter 8, including penetration, shielding, sublevel energy splitting in multielectron atoms, and effective nuclear charge.
- I have reorganized Chapter 12 (solutions) so that all the colligative properties are now covered in one section (12.6) entitled Colligative Properties: Vapor Pressure Lowering, Freezing Point Depression, Boiling Point Elevation, and Osmotic Pressure. A separate section (12.7) covers the colligative properties of strong electrolyte solutions. The new organization groups conceptually similar concepts together and makes the chapter progress more logically.
- I have added a new section to Chapter 17 (Free Energy and Thermodynamics) that better describes the concepts of microstates and macrostates. This addition to Section 17.3 helps lay the foundation for a better understanding of the concept of entropy.
- I have replaced the chapter opening sections for Chapter 5 (gases) and Chapter 6 (thermochemistry) with examples that are more student-accessible and relevant.
- I have worked with Pearson and the solutions manual authors to create an improved solutions manual that is easier to use.
- The MasteringChemistry® team has greatly increased the number of end-of-chapter problems that are randomizable. The new algorithmic feature can now be applied to problems other than just the numeric ones.

Supplements

For the Instructor

MasteringChemistry®
(http://www.masteringchemistry.com)   MasteringChemistry® is the best adaptive-learning online homework and tutorial system. Instructors can create online assignments for their students by choosing from a wide range of items, including end-of-chapter problems and research-enhanced tutorials. Assignments are automatically graded with up-to-date diagnostic information, helping instructors pinpoint where students struggle either individually or as a class as a whole.

Instructor Resource DVD (0-321-66749-2)   This DVD provides an integrated collection of resources designed to help you make efficient and effective use of your time. It features four pre-built PowerPoint™ presentations. The first presentation contains all the images/figures/tables from the text embedded within the PowerPoint slides, while the second includes a complete modifiable lecture outline. The final two presentations contain worked "in-chapter" sample exercises and questions to be used with Classroom Response Systems. This DVD also contains movies and animations, as well as the TestGen version of the Test Bank, which allows you to create and tailor exams to your needs.

Solutions Manual (0-321-66796-4)   Prepared by MaryBeth Kramer of the University of Delaware and Kathleen Thrush Shaginaw, this manual contains step-by-step solutions to all

complete, end-of-chapter exercises. The Solutions Manual to accompany the second edition has been extensively revised. All problems have been accuracy checked and the design has been upgraded to improve clarity and ease of use. With instructor permission, this manual may be made available to students.

Instructor Resource Manual (0-321-66787-5)   Organized by chapter, this useful guide includes objectives, lecture outlines, references to figures and solved problems, as well as teaching tips.

Printed Test Bank (0-321-66786-7)   Prepared by Christine Hermann of Radford University. The printed test bank contains more than 2000 multiple choice, true/false, and short-answer questions. The second edition also contains more than 500 algorithmic questions.

Transparency Acetates (0-321-66748-4)   This set of transparencies has been chosen specifically to focus on the illustrations that provide a visual perspective of the key principles.

Blackboard® and WebCT®   All test questions are available formatted for either Blackboard or WebCT.

For the Student

MasteringChemistry® (http://www.masteringchemistry.com)
MasteringChemistry® provides you with two learning systems: an extensive self-study area with an interactive eBook and the most widely used chemistry homework and tutorial system (if your instructor chooses to make online assignments part of your course).

Pearson eText: The integration of Pearson eText within MasteringChemistry® gives students, with new books, easy access to the electronic text when they are logged into MasteringChemistry. Pearson eText pages look exactly like the printed text, offering powerful new functionality for students and instructors. Users can create notes, highlight text in different colors, create bookmarks, zoom, view in single-page or two-page view, etc.

Selected Solutions Manual (0-321-66754-9)   Prepared by MaryBeth Kramer of the University of Delaware and Kathleen Thrush Shaginaw, this manual for students contains complete, step-by-step solutions to selected odd-numbered end-of-chapter problems. The Selected Solutions Manual to accompany the second edition has been extensively revised. All problems have been accuracy checked and the design has been upgraded to improve clarity and ease of use.

Study Guide (0-321-66788-3)   Prepared by Jennifer Shanoski of Merritt College. This Study Guide was written specifically to assist students using the second edition of *Chemistry: A Molecular Approach*. It presents the major concept, theories, and applications discussed in the text in a comprehensive and accessible manner for students. It contains learning objectives, chapter summaries, and outlines, as well as examples, self test, and concept questions.

Laboratory Manual (0-321-66785-9)   Prepared by John B. Vincent and Erica Livingston, both of the University of Alabama. This manual contains twenty-eight experiments with a focus on real-world applications. Each experiment contains a

set of pre-laboratory questions, an introduction, a step-by-step procedure (including safety information), and a report section featuring post-laboratory questions. Additional features include a section on laboratory safety rules, an overview on general techniques and equipment, and a detailed tutorial on graphing data in Excel.

Acknowledgments

The book you hold in your hands bears my name on the cover, but I am really only one member of a large team that carefully crafted the first edition and now the second edition of this book over several years. Most importantly, I thank my new editor on this edition, Dan Kaveney. Dan and I have become co-workers and friends. We share a drive and vision that refuses to settle for anything but the clearest and best presentation of the material. Thank you, Dan, for your experience, wisdom, focus, support, and enthusiasm. I am so grateful. Also new to this edition is my developmental editor Erin Mulligan. Erin is an excellent wordsmith, clear thinker (and fellow foodie). Thanks, Erin, for helping me to stay in the active voice, for reminding me when I have forgotten to define terms, and for some really good recipes. I am also indebted to Jennifer Hart, the project editor for this book. Jennifer's attention to detail and help in time of need have gotten me through the tough times. Thanks, Jennifer.

A significant factor in the success of the first edition of this book was MasteringChemistry®, and I owe the entire MasteringChemistry® team a debt of gratitude. In particular I would like to thank Brian Buckley, who has been a tireless advocate of Mastering Chemistry and my book. Thanks Brian for all you have done to make this project a success.

I am also incredibly grateful to the chemistry editor in chief, Nicole Folchetti. Nicole and I have become good friends over the years, and I am grateful for her unrelenting support of my work. Thanks, Nicole, for all you have done for me (and for the two bottles of Seasmoke Pinot Noir—wow!). I continue to be inspired by and grateful to Paul Corey. Paul is a man of incredible energy and vision—he has been an inspiration to me. When I first met Paul, he told me to dream big, and then he provided the resources I needed to make those dreams come true. Thanks, Paul.

New to the team is Erin Gardner, and although we have worked together for only a short while, I am already impressed by her energy in marketing this book. I continue to owe a special word of thanks to Glenn and Meg Turner of Burrston House, ideal collaborators whose contributions to the first edition of the book were extremely important and much appreciated, as well as Fran Falk and Kristen Wallerius who commissioned reviews from my colleagues. Quade and Emiko Paul, who make my ideas come alive with their art, have been with us from the beginning, and I owe a special debt of gratitude to them. I am also grateful to Laura Gardner for her creativity and hard work in crafting the design of this text; to Francesca Monaco, Shari Toron, and Gina Cheselka, whose skill and diligence gave this book its physical existence; and to Connie Long who managed the extensive art program. Finally, I would like to thank my copy editor, Michael Rossa, for his dedication and professionalism, Donna Young for her detailed proofreading, and Clare Maxwell for her exemplary photo research. The team at Prentice Hall is a first-class operation—this text has benefited immeasurably from their talents and hard work.

I acknowledge the help of my colleagues Allan Nishimura, David Marten, Stephen Contakes, and Mako Masuno who have supported me in my department while I worked on this book. I am also grateful to Gayle Beebe, the President of Westmont College, who has allowed me the time and space to work on my books. Thank you, Gayle, for allowing me to pursue my gifts and my vision. I am also grateful to those who have supported me personally. First on that list is my wife, Ann. Her patience and love for me are beyond description, and without her, this book would never have been written. I am also indebted to my children, Michael, Ali, Kyle, and Kaden, whose smiling faces and love of life always inspire me. I come from a large Cuban family whose closeness and support most people would envy. Thanks to my parents, Nivaldo and Sara; my siblings, Sarita, Mary, and Jorge; my siblings-in-law, Jeff, Nachy, Karen, and John; my nephews and nieces, Germain, Danny, Lisette, Sara, and Kenny. These are the people with whom I celebrate life.

I would like to thank all of the general chemistry students who have been in my classes throughout my 20 years as a professor at Westmont College. You have taught me much about teaching that is now in this book. I am especially grateful to Zachary Conley who put in many hours proofreading my manuscript, working problems, and organizing art codes and appendices. Zack, you are extremely intelligent and diligent, and I thank you for your help. I would also like to express my appreciation to Mary Jones, Tammy Tong, and Ryan Fields who helped in the development of the manuscript.

Lastly, I am indebted to the many reviewers, listed on the following pages, whose ideas are imbedded throughout this book. They have corrected me, inspired me, and sharpened my thinking on how best to teach this subject we call chemistry. I deeply appreciate their commitment to this project. I am particularly grateful to Bob Boikess for his important contributions to the book. Thanks also to Frank Lambert for his review of the entropy sections in the first edition of the book, and to Diane K. Smith for her review of and input on the electrochemistry chapter. Last but by no means least, I would like to thank Nancy Lee for her suggestions on the origin of elements box, and Paul Brandt, Greg Owen, and Louis J. Kirschenbaum for their help in reviewing page proofs.

Reviewers

Michael R. Adams, *Xavier University of Louisiana*
Patricia G. Amateis, *Virginia Tech*
Margaret R. Asirvatham, *University of Colorado*
Paul Badger, *Robert Morris University*
Monica H. Baloga, *Florida Institute of Technology*
Rebecca Barlag, *Ohio University*
Mufeed M. Basti, *North Carolina Agricultural & Technological State University*
Amy E. Beilstein, *Centre College*
Maria Benavides, *University of Houston, Downtown*
Kyle A. Beran, *University of Texas of the Permian Basin*
Christine V. Bilicki, *Pasadena City College*
Silas C. Blackstock, *The University of Alabama*
Robert E. Blake, *Texas Tech University*
Angela E. Boerger, *Loyola University*
Robert S. Boikess, *Rutgers University*
Paul Brandt, *North Central College*
Michelle M. Brooks, *College of Charleston*
Joseph H. Bularzik, *Purdue University, Calumet*
Cindy M. Burkhardt, *Radford University*
Andrew E. Burns, *Kent State University, Stark Campus*
Kim C. Calvo, *University of Akron*
Stephen C. Carlson, *Lansing Community College*

David A. Carter, *Angelo State University*
Eric G. Chesloff, *Villanova University*
William M. Cleaver, *University of Vermont*
Charles T. Cox, Jr., *Georgia Institute of Technology*
J. Ricky Cox, *Murray State University*
Samuel R. Cron, *Arkansas State*
Darwin B. Dahl, *Western Kentucky University*
Robert F. Dias, *Old Dominion University*
Daniel S. Domin, *Tennessee State University*
Alan D. Earhart, *Southeast Community College*
Amina K. El-Ashmawy, *Collin County Community College*
Joseph P. Ellison, *United States Military Academy, West Point*
Joseph M. Eridon, *Albuquerque TVI*
Deborah B. Exton, *University of Oregon*
William A. Faber, *Grand Rapids Community College*
Maria C. Fermin-Ennis, *Gordon College*
Jan Florian, *Loyola University*
Candice E. Fulton, *Midwestern State*
Carlos D. Garcia, *University of Texas, San Antonio*
Eric S. Goll, *Brookdale Community College*
Robert A. Gossage, *Acadia University*
Pierre Y. Goueth, *Santa Monica College*
Thomas J. Greenbowe, *Iowa State*
Jason A. Halfen, *University of Wisconsin, Eau Claire*
Michael D. Hampton, *University of Central Florida*
Lois Hansen-Polcar, *Cuyahoga Community College West*
Monte L. Helm, *Fort Lewis College*
David E. Henderson, *Trinity College*
Susan K. Henderson, *Quinnipiac University*
Peter M. Hierl, *University of Kansas*
Angela Hoffman, *University of Portland*
Todd A. Hopkins, *Butler University*
Byron E. Howell, *Tyler Junior College*
Ralph Isovitsch, *Xavier University of Louisiana*
Kenneth C. Janda, *University of California, Irvine*
Jason A. Kautz, *University of Nebraska, Lincoln*
Catherine A. Keenan, *Chaffey College*
Steven W. Keller, *University of Missouri, Columbia*
Resa Kelly, *San Jose State University*
Chulsung Kim, *Georgia Gwinnett College*
Louis J. Kirschenbaum, *University of Rhode Island*
Bette Kreuz, *University of Michigan, Dearborn*
Tim Krieder
Sergiy Kryatov, *Tufts University*
Richard H. Langley, *Stephen F. Austin State University*
Clifford B. Lemaster, *Boise State University*
Christopher Lovallo, *Mount Royal College*
Eric Malina, *University of Nebraska, Lincoln*
Benjamin R. Martin, *Texas State*
Lydia J. Martinez-Rivera, *University of Texas, San Antonio*
Marcus T. McEllistrem, *University of Wisconsin, Eau Claire*
Danny G. McGuire, *Cameron University*
Charles W. McLaughlin, *University of Nebraska, Lincoln*
Curt L. McLendon, *Saddleback College*
Robert C. McWilliams, *United States Military Academy*
David H. Metcalf, *University of Virginia*
Ray Mohseni, *East Tennessee State University*
Elisabeth A. Morlino, *The University of the Science, Philadelphia*
James E. Murphy, *Santa Monica College*
Maria C. Nagan, *Truman State University*
Edward J. Neth, *University of Connecticut*
Kenneth S. Overway, *Bates College*
Greg Owens, *University of Utah*
Gerard Parkin, *Columbia University*
Yasmin Patell, *Kansas State University*
Tom Pentecost, *Grand Valley State University*
Glenn A. Petrie, *Central Missouri State*
Norbert J. Pienta, *University of Iowa*
Louis H. Pignolet, *University of Minnesota*
Valerie Reeves, *University of New Brunswick*
Dawn J. Richardson, *Colin College*
Thomas G. Richmond, *University of Utah*
Dana L. Richter-Egger, *University of Nebraska*
Jason Ritchie, *The University of Mississippi*
Christopher P. Roy, *Duke University*
A. Timothy Royappa, *University of West Florida*
Stephen P. Ruis, *American River College*
Alan E. Sadurski, *Ohio Northern University*
Thomas W. Schleich, *University of California, Santa Cruz*

Rod Schoonover, *CA Polytechnic State University*
Tom Selegue, *Pima Community College, West*
Anju H. Sharma, *Stevens Institute of Technology*
Sherril A. Soman, *Grand Valley State University*
Michael S. Sommer, *University of Wyoming*
Jie S. Song, *University of Michigan, Flint*
Mary Kay Sorenson, *University of Wisconsin, Milwaukee*
Stacy E. Sparks, *University of Texas, Austin*
William H. Steel, *York College of Pennsylvania*
Vinodhkumar Subramaniam, *East Carolina University*
Jerry Suits, *University of Northern Colorado*
Tamar Y. Susskind, *Oakland Community College*
Ryan Sweeder, *Michigan State University*
Dennis Taylor, *Clemson University*
Jacquelyn Thomas, *Southwestern College*
Kathleen Thrush Shaginaw, *Villanova University*
Lydia Tien, *Monroe Community College*
David Livingstone Toppen, *California State University Northridge*
Marcy Towns, *Purdue University*
Harold Trimm, *Broome Community College*
Susan Varkey, *Mount Royal College*
Ramaiyer Venkatraman, *Jackson State University*
John B. Vincent, *University of Alabama, Tuscaloosa*
Kent S. Voelkner, *Lake Superior College*
Sheryl K. Wallace, *South Plains College*
Wayne E. Wesolowski, *University of Arizona*
Sarah E. West, *Notre Dame University*
Kurt J. Winkelmann, *Florida Institute of Technology*
Troy D. Wood, *University of Buffalo*
Servet M. Yatin, *Quincy College*
Kazushige Yokoyama, *SUNY Geneseo*

Focus Group Participants

We would like to thank the following professors for contributing their valuable time to meet with the author and the publishing team in order to provide a meaningful perspective on the most important challenges they face in teaching general chemistry and give us insight into creating a new general chemistry text that successfully responds to those challenges.

Focus Group 1

Michael R. Abraham, *University of Oklahoma*
Steven W. Keller, *University of Missouri, Columbia*
Roy A. Lacey, *State University of New York, Stony Brook*
Norbert J. Pienta, *University of Iowa*
Cathrine E. Reck, *Indiana University*
Reva A. Savkar, *Northern Virginia Community College*

Focus Group 2

Amina K. El-Ashmawy, *Collin County Community College*
Steven W. Keller, *University of Missouri, Columbia*
Joseph L. March, *University of Alabama, Birmingham*
Norbert J. Pienta, *University of Iowa*

Focus Group 3

James A. Armstrong, *City College of San Francisco*
Roberto A. Bogomolni, *University of California, Santa Cruz*
Kate Deline, *College of San Mateo*
Greg M. Jorgensen, *American River College*
Dianne Meador, *American River College*
Heino Nitsche, *University of California at Berkeley*
Thomas W. Schleich, *University of California, Santa Cruz*

Focus Group 4

Ramesh D. Arasasingham, *University of California, Irvine*
Raymond F. Glienna, *Glendale Community College*
Pierre Y. Goueth, *Santa Monica College*
Catherine A. Keenan, *Chaffey College*
Ellen Kime-Hunt, *Riverside Community College, Riverside Campus*
David P. Licata, *Coastline Community College*
Curtis L. McLendon, *Saddleback College*
John A. Milligan, *Los Angeles Valley College*

Focus Group 5

Eric S. Goll, *Brookdale Community College*
Kamal Ismail, *CUNY, Bronx Community College*
Sharon K. Kapica, *County College of Morris*
Richard Rosso, *St. John's University*
Steven Rowley, *Middlesex County College*
David M. Sarno, *CUNY, Queensborough Community College*
Donald L. Siegel, *Rutgers University, New Brunswick*
Servet M. Yatin, *Quincy College*

Focus Group 6

William Eck, *University of Wisconsin, Marshfield/Wood County*
Richard W. Frazee, *Rowan University*
Barbara A. Gage, *Prince George's Community College*
John A. W. Harkless, *Howard University*
Patrick M. Lloyd, *CUNY, Kingsborough Community College*
Boon H. Loo, *Towson University*
Elisabeth A. Morlino, *The University of the Science, Philadelphia*
Benjamin E. Rusiloski, *Delaware Valley College*
Louise S. Sowers, *Richard Stockton College of New Jersey*
William H. Steel, *York College of Pennsylvania*
Galina G. Talanova, *Howard University*
Kathleen Thrush Shaginaw, *Villanova University*

Focus Group 7

Stephen C. Carlson, *Lansing Community College*
Darwin B. Dahl, *Western Kentucky University*
Robert J. Eierman, *University of Wisconsin, Eau Claire*
William A. Faber, *Grand Rapids Community College*
Jason A. Halfen, *University of Wisconsin, Eau Claire*
Todd A. Hopkins, *Butler University*
Michael E. Lipschutz, *Purdue University*
Jack F. McKenna, *St. Cloud State University*
Claire A. Tessier, *University of Akron*

Focus Group 8

Charles E. Carraher, *Florida Atlantic University*
Jerome E. Haky, *Florida Atlantic University*
Paul I. Higgs, *Barry University*
Moheb Ishak, *St. Petersburg College, St. Petersburg*
Peter J. Krieger, *Palm Beach Community College, Lake Worth*
Jeanette C. Madea, *Broward Community College, North*
Alice J. Monroe, *St. Petersburg College, Clearwater*
Mary L. Sohn, *Florida Institute of Technology*

Focus Group 9

Silas C. Blackstock, *University of Alabama*
Kenneth Capps, *Central Florida Community College*
Ralph C. Dougherty, *Florida State University*
W. Tandy Grubbs, *Stetson University*
Norris W. Hoffman, *University of South Alabama*
Tony Holland, *Wallace Community College*
Paul I. Higgs, *Barry University*
James L. Mack, *Fort Valley State University*
Karen Sanchez, *Florida Community College, Jacksonville*
Richard E. Sykora, *University of South Alabama*
Gary L. Wood, *Valdosta State University*

Focus Group 10

Kenneth Caswell, *University of South Florida*
Mohammed Daoudi, *University of Central Florida*
Stephanie Dillon, *Florida State University*
Simon Garrett, *California State University, Northridge*
Jason Kautz, *University of Nebraska, Lincoln*
David Metcalf, *University of Virginia*
Pedro Patino, *University of Central Florida*
Jeremy Perotti, *Nova Southeastern University*
Uma Swamy, *Florida International University*
Robert Craig Taylor, *Oakland University*
John Vincent, *University of Alabama*

Student Focus Groups

We are very grateful to the students who gave part of their day to share with the chemistry team their experience in using textbooks and their ideas on how to make a general chemistry text a more valuable reference.

Bryan Aldea, *Brookdale Community College*
Corinthia Andres, *The University of the Science, Philadelphia*
Hadara Biala, *Brookdale Community College*
Eric Bowes, *Villanova University*
Adrian Danemayer, *Drexel University*
Daniel Fritz, *Middlesex County College*
Olga Ginsburg, *Rutgers University*
Kira Gordin, *The University of the Science, Philadelphia*
Geoffrey Haas, *Villanova University*
Hadi Dharma Halim, *Middlesex County College*
Heather Hartman, *Bucks County Community College*
Stephen A. Horvath, *Rutgers University*
Mark Howell, *Villanova University*
Gene Iucci, *Rutgers University*
Adrian Kochan, *Villanova University*
Jeffrey D. Laszczyk Jr., *The University of the Science, Philadelphia*
Allison Lucci, *Drexel University*
Mallory B. McDonnell, *Villanova University*
Brian McLaughlin, *Brookdale Community College*
Michael McVann, *Villanova University*
Stacy L. Molnar, *Bucks County Community College*
Jenna Munnelly, *Villanova University*
Lauren Papa, *Rutgers University*
Ankur Patel, *Drexel University*
Janaka P. Peiris, *Middlesex County College*
Ann Mary Sage, *Brookdale Community College*
Salvatore Sansone, *Bucks County Community College*
Michael Scarneo, *Drexel University*
Puja Shahi, *Drexel University*
Rebeccah G. Steinberg, *Brookdale Community College*
Alyssa J. Urick, *The University of the Science, Philadelphia*
Padma Vemuri, *Villanova University*
Joni Vitale, *Brookdale Community College*
Kyle Wright, *Rowan Uninversity*
Joseph L. Yobb, *Bucks County Community College*

Reviewer Conference Participants: Group 1

Mufeed M. Basti, *North Carolina Agricultural & Technical State University*
Robert S. Boikess, *Rutgers University*
Jason A. Kautz, *University of Nebraska, Lincoln*
Curtis L. McLendon, *Saddleback College*
Norbert J. Pienta, *University of Iowa*
Alan E. Sadurski, *Ohio Northern University*
Jie S. Song, *University of Michigan, Flint*
John B. Vincent, *University of Alabama, Tuscaloosa*

Reviewer Conference Participants: Group 2

Titus Albu, *Tennessee Tech University*
Donovan Dixon, *University of Central Florida*
Jason Kautz, *University of Nebraska at Lincoln*
Bill McLaughlin, *Montana State University*
Heino Nitsche, *University of CA Berkeley*
Greg Owens, *University of Utah*
Pedro Patino, *University of Central Florida*
Joel Russell, *Oakland University*
Rod Schoonover, *CA Polytechnic State University*
Apryll Stalcup, *University of Cincinnati*
Dennis Taylor, *Clemson University*

How this text will help you
LEARN CHEMISTRY

N iva Tro's true passion is teaching chemistry. Every day he finds new and innovative ways of presenting chemical concepts to his students.

Chemistry: A Molecular Approach, **Second Edition** was written from Niva's classroom experience to address the challenges his students face. Niva's writing is known for a rigorous, yet accessible treatment of general chemistry—always in the context of its relevance to everyday life.

Chemistry is presented visually through macroscopic, molecular, and symbolic representations, allowing you to see the connections among the formulas (symbolic), the world around you (macroscopic), and the atoms and molecules that make up the world (molecular).

Your book includes the premier online homework and assessment tool that will truly deepen your understanding of chemistry and enhance your success in this course.

Mastering CHEMISTRY®
Make Learning Part of the Grade®
www.masteringchemistry.com

Highlights of this text

Relevance and Writing Style
Chemistry becomes both meaningful and understandable.

(Pages xxvi-xxvii)

Pioneering Artwork
Superlative images help you grasp concepts.

(Pages xxviii-xxix)

Problem-Solving
Proven strategies foster your problem-solving skills.

(Pages xxx-xxxi)

End-of-Chapter Material
Helpful learning aids reinforce concepts.

(Pages xxxii-xxxiii)

MasteringChemistry
Improve your understanding of chemistry and class performance with this online homework and assessment tool.

(Pages xxxiv-xxxv)

Supplements
A wide selection of support materials is available with this text.

(Page xxxvi)

Relevant examples and clear language

Chemistry is relevant to every process occurring around you, at every second. Niva Tro helps you understand this connection by weaving specific, vivid examples throughout the text that tell the story of chemistry. Every chapter begins with a brief story that illustrates how chemistry is relevant to all people, at every moment.

◄···Are you interested in knowing how nerve cells transmit signals?

See Chapter 8 to learn why periodic properties are essential to understanding this process.

What about global··· ► climate change?

Start by studying the material presented in Chapter 4 that explains how to use chemistry to understand the genesis of the problem.

These examples make the material more accessible by contextualizing the chemistry and grounding it in the world you live in.

connect chemistry to
YOUR WORLD

Student Interest

Throughout the narrative and in special boxed features, interesting descriptions of chemistry in the modern world demonstrate its importance.

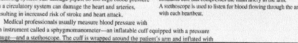

CHEMISTRY AND MEDICINE Blood Pressure

Blood pressure is the force within arteries that drives the circulation of blood throughout the body. Blood pressure in the body is analogous to water pressure in a plumbing system. Just as water pressure pushes water through the pipes to faucets and fixtures throughout a house, blood pressure pushes blood to muscles and other tissues throughout the body. However, unlike the water pressure in a plumbing system—which is typically nearly constant—our blood pressure varies with each heartbeat. When the heart muscle contracts, blood pressure increases; between contractions it decreases. Systolic blood pressure is the peak pressure during a contraction, and diastolic blood pressure is the lowest pressure between contractions. Just as excessively high water pressure in a plumbing system can damage pipes, so too high blood pressure in a circulatory system can damage the heart and arteries, resulting in increased risk of stroke and heart attack.

Medical professionals usually measure blood pressure with an instrument called a sphygmomanometer—an inflatable cuff equipped with a pressure gauge—and a stethoscope. The cuff is wrapped around the patient's arm and inflated with

▲ A doctor or a nurse typically measures blood pressure with an inflatable cuff that compresses the main artery in the arm. A stethoscope is used to listen for blood flowing through the artery with each heartbeat.

CHEMISTRY AND THE ENVIRONMENT Renewable Energy

Because of their finite supply and environmental impacts, fossil fuels will not be our major source of energy in the future. What will replace them? Although the answer is not clear, several alternative energy technologies are beginning to emerge. Unlike fossil fuels, these technologies are renewable, and we can use them indefinitely.

Our planet's greatest source of renewable energy is the sun. If we could capture and harness just a small fraction of the total sunlight falling on Earth, we could meet our energy needs several times over. The main problem with solar energy, however, is diffuseness—the sun's energy falls over an enormous area. How do we concentrate and store it? In California, some of the state's electricity is generated by parabolic troughs, solar power towers, and dish/engines.

These devices use reflective surfaces to focus the sun's energy and produce enough heat to generate electricity. Although the direct cost of generating electricity this way is higher than using fossil fuels, the benefits to the environment are obvious. In addition, with time, the costs are expected to fall.

Another way to capture the sun's energy is in chemical bonds. For example, solar energy could be used to drive the decomposition of water:

$$H_2O(l) \longrightarrow H_2(g) + \tfrac{1}{2} O_2(g) \quad \Delta H^\circ_{rxn} = +285.8 \text{ kJ}$$

The hydrogen gas produced could be stored until needed to provide energy by re-forming water in the reverse reaction:

$$H_2(g) + \tfrac{1}{2} O_2(g) \longrightarrow H_2O(l) \quad \Delta H^\circ_{rxn} = -285.8 \text{ kJ}$$

This reaction can be carried out in an electrochemical device called a fuel cell. In a fuel cell, hydrogen and oxygen gas combine to form water and produce electricity. In 2005, General Motors demonstrated the Sequel: a fuel cell SUV with a 300-mile range and quick acceleration (0–60 mph in 10 seconds). According to the company, the Sequel is quicker, easier to handle, easier to build, and safer than gasoline-powered vehicles, and its only emission is water vapor. In 2008, Honda's FCX Clarity, a four-passenger fuel cell vehicle with a 280-mile range, became selectively available for lease in Southern California. The main challenge for these vehicles at

the moment is refueling. The FCX requires hydrogen fuel, which can only be obtained at a small number of refueling stations. Other automakers have similar prototype models in development.

▲ Honda made its 2009 FCX Clarity, a fuel cell vehicle that runs on hydrogen gas and produces only water as exhaust, selectively available for lease in Southern California in the summer of 2008.

Other renewable energy sources are wind power and hydroelectric power. Hydroelectric power plants—which generate approximately 8% of U.S. electricity—harness the gravitational potential energy of water held behind a dam. Water is released at a controlled rate. As it falls, it acquires kinetic energy that is used to spin a turbine, generating electricity. Wind power plants—which produced about 2.3% of California's electricity in 2007—consist of hundreds of turbines that are spun by the wind to generate electricity. Both of these technologies are cost competitive with fossil fuels, have no emissions, and are completely renewable.

Our energy future will probably involve a combination of these technologies and some new ones, combined with a focus on greater efficiency and conservation. One thing, however, is clear—the future of fossil fuels is limited.

▲ Wind turbines such as these generate about 2.3% of California's electricity.

▼ The sun's energy, concentrated by reflective surfaces in various arrangements, can produce enough heat to generate electricity.

Parabolic troughs

Solar power tower

Dish/engine

▲ **Chemistry and Medicine** boxes show applications relevant to biomedical and health-related topics.

◄ **Chemistry and the Environment** boxes relate chapter topics to current environmental and societal issues.

▼ **Chemistry In Your Day** boxes demonstrate the importance of chemistry in everyday situations.

CHEMISTRY IN YOUR DAY Bleached Blonde

Have you ever bleached your hair? Most home kits for hair bleaching contain hydrogen peroxide (H_2O_2), an excellent oxidizing agent. When applied to hair, hydrogen peroxide oxidizes melanin, the dark pigment that gives hair its color. Once melanin is oxidized, it no longer imparts a dark color to hair, leaving the hair with the familiar bleached look. Hydrogen peroxide also oxidizes other components of hair. For example, protein molecules in hair contain —SH groups called thiols. Hydrogen peroxide oxidizes these thiol groups to sulfonic acid groups, —SO_3H. The oxidation of thiol groups to sulfonic acid groups causes changes in the proteins that compose hair, making the hair more brittle and more likely to tangle. Consequently, people with heavily bleached hair generally use conditioners, which contain compounds that form thin, lubricating coatings on individual hair shafts. These coatings prevent tangling and make hair softer and more manageable.

Question
The following is a reaction of hydrogen peroxide with an alkene:

$$H_2O_2 + C_2H_4 \longrightarrow C_2H_4O + H_2O$$

Can you see why this reaction is a redox reaction? Can you identify the oxidizing and reducing agents?

▶ The bleaching of hair involves a redox reaction in which melanin—the main pigment in hair—is oxidized.

Pioneering artwork makes CONCEPTS CLEAR

Annotated Molecular Art

Many illustrations have three parts:

- a macroscopic image (what you can see with your eyes)
- a molecular image (what the molecules are doing)
- a symbolic representation (how chemists represent the process with symbols and equations)

The goal is for you to connect what you see and experience (the macroscopic world) with the molecules responsible for that world, and with the way chemists represent those molecules. After all, this is what chemistry is all about.

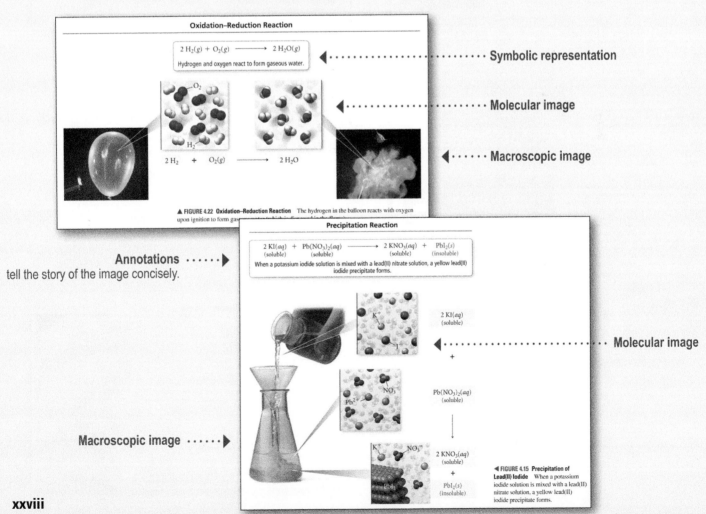

Oxidation–Reduction Reaction

$2\,H_2(g) + O_2(g) \longrightarrow 2\,H_2O(g)$
Hydrogen and oxygen react to form gaseous water.

$2\,H_2 \quad + \quad O_2(g) \quad \longrightarrow \quad 2\,H_2O$

Symbolic representation

Molecular image

Macroscopic image

▲ FIGURE 4.22 **Oxidation–Reduction Reaction** The hydrogen in the balloon reacts with oxygen upon ignition to form gas...

Annotations tell the story of the image concisely.

Precipitation Reaction

$2\,KI(aq) + Pb(NO_3)_2(aq) \longrightarrow 2\,KNO_3(aq) + PbI_2(s)$
(soluble)   (soluble)   (soluble)   (insoluble)
When a potassium iodide solution is mixed with a lead(II) nitrate solution, a yellow lead(II) iodide precipitate forms.

$2\,KI(aq)$ (soluble)

$Pb(NO_3)_2(aq)$ (soluble)

$2\,KNO_3(aq)$ (soluble)

$PbI_2(s)$ (insoluble)

Molecular image

Macroscopic image

◀ FIGURE 4.15 **Precipitation of Lead(II) Iodide** When a potassium iodide solution is mixed with a lead(II) nitrate solution, a yellow lead(II) iodide precipitate forms.

Multipart Images

Multipart Images make connections among graphical representations, molecular processes, and the macroscopic world.

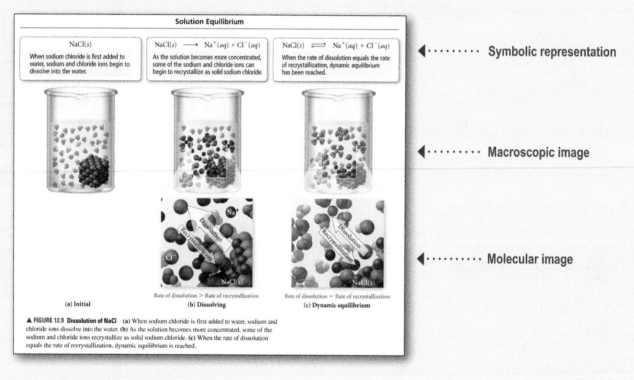

Solution Equilibrium

NaCl(s)

When sodium chloride is first added to water, sodium and chloride ions begin to dissolve into the water.

$NaCl(s) \longrightarrow Na^+(aq) + Cl^-(aq)$

As the solution becomes more concentrated, some of the sodium and chloride ions can begin to recrystallize as solid sodium chloride.

$NaCl(s) \rightleftharpoons Na^+(aq) + Cl^-(aq)$

When the rate of dissolution equals the rate of recrystallization, dynamic equilibrium has been reached.

◄ ·········· **Symbolic representation**

◄ ·········· **Macroscopic image**

◄ ·········· **Molecular image**

(a) Initial

Rate of dissolution > Rate of recrystallization
(b) Dissolving

Rate of dissolution = Rate of recrystallization
(c) Dynamic equilibrium

▲ FIGURE 12.9 **Dissolution of NaCl** (a) When sodium chloride is first added to water, sodium and chloride ions dissolve into the water. (b) As the solution becomes more concentrated, some of the sodium and chloride ions recrystallize as solid sodium chloride. (c) When the rate of dissolution equals the rate of recrystallization, dynamic equilibrium is reached.

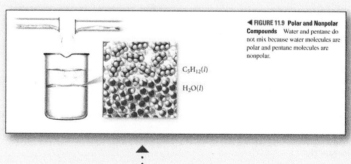

◄ FIGURE 11.9 **Polar and Nonpolar Compounds** Water and pentane do not mix because water molecules are polar and pentane molecules are nonpolar.

$C_5H_{12}(l)$

$H_2O(l)$

⋮ **Graphical representation**

Consistent strategies help you
SOLVE PROBLEMS

Two-Column Example

A consistent approach to problem solving is used throughout the book.

Units Raised to a Power

When building conversion factors for units raised to a power, remember to raise both the number and the unit to the power. For example, to convert from in^2 to cm^2, we construct the conversion factor as follows:

$$2.54 \text{ cm} = 1 \text{ in}$$
$$(2.54 \text{ cm})^2 = (1 \text{ in})^2$$
$$(2.54)^2 \text{ cm}^2 = 1^2 \text{ in}^2$$
$$6.45 \text{ cm}^2 = 1 \text{ in}^2$$
$$\frac{6.45 \text{ cm}^2}{1 \text{ in}^2} = 1$$

The following example shows how to use conversion factors involving units raised to a power.

> The **left column** explains how the problem is solved.

> The **right column** shows the implementation of the steps explained in the left column.

EXAMPLE 1.9 Unit Conversions Involving Units Raised to a Power

Calculate the displacement (the total volume of the cylinders through which the pistons move) of a 5.70-L automobile engine in cubic inches.

> A **four-part structure** ("Sort, Strategize, Solve, Check") provides you with a framework for analyzing and solving problems.

SORT Sort the information in the problem into *Given* and *Find*.

GIVEN: 5.70 L
FIND: in^3

STRATEGIZE Write a conceptual plan. Begin with the given information and devise a path to the information that you are asked to find. Notice that for cubic units, you must cube the conversion factors.

CONCEPTUAL PLAN ◄

$$L \xrightarrow{\frac{1 \text{ mL}}{10^{-3} \text{ L}}} mL \xrightarrow{\frac{1 \text{ cm}^3}{1 \text{ mL}}} cm^3 \xrightarrow{\frac{(1 \text{ in})^3}{(2.54 \text{ cm})^3}} in^3$$

RELATIONSHIPS USED
$1 \text{ mL} = 10^{-3} \text{ L}$
$1 \text{ mL} = 1 \text{ cm}^3$
$2.54 \text{ cm} = 1 \text{ in}$
(These conversion factors are from Tables 1.2 and 1.3.)

> Many problems are solved with a **conceptual plan** that provides a visual outline of the steps leading from the given information to the solution.

SOLVE Follow the conceptual plan to solve the problem. Round the answer to three significant figures to reflect the three significant figures in the least precisely known quantity (5.70 L). These conversion factors are all exact and therefore do not limit the number of significant figures.

SOLUTION

$$5.70 \text{ L} \times \frac{1 \text{ mL}}{10^{-3} \text{ L}} \times \frac{1 \text{ cm}^3}{1 \text{ mL}} \times \frac{(1 \text{ in})^3}{(2.54 \text{ cm})^3} = 347.835 \text{ in}^3$$
$$= 348 \text{ in}^3$$

CHECK The units of the answer are correct and the magnitude makes sense. The unit cubic inches is smaller than liters, so the volume in cubic inches should be larger than the volume in liters.

FOR PRACTICE 1.9 ◄
How many cubic centimeters are there in 2.11 yd^3?

FOR MORE PRACTICE 1.9
A vineyard has 145 acres of Chardonnay grapes. A particular soil supplement requires 5.50 grams for every square meter of vineyard. How many kilograms of the soil supplement are required for the entire vineyard? ($1 \text{ km}^2 = 247$ acres)

> Every worked Example is followed by a "For Practice" problem that you can try to solve on your own. Answers to "For Practice" Problems are in Appendix IV.

Three-Column Example

Problem-Solving Procedure Boxes for important categories of problems enable you to see how the same reasoning applies to different problems.

The **general procedure** is shown in the left column.

PROCEDURE FOR... **Writing Equations for Precipitation Reactions**	**EXAMPLE 4.10** **Writing Equations for Precipitation Reactions** Write an equation for the precipitation reaction that occurs (if any) when solutions of potassium carbonate and nickel(II) chloride are mixed.	**EXAMPLE 4.11** **Writing Equations for Precipitation Reactions** Write an equation for the precipitation reaction that occurs (if any) when solutions of sodium nitrate and lithium sulfate are mixed.
1. Write the formulas of the two compounds being mixed as reactants in a chemical equation.	$K_2CO_3(aq) + NiCl_2(aq) \longrightarrow$	$NaNO_3(aq) + Li_2SO_4(aq) \longrightarrow$
2. Below the equation, write the formulas of the products that could form from the reactants. Obtain these by combining the cation from each reactant with the anion from the other. Make sure to write correct formulas for these ionic compounds, as described in Section 3.5.	$K_2CO_3(aq) + NiCl_2(aq) \longrightarrow$ Possible products KCl NiCO$_3$	$NaNO_3(aq) + Li_2SO_4(aq) \longrightarrow$ Possible products LiNO$_3$ Na$_2$SO$_4$
3. Use the solubility rules to determine whether any of the possible products are insoluble.	KCl is soluble. (Compounds containing Cl$^-$ are usually soluble and K$^+$ is not an exception.) NiCO$_3$ is insoluble. (Compounds containing CO$_3{}^{2-}$ are usually insoluble and Ni^{2+} is not an exception.)	LiNO$_3$ is soluble. (Compounds containing NO$_3{}^-$ are soluble and Li$^+$ is not an exception.) Na$_2$SO$_4$ is soluble. (Compounds containing SO$_4{}^{2-}$ are generally soluble and Na$^+$ is not an exception.)
4. If all of the possible products are soluble, there will be no precipitate. Write NO REACTION after the arrow.	Since this example has an insoluble product, we proceed to the next step.	Since this example has no insoluble product, there is no reaction. $NaNO_3(aq) + Li_2SO_4(aq) \longrightarrow$ NO REACTION
5. If any of the possible products are insoluble, write their formulas as the products of the reaction using (s) to indicate solid. Write any soluble products with (aq) to indicate aqueous.	$K_2CO_3(aq) + NiCl_2(aq) \longrightarrow$ $NiCO_3(s) + KCl(aq)$	
6. Balance the equation. Remember to adjust only coefficients here, not subscripts.	$K_2CO_3(aq) + NiCl_2(aq) \longrightarrow$ $NiCO_3(s) + 2KCl(aq)$	
	FOR PRACTICE 4.10 Write an equation for the precipitation reaction that occurs (if any) when solutions of ammonium chloride and iron(III) nitrate are mixed.	**FOR PRACTICE 4.11** Write an equation for the precipitation reaction that occurs (if any) when solutions of sodium hydroxide and copper(II) bromide are mixed.

Two worked examples, side by side, make it easy to see how differences are handled.

Every worked Example is followed by one or more "For Practice" problems that you can try to solve on your own. Answers to "For Practice" Problems are in Appendix IV.

4.7 Representing Aqueous Reactions: Molecular, Ionic, and Complete Ionic Equations

Consider the following equation for a precipitation reaction:

$$Pb(NO_3)_2 \, (aq) + 2\, KCl(aq) \longrightarrow PbCl_2 \, (s) + 2\, KNO_3(aq)$$

This equation is a **molecular equation**, an equation showing the complete neutral formulas for each compound in the reaction as if they existed as molecules. However, in actual

End-of-chapter
MATERIAL AIDS STUDY AND TEST PREP

End-of-Chapter Review Section

The end-of-chapter review section helps you study the chapter's concepts and skills in a systematic way that is ideal for test preparation. Approximately 250 new end-of-chapter problems have been added, most of these in the cumulative and challenge categories. As a result, the book now has about 20% more cumulative problems and about 50% more challenge problems.

Key Concepts

Pressure (5.1, 5.2)

Gas pressure is the force per unit area that results from gas particles colliding with the surfaces around them. Pressure is measured in a number of units including mmHg, torr, Pa, psi, in Hg, and atm.

The Simple Gas Laws (5.3)

The simple gas laws express relationships between pairs of variables when the other variables are held constant. Boyle's law states that the volume of a gas is inversely proportional to its pressure. Charles's law states that the volume of a gas is directly proportional to its temperature. Avogadro's law states that the volume of a gas is directly proportional to the amount (in moles).

The Ideal Gas Law and Its Applications (5.4, 5.5)

The ideal gas law, $PV = nRT$, gives the relationship among all four gas variables and contains the simple gas laws within it. We can use the ideal gas law to find one of the four variables given the other three. We can use it to calculate the molar volume of an ideal gas, which is 22.4 L at STP, and to calculate the density and molar mass of a gas.

Mixtures of Gases and Partial Pressures (5.6)

In a mixture of gases, each gas acts independently of the others so that any overall property of the mixture is the sum of the properties of the individual components. The pressure of any individual component is its partial pressure.

Gas Stoichiometry (5.7)

In reactions involving gaseous reactants and products, quantities are often reported in volumes at specified pressures and temperatures. We can convert these quantities to amounts (in moles) using the ideal gas law. Then we can use the stoichiometric coefficients from the balanced equation to determine the stoichiometric amounts of other reactants or products. The general form for these types of calculations is often as follows: volume A → amount A (in moles) → amount B (in moles) → quantity of B (in desired units). In cases where the reaction is carried out at STP, the molar volume at STP (22.4 L ≈ 1 mol) can be used to convert between volume in liters and amount in moles.

Kinetic Molecular Theory and Its Applications (5.8, 5.9)

Kinetic molecular theory is a quantitative model for gases. The theory has three main assumptions: (1) the gas particles are negligibly small; (2) the average kinetic energy of a gas particle is proportional to the temperature in kelvins; and (3) the collision of one gas particle with another is completely elastic (the particles do not stick together). The gas laws all follow from the kinetic molecular theory.

We can also use the theory to derive the expression for the root mean square velocity of gas particles. This velocity is inversely proportional to the molar mass of the gas, and therefore—at a given temperature—smaller gas particles are (on average) moving more quickly than larger ones. The kinetic molecular theory also allows us to predict the mean free path of a gas particle (the distance it travels between collisions) and relative rates of diffusion or effusion.

Real Gases (5.10)

Real gases differ from ideal gases to the extent that they do not always fit the assumptions of kinetic molecular theory. These assumptions tend to break down at high pressures, where the volume is higher than predicted for an ideal gas because the particles are no longer negligibly small compared to the space between them. The assumptions also break down at low temperatures where the pressure is lower than predicted because the attraction between molecules combined with low kinetic energies causes partially inelastic collisions. The Van der Waals equation predicts gas properties under nonideal conditions.

The Atmosphere (5.11)

Our atmosphere is primarily nitrogen (78%) and oxygen (21%). Common gaseous pollutants in our atmosphere include sulfur dioxide, carbon monoxide, ozone, and nitrogen dioxide. These pollutants affect exposed organs, such as the eyes and lungs, and force our cardiovascular system to work harder. Other pollutants include chlorofluorocarbons that contribute to the depletion of upper atmospheric ozone, which results in higher levels of ultraviolet radiation and an increase in our risk of skin cancer and cataracts.

▲ The **Key Concepts** section summarizes the chapter's most important ideas.

Key Terms

Section 5.1
pressure (179)

Section 5.2
millimeter of mercury (mmHg) (181)
barometer (181)
torr (181)
atmosphere (atm) (181)
pascal (Pa) (181)
manometer (182)

Section 5.3
Boyle's law (184)

Charles's law (187)
Avogadro's law (189)

Section 5.4
ideal gas law (191)
ideal gas (191)
ideal gas constant (191)

Section 5.5
molar volume (193)
standard temperature and pressure (STP) (193)

Section 5.6
partial pressure (P_n) (197)
Dalton's law of partial pressures (197)
mole fraction (χ_a) (197)
hypoxia (199)
oxygen toxicity (199)
nitrogen narcosis (199)
vapor pressure (201)

Section 5.8
kinetic molecular theory (206)

Section 5.9
mean free path (212)
diffusion (212)
effusion (212)
Graham's law of effusion (213)

Section 5.10
van der Waals equation (216)

▲ **Key Terms** list all of the chapter's boldfaced terms, organized by section in order of appearance, with page references. Definitions are found in the Glossary.

Key Equations and Relationships

Relationship between Pressure (P), Force (F), and Area (A) (5.2)

$$P = \frac{F}{A}$$

Boyle's Law: Relationship between Pressure (P) and Volume (V) (5.3)

$$V \propto \frac{1}{P}$$
$$P_1 V_1 = P_2 V_2$$

Charles's Law: Relationship between Volume (V) and Temperature (T) (5.3)

$$V \propto T \quad (\text{in K})$$
$$\frac{V_1}{T_1} = \frac{V_2}{T_2}$$

Avogadro's Law: Relationship between Volume (V) and Amount in Moles (n) (5.3)

$$V \propto n$$
$$\frac{V_1}{n_1} = \frac{V_2}{n_2}$$

Ideal Gas Law: Relationship between Volume (V), Pressure (P), Temperature (T), and Amount (n) (5.4)

$$PV = nRT$$

Dalton's Law: Relationship between Partial Pressures (P_a) in Mixture of Gases and Total Pressure (P_{total}) (5.6)

$$P_{total} = P_a + P_b + P_c + \cdots$$
$$P_a = \frac{n_a RT}{V} \quad P_b = \frac{n_b RT}{V} \quad P_c = \frac{n_c RT}{V}$$

▲ The **Key Equations and Relationships** section lists each of the key equations and important quantitative relationships from the chapter.

Key Skills

Converting between Pressure Units (5.2)
• Example 5.1 • For Practice 5.1 • For More Practice 5.1 • Exercises 29–32

Relating Volume and Pressure: Boyle's Law (5.3)
• Example 5.2 • For Practice 5.2 • Exercises 35, 36

Relating Volume and Temperature: Charles's Law (5.3)
• Example 5.3 • For Practice 5.3 • Exercises 37, 38

Relating Volume and Moles: Avogadro's Law (5.3)
• Example 5.4 • For Practice 5.4 • Exercises 39, 40

Determining P, V, n, or T using the Ideal Gas Law (5.4)
• Examples 5.5, 5.6 • For Practice 5.5, 5.6 • For More Practice 5.6 • Exercises 41–50, 55, 56

Relating the Density of a Gas to Its Molar Mass (5.5)
• Example 5.7 • For Practice 5.7 • For More Practice 5.7 • Exercises 59, 60

Calculating the Molar Mass of a Gas with the Ideal Gas Law (5.5)
• Example 5.8 • For Practice 5.8 • Exercises 61–64

Calculating Total Pressure, Partial Pressures, and Mole Fractions of Gases in a Mixture (5.6)
• Examples 5.9, 5.10, 5.11 • For Practice 5.9, 5.10, 5.11 • Exercises 65, 66, 69, 71, 72, 74

Relating the Amounts of Reactants and Products in Gaseous Reactions: Stoichiometry (5.7)
• Examples 5.12, 5.13 • For Practice 5.12, 5.13 • For More Practice 5.12 • Exercises 75–81

Calculating the Root Mean Square Velocity of a Gas (5.8)
• Example 5.14 • For Practice 5.14 • Exercises 85, 86

Calculating the Effusion Rate or the Ratio of Effusion Rates of Two Gases (5.9)
• Example 5.15 • For Practice 5.15 • Exercises 87–90

▲ The **Key Skills** section lists the major types of problems that you should be able to solve, with the chapter examples that show the techniques needed—along with the For Practice problems and end-of-chapter exercises that offer practice in those skills.

End-of-Chapter Review Exercises

Answers to odd-numbered questions in Appendix III

Review Questions

1. What is pressure? What causes pressure?

2. Explain what happens when you inhale. What forces air into your lungs?

3. Explain what happens when you exhale. What forces air out of your lungs?

4. What are some common units of pressure? List these in order of smallest to largest unit.

5. What is a manometer? How does it measure the pressure of a sample of gas?

6. Summarize each of the simple gas laws (Boyle's law, Charles's law, and Avogadro's law). For each law, explain the relationship between the two variables and also state which variables must be kept constant.

7. Explain the source of ear pain that is often experienced due to a rapid change in altitude.

▲ **Review Questions** can be used to review chapter content.

Cumulative Problems

97. Modern pennies are composed of zinc coated with copper. A student determines the mass of a penny to be 2.482 g and then makes several scratches in the copper coating (to expose the underlying zinc). The student puts the scratched penny in hydrochloric acid, where the following reaction occurs between the zinc and the HCl (the copper remains undissolved):

$$Zn(s) + 2 HCl(aq) \longrightarrow H_2(g) + ZnCl_2(aq)$$

The student collects the hydrogen produced over water at 25 °C. The collected gas occupies a volume of 0.899 L at a total pressure of 791 mmHg. Calculate the percent zinc (by mass) in the penny. (Assume that all the Zn in the penny dissolves.)

98. A 2.85-g sample of an unknown chlorofluorocarbon decomposes and produces 564 mL of chlorine gas at a pressure of 752 mmHg and a temperature of 298 K. What is the percent chlorine (by mass) in the unknown chlorofluorocarbon?

99. The mass of an evacuated 255-mL flask is 143.187 g. The mass of the flask filled with 267 torr of an unknown gas at 25 °C is 143.289 g. Calculate the molar mass of the unknown gas.

100. A 118-mL flask is evacuated and found to have a mass of 97.129 g. When the flask is filled with 768 torr of helium gas at 35 °C, it has a mass of 97.171 g. Was the helium gas pure?

101. A gaseous hydrogen and carbon containing compound is decomposed and found to contain 82.66% carbon and 17.34% hy-

▲ **Cumulative Problems** combine material from different parts of the chapter, and often from previous chapters as well, allowing you to see how well you can integrate the course material.

Conceptual Problems

141. When the driver of an automobile applies the brakes, the passengers are pushed toward the front of the car, but a helium balloon is pushed toward the back of the car. Upon forward acceleration, the passengers are pushed toward the back of the car, but the helium balloon is pushed toward the front of the car. Why?

142. Suppose that a liquid is 10 times denser than water. If you were to sip this liquid at sea level using a straw, what would be the maximum length of the straw?

143. The reaction occurs in a closed container:

$$A(g) + 2 B(g) \longrightarrow 2 C(g)$$

A reaction mixture initially contains 1.5 L of A and 2.0 L of B. Assuming that the volume and temperature of the reaction mixture remain constant, what is the percent change in pressure if the reaction goes to completion?

144. One mole of nitrogen and one mole of neon are combined in a closed container at STP. How big is the container?

145. Exactly equal amounts (in moles) of gas A and gas B are combined in a 1-L container at room temperature. Gas B has a molar mass that is twice that of gas A. Which statement is true for the mixture of gases and why?
   a. The molecules of gas B have greater kinetic energy than those of gas A.
   b. Gas B has a greater partial pressure than gas A.
   c. The molecules of gas B have a greater average velocity than those of gas A.
   d. Gas B makes a greater contribution to the average density of the mixture than gas A.

146. Which gas would you expect to deviate most from ideal behavior under conditions of low temperature: F_2, Cl_2, or Br_2? Explain.

▲ **Conceptual Problems** let you test your grasp of key chapter concepts, often through reasoning that involves little or no math.

Problems by Topic

Converting between Pressure Units

29. The pressure in Denver, Colorado (elevation 5280 ft), averages about 24.9 in Hg. Convert this pressure to
   a. atm   b. mmHg   c. psi   d. Pa

30. The pressure on top of Mt. Everest averages about 235 mmHg. Convert this pressure to
   a. torr   b. psi   c. in Hg   d. atm

31. The North American record for highest recorded barometric pressure is 31.85 in Hg, set in 1989 in Northway, Alaska. Convert this pressure to
   a. mmHg   b. atm   c. torr   d. kPa (kilopascals)

32. The world record for lowest pressure (at sea level) was 652.5 mmHg recorded inside Typhoon Tip on October 12, 1979, in the Western Pacific Ocean. Convert this pressure to
   a. torr   b. atm   c. in Hg   d. psi

33. Given a barometric pressure of 762.4 mmHg, calculate the pressure of each gas sample as indicated by the manometer.

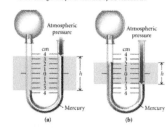

34. Given a barometric pressure of 751.5 mmHg, calculate the pressure of each gas sample as indicated by the manometer.

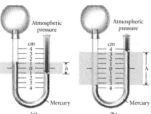

Simple Gas Laws

35. A sample of gas has an initial volume of 5.6 L at a pressure of 735 mmHg. If the volume of the gas is increased to 9.4 L, what will the pressure be?

36. A sample of gas has an initial volume of 13.9 L at a pressure of 1.22 atm. If the sample is compressed to a volume of 10.3 L, what will its pressure be?

37. A 48.3-mL sample of gas in a cylinder is warmed from 22 °C to 87 °C. What is its volume at the final temperature?

38. A syringe containing 1.55 mL of oxygen gas is cooled from 95.3 °C to 0.0 °C. What is the final volume of oxygen gas?

39. A balloon contains 0.158 mol of gas and has a volume of 2.46 L. If an additional 0.113 mol of gas is added to the balloon

▲ **Problems By Topic** are paired, with answers to the odd-numbered questions appearing in the appendix.

Challenge Problems

132. A 10-liter container is filled with 0.10 mol of $H_2(g)$ and heated to 3000 K causing some of the $H_2(g)$ to decompose into $H(g)$. The pressure is found to be 3.0 atm. Find the partial pressure of the $H(g)$ that forms from H_2 at this temperature. (Assume two significant figures for the temperature.)

133. A mixture of $NH_3(g)$ and $N_2H_4(g)$ is placed in a sealed container at 300 K. The total pressure is 0.50 atm. The container is heated to 1200 K at which time both substances decompose completely according to the equations $2 NH_3(g) \longrightarrow N_2(g) + 3 H_2(g)$; $N_2H_4(g) \longrightarrow N_2(g) + 2 H_2(g)$. After decomposition is complete the total pressure at 1200 K is found to be 4.5 atm. Find the percent of $N_2H_4(g)$ in the original mixture. (Assume two significant figures for the temperature.)

134. A quantity of CO gas occupies a volume of 0.48 L at 1.0 atm and 275 K. The pressure of the gas is lowered and its temperature is raised until its volume is 1.3 L. Find the density of the CO under the new conditions.

135. When $CO_2(g)$ is put in a sealed container at 701 K and a pressure of 10.0 atm and is heated to 1401 K, the pressure rises to 22.5 atm. Some of the CO_2 decomposes to CO and O_2. Calculate the mole percent of CO_2 that decomposes.

136. The world burns approximately 9.0×10^{12} kg of fossil fuel per year. Use the combustion of octane as the representative reaction and determine the mass of carbon dioxide (the most significant greenhouse gas) formed per year. The current concentration of carbon dioxide in the atmosphere is approximately 387 ppm (by volume). By what percentage does the concentration increase each year due to fossil fuel combustion? Approximate the average properties of the entire atmosphere by assuming that the atmosphere extends from sea level to 15 km and that it has an average pressure of 381 torr and average temperature of 275 K. Assume Earth is a perfect sphere with a radius of 6371 km.

137. The atmosphere slowly oxidizes hydrocarbons in a number of steps that eventually convert the hydrocarbon into carbon dioxide and water. The overall reaction of a number of such steps for methane gas is

$$CH_4(g) + 5 O_2(g) + 5 NO(g) \longrightarrow CO_2(g) + H_2O(g) + 5 NO_2(g) + 2 OH(g)$$

Suppose that an atmospheric chemist combines 155 mL of methane at STP, 885 mL of oxygen at STP, and 55.5 mL of NO

▲ **Challenge Problems** are designed to challenge stronger students.

Extend learning
BEYOND THE CLASSROOM

MasteringChemistry® emulates the instructor's office-hour environment, coaching you on problem-solving techniques by asking questions that reveal gaps in understanding, and giving you the power to answer questions on your own. It tutors individually—with feedback specific to your errors, offering optional simpler steps. To learn more, visit **www.masteringchemistry.com**.

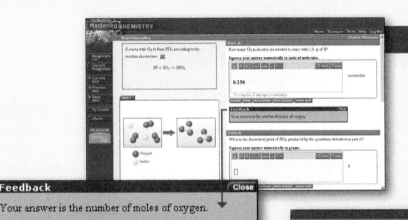

Student Tutorial

MasteringChemistry is the only system to provide instantaneous feedback specific to the most-common wrong answers. Students can submit an answer and receive immediate, error-specific feedback. Simpler sub-problems— "hints"—are provided upon request.

Gradebook

MasteringChemistry is the only system to capture the step-by-step work of each student in your class, including wrong answers submitted, hints requested, and time taken on every step. This data powers an unprecedented gradebook.

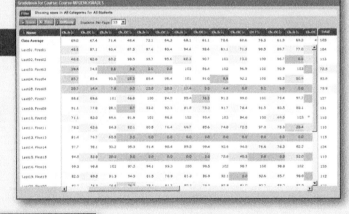

Diagnostics At-A-Glance

Instructors can identify students who are having difficulty at a glance with the color-coded gradebook, identify the most difficult problem (and step within that problem) in each assignment, or critique the detailed work of anyone who needs more help. They can even compare results on any problem and any step with a previous class, or with the national average.

Mastering CHEMISTRY®

Make Learning Part of the Grade®

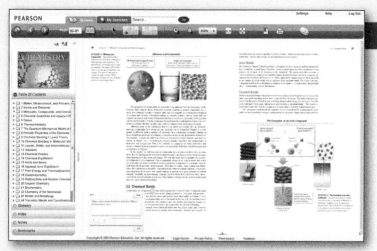

eText

Pearson eText gives students access to the text whenever and wherever they can access the Internet. The eText pages look exactly like the printed text, and include powerful interactive and customization functions.

• You can create notes, highlight text in different colors, create book marks, zoom, click hyperlinked words and phrases to view definitions, and view in single-page or two-page view.

• You can link directly to associated media files, enabling them to view an animation as they read the text.

• You can perform a full-text search and have the ability to save and export notes.

• Instructors can share their notes and highlights with students and can also hide chapters that they do not want their students to read.

Chapter-specific Quizzes

Chapter-specific quizzes and activities focus on important, hard-to-grasp chemistry concepts. Icons throughout the textbook direct you to specific lessons related to the topics discussed in a given section.

Math Review

The Math Review provides a basic review of math that you will need in your chemistry course. You will find reminders on how to round decimals and write basic equations, as well as insights on how math and chemistry work together.

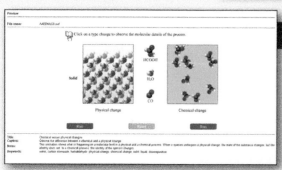

Flashcards

Flashcards of key terms will help you learn the key concepts from the text.

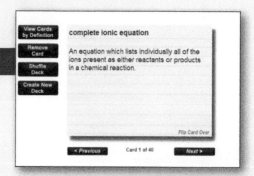

SUPPLEMENTS

For Instructors

Solutions Manual
978-0-321-66796-0 • 0-321-66796-4

Printed Test Bank
978-0-321-66786-1 • 0-321-66786-7

Instructor Resource Manual
978-0-321-66787-8 • 0-321-66787-5

Transparency Acetates
978-0-321-66748-9 • 0-321-66748-4

Instructor Resource DVD/CD
978-0-321-66749-6 • 0-321-66749-2

(Instructor Resource Center Download)
BlackBoard Test Item File
978-0-321-66822-6 • 0-321-66822-7

(Instructor Resource Center Download)
WebCT Test Item File
978-0-321-67630-6 • 0-321-67630-0

For Students

Laboratory Manual
978-0-321-66785-4 • 0-321-66785-9

Selected Solutions Manual
978-0-321-66754-0 • 0-321-66754-9

Study Guide
978-0-321-66788-5 • 0-321-66788-3

MasteringChemistry®
www.masteringchemistry.com

MasteringChemistry with Pearson eText
www.masteringchemistry.com

CHEMISTRY

A MOLECULAR APPROACH

1

Matter, Measurement, and Problem Solving

The most incomprehensible thing about the universe is that it is comprehensible.

—Albert Einstein (1879–1955)

WHAT DO YOU THINK is the most important idea in all of human knowledge? There are, of course, many possible answers to this question—some practical, some philosophical, and some scientific. If we limit ourselves only to scientific answers, mine would be this: **the properties of matter are determined by the properties of molecules and atoms**. Atoms and molecules determine how matter behaves—if they were different, matter would be different. The properties of water molecules determine how water behaves; the properties of sugar molecules determine how sugar behaves; and the properties of the molecules that compose our bodies determine how our bodies behave. The understanding of matter at the molecular level gives us unprecedented control over that matter. In fact, our expanded understanding of the molecules that compose living organisms has made possible the biological revolution of the last 50 years.

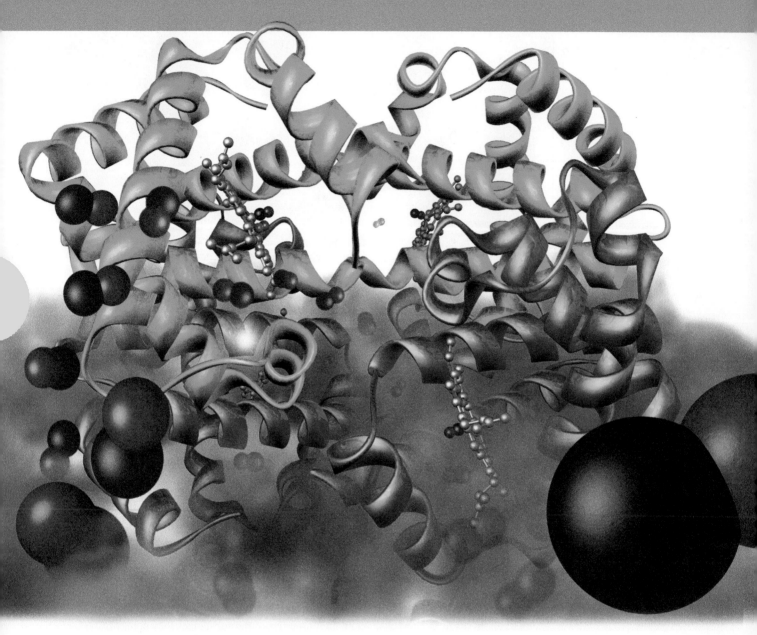

Hemoglobin (depicted in blue and green) is the oxygen-carrying protein in blood. Hemoglobin can also bind carbon monoxide molecules (the linked red and black spheres).

1.1 Atoms and Molecules

The air over most U.S. cities, including my own, contains at least some pollution. A significant component of that pollution is carbon monoxide, a colorless gas emitted in the exhaust of cars and trucks. Carbon monoxide gas is composed of carbon monoxide molecules, each of which contains a carbon *atom* and an oxygen *atom* held together by a chemical bond. **Atoms** are the submicroscopic particles that constitute the fundamental building blocks of ordinary matter. They are most often found in **molecules**, two or more atoms joined in a specific geometrical arrangement.

   The properties of the substances around us depend on the atoms and molecules that compose them, so the properties of carbon monoxide *gas* depend on the properties of carbon monoxide *molecules*. Carbon monoxide molecules happen to be just the right size and shape, and happen to have just the right chemical properties, to fit neatly into cavities within hemoglobin molecules in blood that are normally reserved for oxygen molecules (Figure 1.1 ▶ on the next page). Consequently, carbon monoxide diminishes the oxygen-carrying capacity of blood. Breathing air containing too much carbon monoxide (greater than 0.04% by volume) can lead to unconsciousness and even death because not enough

Carbon monoxide molecule

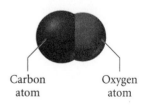

Carbon   Oxygen
atom   atom

1

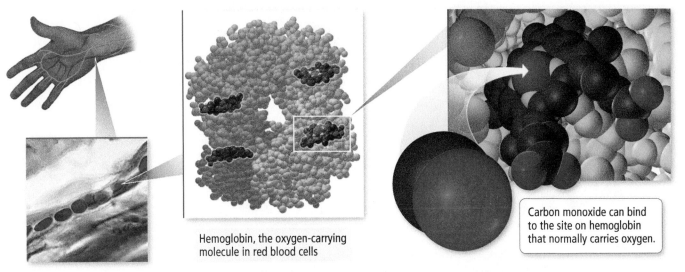

Hemoglobin, the oxygen-carrying molecule in red blood cells

Carbon monoxide can bind to the site on hemoglobin that normally carries oxygen.

▲ **FIGURE 1.1 Binding of Oxygen and Carbon Monoxide to Hemoglobin**   Hemoglobin, a large protein molecule, is the oxygen carrier in red blood cells. Each subunit of the hemoglobin molecule contains an iron atom to which oxygen binds. Carbon monoxide molecules can take the place of oxygen, thus reducing the amount of oxygen reaching the body's tissues.

oxygen reaches the brain. Carbon monoxide deaths can occur as a result of running an automobile in a closed garage or using a propane burner in an enclosed space for too long. In smaller amounts, carbon monoxide causes the heart and lungs to work harder and can result in headache, dizziness, weakness, and confused thinking.

Cars and trucks emit another closely related molecule, called carbon dioxide, in far greater quantities than carbon monoxide. The only difference between carbon dioxide and carbon monoxide is that carbon dioxide molecules contain two oxygen atoms instead of just one. However, this extra oxygen atom dramatically affects the properties of the gas. We breathe much more carbon dioxide—which is naturally 0.03% of air, and a product of our own respiration as well—than carbon monoxide, yet it does not kill us. Why? Because the presence of the second oxygen atom prevents carbon dioxide from binding to the oxygen-carrying site in hemoglobin, making it far less toxic. Although high levels of carbon dioxide (greater than 10% of air) can be hazardous for other reasons, lower levels can enter the bloodstream with no adverse effects. Such is the molecular world. Any changes in molecules—such as the addition of an oxygen atom to carbon monoxide—are likely to result in large changes in the properties of the substances they compose.

As another example, consider two other closely related molecules, water and hydrogen peroxide:

Carbon dioxide molecule

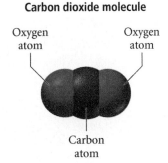

Oxygen atom

Oxygen atom

Carbon atom

In the study of chemistry, atoms are often portrayed as colored spheres, with each color representing a different kind of atom. For example, a black sphere represents a carbon atom, a red sphere represents an oxygen atom, and a white sphere represents a hydrogen atom. For a complete color code of atoms, see Appendix IIA.

Water molecule

Oxygen atom

Hydrogen atoms

Hydrogen peroxide molecule

Oxygen atoms

Hydrogen atoms

A water molecule is composed of *one* oxygen atom and two hydrogen atoms. A hydrogen peroxide molecule is composed of *two* oxygen atoms and two hydrogen atoms. This seemingly small molecular difference results in a huge difference between water and hydrogen peroxide. Water is the familiar and stable liquid we all drink and bathe in. Hydrogen peroxide, in contrast, is an unstable liquid that, in its pure form, burns the skin on contact and is used in rocket fuel. When you pour water onto your hair, your hair simply becomes wet. However, if you put hydrogen peroxide in your hair—which you may have done if you have bleached your hair—a chemical reaction occurs that strips your hair of its color.

The hydrogen peroxide we use as an antiseptic or bleaching agent is considerably diluted.

The details of how specific atoms bond to form a molecule—in a straight line, at a particular angle, in a ring, or in some other pattern—as well as the type of atoms in the molecule, determine everything about the substance that the molecule composes. If we want to understand the substances around us, we must understand the atoms and molecules that compose them—this is the central goal of chemistry. A good simple definition of **chemistry** is

> **Chemistry—the science that seeks to understand the behavior of matter by studying the behavior of atoms and molecules.**

The term *atoms* in this definition can be interpreted loosely to include atoms that have lost or gained electrons.

1.2   The Scientific Approach to Knowledge

Throughout history, humans have approached knowledge about the physical world in different ways. For example, the Greek philosopher Plato (427–347 B.C.) thought that the best way to learn about reality was not through the senses, but through reason. He believed that the physical world was an imperfect representation of a perfect and transcendent world (a world beyond space and time). For him, true knowledge came, not through observing the real physical world, but through reasoning and thinking about the ideal one.

Although some Greek philosophers, such as Aristotle, did use observation to attain knowledge, they did not emphasize experiment and measurement to the extent that modern science does.

The *scientific* approach to knowledge, however, is exactly the opposite of Plato's. Scientific knowledge is empirical—that is, it is based on *observation* and *experiment*. Scientists observe and perform experiments on the physical world to learn about it. Some observations and experiments are qualitative (noting or describing how a process happens), but many are quantitative (measuring or quantifying something about the process). For example, Antoine Lavoisier (1743–1794), a French chemist who studied combustion, made careful measurements of the mass of objects before and after burning them in closed containers. He noticed that there was no change in the total mass of material within the container during combustion. In doing so, Lavoisier made an important *observation* about the physical world.

Observations often lead scientists to formulate a **hypothesis**, a tentative interpretation or explanation of the observations. For example, Lavoisier explained his observations on combustion by hypothesizing that when a substance combusts, it combines with a component of air. A good hypothesis is *falsifiable*, which means that it makes predictions that can be confirmed or refuted by further observations. Scientists test hypotheses by **experiments**, highly controlled procedures designed to generate observations. The results of an experiment may support a hypothesis or prove it wrong—in which case the scientist must modify or discard the hypothesis.

In some cases, a series of similar observations can lead to the development of a **scientific law**, a brief statement that summarizes past observations and predicts future ones. Lavoisier summarized his observations on combustion with the **law of conservation of mass**, which states, "In a chemical reaction, matter is neither created nor destroyed." This statement summarized his observations on chemical reactions and predicted the outcome of future observations on reactions. Laws, like hypotheses, are also subject to experiments, which can support them or prove them wrong.

Scientific laws are not *laws* in the same sense as civil or governmental laws. Nature does not follow laws in the way that we obey the laws against speeding or running a stop sign. Rather, scientific laws *describe* how nature behaves—they are generalizations about what nature does. For that reason, some people find it more appropriate to refer to them as *principles* rather than *laws*.

One or more well-established hypotheses may form the basis for a scientific **theory**. A scientific theory is a model for the way nature is and tries to explain not merely what nature does but why. As such, well-established theories are the pinnacle of scientific knowledge, often predicting behavior far beyond the observations or laws from which they were developed. A good example of a theory is the **atomic theory** proposed by English chemist John Dalton (1766–1844). Dalton explained the law of conservation of mass, as well as other laws and observations of the time, by proposing that matter is composed of small, indestructible particles called atoms. Since these particles are merely rearranged in chemical changes (and not created or destroyed), the total amount of mass remains the same. Dalton's theory is a model for the physical world—it gives us insight into how nature works, and therefore *explains* our laws and observations.

▲ A painting of the French chemist Antoine Lavoisier with his wife, Marie, who helped him in his work by illustrating his experiments and translating scientific articles from English. Lavoisier, who also made significant contributions to agriculture, industry, education, and government administration, was executed during the French Revolution. (The Metropolitan Museum of Art)

In Dalton's time, people thought atoms were indestructible. Today, because of nuclear reactions, we know that atoms can be broken apart into their smaller components.

The Scientific Method

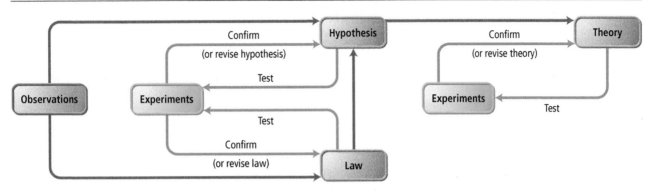

▲ FIGURE 1.2 **The Scientific Method**

Finally, the scientific approach returns to observation to test theories. Experiments validate theories, but theories can never be conclusively proved—there is always the possibility that a new observation or experiment will reveal a flaw. For example, the atomic theory can be tested by trying to isolate single atoms, or by trying to image them (both of which, by the way, have already been accomplished). Notice that the scientific approach to knowledge begins with observation and ends with observation. An experiment is in essence a highly controlled procedure for generating critical observations designed to test a theory or hypothesis. Each new set of observations allows refinement of the original model. Figure 1.2 ▲ summarizes this approach, often called the **scientific method**. Scientific laws, hypotheses, and theories are all subject to continued experimentation. If a law, hypothesis, or theory is proved wrong by an experiment, it must be revised and tested with new experiments. Over time, the scientific community eliminates or corrects poor theories and laws, and good theories and laws—those consistent with experimental results—remain.

Established theories with strong experimental support are the most powerful pieces of scientific knowledge. You may have heard the phrase, "That is just a theory," as if theories were easily dismissible. Such a statement reveals a deep misunderstanding of the nature of a scientific theory. Well-established theories are as close to truth as we get in science. The idea that all matter is made of atoms is "just a theory," but it has over 200 years of experimental evidence to support it. It is a powerful piece of scientific knowledge on which many other scientific ideas have been built.

One last word about the scientific method: some people wrongly imagine science to be a strict set of rules and procedures that automatically lead to inarguable, objective facts. This is not the case. Even our diagram of the scientific method is only an idealization of real science, useful to help us see the key distinctions of science. Real science requires hard work, care, creativity, and even a bit of luck. Scientific theories do not just arise out of data—men and women of great genius and creativity craft theories. A great theory is not unlike a master painting and many see a similar kind of beauty in both. (For more on this aspect of science, see the box entitled *Thomas S. Kuhn and Scientific Revolutions*.)

 Conceptual Connection 1.1 Laws and Theories

Which of the following best explains the difference between a law and a theory?

(a) A law is truth whereas a theory is mere speculation.

(b) A law summarizes a series of related observations, while a theory gives the underlying reasons for them.

(c) A theory describes *what* nature does; a law describes *why* nature does it.

ANSWER: (b) A law only summarizes a series of related observations, while a theory gives the underlying reasons for them.

THE NATURE OF SCIENCE Thomas S. Kuhn and Scientific Revolutions

When scientists talk about science, they often talk in ways that imply that their theories are "true." Further, they talk as if they arrive at theories in logical and unbiased ways. For example, a theory central to chemistry is John Dalton's atomic theory—the idea that all matter is composed of atoms. Is this theory "true"? Was it reached in logical, unbiased ways? Will this theory still be around in 200 years?

The answers to these questions depend on how we view science and its development. One way to view science—let's call it the *traditional view*—is as the continual accumulation of knowledge and the building of increasingly precise theories. In this view, a scientific theory is a model of the world that reflects what is *actually in* nature. New observations and experiments result in gradual adjustments to theories. Over time, theories get better, giving us a more accurate picture of the physical world.

In the twentieth century, a different view of scientific knowledge began to develop. A book by Thomas Kuhn, published in 1964 and entitled *The Structure of Scientific Revolutions*, challenged the traditional view. Kuhn's ideas came from his study of the history of science, which, he argued, does not support the idea that science progresses in a smooth cumulative way. According to Kuhn, science goes through fairly quiet periods that he called *normal science.* In these periods, scientists make their data fit the reigning theory, or paradigm. Small inconsistencies are swept aside during periods of normal science. However, when too many inconsistencies and anomalies develop, a crisis emerges. The crisis brings about a *revolution* and a new reigning theory. According to Kuhn, the new theory is usually quite different from the old one; it not

only helps us to make sense of new or anomalous information, but also enables us to see accumulated data from the past in a dramatically new way.

Kuhn further contended that theories are held for reasons that are not always logical or unbiased, and that theories are not *true* models—in the sense of a one-to-one mapping—of the physical world. Because new theories are often so different from the ones they replace, he argued, and because old theories always make good sense to those holding them, they must not be "True" with a capital *T*, otherwise "truth" would be constantly changing.

Kuhn's ideas created a controversy among scientists and science historians that continues to this day. Some, especially postmodern philosophers of science, have taken Kuhn's ideas one step further. They argue that scientific knowledge is *completely* biased and lacks any objectivity. Most scientists, including Kuhn, would disagree. Although Kuhn pointed out that scientific knowledge has *arbitrary elements*, he also said, "*Observation . . . can and must drastically restrict the range of admissible scientific belief, else there would be no science.*" In other words, saying that science contains arbitrary elements is quite different from saying that science itself is arbitrary.

Question

In his book, Kuhn stated, "*A new theory . . . is seldom or never just an increment to what is already known.*" Can you think of any examples of this from your knowledge of the history of science? In other words, can you think of instances in which a new theory or model was drastically different from the one it replaced?

1.3 The Classification of Matter

Matter is anything that occupies space and has mass. For example, this book, your desk, your chair, and even your body are all composed of matter. Less obviously, the air around you is also matter—it too occupies space and has mass. We call a specific instance of matter—such as air, water, or sand—a **substance**. We can classify matter according to its **state** (its physical form) and its **composition** (the basic components that make it up).

The States of Matter: Solid, Liquid, and Gas

Matter can exist in three different states: **solid**, **liquid**, and **gas**. In *solid matter*, atoms or molecules pack close to each other in fixed locations. Although the atoms and molecules in a solid vibrate, they do not move around or past each other. Consequently, a solid has a fixed volume and rigid shape. Ice, aluminum, and diamond are good examples of solids. Solid matter may be **crystalline**, in which case its atoms or molecules are in patterns with long-range, repeating order (Figure 1.3 ▶ on the next page), or it may be **amorphous**, in which case its atoms or molecules do not have any long-range order. Table salt and diamond are examples of *crystalline* solids; the well-ordered geometric shapes of salt and diamond crystals reflect the well-ordered geometric arrangement of their atoms (although this is not the case for *all* crystalline solids). Examples of *amorphous* solids include glass and plastic. In *liquid matter*, atoms or molecules pack about as closely as they do in solid matter, but they are free to move relative to each other, giving liquids a fixed volume but not a fixed shape. Liquids assume the shape of

The state of matter changes from solid to liquid to gas with increasing temperature.

Glasses and other amorphous solids can be thought of, from one point of view, as intermediate between solids and liquids—their atoms are fixed in position at room temperature, but they have no long-range structure and do not have distinct melting points.

Crystalline Solid:
Regular 3-dimensional pattern

Diamond
C (*s*, diamond)

▲ **FIGURE 1.3 Crystalline Solid**
Diamond is a crystalline solid composed of carbon atoms arranged in a regular, repeating pattern.

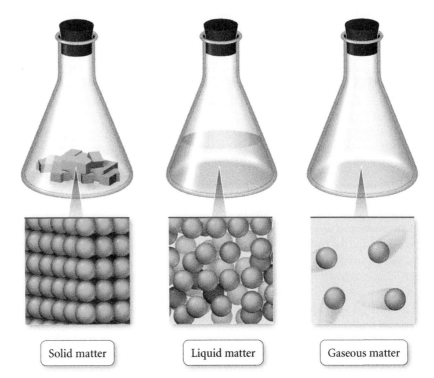

Solid matter   Liquid matter   Gaseous matter

▲ In a solid, the atoms or molecules are fixed in place and can only vibrate. In a liquid, although the atoms or molecules are closely packed, they can move past one another, allowing the liquid to flow and assume the shape of its container. In a gas, the atoms or molecules are widely spaced, making gases compressible as well as fluid.

their container. Water, alcohol, and gasoline are all good examples of substances that are liquids at room temperature.

In *gaseous matter*, atoms or molecules have a lot of space between them and are free to move relative to one another, making gases *compressible* (Figure 1.4 ▼). When you squeeze a balloon or sit down on an air mattress, you force the atoms and molecules into a smaller space, so that they are closer together. Gases always assume the shape *and* volume of their container. Substances that are gases at room temperature include helium, nitrogen (the main component of air), and carbon dioxide.

🔵 **Conceptual Connection 1.2 The Mass of a Gas**

We put a drop of water into a container and seal the container. The drop of water then vaporizes. Does the mass of the sealed container and its contents change upon vaporization?

ANSWER: No. The water vaporizes and becomes a gas, but the water molecules are still present within the flask and have the same mass.

▶ **FIGURE 1.4 The Compressibility of Gases** Gases can be compressed—squeezed into a smaller volume—because there is so much empty space between atoms or molecules in the gaseous state.

Solid—not compressible   Gas—compressible

Classifying Matter according to Its Composition: Elements, Compounds, and Mixtures

In addition to classifying matter according to its state, we can classify it according to its composition, as shown in the following chart:

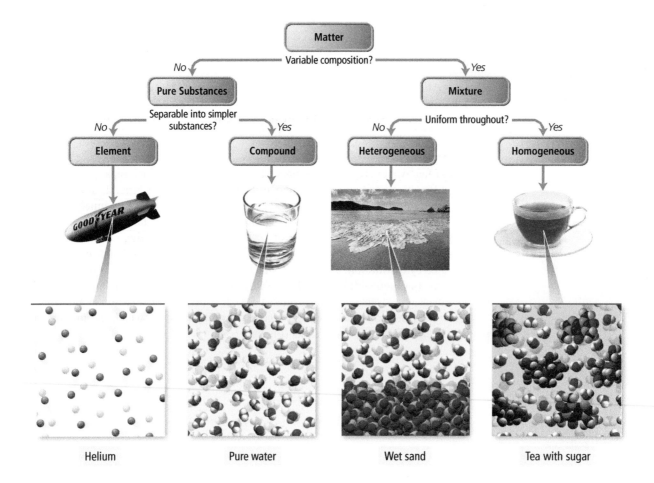

Helium   Pure water   Wet sand   Tea with sugar

The first division in the classification of matter is between a *pure substance* and a *mixture*. A **pure substance** is made up of only one component and its composition is invariant (it does not vary from one sample to another). The *components* of a pure substance can be individual atoms, or groups of atoms joined together. For example, helium, water, and table salt (sodium chloride) are all pure substances. Each of these substances is made up of only one component: helium is made up of helium atoms; water is made up of water molecules; and sodium chloride is made up of sodium chloride units. The composition of a pure sample of any one of these must always be exactly the same (because you can't vary the composition of a substance made up of only one component).

A **mixture**, by contrast, is a substance composed of two or more components in proportions that can vary from one sample to another. For example, sugar water, composed of water molecules and sugar molecules, is a mixture. We can make sugar water slightly sweet (a small proportion of sugar to water) or very sweet (a large proportion of sugar to water) or any level of sweetness in between.

Pure substances can themselves be divided into two types—*elements* and *compounds*—depending on whether or not they can be broken down (or decomposed) into simpler substances. Helium, which we just noted is a pure substance, is also a good example of an **element**, a substance that cannot be chemically broken down into simpler substances. Water, also a pure substance, is a good example of a **compound**, a substance composed of two or more elements (in this case hydrogen and oxygen) in fixed, definite proportions. On Earth, compounds are more common than pure elements because most elements combine with other elements to form compounds.

We can also divide mixtures into two types—heterogeneous and homogeneous—depending on how *uniformly* the substances within them mix. Wet sand is a **heterogeneous mixture**, one in which the composition varies from one region to another. Sugar water is a **homogeneous mixture**, one with the same composition throughout. Homogeneous mixtures have uniform compositions because the atoms or molecules that compose them mix uniformly. Heterogeneous mixtures are made up of distinct regions because the atoms or molecules that compose them separate. Here again we see that the properties of matter are determined by the atoms or molecules that compose it.

Classifying a substance according to its composition is not always obvious and requires that we either know the true composition of the substance or are able to test it in a laboratory. For now, we will focus on relatively common substances with which you likely have some experience. Throughout this course, you will gain the knowledge to understand the composition of a larger variety of substances.

Separating Mixtures

Chemists often want to separate mixtures into their components. Such separations can be easy or difficult, depending on the components in the mixture. In general, mixtures are separable because the different components have different physical or chemical properties. We can use various techniques that exploit these differences to achieve separation. For example, we can separate a mixture of sand and water by **decanting**—carefully pouring off—the water into another container. A homogeneous mixture of liquids can usually be separated by **distillation**, a process in which the mixture is heated to boil off the more **volatile** (easily vaporizable) liquid. The volatile liquid is then recondensed in a condenser and collected in a separate flask (Figure 1.5 ▼). If a mixture is composed of an insoluble solid and a liquid, we can separate the two by **filtration**, in which the mixture is poured through filter paper in a funnel (Figure 1.6 ▼).

Distillation

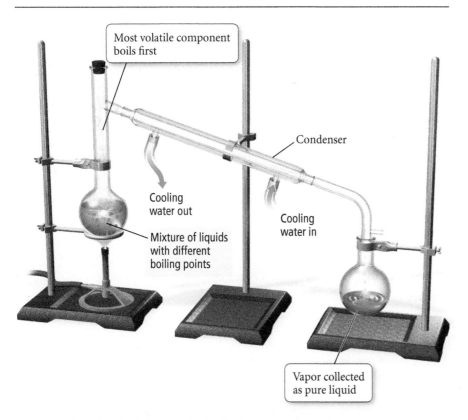

▲ **FIGURE 1.5 Separating Substances by Distillation**   When a liquid mixture is heated, the component with the lowest boiling point vaporizes first, leaving behind less volatile liquids or dissolved solids. The vapor is then cooled, condensing it back to a liquid, and collected.

Filtration

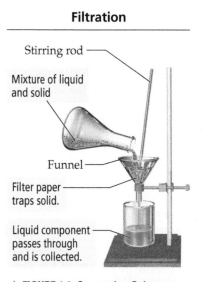

▲ **FIGURE 1.6 Separating Substances by Filtration**   A solid and liquid mixture can be separated by pouring the mixture through a funnel containing filter paper designed to pass only the liquid.

1.4 Physical and Chemical Changes and Physical and Chemical Properties

Every day we witness changes in matter: ice melts, iron rusts, gasoline burns, fruit ripens, and water evaporates. What happens to the molecules that compose these samples of matter during such changes? The answer depends on the type of change. Changes that alter only state or appearance, but not composition, are **physical changes**. The atoms or molecules that compose a substance *do not change* their identity during a physical change. For example, when water boils, it changes its state from a liquid to a gas, but the gas remains composed of water molecules, so this is a physical change (Figure 1.7 ▼).

In contrast, changes that alter the composition of matter are **chemical changes**. During a chemical change, atoms rearrange, transforming the original substances into different substances. For example, the rusting of iron is a chemical change. The atoms that compose iron (iron atoms) combine with oxygen molecules from air to form iron oxide, the orange substance we call rust (Figure 1.8 ▼). Some other examples of physical and chemical changes are shown in Figure 1.9 ▶ on the next page.

Physical and chemical changes are manifestations of physical and chemical properties. A **physical property** is one that a substance displays without changing its composition, whereas a **chemical property** is one that a substance displays only by changing its composition via a chemical change. The smell of gasoline is a physical property—gasoline does not change its composition when it exhibits its odor. The flammability of gasoline, in contrast, is a chemical property—gasoline does change its composition when it burns, turning into completely new substances (primarily carbon dioxide and water). Physical properties include odor, taste, color, appearance, melting point, boiling point, and density. Chemical properties include corrosiveness, flammability, acidity, toxicity, and other such characteristics.

The differences between physical and chemical changes are not always apparent. Only chemical examination can confirm whether any particular change is physical or chemical. In many cases, however, we can identify chemical and physical changes based on what we know about the changes. Changes in the state of matter, such as melting or boiling, or changes in the physical condition of matter, such as those that result from cutting or crushing, are typically physical changes. Changes involving chemical reactions—often evidenced by temperature or color changes—are chemical changes.

A physical change results in a different form of the same substance, while a chemical change results in a completely different substance.

In Chapter 19 we will also learn about *nuclear changes*, which can involve atoms of one element changing into atoms of a different element.

▲ **FIGURE 1.7 Boiling, a Physical Change**   When water boils, it turns into a gas but does not alter its chemical identity—the water molecules are the same in both the liquid and gaseous states. Boiling is thus a physical change, and the boiling point of water is a physical property.

Water molecules change from liquid to gaseous state: physical change.

$H_2O(g)$

$H_2O(l)$

Iron atoms

Iron oxide
(rust)

▲ **FIGURE 1.8 Rusting, a Chemical Change**   When iron rusts, the iron atoms combine with oxygen atoms to form a different chemical substance, the compound iron oxide. Rusting is therefore a chemical change, and the tendency of iron to rust is a chemical property.

Physical Change and Chemical Change

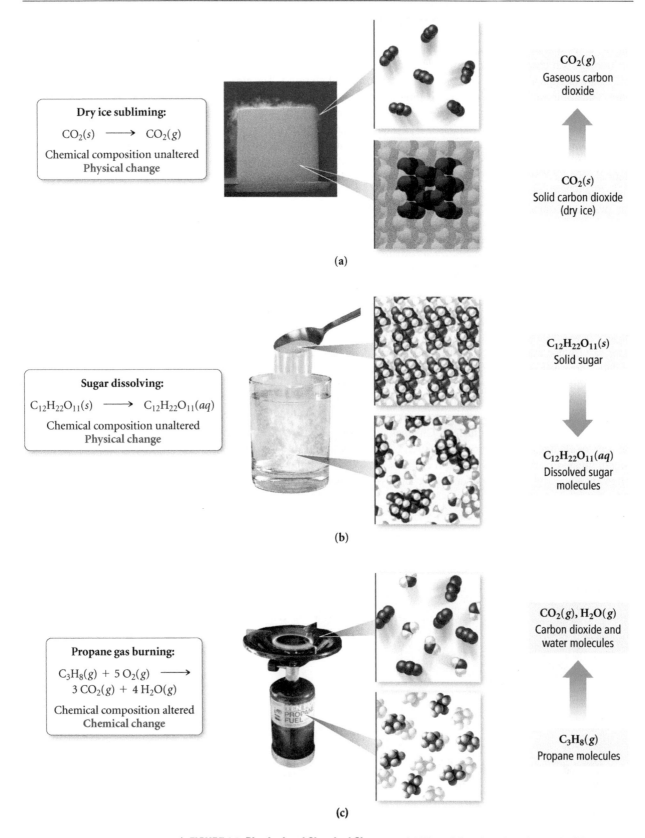

Dry ice subliming:

$$CO_2(s) \longrightarrow CO_2(g)$$

Chemical composition unaltered
Physical change

$CO_2(g)$
Gaseous carbon dioxide

$CO_2(s)$
Solid carbon dioxide (dry ice)

(a)

Sugar dissolving:

$$C_{12}H_{22}O_{11}(s) \longrightarrow C_{12}H_{22}O_{11}(aq)$$

Chemical composition unaltered
Physical change

$C_{12}H_{22}O_{11}(s)$
Solid sugar

$C_{12}H_{22}O_{11}(aq)$
Dissolved sugar molecules

(b)

Propane gas burning:

$$C_3H_8(g) + 5\,O_2(g) \longrightarrow$$
$$3\,CO_2(g) + 4\,H_2O(g)$$

Chemical composition altered
Chemical change

$CO_2(g), H_2O(g)$
Carbon dioxide and water molecules

$C_3H_8(g)$
Propane molecules

(c)

▲ **FIGURE 1.9 Physical and Chemical Changes** (a) The sublimation of dry ice (solid CO_2) is a physical change. (b) The dissolution of sugar is a physical change. (c) The burning of propane is a chemical change.

EXAMPLE 1.1 Physical and Chemical Changes and Properties

Determine whether each change is physical or chemical. What kind of property (chemical or physical) is demonstrated in each case?

(a) the evaporation of rubbing alcohol

(b) the burning of lamp oil

(c) the bleaching of hair with hydrogen peroxide

(d) the forming of frost on a cold night

SOLUTION

(a) When rubbing alcohol evaporates, it changes from liquid to gas, but it remains alcohol—this is a physical change. The volatility (i.e., ability to evaporate easily) of alcohol is a therefore a physical property.

(b) Lamp oil burns because it reacts with oxygen in air to form carbon dioxide and water—this is a chemical change. The flammability of lamp oil is therefore a chemical property.

(c) Applying hydrogen peroxide to hair changes pigment molecules in hair that give it color—this is a chemical change. The susceptibility of hair to bleaching is therefore a chemical property.

(d) Frost forms on a cold night because water vapor in air changes its state to form solid ice—this is a physical change. The temperature at which water freezes is therefore a physical property.

FOR PRACTICE 1.1

Determine whether each change is physical or chemical. What kind of property (chemical or physical) is demonstrated in each case?

(a) A copper wire is hammered flat.

(b) A nickel dissolves in acid to form a blue-green solution.

(c) Dry ice sublimes (i.e., changes from solid to gas) without melting.

(d) A match ignites when struck on a flint.

Answers to For Practice and For More Practice problems can be found in Appendix IV.

 Conceptual Connection 1.3 Chemical and Physical Changes

The diagram to the left represents liquid water molecules in a pan.

Which of the three diagrams on the right best represents the water molecules after they have been vaporized by the boiling of liquid water?

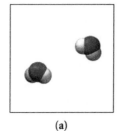
(a)

(b)

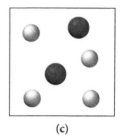
(c)

ANSWER: View **(a)** best represents the water after vaporization. Vaporization is a physical change, so the molecules must remain the same before and after the change.

1.5 Energy: A Fundamental Part of Physical and Chemical Change

The physical and chemical changes that we have just discussed are usually accompanied by energy changes. For example, when water evaporates from your skin (a physical change), the water molecules absorb energy from your body, making you feel cooler. When you burn natural gas on the stove (a chemical change), energy is released, heating the food you are cooking. Understanding the physical and chemical changes of matter—that is, understanding chemistry—requires that we understand energy changes and energy flow.

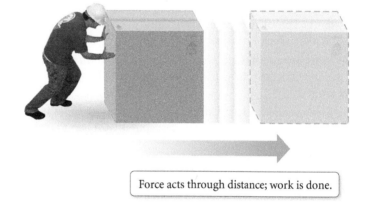

Force acts through distance; work is done.

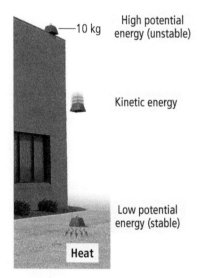

—10 kg

High potential energy (unstable)

Kinetic energy

Low potential energy (stable)

Heat

▲ **FIGURE 1.10 Energy Conversions**
Gravitational potential energy is converted into kinetic energy when the weight is released. The kinetic energy is converted mostly to thermal energy when the weight strikes the ground.

We will find in Chapter 19 that energy conservation is actually part of a more general law that allows for the interconvertibility of mass and energy.

The scientific definition of **energy** is *the capacity to do work*. **Work** is defined as the action of a force through a distance. For instance, when you push a box across the floor or pedal your bicycle across the street, you have done work.

The *total energy* of an object is a sum of its **kinetic energy**, the energy associated with its motion, and its **potential energy**, the energy associated with its position or composition. For example, a weight held several meters from the ground has potential energy due to its position within Earth's gravitational field (Figure 1.10 ◄). If you drop the weight, it accelerates, and the potential energy is converted to kinetic energy. When the weight hits the ground, its kinetic energy is converted primarily to **thermal energy**, the energy associated with the temperature of an object. Thermal energy is actually a type of kinetic energy because it arises from the motion of the individual atoms or molecules that make up an object. In other words, when the weight hits the ground its kinetic energy is essentially transferred to the atoms and molecules that compose the ground, raising the temperature of the ground ever so slightly.

The first principle to note about the way that energy changes as the weight falls to the ground is that *energy is neither created nor destroyed*. The potential energy of the weight becomes kinetic energy as the weight accelerates toward the ground. The kinetic energy then becomes thermal energy when the weight hits the ground. The total amount of thermal energy that is released through the process is exactly equal to the initial potential energy of the weight. The generalization that energy is neither created nor destroyed is known as the **law of conservation of energy**. Although energy can change from one kind into another, and although it can flow from one object to another, the *total quantity* of energy does not change—it remains constant.

The second principle to note is *the tendency of systems with high potential energy to change in a way that lowers their potential energy*. For this reason, objects or systems with high potential energy tend to be *unstable*. The weight lifted several meters from the ground is unstable because it contains a significant amount of localized potential energy. Unless restrained, the weight will naturally fall, lowering its potential energy. We can harness some of the raised weight's potential energy to do work. For example, we can attach the weight to a rope that turns a paddle wheel or spins a drill as the weight falls. After it falls to the ground, the weight contains less potential energy—it has become more *stable*.

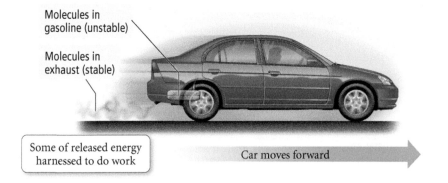

Molecules in gasoline (unstable)

Molecules in exhaust (stable)

Some of released energy harnessed to do work

Car moves forward

◀ **FIGURE 1.11 Using Chemical Energy to Do Work** The compounds produced when gasoline burns have less chemical potential energy than the gasoline molecules.

Some chemical substances are like the raised weight just described. For example, the molecules that compose gasoline have a relatively high potential energy—energy is concentrated in them just as energy is concentrated in the raised weight. The molecules in the gasoline therefore tend to undergo chemical changes (specifically combustion) that will lower their potential energy. As the energy of the molecules is released, some of it can be harnessed to do work, such as moving a car down the street (Figure 1.11 ▲). The molecules that result from the chemical change have less potential energy than the original molecules in gasoline and are more stable.

Chemical potential energy, such as that contained in the molecules that compose gasoline, arises primarily from electrostatic forces between the electrically charged particles (protons and electrons) that compose atoms and molecules. We will learn more about those particles, as well as the properties of electrical charge, in Chapter 2, but for now, know that molecules contain specific, sometimes complex, arrangements of these charged particles. Some of these arrangements—such as the one within the molecules that compose gasoline—have a much higher potential energy than others. When gasoline undergoes combustion the arrangement of these particles changes, creating molecules with much lower potential energy and transferring a great deal of energy (mostly in the form of heat) to the surroundings.

Summarizing Energy:

▶ Energy is always conserved in a physical or chemical change; it is neither created nor destroyed.

▶ Systems with high potential energy tend to change in a direction of lower potential energy, releasing energy into the surroundings.

1.6 The Units of Measurement

In 1999, NASA lost the $125 million *Mars Climate Orbiter* (pictured here). The chairman of the commission that investigated the disaster concluded, "The root cause of the loss of the spacecraft was a failed translation of English units into metric units." As a result, the orbiter—which was supposed to monitor weather on Mars—descended too far into the Martian atmosphere and burned up. In chemistry as in space exploration, **units**— standard quantities used to specify measurements—are critical. If you get them wrong, the consequences can be disastrous.

The two most common unit systems are the **English system**, used in the United States, and the **metric system**, used in most of the rest of the world. Scientists use the **International System of Units (SI)**, which is based on the metric system.

▲ The $125 million *Mars Climate Orbiter* was lost in the Martian atmosphere in 1999 because two groups of engineers failed to communicate to each other the units that they used in their calculations.

The Standard Units

Table 1.1 shows the standard SI base units. For now, we will focus on the first four of these units: the *meter,* the standard unit of length; the *kilogram*, the standard unit of mass; the *second*, the standard unit of time; and the *kelvin*, the standard unit of temperature.

The abbreviation *SI* comes from the French, *Système International d'Unités.*

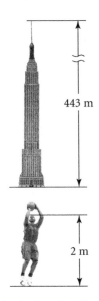

▲ The Empire State Building is 443 meters tall. A basketball player stands about 2 meters tall.

TABLE 1.1 SI Base Units

Quantity	Unit	Symbol
Length	Meter	m
Mass	Kilogram	kg
Time	Second	s
Temperature	Kelvin	K
Amount of substance	Mole	mol
Electric current	Ampere	A
Luminous intensity	Candela	cd

The Meter: A Measure of Length

The **meter (m)** is slightly longer than a yard (1 yard is 36 inches while 1 meter is 39.37 inches).

Yardstick

Meterstick

Thus, a 100-yard football field measures only 91.4 meters. The meter was originally defined as 1/10,000,000 of the distance from the equator to the North Pole (through Paris). The International Bureau of Weights and Measures now defines it more precisely as the distance light travels through a vacuum in a certain period of time, 1/299,792,458 second. A tall human is about 2 m tall and the Empire State Building stands 443 m tall (including its mast).

Scientists commonly deal with a wide range of lengths and distances. The separation between the sun and the closest star (Proxima Centauri) is about 3.8×10^{16} m, while many chemical bonds measure about 1.5×10^{-10} m.

The velocity of light in a vacuum is 3.00×10^8 m/s.

The Kilogram: A Measure of Mass

The **kilogram (kg)**, defined as the mass of a metal cylinder kept at the International Bureau of Weights and Measures at Sèvres, France, is a measure of *mass*, a quantity different from *weight*. The **mass** of an object is a measure of the quantity of matter within it, while the weight of an object is a measure of the *gravitational pull* on its matter. If you weigh yourself on the moon, for example, its weaker gravity pulls on you with less force than does Earth's gravity, resulting in a lower weight. A 130-pound (lb) person on Earth weighs 21.5 lb on the moon. However, the person's mass—the quantity of matter in his or her body—remains the same on every planet. One kilogram of mass is the equivalent of 2.205 lb of weight on Earth, so if we express mass in kilograms, a 130-lb person has a mass of approximately 59 kg and this book has a mass of about 2.5 kg. A second common unit of mass is the gram (g). One gram is 1/1000 kg. A nickel (5¢) has a mass of about 5 g.

▲ A nickel (5 cents) weighs about 5 grams.

The Second: A Measure of Time

If you live in the United States, the **second (s)** is perhaps the most familiar SI unit. The International Bureau of Weights and Measures originally defined the second in terms of the day and the year, but a second is now defined more precisely as the duration of 9,192,631,770 periods of the radiation emitted from a certain transition in a cesium-133 atom. (We discuss transitions and the emission of radiation by atoms in Chapter 7.) Scientists measure time on a large range of scales. The human heart beats about once every second; the age of the universe is estimated to be about 4.32×10^{17} s (13.7 billion years); and some molecular bonds break or form in time periods as short as 1×10^{-15} s.

The Kelvin: A Measure of Temperature

The **kelvin (K)** is the SI unit of **temperature**. The temperature of a sample of matter is a measure of the amount of average kinetic energy—the energy due to motion—of the atoms or molecules that compose the matter. The molecules in a *hot* glass of water are, on average, moving faster than the molecules in a *cold* glass of water. Temperature is a measure of this molecular motion.

Temperature also determines the direction of thermal energy transfer, or what we commonly call *heat*. Thermal energy transfers from hot objects to cold ones. For example, when you touch another person's warm hand (and yours is cold), thermal energy flows *from their hand to yours,* making your hand feel warmer. However, if you touch an ice cube, thermal energy flows *out of your hand* to the ice, cooling your hand (and possibly melting some of the ice cube).

Temperature Scales

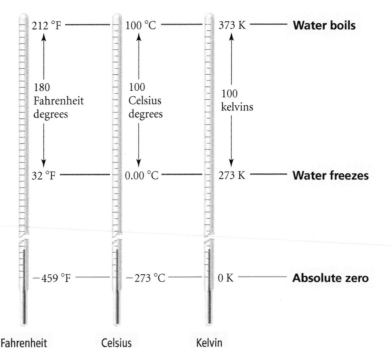

◀ FIGURE 1.12 **Comparison of the Fahrenheit, Celsius, and Kelvin Temperature Scales** The Fahrenheit degree is five-ninths the size of the Celsius degree and the kelvin. The zero point of the Kelvin scale is absolute zero (the lowest possible temperature), whereas the zero point of the Celsius scale is the freezing point of water.

Figure 1.12 ▲ shows the three common temperature scales. The most familiar in the United States is the **Fahrenheit (°F) scale**, shown on the left. On the Fahrenheit scale, water freezes at 32 °F and boils at 212 °F at sea level. Room temperature is approximately 72 °F. The Fahrenheit scale was originally determined by assigning 0 °F to the freezing point of a concentrated saltwater solution and 96 °F to normal body temperature.

Scientists and citizens of most countries other than the United States typically use the **Celsius (°C) scale**, shown in the middle. On this scale, pure water freezes at 0 °C and boils at 100 °C (at sea level). Room temperature is approximately 22 °C. The Fahrenheit scale and the Celsius scale differ both in the size of their respective degrees and the temperature each designates as "zero." Both the Fahrenheit and Celsius scales allow for negative temperatures.

The SI unit for temperature, as we have seen, is the kelvin, shown on the right in Figure 1.12. The **Kelvin scale** (sometimes also called the *absolute scale*) avoids negative temperatures by assigning 0 K to the coldest temperature possible, absolute zero. Absolute zero (−273 °C or −459 °F) is the temperature at which molecular motion virtually stops. Lower temperatures do not exist. The size of the kelvin is identical to that of the Celsius degree—the only difference is the temperature that each designates as zero. You can convert between the temperature scales with the following formulas:

$$°C = \frac{(°F - 32)}{1.8}$$

$$K = °C + 273.15$$

Normal body temperature was later measured more accurately to be 98.6 °F.

Molecular motion does not *completely* stop at absolute zero because of the uncertainty principle in quantum mechanics, which we will discuss in Chapter 7.

Note that we give Kelvin temperatures in kelvins (*not* "degrees Kelvin") or K (*not* °K).

The Celsius Temperature Scale

0 °C – Water freezes

10 °C – Brisk fall day

22 °C – Room temperature

45 °C – Summer day in Death Valley

Throughout this book you will see examples worked out in formats that are designed to help you develop problem-solving skills. The most common format uses two columns to guide you through the worked example. The left column describes the thought processes and steps used in solving the problem while the right column shows the implementation. The first example in this two-column format follows.

EXAMPLE 1.2 Converting between Temperature Scales

A sick child has a temperature of 40.00 °C. What is the child's temperature in **(a)** K and **(b)** °F?

SOLUTION

(a) Begin by finding the equation that relates the quantity that is given (°C) and the quantity you are trying to find (K).	$K = {}^\circ C + 273.15$
Since this equation gives the temperature in K directly, substitute in the correct value for the temperature in °C and compute the answer.	$K = {}^\circ C + 273.15$ $K = 40.00 + 273.15 = 313.15 \ K$
(b) To convert from °C to °F, first find the equation that relates these two quantities.	$^\circ C = \dfrac{({}^\circ F - 32)}{1.8}$
Since this equation expresses °C in terms of °F, you must solve the equation for °F.	$^\circ C = \dfrac{({}^\circ F - 32)}{1.8}$ $1.8({}^\circ C) = ({}^\circ F - 32)$ $^\circ F = 1.8({}^\circ C) + 32$
Now substitute °C into the equation and compute the answer. *Note: The number of digits reported in this answer follows significant figure conventions, covered in Section 1.7.*	$^\circ F = 1.8({}^\circ C) + 32$ $^\circ F = 1.8(40.00 \ {}^\circ C) + 32 = 104.00 \ {}^\circ F$

FOR PRACTICE 1.2

Gallium is a solid metal at room temperature, but will melt to a liquid in your hand. The melting point of gallium is 85.6 °F. What is this temperature on (a) the Celsius scale and (b) the Kelvin scale?

Prefix Multipliers

Scientific notation (see Appendix IA) allows us to express very large or very small quantities in a compact manner by using exponents. For example, the diameter of a hydrogen atom can be written as 1.06×10^{-10} m. The International System of Units uses the

TABLE 1.2 SI Prefix Multipliers

Prefix	Symbol	Multiplier	
exa	E	1,000,000,000,000,000,000	(10^{18})
peta	P	1,000,000,000,000,000	(10^{15})
tera	T	1,000,000,000,000	(10^{12})
giga	G	1,000,000,000	(10^{9})
mega	M	1,000,000	(10^{6})
kilo	k	1000	(10^{3})
deci	d	0.1	(10^{-1})
centi	c	0.01	(10^{-2})
milli	m	0.001	(10^{-3})
micro	μ	0.000001	(10^{-6})
nano	n	0.000000001	(10^{-9})
pico	p	0.000000000001	(10^{-12})
femto	f	0.000000000000001	(10^{-15})
atto	a	0.000000000000000001	(10^{-18})

prefix multipliers shown in Table 1.2 with the standard units. These multipliers change the value of the unit by powers of 10. For example, the kilometer has the prefix "kilo" meaning 1000 or 10^3. Therefore,

$$1 \text{ kilometer} = 1000 \text{ meters} = 10^3 \text{ meters}$$

Similarly, the millimeter has the prefix "milli" meaning 0.001 or 10^{-3}.

$$1 \text{ millimeter} = 0.001 \text{ meters} = 10^{-3} \text{ meters}$$

When reporting a measurement, choose a prefix multiplier close to the size of the quantity being measured. For example, to state the diameter of a hydrogen atom, which is 1.06×10^{-10} m, use picometers (106 pm) or nanometers (0.106 nm) rather than micrometers or millimeters. Choose the prefix multiplier that is most convenient for a particular number.

Derived Units: Volume and Density

A **derived unit** is a combination of other units. For example, the SI unit for speed is meters per second (m/s), a derived unit. Notice that this unit is formed from two other SI units—meters and seconds—put together. You are probably more familiar with speed in miles/hour or kilometers/hour—these are also examples of derived units. Two other common derived units are those for volume (SI base unit is m^3) and density (SI base unit is kg/m^3). We will look at each of these individually.

Volume Volume is a measure of space. Any unit of length, when cubed (raised to the third power), becomes a unit of volume. Thus, the cubic meter (m^3), cubic centimeter (cm^3), and cubic millimeter (mm^3) are all units of volume. The cubic nature of volume is not always intuitive, and studies have shown that our brains are not naturally wired to think abstractly, which we need to do in order to think about volume. For example, consider the following question: How many small cubes measuring 1 cm on each side are required to construct a large cube measuring 10 cm (or 1 dm) on a side?

The answer to this question, as you can see by carefully examining the unit cube in Figure 1.13 ▶, is 1000 small cubes. When you go from a linear, one-dimensional distance to three-dimensional volume, you must raise both the linear dimension *and* its unit to the third power (not multiply by 3). Thus the volume of a cube is equal to the length of its edge cubed:

$$\text{volume of cube} = (\text{edge length})^3$$

Relationship between Length and Volume

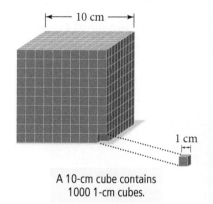

A 10-cm cube contains 1000 1-cm cubes.

▲ **FIGURE 1.13 The Relationship between Length and Volume**

TABLE 1.3 Some Common Units and Their Equivalents

Length	Mass	Volume
1 kilometer (km) = 0.6214 mile (mi)	1 kilogram (kg) = 2.205 pounds (lb)	1 liter (L) = 1000 mL = 1000 cm^3
1 meter (m) = 39.37 inches (in) = 1.094 yards (yd)	1 pound (lb) = 453.59 grams (g)	1 liter (L) = 1.057 quarts (qt)
1 foot (ft) = 30.48 centimeters (cm)	1 ounce (oz) = 28.35 grams (g)	1 U.S. gallon (gal) = 3.785 liters (L)
1 inch (in) = 2.54 centimeter (cm) (exact)		

A cube with a 10-cm edge length has a volume of $(10 \text{ cm})^3$ or 1000 cm^3, and a cube with a 100-cm edge length has a volume of $(100 \text{ cm})^3 = 1,000,000 \text{ cm}^3$.

Other common units of volume in chemistry are the **liter (L)** and the **milliliter (mL)**. One milliliter $\left(10^{-3} \text{ L}\right)$ is equal to 1 cm^3. A gallon of gasoline contains 3.785 L. Table 1.3 lists some common units—for volume and other quantities—and their equivalents.

Density An old riddle asks, 'Which weighs more, a ton of bricks or a ton of feathers?' The answer, of course, is neither—they both weigh the same (1 ton). If you answered bricks, you confused weight with density. The **density** (d) of a substance is the ratio of its mass (m) to its volume (V):

> The m in the equation for density is in italic type, meaning that it stands for mass rather than for meters. In general, the symbols for units such as meters (m), seconds (s), or kelvins (K) appear in regular type while those for variables such as mass (m), volume (V), and time (t) appear in italics.

$$\text{Density} = \frac{\text{mass}}{\text{volume}} \quad \text{or} \quad d = \frac{m}{V}$$

Density is a characteristic physical property of materials and differs from one substance to another, as you can see in Table 1.4. The density of a substance also depends on its temperature. Density is an example of an **intensive property**, one that is *independent* of the amount of the substance. The density of aluminum, for example, is the same whether you have an ounce or a ton. Intensive properties are often used to identify substances because these properties depend only on the type of substance, not on the amount of it. For example, from Table 1.4 you can see that pure gold has a density of 19.3 g/cm^3. One way to determine whether a substance is pure gold is to measure its density and compare it to 19.3 g/cm^3. Mass, in contrast, is an **extensive property**, one that depends on the amount of the substance.

The units of density are those of mass divided by volume. Although the SI derived unit for density is kg/m^3, the density of liquids and solids is most often expressed in g/cm^3 or g/mL. (Remember that cm^3 and mL are equivalent units: 1 cm^3 = 1 mL.) Aluminum is one of the least dense structural metals with a density of 2.7 g/cm^3, while platinum is one of the densest metals with a density of 21.4 g/cm^3.

TABLE 1.4 The Density of Some Common Substances at 20 °C

Substance	Density (g/cm^3)
Charcoal (from oak)	0.57
Ethanol	0.789
Ice	0.917 (at 0 °C)
Water	1.00 (at 4 °C)
Sugar (sucrose)	1.58
Table salt (sodium chloride)	2.16
Glass	2.6
Aluminum	2.70
Titanium	4.51
Iron	7.86
Copper	8.96
Lead	11.4
Mercury	13.55
Gold	19.3
Platinum	21.4

Calculating Density

We calculate the density of a substance by dividing the mass of a given amount of the substance by its volume. For example, suppose a small nugget we suspect to be gold has a mass of 22.5 g and a volume of 2.38 cm^3. To find its density, we divide the mass by the volume:

$$d = \frac{m}{V} = \frac{22.5 \text{ g}}{2.38 \text{ cm}^3} = 9.45 \text{ g/cm}^3$$

In this case, the density reveals that the nugget is not pure gold.

EXAMPLE 1.3 Calculating Density

A man receives a platinum ring from his fiancée. Before the wedding, he notices that the ring feels a little light for its size and decides to measure its density. He places the ring on a balance and finds that it has a mass of 3.15 grams. He then finds that the ring displaces 0.233 cm³ of water. Is the ring made of platinum? (Note: The volume of irregularly shaped objects is often measured by the displacement of water. To use this method, the object is placed in water and the change in volume of the water is measured. This increase in the total volume represents the volume of water *displaced* by the object, and is equal to the volume of the object.)

Set up the problem by writing the important information that is *given* as well as the information that you are asked to *find*. In this case, we are to find the density of the ring and compare it to that of platinum. *Note: This standard way of setting up problems is discussed in detail in Section 1.7.*	**GIVEN:** $m = 3.15 \text{ g}$ $V = 0.233 \text{ cm}^3$ **FIND:** Density in g/cm^3
Next, write down the equation that defines density.	**EQUATION:** $d = \dfrac{m}{V}$
Solve the problem by substituting the correct values of mass and volume into the expression for density.	**SOLUTION:** $d = \dfrac{m}{V} = \dfrac{3.15 \text{ g}}{0.233 \text{ cm}^3} = 13.5 \text{ g/cm}^3$

The density of the ring is much too low to be platinum (platinum density is 21.4 g/cm³), and the ring is therefore a fake.

FOR PRACTICE 1.3

The woman in the above example is shocked that the ring is fake and returns it. She buys a new ring that has a mass of 4.53 g and a volume of 0.212 cm³. Is this ring genuine?

FOR MORE PRACTICE 1.3

A metal cube has an edge length of 11.4 mm and a mass of 6.67 g. Calculate the density of the metal and use Table 1.4 to determine the likely identity of the metal.

 Conceptual Connection 1.4 Density

The density of copper decreases as temperature increases (as does the density of most substances). Which of the following will be true upon changing the temperature of a sample of copper from room temperature to 95 °C?

(a) the copper sample will become lighter

(b) the copper sample will become heavier

(c) the copper sample will expand

(d) the copper sample will contract

ANSWER: **(c)** The sample expands. However, because its mass remains constant while its volume increases, its density decreases.

CHEMISTRY AND MEDICINE   Bone Density

Osteoporosis—which means *porous bone*—is a condition in which bone density becomes too low. The healthy bones of a young adult have a density of about $1.0 \ g/cm^3$. Patients suffering from osteoporosis, however, can have bone densities as low as $0.22 \ g/cm^3$. These low densities mean the bones have deteriorated and weakened, resulting in increased susceptibility to fractures, especially hip fractures. Patients suffering from osteoporosis can also experience height loss and disfiguration such as dowager's hump, a condition in which the patient becomes hunched over due to compression of the vertebrae. Osteoporosis is most common in postmenopausal women, but it can also occur in people (including men) who have certain diseases, such as insulin-dependent diabetes, or who take certain medications, such as prednisone. Osteoporosis is usually diagnosed and monitored with hip X-rays. Low-density bones absorb less of the X-rays than do high-density bones, producing characteristic differences in the X-ray image. Treatments for osteoporosis include additional calcium and vitamin D, drugs that prevent bone weakening, exercise and strength training, and, in extreme cases, hip-replacement surgery.

Question

Suppose you find a large animal bone in the woods, too large to fit in a beaker or flask. How might you approximate its density?

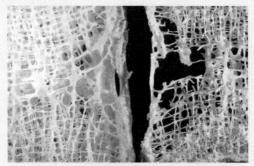

▲ Magnified views of the bone matrix in a normal vertebra (left) and one weakened by osteoporosis (right).

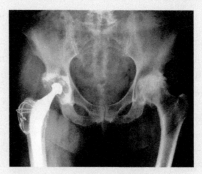

▲ Severe osteoporosis can necessitate surgery to implant an artificial hip joint, seen at left in this X-ray image.

1.7 The Reliability of a Measurement

Recall from our opening example (Section 1.1) that carbon monoxide is a colorless gas emitted by motor vehicles and found in polluted air. The table below shows carbon monoxide concentrations in Los Angeles County as reported by the U.S. Environmental Protection Agency (EPA) over the period 1997–2007:

Year	Carbon Monoxide Concentration (ppm)*
1997	15.0
1999	11.1
2001	7.2
2003	7.2
2005	5.6
2007	4.9

*Second maximum, 8 hour average; ppm = *parts per million*, defined as mL pollutant per million mL of air.

The first thing you should notice about these values is that they decrease over time. For this decrease, we can thank the Clean Air Act and its amendments, which have resulted in more efficient engines, in specially blended fuels, and consequently in cleaner air in all major U.S. cities over the last 30 years. The second thing you might notice is the number of digits to which the measurements are reported. The number of digits in a reported measurement indicates the certainty associated with that measurement. For example, a less certain measurement of carbon monoxide levels might be reported as follows:

Year	Carbon Monoxide Concentration (ppm)
1997	15
1999	11
2001	7
2003	7
2005	6
2007	5

Notice that the first set of data is reported to the nearest 0.1 ppm while the second set is reported to the nearest 1 ppm. Scientists agree on a standard way of reporting measured quantities in which the number of reported digits reflects the certainty in the measurement: more digits, more certainty; fewer digits, less certainty. Numbers are usually written so that the uncertainty is in the last reported digit. (That uncertainty is assumed to be ±1 in the last digit unless otherwise indicated.) By reporting the 1997 carbon monoxide concentration as 15.0 ppm, the scientists mean 15.0 ± 0.1 ppm. The carbon monoxide concentration is between 14.9 and 15.1 ppm—it might be 15.1 ppm, for example, but it could not be 16.0 ppm. In contrast, if the reported value was 15 ppm (without the .0), this would mean 15 ± 1 ppm, or between 14 and 16 ppm. In general,

Scientific measurements are reported so that every digit is certain except the last, which is estimated.

For example, consider the following reported number:

5.213

certain   estimated

The first three digits are certain; the last digit is estimated.

The number of digits reported in a measurement depends on the measuring device. Consider weighing a pistachio nut on two different balances (Figure 1.14 ▸). The balance on the top has marks every 1 gram, while the balance on the bottom has marks every 0.1 gram. For the balance on the top, we mentally divide the space between the 1- and 2-gram marks into ten equal spaces and estimate that the pointer is at about 1.2 grams. We then write the measurement as 1.2 grams indicating that we are sure of the "1" but have estimated the ".2." The balance on the bottom, with marks every *tenth* of a gram, requires us to write the result with more digits. The pointer is between the 1.2-gram mark and the 1.3-gram mark. We again divide the space between the two marks into ten equal spaces and estimate the third digit. For the figure shown, we report 1.27 g.

(a)

Markings every 1 g
Estimated reading 1.2 g

(b)

Markings every 0.1 g
Estimated reading 1.27 g

▲ **FIGURE 1.14 Estimation in Weighing** (a) This scale has markings every 1 g, so we estimate to the tenths place by mentally dividing the space into ten equal spaces to estimate the last digit. This reading is 1.2 g. (b) Because this balance has markings every 0.1 g, we estimate to the hundredths place. This reading is 1.27 g.

EXAMPLE 1.4 Reporting the Correct Number of Digits

The graduated cylinder shown at right has markings every 0.1 mL. Report the volume (which is read at the bottom of the meniscus) to the correct number of digits. (Note: The meniscus is the crescent-shaped surface at the top of a column of liquid.)

SOLUTION

Since the bottom of the meniscus is between the 4.5 and 4.6 mL markings, mentally divide the space between the markings into ten equal spaces and estimate the next digit. In this case, you should report the result as 4.57 mL.

What if you estimated a little differently and wrote 4.56 mL? In general, one unit difference in the last digit is acceptable because the last digit is estimated and different people might estimate it slightly differently. However, if you wrote 4.63 mL, you would have misreported the measurement.

FOR PRACTICE 1.4

Record the temperature on the thermometer shown at right to the correct number of digits.

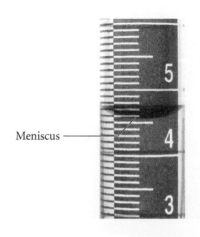

Meniscus

Counting Significant Figures

The precision of a measurement—which depends on the instrument used to make the measurement—must be preserved, not only when recording the measurement, but also when performing calculations that use the measurement. We can accomplish the preservation of this precision by using *significant figures*. In any reported measurement, the non-place-holding digits—those that are not simply marking the decimal place—are called **significant figures** (or **significant digits**). *The greater the number of significant figures, the greater the certainty of the measurement.* For example, the number 23.5 has three significant figures while the number 23.56 has four. To determine the number of significant figures in a number containing zeroes, we must distinguish between zeroes that are significant and those that simply mark the decimal place. For example, in the number 0.0008, the leading zeroes mark the decimal place but *do not* add to the certainty of the measurement and are therefore not significant; this number has only one significant figure. In contrast, the trailing zeroes in the number 0.000800 *do add* to the certainty of the measurement and are therefore counted as significant; this number has three significant figures.

To determine the number of significant figures in a number, follow these rules (with examples shown on the right).

Significant Figure Rules	Examples	
1. All nonzero digits are significant.	28.03	0.0540
2. Interior zeroes (zeroes between two non-zero digits) are significant.	408	7.0301
3. Leading zeroes (zeroes to the left of the first non-zero digit) are not significant. They only serve to locate the decimal point.	⓪.00⃝32	⓪.0000⃝6

not significant

4. Trailing zeroes (zeroes at the end of a number) are categorized as follows:

• Trailing zeroes after a decimal point are always significant.	45.000	3.5600
• Trailing zeroes before a decimal point (and after a non-zero number) are always significant.	140.00	2500.55
• Trailing zeroes before an *implied* decimal point are ambiguous and should be avoided by using scientific notation.	1200 1.2×10^3 1.20×10^3 1.200×10^3	ambiguous 2 significant figures 3 significant figures 4 significant figures
• Some textbooks put a decimal point after one or more trailing zeroes if the zeroes are to be considered significant. We avoid that practice in this book, but you should be aware of it.	1200.	4 significant figures (common in some textbooks)

Exact Numbers

Exact numbers have no uncertainty, and thus do not limit the number of significant figures in any calculation. We can regard an exact number as having an unlimited number of significant figures. Exact numbers originate from three sources:

- From the accurate counting of discrete objects. For example, 3 atoms means 3.00000. . . atoms.
- From defined quantities, such as the number of centimeters in 1 m. Because 100 cm is defined as 1 m,

$$100 \, cm = 1 \, m \text{ means } 100.00000. . . cm = 1.0000000. . . m$$

• From integral numbers that are part of an equation. For example, in the equation,

$radius = \dfrac{diameter}{2}$, the number 2 is exact and therefore has an unlimited number of

significant figures.

EXAMPLE 1.5 Determining the Number of Significant Figures in a Number

How many significant figures are in each number?

(a) 0.04450 m   (b) 5.0003 km

(c) 10 dm = 1 m   (d) 1.000×10^5 s

(e) 0.00002 mm   (f) 10,000 m

SOLUTION

(a) 0.04450 m	*Four significant figures.* The two 4's and the 5 are significant (rule 1). The trailing zero is after a decimal point and is therefore significant (rule 4). The leading zeroes only mark the decimal place and are therefore not significant (rule 3).
(b) 5.0003 km	*Five significant figures.* The 5 and 3 are significant (rule 1) as are the three interior zeroes (rule 2).
(c) 10 dm = 1 m	*Unlimited significant figures.* Defined quantities have an unlimited number of significant figures.
(d) 1.000×10^5 s	*Four significant figures.* The 1 is significant (rule 1). The trailing zeroes are after a decimal point and therefore significant (rule 4).
(e) 0.00002 mm	*One significant figure.* The 2 is significant (rule 1). The leading zeroes only mark the decimal place and are therefore not significant (rule 3).
(f) 10,000 m	*Ambiguous.* The 1 is significant (rule 1) but the trailing zeroes occur before an implied decimal point and are therefore ambiguous (rule 4). Without more information, we would assume 1 significant figure. It is better to write this as 1×10^5 to indicate one significant figure or as 1.0000×10^5 to indicate five (rule 4).

FOR PRACTICE 1.5

How many significant figures are in each of the following numbers?

(a) 554 km   (b) 7 pennies

(c) 1.01×10^5 m   (d) 0.00099 s

(e) 1.4500 km   (f) 21,000 m

Significant Figures in Calculations

When you use measured quantities in calculations, the results of the calculation must reflect the precision of the measured quantities. You should not lose or gain precision during mathematical operations. Follow these rules when carrying significant figures through calculations.

Rules for Calculations	Examples
1. In multiplication or division, the result carries the same number of significant figures as the factor with the fewest significant figures.	$1.052 \times 12.054 \times 0.53 = 6.7208 = 6.7$ (4 sig. figures) (5 sig. figures) (2 sig. figures) (2 sig. figures) $2.0035 \div 3.20 = 0.626094 = 0.626$ (5 sig. figures) (3 sig. figures) (3 sig. figures)

2. In addition or subtraction the result carries the same number of decimal places as the quantity with the fewest decimal places.

$$
\begin{array}{r}
2.34|5 \\
0.07| \\
\underline{2.99|75} \\
5.41|25 = 5.41
\end{array}
\qquad
\begin{array}{r}
5.9| \\
\underline{-0.2|21} \\
5.6|79 = 5.7
\end{array}
$$

In addition and subtraction, it is helpful to draw a line next to the number with the fewest decimal places. This line determines the number of decimal places in the answer.

A few books recommend a slightly different rounding procedure for cases where the last digit is 5. However, the procedure presented here is consistent with electronic calculators and will be used throughout this book.

3. When rounding to the correct number of significant figures, round down if the last (or leftmost) digit dropped is four or less; round up if the last (or leftmost) digit dropped is five or more.

To two significant figures:

5.37 rounds to 5.4
5.34 rounds to 5.3
5.35 rounds to 5.4
5.349 rounds to 5.3

Notice in the last example that only the *last (or leftmost) digit being dropped* determines in which direction to round—ignore all digits to the right of it.

4. To avoid rounding errors in multistep calculations round only the final answer—do not round intermediate steps. If you write down intermediate answers, keep track of significant figures by underlining the least significant digit.

$$
6.78 \times 5.903 \times (5.489 - 5.01)
$$
$$
= 6.78 \times 5.903 \times 0.47\underline{9}
$$
$$
= 19.1707
$$
$$
= 19
$$

underline least significant digit

Notice that for multiplication or division, the quantity with the fewest *significant figures* determines the number of *significant figures* in the answer, but for addition and subtraction, the quantity with the fewest *decimal places* determines the number of *decimal places* in the answer. In multiplication and division, we focus on significant figures, but in addition and subtraction we focus on decimal places. When a problem involves addition or subtraction, the answer may have a different number of significant figures than the initial quantities. Keep this in mind in problems that involve both addition or subtraction and multiplication or division. For example,

$$
\frac{1.002 - 0.999}{3.754} = \frac{0.003}{3.754}
$$
$$
= 7.99 \times 10^{-4}
$$
$$
= 8 \times 10^{-4}
$$

The answer has only one significant figure, even though the initial numbers had three or four.

EXAMPLE 1.6 Significant Figures in Calculations

Perform each calculation to the correct number of significant figures.

(a) $1.10 \times 0.5120 \times 4.0015 \div 3.4555$

(b)
$$
\begin{array}{r}
0.355 \\
+105.1 \\
\underline{-100.5820}
\end{array}
$$

(c) $4.562 \times 3.99870 \div (452.6755 - 452.33)$

(d) $(14.84 \times 0.55) - 8.02$

SOLUTION

(a) Round the intermediate result (in blue) to three significant figures to reflect the three significant figures in the least precisely known quantity (1.10).	$1.10 \times 0.5120 \times 4.0015 \div 3.4555$ $= 0.65219$ $= 0.652$
(b) Round the intermediate answer (in blue) to one decimal place to reflect the quantity with the fewest decimal places (105.1). Notice that 105.1 is *not* the quantity with the fewest significant figures, but it has the fewest decimal places and therefore determines the number of decimal places in the answer.	$\begin{array}{r} 0.3\vert55 \\ +105.1\vert \\ -100.5\vert820 \\ \hline 4.8\vert730 = 4.9 \end{array}$
(c) Mark the intermediate result to two decimal places to reflect the number of decimal places in the quantity within the parentheses having the fewest number of decimal places (452.33). Round the final answer to two significant figures to reflect the two significant figures in the least precisely known quantity (0.3455).	$4.562 \times 3.99870 \div (452.6755 - 452.33)$ $= 4.562 \times 3.99870 \div 0.3455$ $= 52.79904$ $= 53$ 2 places of the decimal
(d) Mark the intermediate result to two significant figures to reflect the number of significant figures in the quantity within the parentheses having the fewest number of significant figures (0.55). Round the final answer to one decimal place to reflect the one decimal place in the least precisely known quantity (8.162).	$(14.84 \times 0.55) - 8.02 = 8.162 - 8.02$ $= 0.142$ $= 0.1$

FOR PRACTICE 1.6

Perform each calculation to the correct number of significant figures.

(a) $3.10007 \times 9.441 \times 0.0301 \div 2.31$ (b) $\begin{array}{r} 0.881 \\ +132.1 \\ -12.02 \\ \hline \end{array}$

(c) $2.5110 \times 21.20 \div (44.11 + 1.223)$ (d) $(12.01 \times 0.3) + 4.811$

Precision and Accuracy

Scientists often repeat measurements several times to increase confidence in the result. We can distinguish between two different kinds of certainty—called accuracy and precision—associated with such measurements. **Accuracy** refers to how close the measured value is to the actual value. **Precision** refers to how close a series of measurements are to one another or how reproducible they are. A series of measurements can be precise (close to one another in value and reproducible) but not accurate (not close to the true value). Consider the results of three students who repeatedly weighed a lead block known to have a true mass of 10.00 g (indicated by the solid horizontal blue line on the graphs on the next page).

	Student A	Student B	Student C
Trial 1	10.49 g	9.78 g	10.03 g
Trial 2	9.79 g	9.82 g	9.99 g
Trial 3	9.92 g	9.75 g	10.03 g
Trial 4	10.31 g	9.80 g	9.98 g
Average	**10.13 g**	**9.79 g**	**10.01 g**

- The results of student A are both inaccurate (not close to the true value) and imprecise (not consistent with one another). The inconsistency is the result of **random error**, error that has equal probability of being too high or too low. Almost all measurements have some degree of random error. Random error can, with enough trials, average itself out.

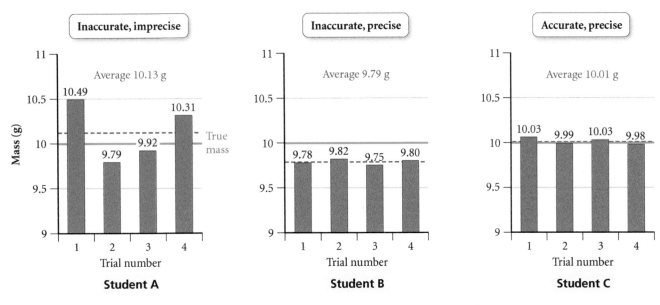

▲ Measurements are said to be precise if they are consistent with one another, but they are accurate only if they are close to the actual value.

- The results of student B are precise (close to one another in value) but inaccurate. The inaccuracy is the result of **systematic error**, error that tends toward being either too high or too low. Systematic error does not average out with repeated trials. For instance, if a balance is not properly calibrated, it may systematically read too high or too low.

- The results of student C display little systematic error or random error—they are both accurate and precise.

CHEMISTRY IN YOUR DAY Integrity in Data Gathering

Most scientists spend many hours collecting data in the laboratory. Often, the data do not turn out exactly as the scientist had expected (or hoped). A scientist may then be tempted to "fudge" his or her results. For example, suppose you are expecting a particular set of measurements to follow a certain pattern. After working hard over several days or weeks to make the measurements, you notice that a few of them do not quite fit the pattern that you anticipated. You might find yourself wishing that you could simply change or omit the "faulty" measurements. Altering data in this way is considered highly unethical in the scientific community and, when discovered, is usually punished severely.

In 2004, Dr. Hwang Woo Suk, a stem cell researcher at the Seoul National University in Korea, published a research paper in *Science* (a highly respected research journal) claiming that he and his colleagues had cloned human embryonic stem cells. As part of his evidence, he showed photographs of the cells. The paper was hailed as an incredible breakthrough, and Dr. Hwang traveled the world lecturing on his work. *Time* magazine even listed him among their "people that matter"

for 2004. Several months later, however, one of his co-workers revealed that the photographs were fraudulent. According to the co-worker, the photographs came from a computer data bank of stem cell photographs, not from a cloning experiment. A university panel investigated the results and confirmed that the photographs and other data had indeed been faked. Dr. Hwang was forced to resign his prestigious post at the university.

Although not common, incidents like this do occur from time to time. They are damaging to a community that is largely built on trust. A scientist's peers (other researchers in similar fields) review all published research papers, but usually they are judging whether the data support the conclusion—they assume that the experimental measurements are authentic. The pressure to succeed sometimes leads researchers to betray that trust. However, over time, the tendency of scientists to reproduce and build upon one another's work results in the discovery of the fraudulent data. When that happens, the researchers at fault are usually banished from the community and their careers are ruined.

1.8 Solving Chemical Problems

Learning to solve problems is one of the most important skills you will acquire in this course. No one succeeds in chemistry—or in life, really—without the ability to solve problems. Although no simple formula applies to every chemistry problem, you can learn problem-solving strategies and begin to develop some chemical intuition. Many of the problems you will solve in this course can be thought of as *unit conversion problems*, where you are given one or more quantities and asked to convert them into different units. Other problems require that you use *specific equations* to get to the information you are trying to find. In the sections that follow, you will find strategies to help you solve both of these types of problems. Of course, many problems contain both conversions and equations, requiring the combination of these strategies, and some problems may require an altogether different approach.

Converting from One Unit to Another

In Section 1.6, we learned the SI unit system, the prefix multipliers, and a few other units. Knowing how to work with and manipulate these units in calculations is central to solving chemical problems. In calculations, units help to determine correctness. Using units as a guide to solving problems is often called **dimensional analysis**. Units should always be included in calculations; they are multiplied, divided, and canceled like any other algebraic quantity.

Consider converting 12.5 inches (in) to centimeters (cm). We know from Table 1.3 that 1 in = 2.54 cm (exact), so we can use this quantity in the calculation as follows:

$$12.5 \; \cancel{\text{in}} \times \frac{2.54 \text{ cm}}{1 \; \cancel{\text{in}}} = 31.8 \text{ cm}$$

The unit, in, cancels and we are left with cm as our final unit. The quantity $\frac{2.54 \text{ cm}}{1 \text{ in}}$ is a **conversion factor**—a fractional quantity with the units we are *converting from* on the bottom and the units we are *converting to* on the top. Conversion factors are constructed from any two equivalent quantities. In this example, 2.54 cm = 1 in, so we construct the conversion factor by dividing both sides of the equality by 1 in and canceling the units

$$2.54 \text{ cm} = 1 \text{ in}$$

$$\frac{2.54 \text{ cm}}{1 \text{ in}} = \frac{1 \; \cancel{\text{in}}}{1 \; \cancel{\text{in}}}$$

$$\frac{2.54 \text{ cm}}{1 \text{ in}} = 1$$

The quantity $\frac{2.54 \text{ cm}}{1 \text{ in}}$ is equivalent to 1, so multiplying by the conversion factor affects only the units, not the actual quantity. To convert the other way, from centimeters to inches, we must—using units as a guide—use a different form of the conversion factor. If you accidentally use the same form, you will get the wrong result, indicated by erroneous units. For example, suppose that you want to convert 31.8 cm to inches.

$$31.8 \text{ cm} \times \frac{2.54 \text{ cm}}{1 \text{ in}} = \frac{80.8 \text{ cm}^2}{\text{in}}$$

The units in the above answer (cm^2/in), as well as the value of the answer, are obviously wrong. When you solve a problem, always look at the final units. Are they the desired units? Always look at the magnitude of the numerical answer as well. Does it make sense? In this case, our mistake was the form of the conversion factor. It should have been inverted so that the units cancel as follows:

$$31.8 \; \cancel{\text{cm}} \times \frac{1 \text{ in}}{2.54 \; \cancel{\text{cm}}} = 12.5 \text{ in}$$

Conversion factors can be inverted because they are equal to 1 and the inverse of 1 is 1. Therefore,

$$\frac{2.54 \text{ cm}}{1 \text{ in}} = 1 = \frac{1 \text{ in}}{2.54 \text{ cm}}$$

Most unit conversion problems take the following form:

Information given × conversion factor(s) = information sought

$$\cancel{\text{Given unit}} \times \frac{\text{desired unit}}{\cancel{\text{given unit}}} = \text{desired unit}$$

In this book, we diagram problem solutions using a *conceptual plan*. A conceptual plan is a visual outline that helps you to see the general flow of the problem solution. For unit conversions, the conceptual plan focuses on units and the conversion from one unit to another. The conceptual plan for converting in to cm is as follows:

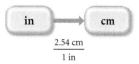

The conceptual plan for converting the other way, from cm to in, is just the reverse, with the reciprocal conversion factor:

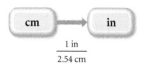

Each arrow in a conceptual plan for a unit conversion has an associated conversion factor with the units of the previous step in the denominator and the units of the following step in the numerator. In the following section, we incorporate the idea of a conceptual plan into an overall approach to solving numerical chemical problems.

General Problem-Solving Strategy

In this book, we use a standard problem-solving procedure that can be adapted to many of the problems encountered in general chemistry and beyond. To solve any problem you need to assess the information given in the problem and devise a way to get to the information asked for. In other words, you must

- Identify the starting point (the *given* information).
- Identify the end point (what you must *find*).
- Devise a way to get from the starting point to the end point using what is given as well as what you already know or can look up. (We call this the *conceptual plan*.)

In graphic form, we can represent this progression as

$$\textbf{Given} \longrightarrow \textbf{Conceptual Plan} \longrightarrow \textbf{Find}$$

One of the main difficulties beginning students have when trying to solve problems in general chemistry is not knowing where to start. While no problem-solving procedure is applicable to all problems, the following four-step procedure can be helpful in working through many of the numerical problems you will encounter in this book.

1. **Sort.** Begin by sorting the information in the problem. *Given* information is the basic data provided by the problem—often one or more numbers with their associated units. *Find* indicates what information you will need for your answer.

2. **Strategize.** This is usually the hardest part of solving a problem. In this process, you must develop a *conceptual plan*—a series of steps that will get you from the given information to the information you are trying to find. You have already seen conceptual plans for simple unit conversion problems. Each arrow in a conceptual plan represents a computational step. On the left side of the arrow is the quantity you had before the step; on the right side of the arrow is the quantity you will have after the step; and below the arrow is the information you need to get from one to the other—the relationship between the quantities.

Often such relationships will take the form of conversion factors or equations. These may be given in the problem, in which case you will have written them down under "Given" in step 1. Usually, however, you will need other information—which may include physical constants, formulas, or conversion factors—to help get you from what you are given to what you must find. This information comes from what you have learned or can look up in the chapter or in tables within the book.

In some cases, you may get stuck at the strategize step. If you cannot figure out how to get from the given information to the information you are asked to find, you might try working backwards. For example, you may want to look at the units of the quantity you are trying to find and try to find conversion factors to get to the units of the given quantity. You may even try a combination of strategies; work forward, backward, or some of both. If you persist, you will develop a strategy to solve the problem.

Most problems can be solved in more than one way. The solutions we derive in this book will tend to be the most straightforward but certainly not the only way to solve the problem.

3. **Solve.** This is the easiest part of solving a problem. Once you set up the problem properly and devise a conceptual plan, you simply follow the plan to solve the problem. Carry out any mathematical operations (paying attention to the rules for significant figures in calculations) and cancel units as needed.

4. **Check.** This is the step beginning students most often overlook. Experienced problem solvers always ask, does this answer make sense? Are the units correct? Is the number of significant figures correct? When solving multistep problems, errors easily creep into the solution. You can catch most of these errors by simply checking the answer. For example, suppose you are calculating the number of atoms in a gold coin and end up with an answer of 1.1×10^{-6} atoms. Could the gold coin really be composed of one-millionth of one atom?

In the following pages, we apply this problem-solving procedure to unit conversion problems. The procedure is summarized in the left column and two examples of applying the procedure are shown in the middle and right columns. This three-column format will be used in selected examples throughout this text. It allows you to see how you can apply a particular procedure to two different problems. Work through one problem first (from top to bottom) and then see how you can apply the same procedure to the other problem. Being able to see the commonalities and differences between problems is a key part of developing problem-solving skills.

PROCEDURE FOR... Solving Unit Conversion Problems	EXAMPLE 1.7 Unit Conversion Convert 1.76 yards to centimeters.	EXAMPLE 1.8 Unit Conversion Convert 1.8 quarts to cubic centimeters.
SORT Begin by sorting the information in the problem into *Given* and *Find*.	**GIVEN:** 1.76 yd **FIND:** cm	**GIVEN:** 1.8 qt **FIND:** cm^3
STRATEGIZE Devise a *conceptual plan* for the problem. Begin with the *given* quantity and symbolize each conversion step with an arrow. Below each arrow, write the appropriate conversion factor for that step. Focus on the units. The conceptual plan should end at the *find* quantity and its units. In these examples, the other information needed consists of relationships between the various units as shown.	**CONCEPTUAL PLAN** 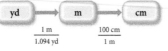 **RELATIONSHIPS USED** 1.094 yd = 1 m 1 m = 100 cm (These conversion factors are from Tables 1.2 and 1.3.)	**CONCEPTUAL PLAN** 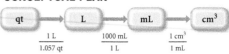 **RELATIONSHIPS USED** 1.057 qt = 1 L 1 L = 1000 mL 1 mL = 1 cm^3 (These conversion factors are from Tables 1.2 and 1.3.)
SOLVE Follow the conceptual plan. Begin with the *given* quantity and its units. Multiply by the appropriate conversion factor(s), canceling units, to arrive at the *find* quantity. Round the answer to the correct number of significant figures following the rules in Section 1.7. Remember that exact conversion factors do not limit significant figures.	**SOLUTION** $1.76 \text{ yd} \times \dfrac{1 \text{ m}}{1.094 \text{ yd}} \times \dfrac{100 \text{ cm}}{1 \text{ m}}$ $= 160.8775 \text{ cm}$ 160.8775 cm = 161 cm	**SOLUTION** $1.8 \text{ qt} \times \dfrac{1 \text{ L}}{1.057 \text{ qt}} \times \dfrac{1000 \text{ mL}}{1 \text{ L}} \times \dfrac{1 \text{ cm}^3}{1 \text{ mL}}$ $= 1.70293 \times 10^3 \text{ cm}^3$ $1.70293 \times 10^3 \text{ cm}^3 = 1.7 \times 10^3 \text{ cm}^3$
CHECK Check your answer. Are the units correct? Does the answer make sense?	The units (cm) are correct. The magnitude of the answer (161) makes sense because a centimeter is a much smaller unit than a yard.	The units (cm^3) are correct. The magnitude of the answer (1700) makes sense because a cubic centimeter is a much smaller unit than a quart.
	FOR PRACTICE 1.7 Convert 288 cm to yards.	**FOR PRACTICE 1.8** Convert 9255 cm^3 to gallons.

Units Raised to a Power

When building conversion factors for units raised to a power, remember to raise both the number and the unit to the power. For example, to convert from in^2 to cm^2, we construct the conversion factor as follows:

$$2.54 \text{ cm} = 1 \text{ in}$$
$$(2.54 \text{ cm})^2 = (1 \text{ in})^2$$
$$(2.54)^2 \text{ cm}^2 = 1^2 \text{ in}^2$$
$$6.45 \text{ cm}^2 = 1 \text{ in}^2$$
$$\frac{6.45 \text{ cm}^2}{1 \text{ in}^2} = 1$$

The following example shows how to use conversion factors involving units raised to a power.

EXAMPLE 1.9 Unit Conversions Involving Units Raised to a Power

Calculate the displacement (the total volume of the cylinders through which the pistons move) of a 5.70-L automobile engine in cubic inches.

SORT Sort the information in the problem into *Given* and *Find*.	**GIVEN:** 5.70 L **FIND:** in^3
STRATEGIZE Write a conceptual plan. Begin with the given information and devise a path to the information that you are asked to find. Notice that for cubic units, you must cube the conversion factors.	**CONCEPTUAL PLAN** 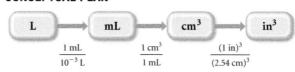 **RELATIONSHIPS USED** $1 \text{ mL} = 10^{-3} \text{ L}$ $1 \text{ mL} = 1 \text{ cm}^3$ $2.54 \text{ cm} = 1 \text{ in}$ (These conversion factors are from Tables 1.2 and 1.3.)
SOLVE Follow the conceptual plan to solve the problem. Round the answer to three significant figures to reflect the three significant figures in the least precisely known quantity (5.70 L). These conversion factors are all exact and therefore do not limit the number of significant figures.	**SOLUTION** $5.70 \text{ L} \times \dfrac{1 \text{ mL}}{10^{-3} \text{ L}} \times \dfrac{1 \text{ cm}^3}{1 \text{ mL}} \times \dfrac{(1 \text{ in})^3}{(2.54 \text{ cm})^3} = 347.835 \text{ in}^3$ $= 348 \text{ in}^3$

CHECK The units of the answer are correct and the magnitude makes sense. The unit cubic inches is smaller than liters, so the volume in cubic inches should be larger than the volume in liters.

FOR PRACTICE 1.9

How many cubic centimeters are there in 2.11 yd^3?

FOR MORE PRACTICE 1.9

A vineyard has 145 acres of Chardonnay grapes. A particular soil supplement requires 5.50 grams for every square meter of vineyard. How many kilograms of the soil supplement are required for the entire vineyard? ($1 \text{ km}^2 = 247$ acres)

EXAMPLE 1.10 Density as a Conversion Factor

The mass of fuel in a jet must be calculated before each flight to ensure that the jet is not too heavy to fly. A 747 is fueled with 173,231 L of jet fuel. If the density of the fuel is 0.768 g/cm³, what is the mass of the fuel in kilograms?

SORT Begin by *sorting* the information in the problem into *Given* and *Find*.	**GIVEN:** fuel volume = 173,231 L density of fuel = 0.768 g/cm³ **FIND:** mass in kg
STRATEGIZE Draw the conceptual plan by beginning with the given quantity, in this case the volume in liters (L). The overall goal of this problem is to find the mass. You can convert between volume and mass using density (g/cm^3). However, you must first convert the volume to cm^3. Once you have converted the volume to cm^3, use the density to convert to g. Finally convert g to kg.	**CONCEPTUAL PLAN** 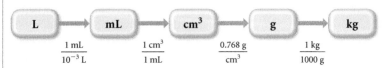 **RELATIONSHIPS USED** $1 \text{ mL} = 10^{-3} \text{ L}$ $1 \text{ mL} = 1 \text{ cm}^3$ $d = 0.768 \text{ g/cm}^3$ $1000 \text{ g} = 1 \text{ kg}$ (These conversion factors are from Tables 1.2 and 1.3.)
SOLVE Follow the conceptual plan to solve the problem. Round the answer to three significant figures to reflect the three significant figures in the density.	**SOLUTION** $$173,231 \text{ L} \times \frac{1 \text{ mL}}{10^{-3} \text{ L}} \times \frac{1 \text{ cm}^3}{1 \text{ mL}} \times \frac{0.768 \text{ g}}{1 \text{ cm}^3} \times \frac{1 \text{ kg}}{1000 \text{ g}} = 1.33 \times 10^5 \text{ kg}$$

CHECK The units of the answer (kg) are correct. The magnitude makes sense because the mass (1.33×10^5 kg) is similar in magnitude to the given volume (173,231 L or 1.73231×10^5 L), as expected for a density close to one (0.768 g/cm³).

FOR PRACTICE 1.10

Backpackers often use canisters of white gas to fuel a cooking stove's burner. If one canister contains 1.45 L of white gas, and the density of the gas is 0.710 g/cm³, what is the mass of the fuel in kilograms?

FOR MORE PRACTICE 1.10

A drop of gasoline has a mass of 22 mg and a density of 0.754 g/cm³. What is its volume in cubic centimeters?

Order-of-Magnitude Estimations

Calculation plays a major role in chemical problem solving. But precise numerical calculation is not always necessary, or even possible. Sometimes data are only approximate, so there is no point in trying to determine an extremely precise answer. At other times, you simply don't need a high degree of precision—a rough estimate or a simplified "back of the envelope" calculation is enough. Scientists often use these kinds of calculations to get an initial feel for a problem, or as a quick check to see whether a proposed solution is "in the right ballpark."

One way to make such estimates is to simplify the numbers so that they can be manipulated easily. The technique known as *order-of-magnitude estimation* is based on focusing only on the exponential part of numbers written in scientific notation, according to the following guidelines:

- If the decimal part of the number is less than 5, just drop it. Thus, 4.36×10^5 becomes 10^5 and 2.7×10^{-3} becomes 10^{-3}.

- If the decimal part is 5 or more, round it up to 10 and rewrite the number as a power of 10. Thus, 5.982×10^7 becomes $10 \times 10^7 = 10^8$, and 6.1101×10^{-3} becomes $10 \times 10^{-3} = 10^{-2}$.

When you make these approximations, you are left with powers of 10, which are easily multiplied and divided—often in your head. It's important to remember, however, that your answer is only as reliable as the numbers used to get it, so never assume that the results of an order-of-magnitude calculation are accurate to more than an order of magnitude.

Suppose, for example, that you want to estimate the number of atoms an immortal being could have counted in the 14 billion (1.4×10^{10}) years that the universe has been in existence, assuming a counting rate of 10 atoms per second. Since a year has 3.2×10^7 seconds, you can approximate the number of atoms counted as follows:

$$10^{10} \ \cancel{\text{years}} \quad \times \quad 10^7 \ \frac{\cancel{\text{seconds}}}{\cancel{\text{year}}} \quad \times \quad 10^1 \ \frac{\text{atoms}}{\cancel{\text{second}}} \quad \approx \quad 10^{18} \ \text{atoms}$$

(number of years) (number of seconds number of atoms
per year) counted per second)

A million trillion atoms (10^{18}) may seem like a lot, but as you will see in Chapter 2, a speck of matter made up of a million trillion atoms is nearly impossible to see without a microscope.

In our general problem-solving procedure, the last step is to check whether the results seem reasonable. Order-of-magnitude estimations can often help you catch the kinds of mistakes that may happen in a detailed calculation, such as entering an incorrect exponent or sign into your calculator, or multiplying when you should have divided.

Problems Involving an Equation

Problems involving equations can be solved in much the same way as problems involving conversions. Usually, in problems involving equations, you must find one of the variables in the equation, given the others. The *conceptual plan* concept outlined above can be used for problems involving equations. For example, suppose you are given the mass (*m*) and volume (*V*) of a sample and asked to calculate its density. The conceptual plan shows how the *equation* takes you from the *given* quantities to the *find* quantity.

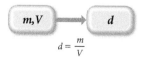

$$d = \frac{m}{V}$$

Here, instead of a conversion factor under the arrow, this conceptual plan has an equation. The equation shows the *relationship* between the quantities on the left of the arrow and the quantities on the right. Note that at this point, the equation need not be solved for the quantity on the right (although in this particular case it is). The procedure that follows, as well as the two examples, will guide you in developing a strategy to solve problems involving equations. We again use the three-column format here. Work through one problem from top to bottom and then see how you can apply the same general procedure to the second problem.

PROCEDURE FOR... Solving Problems Involving Equations	**EXAMPLE 1.11** Problems with Equations Find the radius (r), in centimeters, of a spherical water droplet with a volume (V) of 0.058 cm^3. For a sphere, $V = (4/3)\,\pi r^3$.	**EXAMPLE 1.12** Problems with Equations Find the density (in g/cm^3) of a metal cylinder with a mass (m) of 8.3 g, a length (l) of 1.94 cm, and a radius (r) of 0.55 cm. For a cylinder, $V = \pi r^2 l$.
SORT Begin by sorting the information in the problem into *given* and *find*.	**GIVEN:** $V = 0.058$ cm^3 **FIND:** r in cm	**GIVEN:** $m = 8.3$ g $l = 1.94$ cm $r = 0.55$ cm **FIND:** d in g/cm^3
STRATEGIZE Write a *conceptual plan* for the problem. Focus on the equation(s). The conceptual plan shows how the equation takes you from the *given* quantity (or quantities) to the *find* quantity. The conceptual plan may have several parts, involving other equations or required conversions. In these examples, you use the geometrical relationships given in the problem statements as well as the definition of density, $d = m/V$, which you learned in this chapter.	**CONCEPTUAL PLAN** 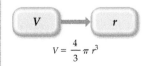 $$V = \frac{4}{3}\,\pi\,r^3$$ **RELATIONSHIPS USED** $$V = \frac{4}{3}\,\pi r^3$$	**CONCEPTUAL PLAN**  $$V = \pi r^2 l$$ $$d = m/V$$ **RELATIONSHIPS USED** $$V = \pi r^2 l$$ $$d = \frac{m}{V}$$
SOLVE Follow the conceptual plan. Solve the equation(s) for the *find* quantity (if it is not already). Gather each of the quantities that must go into the equation in the correct units. (Convert to the correct units if necessary.) Substitute the numerical values and their units into the equation(s) and compute the answer. Round the answer to the correct number of significant figures.	**SOLUTION** $$V = \frac{4}{3}\,\pi r^3$$ $$r^3 = \frac{3}{4\pi}V$$ $$r = \left(\frac{3}{4\pi}V\right)^{1/3}$$ $$= \left(\frac{3}{4\pi}\,0.058\ \text{cm}^3\right)^{1/3}$$ $$= 0.24013\ \text{cm}$$ 0.24013 cm = 0.24 cm	**SOLUTION** $$V = \pi r^2 l$$ $$= \pi(0.55\ \text{cm})^2\,(1.94\ \text{cm})$$ $$= 1.8436\ \text{cm}^3$$ $$d = \frac{m}{V}$$ $$= \frac{8.3\ \text{g}}{1.8436\ \text{cm}^3} = 4.50195\ \text{g/cm}^3$$ 4.50195 g/cm^3 = 4.5 g/cm^3
CHECK Check your answer. Are the units correct? Does the answer make sense?	The units (cm) are correct and the magnitude makes sense.	The units (g/cm^3) are correct. The magnitude of the answer seems correct for one of the lighter metals (see Table 1.4).
	FOR PRACTICE 1.11 Find the radius (r) of an aluminum cylinder that is 2.00 cm long and has a mass of 12.4 g. For a cylinder, $V = \pi r^2 l$.	**FOR PRACTICE 1.12** Find the density, in g/cm^3, of a metal cube with a mass of 50.3 g and an edge length (l) of 2.65 cm. For a cube, $V = l^3$.

CHAPTER IN REVIEW

Key Terms

Section 1.1
atoms (1)
molecules (1)
chemistry (3)

Section 1.2
hypothesis (3)
experiment (3)
scientific law (3)
law of conservation of mass (3)
theory (3)
atomic theory (3)
scientific method (4)

Section 1.3
matter (5)
substance (5)
state (5)
composition (5)
solid (5)
liquid (5)
gas (5)

crystalline (5)
amorphous (5)
pure substance (7)
mixture (7)
element (7)
compound (7)
heterogeneous mixture (8)
homogeneous mixture (8)
decanting (8)
distillation (8)
volatile (8)
filtration (8)

Section 1.4
physical change (9)
chemical change (9)
physical property (9)
chemical property (9)

Section 1.5
energy (12)
work (12)

kinetic energy (12)
potential energy (12)
thermal energy (12)
law of conservation
    of energy (12)

Section 1.6
units (13)
English system (13)
metric system (13)
International System of Units
    (SI) (13)
meter (m) (14)
kilogram (kg) (14)
mass (14)
second (s) (14)
kelvin (K) (15)
temperature (15)
Fahrenheit (°F) scale (15)
Celsius (°C) scale (15)
Kelvin scale (15)
prefix multipliers (17)

derived unit (17)
volume (17)
liter (L) (18)
milliliter (mL) (18)
density (d) (18)
intensive property (18)
extensive property (18)

Section 1.7
significant figures (significant
    digits) (22)
exact numbers (22)
accuracy (25)
precision (25)
random error (25)
systematic error (26)

Section 1.8
dimensional analysis (27)
conversion factor (27)

Key Concepts

Atoms and Molecules (1.1)

All matter is composed of atoms and molecules. Chemistry is the science that investigates the properties of matter by examining the atoms and molecules that compose it.

The Scientific Method (1.2)

Science begins with the observation of the physical world. A number of related observations can often be subsumed in a summary statement or generalization called a scientific law. Observations may suggest a hypothesis, a tentative interpretation or explanation of the observed phenomena. One or more well-established hypotheses may prompt the development of a scientific theory, a model for nature that explains the underlying reasons for observations and laws. Laws, hypotheses, and theories all give rise to predictions that can be tested by experiments, carefully controlled procedures designed to produce critical new observations. If scientists cannot confirm the predictions, they must modify or replace the law, hypothesis, or theory.

The Classification of Matter (1.3)

We classify matter according to its state (solid, liquid, or gas) or according to its composition (pure substance or mixture). A pure substance can either be an element, which cannot be chemically broken down into simpler substances, or a compound, which is composed of two or more elements in fixed proportions. A mixture can be either homogeneous, with the same composition throughout, or heterogeneous, with different compositions in different regions.

The Properties of Matter (1.4)

The properties of matter can be divided into two kinds: physical and chemical. Matter displays its physical properties without changing its composition. Matter displays its chemical properties only through changing its composition. Changes in matter in which its composition does not change are called physical changes. Changes in matter in which its composition does change are called chemical changes.

Energy (1.5)

In chemical and physical changes, matter often exchanges energy with its surroundings. In these exchanges, the total energy is always conserved; energy is neither created nor destroyed. Systems with high potential energy tend to change in the direction of lower potential energy, releasing energy into the surroundings.

The Units of Measurement and Significant Figures (1.6, 1.7)

Scientists use primarily SI units, which are based on the metric system. The SI base units include the meter (m) for length, the kilogram (kg) for mass, the second (s) for time, and the kelvin (K) for temperature. Derived units are those formed from a combination of other units. Common derived units include volume (cm^3 or m^3) and density $\left(g/cm^3\right)$. Measured quantities are reported so that the number of digits reflects the uncertainty in the measurement. Significant figures are the non-place-holding digits in a reported number.

Key Equations and Relationships

Relationship between Kelvin (K) and Celsius (°C) Temperature Scales (1.6)

$$K = °C + 273.15$$

Relationship between Celsius (°C) and Fahrenheit (°F) Temperature Scales (1.6)

$$°C = \frac{(°F - 32)}{1.8}$$

Relationship between Density (*d*), Mass (*m*), and Volume (*V*) (1.6)

$$d = \frac{m}{V}$$

Key Skills

Determining Physical and Chemical Changes and Properties (1.4)
  • Example 1.1 • For Practice 1.1 • Exercises 43–50

Converting between the Temperature Scales: Fahrenheit, Celsius, and Kelvin (1.6)
  • Example 1.2 • For Practice 1.2 • Exercises 51–54

Calculating the Density of a Substance (1.6)
  • Example 1.3 • For Practice 1.3 • For More Practice 1.3 • Exercises 65–68

Reporting Scientific Measurements to the Correct Digit of Uncertainty (1.7)
  • Example 1.4 • For Practice 1.4 • Exercises 73, 74

Working with Significant Figures (1.7)
  • Examples 1.5, 1.6 • For Practice 1.5, 1.6 • Exercises 77, 78, 80, 83–88

Using Conversion Factors (1.8)
  • Examples 1.7, 1.8, 1.9, 1.10 • For Practice 1.7, 1.8, 1.9, 1.10 • For More Practice 1.9, 1.10 • Exercises 89, 90, 94–97, 99, 100

Solving Problems Involving Equations (1.8)
  • Examples 1.11, 1.12 • For Practice 1.11, 1.12 • Exercises 115, 116

EXERCISES

Review Questions

1. Explain the following statement in your own words and give an example. *The properties of the substances around us depend on the atoms and molecules that compose them.*
2. Explain the main goal of chemistry.
3. Describe the scientific approach to knowledge. How does it differ from other approaches?
4. Explain the differences between a hypothesis, a law, and a theory.
5. What observations did Antoine Lavoisier make? What law did he formulate?
6. What theory did John Dalton formulate?
7. What is wrong with the expression, "That is just a theory," if by theory you mean a scientific theory?
8. What are two different ways to classify matter?
9. How do solids, liquids, and gases differ?
10. What is the difference between a crystalline solid and an amorphous solid?
11. Explain the difference between a pure substance and a mixture.
12. Explain the difference between an element and a compound.
13. Explain the difference between a homogeneous and a heterogeneous mixture.
14. What kind of mixtures can be separated by filtration?
15. Explain how distillation works to separate mixtures.
16. What is the difference between a physical property and a chemical property?

17. What is the difference between a physical change and a chemical change? Give some examples of each.
18. Explain the significance of the law of conservation of energy.
19. What kind of energy is chemical energy? In what way is an elevated weight similar to a tank of gasoline?
20. What are the standard SI base units of length, mass, time, and temperature?
21. What are the three common temperature scales? Does the size of a degree differ among them?
22. What are prefix multipliers? Give some examples.
23. What is a derived unit? Give an example.
24. Explain the difference between density and mass.
25. Explain the difference between *intensive* and *extensive* properties.
26. What is the meaning of the number of digits reported in a measured quantity?
27. When multiplying or dividing measured quantities, what determines the number of significant figures in the result?
28. When adding or subtracting measured quantities, what determines the number of significant figures in the result?
29. What are the rules for rounding off the results of calculations?
30. Explain the difference between precision and accuracy.
31. Explain the difference between random error and systematic error.
32. What is dimensional analysis?

Problems by Topic

Note: Answers to all odd-numbered Problems, numbered in blue, can be found in Appendix III. Exercises in the Problems by Topic section are paired, with each odd-numbered problem followed by a similar even-numbered problem. Exercises in the Cumulative Problems section are also paired, but somewhat more loosely. (Challenge Problems and Conceptual Problems, because of their nature, are unpaired.)

The Scientific Approach to Knowledge

33. Classify each statement as an observation, a law, or a theory.

    a. All matter is made of tiny, indestructible particles called atoms.

    b. When iron rusts in a closed container, the mass of the container and its contents does not change.

    c. In chemical reactions, matter is neither created nor destroyed.

    d. When a match burns, heat is released.

34. Classify each statement as an observation, a law, or a theory.

    a. Chlorine is a highly reactive gas.

    b. If elements are listed in order of increasing mass of their atoms, their chemical reactivity follows a repeating pattern.

    c. Neon is an inert (or nonreactive) gas.

    d. The reactivity of elements depends on the arrangement of their electrons.

35. A chemist decomposes several samples of carbon monoxide into carbon and oxygen and weighs the resultant elements. The results are shown below:

Sample	Mass of Carbon (g)	Mass of Oxygen (g)
1	6	8
2	12	16
3	18	24

a. Do you notice a pattern in these results?
Next, the chemist decomposes several samples of hydrogen peroxide into hydrogen and oxygen. The results are shown below:

Sample	Mass of Hydrogen (g)	Mass of Oxygen (g)
1	0.5	8
2	1	16
3	1.5	24

b. Do you notice a similarity between these results and those for carbon monoxide in part a?

c. Can you formulate a law from the observations in a and b?

d. Can you formulate a hypothesis that might explain your law in c?

36. When astronomers observe distant galaxies, they can tell that most of them are moving away from one another. In addition, the more distant the galaxies, the more rapidly they are likely to be moving away from each other. Can you devise a hypothesis to explain these observations?

The Classification and Properties of Matter

37. Classify each substance as a pure substance or a mixture. If it is a pure substance, classify it as an element or a compound. If it is a mixture, classify it as homogeneous or heterogeneous.

    a. sweat   b. carbon dioxide
    c. aluminum   d. vegetable soup

38. Classify each substance as a pure substance or a mixture. If it is a pure substance, classify it as an element or a compound. If it is a mixture, classify it as homogeneous or heterogeneous.

    a. wine   b. beef stew
    c. iron   d. carbon monoxide

39. Complete the table.

Substance	Pure or mixture	Type (element or compound)
aluminum	pure	element
apple juice	_____	_____
hydrogen peroxide	_____	_____
chicken soup	_____	_____

40. Complete the table.

Substance	Pure or mixture	Type (element or compound)
water	pure	compound
coffee	_____	_____
ice	_____	_____
carbon	_____	_____

41. Determine whether each molecular diagram represents a pure substance or a mixture. If it represents a pure substance, classify the substance as an element or a compound. If it represents a mixture, classify the mixture as homogeneous or heterogeneous.

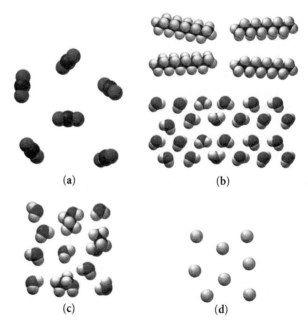

(a)   (b)

(c)   (d)

42. Determine whether each molecular diagram represents a pure substance or a mixture. If it represents a pure substance, classify

the substance as an element or a compound. If it represents a mixture, classify the mixture as homogeneous or heterogeneous.

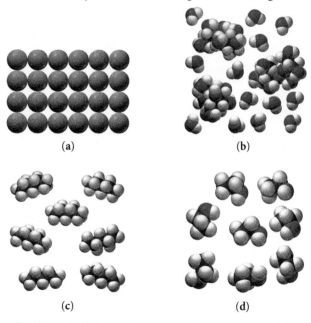

(a)

(b)

(c)

(d)

43. Classify each of the listed properties of isopropyl alcohol (also known as rubbing alcohol) as physical or chemical.
  a. colorless
  b. flammable
  c. liquid at room temperature
  d. density = 0.79 g/mL
  e. mixes with water

44. Classify each of the listed properties of ozone (a pollutant in the lower atmosphere, but part of a protective shield against UV light in the upper atmosphere) as physical or chemical.
  a. bluish color
  b. pungent odor
  c. very reactive
  d. decomposes on exposure to ultraviolet light
  e. gas at room temperature

45. Classify each property as physical or chemical.
  a. the tendency of ethyl alcohol to burn
  b. the shine of silver
  c. the odor of paint thinner
  d. the flammability of propane gas

46. Classify each property as physical or chemical.
  a. the boiling point of ethyl alcohol
  b. the temperature at which dry ice evaporates
  c. the tendency of iron to rust
  d. the color of gold

47. Classify each change as physical or chemical.
  a. Natural gas burns in a stove.
  b. The liquid propane in a gas grill evaporates because the valve was left open.
  c. The liquid propane in a gas grill burns in a flame.
  d. A bicycle frame rusts on repeated exposure to air and water.

48. Classify each change as physical or chemical.
  a. Sugar burns when heated on a skillet.
  b. Sugar dissolves in water.
  c. A platinum ring becomes dull because of continued abrasion.
  d. A silver surface becomes tarnished after exposure to air for a long period of time.

49. Based on the molecular diagram, classify each change as physical or chemical.

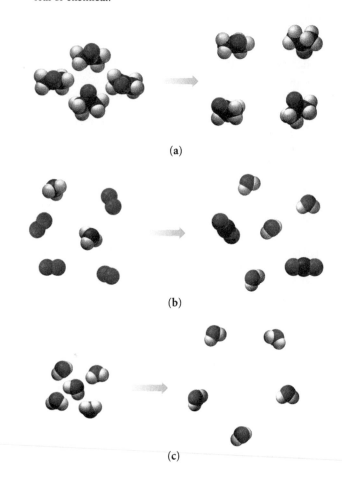

(a)

(b)

(c)

50. Based on the molecular diagram, classify each change as physical or chemical.

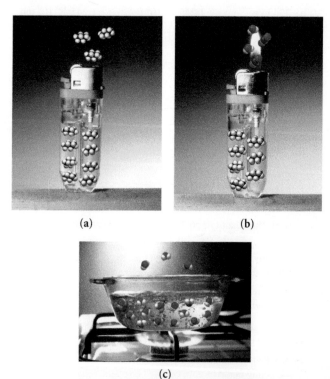

(a)

(b)

(c)

Units in Measurement

51. Convert each temperature.
    a. 32 °F to °C (temperature at which water freezes)
    b. 77 K to °F (temperature of liquid nitrogen)
    c. –109 °F to °C (temperature of dry ice)
    d. 98.6 °F to K (body temperature)

52. Convert each temperature.
    a. 212 °F to °C (temperature of boiling water at sea level)
    b. 22 °C to K (approximate room temperature)
    c. 0.00 K to °F (coldest temperature possible, also known as absolute zero)
    d. 2.735 K to °C (average temperature of the universe as measured from background black body radiation)

53. The coldest temperature ever measured in the United States is –80 °F on January 23, 1971, in Prospect Creek, Alaska. Convert that temperature to °C and K. (Assume that –80 °F is accurate to two significant figures.)

54. The warmest temperature ever measured in the United States is 134 °F on July 10, 1913, in Death Valley, California. Convert that temperature to °C and K.

55. Use the prefix multipliers to express each measurement without any exponents.
    a. 1.2×10^{-9} m
    b. 22×10^{-15} s
    c. 1.5×10^{9} g
    d. 3.5×10^{6} L

56. Use prefix multipliers to express each measurement without any exponents.
    a. 38.8×10^{5} g
    b. 55.2×10^{-10} s
    c. 23.4×10^{11} m
    d. 87.9×10^{-7} L

57. Use scientific notation to express each quantity with only the base units (no prefix multipliers).
    a. 4.5 ns
    b. 18 fs
    c. 128 pm
    d. 35 μm

58. Use scientific notation to express each quantity with only the base units (no prefix multipliers).
    a. 35 μL
    b. 225 Mm
    c. 133 Tg
    d. 1.5 cg

59. Complete the table:

a.	1245 kg	1.245×10^{6} g	1.245×10^{9} mg
b.	515 km	_____ dm	_____ cm
c.	122.355 s	_____ ms	_____ ks
d.	3.345 kJ	_____ J	_____ mJ

60. Complete the table:

a.	355 km/s	_____ cm/s	_____ m/ms
b.	1228 g/L	_____ g/mL	_____ kg/ML
c.	554 mK/s	_____ K/s	_____ μK/ms
d.	2.554 mg/mL	_____ g/L	_____ μg/mL

61. Express the quantity 254,998 m in each unit.
    a. km
    b. Mm
    c. mm
    d. cm

62. Express the quantity 556.2×10^{-12} s in each unit.
    a. ms
    b. ns
    c. ps
    d. fs

63. How many 1-cm squares would it take to construct a square that is 1 m on each side?

64. How many 1-cm cubes would it take to construct a cube that is 4 cm on edge?

Density

65. A new penny has a mass of 2.49 g and a volume of 0.349 cm³. Is the penny made of pure copper? Explain.

66. A titanium bicycle frame displaces 0.314 L of water and has a mass of 1.41 kg. What is the density of the titanium in g/cm³?

67. Glycerol is a syrupy liquid often used in cosmetics and soaps. A 3.25-L sample of pure glycerol has a mass of 4.10×10^{3} g. What is the density of glycerol in g/cm³?

68. A supposedly gold nugget is tested to determine its density. It is found to displace 19.3 mL of water and has a mass of 371 grams. Could the nugget be made of gold?

69. Ethylene glycol (antifreeze) has a density of 1.11 g/cm³.
    a. What is the mass in g of 417 mL of this liquid?
    b. What is the volume in L of 4.1 kg of this liquid?

70. Acetone (nail polish remover) has a density of 0.7857 g/cm³.
    a. What is the mass, in g, of 28.56 mL of acetone?
    b. What is the volume, in mL, of 6.54 g of acetone?

71. A small airplane takes on 245 L of fuel. If the density of the fuel is 0.821 g/mL, what mass of fuel has the airplane taken on?

72. Human fat has a density of 0.918 g/cm³. How much volume (in cm³) is gained by a person who gains 10.0 lbs of pure fat?

The Reliability of a Measurement and Significant Figures

73. Read each measurement to the correct number of significant figures. Note: Laboratory glassware should always be read from the bottom of the meniscus.

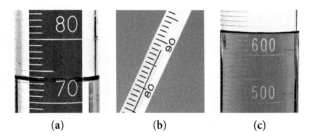

(a)	(b)	(c)

74. Read each measurement to the correct number of significant figures. Note: Laboratory glassware should always be read from the bottom of the meniscus. Digital balances normally display mass to the correct number of significant figures for that particular balance.

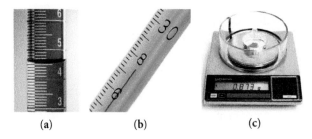

(a)	(b)	(c)

75. For each number, underline the zeroes that are significant and draw an x through the zeroes that are not:
    a. 1,050,501 km
    b. 0.0020 m
    c. 0.000000000000002 s
    d. 0.001090 cm

76. For each number, underline the zeroes that are significant and draw an x through the zeroes that are not:
    a. 180,701 mi
    b. 0.001040 m
    c. 0.005710 km
    d. 90,201 m

77. How many significant figures are in each number?
    a. 0.000312 m
    b. 312,000 s
    c. 3.12×10^{5} km
    d. 13,127 s
    e. 2000

78. How many significant figures are in each number?
  a. 0.1111 s   **b.** 0.007 m   **c.** 108,700 km
  d. 1.563300×10^{11} m   **e.** 30,800

79. Which numbers are exact (and therefore have an unlimited number of significant figures)?
  a. $\pi = 3.14$ **b.** 12 inches = 1 foot
  c. EPA gas mileage rating of 26 miles per gallon
  d. 1 gross = 144

80. Indicate the number of significant figures in each number. If the number is an exact number, indicate an unlimited number of significant figures.
  a. 305,435,087 (2008 U.S. population)
  b. 2.54 cm = 1 in
  c. 11.4 g/cm^3 (density of lead)
  d. 12 = 1 dozen

81. Round each number to four significant figures.
  a. 156.852   **b.** 156.842   **c.** 156.849   **d.** 156.899

82. Round each number to three significant figures.
  a. 79,845.82   **b.** 1.548937×10^7
  c. 2.3499999995   **d.** 0.000045389

Significant Figures in Calculations

83. Calculate to the correct number of significant figures.
  a. $9.15 \div 4.970$ **b.** $1.54 \times 0.03060 \times 0.69$
  c. $27.5 \times 1.82 \div 100.04$ **d.** $(2.290 \times 10^6) \div (6.7 \times 10^4)$

84. Calculate to the correct number of significant figures.
  a. $89.3 \times 77.0 \times 0.08$ **b.** $(5.01 \times 10^5) \div (7.8 \times 10^2)$
  c. $4.005 \times 74 \times 0.007$ **d.** $453 \div 2.031$

85. Calculate to the correct number of significant figures.
  a. $43.7 - 2.341$
  b. $17.6 + 2.838 + 2.3 + 110.77$
  c. $19.6 + 58.33 - 4.974$
  d. $5.99 - 5.572$

86. Calculate to the correct number of significant figures.
  a. $0.004 + 0.09879$ **b.** $1239.3 + 9.73 + 3.42$
  c. $2.4 - 1.777$ **d.** $532 + 7.3 - 48.523$

87. Calculate to the correct number of significant figures.
  a. $(24.6681 \times 2.38) + 332.58$
  b. $(85.3 - 21.489) \div 0.0059$
  c. $(512 \div 986.7) + 5.44$
  d. $[(28.7 \times 10^5) \div 48.533] + 144.99$

88. Calculate to the correct number of significant figures.
  a. $[(1.7 \times 10^6) \div (2.63 \times 10^5)] + 7.33$
  b. $(568.99 - 232.1) \div 5.3$
  c. $(9443 + 45 - 9.9) \times 8.1 \times 10^6$
  d. $(3.14 \times 2.4367) - 2.34$

Unit Conversions

89. Convert:
  a. 154 cm to in   **b.** 3.14 kg to g
  c. 3.5 L to qt   **d.** 109 mm to in

90. Convert:
  a. 1.4 in to mm   **b.** 116 ft to cm
  c. 1845 kg to lb   **d.** 815 yd to km

91. A runner wants to run 10.0 km. She knows that her running pace is 7.5 miles per hour. How many minutes must she run?

92. A cyclist rides at an average speed of 18 miles per hour. If she wants to bike 212 km, how long (in hours) must she ride?

93. A European automobile has a gas mileage of 17 km/L. What is the gas mileage in miles per gallon?

94. A gas can holds 5.0 gallons of gasoline. What is this quantity in cm^3?

95. A house has an area of 195 m^2. What is its area in:
  a. km^2 **b.** dm^2 **c.** cm^2

96. A bedroom has a volume of 115 m^3. What is its volume in:
  a. km^3 **b.** dm^3 **c.** cm^3

97. The average U.S. farm occupies 435 acres. How many square miles is this? (1 acre = 43,560 ft^2, 1 mile = 5280 ft)

98. Total U.S. farmland occupies 954 million acres. How many square miles is this? (1 acre = 43,560 ft^2, 1 mile = 5280 ft). Total U.S. land area is 3.537 million square miles. What percentage of U.S. land is farmland?

99. An acetaminophen suspension for infants contains 80 mg/0.80 mL suspension. The recommended dose is 15 mg/kg body weight. How many mL of this suspension should be given to an infant weighing 14 lb? (Assume two significant figures.)

100. An ibuprofen suspension for infants contains 100 mg/5.0 mL suspension. The recommended dose is 10 mg/kg body weight. How many mL of this suspension should be given to an infant weighing 18 lb? (Assume two significant figures.)

Cumulative Problems

101. There are exactly 60 seconds in a minute, there are exactly 60 minutes in an hour, there are exactly 24 hours in a mean solar day, and there are 365.24 solar days in a solar year. Find the number of seconds in a solar year. Be sure to give your answer with the correct number of significant figures.

102. Use exponential notation to indicate the number of significant figures in each statement:
  a. Fifty million Frenchmen can't be wrong.
  b. "For every ten jokes, thou hast got an hundred enemies" (Laurence Sterne, 1713–1768).
  c. The diameter of a Ca atom is 1.8 one hundred millionths of a centimeter.
  d. Sixty thousand dollars is a lot of money to pay for a car.
  e. The density of platinum (Table 1.4).

103. Classify each property as intensive or extensive.
  a. volume   **b.** boiling point
  c. temperature   **d.** electrical conductivity
  e. energy

104. At what temperatures will the readings on the Fahrenheit and Celsius thermometers be the same?

105. Suppose you design a new thermometer called the X thermometer. On the X scale the boiling point of water is 130 °X and the freezing point of water is 10 °X. At what temperature will the readings on the Fahrenheit and X thermometers be the same?

106. On a new Jekyll temperature scale, water freezes at 17 °J and boils at 97 °J. On another new temperature scale, the Hyde scale, water freezes at 0 °H and boils at 120 °H. If methyl alcohol boils at 84 °H, what is its boiling point on the Jekyll scale?

107. Force is defined as mass times acceleration. Starting with SI base units, derive a unit for force. Using SI prefixes suggest a convenient unit for the force resulting from a collision with a 10-ton trailer truck moving at 55 miles per hour and for the force resulting from the collision of a molecule of mass around 10^{-20} kg moving almost at the speed of light $(3 \times 10^8$ m/s$)$ with the wall of its container. (Assume a 1 second deceleration time for both collisions.)

108. A temperature measurement of 25 °C has three significant figures, while a temperature measurement of –196 °C has only two significant figures. Explain.

109. Do each calculation without using your calculator and give the answers to the correct number of significant figures.
   a. $1.76 \times 10^{-3}/8.0 \times 10^2$
   b. $1.87 \times 10^{-2} + 2 \times 10^{-4} - 3.0 \times 10^{-3}$
   c. $[(1.36 \times 10^5)(0.000322)/0.082](129.2)$

110. The value of the Euro is currently $1.35 U.S. and the price of 1 liter of gasoline in France is 0.97 Euro. What is the price of 1 gallon of gasoline in U.S. dollars in France?

111. A thief uses a can of sand to replace a solid gold cylinder that sits on a weight-sensitive, alarmed pedestal. The can of sand and the gold cylinder have exactly the same dimensions (length = 22 cm and radius = 3.8 cm).
   a. Calculate the mass of each cylinder (ignore the mass of the can itself). (density of gold = 19.3 g/cm^3, density of sand = 3.00 g/cm^3)
   b. Did the thief set off the alarm? Explain.

112. The proton has a radius of approximately 1.0×10^{-13} cm and a mass of 1.7×10^{-24} g. Determine the density of a proton. For a sphere $V = (4/3)\pi r^3$.

113. The density of titanium is 4.51 g/cm^3. What is the volume (in cubic inches) of 3.5 lb of titanium?

114. The density of iron is 7.86 g/cm^3. What is its density in pounds per cubic inch (lb/in^3)?

115. A steel cylinder has a length of 2.16 in, a radius of 0.22 in, and a mass of 41 g. What is the density of the steel in g/cm^3?

116. A solid aluminum sphere has a mass of 85 g. Use the density of aluminum to find the radius of the sphere in inches.

117. A backyard swimming pool holds 185 cubic yards (yd^3) of water. What is the mass of the water in pounds?

118. An iceberg has a volume of 7655 cubic feet. What is the mass of the ice (in kg) composing the iceberg (at 0 °C)?

119. The Toyota Prius, a hybrid electric vehicle, has an EPA gas mileage rating of 52 mi/gal in the city. How many kilometers can the Prius travel on 15 liters of gasoline?

120. The Honda Insight, a hybrid electric vehicle, has an EPA gas mileage rating of 57 mi/gal in the city. How many kilometers can the Insight travel on the amount of gasoline that would fit in a soda pop can? The volume of a soda pop can is 355 mL.

121. The single proton that forms the nucleus of the hydrogen atom has a radius of approximately 1.0×10^{-13} cm. The hydrogen atom itself has a radius of approximately 52.9 pm. What fraction of the space within the atom is occupied by the nucleus?

122. A sample of gaseous neon atoms at atmospheric pressure and 0 °C contains 2.69×10^{22} atoms per liter. The atomic radius of neon is 69 pm. What fraction of the space is occupied by the atoms themselves? What does this reveal about the separation between atoms in the gaseous phase?

123. The diameter of a hydrogen atom is 212 pm. Find the length in kilometers of a row of 6.02×10^{23} hydrogen atoms. The diameter of a ping pong ball is 4.0 cm. Find the length in kilometers of a row of 6.02×10^{23} ping pong balls.

124. The world's record in the 100 m dash is 9.69 s and in the 100 yard dash is 9.21 s. Find the speed in miles/hr of the runners who set these records.

125. Table salt contains 39.33 g of sodium per 100 g of salt. The U.S. Food and Drug Administration (FDA) recommends that adults consume less than 2.40 g of sodium per day. A particular snack mix contains 1.25 g of salt per 100 g of the mix. What mass of the snack mix can you consume and still be within the FDA limit?

126. Lead metal can be extracted from a mineral called galena, which contains 86.6% lead by mass. A particular ore contains 68.5% galena by mass. If the lead can be extracted with 92.5% efficiency, what mass of ore is required to make a lead sphere with a 5.00 cm radius?

127. Liquid nitrogen has a density of 0.808 g/mL and boils at 77 K. Researchers often purchase liquid nitrogen in insulated 175-L tanks. The liquid vaporizes quickly to gaseous nitrogen (which has a density of 1.15 g/L at room temperature and atmospheric pressure) when the liquid is removed from the tank. Suppose that all 175 L of liquid nitrogen in a tank accidentally vaporized in a lab that measured 10.00 m × 10.00 m × 2.50 m. What maximum fraction of the air in the room could be displaced by the gaseous nitrogen?

128. Mercury is often used as an expansion medium in a thermometer. The mercury sits in a bulb on the bottom of the thermometer and rises up a thin capillary as the temperature rises. Suppose a mercury thermometer contains 3.380 g of mercury and has a capillary that is 0.200 mm in diameter. How far does the mercury rise in the capillary when the temperature changes from 0.0 °C to 25.0 °C? The density of mercury at these temperatures is 13.596 g/cm^3 and 13.534 g/cm^3, respectively.

Challenge Problems

129. A force of 2.31×10^4 N is applied to a diver's face mask that has an area of 125 cm^2. Find the pressure in atm on the face mask.

130. The SI unit of force is the Newton, derived from the base units by using the definition of force, $F = ma$. The dyne is a non-SI unit of force in which mass is measured in grams and time is measured in seconds. The relationship between the two units is 1 dyne = 10^{-5} N. Find the unit of length used to define the dyne.

131. Kinetic energy can be defined as $\frac{1}{2}mv^2$ or as $3/2\ PV$. Show that the derived SI units of each of these terms are those of energy. (Pressure is force/area and force is mass × acceleration.)

132. In 1999, scientists discovered a new class of black holes with masses 100 to 10,000 times the mass of our sun, but occupying less space than our moon. Suppose that one of these black holes has a mass of 1×10^3 suns and a radius equal to one-half the radius of our moon. What is the density of the black hole in g/cm^3? The radius of our sun is 7.0×10^5 km and it has an average density of 1.4×10^3 kg/m^3. The diameter of the moon is 2.16×10^3 miles.

133. Section 1.7 showed that in 1997 Los Angeles County air had carbon monoxide (CO) levels of 15.0 ppm. An average human inhales about 0.50 L of air per breath and takes about 20 breaths per minute. How many milligrams of carbon monoxide does the average person inhale in an 8-hour period for this level of carbon monoxide pollution? Assume that the carbon monoxide has a density of 1.2 g/L. (Hint: 15.0 ppm CO means 15.0 L CO per 10^6 L air.)

134. Nanotechnology, the field of trying to build ultrasmall structures one atom at a time, has progressed in recent years. One potential application of nanotechnology is the construction of artificial cells. The simplest cells would probably mimic red blood cells, the body's oxygen transporters. For example, nanocontainers, perhaps constructed of carbon, could be pumped full of oxygen and injected into a person's bloodstream. If the person needed additional oxygen—due to a heart attack perhaps, or for the purpose of space travel—these containers could slowly release oxygen into the blood, allowing tissues that would otherwise die to remain alive. Suppose that the nanocontainers were cubic and had an edge length of 25 nanometers.
    a. What is the volume of one nanocontainer? (Ignore the thickness of the nanocontainer's wall.)
    b. Suppose that each nanocontainer could contain pure oxygen pressurized to a density of 85 g/L. How many grams of oxygen could be contained by each nanocontainer?

    c. Normal air contains about 0.28 g of oxygen per liter. An average human inhales about 0.50 L of air per breath and takes about 20 breaths per minute. How many grams of oxygen does a human inhale per hour? (Assume two significant figures.)
    d. What is the minimum number of nanocontainers that a person would need in their bloodstream to provide 1 hour's worth of oxygen?
    e. What is the minimum volume occupied by the number of nanocontainers computed in part d? Is such a volume feasible, given that total blood volume in an adult is about 5 liters?

135. Approximate the percent increase in waist size that occurs when a 155-lb person gains 40.0 lbs of fat. Assume that the volume of the person can be modeled by a cylinder that is 4.0 feet tall. The average density of a human is about 1.0 g/cm³ and the density of fat is 0.918 g/cm³.

136. A box contains a mixture of small copper spheres and small lead spheres. The total volume of both metals is measured by the displacement of water to be 427 cm³ and the total mass is 4.36 kg. What percentage of the spheres are copper?

Conceptual Problems

137. A volatile liquid (one that easily evaporates) is put into a jar and the jar is then sealed. Does the mass of the sealed jar and its contents change upon the vaporization of the liquid?

138. The diagram represents solid carbon dioxide, also known as dry ice.

    Which of the diagrams below best represents the dry ice after it has sublimed into a gas?

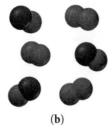

(a)   (b)   (c)

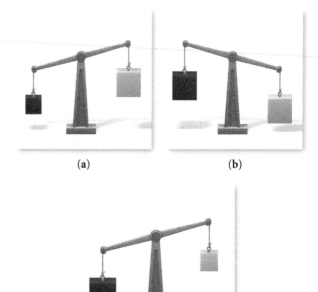

(a)   (b)

(c)

139. A cube has an edge length of 7 cm. If it is divided up into 1-cm cubes, how many 1-cm cubes would there be?

140. Substance A has a density of 1.7 g/cm³. Substance B has a density of 1.7 kg/m³. Without doing any calculations, determine which substance is most dense.

141. For each box, examine the blocks attached to the balances. Based on their positions and sizes, determine which block is more dense (the dark block or the lighter-colored block), or if the relative densities cannot be determined. (Think carefully about the information being shown.)

142. Identify each statement as being most like an observation, a law, or a theory.
    a. All coastal areas experience two high tides and two low tides each day.
    b. The tides in Earth's oceans are caused mainly by the gravitational attraction of the moon.
    c. Yesterday, high tide in San Francisco Bay occurred at 2:43 A.M. and 3:07 P.M.
    d. Tides are higher at the full moon and new moon than at other times of the month.

2 Atoms and Elements

These observations have tacitly led to the conclusion which seems universally adopted, that all bodies of sensible magnitude . . . are constituted of a vast number of extremely small particles, or atoms of matter . . . .

—John Dalton (1766–1844)

IF YOU CUT A PIECE OF GRAPHITE from the tip of a pencil into smaller and smaller pieces, how far could you go? Could you divide it forever? Would you eventually run into some basic particles that were no longer divisible, not because of their sheer smallness, but because of the nature of matter? This fundamental question about the nature of matter has been asked by thinkers for over two millennia. The answers they reached, however, have varied over time. On the scale of everyday objects, matter appears continuous, or infinitely divisible. Until about 200 years ago, many scientists thought that matter was indeed continuous—but they were proven wrong. If you were to divide the graphite from your pencil tip into smaller and smaller pieces (far smaller than the eye could see), you would eventually end up with individual carbon atoms. The word atom comes from the Greek *atomos*, meaning "indivisible." You cannot divide a carbon atom into smaller pieces and still have carbon. Atoms compose all ordinary matter—if you want to understand matter, you must begin by understanding atoms.

The tip of a scanning tunneling microscope (STM) moves across an atomic surface.

2.1 Imaging and Moving Individual Atoms

On March 16, 1981, Gerd Binnig and Heinrich Rohrer worked late into the night in their laboratory at IBM in Zurich, Switzerland. They were measuring how an electrical current—flowing between a sharp metal tip and a flat metal surface—varied as the distance between the tip and the surface varied. The results of that night's experiment and subsequent results over the next several months won Binnig and Rohrer a share of the 1986 Nobel Prize in Physics. They had discovered *scanning tunneling microscopy (STM),* a technique that can image, and even move, individual atoms and molecules.

A scanning tunneling microscope works by moving an extremely sharp *electrode* (an electrical conductor) over a surface and measuring the resulting *tunneling current,* the electrical current that flows between the tip of the electrode and the surface even though the two are not in physical contact (Figure 2.1 ▶ on the next page).

The tunneling current, as Binnig and Rohrer found that night in their laboratory at IBM, is extremely sensitive to distance, making it possible to maintain a precise separation of approximately two atomic diameters between the tip and the surface simply by

▶ FIGURE 2.1 **Scanning Tunneling Microscopy** In this technique, an atomically sharp tip is scanned across a surface. The tip is kept at a fixed distance from the surface by moving it up and down so as to maintain a constant tunneling current. The motion of the tip is recorded to create an image of the surface with atomic resolution.

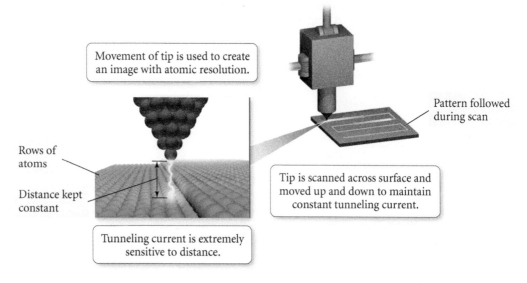

Movement of tip is used to create an image with atomic resolution.

Pattern followed during scan

Rows of atoms

Distance kept constant

Tip is scanned across surface and moved up and down to maintain constant tunneling current.

Tunneling current is extremely sensitive to distance.

moving the tip so as to keep the current constant. If the current starts to drop a bit, the tip is moved down towards the surface to increase the current. If the current starts to increase a bit, the tip is moved up, away from the surface to decrease the current. As long as the current is constant, the separation between the tip and the surface is constant. As the tip goes over an atom, therefore, the tip must move up (away from the surface) to maintain constant current. By measuring the up-and-down movement of the tip as it scans a surface, the microscope creates an image, which shows the location of individual atoms on that surface (see Figure 2.2(a) ▼).

In other words, Binnig and Rohrer had discovered a type of microscope that could "see" atoms. When I was a child taking science in elementary school, my teachers always told me that, although scientists were certain that matter was made of atoms, we could not see them even with the most powerful microscopes (and probably never would) because they were too small. Today, with the STM, we can form incredible images of atoms and molecules. Later work by other scientists showed that the STM could also be used to *pick up and move* individual atoms or molecules, allowing structures and patterns to be made one atom at a time. Figure 2.2(b), for example, shows the Kanji characters for the word "atom" written with individual iron atoms on top of a copper surface. If all of the words in the books in the Library of Congress—29 million books on 530 miles of shelves—were written in letters the size of these Kanji characters, they would fit in an area of about 5 square millimeters.

As we discussed in Chapter 1, it was only 200 years ago that John Dalton proposed his atomic theory. Now we can image atoms, move them, and are even beginning to build

▶ FIGURE 2.2 **Imaging Atoms** (a) A scanning tunneling microscope image of iodine atoms (green) on a platinum surface (blue). (b) The Kanji characters for "atom" written with iron atoms (red) on a copper surface (blue). The copper atoms are not as distinct as the iron atoms, but they appear as blue ripples in the background.

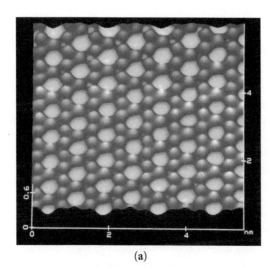

(a)

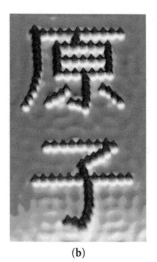

(b)

tiny machines out of just a few dozen atoms (an area of research called nanotechnology). These atomic machines, and the atoms that compose them, are almost unimaginably small. To get an idea of the size of an atom, imagine picking up a grain of sand at a beach. That grain contains more atoms than you could count in a lifetime. In fact, the number of atoms in one sand grain far exceeds the number of grains on the entire beach. If every atom within the sand grain were the size of the grain itself, the sand grain would be the size of a large mountain range.

Despite their size, atoms are the key to connecting the macroscopic and microscopic worlds. An *atom* is the smallest identifiable unit of an *element*. There are about 91 different naturally occurring elements. In addition, scientists have succeeded in making over 20 synthetic elements (not found in nature). In this chapter, we learn about atoms: what they are made of, how they differ from one another, and how they are structured. We also learn about the elements made up of these different kinds of atoms, and about some of their characteristic properties. We will discover that the elements can be organized in a way that reveals patterns in their properties and helps us to understand what underlies those properties.

The exact number of naturally occurring elements is controversial, because some elements that were first discovered when they were synthesized are believed to also be present in trace amounts in nature.

2.2 Early Ideas about the Building Blocks of Matter

The first people to propose that matter was composed of small, indestructible particles were Leucippus (fifth century B.C., exact dates unknown) and his student Democritus (460–370 B.C.). These Greek philosophers theorized that matter was ultimately composed of small, indivisible particles they named *atomos*. Democritus wrote, "Nothing exists except atoms and empty space; everything else is opinion." Leucippus and Democritus proposed that many different kinds of atoms existed, each different in shape and size, and that they moved randomly through empty space. Other influential Greek thinkers of the time, such as Plato and Aristotle, did not embrace the atomic ideas of Leucippus and Democritus. Instead, they held that matter had no smallest parts and that different substances were composed of various proportions of fire, air, earth, and water. Since there was no experimental way to test the relative merits of the competing ideas, Aristotle's view prevailed, largely because he was so influential. The idea that matter was composed of atoms took a back seat in intellectual thought for nearly 2000 years.

In the sixteenth century modern science began to emerge. A greater emphasis on observation led Nicolaus Copernicus (1473–1543) to publish *On the Revolution of the Heavenly Orbs* in 1543. The publication of that book—which proposed that the sun, not Earth, was at the center of the universe—marks the beginning of what we now call the *scientific revolution*. The next 200 years—and the work of scientists such as Francis Bacon (1561–1626), Johannes Kepler (1571–1630), Galileo Galilei (1564–1642), Robert Boyle (1627–1691), and Isaac Newton (1642–1727)—brought rapid advancement as the scientific method became the established way to learn about the physical world. By the early 1800s certain observations led the English chemist John Dalton (1766–1844) to offer convincing evidence that supported the early atomic ideas of Leucippus and Democritus.

2.3 Modern Atomic Theory and the Laws That Led to It

Recall the discussion of the scientific method from Chapter 1. The theory that all matter is composed of atoms grew out of observations and laws. The three most important laws that led to the development and acceptance of the atomic theory were the law of conservation of mass, the law of definite proportions, and the law of multiple proportions.

The Law of Conservation of Mass

In 1789, as we saw in Chapter 1, Antoine Lavoisier formulated the **law of conservation of mass**, which states the following:

In a chemical reaction, matter is neither created nor destroyed.

We will see in Chapter 19 that this law is a slight oversimplification. However, the changes in mass in ordinary chemical processes are so minute that they can be ignored for all practical purposes.

In other words, when a chemical reaction occurs, the total mass of the substances involved in the reaction does not change. For example, consider the reaction between sodium and chlorine to form sodium chloride.

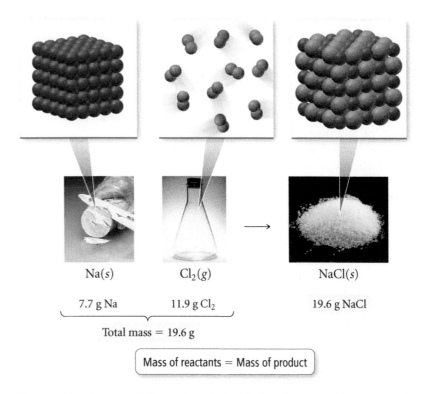

$Na(s)$ $Cl_2(g)$ $NaCl(s)$

7.7 g Na   11.9 g Cl$_2$ 19.6 g NaCl

Total mass = 19.6 g

Mass of reactants = Mass of product

The combined mass of the sodium and chlorine that react (the reactants) exactly equals the mass of the sodium chloride that forms (the product). This law is consistent with the idea that matter is composed of small, indestructible particles. The particles rearrange during a chemical reaction, but the amount of matter is conserved because the particles themselves are indestructible (at least by chemical means).

Conceptual Connection 2.1 The Law of Conservation of Mass

When a small log completely burns in a campfire, the mass of the ash is much less than the mass of the log. What happened to the matter that composed the log?

ANSWER: Most of the matter that composed the log underwent a chemical change by reacting with oxygen molecules in the air. The products of the reaction (mostly carbon dioxide and water) were released as gases into the air.

The Law of Definite Proportions

In 1797, a French chemist named Joseph Proust (1754–1826) made observations on the composition of compounds. He found that the elements composing a given compound always occurred in fixed (or definite) proportions in all samples of the compound. In contrast, the components of a mixture could be present in any proportions whatsoever. He summarized his observations in the **law of definite proportions**:

The law of definite proportions is sometimes called the law of constant composition.

> **All samples of a given compound, regardless of their source or how they were prepared, have the same proportions of their constituent elements.**

For example, the decomposition of 18.0 g of water results in 16.0 g of oxygen and 2.0 g of hydrogen, or an oxygen-to-hydrogen mass ratio of:

$$\text{Mass ratio} = \frac{16.0\ \text{g O}}{2.0\ \text{g H}} = 8.0 \text{ or } 8{:}1$$

This ratio holds for any sample of pure water, regardless of its origin. The law of definite proportions applies to every compound. Consider ammonia, a compound composed of nitrogen and hydrogen. Ammonia contains 14.0 g of nitrogen for every 3.0 g of hydrogen, resulting in a nitrogen-to-hydrogen mass ratio of:

$$\text{Mass ratio} = \frac{14.0 \text{ g N}}{3.0 \text{ g H}} = 4.7 \text{ or } 4.7:1$$

Again, this ratio is the same for every sample of ammonia. The law of definite proportions also hints at the idea that matter might be composed of atoms. Compounds have definite proportions of their constituent elements because the atoms that compose them, each with its own specific mass, occur in a definite ratio. Since the ratio of atoms is the same for all samples of a particular compound, the ratio of masses is also the same.

EXAMPLE 2.1 Law of Definite Proportions

Two samples of carbon dioxide are decomposed into their constituent elements. One sample produces 25.6 g of oxygen and 9.60 g of carbon, and the other produces 21.6 g of oxygen and 8.10 g of carbon. Show that these results are consistent with the law of definite proportions.

SOLUTION

To show this, compute the mass ratio of one element to the other for both samples by dividing the mass of one element by the mass of the other. For convenience, divide the larger mass by the smaller one.	For the first sample: $$\frac{\text{Mass oxygen}}{\text{Mass carbon}} = \frac{25.6}{9.60} = 2.67 \text{ or } 2.67:1$$ For the second sample: $$\frac{\text{Mass oxygen}}{\text{Mass carbon}} = \frac{21.6}{8.10} = 2.67 \text{ or } 2.67:1$$

The ratios are the same for the two samples, so these results are consistent with the law of definite proportions.

FOR PRACTICE 2.1

Two samples of carbon monoxide are decomposed into their constituent elements. One sample produces 17.2 g of oxygen and 12.9 g of carbon, and the other sample produces 10.5 g of oxygen and 7.88 g of carbon. Show that these results are consistent with the law of definite proportions.

Answers to For Practice and For More Practice Problems can be found in Appendix IV.

The Law of Multiple Proportions

In 1804, John Dalton published his **law of multiple proportions**, which asserts the following principle:

> **When two elements (call them A and B) form two different compounds, the masses of element B that combine with 1 g of element A can be expressed as a ratio of small whole numbers.**

Dalton already suspected that matter was composed of atoms, so that when two elements A and B combined to form more than one compound, an atom of A combined with either one, two, three, or more atoms of B (AB_1, AB_2, AB_3, etc.). Therefore the ratio of the masses of B that reacted with a fixed mass of A would always be small whole numbers. Consider the compounds carbon monoxide and carbon dioxide, which we discussed in the opening section of Chapter 1 and in Example 2.1. Carbon monoxide and carbon dioxide are two compounds composed of the same two elements: carbon and oxygen. We saw in Example 2.1 that the mass ratio of oxygen to carbon in carbon dioxide is 2.67:1;

therefore, 2.67 g of oxygen would react with 1 g of carbon. In carbon monoxide, however, the mass ratio of oxygen to carbon is 1.33:1, or 1.33 g of oxygen to every 1 g of carbon.

Carbon dioxide   Mass oxygen that combines with 1 g carbon = 2.67 g

Carbon monoxide   Mass oxygen that combines with 1 g carbon = 1.33 g

The ratio of these two masses is itself a small whole number.

$$\frac{\text{Mass oxygen to 1 g carbon in carbon dioxide}}{\text{Mass oxygen to 1 g carbon in carbon monoxide}} = \frac{2.67}{1.33} = 2$$

With the help of the molecular models, we can see why the ratio is 2:1—carbon dioxide contains two oxygen atoms to every carbon atom while carbon monoxide contains only one.

EXAMPLE 2.2 Law of Multiple Proportions

Nitrogen forms several compounds with oxygen, including nitrogen dioxide and dinitrogen monoxide. Nitrogen dioxide contains 2.28 g oxygen to every 1.00 g nitrogen while dinitrogen monoxide contains 0.570 g oxygen to every 1.00 g nitrogen. Show that these results are consistent with the law of multiple proportions.

SOLUTION

To show this, compute the ratio of the mass of oxygen from one compound to the mass of oxygen in the other. Always divide the larger of the two masses by the smaller one.	$\dfrac{\text{Mass oxygen to 1 g nitrogen in nitrogen dioxide}}{\text{Mass oxygen to 1 g nitrogen in dinitrogen monoxide}} = \dfrac{2.28}{0.570} = 4.00$

The ratio is a small whole number (4); these results are consistent with the law of multiple proportions.

FOR PRACTICE 2.2

Hydrogen and oxygen form both water and hydrogen peroxide. The decomposition of a sample of water forms 0.125 g hydrogen to every 1.00 g oxygen. The decomposition of a sample of hydrogen peroxide forms 0.250 g hydrogen to every 1.00 g oxygen. Show that these results are consistent with the law of multiple proportions.

 Conceptual Connection 2.2 **The Laws of Definite and Multiple Proportions**

Explain the difference between the law of definite proportions and the law of multiple proportions.

ANSWER: The law of definite proportions applies to two or more samples of the *same compound* and states that the ratio of one element to the other will always be the same. The law of multiple proportions applies to two *different compounds* containing the same two elements (A and B) and states that the masses of B that combine with 1 g of A are always related as a small whole-number ratio.

John Dalton and the Atomic Theory

In 1808, John Dalton explained the laws just discussed with his **atomic theory**, which included the following concepts:

1. Each element is composed of tiny, indestructible particles called atoms.

CHEMISTRY IN YOUR DAY **Atoms and Humans**

You and I are composed of atoms. We get those atoms from the food we eat. Yesterday's cheeseburger contributes to today's skin, muscle, and hair. Not only are we made of atoms, but we are made of *recycled* atoms. The carbon atoms that compose our bodies were used by other living organisms before we got them. And they will be used by still others when we are done with them. In fact, it is likely that at this moment, your body contains some carbon atoms (over one trillion*) that were at one time part of your chemistry professor.

The idea that humans are composed of atoms acting in accord with the laws of chemistry and physics has significant implications and raises important questions. If atoms compose our brains, for example, do those atoms determine our thoughts and emotions? Are our feelings caused by atoms acting according to the laws of chemistry and physics?

*This calculation assumes that all of the carbon atoms metabolized by your professor over the last 40 years have been uniformly distributed into atmospheric carbon dioxide, and subsequently incorporated into the plants that you eat.

Richard Feynman (1918–1988), a Nobel Prize–winning physicist, said that "The most important hypothesis in all of biology is that everything that animals do, atoms do. In other words, there is nothing that living things do that cannot be understood from the point of view that they are made of atoms acting according to the laws of physics." Indeed, biology has undergone a revolution throughout the last 50 years, mostly through the investigation of the atomic and molecular basis for life. Some people have seen the atomic view of life as a devaluation of human life. We have always wanted to distinguish ourselves from everything else, and the idea that we are made of the same basic particles as all other matter takes something away from that distinction. . . . Or does it?

Questions

Do you find the idea that you are made of recycled atoms disturbing? Why or why not? *Reductionism* is the idea that complex systems can be understood by understanding their parts. Is reductionism a good way to understand humans? Is it the only way?

---

2. All atoms of a given element have the same mass and other properties that distinguish them from the atoms of other elements.

3. Atoms combine in simple, whole-number ratios to form compounds.

4. Atoms of one element cannot change into atoms of another element. In a chemical reaction, atoms only change the way that they are *bound together* with other atoms.

> In Section 2.6, we will see that, contrary to Dalton's theory, all atoms of a given element do not have exactly the same mass.

Today, the evidence for the atomic theory is overwhelming. Matter is indeed composed of atoms.

2.4 The Discovery of the Electron

By the end of the nineteenth century, scientists were convinced that matter was made up of atoms, the permanent, supposedly indestructible building blocks that composed everything. However, further experiments revealed that the atom itself was composed of even smaller, more fundamental particles.

Cathode Rays

In the late 1800s an English physicist named J. J. Thomson (1856–1940), working at Cambridge University, performed experiments to probe the properties of **cathode rays**. Thomson constructed a glass tube called a **cathode ray tube**, shown in Figure 2.3 ▾. The

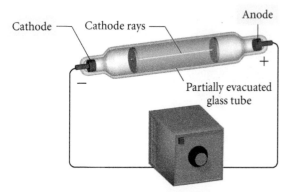

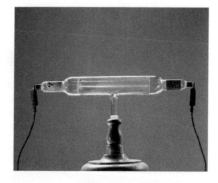

◀ **FIGURE 2.3 Cathode Ray Tube**

tube was partially evacuated, which means that much of the air was pumped out of the tube (because air interferes with cathode rays). Thomson then applied a high electrical voltage between two electrodes at either end of the tube. Thomson found that a beam of particles, called cathode rays, traveled from the negatively charged electrode (which is called the cathode) to the positively charged one.

Thomson found that these particles had the following properties: they traveled in straight lines; they were independent of the composition of the material from which they originated (the cathode); and they carried a negative **electrical charge**. Electrical charge is a fundamental property of some of the particles that compose atoms, and it results in attractive and repulsive forces—called *electrostatic forces*—between those particles. The area around a charged particle where these forces exist is called an *electric field.* The characteristics of electrical charge are summarized in the figure in the margin. You have probably experienced excess electrical charge when brushing your hair on a dry day. The brushing action causes the accumulation of charged particles in your hair, which repel each other, making your hair stand on end.

J. J. Thomson measured the charge-to-mass ratio of the cathode ray particles by deflecting them using electric and magnetic fields, as shown in Figure 2.4 ▼. The value he measured, -1.76×10^8 coulombs (C) per gram, implied that the cathode ray particle was about 2000 times lighter (less massive) than hydrogen, the lightest known atom. These results were incredible—the indestructible atom could apparently be chipped!

J. J. Thomson had discovered the **electron**, a negatively charged, low mass particle present within all atoms. Thomson wrote, "We have in the cathode rays matter in a new state, a state in which the subdivision of matter is carried very much further . . . a state in which all matter . . . is of one and the same kind; this matter being the substance from which all the chemical elements are built up."

Properties of Electrical Charge

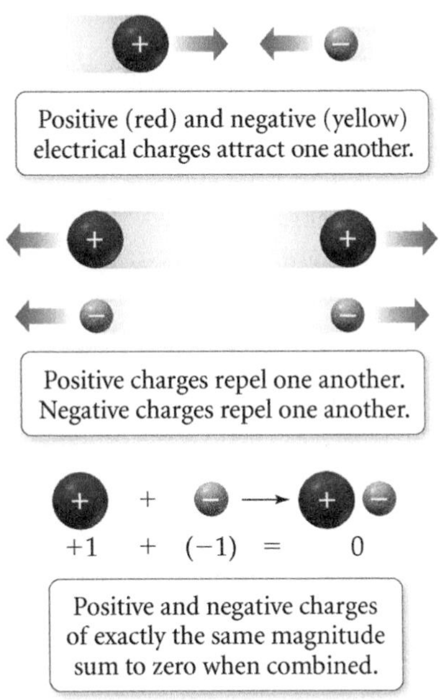
Positive (red) and negative (yellow) electrical charges attract one another.
Positive charges repel one another. Negative charges repel one another.
+1 + (−1) = 0
Positive and negative charges of exactly the same magnitude sum to zero when combined.

For a full explanation of electrical voltage, see Chapter 18.

The coulomb (C) is the SI unit for charge.

Millikan's Oil Drop Experiment: The Charge of the Electron

In 1909, American physicist Robert Millikan (1868–1953), working at the University of Chicago, performed his now famous oil drop experiment in which he deduced the charge of a single electron. The apparatus for the oil drop experiment is shown in Figure 2.5 ►.

In his experiment, Millikan sprayed oil into fine droplets using an atomizer. The droplets were allowed to fall under the influence of gravity through a small hole into the lower portion of the apparatus where Millikan viewed them with the aid of a light source and a viewing microscope. During their fall, the drops acquired electrons that had been produced by bombarding the air in the chamber with ionizing radiation (a kind of energy which we will learn more about in Chapter 7). The electrons imparted a negative charge to the drops. In the lower portion of the apparatus, Millikan could create an electric field between two metal plates. Since the lower plate was negatively charged, and since Millikan could vary the strength of the electric field, the free fall of the negatively charged drops could be slowed and even reversed. (Remember that like charges repel each other.)

Charge-to-Mass Ratio of the Electron

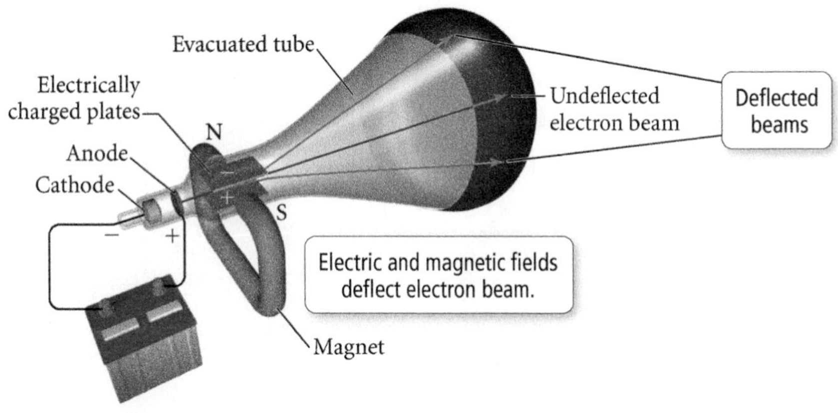
Evacuated tube
Electrically charged plates
Anode
Cathode
N
S
Undeflected electron beam
Deflected beams
Electric and magnetic fields deflect electron beam.
Magnet

► **FIGURE 2.4 Thomson's Measurement of the Charge-to-Mass Ratio of the Electron** J. J. Thomson used electric and magnetic fields to deflect the electron beam in a cathode ray tube. By measuring the strengths at which the effects of the two fields (electric and magnetic) canceled exactly, leaving the beam undeflected, he was able to calculate the charge-to-mass ratio of the electron.

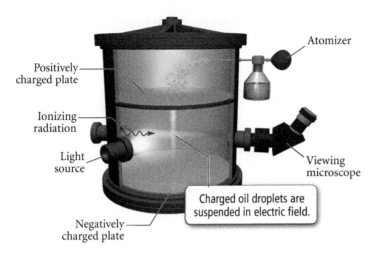

FIGURE 2.5 Millikan's Measurement of the Electron's Charge Millikan calculated the charge on oil droplets falling in an electric field. He found that it was always a whole-number multiple of -1.60×10^{-19} C, the charge of a single electron.

By measuring the size of the electric field required to halt the free fall of the drops, and figuring out the masses of the drops themselves (determined from their radii and density), Millikan calculated the charge of each drop. He then reasoned that, since each drop must contain an integral (or whole) number of electrons, the charge of each drop must be a whole-number multiple of the electron's charge. Indeed, Millikan was correct; the measured charge on any drop was always a whole-number multiple of -1.60×10^{-19} C, the fundamental charge of a single electron. With this number in hand, and knowing Thomson's mass-to-charge ratio for electrons, we can deduce the mass of an electron as follows:

$$\text{Charge} \times \frac{\text{mass}}{\text{charge}} = \text{mass}$$

$$-1.60 \times 10^{-19} \, \cancel{C} \times \frac{\text{g}}{-1.76 \times 10^{8} \, \cancel{C}} = 9.10 \times 10^{-28} \, \text{g}$$

As Thomson had correctly deduced, this mass is about 2000 times lighter than hydrogen, the lightest atom.

Why did scientists work so hard to measure the charge of the electron? Since the electron is a fundamental building block of matter, scientists want to know its properties, including its charge. The magnitude of the charge of the electron is of tremendous importance because it determines how strongly an atom holds its electrons. Imagine how matter would be different if electrons had a much smaller charge, so that atoms held them more loosely. Many atoms might not even be stable. On the other hand, imagine how matter would be different if electrons had a much greater charge, so that atoms held them more tightly. Since atoms form compounds by exchanging and sharing electrons (more on this in Chapter 3), the result could be fewer compounds or maybe even none. Without the abundant diversity of compounds, life would not be possible. So, the magnitude of the charge of the electron—even though it may seem like an insignificantly small number—has great importance.

2.5 The Structure of the Atom

The discovery of negatively charged particles within atoms raised a new question. Since atoms are charge-neutral, they must contain positive charge that neutralizes the negative charge of the electrons—but how do the positive and negative charges within the atom fit together? Are atoms just a jumble of even more fundamental particles? Are they solid spheres? Do they have some internal structure? J. J. Thomson proposed that the negatively charged electrons were small particles held within a positively charged sphere, as shown in the margin figure.

This model, the most popular of the time, became known as the plum-pudding model. The picture suggested by Thomson, to those of us not familiar with plum pudding (an English dessert), was like a blueberry muffin, where the blueberries are the electrons and the muffin is the positively charged sphere.

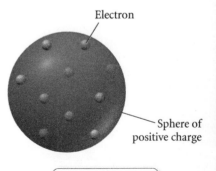

Plum-pudding model

Rutherford's Gold Foil Experiment

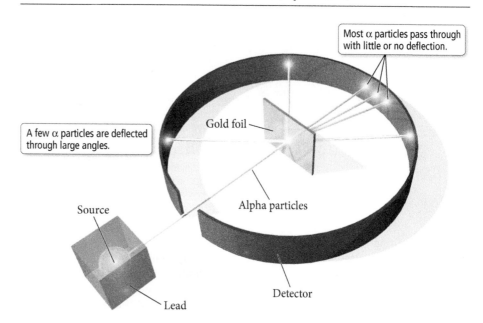

Most α particles pass through
with little or no deflection.

A few α particles are deflected
through large angles.

Gold foil

Alpha particles

Source

Detector

Lead

▶ **FIGURE 2.6 Rutherford's Gold Foil Experiment**   Alpha particles were directed at a thin sheet of gold foil. Most of the particles passed through the foil, but a small fraction were deflected, and a few even bounced backward.

Alpha particles are about 7000 times more massive than electrons.

The discovery of **radioactivity**—the emission of small energetic particles from the core of certain unstable atoms—by scientists Henri Becquerel (1852–1908) and Marie Curie (1867–1934) at the end of the nineteenth century allowed researchers to experimentally probe the structure of the atom. At the time, scientists had identified three different types of radioactivity: alpha (α) particles, beta (β) particles, and gamma (γ) rays. We will discuss these and other types of radioactivity in more detail in Chapter 19. For now, just know that α particles are positively charged and that they are by far the most massive of the three.

In 1909, Ernest Rutherford (1871–1937), who had worked under Thomson and subscribed to his plum-pudding model, performed an experiment in an attempt to confirm it. His experiment, which employed α particles, proved it wrong instead. In the experiment, Rutherford directed the positively charged α particles at an ultrathin sheet of gold foil, as shown in Figure 2.6 ▲.

These particles were to act as probes of the gold atoms' structure. If the gold atoms were indeed like blueberry muffins or plum pudding—with their mass and charge spread throughout the entire volume of the atom—these speeding probes should pass right through the gold foil with minimum deflection.

Rutherford performed the experiment, but the results were not as he expected. A majority of the particles did pass directly through the foil, but some particles were deflected, and some (approximately 1 in 20,000) even bounced back. The results puzzled Rutherford, who wrote that they were "about as credible as if you had fired a 15-inch shell at a piece of tissue paper and it came back and hit you." What sort of atomic structure could explain this odd behavior?

Rutherford created a new model—a modern version of which is shown in Figure 2.7 ▶ alongside the plum-pudding model—to explain his results.

He realized that to account for the deflections he observed, the mass and positive charge of an atom must be concentrated in a space much smaller than the size of the atom itself. He concluded that, in contrast to the plum-pudding model, matter must not be as uniform as it appears. It must contain large regions of empty space dotted with small regions of very dense matter. Building on this idea, he proposed the **nuclear theory** of the atom, with three basic parts:

1. Most of the atom's mass and all of its positive charge are contained in a small core called the **nucleus**.

2. Most of the volume of the atom is empty space, throughout which tiny, negatively charged electrons are dispersed.

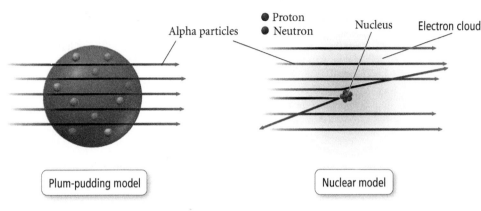

Alpha particles ● Proton ● Neutron Nucleus Electron cloud

Plum-pudding model

Nuclear model

3. There are as many negatively charged electrons outside the nucleus as there are positively charged particles (named **protons**) within the nucleus, so that the atom is electrically neutral.

Although Rutherford's model was highly successful, scientists realized that it was incomplete. For example, hydrogen atoms contain one proton, and helium atoms contain two, yet a hydrogen atom has only one-fourth the mass of a helium atom. Why? The helium atom must contain some additional mass. Later work by Rutherford and one of his students, British scientist James Chadwick (1891–1974), demonstrated that the previously unaccounted for mass was due to **neutrons**, neutral particles within the nucleus. The mass of a neutron is similar to that of a proton, but a neutron has no electrical charge. The helium atom is four times as massive as the hydrogen atom because it contains two protons *and two neutrons* (while hydrogen contains only 1 proton and no neutrons).

The dense nucleus contains over 99.9% of the mass of the atom, but occupies very little of its volume. For now, we can think of the electrons that surround the nucleus in analogy to the water droplets that make up a cloud—although their mass is almost negligibly small, they are dispersed over a very large volume. Consequently, an atom, like a cloud, is mostly empty space.

Rutherford's nuclear theory was a success and is still valid today. The revolutionary part of this theory is the idea that matter—at its core—is much less uniform than it appears. If the nucleus of the atom were the size of the period at the end of this sentence, the average electron would be about 10 meters away. Yet the period would contain nearly all of the atom's mass. Imagine what matter would be like if atomic structure were different. What if matter were composed of atomic nuclei piled on top of each other like marbles in a box? Such matter would be incredibly dense; a single grain of sand composed of solid atomic nuclei would have a mass of 5 million kilograms (or a weight of about 11 million pounds). Astronomers believe there are some objects in the universe composed of such matter—neutron stars.

If matter really is mostly empty space, as Rutherford suggested, then why does it appear so solid? Why can we tap our knuckles on a table and feel a solid thump? Matter appears solid because the variation in its density is on such a small scale that our eyes cannot see it. Imagine a scaffolding 100 stories high and the size of a football field as shown in the margin. The volume of the scaffolding is mostly empty space. Yet if you viewed it from an airplane, it would appear as a solid mass. Matter is similar. When you tap your knuckle on the table, it is much like one giant scaffolding (your finger) crashing into another (the table). Even though they are both primarily empty space, one does not fall into the other.

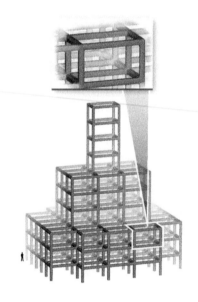

2.6 Subatomic Particles: Protons, Neutrons, and Electrons in Atoms

We have just learned that all atoms are composed of the same subatomic particles: protons, neutrons, and electrons. Protons and neutrons, as we saw earlier, have nearly identical masses. In SI units, the mass of the proton is 1.67262×10^{-27} kg, and the mass of the neutron is 1.67493×10^{-27} kg. A more common unit to express these masses, however, is the **atomic mass unit (amu)**, defined as 1/12 the mass of a carbon atom containing six protons and six neutrons. Expressed in this unit, the mass of a proton or neutron is approximately 1 amu. Electrons, by contrast, have an almost negligible mass of 0.00091×10^{-27} kg or 0.00055 amu.

If a proton had the mass of a baseball, an electron would have the mass of a rice grain.

TABLE 2.1 Subatomic Particles

	Mass (kg)	Mass (amu)	Charge (relative)	Charge (C)
Proton	1.67262×10^{-27}	1.00727	+1	$+1.60218 \times 10^{-19}$
Neutron	1.67493×10^{-27}	1.00866	0	0
Electron	0.00091×10^{-27}	0.00055	−1	-1.60218×10^{-19}

Negative charge builds up on clouds.

Electrical discharge equalizes charge imbalance.

Positive charge builds up on ground.

▲ When the normal charge balance of matter is disturbed, as happens during an electrical storm, it quickly equalizes, often in dramatic ways.

The proton and the electron both have electrical *charge*. We know from Millikan's oil drop experiment that the electron has a charge of -1.60×10^{-19} C. In atomic (or relative) units, the electron is assigned a charge of –1 and the proton is assigned a charge of +1. *The charge of the proton and the electron are equal in magnitude but opposite in sign*, so that when the two particles are paired, the charges sum to zero. The neutron has no charge.

Notice that matter is usually charge-neutral (it has no overall charge) because protons and electrons are normally present in equal numbers. When matter does acquire charge imbalances, these imbalances usually equalize quickly, often in dramatic ways. For example, the shock you receive when touching a doorknob during dry weather is the equalization of a charge imbalance that developed as you walked across the carpet. Lightning, as shown here, is an equalization of charge imbalances that develop during electrical storms.

A sample of matter—even a tiny sample, such as a sand grain—composed of only protons or only electrons, would have extraordinary repulsive forces inherent within it, and would be unstable. Luckily, matter is not that way. The properties of protons, neutrons, and electrons are summarized in Table 2.1.

Elements: Defined by Their Numbers of Protons

If all atoms are composed of the same subatomic particles, what makes the atoms of one element different from those of another? The answer is the *number* of these particles. The most important number to the *identity* of an atom is the number of protons in its nucleus. In fact, the number of protons defines the element. For example, an atom with 2 protons in its nucleus is a helium atom; an atom with 6 protons in its nucleus is a carbon atom (Figure 2.8 ▼); and an atom with 92 protons in its nucleus is a uranium atom. The number of protons in an atom's nucleus is its **atomic number** and is given the symbol **Z**. The atomic numbers of known elements range from 1 to 116 (although additional elements may still be discovered), as shown in the periodic table of the elements (Figure 2.9 ▶). In the periodic table, described in more detail in Section 2.7, the elements are arranged so that those with similar properties are in the same column.

▶ FIGURE 2.8 **How Elements Differ** Each element is defined by a unique atomic number (Z), the number of protons in the nucleus of every atom of that element.

The Number of Protons Defines the Element

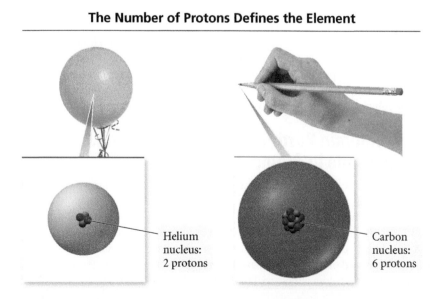

Helium nucleus: 2 protons

Carbon nucleus: 6 protons

The Periodic Table

Atomic number (Z)

4
Be
beryllium

Chemical symbol

Name

1 H hydrogen																	2 He helium
3 Li lithium	4 Be beryllium											5 B boron	6 C carbon	7 N nitrogen	8 O oxygen	9 F fluorine	10 Ne neon
11 Na sodium	12 Mg magnesium											13 Al aluminum	14 Si silicon	15 P phosphorus	16 S sulfur	17 Cl chlorine	18 Ar argon
19 K potassium	20 Ca calcium	21 Sc scandium	22 Ti titanium	23 V vanadium	24 Cr chromium	25 Mn manganese	26 Fe iron	27 Co cobalt	28 Ni nickel	29 Cu copper	30 Zn zinc	31 Ga gallium	32 Ge germanium	33 As arsenic	34 Se selenium	35 Br bromine	36 Kr krypton
37 Rb rubidium	38 Sr strontium	39 Y yttrium	40 Zr zirconium	41 Nb niobium	42 Mo molybdenum	43 Tc technetium	44 Ru ruthenium	45 Rh rhodium	46 Pd palladium	47 Ag silver	48 Cd cadmium	49 In indium	50 Sn tin	51 Sb antimony	52 Te tellurium	53 I iodine	54 Xe xenon
55 Cs cesium	56 Ba barium	57 La lanthanum	72 Hf hafnium	73 Ta tantalum	74 W tungsten	75 Re rhenium	76 Os osmium	77 Ir iridium	78 Pt platinum	79 Au gold	80 Hg mercury	81 Tl thallium	82 Pb lead	83 Bi bismuth	84 Po polonium	85 At astatine	86 Rn radon
87 Fr francium	88 Ra radium	89 Ac actinium	104 Rf rutherfordium	105 Db dubnium	106 Sg seaborgium	107 Bh bohrium	108 Hs hassium	109 Mt meitnerium	110 Ds darmstadtium	111 Rg roentgenium	112 **	113 **	114 **	115 **	116 **		

58 Ce cerium	59 Pr praseodymium	60 Nd neodymium	61 Pm promethium	62 Sm samarium	63 Eu europium	64 Gd gadolinium	65 Tb terbium	66 Dy dysprosium	67 Ho holmium	68 Er erbium	69 Tm thulium	70 Yb ytterbium	71 Lu lutetium
90 Th thorium	91 Pa protactinium	92 U uranium	93 Np neptunium	94 Pu plutonium	95 Am americium	96 Cm curium	97 Bk berkelium	98 Cf californium	99 Es einsteinium	100 Fm fermium	101 Md mendelevium	102 No nobelium	103 Lr lawrencium

▲ **FIGURE 2.9 The Periodic Table**   Each element is represented by its symbol and atomic number. Elements in the same column have similar properties.

Each element, identified by its unique atomic number, is represented with a unique **chemical symbol**, a one- or two-letter abbreviation listed directly below its atomic number on the periodic table. The chemical symbol for helium is He; for carbon, it is C; and for uranium, it is U. The chemical symbol and the atomic number always go together. If the atomic number is 2, the chemical symbol *must be* He. If the atomic number is 6, the chemical symbol *must be* C. This is just another way of saying that the number of protons defines the element.

Most chemical symbols are based on the English name of the element. For example, the symbol for sulfur is S; for oxygen, O; and for chlorine, Cl. Several of the oldest known elements, however, have symbols based on their original Latin names. For example, the symbol for sodium is Na from the Latin *natrium*, and the symbol for tin is Sn from the Latin *stannum*. Early scientists often gave newly discovered elements names that reflect their properties. For example, argon originates from the Greek word *argos* meaning inactive, referring to argon's chemical inertness (it does not react with other elements). Chlorine originates from the Greek word *chloros* meaning pale green, referring to chlorine's pale green color. Other elements, including helium, selenium, and mercury, were named after figures from Greek or Roman mythology or astronomical bodies. Still others (such as europium, polonium, and berkelium) were named for the places where they were discovered or where their discoverer was born. More recently, elements have been named after scientists; for example, curium was named for Marie Curie, einsteinium for Albert Einstein, and rutherfordium for Ernest Rutherford.

Isotopes: When the Number of Neutrons Varies

All atoms of a given element have the same number of protons; however, they do not necessarily have the same number of neutrons. Since neutrons have nearly the same mass as protons (1 amu), this means that—contrary to what John Dalton originally proposed in

96
Cm
Curium

▲ Element 96 is named curium, after Marie Curie, co-discoverer of radioactivity.

his atomic theory—all atoms of a given element *do not* have the same mass. For example, all neon atoms contain 10 protons, but they may contain 10, 11, or 12 neutrons. All three types of neon atoms exist, and each has a slightly different mass. Atoms with the same number of protons but different numbers of neutrons are called **isotopes**. Some elements, such as beryllium (Be) and aluminum (Al), have only one naturally occurring isotope, while other elements, such as neon (Ne) and chlorine (Cl), have two or more.

The relative amount of each different isotope in a naturally occurring sample of a given element is usually constant. For example, in any natural sample of neon atoms, 90.48% of them are the isotope with 10 neutrons, 0.27% are the isotope with 11 neutrons, and 9.25% are the isotope with 12 neutrons. These percentages are called the **natural abundance** of the isotopes. Each element has its own characteristic natural abundance of isotopes.

The sum of the number of neutrons and protons in an atom is its **mass number** and is represented by the symbol A:

$$A = \text{number of protons (p)} + \text{number of neutrons (n)}$$

For neon, with 10 protons, the mass numbers of the three different naturally occurring isotopes are 20, 21, and 22, corresponding to 10, 11, and 12 neutrons, respectively.

Isotopes are often symbolized in the following way:

Mass number $\longrightarrow$ $^{A}_{Z}X$ $\longleftarrow$ Chemical symbol
Atomic number $\longrightarrow$

where X is the chemical symbol, A is the mass number, and Z is the atomic number. Therefore, the symbols for the neon isotopes are

$$^{20}_{10}\text{Ne} \quad ^{21}_{10}\text{Ne} \quad ^{22}_{10}\text{Ne}$$

Notice that the chemical symbol, Ne, and the atomic number, 10, are redundant: if the atomic number is 10, the symbol must be Ne. The mass numbers, however, are different for the different isotopes, reflecting the different number of neutrons in each one.

A second common notation for isotopes is the chemical symbol (or chemical name) followed by a dash and the mass number of the isotope.

Chemical symbol or name $\longrightarrow$ X-A $\longleftarrow$ Mass number

In this notation, the neon isotopes are

| Ne-20 | Ne-21 | Ne-22 |
| neon-20 | neon-21 | neon-22 |

We summarize what we have learned about the neon isotopes in the following table:

Symbol	Number of Protons	Number of Neutrons	A (Mass Number)	Natural Abundance (%)
Ne-20 or $^{20}_{10}$Ne	10	10	20	90.48
Ne-21 or $^{21}_{10}$Ne	10	11	21	0.27
Ne-22 or $^{22}_{10}$Ne	10	12	22	9.25

Notice that all isotopes of a given element have the same number of protons (otherwise they would be different elements). Notice also that the mass number is the *sum* of the number of protons and the number of neutrons. The number of neutrons in an isotope is therefore the difference between the mass number and the atomic number ($A - Z$). The different isotopes of an element generally exhibit the same chemical behavior—the three isotopes of neon, for example, all exhibit the same chemical inertness.

EXAMPLE 2.3 Atomic Numbers, Mass Numbers, and Isotope Symbols

(a) What are the atomic number (Z), mass number (A), and symbol of the chlorine isotope with 18 neutrons?

(b) How many protons, electrons, and neutrons are present in an atom of $^{52}_{24}Cr$?

SOLUTION

(a) Look up the atomic number (Z) for chlorine on the periodic table. The atomic number specifies the number of protons.	$Z = 17$, so chlorine has 17 protons.
The mass number (A) for an isotope is the sum of the number of protons and the number of neutrons.	A = number of protons + number of neutrons $= 17 + 18 = 35$
The symbol for an isotope is its two-letter abbreviation with the atomic number (Z) in the lower left corner and the mass number (A) in the upper left corner.	$^{35}_{17}Cl$
(b) For any isotope (in this case $^{52}_{24}Cr$) the number of protons is indicated by the atomic number located at the lower left. Since this is a neutral atom, the number of electrons equals the number of protons.	Number of protons = Z = 24 Number of electrons = 24 (neutral atom)
The number of neutrons is equal to the mass number (upper left) minus the atomic number (lower left).	Number of neutrons = $52 - 24 = 28$

FOR PRACTICE 2.3

(a) What are the atomic number, mass number, and symbol for the carbon isotope with 7 neutrons?

(b) How many protons and neutrons are present in an atom of $^{39}_{19}K$?

Ions: Losing and Gaining Electrons

The number of electrons in a neutral atom is equal to the number of protons in its nucleus (designated by its atomic number Z). During chemical changes, however, atoms can lose or gain electrons and become charged particles called **ions**. For example, neutral lithium (Li) atoms contain 3 protons and 3 electrons; however, in many chemical reactions lithium atoms lose one electron (e^-) to form Li^+ ions.

$$Li \longrightarrow Li^+ + 1\,e^-$$

The charge of an ion depends on the relative number of protons and electrons and is indicated in the upper right corner of the symbol. Since the Li^+ *ion* contains 3 protons and only 2 electrons, its charge is 1+.

Ions can also be negatively charged. For example, neutral fluorine (F) atoms contain 9 protons and 9 electrons; however, in many chemical reactions fluorine atoms gain one electron to form F^- ions.

$$F + 1\,e^- \longrightarrow F^-$$

The F^- *ion* contains 9 protons and 10 electrons, resulting in a charge of 1−. For many elements, such as lithium and fluorine, the ion is much more common than the neutral atom. In fact, virtually all of the lithium and fluorine in nature exist as ions.

Positively charged ions, such as Li^+, are called **cations** and negatively charged ions, such as F^-, are called **anions**. Ions act very differently than the atoms from which they are formed. Neutral sodium atoms, for example, are extremely unstable, reacting violently with most things they contact. Sodium cations (Na^+), by contrast, are relatively inert—we eat them all the time in sodium chloride (table salt). In ordinary matter, cations and anions always occur together so that matter is charge-neutral overall.

Conceptual Connection 2.3 **The Nuclear Atom, Isotopes, and Ions**

In light of the nuclear model for the atom, which statement is most likely true?

(a) The size of an isotope with more neutrons is larger than one with fewer neutrons.

(b) The mass of an isotope with more neutrons is greater than one with fewer neutrons.

(c) Both (a) and (b) are true.

ANSWER: (b) The number of neutrons in the nucleus of an atom does not affect the atom's size because the nucleus is miniscule compared to the atom itself. The number of neutrons, however, does affect the mass of the isotope; more neutrons means more mass.

 CHEMISTRY IN YOUR DAY **Where Did Elements Come From?**

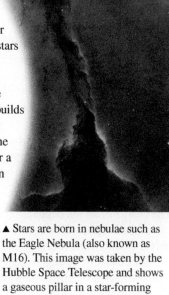

We find ourselves on a planet containing many different kinds of elements. If it were otherwise, we would not exist, and would not be here to reflect on why. But we are here, and so we ask, where did these elements come from? The story of element formation is as old as the universe itself, and we have to go back to the very beginning to tell the story.

The birth of the universe is described by the Big Bang Theory, which asserts that the universe began as a hot, dense collection of matter and energy that expanded rapidly. As it expanded, it cooled, and within the first several hours, subatomic particles formed the first atomic nuclei: hydrogen and helium. These two elements were (and continue to be) the most abundant in the universe. As the universe continued expanding, some of the hydrogen and helium clumped together under the influence of gravity to form nebulae (clouds of gas) that eventually gave birth to stars and galaxies. These stars and galaxies became the nurseries where all other elements form.

Stars are fueled by nuclear fusion, which we discuss in more detail in Chapter 19. Under the conditions within the core of a star, hydrogen nuclei can combine (or fuse) to form helium. Fusion gives off enormous quantities of energy; this is why stars emit so much heat and light. The fusion of hydrogen to helium can fuel a star for billions of years.

After it burns through large quantities of hydrogen, if a star is large enough, the helium that builds up in its core can in turn fuse to form carbon. The carbon then builds up in the core and (again, if the star is large enough) can fuse to form even heavier elements. The fusion process ends at iron, which has a highly stable nucleus. By the time iron is formed, however, the star is near the end of its existence and may enter a phase of expansion, transforming into a supernova. Within a supernova, which is in essence a large exploding star, a shower of neutrons allows the lighter elements (which formed during the lifetime of the star through the fusion processes just described) to capture extra neutrons. These neutrons can transform into protons (through processes that we discuss in Chapter 19) contributing ultimately to the formation of elements heavier than iron, all the way up to uranium. As the supernova continues to expand, the elements present within it are blown out into space, where they can incorporate into other nebulae and perhaps even form planets that orbit a star like our own sun.

▲ Stars are born in nebulae such as the Eagle Nebula (also known as M16). This image was taken by the Hubble Space Telescope and shows a gaseous pillar in a star-forming region of the Eagle Nebula.

2.7 Finding Patterns: The Periodic Law and the Periodic Table

The modern periodic table grew out of the work of Dmitri Mendeleev (1834–1907), a nineteenth-century Russian chemistry professor. In his time, scientists had discovered about 65 different elements, and chemists had identified many of the properties of these elements—such as their relative masses, their chemical activity, and some of their physical properties. However, no one had developed any systematic way of organizing them.

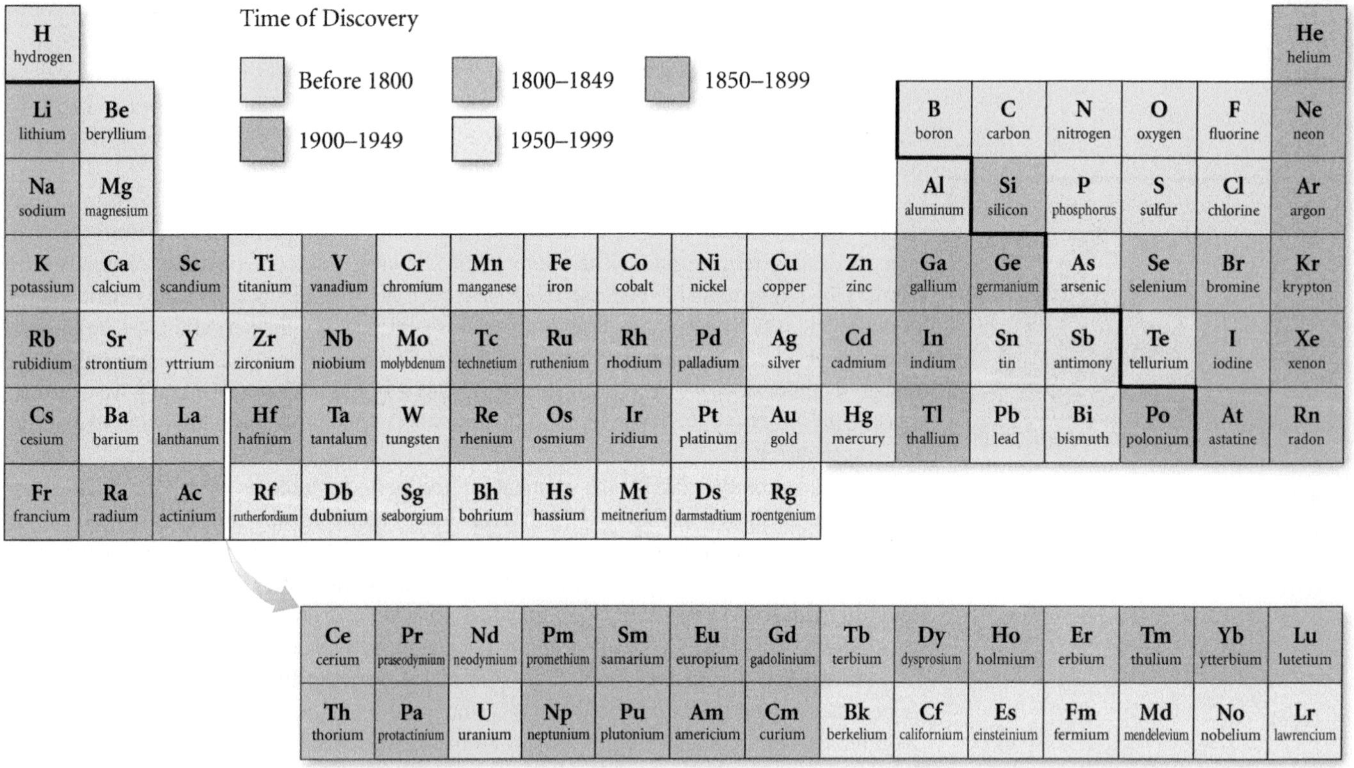

Time of Discovery
Before 1800
1800–1849
1850–1899
1900–1949
1950–1999
H hydrogen
He helium
Li lithium
Be beryllium
B boron
C carbon
N nitrogen
O oxygen
F fluorine
Ne neon
Na sodium
Mg magnesium
Al aluminum
Si silicon
P phosphorus
S sulfur
Cl chlorine
Ar argon
K potassium
Ca calcium
Sc scandium
Ti titanium
V vanadium
Cr chromium
Mn manganese
Fe iron
Co cobalt
Ni nickel
Cu copper
Zn zinc
Ga gallium
Ge germanium
As arsenic
Se selenium
Br bromine
Kr krypton
Rb rubidium
Sr strontium
Y yttrium
Zr zirconium
Nb niobium
Mo molybdenum
Tc technetium
Ru ruthenium
Rh rhodium
Pd palladium
Ag silver
Cd cadmium
In indium
Sn tin
Sb antimony
Te tellurium
I iodine
Xe xenon
Cs cesium
Ba barium
La lanthanum
Hf hafnium
Ta tantalum
W tungsten
Re rhenium
Os osmium
Ir iridium
Pt platinum
Au gold
Hg mercury
Tl thallium
Pb lead
Bi bismuth
Po polonium
At astatine
Rn radon
Fr francium
Ra radium
Ac actinium
Rf rutherfordium
Db dubnium
Sg seaborgium
Bh bohrium
Hs hassium
Mt meitnerium
Ds darmstadtium
Rg roentgenium
Ce cerium
Pr praseodymium
Nd neodymium
Pm promethium
Sm samarium
Eu europium
Gd gadolinium
Tb terbium
Dy dysprosium
Ho holmium
Er erbium
Tm thulium
Yb ytterbium
Lu lutetium
Th thorium
Pa protactinium
U uranium
Np neptunium
Pu plutonium
Am americium
Cm curium
Bk berkelium
Cf californium
Es einsteinium
Fm fermium
Md mendelevium
No nobelium
Lr lawrencium

▲ Many of the elements that we know today were discovered during Mendeleev's lifetime.

In 1869, Mendeleev noticed that certain groups of elements had similar properties. He also found that when he listed elements in order of increasing mass, these similar properties recurred in a periodic pattern (Figure 2.10 ▾).

Periodic means exhibiting a repeating pattern.

The Periodic Law
1 H
2 He
3 Li
4 Be
5 B
6 C
7 N
8 O
9 F
10 Ne
11 Na
12 Mg
13 Al
14 Si
15 P
16 S
17 Cl
18 Ar
19 K
20 Ca
Elements with similar properties recur in a regular pattern.

◀ **FIGURE 2.10 Recurring Properties** These elements are listed in order of increasing atomic number. Elements with similar properties are the same color. Notice that the colors form a repeating pattern, much like musical notes, which form a repeating pattern on a piano keyboard.

Mendeleev summarized these observations in the **periodic law**:

When the elements are arranged in order of increasing mass, certain sets of properties recur periodically.

Mendeleev organized the known elements in a table consisting of a series of rows in which mass increased from left to right. He arranged the rows so that elements with similar properties fell in the same vertical columns (Figure 2.11 ▾).

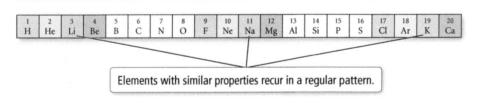

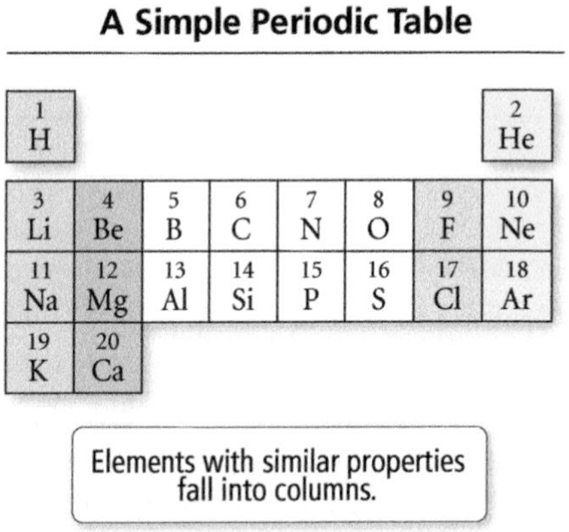

A Simple Periodic Table
1 H
2 He
3 Li
4 Be
5 B
6 C
7 N
8 O
9 F
10 Ne
11 Na
12 Mg
13 Al
14 Si
15 P
16 S
17 Cl
18 Ar
19 K
20 Ca
Elements with similar properties fall into columns.

◀ **FIGURE 2.11 Making a Periodic Table** We can arrange the elements in Figure 2.10 in a table in which atomic number increases from left to right and elements with similar properties (as represented by the different colors) are aligned in columns.

Eka means the one beyond or the next one in a family of elements. So, eka-silicon means the element beyond silicon in the same family as silicon.

▲ Dmitri Mendeleev, a Russian chemistry professor who proposed the periodic law and arranged early versions of the periodic table, was honored on a Soviet postage stamp.

Since many elements had not yet been discovered, Mendeleev's table contained some gaps, which allowed him to predict the existence (and even the properties) of yet undiscovered elements. For example, Mendeleev predicted the existence of an element he called eka-silicon, which fell below silicon on the table and between gallium and arsenic. In 1886, eka-silicon was discovered by German chemist Clemens Winkler (1838–1904), who named it germanium, after his home country.

Mendeleev's original listing evolved into the modern periodic table shown in Figure 2.12 ▼. In the modern table, elements are listed in order of increasing atomic number rather than increasing relative mass. The modern periodic table also contains more elements than Mendeleev's original table because more have been discovered since his time. Mendeleev's periodic law was based on observation. Like all scientific laws, the periodic law summarizes many observations but does not give the underlying reason for the observations—only theories do that. For now, we accept the periodic law as it is, but in Chapters 7 and 8 we examine a powerful theory—called quantum mechanics—that explains the law and gives the underlying reasons for it.

We can broadly classify the elements in the periodic table as metals, nonmetals, or metalloids, as shown in Figure 2.12. **Metals** lie on the lower left side and middle of the periodic table and share some common properties: they are good conductors of heat and electricity; they can be pounded into flat sheets (malleability); they can be drawn into wires (ductility); they are often shiny; and they tend to lose electrons when they undergo chemical changes. Chromium, copper, strontium, and lead are typical metals.

Nonmetals lie on the upper right side of the periodic table. The dividing line between metals and nonmetals is the zigzag diagonal line running from boron to astatine. Nonmetals have more varied properties—some are solids at room temperature, others are liquids or gases—but as a whole they tend to be poor conductors of heat and electricity

Major Divisions of the Periodic Table

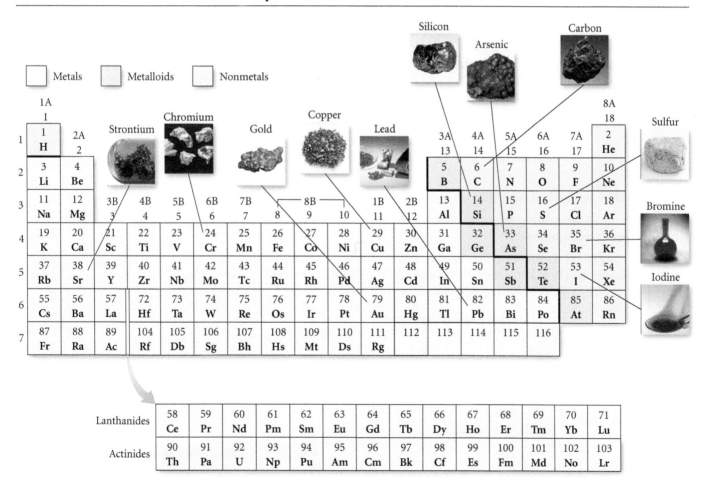

▲ **FIGURE 2.12 Metals, Nonmetals, and Metalloids** The elements in the periodic table fall into these three broad classes.

| Main-group elements | | Transition elements | | | | | | | | | Main-group elements | | | | | | |

1A 1	Group number																8A 18
1 H	2A 2											3A 13	4A 14	5A 15	6A 16	7A 17	**2** He
3 Li	**4** Be											**5** B	**6** C	**7** N	**8** O	**9** F	**10** Ne
11 Na	**12** Mg	3B 3	4B 4	5B 5	6B 6	7B 7	8	8B 9	10	1B 11	2B 12	**13** Al	**14** Si	**15** P	**16** S	**17** Cl	**18** Ar
19 K	**20** Ca	**21** Sc	**22** Ti	**23** V	**24** Cr	**25** Mn	**26** Fe	**27** Co	**28** Ni	**29** Cu	**30** Zn	**31** Ga	**32** Ge	**33** As	**34** Se	**35** Br	**36** Kr
37 Rb	**38** Sr	**39** Y	**40** Zr	**41** Nb	**42** Mo	**43** Tc	**44** Ru	**45** Rh	**46** Pd	**47** Ag	**48** Cd	**49** In	**50** Sn	**51** Sb	**52** Te	**53** I	**54** Xe
55 Cs	**56** Ba	**57** La	**72** Hf	**73** Ta	**74** W	**75** Re	**76** Os	**77** Ir	**78** Pt	**79** Au	**80** Hg	**81** Tl	**82** Pb	**83** Bi	**84** Po	**85** At	**86** Rn
87 Fr	**88** Ra	**89** Ac	**104** Rf	**105** Db	**106** Sg	**107** Bh	**108** Hs	**109** Mt	**110** Ds	**111** Rg	**112**	**113**	**114**	**115**	**116**		

Periods: 1, 2, 3, 4, 5, 6, 7

▲ **FIGURE 2.13 The Periodic Table: Main-Group and Transition Elements** The elements in the periodic table fall into columns. The two columns at the left and the six columns at the right comprise the main-group elements. Each of these eight columns is a group or family. The properties of main-group elements can generally be predicted from their position in the periodic table. The properties of the elements in the middle of the table, known as transition elements, are less predictable.

and they all tend to gain electrons when they undergo chemical changes. Oxygen, carbon, sulfur, bromine, and iodine are nonmetals.

Many of the elements that lie along the zigzag diagonal line that divides metals and nonmetals are **metalloids** and exhibit mixed properties. Several metalloids are also classified as **semiconductors** because of their intermediate (and highly temperature-dependent) electrical conductivity. The ability to change and control the conductivity of semiconductors makes them useful in the manufacture of the electronic chips and circuits central to computers, cellular telephones, and many other modern devices. Good examples of metalloids include silicon, arsenic, and antimony.

Metalloids are sometimes called semimetals.

The periodic table, as shown in Figure 2.13 ▲, can also be divided into **main-group elements**, whose properties tend to be largely predictable based on their position in the periodic table, and **transition elements** or **transition metals**, whose properties tend to be less predictable based simply on their position in the periodic table. Main-group elements are in columns labeled with a number and the letter A. Transition elements are in columns labeled with a number and the letter B. An alternative numbering system does not use letters, but only the numbers 1–18. Both numbering systems are shown in most of the periodic tables in this book. Each column within the main-group regions of the periodic table is called a **family** or **group** of elements.

The elements within a group usually have similar properties. For example, the group 8A elements, called the **noble gases**, are mostly unreactive. The most familiar noble gas is probably helium, used to fill buoyant balloons. Helium is chemically stable—it does not combine with other elements to form compounds—and is therefore safe to put into balloons. Other noble gases are neon (often used in electronic signs), argon (a small component of our atmosphere), krypton, and xenon.

The group 1A elements, called the **alkali metals**, are all reactive metals. A marble-sized piece of sodium explodes violently when dropped into water. Lithium, potassium, and rubidium are also alkali metals.

The group 2A elements, called the **alkaline earth metals**, are also fairly reactive, although not quite as reactive as the alkali metals. Calcium for example, reacts fairly vigorously when dropped into water but will not explode as dramatically as sodium. Other alkaline earth metals include magnesium (a common low-density structural metal), strontium, and barium.

Alkali metals

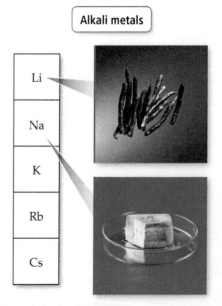

Li
Na
K
Rb
Cs

Halogens

The group 7A elements, called the **halogens**, are very reactive nonmetals. One of the most familiar halogens is chlorine, a greenish-yellow gas with a pungent odor. Because of its reactivity, chlorine is used as a sterilizing and disinfecting agent. Other halogens include bromine, a red-brown liquid that easily evaporates into a gas; iodine, a purple solid; and fluorine, a pale-yellow gas.

Ions and the Periodic Table

We have learned that, in chemical reactions, metals tend to lose electrons (forming cations) and nonmetals tend to gain them (forming anions). The number of electrons lost or gained, and therefore the charge of the resulting ion, is often predictable for a given element, especially main-group elements. Main-group elements tend to form ions that have the same number of electrons as the nearest noble gas (i.e., the noble gas that has the number of electrons closest to that of the element).

• **A main-group metal tends to lose electrons, forming a cation with the same number of electrons as the nearest noble gas.**

• **A main-group nonmetal tends to gain electrons, forming an anion with the same number of electrons as the nearest noble gas.**

For example, lithium, a metal with three electrons, tends to lose one electron, forming a 1+ cation that has the same number of electrons (two) as helium. Chlorine, a nonmetal with 17 electrons, tends to gain one electron, forming a 1– anion that has the same number of electrons (18) as argon.

In general, the alkali metals (group 1A) have a tendency to lose one electron and form 1+ ions. The alkaline earth metals (group 2A) tend to lose two electrons and form 2+ ions. The halogens (group 7A) tend to gain one electron and form 1– ions. The oxygen family nonmetals (group 6A) tend to gain two electrons and form 2– ions. More generally, for the main-group elements that form cations with predictable charge, the charge is equal to the group number. For main-group elements that form anions with predictable charge, the charge is equal to the group number minus eight. Transition elements may form various different ions with different charges. Figure 2.14 ▼ shows the ions formed by the main-group elements that form ions with predictable charges. In Chapters 7 and 8, we learn about quantum-mechanical theory, which more fully explains *why* these groups form ions as they do.

Elements That Form Ions with Predictable Charges

1A												3A	4A	5A	6A	7A	8A
H^+	2A															H^-	N
Li^+														N^{3-}	O^{2-}	F^-	o
Na^+	Mg^{2+}				Transition metals							Al^{3+}			S^{2-}	Cl^-	b l e
K^+	Ca^{2+}														Se^{2-}	Br^-	G a
Rb^+	Sr^{2+}														Te^{2-}	I^-	s e
Cs^+	Ba^{2+}																s

▲ FIGURE 2.14 **Elements That Form Ions with Predictable Charges**

EXAMPLE 2.4 Predicting the Charge of Ions

Predict the charges of the monoatomic (single atom) ions formed by the following main-group elements.

(a) Al   **(b)** S

SOLUTION

(a) Aluminum is a main-group metal and therefore tends to lose electrons to form a cation with the same number of electrons as the nearest noble gas. Aluminum atoms have 13 electrons and the nearest noble gas is neon, which has 10 electrons. Aluminum therefore loses 3 electrons to form a cation with a 3+ charge (Al^{3+}).

(b) Sulfur is a nonmetal and therefore tends to gain electrons to form an anion with the same number of electrons as the nearest noble gas. Sulfur atoms have 16 electrons and the nearest noble gas is argon, which has 18 electrons. Sulfur therefore gains 2 electrons to form an anion with a 2– charge (S^{2-}).

FOR PRACTICE 2.4

Predict the charges of the monoatomic ions formed by the following main-group elements.

(a) N   **(b)** Rb

CHEMISTRY AND MEDICINE   The Elements of Life

What kind of atoms compose living things such as humans? In terms of sheer mass, our bodies are 65% oxygen (because of the large amount of water), 18% carbon, and 10% hydrogen, with a few other elements present in smaller quantities, as shown in Figure 2.15 ▶ and Table 2.2. Because the atoms of different elements have different masses (more on this in Sections 2.8 and 2.9), when expressed in terms of number of atoms, hydrogen comes in first (because hydrogen atoms are so light), with oxygen second and carbon third.

TABLE 2.2 **Approximate Percent Elemental Composition of Humans**

Element	% by Mass	% by Number of Atoms
Oxygen	65	26.4
Carbon	18	9.2
Hydrogen	10	62.3
Nitrogen	3	1.4
Calcium	1.5	0.2
Phosphorus	1	0.3
Other	1.5	0.2

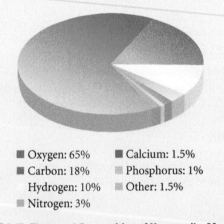

Oxygen: 65%   Calcium: 1.5%
Carbon: 18%   Phosphorus: 1%
Hydrogen: 10%   Other: 1.5%
Nitrogen: 3%

▲ FIGURE 2.15 **Elemental Composition of Humans (by Mass)**

Much of the *chemistry* of life revolves, not around oxygen or hydrogen, however, but around the chemistry of carbon, an element that forms a disproportionately large number of compounds with a few other elements such as hydrogen, oxygen, and nitrogen. We will first encounter the chemistry of carbon—called organic chemistry—in Chapter 3 and then examine it in more detail in Chapter 20.

2.8 Atomic Mass: The Average Mass of an Element's Atoms

Atomic mass is sometimes called *atomic weight, average atomic mass,* or *average atomic weight.*

An important part of Dalton's atomic theory is that all atoms of a given element have the same mass. In Section 2.6, we learned that because of isotopes, the atoms of a given element often have different masses, so Dalton was not completely correct. We can, however, calculate an average mass—called the **atomic mass**—for each element.

The atomic mass of each element is listed directly beneath the element's symbol in the periodic table and represents the average mass of the isotopes that compose that element, *weighted according to the natural abundance of each isotope*. For example, the periodic table lists the atomic mass of chlorine as 35.45 amu. Naturally occurring chlorine consists of 75.77% chlorine-35 atoms (mass 34.97 amu) and 24.23% chlorine-37 atoms (mass 36.97 amu). We can calculate its atomic mass as follows:

17
Cl
35.45
chlorine

$$\text{Atomic mass} = 0.7577(34.97 \text{ amu}) + 0.2423(36.97 \text{ amu}) = 35.45 \text{ amu}$$

Notice that the atomic mass of chlorine is closer to 35 than 37. Naturally occurring chlorine contains more chlorine-35 atoms than chlorine-37 atoms, so the weighted average mass of chlorine is closer to 35 amu than to 37 amu.

In general, the atomic mass is calculated according to the following equation:

When percentages are used in calculations, they are converted to their decimal value by dividing by 100.

$$\textbf{Atomic mass} = \sum_{n} (\textbf{fraction of isotope } n) \times (\textbf{mass of isotope } n)$$
$$= (\textbf{fraction of isotope 1} \times \textbf{mass of isotope 1})$$
$$+ (\textbf{fraction of isotope 2} \times \textbf{mass of isotope 2})$$
$$+ (\textbf{fraction of isotope 3} \times \textbf{mass of isotope 3}) +$$

where the fractions of each isotope are the percent natural abundances converted to their decimal values. The concept of atomic mass is useful because it allows us to assign a characteristic mass to each element and, as we will see shortly, it allows us to quantify the number of atoms in a sample of that element.

EXAMPLE 2.5 Atomic Mass

Copper has two naturally occurring isotopes: Cu-63 with mass 62.9396 amu and a natural abundance of 69.17%, and Cu-65 with mass 64.9278 amu and a natural abundance of 30.83%. Calculate the atomic mass of copper.

SOLUTION

Convert the percent natural abundances into decimal form by dividing by 100.	$$\text{Fraction Cu-63} = \frac{69.17}{100} = 0.6917$$ $$\text{Fraction Cu-65} = \frac{30.83}{100} = 0.3083$$
Compute the atomic mass using the equation given in the text.	Atomic mass = 0.6917(62.9396 amu) + 0.3083(64.9278 amu) = 43.5353 amu + 20.0172 amu = 63.5525 = 63.55 amu

FOR PRACTICE 2.5

Magnesium has three naturally occurring isotopes with masses of 23.99 amu, 24.99 amu, and 25.98 amu and natural abundances of 78.99%, 10.00%, and 11.01%, respectively. Calculate the atomic mass of magnesium.

FOR MORE PRACTICE 2.5

Gallium has two naturally occurring isotopes: Ga-69 with a mass of 68.9256 amu and a natural abundance of 60.11%, and Ga-71. Use the atomic mass of gallium listed in the periodic table to find the mass of Ga-71.

Mass Spectrometer

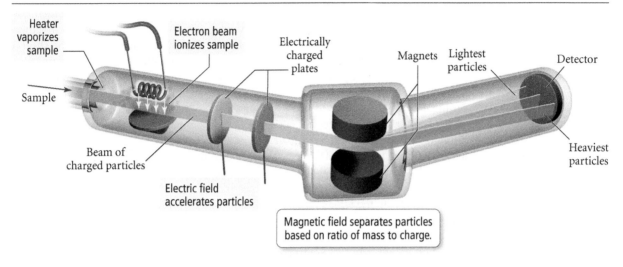

▲ **FIGURE 2.16 The Mass Spectrometer**   Atoms are converted to positively charged ions, accelerated, and passed through a magnetic field that deflects their path. The heaviest ions undergo the least deflection.

Mass Spectrometry: Measuring the Mass of Atoms and Molecules

The masses of atoms and the percent abundances of isotopes of elements are measured using **mass spectrometry**. In a mass spectrometer, such as the one in Figure 2.16 ▲, the sample (containing the atoms whose mass is to be measured) is injected into the instrument and vaporized. The vaporized atoms are then ionized by an electron beam—the electrons in the beam collide with the atoms, removing electrons and creating positively charged ions. Charged plates with slits in them accelerate the positively charged ions into a magnetic field, which deflects them. The amount of deflection depends on the mass of the ions—lighter ions are deflected more than heavier ones.

In the right side of the spectrometer shown in Figure 2.16, you can see three different paths, each corresponding to atoms of different mass. Finally, the ions strike a detector and produce an electrical signal that is recorded. The result is the separation of the atoms in the sample according to their mass, producing a mass spectrum such as the one in Figure 2.17 ▶. The *position* of each peak on the *x*-axis indicates the *mass of the isotope* that was ionized, and the *intensity* (indicated by the height of the peak) indicates the *relative abundance of that isotope*.

Mass spectrometry can also be used on molecules. Because molecules often fragment (break apart) during ionization, the mass spectrum of a molecule usually contains many peaks representing the masses of different parts of the molecule, as well as a peak representing the mass of the molecule as a whole. The fragments that form upon ionization, and therefore the corresponding peaks that appear in the mass spectrum, are specific to the molecule, so that a mass spectrum is like a molecular fingerprint. Mass spectroscopy can therefore be used to identify an unknown molecule and to determine how much of it is present in a particular sample. For example, mass spectrometry has been used to detect organic (carbon-containing) compounds present in meteorites, a puzzling observation, which some scientists speculate may be evidence of life outside of our planet. Most scientists, however, think that the compounds probably formed in the same way as the first organic molecules on Earth, indicating that the formation of organic molecules may be common in the universe.

Since the early 1990s, researchers have also successfully applied mass spectrometry to biological molecules, including proteins (the workhorse molecules in cells) and nucleic acids (the molecules that carry genetic information). For a long time, these molecules could not be analyzed by mass spectrometry because they were difficult to vaporize and ionize without destroying them, but modern techniques have overcome this problem. A tumor, for example, can now be instantly analyzed by mass spectrometry to determine whether it contains specific proteins associated with cancer.

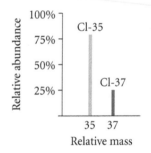

▲ **FIGURE 2.17 The Mass Spectrum of Chlorine**   The position of each peak on the *x*-axis indicates the mass of the isotope. The intensity (or height) of the peak indicates the relative abundance of the isotope.

2.9 Molar Mass: Counting Atoms by Weighing Them

Have you ever bought shrimp by *count*? Shrimp is normally sold by count, which tells you the number of shrimp per pound. For example, 41–50 count shrimp means that there are between 41 and 50 shrimp per pound. The smaller the count, the larger the shrimp. The big tiger prawns have counts as low as 10–15, which means that each shrimp can weigh up to 1/10 of a pound. One advantage of categorizing shrimp in this way is that you can count the shrimp by weighing them. For example, two pounds of 41–50 count shrimp contains between 82 and 100 shrimp.

A similar (but more precise) concept exists for atoms. Counting atoms is much more difficult than counting shrimp, yet we often need to know the number of atoms in a given mass of atoms. For example, intravenous fluids—fluids that are delivered to patients by directly dripping them into their veins—are saline (salt) solutions that must have a specific number of sodium and chloride ions per liter of fluid. The result of using an intravenous fluid with the wrong number of sodium and chloride ions could be fatal.

Atoms are far too small to count by any ordinary means. As we saw earlier, even if you could somehow count atoms, and counted them 24 hours a day for as long as you lived, you would barely begin to count the number of atoms in something as small as a sand grain. Therefore, if we want to know the number of atoms in anything of ordinary size, we must count them by weighing.

Twenty-two copper pennies contain approximately 1 mol of copper atoms.

Beginning in 1982, pennies became almost all zinc, with only a copper coating. Before this date, pennies were mostly copper.

The Mole: A Chemist's "Dozen"

When we count large numbers of objects, we often use units such as a dozen (12 objects) or a gross (144 objects) to organize our counting and to keep our numbers more manageable. With atoms, quadrillions of which may be in a speck of dust, we need a much larger number for this purpose. The chemist's "dozen" is the **mole** (abbreviated mol). A mole is the *amount* of material containing 6.02214×10^{23} particles.

$$1 \text{ mol} = 6.02214 \times 10^{23} \text{ particles}$$

This number is also called **Avogadro's number**, named after Italian physicist Amedeo Avogadro (1776–1856), and is a convenient number to use when working with atoms, molecules, and ions. In this book, we usually round Avogadro's number to four significant figures or 6.022×10^{23}. Notice that the definition of the mole is an *amount* of a substance. We will often refer to the number of moles of substance as the *amount* of the substance.

The first thing to understand about the mole is that it can specify Avogadro's number of anything. For example, 1 mol of marbles corresponds to 6.022×10^{23} marbles, and 1 mol of sand grains corresponds to 6.022×10^{23} sand grains. *One mole of anything is 6.022×10^{23} units of that thing.* One mole of atoms, ions, or molecules, however, makes up objects of everyday sizes. Twenty-two copper pennies, for example, contain approximately 1 mol of copper atoms and one tablespoon of water contains approximately 1 mol of water molecules.

The second, and more fundamental, thing to understand about the mole is how it gets its specific value.

The value of the mole is equal to the number of atoms in exactly 12 grams of pure carbon-12 (12 g C = 1 mol C atoms = 6.022×10^{23} C atoms).

The definition of the mole gives us a relationship between mass (grams of carbon) and number of atoms (Avogadro's number). This relationship, as we will see shortly, allows us to count atoms by weighing them.

One tablespoon of water contains approximately one mole of water molecules.

One tablespoon is approximately 15 mL; one mole of water occupies 18 mL.

Converting between Number of Moles and Number of Atoms

Converting between number of moles and number of atoms is similar to converting between dozens of eggs and number of eggs. For eggs, you use the conversion factor 1 dozen eggs = 12 eggs. For atoms you use the conversion factor 1 mol atoms = 6.022×10^{23} atoms. The conversion factors take the following forms:

$$\frac{1 \text{ mol atoms}}{6.022 \times 10^{23} \text{ atoms}} \quad \text{or} \quad \frac{6.022 \times 10^{23} \text{ atoms}}{1 \text{ mol atoms}}$$

The following example shows how to use these conversion factors in calculations.

EXAMPLE 2.6 Converting between Number of Moles and Number of Atoms

Calculate the number of copper atoms in 2.45 mol of copper.

SORT You are given the amount of copper in moles and asked to find the number of copper atoms.	**GIVEN:** 2.45 mol Cu **FIND:** Cu atoms
STRATEGIZE Convert between number of moles and number of atoms by using Avogadro's number as a conversion factor.	**CONCEPTUAL PLAN** mol Cu ⟶ Cu atoms $$\frac{6.022 \times 10^{23} \text{ Cu atoms}}{1 \text{ mol Cu}}$$ **RELATIONSHIPS USED** $6.022 \times 10^{23} = 1$ mol (Avogadro's number)
SOLVE Follow the conceptual plan to solve the problem. Begin with 2.45 mol Cu and multiply by Avogadro's number to get to the number of Cu atoms.	**SOLUTION** $2.45 \text{ mol Cu} \times \dfrac{6.022 \times 10^{23} \text{ Cu atoms}}{1 \text{ mol Cu}} = 1.48 \times 10^{24}$ Cu atoms

CHECK Since atoms are small, it makes sense that the answer is large. The given number of moles of copper is almost 2.5, so the number of atoms is almost 2.5 times Avogadro's number.

FOR PRACTICE 2.6

A pure silver ring contains 2.80×10^{22} silver atoms. How many moles of silver atoms does it contain?

Converting between Mass and Amount (Number of Moles)

To count atoms by weighing them, we need one other conversion factor—the mass of 1 mol of atoms. For the isotope carbon-12, we know that the mass of 1 mol of atoms is exactly 12 grams, which is numerically equivalent to carbon-12's atomic mass in atomic mass units. Since the masses of all other elements are defined relative to carbon-12, the same relationship holds for all elements.

The mass of 1 mol of atoms of an element is called the **molar mass**.

An element's molar mass in grams per mole is numerically equal to the element's atomic mass in atomic mass units.

For example, copper has an atomic mass of 63.55 amu and a molar mass of 63.55 g/mol. One mole of copper atoms therefore has a mass of 63.55 g. Just as the count for shrimp depends on the size of the shrimp, so the mass of 1 mol of atoms depends on the element: 1 mol of aluminum atoms (which are lighter than copper atoms) has a mass of 26.98 g; 1 mol of carbon atoms (which are even lighter than aluminum atoms) has a mass of 12.01 g; and 1 mol of helium atoms (lighter yet) has a mass of 4.003 g.

26.98 g aluminum = 1 mol aluminum = 6.022×10^{23} Al atoms   ⬤ Al

12.01 g carbon = 1 mol carbon = 6.022×10^{23} C atoms   ⬤ C

4.003 g helium = 1 mol helium = 6.022×10^{23} He atoms   ● He

The lighter the atom, the less mass in 1 mol.

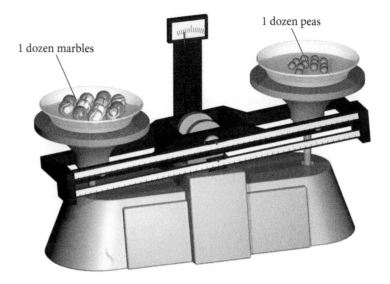

1 dozen marbles

1 dozen peas

▶ The two pans contain the same number of objects (12), but the masses are different because peas are less massive than marbles. Similarly, a mole of light atoms will have less mass than a mole of heavier atoms.

The molar mass of any element is the conversion factor between the mass (in grams) of that element and the amount (in moles) of that element. For carbon:

$$12.01 \text{ g C} = 1 \text{ mol C} \quad \text{or} \quad \frac{12.01 \text{ g C}}{\text{mol C}} \quad \text{or} \quad \frac{1 \text{ mol C}}{12.01 \text{ g C}}$$

The following example shows how to use these conversion factors.

EXAMPLE 2.7 Converting between Mass and Amount (Number of Moles)

Calculate the amount of carbon (in moles) contained in a 0.0265-g pencil "lead." (Assume that the pencil lead is made of pure graphite, a form of carbon.)

SORT You are given the mass of carbon and asked to find the amount of carbon in moles.	**GIVEN:** 0.0265 g C **FIND:** mol C
STRATEGIZE Convert between mass and amount (in moles) of an element by using the molar mass of the element.	**CONCEPTUAL PLAN** g C → mol C $\dfrac{1 \text{ mol}}{12.01 \text{ g}}$ **RELATIONSHIPS USED** 12.01 g C = 1 mol C (carbon molar mass)
SOLVE Follow the conceptual plan to solve the problem.	**SOLUTION** $0.0265 \text{ g C} \times \dfrac{1 \text{ mol C}}{12.01 \text{ g C}} = 2.21 \times 10^{-3} \text{ mol C}$

CHECK The given mass of carbon is much less than the molar mass of carbon, so it makes sense that the answer (the amount in moles) is much less than 1 mol of carbon.

FOR PRACTICE 2.7

Calculate the amount of copper (in moles) in a 35.8-g pure copper sheet.

FOR MORE PRACTICE 2.7

Calculate the mass (in grams) of 0.473 mol of titanium.

We now have all the tools to count the number of atoms in a sample of an element by weighing it. First, obtain the mass of the sample. Then convert it to amount in moles using the element's molar mass. Finally, convert to number of atoms using Avogadro's number. The conceptual plan for these kinds of calculations takes the following form:

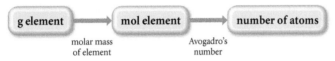

g element →(molar mass of element)→ mol element →(Avogadro's number)→ number of atoms

The examples that follow demonstrate these conversions.

EXAMPLE 2.8   The Mole Concept—Converting between Mass and Number of Atoms

How many copper atoms are in a copper penny with a mass of 3.10 g? (Assume that the penny is composed of pure copper.)

SORT You are given the mass of copper and asked to find the number of copper atoms.	**GIVEN:** 3.10 g Cu **FIND:** Cu atoms
STRATEGIZE Convert between the mass of an element in grams and the number of atoms of the element by first converting to moles (using the molar mass of the element) and then to number of atoms (using Avogadro's number).	**CONCEPTUAL PLAN** 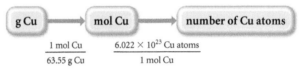 g Cu →($\frac{1 \text{ mol Cu}}{63.55 \text{ g Cu}}$)→ mol Cu →($\frac{6.022 \times 10^{23} \text{ Cu atoms}}{1 \text{ mol Cu}}$)→ number of Cu atoms **RELATIONSHIPS USED** 63.55 g Cu = 1 mol Cu (molar mass of copper) 6.022×10^{23} = 1 mol (Avogadro's number)
SOLVE Follow the conceptual plan to solve the problem. Begin with 3.10 g Cu and multiply by the appropriate conversion factors to arrive at the number of Cu atoms.	**SOLUTION** $3.10 \text{ g Cu} \times \dfrac{1 \text{ mol Cu}}{63.55 \text{ g Cu}} \times \dfrac{6.022 \times 10^{23} \text{ Cu atoms}}{1 \text{ mol Cu}} = 2.94 \times 10^{22} \text{ Cu atoms}$

CHECK The answer (the number of copper atoms) is less than 6.022×10^{23} (one mole). This is consistent with the given mass of copper atoms, which is less than the molar mass of copper.

FOR PRACTICE 2.8

How many carbon atoms are there in a 1.3-carat diamond? Diamonds are a form of pure carbon. (1 carat = 0.20 grams)

FOR MORE PRACTICE 2.8

Calculate the mass of 2.25×10^{22} tungsten atoms.

Notice that numbers with large exponents, such as 6.022×10^{23}, are almost unbelievably large. Twenty-two copper pennies contain 6.022×10^{23} or 1 mol of copper atoms, but 6.022×10^{23} pennies would cover the Earth's entire surface to a depth of 300 m. Even objects small by everyday standards occupy a huge space when we have a mole of them. For example, a grain of sand has a mass of less than 1 mg and a diameter of less than 0.1 mm, yet 1 mol of sand grains would cover the state of Texas to a depth of several feet. For every increase of 1 in the exponent of a number, the number increases by a factor of 10, so 10^{23} is incredibly large. Of course one mole has to be a large number if it is to have practical value, because atoms are so small.

EXAMPLE 2.9 The Mole Concept

An aluminum sphere contains 8.55×10^{22} aluminum atoms. What is the radius of the sphere in centimeters? The density of aluminum is 2.70 g/cm^3.

SORT You are given the number of aluminum atoms in a sphere and the density of aluminum. You are asked to find the radius of the sphere.	**GIVEN:** 8.55×10^{22} Al atoms $\qquad d = 2.70 \text{ g/cm}^3$ **FIND:** radius (r) of sphere

STRATEGIZE The heart of this problem is density, which relates mass to volume, and though you aren't given the mass directly, you are given the number of atoms, which you can use to find mass.

1. Convert from number of atoms to number of moles using Avogadro's number as a conversion factor.
2. Convert from number of moles to mass using molar mass as a conversion factor.
3. Convert from mass to volume (in cm^3) using density as a conversion factor.
4. Once you compute the volume, find the radius from the volume using the formula for the volume of a sphere.

CONCEPTUAL PLAN

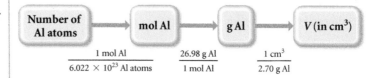

$$\frac{1 \text{ mol Al}}{6.022 \times 10^{23} \text{ Al atoms}} \qquad \frac{26.98 \text{ g Al}}{1 \text{ mol Al}} \qquad \frac{1 \text{ cm}^3}{2.70 \text{ g Al}}$$

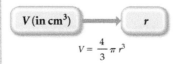

$$V = \frac{4}{3} \pi r^3$$

RELATIONSHIPS AND EQUATIONS USED

$6.022 \times 10^{23} = 1 \text{ mol}$ (Avogadro's number)

$26.98 \text{ g Al} = 1 \text{ mol Al}$ (molar mass of aluminum)

2.70 g/cm^3 (density of aluminum)

$V = \dfrac{4}{3}\pi r^3$ (volume of a sphere)

SOLVE Finally, follow the conceptual plan to solve the problem. Begin with 8.55×10^{22} Al atoms and multiply by the appropriate conversion factors to arrive at volume in cm^3.

Then solve the equation for the volume of a sphere for r and substitute the volume to compute r.

SOLUTION

$$8.55 \times 10^{22} \text{ Al atoms} \times \frac{1 \text{ mol Al}}{6.022 \times 10^{23} \text{ Al atoms}}$$

$$\times \frac{26.98 \text{ g Al}}{1 \text{ mol Al}} \times \frac{1 \text{ cm}^3}{2.70 \text{ g Al}} = 1.4187 \text{ cm}^3$$

$$V = \frac{4}{3}\pi r^3$$

$$r = \sqrt[3]{\frac{3V}{4\pi}} = \sqrt[3]{\frac{3(1.4187 \text{ cm}^3)}{4\pi}} = 0.697 \text{ cm}$$

CHECK The units of the answer (cm) are correct. The magnitude cannot be estimated accurately, but a radius of about one-half of a centimeter is reasonable for just over one-tenth of a mole of aluminum atoms.

FOR PRACTICE 2.9

A titanium cube contains 2.86×10^{23} atoms. What is the edge length of the cube? The density of titanium is 4.50 g/cm^3.

FOR MORE PRACTICE 2.9

Find the number of atoms in a copper rod with a length of 9.85 cm and a radius of 1.05 cm. The density of copper is 8.96 g/cm^3.

Conceptual Connection 2.4 Avogadro's Number

Why is Avogadro's number defined as 6.022×10^{23} and not a simpler round number such as 1.00×10^{23}?

ANSWER: Remember that Avogadro's number is defined with respect to carbon-12—it is the number equal to the number of atoms in exactly 12 g of carbon-12. If Avogadro's number was defined as 1.00×10^{23} (a nice round number), it would correspond to 1.99 g of carbon-12 atoms (an inconvenient number). Avogadro's number is defined with respect to carbon-12 because, as you recall from Section 2.6, the amu (the basic mass unit used for all atoms) is defined relative to carbon-12. Therefore, the mass in grams of 1 mol of *any* element is equal to its atomic mass. As we have seen, these two definitions together make it possible to determine the number of atoms in a known mass of any element.

 Conceptual Connection 2.5 The Mole

Without doing any calculations, determine which of the following contains the most atoms.

(a) a 1-g sample of copper
(b) a 1-g sample of carbon
(c) a 10-g sample of uranium

ANSWER: (b) The carbon sample contains more atoms than the copper sample because carbon has a lower molar mass than copper. Carbon atoms are lighter than copper atoms, so a 1-g sample of carbon contains more atoms than a 1-g sample of copper. The carbon sample also contains more atoms than the uranium sample because, even though the uranium sample has 10 times the mass of the carbon sample, a uranium atom is more than 10 times as massive (238 g/mol for U versus 12 g/mol for carbon).

CHAPTER IN REVIEW

Key Terms

Section 2.3
law of conservation of mass (45)
law of definite proportions (46)
law of multiple proportions (47)
atomic theory (48)

Section 2.4
cathode rays (49)
cathode rays tube (49)
electrical charge (50)
electron (50)

Section 2.5
radioactivity (52)

nuclear theory (52)
nucleus (52)
proton (53)
neutron (53)

Section 2.6
atomic mass unit (amu) (53)
atomic number (Z) (54)
chemical symbol (55)
isotope (56)
natural abundance (56)
mass number (A) (56)
ion (57)

cation (57)
anion (57)

Section 2.7
periodic law (59)
metal (60)
nonmetal (60)
metalloid (61)
semiconductor (61)
main-group elements (61)
transition elements
    (transition metals) (61)
family (group) (61)

noble gases (61)
alkali metals (61)
alkaline earth metals (61)
halogens (62)

Section 2.8
atomic mass (64)
mass spectrometry (65)

Section 2.9
mole (mol) (66)
Avogadro's number (66)
molar mass (67)

Key Concepts

Imaging and Moving Individual Atoms (2.1)

Although it was only 200 years ago that John Dalton proposed his atomic theory, technology has since progressed to the level where individual atoms can be imaged and moved by techniques such as *scanning tunneling microscopy* (STM).

The Atomic Theory (2.2, 2.3)

The idea that all matter is composed of small, indestructible particles called atoms dates back to the fifth century B.C.; however, at the time the atomic idea was rejected by most Greek thinkers. At about A.D. 1800 certain observations and laws including the law of conservation of mass, the law of constant composition, and the law of multiple proportions led John Dalton to reformulate the atomic theory with the following postulates: (1) each element is composed of indestructible particles called atoms; (2) all atoms of a given element have the same mass and other properties; (3) atoms combine in simple, whole-number ratios to form compounds; and (4) atoms of one element cannot change into atoms of another element. In a chemical reaction, atoms change the way that they are bound together with other atoms to form new substances.

The Electron (2.4)

J. J. Thomson discovered the electron in the late 1800s through experiments with cathode rays. He deduced that electrons were negatively charged, and then measured their charge-to-mass ratio. Later, Robert Millikan measured the charge of the electron, which—in conjunction with Thomson's results—led to the calculation of the mass of an electron.

The Nuclear Atom (2.5)

In 1909, Ernest Rutherford probed the inner structure of the atom by working with a form of radioactivity called alpha radiation and developed the nuclear theory of the atom. This theory states that the atom is mainly empty space, with most of its mass concentrated in a tiny region called the nucleus and most of its volume occupied by relatively light electrons.

Subatomic Particles (2.6)

Atoms are composed of three fundamental particles: the proton (1 amu, +1 charge), the neutron (1 amu, 0 charge), and the electron (~0 amu, –1 charge). The number of protons in the nucleus of the atom is its atomic number (Z) and defines the element. The sum of the number of protons and neutrons is the mass number (A). Atoms of an element that have different numbers of neutrons (and therefore different mass numbers) are isotopes. Atoms that have lost or gained electrons become charged and are ions. Cations are positively charged and anions are negatively charged.

The Periodic Table (2.7)

The periodic table tabulates all known elements in order of increasing atomic number. The periodic table is arranged so that similar elements are grouped together in columns. Elements on the left side and in the center of the periodic table are metals and tend to lose electrons in their chemical changes. Elements on the upper right side of the periodic table are nonmetals and tend to gain electrons in their chemical changes. Elements located on the boundary between these two classes are metalloids.

Atomic Mass and the Mole (2.8, 2.9)

The atomic mass of an element, listed directly below its symbol in the periodic table, is a weighted average of the masses of the naturally occurring isotopes of the element.

One mole of an element is the amount of that element that contains Avogadro's number (6.022×10^{23}) of atoms. Any sample of an element with a mass (in grams) that equals its atomic mass contains one mole of the element. For example, the atomic mass of carbon is 12.011 amu, therefore 12.011 grams of carbon contains 1 mol of carbon atoms.

Key Equations and Relationships

Relationship between Mass Number (A), Number of Protons (p), and Number of Neutrons (n) (2.6)

$$A = \text{number of protons (p)} + \text{number of neutrons (n)}$$

Atomic Mass (2.8)

$$\text{Atomic mass} = \sum_n (\text{fraction of isotope } n) \times (\text{mass of isotope } n)$$

Avogadro's Number (2.9)

$$1 \text{ mol} = 6.0221421 \times 10^{23} \text{ particles}$$

Key Skills

Using the Law of Definite Proportions (2.3)
  • Example 2.1   • For Practice 2.1   • Exercises 31, 32

Using the Law of Multiple Proportions (2.3)
  • Example 2.2   • For Practice 2.2   • Exercises 35–38

Working with Atomic Numbers, Mass Numbers, and Isotope Symbols (2.6)
  • Example 2.3   • For Practice 2.3   • Exercises 51–58

Predicting the Charge of Ions (2.7)
  • Example 2.4   • For Practice 2.4   • Exercises 59–62

Calculating Atomic Mass (2.8)
  • Example 2.5   • For Practice 2.5   • For More Practice 2.5   • Exercises 71, 72, 74–77

Converting between Moles and Number of Atoms (2.9)
  • Example 2.6   • For Practice 2.6   • Exercises 79, 80

Converting between Mass and Amount (in Moles) (2.9)
  • Example 2.7   • For Practice 2.7   • For More Practice 2.7   • Exercises 81, 82

Using the Mole Concept (2.9)
  • Examples 2.8, 2.9   • For Practice 2.8, 2.9   • For More Practice 2.8, 2.9   • Exercises 83–92, 108, 109

EXERCISES

Review Questions

1. What is scanning tunneling microscopy? How does it work?
2. Summarize the history of the atomic idea. How was Dalton able to convince others to accept an idea that had been controversial for 2000 years?
3. State the law of conservation of mass and explain what it means.
4. State the law of definite proportions and explain what it means.
5. State the law of multiple proportions and explain what it means. How is the law of multiple proportions different from the law of definite proportions?
6. What are the main ideas in Dalton's atomic theory? How do they help explain the laws of conservation of mass, of constant composition, and of definite proportions?
7. How and by whom was the electron discovered? What basic properties of the electron were reported with its discovery?
8. Explain Millikan's oil drop experiment and how it led to the measurement of the electron's charge. Why is the magnitude of the charge of the electron so important?
9. Explain the plum-pudding model of the atom.
10. Describe Rutherford's gold foil experiment. How did the experiment show that the plum-pudding model of the atom was wrong?
11. Describe Rutherford's nuclear model of the atom. What was revolutionary about his model?
12. If matter is mostly empty space, as suggested by Rutherford, then why does it appear so solid?
13. List the three subatomic particles that compose atoms and give the basic properties (mass and charge) of each.
14. What defines an element?
15. Explain the difference between Z (the atomic number) and A (the mass number).
16. Where do elements get their names?
17. What are isotopes? What is percent natural abundance of isotopes?
18. Describe the two different notations used to specify isotopes and give an example of each.
19. What is an ion? A cation? An anion?
20. What is the periodic law? How did it lead to the periodic table?
21. What are the characteristic properties of metals, nonmetals, and metalloids?
22. What are the characteristic properties of each of the following groups?
    a. noble gases   b. alkali metals
    c. alkaline earth metals   d. halogens
23. How do you predict the charges of ions formed by main-group elements?
24. What is atomic mass? How is it computed?
25. Explain how a mass spectrometer works.
26. What kind of information can be determined from a mass spectrum?
27. What is a mole? How is the mole concept useful in chemical calculations?
28. Why is the mass corresponding to a mole of one element different from the mass corresponding to a mole of another element?

Problems by Topic

Note: Answers to all odd-numbered Problems, numbered in blue, can be found in Appendix III. Exercises in the Problems by Topic section are paired, with each odd-numbered problem followed by a similar even-numbered problem. Exercises in the Cumulative Problems section are also paired, but somewhat more loosely. (Challenge Problems and Conceptual Problems, because of their nature, are unpaired.)

The Laws of Conservation of Mass, Definite Proportions, and Multiple Proportions

29. A hydrogen-filled balloon was ignited and 1.50 g of hydrogen reacted with 12.0 g of oxygen. How many grams of water vapor were formed? (Assume that water vapor is the only product.)
30. An automobile gasoline tank holds 21 kg of gasoline. When the gasoline burns, 84 kg of oxygen is consumed, and carbon dioxide and water are produced. What is the total combined mass of carbon dioxide and water that is produced?
31. Two samples of carbon tetrachloride were decomposed into their constituent elements. One sample produced 38.9 g of carbon and 448 g of chlorine, and the other sample produced 14.8 g of carbon and 134 g of chlorine. Are these results consistent with the law of definite proportions? Show why or why not.
32. Two samples of sodium chloride were decomposed into their constituent elements. One sample produced 6.98 g of sodium and 10.7 g of chlorine, and the other sample produced 11.2 g of sodium and 17.3 g of chlorine. Are these results consistent with the law of definite proportions?
33. The mass ratio of sodium to fluorine in sodium fluoride is 1.21:1. A sample of sodium fluoride produced 28.8 g of sodium upon decomposition. How much fluorine (in grams) was formed?
34. Upon decomposition, one sample of magnesium fluoride produced 1.65 kg of magnesium and 2.57 kg of fluorine. A second sample produced 1.32 kg of magnesium. How much fluorine (in grams) did the second sample produce?
35. Two different compounds containing osmium and oxygen have the following masses of oxygen per gram of osmium: 0.168 and 0.3369 g. Show that these amounts are consistent with the law of multiple proportions.
36. Palladium forms three different compounds with sulfur. The mass of sulfur per gram of palladium in each compound is listed below:

Compound	Grams S per Gram Pd
A	0.603
B	0.301
C	0.151

Show that these masses are consistent with the law of multiple proportions.

37. Sulfur and oxygen form both sulfur dioxide and sulfur trioxide. When samples of these were decomposed the sulfur dioxide produced 3.49 g oxygen and 3.50 g sulfur, while the sulfur trioxide produced 6.75 g oxygen and 4.50 g sulfur. Calculate the mass of oxygen per gram of sulfur for each sample and show that these results are consistent with the law of multiple proportions.

38. Sulfur and fluorine form several different compounds including sulfur hexafluoride and sulfur tetrafluoride. Decomposition of a sample of sulfur hexafluoride produced 4.45 g of fluorine and 1.25 g of sulfur, while decomposition of a sample of sulfur tetrafluoride produced 4.43 g of fluorine and 1.87 g of sulfur. Calculate the mass of fluorine per gram of sulfur for each sample and show that these results are consistent with the law of multiple proportions.

Atomic Theory, Nuclear Theory, and Subatomic Particles

39. Which statements are *consistent* with Dalton's atomic theory as it was originally stated? Why?
    a. Sulfur and oxygen atoms have the same mass.
    b. All cobalt atoms are identical.
    c. Potassium and chlorine atoms combine in a 1:1 ratio to form potassium chloride.
    d. Lead atoms can be converted into gold.

40. Which statements are *inconsistent* with Dalton's atomic theory as it was originally stated? Why?
    a. All carbon atoms are identical.
    b. An oxygen atom combines with 1.5 hydrogen atoms to form a water molecule.
    c. Two oxygen atoms combine with a carbon atom to form a carbon dioxide molecule.
    d. The formation of a compound often involves the destruction of one or more atoms.

41. Which statements are *consistent* with Rutherford's nuclear theory as it was originally stated? Why?
    a. The volume of an atom is mostly empty space.
    b. The nucleus of an atom is small compared to the size of the atom.
    c. Neutral lithium atoms contain more neutrons than protons.
    d. Neutral lithium atoms contain more protons than electrons.

42. Which statements are *inconsistent* with Rutherford's nuclear theory as it was originally stated? Why?
    a. Since electrons are smaller than protons, and since a hydrogen atom contains only one proton and one electron, it must follow that the volume of a hydrogen atom is mostly due to the proton.
    b. A nitrogen atom has seven protons in its nucleus and seven electrons outside of its nucleus.
    c. A phosphorus atom has 15 protons in its nucleus and 150 electrons outside of its nucleus.
    d. The majority of the mass of a fluorine atom is due to its nine electrons.

43. A chemist in an imaginary universe, where electrons have a different charge than they do in our universe, performs the Millikan oil drop experiment to measure the electron's charge. The charges of several drops are recorded below. What is the charge of the electron in this imaginary universe?

Drop #	Charge
A	-6.9×10^{-19} C
B	-9.2×10^{-19} C
C	-11.5×10^{-19} C
D	-4.6×10^{-19} C

44. Imagine a unit of charge called the zorg. A chemist performs the oil drop experiment and measures the charge of each drop in zorgs. Based on the results below, what is the charge of the electron in zorgs (z)? How many electrons are in each drop?

Drop #	Charge
A	-4.8×10^{-9} z
B	-9.6×10^{-9} z
C	-6.4×10^{-9} z
D	-12.8×10^{-9} z

45. On a dry day, your body can accumulate static charge from walking across a carpet or from brushing your hair. If your body develops a charge of $-15 \, \mu C$ (microcoulombs), how many excess electrons has it acquired? What is their collective mass?

46. How many electrons are necessary to produce a charge of -1.0 C? What is the mass of this many electrons?

47. Which statements about subatomic particles are true?
    a. If an atom has an equal number of protons and electrons, it will be charge-neutral.
    b. Electrons are attracted to protons.
    c. Electrons are much lighter than neutrons.
    d. Protons have twice the mass of neutrons.

48. Which statements about subatomic particles are false?
    a. Protons and electrons have charges of the same magnitude but opposite sign.
    b. Protons have about the same mass as neutrons.
    c. Some atoms don't have any protons.
    d. Protons and neutrons have charges of the same magnitude but opposite signs.

49. How many electrons would it take to equal the mass of a proton?

50. A helium nucleus has two protons and two neutrons. How many electrons would it take to equal the mass of a helium nucleus?

Isotopes and Ions

51. Write isotopic symbols of the form $^A_Z X$ for each isotope.
    a. the copper isotope with 34 neutrons
    b. the copper isotope with 36 neutrons
    c. the potassium isotope with 21 neutrons
    d. the argon isotope with 22 neutrons

52. Write isotopic symbols of the form X-A (e.g., C-13) for each isotope.
    a. the silver isotope with 60 neutrons
    b. the silver isotope with 62 neutrons
    c. the uranium isotope isotope with 146 neutrons
    d. the hydrogen isotope with 1 neutron

53. Determine the number of protons and neutrons in each isotope.
    a. $^{14}_7 N$ b. $^{23}_{11} Na$ c. $^{222}_{86} Rn$ d. $^{208}_{82} Pb$

54. Determine the number of protons and neutrons in each isotope.
    a. $^{40}_{19} K$ b. $^{226}_{88} Ra$ c. $^{99}_{43} Tc$ d. $^{33}_{15} P$

55. The amount of carbon-14 in ancient artifacts and fossils is often used to establish their age. Determine the number of protons and neutrons in a carbon-14 isotope and write its symbol in the form $^A_Z X$.

56. Uranium-235 is used in nuclear fission. Determine the number of protons and neutrons in uranium-235 and write its symbol in the form $^A_Z X$.

57. Determine the number of protons and electrons in each ion.
    a. Ni^{2+} b. S^{2-} c. Br^- d. Cr^{3+}

58. Determine the number of protons and electrons in each ion.
    a. Al^{3+} b. Se^{2-} c. Ga^{3+} d. Sr^{2+}

59. Predict the charge of the ion formed by each element.
    a. O   **b.** K   **c.** Al   **d.** Rb

60. Predict the charge of the ion formed by each element.
    a. Mg   **b.** N   **c.** F   **d.** Na

61. Fill in the blanks to complete the table.

Symbol	Ion Formed	Number of Electrons in Ion	Number of Protons in Ion
Ca	Ca^{2+}	____	____
____	Be^{2+}	2	____
Se	____	____	34
In	____	____	49

62. Fill in the blanks to complete the table.

Symbol	Ion Formed	Number of Electrons in Ion	Number of Protons in Ion
Cl	____	____	17
Te	____	54	____
Br	Br^-	____	____
____	Sr^{2+}	____	38

The Periodic Table and Atomic Mass

63. Write the name of each element and classify it as a metal, nonmetal, or metalloid.
    a. K   **b.** Ba   **c.** I   **d.** O   **e.** Sb

64. Write the symbol for each element and classify it as a metal, nonmetal, or metalloid.
    a. gold   **b.** fluorine   **c.** sodium
    d. tin   **e.** argon

65. Which elements from this list are main group elements?
    a. tellurium   **b.** potassium
    c. vanadium   **d.** manganese

66. Which elements from this list are transition elements?
    a. Cr   **b.** Br   **c.** Mo   **d.** Cs

67. Classify each element as an alkali metal, alkaline earth metal, halogen, or noble gas.
    a. sodium   **b.** iodine   **c.** calcium
    d. barium   **e.** krypton

68. Classify each element as an alkali metal, alkaline earth metal, halogen, or noble gas.
    a. F   **b.** Sr   **c.** K   **d.** Ne   **e.** At

69. Which pair of elements do you expect to be most similar? Why?
    a. N and Ni   **b.** Mo and Sn   **c.** Na and Mg
    d. Cl and F   **e.** Si and P

70. Which pair of elements do you expect to be most similar? Why?
    a. nitrogen and oxygen   **b.** titanium and gallium
    c. lithium and sodium   **d.** germanium and arsenic
    e. argon and bromine

71. Gallium has two naturally occurring isotopes with the following masses and natural abundances:

Isotope	Mass (amu)	Abundance (%)
Ga-69	68.92558	60.108
Ga-71	70.92470	39.892

Calculate the atomic mass of gallium and sketch its mass spectrum.

72. Magnesium has three naturally occurring isotopes with the following masses and natural abundances:

Isotope	Mass (amu)	Abundance (%)
Mg-24	23.9850	78.99
Mg-25	24.9858	10.00
Mg-26	25.9826	11.01

Calculate the atomic mass of magnesium and sketch its mass spectrum.

73. The atomic mass of fluorine is 18.998 amu and its mass spectrum shows a large peak at this mass. The atomic mass of chlorine is 35.45 amu, yet the mass spectrum of chlorine does not show a peak at this mass. Explain the difference.

74. The atomic mass of copper is 63.546 amu. Do any copper isotopes have a mass of 63.546 amu? Explain.

75. An element has two naturally occurring isotopes. Isotope 1 has a mass of 120.9038 amu and a relative abundance of 57.4%, and isotope 2 has a mass of 122.9042 amu. Find the atomic mass of this element and identify it.

76. An element has four naturally occurring isotopes with the masses and natural abundances given here. Find the atomic mass of the element and identify it.

Isotope	Mass (amu)	Abundance (%)
1	135.90714	0.19
2	137.90599	0.25
3	139.90543	88.43
4	141.90924	11.13

77. Bromine has two naturally occurring isotopes (Br-79 and Br-81) and has an atomic mass of 79.904 amu. The mass of Br-81 is 80.9163 amu, and its natural abundance is 49.31%. Calculate the mass and natural abundance of Br-79.

78. Silicon has three naturally occurring isotopes (Si-28, Si-29, and Si-30). The mass and natural abundance of Si-28 are 27.9769 amu and 92.2%, respectively. The mass and natural abundance of Si-29 are 28.9765 amu and 4.67%, respectively. Find the mass and natural abundance of Si-30.

The Mole Concept

79. How many sulfur atoms are there in 3.8 mol of sulfur?

80. How many moles of aluminum do 5.8×10^{24} aluminum atoms represent?

81. What is the amount, in moles, of each elemental sample?
    a. 11.8 g Ar   **b.** 3.55 g Zn
    c. 26.1 g Ta   **d.** 0.211 g Li

82. What is the mass, in grams, of each elemental sample?
    a. 2.3×10^{-3} mol Sb   **b.** 0.0355 mol Ba
    c. 43.9 mol Xe   **d.** 1.3 mol W

83. How many silver atoms are there in 3.78 g of silver?

84. What is the mass of 4.91×10^{21} platinum atoms?

85. Calculate the number of atoms in each sample.
    a. 5.18 g P   **b.** 2.26 g Hg
    c. 1.87 g Bi   **d.** 0.082 g Sr

86. Calculate the number of atoms in each sample.
    a. 14.955 g Cr   **b.** 39.733 g S
    c. 12.899 g Pt   **d.** 97.552 g Sn

87. Calculate the mass, in grams, of each sample.
    a. 1.1×10^{23} gold atoms   **b.** 2.82×10^{22} helium atoms
    c. 1.8×10^{23} lead atoms   **d.** 7.9×10^{21} uranium atoms

88. Calculate the mass, in kg, of each sample.
    a. 7.55×10^{26} cadmium atoms
    b. 8.15×10^{27} nickel atoms
    c. 1.22×10^{27} manganese atoms
    d. 5.48×10^{29} lithium atoms

89. How many carbon atoms are there in a diamond (pure carbon) with a mass of 52 mg?

90. How many helium atoms are there in a helium blimp containing 536 kg of helium?

91. Calculate the average mass, in grams, of one platinum atom.

92. Using scanning tunneling microscopy, scientists at IBM wrote the initials of their company with 35 individual xenon atoms (as shown below). Calculate the total mass of these letters in grams.

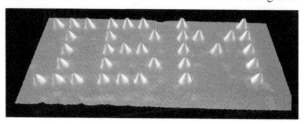

Cumulative Problems

93. A 7.83-g sample of HCN is found to contain 0.290 g of H and 4.06 g of N. Find the mass of carbon in a sample of HCN with a mass of 3.37 g.

94. The ratio of sulfur to oxygen by mass in SO_2 is 1.0:1.0.
    a. Find the ratio of sulfur to oxygen by mass in SO_3.
    b. Find the ratio of sulfur to oxygen by mass in S_2O.

95. The ratio of oxygen to carbon by mass in carbon monoxide is 1.33:1.00. Find the formula of an oxide of carbon in which the ratio by mass of oxygen to carbon is 2.00:1.00.

96. The ratio of the mass of a nitrogen atom to the mass of an atom of ^{12}C is 7:6 and the ratio of the mass of nitrogen to oxygen in N_2O is 7:4. Find the mass of 1 mol of oxygen atoms.

97. An α particle, $^{4}He^{2+}$, has a mass of 4.00151 amu. Find the value of its charge-to-mass ratio in C/kg.

98. Naturally occurring iodine has an atomic mass of 126.9045. A 12.3849-g sample of iodine is accidentally contaminated with an additional 1.00070 g of ^{129}I, a synthetic radioisotope of iodine used in the treatment of certain diseases of the thyroid gland. The mass of ^{129}I is 128.9050 amu. Find the apparent "atomic mass" of the contaminated iodine.

99. Nuclei with the same number of *neutrons* but different mass numbers are called *isotones*. Write the symbols of four isotones of ^{236}Th.

100. Fill in the blanks to complete the table.

Symbol	Z	A	Number of p	Number of e$^-$	Number of n	Charge
Si	14	___	___	14	14	___
S^{2-}	___	32	___	___	___	2−
Cu^{2+}	___	___	___	___	34	2+
___	15	___	___	15	16	___

101. Fill in the blanks to complete the table.

Symbol	Z	A	Number of p	Number of e$^-$	Number of n	Charge
___	8	___	___	___	8	2−
Ca^{2+}	20	___	___	___	20	___
Mg^{2+}	___	25	___	___	13	2+
N^{3-}	___	14	___	10	___	___

102. Neutron stars are composed of solid nuclear matter, primarily neutrons. Assume the radius of a neutron is approximately 1.0×10^{-13} cm, and calculate the density of a neutron. [*Hint:*

For a sphere $V = (4/3)\pi r^3$.] Assuming that a neutron star has the same density as a neutron, calculate the mass (in kg) of a small piece of a neutron star the size of a spherical pebble with a radius of 0.10 mm.

103. Carbon-12 contains 6 protons and 6 neutrons. The radius of the nucleus is approximately 2.7 fm (femtometers) and the radius of the atom is approximately 70 pm (picometers). Calculate the volume of the nucleus and the volume of the atom. What percentage of the carbon atom's volume is occupied by the nucleus? (Assume two significant figures.)

104. A penny has a thickness of approximately 1.0 mm. If you stacked Avogadro's number of pennies one on top of the other on Earth's surface, how far would the stack extend (in km)? [For comparison, the sun is about 150 million km from Earth and the nearest star (Proxima Centauri) is about 40 trillion km from Earth.]

105. Consider the stack of pennies in the previous problem. How much money (in dollars) would this represent? If this money were equally distributed among the world's population of 6.5 billion people, how much would each person receive? Would each person be a millionaire? Billionaire? Trillionaire?

106. The mass of an average blueberry is 0.75 g and the mass of an automobile is 2.0×10^3 kg. Find the number of automobiles whose total mass is the same as 1.0 mol blueberries.

107. Suppose that atomic masses were based on the assignment of a mass of 12.000 g to 1 mol of carbon, rather than 1 mol of ^{12}C. What would the atomic mass of oxygen be? (The atomic masses of carbon and oxygen based on the assignment of 12.000 g to 1 mol of ^{12}C are 12.011 amu and 15.994 amu, respectively.)

108. A pure titanium cube has an edge length of 2.78 in. How many titanium atoms does it contain? Titanium has a density of 4.50 g/cm^3.

109. A pure copper sphere has a radius of 0.935 in. How many copper atoms does it contain? [The volume of a sphere is $(4/3)\pi r^3$ and the density of copper is 8.96 g/cm^3.]

110. Boron has only two naturally occurring isotopes. The mass of boron-10 is 10.01294 amu and the mass of boron-11 is 11.00931 amu. Calculate the relative abundances of the two isotopes.

111. Lithium has only two naturally occurring isotopes. The mass of lithium-6 is 6.01512 amu and the mass of lithium-7 is 7.01601 amu. Calculate the relative abundances of the two isotopes.

112. Common brass is a copper and zinc alloy containing 37.0% zinc by mass and having a density of 8.48 g/cm^3. A fitting composed of common brass has a total volume of 112.5 cm^3. How many atoms (copper and zinc) does the fitting contain?

113. A 67.2 g sample of a gold and palladium alloy contains 2.49×10^{23} atoms. What is the composition (by mass) of the alloy?

114. Naturally occurring chlorine is composed of two isotopes: 75.76% Cl-35 (mass 34.9688 amu) and 24.24% Cl-37 (mass

36.9659 amu). Naturally occurring oxygen is composed of three isotopes: 99.757% O-16 (mass 15.9949 amu); 0.038% O-17 (mass 16.9991 amu); and 0.205% O-18 (mass 17.9991 amu). The compound dichloromonoxide is composed of two chlorine atoms and one oxygen atom bonded together to form the Cl_2O molecule. How many Cl_2O molecules of different masses naturally exist? Give the masses of the three most abundant Cl_2O molecules.

115. Silver is composed of two naturally occurring isotopes: Ag-107 (51.839%) and Ag-109. The ratio of the masses of the two isotopes is 1.0187. What is the mass of Ag-107?

116. The U.S. Environmental Protection Agency (EPA) sets limits on healthful levels of air pollutants. The maximum level that the EPA considers safe for lead air pollution is 1.5 $\mu g/m^3$. If your lungs were filled with air containing this level of lead, how many lead atoms would be in your lungs? (Assume a total lung volume of 5.50 L.)

117. Pure gold is usually too soft for jewelry, so it is often alloyed with other metals. How many gold atoms are in an 0.255 ounce, 18 K gold bracelet? (18 K gold is 75% gold by mass.)

Challenge Problems

118. In Section 2.9, it was stated that 1 mol of sand grains would cover the state of Texas to several feet. Estimate how many feet by assuming that the sand grains are roughly cube-shaped, each one with an edge length of 0.10 mm. Texas has a land area of 268,601 square miles.

119. Use the concepts in this chapter to obtain an estimate for the number of atoms in the universe. Make the following assumptions: **(a)** All of the atoms in the universe are hydrogen atoms in stars. (This is not a ridiculous assumption because over three-fourths of the atoms in the universe are in fact hydrogen. Gas and dust between the stars represent only about 15% of the visible matter of our galaxy, and planets compose a far tinier fraction.) **(b)** The sun is a typical star composed of pure hydrogen with a density of 1.4 g/cm^3 and a radius of 7×10^8 m. **(c)** Each of the roughly 100 billion stars in the Milky Way galaxy contains the same number of atoms as our sun. **(d)** Each of the 10 billion galaxies in the visible universe contains the same number of atoms as our Milky Way galaxy.

120. Below is a representation of 50 atoms of a fictitious element called westmontium (Wt). The red spheres represent Wt-296, the blue spheres Wt-297, and the green spheres Wt-298.

   a. Assuming that the sample is statistically representative of a naturally occurring sample, calculate the percent natural abundance of each Wt isotope.

   b. Draw the mass spectrum for a naturally occurring sample of Wt.

   c. The mass of each Wt isotope is measured relative to C-12 and tabulated below. Use the mass of C-12 to convert each of the masses to amu and calculate the atomic mass of Wt.

Isotope	Mass
Wt-296	24.6630 × Mass(^{12}C)
Wt-297	24.7490 × Mass(^{12}C)
Wt-298	24.8312 × Mass(^{12}C)

121. The ratio of oxygen to nitrogen by mass in NO_2 is 2.29. The ratio of fluorine to nitrogen by mass in NF_3 is 4.07. Find the ratio of oxygen to fluorine by mass in OF_2.

122. Naturally occurring cobalt consists of only one isotope, ^{59}Co, whose relative atomic mass is 58.9332. A synthetic radioactive isotope of cobalt, ^{60}Co, relative atomic mass 59.9338, is used in radiation therapy for cancer. A 1.5886-g sample of cobalt has an apparent "atomic mass" of 58.9901. Find the mass of ^{60}Co in this sample.

123. A 7.36-g sample of copper is contaminated with an additional 0.51 g of zinc. Suppose an atomic mass measurement was performed on this sample. What would be the measured atomic mass?

124. The ratio of the mass of O to the mass of N in N_2O_3 is 12:7. Another binary compound of nitrogen has a ratio of O to N of 16:7. What is its formula? What is the ratio of O to N in the next member of this series of compounds?

125. Naturally occurring magnesium has an atomic mass of 24.312 and consists of three isotopes. The major isotope is ^{24}Mg, natural abundance 78.99%, relative atomic mass 23.98504. The next most abundant isotope is ^{26}Mg, relative atomic mass 25.98259. The third isotope is ^{25}Mg whose natural abundance is in the ratio of 0.9083 to that of ^{26}Mg. Find the relative atomic mass of ^{25}Mg.

Conceptual Problems

126. Which of the following is an example of the law of multiple proportions? Explain.

   a. Two different samples of water are found to have the same ratio of hydrogen to oxygen.

   b. When hydrogen and oxygen react to form water, the mass of water formed is exactly equal to the mass of hydrogen and oxygen that reacted.

   c. The mass ratio of oxygen to hydrogen in water is 8:1. The mass ratio of oxygen to hydrogen in hydrogen peroxide (a compound that only contains hydrogen and oxygen) is 16:1.

127. The mole is defined as the amount of a substance containing the same number of particles as exactly 12 grams of C-12. The amu is defined as 1/12 of the mass of an atom of C-12. Why is it important that both of these definitions reference the same isotope? What would be the result, for example, of defining the mole with respect to C-12, but the amu with respect to Ne-20?

128. Without doing any calculations, determine which of the samples contains the greatest amount of the element in moles. Which contains the greatest mass of the element?
   a. 55.0 g Cr   **b.** 45.0 g Ti   **c.** 60.0 g Zn

129. The atomic radii of the isotopes of an element are identical to one another. However, the atomic radii of the ions of an element are significantly different from the atomic radii of the neutral atom of the element. Explain.

3

Molecules, Compounds, and Chemical Equations

Almost all aspects of life are engineered at the molecular level, and without understanding molecules we can only have a very sketchy understanding of life itself.

—Francis Harry Compton Crick (1916–2004)

HOW MANY DIFFERENT substances exist? We learned in Chapter 2 that about 91 different elements exist in nature, so there are at least 91 different substances. However, the world would be dull—not to mention lifeless—with only 91 different substances. Fortunately, elements combine with each other to form *compounds*. Just as combinations of only 26 letters in our English alphabet allow for an almost limitless number of words, each with its own specific meaning, combinations of the 91 naturally occurring elements allow for an almost limitless number of compounds, each with its own specific properties. The great diversity of substances that we find in nature is a direct result of the ability of elements to form compounds. Life, for example, could not exist with just 91 different elements. It takes compounds, in all of their diversity, to make life possible.

3.1 Hydrogen, Oxygen, and Water

Hydrogen (H_2) is an explosive gas used as a fuel in the space shuttle. Oxygen (O_2), also a gas, is a natural component of the air on Earth. Oxygen is not itself flammable, but must be present for combustion (burning) to occur. Hydrogen and oxygen both have extremely low boiling points, as

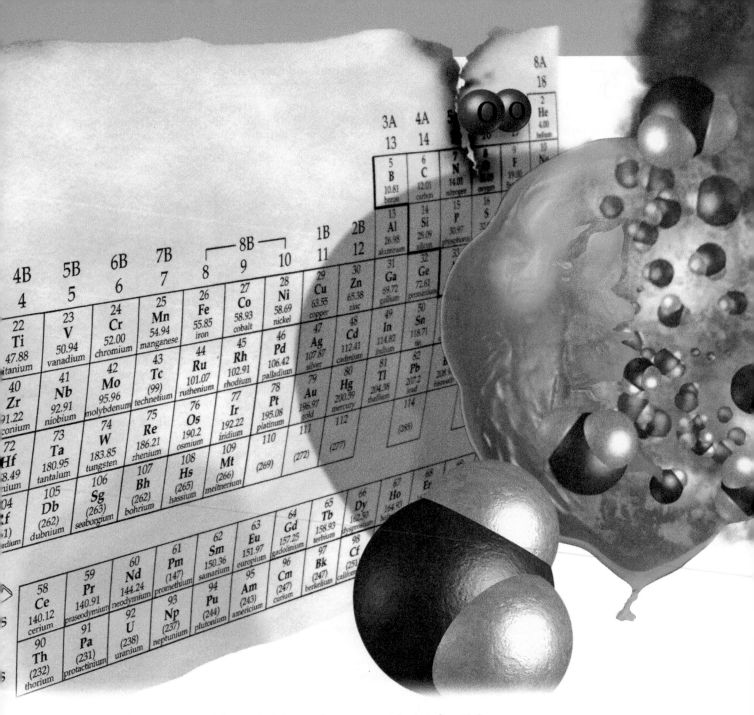

When a balloon filled with H_2 and O_2 is ignited, the two elements react violently to form H_2O.

you can see from the table below. When hydrogen and oxygen combine to form the compound water (H_2O), however, a dramatically different substance results.

Selected Properties	Hydrogen	Oxygen	Water
Boiling Point	−253 °C	−183 °C	100 °C
State at Room Temperature	Gas	Gas	Liquid
Flammability	Explosive	Necessary for combustion	Used to extinguish flame

First of all, water is a liquid rather than a gas at room temperature, and its boiling point is hundreds of degrees above the boiling points of hydrogen and oxygen. Second, instead of being flammable (like hydrogen gas) or supporting combustion (like oxygen gas), water actually smothers flames. Water is nothing like the hydrogen and oxygen from which it was formed.

▶ **FIGURE 3.1 Mixtures and Compounds** The balloon in this illustration is filled with a mixture of hydrogen gas and oxygen gas. The proportions of hydrogen and oxygen are variable. The glass is filled with water, a compound of hydrogen and oxygen. The ratio of hydrogen to oxygen in water is fixed: Water molecules always have two hydrogen atoms for each oxygen atom.

Mixtures and Compounds

Hydrogen and Oxygen Mixture
Can have any ratio of hydrogen to oxygen.

Water (A Compound)
Water molecules have a fixed ratio of hydrogen (2 atoms) to oxygen (1 atom).

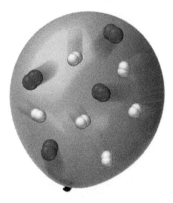

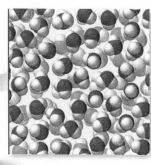

The properties of compounds are generally very different from the properties of the elements that compose them. When two elements combine to form a compound, an entirely new substance results. Common table salt, for example, is a compound composed of sodium and chlorine. Elemental sodium is a highly reactive, silvery metal that can explode on contact with water. Elemental chlorine is a corrosive, greenish-yellow gas that can be fatal if inhaled. Yet the compound formed from the combination of these two elements is sodium chloride (or table salt), a flavor enhancer that tastes great on steak.

Although some of the substances that we encounter in everyday life are elements, most are compounds. Free atoms are rare on Earth. As we learned in Chapter 1, a compound is different from a mixture of elements. In a compound, elements combine in fixed, definite proportions; in a mixture, elements can mix in any proportions whatsoever. For example, consider the difference between a hydrogen–oxygen mixture and water as shown in Figure 3.1 ▲. A hydrogen–oxygen mixture can have any proportions of hydrogen and oxygen gas. Water, by contrast, is composed of water molecules that always contain 2 hydrogen atoms to every 1 oxygen atom. Water has a definite proportion of hydrogen to oxygen.

In this chapter we will learn about compounds: how to represent them, how to name them, how to distinguish between their different types, and how to write chemical equations showing how they form and change. We will also learn how to quantify the elemental composition of a compound. This is important whenever we want to know how much of a particular element is contained within a particular compound. For example, patients with high blood pressure (hypertension) often have to reduce their sodium ion intake. Since the sodium ion is normally consumed in the form of sodium chloride, a hypertension patient needs to know how much sodium is present in a given amount of sodium chloride. Similarly, an iron-mining company needs to know how much iron they can recover from a given amount of iron ore. This chapter will give us the tools to understand and solve these kinds of problems.

3.2 Chemical Bonds

Compounds are composed of atoms held together by *chemical bonds*. Chemical bonds are the result of interactions between the charged particles—electrons and protons—that compose atoms. We discuss these interactions more thoroughly in Chapter 9 (see Section 9.2). For now, remember that, as we discussed in Section 2.4, electrostatic forces exist between charged particles; like charges repel one another and opposite charges attract one another. These electrostatic forces are responsible for chemical bonding.

We can broadly classify most chemical bonds into two types: ionic and covalent. *Ionic bonds*—which occur between metals and nonmetals—involve the *transfer* of

electrons from one atom to another. *Covalent bonds*—which occur between two or more nonmetals—involve the *sharing* of electrons between two atoms.

Ionic Bonds

We learned in Chapter 2 that metals have a tendency to lose electrons and that nonmetals have a tendency to gain them. Therefore, when a metal interacts with a nonmetal, it can transfer one or more of its electrons to the nonmetal. The metal atom then becomes a *cation* (a positively charged ion) and the nonmetal atom becomes an *anion* (a negatively charged ion) as shown in Figure 3.2 ▼. These oppositely charged ions are then attracted to one another by electrostatic forces, and they form an **ionic bond**. The result is an ionic compound which in the solid phase is composed of a lattice—a regular three-dimensional array—of alternating cations and anions.

Covalent Bonds

When a nonmetal bonds with another nonmetal, neither atom transfers its electron to the other. Instead the bonding atoms *share* some of their electrons. The shared electrons interact with the nuclei of both atoms, lowering the potential energy (see Section 1.5) of the system through electrostatic interactions and forming a **covalent bond**. The result is a molecular compound, which is composed of individual covalently-bonded molecules.

We can begin to understand the stability of a covalent bond by considering the most stable (or lowest potential energy) configuration of a negative charge interacting with two

The Formation of an Ionic Compound

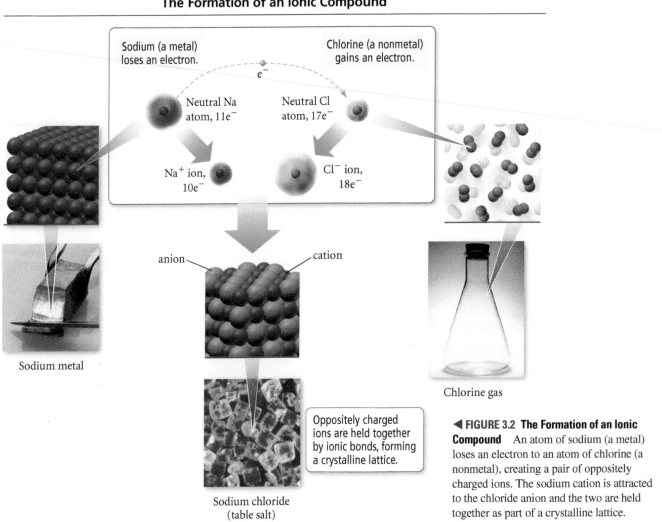

Sodium (a metal) loses an electron.

Chlorine (a nonmetal) gains an electron.

e^-

Neutral Na atom, $11e^-$

Neutral Cl atom, $17e^-$

Na^+ ion, $10e^-$

Cl^- ion, $18e^-$

anion

cation

Sodium metal

Chlorine gas

Oppositely charged ions are held together by ionic bonds, forming a crystalline lattice.

Sodium chloride (table salt)

◀ **FIGURE 3.2 The Formation of an Ionic Compound** An atom of sodium (a metal) loses an electron to an atom of chlorine (a nonmetal), creating a pair of oppositely charged ions. The sodium cation is attracted to the chloride anion and the two are held together as part of a crystalline lattice.

The potential energy of a negative charge interacting with two positive charges is lowest when the negative charge is between the two positive charges.

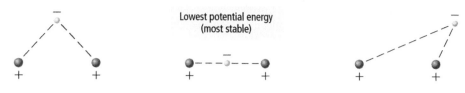

positive charges (which are separated by some small distance). As you can see from Figure 3.3 ▲, the arrangement in which the negative charge lies *between* the two positive charges has the lowest potential energy because the negative charge can interact with *both positive charges*. Similarly, shared electrons in a covalent chemical bond hold the bonding atoms together by attracting the positively charged nuclei of both bonding atoms.

3.3 Representing Compounds: Chemical Formulas and Molecular Models

The quickest and easiest way to represent a compound is with its **chemical formula**, which indicates the elements present in the compound and the relative number of atoms or ions of each. For example, H_2O is the chemical formula for water—it indicates that water consists of hydrogen and oxygen atoms in a two-to-one ratio. The formula contains the symbol for each element and a subscript indicating the relative number of atoms of the element. A subscript of 1 is typically omitted. Chemical formulas normally list the more metallic (or more positively charged) elements first, followed by the less metallic (or more negatively charged) elements. Other examples of common chemical formulas include NaCl for sodium chloride, indicating sodium and chloride ions in a one-to-one ratio; CO_2 for carbon dioxide, indicating carbon and oxygen atoms in a one-to-two ratio; and CCl_4 for carbon tetrachloride, indicating carbon and chlorine in a one-to-four ratio.

Types of Chemical Formulas

Chemical formulas can generally be categorized into three different types: empirical, molecular, and structural. An **empirical formula** gives the *relative* number of atoms of each element in a compound. A **molecular formula** gives the *actual* number of atoms of each element in a molecule of a compound. For example, the empirical formula for hydrogen peroxide is HO, but its molecular formula is H_2O_2. The molecular formula is always a whole-number multiple of the empirical formula. For some compounds, the empirical formula and the molecular formula are identical. For example, the empirical and molecular formula for water is H_2O because water molecules contain 2 hydrogen atoms and 1 oxygen atom, and no simpler whole-number ratio can express the relative number of hydrogen atoms to oxygen atoms.

A **structural formula** uses lines to represent covalent bonds and shows how atoms in a molecule are connected or bonded to each other. The structural formula for H_2O_2 is shown below:

$$H—O—O—H$$

Structural formulas may also be written to give a sense of the molecule's geometry. The structural formula for hydrogen peroxide can be written as follows:

$$\begin{array}{c} H \\ \backslash \\ O—O \\ \quad\ \backslash \\ \quad\ H \end{array}$$

This version of the formula represents the approximate angles between bonds, giving a sense of the molecule's shape. Structural formulas can also depict the different types of bonds that occur between molecules. For example, consider the structural formula for carbon dioxide:

$$O{=}C{=}O$$

The two lines between each carbon and oxygen atom represent a double bond, which is generally stronger and shorter than a single bond (represented by a single line). A single bond

corresponds to one shared electron pair while a double bond corresponds to two shared electron pairs. We will learn more about single, double, and even triple bonds in Chapter 9.

The type of formula you use depends on how much you know about the compound and how much you want to communicate. A structural formula communicates the most information, while an empirical formula communicates the least.

EXAMPLE 3.1 Molecular and Empirical Formulas

Write empirical formulas for the compounds represented by the molecular formulas.

(a) C_4H_8 **(b)** B_2H_6 **(c)** CCl_4

SOLUTION

To find the empirical formula from a molecular formula, divide the subscripts by the greatest common factor (the largest number that divides exactly into all of the subscripts).

(a) For C_4H_8, the greatest common factor is 4. The empirical formula is therefore CH_2.

(b) For B_2H_6, the greatest common factor is 2. The empirical formula is therefore BH_3.

(c) For CCl_4, the only common factor is 1, so the empirical formula and the molecular formula are identical.

FOR PRACTICE 3.1

Write the empirical formula for the compounds represented by the molecular formulas.

(a) C_5H_{12} **(b)** Hg_2Cl_2 **(c)** $C_2H_4O_2$

Answers to For Practice and For More Practice problems can be found in Appendix IV.

Molecular Models

A more accurate and complete way to specify a compound is with a molecular model. **Ball-and-stick models** represent atoms as balls and chemical bonds as sticks; how the two connect reflects a molecule's shape. The balls are typically color-coded to specific elements. For example, carbon is customarily black, hydrogen is white, nitrogen is blue, and oxygen is red. (For a complete list of colors of elements in the molecular models used in this book see Appendix IIA.)

In **space-filling molecular models**, atoms fill the space between each other to more closely represent our best estimates for how a molecule might appear if scaled to a visible size. Consider the following ways to represent a molecule of methane, the main component of natural gas:

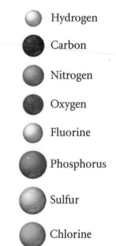

Hydrogen

Carbon

Nitrogen

Oxygen

Fluorine

Phosphorus

Sulfur

Chlorine

CH_4

$$H-\overset{\displaystyle H}{\underset{\displaystyle H}{C}}-H$$

Molecular formula   Structural formula   Ball-and-stick model   Space-filling model

The molecular formula of methane indicates the number and type of each atom in the molecule: one carbon atom and four hydrogen atoms. The structural formula shows how the atoms are connected: the carbon atom is bonded to the four hydrogen atoms. The ball-and-stick model clearly portrays the geometry of the molecule: the carbon atom sits in the center of a *tetrahedron* formed by the four hydrogen atoms. And finally, the space-filling model gives the best sense of the relative sizes of the atoms and how they merge together in bonding.

Throughout this book, you will see molecules represented in all of these ways. As you look at these representations, keep in mind what you learned in Chapter 1: the details about a molecule—the atoms that compose it, the lengths of the bonds between atoms,

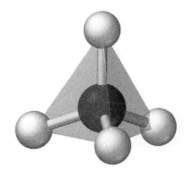

▲ A tetrahedron is a three-dimensional geometrical shape characterized by four equivalent triangular faces.

TABLE 3.1 Benzene, Acetylene, Glucose, and Ammonia

Name of Compound	Empirical Formula	Molecular Formula	Structural Formula	Ball-and-Stick Model	Space-Filling Model
Benzene	CH	C_6H_6			
Acetylene	CH	C_2H_2	H—C≡C—H		
Glucose	CH_2O	$C_6H_{12}O_6$			
Ammonia	NH_3	NH_3			

the angles of the bonds between atoms, and its overall shape—determine the properties of the substance that the molecule composes. Change any of these details and those properties change. Table 3.1 shows various compounds represented in the different ways we have just discussed.

 Conceptual Connection 3.1 Representing Molecules

Based on what you learned in Chapter 2 about atoms, what part of the atom do you think the spheres in the above molecular models represent? If you were to superimpose a nucleus on one of these spheres, how big would you draw it?

ANSWER: The spheres represent the electron cloud of the atom. It would be nearly impossible to draw a nucleus to scale on any of the space-filling molecular models—on this scale, the nucleus would be too small to see.

3.4 An Atomic-Level View of Elements and Compounds

In Chapter 1, we learned that we can categorize pure substances as either elements or compounds. We can subcategorize elements and compounds according to the basic units that compose them, as shown in Figure 3.4 ►. Elements may be either atomic or molecular. Compounds may be either molecular or ionic.

Atomic elements are those that exist in nature with single atoms as their basic units. Most elements fall into this category. For example, helium is composed of helium atoms,

Classification of Elements and Compounds

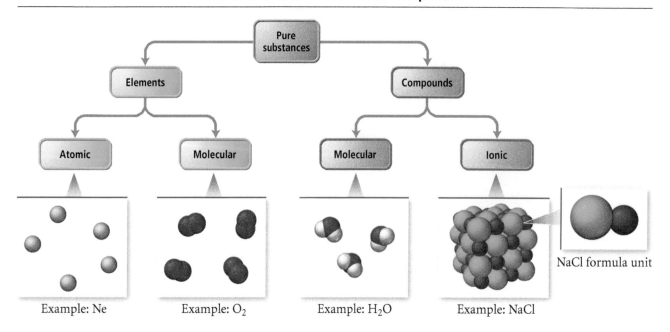

▲ FIGURE 3.4 A Molecular View of Elements and Compounds

aluminum is composed of aluminum atoms, and iron is composed of iron atoms. **Molecular elements** do not normally exist in nature with single atoms as their basic units. Instead, these elements exist as molecules—two or more atoms of the element bonded together. Most molecular elements exist as *diatomic* molecules. For example, hydrogen is composed of H_2 molecules, nitrogen is composed of N_2 molecules, and chlorine is composed of Cl_2 molecules. A few molecular elements exist as *polyatomic molecules*. Phosphorus exists as P_4 and sulfur exists as S_8. Figure 3.5 ▼ shows the elements that exist primarily as diatomic or polyatomic molecules.

Molecular compounds are usually composed of two or more covalently bonded nonmetals. The basic units of molecular compounds are molecules composed of the constituent atoms. For example, water is composed of H_2O molecules, dry ice is composed of CO_2 molecules, and propane (often used as a fuel for grills) is composed of C_3H_8 molecules as shown in Figure 3.6(a) ▶ on the next page.

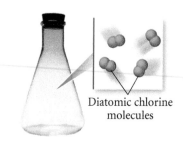

Diatomic chlorine molecules

▲ The basic units that compose chlorine gas are diatomic chlorine molecules.

Molecular Elements

◀ FIGURE 3.5 Molecular Elements The highlighted elements exist primarily as diatomic molecules (yellow) or polyatomic molecules (red).

A Molecular Compound

An Ionic Compound

(a)

(b)

▲ **FIGURE 3.6 Molecular and Ionic Compounds**   (a) Propane is an example of a molecular compound. The basic units that compose propane gas are propane (C_3H_8) molecules. (b) Table salt (NaCl) is an ionic compound. Its formula unit is the simplest charge-neutral collection of ions: one Na^+ ion and one Cl^- ion.

Some ionic compounds, such as K_2NaPO_4, contain more than one type of metal ion.

People occasionally refer to formula units as molecules, but this is *not* correct since ionic compounds do not contain distinct molecules.

DANGER: CORROSIVE. HARMFUL IF SWALLOWED.
Ingredients: Sodium Hypochlorite, Sodium Hydroxide
May cause severe irritation or damage to eyes, skin, and mucous membranes.
Avoid contact with eyes, skin and clothing. Do not ingest. For prolonged use, wear gloves.
FIRST AID: EYES-Rinse with plenty of water for 15 minutes. IF SWALLOWED-Do not induce vomiting. Drink a glassful of water. In either case, call a physician or poison control center immediately. SKIN-Remove contaminated clothing and wash skin thoroughly with water.
PHYSICAL AND CHEMICAL HAZARDS: Ultra Clorox® Fresh Wildflowers™ bleach contains a strong oxidizer. Always flush drains before and after use. **Do not use or mix with other household chemicals,** such as toilet bowl cleaners, rust removers, acids, or products containing ammonia. To do so will release hazardous gases. Prolonged contact with metal may cause pitting or discoloration. Not harmful to septic systems.
STORAGE: Store ultra Clorox® Fresh Wildflowers™ bleach upright in a cool, dry place. Store away from children. Reclose cap tightly after each use.
DISPOSAL: Offer empty container for recycling. If recycling is not available, discard in trash.
Clorox is a reg. trademark of The Clorox Co. Mfd. for & © 1999 The Clorox Company, 1221 Broadway, Oakland, CA 94612. Made in U.S.A.

0 44600 02470 7

62412 1201

▲ Polyatomic ions are common in household products such as bleach, which contains sodium hypochlorite (NaClO).

Ionic compounds are composed of cations (usually one type of metal) and anions (usually one or more nonmetals) bound together by ionic bonds. The basic unit of an ionic compound is the **formula unit**, the smallest, electrically neutral collection of ions. Formula units are different from molecules in that they do not exist as discrete entities, but rather only as part of a larger lattice. For example, the ionic compound table salt, with the formula unit NaCl, is composed of Na^+ and Cl^- ions in a one-to-one ratio. In table salt, Na^+ and Cl^- ions exist in a three-dimensional alternating array. Because ionic bonds are not directional, no one Na^+ ion pairs with a specific Cl^- ion. Rather, as you can see from Figure 3.6(b), any one Na^+ cation is surrounded by Cl^- anions and vice versa.

Many common ionic compounds contain ions that are themselves composed of a group of covalently bonded atoms with an overall charge. For example, the active ingredient in household bleach is sodium hypochlorite, which acts to chemically alter color-causing molecules in clothes (bleaching action) and to kill bacteria (disinfection). Hypochlorite is a **polyatomic ion**—an ion composed of two or more atoms—with the formula ClO^-. (Note that the charge on the hypochlorite ion is a property of the whole ion, not just the oxygen atom; this is true for all polyatomic ions.) The hypochlorite ion is often found as a unit in other compounds as well [such as KClO and $Mg(ClO)_2$]. Other common compounds that contain polyatomic ions include sodium bicarbonate ($NaHCO_3$), also known as baking soda, sodium nitrite ($NaNO_2$), an inhibitor of bacterial growth in packaged meats, and calcium carbonate ($CaCO_3$), the active ingredient in antacids such as Tums and Alka-Mints.

EXAMPLE 3.2 Classifying Substances as Atomic Elements, Molecular Elements, Molecular Compounds, or Ionic Compounds

Classify each of the substances as an atomic element, molecular element, molecular compound, or ionic compound.

(a) xenon   **(b)** $NiCl_2$ **(c)** bromine   **(d)** NO_2 **(e)** $NaNO_3$

SOLUTION

(a) Xenon is an element. It is not a molecular element (see Figure 3.5); therefore, it is an atomic element.

(b) $NiCl_2$ is a compound composed of a metal (left side of the periodic table) and nonmetal (right side of the periodic table); therefore, it is an ionic compound.

(c) Bromine is one of the elements that exists as a diatomic molecule (see Figure 3.5); therefore, it is a molecular element.

(d) NO_2 is a compound composed of a nonmetal and a nonmetal; therefore, it is a molecular compound.

(e) $NaNO_3$ is a compound composed of a metal and a polyatomic ion; therefore, it is an ionic compound.

FOR PRACTICE 3.2
Classify each of the substances as an atomic element, molecular element, molecular compound, or ionic compound.

(a) fluorine   (b) N_2O (c) silver   (d) K_2O (e) Fe_2O_3

Conceptual Connection 3.2 Ionic and Molecular Compounds

Which of the following statements best summarizes the difference between ionic and molecular compounds?

(a) Molecular compounds contain highly directional covalent bonds, which results in the formation of molecules—discrete particles that do not covalently bond to each other. Ionic compounds contain nondirectional ionic bonds, which results (in the solid phase) in the formation of ionic lattices—extended networks of alternating cations and anions.

(b) Molecular compounds contain covalent bonds in which one of the atoms shares an electron with the other one, resulting in a new force that holds the atoms together in a covalent molecule. Ionic compounds contain ionic bonds in which one atom donates an electron to the other, resulting in a new force that holds the ions together in pairs (in the solid phase).

(c) The key difference between ionic and covalent compounds is the types of elements that compose them, not the way that the atoms bond together.

(d) A molecular compound is composed of covalently bonded molecules. An ionic compound is composed of ionically bonded molecules (in the solid phase).

ANSWER: Choice **(a)** best describes the difference between ionic and molecular compounds. The **(b)** answer is incorrect because there are no "new" forces in bonding (just rearrangements that result in lower potential energy), and because ions do not group together in pairs in the solid phase. The **(c)** answer is incorrect because the main difference between ionic and molecular compounds is the way that the atoms bond. The **(d)** answer is incorrect because ionic compounds do not contain molecules.

3.5 Ionic Compounds: Formulas and Names

Ionic compounds occur throughout Earth's crust as minerals. Examples include limestone $(CaCO_3)$, a type of sedimentary rock, gibbsite $[Al(OH)_3]$, an aluminum-containing mineral, and soda ash (Na_2CO_3), a natural deposit. We can also find ionic compounds in the foods that we eat: table salt (NaCl), calcium carbonate $(CaCO_3)$, a source of calcium necessary for bone health, and potassium chloride (KCl), a source of potassium necessary for fluid balance and muscle function. Ionic compounds are generally very stable because the attractions between cations and anions within ionic compounds are strong, and because each ion interacts with several oppositely charged ions in the crystalline lattice.

◀ Calcite (left) is the main component of limestone, marble, and other forms of calcium carbonate $(CaCO_3)$ commonly found in Earth's crust. Trona (right) is a crystalline form of hydrated sodium carbonate $(Na_3H(CO_3)_2 \cdot 2H_2O)$.

▲ Ionic compounds are common in food and consumer products such as light salt (a mixture of NaCl and KCl) and Tums™ ($CaCO_3$).

See Figure 2.14 to review the elements that form ions with a predictable charge.

Writing Formulas for Ionic Compounds

Since ionic compounds are charge-neutral, and since many elements form only one type of ion with a predictable charge, the formulas for many ionic compounds can be deduced from their constituent elements. For example, the formula for the ionic compound composed of sodium and chlorine must be NaCl because, in compounds, Na always forms 1+ cations and Cl always forms 1– anions. In order for the compound to be charge-neutral, it must contain one Na^+ cation to every one Cl^- anion. The formula for the ionic compound composed of *calcium* and chlorine, however, is $CaCl_2$ because Ca always forms 2+ cations and Cl always forms 1– anions. In order for this compound to be charge-neutral, it must contain one Ca^{2+} cation for every two Cl^- anions.

Summarizing Ionic Compound Formulas:

▶ Ionic compounds always contain positive and negative ions.

▶ In a chemical formula, the sum of the charges of the positive ions (cations) must equal the sum of the charges of the negative ions (anions).

▶ A formula reflects the smallest whole-number ratio of ions.

To write the formula for an ionic compound, follow the procedure in the left column in the following example. Two examples of how to apply the procedure are provided in the center and right columns.

PROCEDURE FOR... Writing Formulas for Ionic Compounds	EXAMPLE 3.3 Writing Formulas for Ionic Compounds Write a formula for ionic compound that forms between aluminum and oxygen.	EXAMPLE 3.4 Writing Formulas for Ionic Compounds Write a formula for the ionic compound that forms between calcium and oxygen.
1. Write the symbol for the metal cation and its charge followed by the symbol for the nonmetal anion and its charge. Obtain charges from the element's group number in the periodic table (refer to Figure 2.14).	Al^{3+} O^{2-}	Ca^{2+} O^{2-}
2. Adjust the subscript on each cation and anion to balance the overall charge.	Al^{3+} O^{2-} ↓ Al_2O_3	Ca^{2+} O^{2-} ↓ CaO
3. Check that the sum of the charges of the cations equals the sum of the charges of the anions.	cations: $2(3+) = 6+$ anions: $3(2-) = 6-$ The charges cancel.	cations: $2+$ anions: $2-$ The charges cancel.

FOR PRACTICE 3.3
Write a formula for the compound formed between potassium and sulfur.

FOR PRACTICE 3.4
Write a formula for the compound formed between aluminum and nitrogen.

Naming Ionic Compounds

Some ionic compounds—such as NaCl (table salt) and $NaHCO_3$ (baking soda)—have **common names**, which are nicknames learned by familiarity. However, chemists have developed **systematic names** for different types of compounds including ionic ones. Even if you are not familiar with a compound, you can determine its systematic name from its chemical formula. Conversely, you can deduce the formula of a compound from its systematic name.

The first step in naming an ionic compound is to identify it as one. Remember, *ionic compounds are usually composed of metals and nonmetals*; any time you see a metal and one or more nonmetals together in a chemical formula, assume that you have an ionic compound. Ionic compounds can be categorized into two types, depending on the metal in the compound. The first type contains a metal whose charge is invariant from one compound to another. Whenever the metal in this first type of compound forms an ion, the ion always has the same charge.

Since the charge of the metal in this first type of ionic compound is always the same, it need not be specified in the name of the compound. Sodium, for instance, has a 1+ charge in all of its compounds. Some examples of these types of metals are listed in Table 3.2; the charges of these metals can be inferred from their group number in the periodic table.

The second type of ionic compound contains a metal with a charge that can differ in different compounds. In other words, the metal in this second type of ionic compound can form more than one kind of cation (depending on the compound), and its charge must therefore be specified for a given compound. Iron, for instance, forms a 2+ cation in some of its compounds and a 3+ cation in others. Metals of this type are often *transition metals* (Figure 3.7 ►). However, some transition metals, such as Zn and Ag, form cations with the same charge in all of their compounds (as shown in Table 3.2), and some main group metals, such as Pb and Sn, form more than one type of cation.

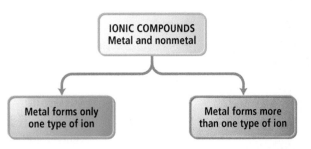

Naming Binary Ionic Compounds Containing a Metal That Forms Only One Type of Cation

Binary compounds are those containing only two different elements. The names for binary ionic compounds take the following form:

| name of cation (metal) | base name of anion (nonmetal) + *-ide* |

For example, the name for KCl consists of the name of the cation, *potassium*, followed by the base name of the anion, *chlor*, with the ending *-ide*. The full name is *potassium chloride*.

KCl   potassium chloride

The name for CaO consists of the name of the cation, *calcium*, followed by the base name of the anion, *ox*, with the ending *-ide*. The full name is *calcium oxide*.

CaO   calcium oxide

The base names for various nonmetals, and their most common charges in ionic compounds, are shown in Table 3.3.

TABLE 3.2 Metals Whose Charge Is Invariant from One Compound to Another

Metal	Ion	Name	Group Number
Li	Li^+	Lithium	1A
Na	Na^+	Sodium	1A
K	K^+	Potassium	1A
Rb	Rb^+	Rubidium	1A
Cs	Cs^+	Cesium	1A
Be	Be^{2+}	Beryllium	2A
Mg	Mg^{2+}	Magnesium	2A
Ca	Ca^{2+}	Calcium	2A
Sr	Sr^{2+}	Strontium	2A
Ba	Ba^{2+}	Barium	2A
Al	Al^{3+}	Aluminum	3A
Zn	Zn^{2+}	Zinc	*
Sc	Sc^{3+}	Scandium	*
Ag**	Ag^+	Silver	*

*The charge of these metals cannot be inferred from their group number.
**Silver sometimes forms compounds with other charges, but these are rare.

TABLE 3.3 Some Common Monoatomic Anions

Nonmetal	Symbol for Ion	Base Name	Anion Name
Fluorine	F^-	fluor	Fluoride
Chlorine	Cl^-	chlor	Chloride
Bromine	Br^-	brom	Bromide
Iodine	I^-	iod	Iodide
Oxygen	O^{2-}	ox	Oxide
Sulfur	S^{2-}	sulf	Sulfide
Nitrogen	N^{3-}	nitr	Nitride
Phosphorus	P^{3-}	phosph	Phosphide

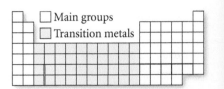

▲ **FIGURE 3.7 Transition Metals** Metals that can have different charges in different compounds are usually (but not always) transition metals.

EXAMPLE 3.5 Naming Ionic Compounds Containing a Metal That Forms Only One Type of Cation

Name the compound $CaBr_2$.

SOLUTION

The cation is *calcium*. The anion is from bromine, which becomes *bromide*. The correct name is *calcium bromide*.

FOR PRACTICE 3.5

Name the compound Ag_3N.

FOR MORE PRACTICE 3.5

Write the formula for rubidium sulfide.

Naming Binary Ionic Compounds Containing a Metal That Forms More than One Kind of Cation

For these types of metals, the name of the cation is followed by a roman numeral (in parentheses) that indicates the charge of the metal in that particular compound. For example, we distinguish between Fe^{2+} and Fe^{3+} as follows:

$$Fe^{2+} \quad iron(II)$$
$$Fe^{3+} \quad iron(III)$$

The full names for these compounds have the following form:

Note that there is no space between the name of the cation and the parenthetical number indicating its charge.

(name of cation (metal)) (charge of cation (metal) in roman numerals in parentheses) (base name of anion (nonmetal) + -ide)

TABLE 3.4 Some Metals That Form Cations with Different Charges

Metal	Ion	Name	Older Name*
Chromium	Cr^{2+}	Chromium(II)	Chromous
	Cr^{3+}	Chromium(III)	Chromic
Iron	Fe^{2+}	Iron(II)	Ferrous
	Fe^{3+}	Iron(III)	Ferric
Cobalt	Co^{2+}	Cobalt(II)	Cobaltous
	Co^{3+}	Cobalt(III)	Cobaltic
Copper	Cu^+	Copper(I)	Cuprous
	Cu^{2+}	Copper(II)	Cupric
Tin	Sn^{2+}	Tin(II)	Stannous
	Sn^{4+}	Tin(IV)	Stannic
Mercury	Hg_2^{2+}	Mercury(I)	Mercurous
	Hg^{2+}	Mercury(II)	Mercuric
Lead	Pb^{2+}	Lead(II)	Plumbous
	Pb^{4+}	Lead(IV)	Plumbic

*An older naming system substitutes the names found in this column for the name of the metal and its charge. Under this system, chromium(II) oxide is named chromous oxide. In this system, the suffix *-ous* indicates the ion with the lesser charge and *-ic* indicates the ion with the greater charge. We will *not* use the older system in this text.

You can determine the charge of the metal cation by inference from the sum of the charges of the nonmetal anions—remember that the sum of all the charges must be zero. Table 3.4 shows some of the metals that form more than one cation and their most common charges. For example, in $CrBr_3$, the charge of chromium must be 3+ in order for the compound to be charge-neutral with three Br^- anions. The cation is named as follows:

$$Cr^{3+} \quad chromium(III)$$

The full name of the compound is

$$CrBr_3 \quad chromium(III) \text{ bromide}$$

Similarly, in CuO, the charge of copper must be 2+ in order for the compound to be charge-neutral with one O^{2-} anion. The cation is therefore named as follows:

$$Cu^{2+} \quad copper(II)$$

The full name of the compound is

$$CuO \quad copper(II) \text{ oxide}$$

EXAMPLE 3.6 Naming Ionic Compounds Containing a Metal That Forms More than One Kind of Cation

Name the compound $PbCl_4$.

SOLUTION

The charge on Pb must be 4+ for the compound to be charge-neutral with 4 Cl^- anions. The name for $PbCl_4$ is the name of the cation, *lead*, followed by the charge of the cation in parentheses *(IV)*, and the base name of the anion, *chlor*, with the ending *-ide*. The full name is *lead(IV) chloride*.

$PbCl_4$ lead(IV) chloride

FOR PRACTICE 3.6

Name the compound FeS.

FOR MORE PRACTICE 3.6

Write the formula for ruthenium(IV) oxide.

Naming Ionic Compounds Containing Polyatomic Ions

Ionic compounds that contain a polyatomic ion are named in the same way as other ionic compounds, except that the name of the polyatomic ion is used whenever it occurs. Table 3.5 lists common polyatomic ions and their formulas. For example, $NaNO_2$ is named according to its cation, Na^+, *sodium*, and its polyatomic anion, NO_2^-, *nitrite*. Its full name is *sodium nitrite*.

$NaNO_2$ sodium nitrite

$FeSO_4$ is named according to its cation, *iron*, its charge *(II)*, and its polyatomic ion *sulfate*. Its full name is *iron(II) sulfate*.

$FeSO_4$ iron(II) sulfate

If the compound contains both a polyatomic cation and a polyatomic anion, use the names of both polyatomic ions. For example, NH_4NO_3 is *ammonium nitrate*.

NH_4NO_3 ammonium nitrate

TABLE 3.5 Some Common Polyatomic Ions

Name	Formula	Name	Formula
Acetate	$C_2H_3O_2^-$	Hypochlorite	ClO^-
Carbonate	CO_3^{2-}	Chlorite	ClO_2^-
Hydrogen carbonate (or bicarbonate)	HCO_3^-	Chlorate	ClO_3^-
Hydroxide	OH^-	Perchlorate	ClO_4^-
Nitrite	NO_2^-	Permanganate	MnO_4^-
Nitrate	NO_3^-	Sulfite	SO_3^{2-}
Chromate	CrO_4^{2-}	Hydrogen sulfite (or bisulfite)	HSO_3^-
Dichromate	$Cr_2O_7^{2-}$	Sulfate	SO_4^{2-}
Phosphate	PO_4^{3-}	Hydrogen sulfate (or bisulfate)	HSO_4^-
Hydrogen phosphate	HPO_4^{2-}	Cyanide	CN^-
Dihydrogen phosphate	$H_2PO_4^-$	Peroxide	O_2^{2-}
Ammonium	NH_4^+		

You should be able to recognize polyatomic ions in a chemical formula, so become familiar with the ions listed in Table 3.5. Most polyatomic ions are **oxyanions**, anions containing oxygen and another element. Notice that when a series of oxyanions contains different numbers of oxygen atoms, they are named systematically according to the number of oxygen atoms in the ion. If there are only two ions in the series, the one with more oxygen atoms has the ending *-ate* and the one with fewer has the ending *-ite*. For example, NO_3^- is *nitrate* and NO_2^- is *nitrite*.

$$NO_3^- \quad \text{nitr\textit{ate}}$$
$$NO_2^- \quad \text{nitr\textit{ite}}$$

If there are more than two ions in the series then the prefixes *hypo-*, meaning *less than*, and *per-*, meaning *more than*, are used. So ClO^- is hypochlorite—less oxygen than chlorite, and ClO_4^- is perchlorate—more oxygen than chlorate.

$$ClO^- \quad \textit{hypo}\text{chlor\textit{ite}}$$
$$ClO_2^- \quad \text{chlor\textit{ite}}$$
$$ClO_3^- \quad \text{chlor\textit{ate}}$$
$$ClO_4^- \quad \textit{per}\text{chlor\textit{ate}}$$

Other halides (halogen ions) form similar series with similar names. Thus, IO_3^- is called iodate and BrO_3^- is called bromate.

EXAMPLE 3.7 Naming Ionic Compounds That Contain a Polyatomic Ion

Name the compound $Li_2Cr_2O_7$.

SOLUTION

The name for $Li_2Cr_2O_7$ is the name of the cation, *lithium*, followed by the name of the polyatomic ion, *dichromate*. Its full name is *lithium dichromate*.

$$Li_2Cr_2O_7 \quad \text{lithium dichromate}$$

FOR PRACTICE 3.7
Name the compound $Sn(ClO_3)_2$.

FOR MORE PRACTICE 3.7
Write the formula for cobalt(II) phosphate.

| Hydrate | Anhydrous |

$$CoCl_2 \cdot 6H_2O \qquad CoCl_2$$

▲ **FIGURE 3.8 Hydrates** Cobalt(II) chloride hexahydrate is pink. Heating the compound removes the waters of hydration, leaving the blue anhydrous cobalt(II) chloride.

Common hydrate prefixes
hemi = 1/2
mono = 1
di = 2
tri = 3
tetra = 4
penta = 5
hexa = 6
hepta = 7
octa = 8

Hydrated Ionic Compounds

Some ionic compounds—called **hydrates**—contain a specific number of water molecules associated with each formula unit. For example, the formula for epsom salts is $MgSO_4 \cdot 7H_2O$ and its systematic name is magnesium sulfate heptahydrate. The seven H_2O molecules associated with the formula unit are *waters of hydration*. Waters of hydration can usually be removed by heating the compound. Figure 3.8 ◄, for example, shows a sample of cobalt(II) chloride hexahydrate ($CoCl_2 \cdot 6H_2O$) before and after heating. The hydrate is pink and the anhydrous salt (the salt without any associated water molecules) is blue. Hydrates are named just as other ionic compounds, but they are given the additional name "*prefix*hydrate," where the *prefix* indicates the number of water molecules associated with each formula unit.

Other common hydrated ionic compounds and their names are as follows:

$$CaSO_4 \cdot \tfrac{1}{2}H_2O \qquad \text{calcium sulfate hemihydrate}$$
$$BaCl_2 \cdot 6H_2O \qquad \text{barium chloride hexahydrate}$$
$$CuSO_4 \cdot 5H_2O \qquad \text{copper(II) sulfate pentahydrate}$$

3.6 Molecular Compounds: Formulas and Names

In contrast to ionic compounds, the formula for a molecular compound *cannot* readily be determined from its constituent elements because the same combination of elements may form many different molecular compounds, each with a different formula. We learned in Chapter 1, for example, that carbon and oxygen form both CO and CO_2, and that hydrogen and oxygen form both H_2O and H_2O_2. Nitrogen and oxygen form all of the following unique molecular compounds: NO, NO_2, N_2O, N_2O_3, N_2O_4, and N_2O_5. In Chapter 9, we will learn how to understand the stability of these various combinations of the same elements. For now, we focus on naming a molecular compound based on its formula and writing its formula based on its name.

Naming Molecular Compounds

Like ionic compounds, many molecular compounds have common names. For example, H_2O and NH_3 are commonly called *water* and *ammonia*. However, the sheer number of existing molecular compounds—numbering in the millions—requires a systematic approach to naming them.

The first step in naming a molecular compound is identifying it as one. Remember, *molecular compounds are composed of two or more nonmetals*. In this section, we learn how to name binary (two-element) molecular compounds. Their names have the following form:

| prefix | name of 1st element | prefix | base name of 2nd element + *-ide* |

When writing the name of a molecular compound, as when writing the formula, the first element is the more metal-like one (toward the left and bottom of the periodic table). Generally, write the name of the element with the smallest group number first. If the two elements lie in the same group, then write the element with the greatest row number first. The prefixes given to each element indicate the number of atoms present:

mono = 1	hexa = 6
di = 2	hepta = 7
tri = 3	octa = 8
tetra = 4	nona = 9
penta = 5	deca = 10

These prefixes are the same as those used in naming hydrates.

If there is only one atom of the *first element* in the formula, the prefix *mono-* is normally omitted. For example, NO_2 is named according to the first element, *nitrogen*, with no prefix because *mono-* is omitted for the first element, followed by the prefix *di*, to indicate two oxygen atoms, and the base name of the second element, *ox*, with the ending *-ide*. The full name is *nitrogen dioxide*.

$$NO_2 \quad \text{nitrogen dioxide}$$

The compound N_2O, sometimes called laughing gas, is named similarly except that we use the prefix *di-* before nitrogen to indicate two nitrogen atoms and the prefix *mono-* before oxide to indicate one oxygen atom. Its entire name is *dinitrogen monoxide*.

When a prefix ends with "o" and the base name begins "o," the first "o" is often dropped. So mono-oxide becomes *monoxide*.

$$N_2O \quad \text{dinitrogen monoxide}$$

EXAMPLE 3.8 Naming Molecular Compounds

Name each molecular compound.

(a) NI_3 **(b)** PCl_5 **(c)** P_4S_{10}

SOLUTION

(a) The name of the compound is the name of the first element, *nitrogen*, followed by the base name of the second element, *iod*, prefixed by *tri-* to indicate three and given the suffix *-ide*.

$$NI_3 \qquad \text{nitrogen triiodide}$$

(b) The name of the compound is the name of the first element, *phosphorus*, followed by the base name of the second element, *chlor*, prefixed by *penta-* to indicate five and given the suffix *-ide*.

$$PCl_5 \qquad \text{phosphorus pentachloride}$$

(c) The name of the compound is the name of the first element, *phosphorus*, prefixed by *tetra-* to indicate four, followed by the base name of the second element, *sulf*, prefixed by *deca* to indicate ten and given the suffix *-ide*.

$$P_4S_{10} \qquad \text{tetraphosphorus decasulfide}$$

FOR PRACTICE 3.8

Name the compound N_2O_5.

FOR MORE PRACTICE 3.8

Write the formula for phosphorus tribromide.

Naming Acids

▲ Many fruits are acidic and have the characteristically sour taste of acids.

Acids are molecular compounds that release hydrogen ions (H^+) when dissolved in water. They are composed of hydrogen, usually written first in their formula, and one or more nonmetals, written second. For example, HCl is a molecular compound that, when dissolved in water, forms $H^+(aq)$ and $Cl^-(aq)$ ions, where *aqueous (aq)* means *dissolved in water*. Therefore, HCl is an acid when dissolved in water. To distinguish between gaseous HCl (which is named hydrogen chloride because it is a molecular compound) and HCl in solution (which is named hydrochloric acid because it is an acid), we write the former as HCl(*g*) and the latter as HCl(*aq*).

Acids are characterized by their sour taste and their ability to dissolve many metals. For example, hydrochloric acid is present in stomach fluids, and its sour taste becomes painfully obvious during vomiting. Hydrochloric acid also dissolves some metals. For example, if you put a strip of zinc into a test tube of hydrochloric acid, it slowly dissolves as the $H^+(aq)$ ions convert the zinc metal into $Zn^{2+}(aq)$ cations (Figure 3.9 ▶).

Acids are present in foods such as lemons and limes and are used in household products such as toilet bowl cleaner and Lime-Away. In this section, we learn how to name them; in Chapter 15 we will learn more about their properties. Acids can be divided into two categories, binary acids and oxyacids.

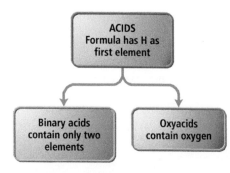

Acids Dissolve Many Metals

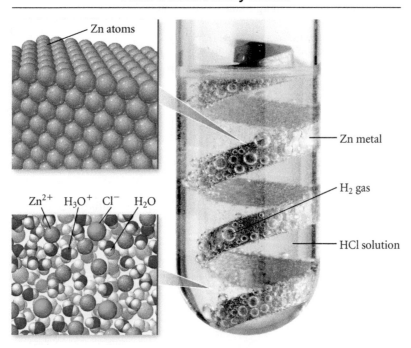

◀ **FIGURE 3.9 Hydrochloric Acid Dissolving Zinc Metal** The zinc atoms are ionized to zinc ions, which dissolve in the water. The HCl forms H_2 gas, which is responsible for the bubbles you can see in the test tube.

Naming Binary Acids

Binary acids are composed of hydrogen and a nonmetal. Names for binary acids have the following form:

For example, HCl(aq) is named hydro*chlor*ic acid and HBr(aq) is named hydro*brom*ic acid.

HCl(aq) hydrochloric acid   HBr(aq) hydrobromic acid

EXAMPLE 3.9 Naming Binary Acids

Name HI(aq).

SOLUTION

The base name of I is *iod* so HI(aq) is hydroiodic acid.

HI(aq)   hydroiodic acid

FOR PRACTICE 3.9

Name HF(aq).

Naming Oxyacids

Oxyacids contain hydrogen and an oxyanion (an anion containing a nonmetal and oxygen). The common oxyanions are listed in the table of polyatomic ions (Table 3.5). For example, $HNO_3(aq)$ contains the nitrate (NO_3^-) ion, $H_2SO_3(aq)$ contains the sulfite (SO_3^{2-}) ion, and $H_2SO_4(aq)$ contains the sulfate (SO_4^{2-}) ion. Oxyacids are a combination of one or more H^+ ions with an oxyanion (see Table 3.5). The number of H^+ ions

depends on the charge of the oxyanion; the formula is always charge-neutral. The names of oxyacids depend on the ending of the oxyanion and take the following forms:

oxyanions ending with *-ate* | base name of oxyanion + *-ic* | | acid |

oxyanions ending with *-ite* | base name of oxyanion + *-ous* | | acid |

So $HNO_3(aq)$ is nitric acid (oxyanion is nitrate), and $H_2SO_3(aq)$ is sulfurous acid (oxyanion is sulfite).

$HNO_3(aq)$ nitric acid $H_2SO_3(aq)$ sulfurous acid

CHEMISTRY IN THE ENVIRONMENT Acid Rain

Certain pollutants—such as NO, NO_2, and SO_2—form acids when mixed with water. NO and NO_2, primarily emitted in vehicular exhaust, combine with atmospheric oxygen and water to form nitric acid, $HNO_3(aq)$. SO_2, emitted primarily from coal-powered electricity generation, combines with atmospheric oxygen and water to form sulfuric acid, $H_2SO_4(aq)$. Both $HNO_3(aq)$ and $H_2SO_4(aq)$ result in acidic rainwater. The problem is greatest in the northeastern United States where pollutants from midwestern electrical power plants combine with rainwater to produce rain that is up to 10 times more acidic than normal.

Acid rain can fall or flow into lakes and streams, making them more acidic. Some species of aquatic animals—such as trout, bass, snails, salamanders, and clams—cannot tolerate the increased acidity and die. This in turn disturbs the ecosystem of the lake, resulting in imbalances that may lead to the death of other aquatic species. Acid rain also weakens trees by dissolving nutrients in the soil (and washing them away) and by damaging leaves. Appalachian red spruce trees have been the hardest hit, with many forests showing significant acid rain damage.

In addition, acid rain degrades building materials because acids dissolve iron, the main component of steel, and $CaCO_3$ (limestone), a main component of marble and concrete. Consequently, acid rain has damaged many statues, buildings,

▼ A forest damaged by acid rain.

◄ Acid rain damages building materials such as the limestone that composes many statues.

and bridges in the northeastern United States. Some historical gravestones, made of limestone, are barely legible due to acid rain damage.

Acid rain has been a problem for many years but legislation passed toward the end of the last century has offered hope for improvement. In 1990, Congress passed several amendments to the Clean Air Act that included provisions requiring electrical utilities to lower SO_2 emissions. Since then, SO_2 emissions have decreased and rain in the northeastern United States has become somewhat less acidic. With time, and with continued enforcement of the acid rain regulation, lakes, streams, and forests damaged by acid rain should recover.

Question
Provide the names for each of the compounds given here as formulas: NO, NO_2, SO_2, H_2SO_4, HNO_3, $CaCO_3$.

EXAMPLE 3.10 **Naming Oxyacids**

Name $HC_2H_3O_2(aq)$.

SOLUTION

The oxyanion is acetate, which ends in *-ate*; therefore, the name of the acid is *acetic acid*.

$$HC_2H_3O_2(aq) \qquad \text{acetic acid}$$

FOR PRACTICE 3.10

Name $HNO_2(aq)$.

FOR MORE PRACTICE 3.10

Write the formula for perchloric acid.

 Conceptual Connection 3.3 **Nomenclature**

The compound NCl_3 is named nitrogen trichloride, but $AlCl_3$ is simply aluminum chloride. Why?

ANSWER: This conceptual connection addresses one of the main errors in nomenclature: the failure to correctly categorize the compound. Remember that you must first determine whether the compound that you are naming is an ionic compound, a molecular compound, or an acid, and then name it accordingly. NCl_3 is a molecular compound (two or more nonmetals), and therefore uses prefixes to indicate the number of each type of atom—so NCl_3 is nitrogen trichloride. The compound $AlCl_3$, however, is an ionic compound (metal and nonmetal), and therefore does not require prefixes—so $AlCl_3$ is aluminum chloride.

3.7 Formula Mass and the Mole Concept for Compounds

In Chapter 2, we defined the average mass of an atom of an element as its *atomic mass*. Similarly, we now define the average mass of a molecule (or a formula unit) of a compound as its **formula mass**. (The terms *molecular mass* or *molecular weight* are synonymous with formula mass and are also common.) For any compound, the formula mass is the sum of the atomic masses of all the atoms in its chemical formula.

$$\text{Formula mass} = \left(\begin{array}{c} \text{Number of atoms} \\ \text{of 1st element in} \\ \text{chemical formula} \end{array} \times \begin{array}{c} \text{Atomic mass} \\ \text{of} \\ \text{1st element} \end{array} \right) + \left(\begin{array}{c} \text{Number of atoms} \\ \text{of 2nd element in} \\ \text{chemical formula} \end{array} \times \begin{array}{c} \text{Atomic mass} \\ \text{of} \\ \text{2nd element} \end{array} \right) + \ldots$$

For example, the formula mass of carbon dioxide, CO_2, is

Multiply by 2 because formula has 2 oxygen atoms.

$$\text{Formula mass} = 12.01 \text{ amu} + 2(16.00 \text{ amu})$$

$$= 44.01 \text{ amu}$$

and that of sodium oxide, Na_2O, is

Multiply by 2 because formula has 2 sodium atoms.

$$\text{Formula mass} = 2(22.99 \text{ amu}) + 16.00 \text{ amu}$$

$$= 61.98 \text{ amu}$$

EXAMPLE 3.11 Calculating Formula Mass

Calculate the formula mass of glucose, $C_6H_{12}O_6$.

SOLUTION

To find the formula mass, we add the atomic masses of each atom in the chemical formula:

$$\text{Formula mass} = 6 \times (\text{atomic mass C}) + 12 \times (\text{atomic mass H}) + 6 \times (\text{atomic mass O})$$

$$= 6(12.01 \text{ amu}) \qquad + 12(1.008 \text{ amu}) \qquad + 6(16.00 \text{ amu})$$

$$= 180.16 \text{ amu}$$

FOR PRACTICE 3.11

Calculate the formula mass of calcium nitrate.

Molar Mass of a Compound

Remember, ionic compounds do not contain individual molecules. In casual language, the smallest electrically neutral collection of ions is sometimes called a molecule but is more correctly called a formula unit.

In Chapter 2 (Section 2.9), we learned that an element's molar mass—the mass in grams of one mole of its atoms—is numerically equivalent to its atomic mass. We then used the molar mass in combination with Avogadro's number to determine the number of atoms in a given mass of the element. The same concept applies to compounds. The *molar mass of a compound*—the mass in grams of 1 mol of its molecules or formula units—is numerically equivalent to its formula mass. For example, we just calculated the formula mass of CO_2 to be 44.01 amu. The molar mass is, therefore,

$$CO_2 \text{ molar mass} = 44.01 \text{ g/mol}$$

Using Molar Mass to Count Molecules by Weighing

The molar mass of CO_2 is a conversion factor between mass (in grams) and amount (in moles) of CO_2. Suppose we want to find the number of CO_2 molecules in a sample of dry ice (solid CO_2) with a mass of 10.8 g. This calculation is analogous to Example 2.8, where we found the number of atoms in a sample of copper of a given mass. We begin with the mass of 10.8 g and use the molar mass to convert to the amount in moles. Then we use Avogadro's number to convert to number of molecules. The conceptual plan is as follows:

Conceptual Plan

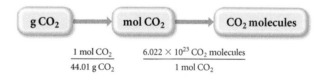

To solve the problem, we follow the conceptual plan, beginning with 10.8 g CO_2, converting to moles, and then to molecules.

Solution

$$10.8 \text{ g } CO_2 \times \frac{1 \text{ mol } CO_2}{44.01 \text{ g } CO_2} \times \frac{6.022 \times 10^{23} \text{ CO}_2 \text{ molecules}}{1 \text{ mol } CO_2} = 1.48 \times 10^{23} \text{ CO}_2 \text{ molecules}$$

EXAMPLE 3.12 The Mole Concept—Converting between Mass and Number of Molecules

An aspirin tablet contains 325 mg of acetylsalicylic acid ($C_9H_8O_4$). How many acetylsalicylic acid molecules does it contain?

SORT You are given the mass of acetylsalicylic acid and asked to find the number of molecules.	**GIVEN:** 325 mg $C_9H_8O_4$ **FIND:** number of $C_9H_8O_4$ molecules

STRATEGIZE First convert to moles (using the molar mass of the compound) and then to number of molecules (using Avogadro's number). You will need both the molar mass of acetylsalicylic acid and Avogadro's number as conversion factors. You will also need the conversion factor between g and mg.

CONCEPTUAL PLAN

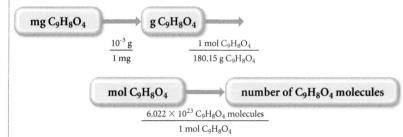

RELATIONSHIPS USED

$C_9H_8O_4$ molar mass = 9(12.01) + 8(1.008) + 4(16.00)

$\qquad\qquad = 180.15$ g/mol

$6.022 \times 10^{23} = 1$ mol

1 mg $= 10^{-3}$ g

SOLVE Follow the conceptual plan to solve the problem.

SOLUTION

$$325 \text{ mg } C_9H_8O_4 \times \frac{10^{-3} \text{ g}}{1 \text{ mg}} \times \frac{1 \text{ mol } C_9H_8O_4}{180.15 \text{ g } C_9H_8O_4} \times$$

$$\frac{6.022 \times 10^{23} \text{ } C_9H_8O_4 \text{ molecules}}{1 \text{ mol } C_9H_8O_4} = 1.09 \times 10^{21} \text{ } C_9H_8O_4 \text{ molecules}$$

CHECK The units of the answer, $C_9H_8O_4$ molecules, are correct. The magnitude is smaller than Avogadro's number, as expected, since we have less than one molar mass of acetylsalicylic acid.

FOR PRACTICE 3.12

Find the number of ibuprofen molecules in a tablet containing 200.0 mg of ibuprofen ($C_{13}H_{18}O_2$).

FOR MORE PRACTICE 3.12

What is the mass of a sample of water containing 3.55×10^{22} H_2O molecules?

 Conceptual Connection 3.4 Molecular Models and the Size of Molecules

Throughout this book, we use space-filling molecular models to represent molecules. Which of the following is the best estimate for the scaling factor used in these models? In other words, by approximately what number would you have to multiply the radius of an actual oxygen atom to get the radius of the sphere used to represent the oxygen atom in the water molecule shown here?

(a) 10 **(b)** 10^4 **(c)** 10^8 **(d)** 10^{16}

ANSWER: (c) Atomic radii range in the hundreds of picometers while the spheres in these models have radii of less than a centimeter. The scaling factor is therefore about 10^8 (100 million).

▲ The chlorine in chlorofluorocarbons caused the ozone hole over Antarctica. The dark blue color indicates depressed ozone levels.

3.8 Composition of Compounds

A chemical formula, in combination with the molar masses of its constituent elements, indicates the relative quantities of each element in a compound, which is extremely useful information. For example, about 30 years ago, scientists began to suspect that synthetic compounds known as chlorofluorocarbons (or CFCs) were destroying ozone (O_3) in Earth's upper atmosphere. Upper atmospheric ozone is important because it acts as a shield, protecting life on Earth from the sun's harmful ultraviolet light.

CFCs are chemically inert compounds that were used primarily as refrigerants and industrial solvents. Over time CFCs began to accumulate in the atmosphere. In the upper atmosphere, sunlight breaks bonds within CFCs, releasing chlorine atoms. The chlorine atoms then react with ozone, converting it into O_2. So the harmful part of CFCs is the chlorine atoms that they carry. How do you determine the mass of chlorine in a given mass of a CFC?

One way to express how much of an element is in a given compound is to use the element's mass percent composition for that compound. The **mass percent composition** or **mass percent** of an element is that element's percentage of the compound's total mass. The mass percent of element X in a compound can be computed from the chemical formula as follows:

$$\text{mass percent of element X} = \frac{\text{mass of element X in 1 mol of compound}}{\text{mass of 1 mol of the compound}} \times 100\%$$

Suppose, for example, that we want to calculate the mass percent composition of Cl in the chlorofluorocarbon CCl_2F_2. The mass percent Cl is given by

$$\text{Mass percent Cl} = \frac{2 \times \text{Molar mass Cl}}{\text{Molar mass } CCl_2F_2} \times 100\%$$

The molar mass of Cl must be multiplied by two because the chemical formula has a subscript of 2 for Cl, indicating that 1 mol of CCl_2F_2 contains 2 mol of Cl atoms. We calculate the molar mass of CCl_2F_2 as follows:

$$\text{Molar mass} = 12.01 \text{ g/mol} + 2(35.45 \text{ g/mol}) + 2(19.00 \text{ g/mol})$$

$$= 120.91 \text{ g/mol}$$

So the mass percent of Cl in CCl_2F_2 is

$$\text{Mass percent Cl} = \frac{2 \times \text{molar mass Cl}}{\text{molar mass } CCl_2F_2} \times 100\%$$

$$= \frac{2 \times 35.45 \text{ g/mol}}{120.91 \text{ g/mol}} \times 100\%$$

$$= 58.64\%$$

EXAMPLE 3.13 Mass Percent Composition

Calculate the mass percent of Cl in Freon-112 ($C_2Cl_4F_2$), a CFC refrigerant.

SORT You are given the molecular formula of Freon-112 and asked to find the mass percent of Cl.	**GIVEN:** $C_2Cl_4F_2$ **FIND:** mass percent Cl
STRATEGIZE The molecular formula tells you that there are 4 mol of Cl in each mole of Freon-112. Find the mass percent composition from the chemical formula by using the equation that defines mass percent. The conceptual plan shows how the mass of Cl in 1 mol of $C_2Cl_4F_2$ and the molar mass of $C_2Cl_4F_2$ are used to find the mass percent of Cl.	**CONCEPTUAL PLAN** $$\text{Mass \% Cl} = \frac{4 \times \text{molar mass Cl}}{\text{molar mass } C_2Cl_4F_2} \times 100\%$$ **RELATIONSHIPS USED** $$\text{Mass percent of element X} = \frac{\text{mass of element X in 1 mol of compound}}{\text{mass of 1 mol of compound}} \times 100\%$$
SOLVE Calculate the necessary parts of the equation and substitute the values into the equation to find mass percent Cl.	**SOLUTION** $4 \times$ molar mass Cl $= 4(35.45 \text{ g/mol}) = 141.8 \text{ g/mol}$ Molar mass $C_2Cl_4F_2 = 2(12.01 \text{ g/mol}) + 4(35.45 \text{ g/mol}) + 2(19.00 \text{ g/mol})$ $= 24.02 \text{ g/mol} + 141.8 \text{ g/mol} + 38.00 \text{ g/mol} = 203.8 \text{ g/mol}$ $$\text{Mass \% Cl} = \frac{4 \times \text{molar mass Cl}}{\text{molar mass } C_2Cl_4F_2} \times 100\%$$ $$= \frac{141.8 \text{ g/mol}}{203.8 \text{ g/mol}} \times 100\%$$ $$= 69.58\%$$

CHECK The units of the answer (%) are correct and the magnitude is reasonable because (a) it is between 0 and 100% and (b) chlorine is the heaviest atom in the molecule and there are four of them.

FOR PRACTICE 3.13

Acetic acid ($C_2H_4O_2$) is the active ingredient in vinegar. Calculate the mass percent composition of oxygen in acetic acid.

FOR MORE PRACTICE 3.13

Calculate the mass percent composition of sodium in sodium oxide.

 Conceptual Connection 3.5 Mass Percent Composition

In For Practice 3.13 you calculated the mass percent of oxygen in acetic acid ($C_2H_4O_2$). Without doing any calculations, predict whether the mass percent of carbon in acetic acid is greater or smaller than that of oxygen. Explain.

ANSWER: The mass percent of carbon in acetic acid will be smaller than the mass percent of oxygen because, even though the formula ($C_2H_4O_2$) contains the same molar amounts of the two elements, carbon is lighter (it has a lower molar mass) than oxygen.

Mass Percent Composition as a Conversion Factor

The mass percent composition of an element in a compound is a conversion factor between mass of the element and mass of the compound. For example, we saw that the mass percent composition of Cl in CCl_2F_2 is 58.64%. Since percent means *per hundred*, there are 58.64 g Cl *per hundred* grams CCl_2F_2, which can be expressed as the following ratio:

$$58.64 \text{ g Cl} : 100 \text{ g } CCl_2F_2$$

or, in fractional form:

$$\frac{58.64 \text{ g Cl}}{100 \text{ g } CCl_2F_2} \quad \text{or} \quad \frac{100 \text{ g } CCl_2F_2}{58.64 \text{ g Cl}}$$

These ratios can function as conversion factors between grams of Cl and grams of CCl_2F_2. For example, to calculate the mass of Cl in 1.00 kg CCl_2F_2, we use the following conceptual plan:

Conceptual Plan

$$\boxed{\text{kg } CCl_2F_2} \longrightarrow \boxed{\text{g } CCl_2F_2} \longrightarrow \boxed{\text{g Cl}}$$
$$\frac{1000 \text{ g}}{1 \text{ kg}} \qquad \frac{58.64 \text{ g Cl}}{100 \text{ g } CCl_2F_2}$$

Notice that the mass percent composition acts as a conversion factor between grams of the compound and grams of the constituent element. To compute grams Cl, follow the conceptual plan:

Solution

$$1.00 \text{ kg } \cancel{CCl_2F_2} \times \frac{1000 \text{ g}}{1 \text{ kg}} \times \frac{58.64 \text{ g Cl}}{100 \text{ g } \cancel{CCl_2F_2}} = 5.86 \times 10^2 \text{ g Cl}$$

EXAMPLE 3.14 Using Mass Percent Composition as a Conversion Factor

The U.S. Food and Drug Administration (FDA) recommends that a person consume less than 2.4 g of sodium per day. What mass of sodium chloride (in grams) can you consume and still be within the FDA guidelines? Sodium chloride is 39% sodium by mass.

SORT You are given a mass of sodium and the mass percent of sodium in sodium chloride. You are asked to find the mass of NaCl that contains the given mass of sodium.	**GIVEN:** 2.4 g Na **FIND:** g NaCl
STRATEGIZE Convert between mass of a constituent element and mass of a compound by using mass percent composition as a conversion factor.	**CONCEPTUAL PLAN**  **RELATIONSHIPS USED** 39 g Na : 100 g NaCl
SOLVE Follow the conceptual plan to solve the problem.	**SOLUTION** $2.4 \text{ g } \cancel{Na} \times \dfrac{100 \text{ g NaCl}}{39 \text{ g } \cancel{Na}} = 6.2 \text{ g NaCl}$ You can consume 6.2 g NaCl and still be within the FDA guidelines.

CHECK The units of the answer are correct. The magnitude seems reasonable because it is larger than the amount of sodium, as expected because sodium is only one of the elements in NaCl.

FOR PRACTICE 3.14

What mass (in grams) of iron(III) oxide contains 58.7 grams of iron? Iron(III) oxide is 69.94% iron by mass.

FOR MORE PRACTICE 3.14

If someone consumes 22 g of sodium chloride per day, what mass (in grams) of sodium does that person consume? Sodium chloride is 39% sodium by mass.

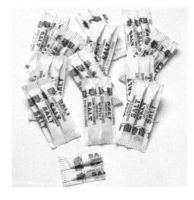

▲ 12.5 packets of salt contain 6.2 g of NaCl.

Conversion Factors from Chemical Formulas

Mass percent composition is one way to understand how much chlorine is in a particular chlorofluorocarbon or, more generally, how much of a constituent element is present in a given mass of any compound. However, we can also approach this type of problem in a different way. Chemical formulas contain within them inherent relationships between atoms (or moles of atoms) and molecules (or moles of molecules). For example, the formula for CCl_2F_2 tells us that 1 mol of CCl_2F_2 contains 2 mol of Cl atoms. We write the ratio as follows:

$$1 \text{ mol } CCl_2F_2 : 2 \text{ mol Cl}$$

With ratios such as these—that come from the chemical formula—we can directly determine the amounts of the constituent elements present in a given amount of a compound without having to compute mass percent composition. For example, we calculate the number of moles of Cl in 38.5 mol of CCl_2F_2 as follows:

Conceptual Plan

$$\boxed{\text{mol } CCl_2F_2} \longrightarrow \boxed{\text{mol Cl}}$$
$$\frac{2 \text{ mol Cl}}{1 \text{ mol } CCl_2F_2}$$

Solution

$$38.5 \text{ mol } CCl_2F_2 \times \frac{2 \text{ mol Cl}}{1 \text{ mol } CCl_2F_2} = 77.0 \text{ mol Cl}$$

As we have seen, however, we often want to know, not the *amount in moles* of an element in a certain number of moles of compound, but the *mass in grams* (or other units) of a constituent element in a given *mass* of the compound. Suppose we want to know the mass (in grams) of Cl contained in 25.0 g CCl_2F_2. The relationship inherent in the chemical formula (2 mol Cl : 1 mol CCl_2F_2) applies to the amount in moles, not to mass. Therefore, we first convert the mass of CCl_2F_2 to moles CCl_2F_2. *Then* we use the conversion factor from the chemical formula to convert to moles Cl. Finally, we use the molar mass of Cl to convert to grams Cl.

Conceptual Plan

$$\boxed{\text{g } CCl_2F_2} \longrightarrow \boxed{\text{mol } CCl_2F_2} \longrightarrow \boxed{\text{mol Cl}} \longrightarrow \boxed{\text{g Cl}}$$
$$\frac{1 \text{ mol } CCl_2F_2}{120.91 \text{ g } CCl_2F_2} \quad \frac{2 \text{ mol Cl}}{1 \text{ mol } CCl_2F_2} \quad \frac{35.45 \text{ g Cl}}{1 \text{ mol Cl}}$$

Solution

$$25.0 \text{ g } CCl_2F_2 \times \frac{1 \text{ mol } CCl_2F_2}{120.91 \text{ g } CCl_2F_2} \times \frac{2 \text{ mol Cl}}{1 \text{ mol } CCl_2F_2} \times \frac{35.45 \text{ g Cl}}{1 \text{ mol Cl}} = 14.7 \text{ g Cl}$$

Notice that we must convert from g CCl_2F_2 to mol CCl_2F_2 *before* we can use the chemical formula as a conversion factor. *Always remember that the chemical formula gives us a relationship between the amounts (in moles) of substances, not between the masses (in grams) of them.*

The general form for solving problems where you are asked to find the mass of an element present in a given mass of a compound is

Mass compound ⟶ moles compound ⟶ moles element ⟶ mass element

The conversions between mass and moles are accomplished using the atomic or molar mass and the conversion between moles and moles is accomplished using the relationships inherent in the chemical formula.

EXAMPLE 3.15 Chemical Formulas as Conversion Factors

Hydrogen may potentially be used in the future to replace gasoline as a fuel. Most major automobile companies are developing vehicles that run on hydrogen. These cars are environmentally friendly because their only emission is water vapor. One way to obtain hydrogen for fuel is to use an emission-free energy source such as wind power to form elemental hydrogen from water. What mass of hydrogen (in grams) is contained in 1.00 gallon of water? (The density of water is 1.00 g/mL.)

SORT You are given a volume of water and asked to find the mass of hydrogen it contains. You are also given the density of water.	**GIVEN:** 1.00 gal H_2O $\qquad d_{H_2O} = 1.00$ g/mL **FIND:** g H

STRATEGIZE The first part of the conceptual plan shows how to convert the units of volume from gallons to liters and then to mL. It also shows how you can then use the density to convert mL to g.

The second part of the conceptual plan is the basic sequence of mass → moles → moles → mass. Convert between moles and mass using the appropriate molar masses, and convert from mol H_2O to mol H using the conversion factor derived from the molecular formula.

CONCEPTUAL PLAN

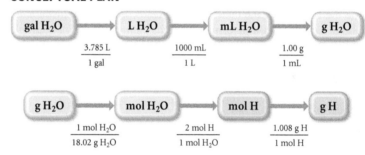

RELATIONSHIPS USED

3.785 L = 1 gal (Table 1.3)

1000 mL = 1 L

1.00 g H_2O = 1 mL H_2O (density of H_2O)

Molar mass H_2O = 2(1.008) + 16.00 = 18.02 g/mol

2 mol H : 1 mol H_2O

1.008 g H = 1 mol H

SOLVE Follow the conceptual plan to solve the problem.

SOLUTION

$$1.00 \text{ gal } H_2O \times \frac{3.785 \text{ L}}{1 \text{ gal}} \times \frac{1000 \text{ mL}}{1 \text{ L}} \times \frac{1.0 \text{ g}}{\text{mL}} = 3.7\underline{8}5 \times 10^3 \text{ g } H_2O$$

$$3.7\underline{8}5 \times 10^3 \text{ g } H_2O \times \frac{1 \text{ mol } H_2O}{18.02 \text{ g } H_2O} \times \frac{2 \text{ mol H}}{1 \text{ mol } H_2O}$$
$$\times \frac{1.008 \text{ g H}}{1 \text{ mol H}} = 4.23 \times 10^2 \text{ g H}$$

CHECK The units of the answer (g H) are correct. Since a gallon of water is about 3.8 L, its mass is about 3.8 kg. H is a light atom, so its mass should be significantly less than 3.8 kg, as it is in the answer.

FOR PRACTICE 3.15

Determine the mass of oxygen in a 7.2-g sample of $Al_2(SO_4)_3$.

FOR MORE PRACTICE 3.15

Butane (C_4H_{10}) is the liquid fuel in lighters. How many grams of carbon are present within a lighter containing 7.25 mL of butane? (The density of liquid butane is 0.601 g/mL.)

Conceptual Connection 3.6 Chemical Formulas and Elemental Composition

The molecular formula for water is H_2O. Which ratio can be correctly derived from this formula? Explain.

(a) 2 g H : 1 g H_2O **(b)** 2 mL H : 1 mL H_2O **(c)** 2 mol H : 1 mol H_2O

ANSWER: **(c)** The chemical formula for a compound gives relationships between *atoms* or *moles of atoms*. The chemical formula for water states that water molecules contain 2 H atoms to every 1 O atom or 2 mol H to every 1 mol H_2O. This *does not* imply a 2-to-1 relationship between *masses* of hydrogen and oxygen because these atoms have different masses. It also does not imply a 2-to-1 relationship between volumes.

CHEMISTRY AND MEDICINE Methylmercury in Fish

In the last decade, the U.S. Environmental Protection Agency (EPA) has grown increasingly concerned about mercury levels in fish. Mercury—which is present in fish as methylmercury—affects the central nervous system, especially in children and developing fetuses. In a developing fetus, excessive mercury exposure can result in slowed mental development and even retardation. Some lakes now have warnings about eating too much fish caught in the lake.

Recent regulations have forced many fish vendors to alert customers about the dangers of eating too much of certain kinds of commercial fish, including shark, tuna, and mackerel. These fish tend to contain high levels of methylmercury and therefore should be eaten in moderation, especially by children and pregnant women. The U.S. Food and Drug Administration (FDA) action level—the level below which the FDA claims the food has no adverse health effects—for methylmercury in fish is 1.0 ppm or 1.0 g of methylmercury per million grams of fish. However, a number of environmental advocacy groups, including the U.S. EPA, have suggested that, while this level may be safe for adults, it is too high for children and pregnant women. Consequently, the FDA suggests that pregnant women limit their intake of fish to 12 ounces per week.

Question

The levels of methylmercury in fish are normally tested by laboratory techniques that measure only the mercury (Hg). Suppose a lab analyzes a 14.5-g sample of fish and finds that it contains 1.03×10^{-5} g of mercury. How much methylmercury ($HgCH_3Cl$) is in the fish in parts per million (ppm)? Is this above the FDA action level?

▲ Lakes containing mercury—either from natural sources or from pollution—often have posted limits for the number of fish from the lake that can be eaten safely.

3.9 Determining a Chemical Formula from Experimental Data

In Section 3.8, we learned how to calculate mass percent composition from a chemical formula. Can we also do the reverse? Can we calculate a chemical formula from mass percent composition? This question is important because many laboratory analyses of compounds give the relative masses of each element present in the compound. For example, if we decompose water into hydrogen and oxygen in the laboratory, we can measure

the masses of hydrogen and oxygen produced. Can we get a chemical formula from this kind of data? The answer is a qualified yes. We can determine a chemical formula, but it is an empirical formula (not a molecular formula). To get a molecular formula, we need additional information, such as the molar mass of the compound.

Suppose we decompose a sample of water in the laboratory and find that it produces 0.857 g of hydrogen and 6.86 g of oxygen. How do we get an empirical formula from these data? We know that an empirical formula represents a ratio of atoms or a ratio of moles of atoms, *not a ratio of masses*. So the first thing we must do is convert our data from mass (in grams) to amount (in moles). How many moles of each element are present in the sample? To convert to moles, we divide each mass by the molar mass of that element:

$$\text{Moles H} = 0.857 \ \text{g H} \times \frac{1 \ \text{mol H}}{1.01 \ \text{g H}} = 0.849 \ \text{mol H}$$

$$\text{Moles O} = 6.86 \ \text{g O} \times \frac{1 \ \text{mol O}}{16.00 \ \text{g O}} = 0.429 \ \text{mol O}$$

From these data, we know there are 0.849 mol H for every 0.429 mol O. We can now write a pseudoformula for water:

$$H_{0.849}O_{0.429}$$

To get the smallest whole-number subscripts in our formula, we divide all the subscripts by the smallest one, in this case 0.429:

$$H_{\frac{0.849}{0.429}}O_{\frac{0.429}{0.429}} = H_{1.98}O = H_2O$$

Our empirical formula for water, which also happens to be the molecular formula, is H_2O. You can use the following procedure to obtain the empirical formula of any compound from experimental data giving the relative masses of the constituent elements. The left column outlines the procedure, and the center and right columns show two examples of how to apply the procedure.

PROCEDURE FOR... **Obtaining an Empirical Formula from Experimental Data**	**EXAMPLE 3.16** **Obtaining an Empirical Formula from Experimental Data** A compound containing nitrogen and oxygen is decomposed in the laboratory and produces 24.5 g nitrogen and 70.0 g oxygen. Calculate the empirical formula of the compound.	**EXAMPLE 3.17** **Obtaining an Empirical Formula from Experimental Data** A laboratory analysis of aspirin determined the following mass percent composition: C 60.00% H 4.48% O 35.52% Find the empirical formula.
1. Write down (or compute) as *given* the masses of each element present in a sample of the compound. If you are given mass percent composition, assume a 100-g sample and compute the masses of each element from the given percentages.	**GIVEN:** 24.5 g N, 70.0 g O **FIND:** empirical formula	**GIVEN:** In a 100-g sample: 60.00 g C, 4.48 g H, 35.52 g O **FIND:** empirical formula
2. Convert each of the masses in step 1 to moles by using the appropriate molar mass for each element as a conversion factor.	$24.5 \ \text{g N} \times \dfrac{1 \ \text{mol N}}{14.01 \ \text{g N}} = 1.75 \ \text{mol N}$ $70.0 \ \text{g O} \times \dfrac{1 \ \text{mol O}}{16.00 \ \text{g O}} = 4.38 \ \text{mol O}$	$60.00 \ \text{g C} \times \dfrac{1 \ \text{mol C}}{12.01 \ \text{g C}} = 4.996 \ \text{mol C}$ $4.48 \ \text{g H} \times \dfrac{1 \ \text{mol H}}{1.008 \ \text{g H}} = 4.44 \ \text{mol H}$ $35.52 \ \text{g O} \times \dfrac{1 \ \text{mol O}}{16.00 \ \text{g O}} = 2.220 \ \text{mol O}$

3. Write down a pseudoformula for the compound using the number of moles of each element (from step 2) as subscripts.	$N_{1.75}O_{4.38}$	$C_{4.996}H_{4.44}O_{2.220}$
4. Divide all the subscripts in the formula by the smallest subscript.	$\dfrac{N_{1.75}O_{4.38}}{1.75 \quad 1.75} \longrightarrow N_1O_{2.5}$	$\dfrac{C_{4.996}H_{4.44}O_{2.220}}{2.220 \ 2.220 \ 2.220} \longrightarrow C_{2.25}H_2O_1$
5. If the subscripts are not whole numbers, multiply all the subscripts by a small whole number (see table) to get whole-number subscripts.	$N_1O_{2.5} \times 2 \longrightarrow N_2O_5$ The correct empirical formula is N_2O_5.	$C_{2.25}H_2O_1 \times 4 \longrightarrow C_9H_8O_4$ The correct empirical formula is $C_9H_8O_4$.

Fractional Subscript	Multiply by This
0.20	5
0.25	4
0.33	3
0.40	5
0.50	2
0.66	3
0.75	4
0.80	5

FOR PRACTICE 3.16

A sample of a compound is decomposed in the laboratory and produces 165 g carbon, 27.8 g hydrogen, and 220.2 g oxygen. Calculate the empirical formula of the compound.

FOR PRACTICE 3.17

Ibuprofen has the following mass percent composition:

C 75.69%, H 8.80%, O 15.51%.

What is the empirical formula of ibuprofen?

Calculating Molecular Formulas for Compounds

We can find the molecular formula of a compound from the empirical formula if we also know the molar mass of the compound. Recall from Section 3.3 that the molecular formula is always a whole-number multiple of the empirical formula:

Molecular formula = empirical formula × n, where n = 1, 2, 3, ...

Suppose we want to find the molecular formula for fructose (a sugar found in fruit) from its empirical formula, CH_2O, and its molar mass, 180.2 g/mol. We know that the molecular formula is a whole-number multiple of CH_2O:

$$\text{Molecular formula} = (CH_2O) \times n$$
$$= C_nH_{2n}O_n$$

We also know that the molar mass is a whole-number multiple of the **empirical formula molar mass**, the sum of the masses of all the atoms in the empirical formula.

Molar mass = empirical formula molar mass × n

For a particular compound, the value of n in both cases is the same. Therefore, we can find n by computing the ratio of the molar mass to the empirical formula molar mass:

$$n = \frac{\text{molar mass}}{\text{empirical formula molar mass}}$$

For fructose, the empirical formula molar mass is

empirical formula molar mass
$$= 12.01 \text{ g/mol} + 2(1.01 \text{ g/mol}) + 16.00 \text{ g/mol} = 30.03 \text{ g/mol}$$

Therefore, n is

$$n = \frac{180.2 \text{ g/mol}}{30.03 \text{ g/mol}} = 6$$

We can then use this value of n to find the molecular formula:

$$\text{Molecular formula} = (CH_2O) \times 6 = C_6H_{12}O_6$$

EXAMPLE 3.18 Calculating a Molecular Formula from an Empirical Formula and Molar Mass

Butanedione—a main component responsible for the smell and taste of butter and cheese—contains the elements carbon, hydrogen, and oxygen. The empirical formula of butanedione is C_2H_3O and its molar mass is 86.09 g/mol. Find its molecular formula.

SORT You are given the empirical formula and molar mass of butanedione and asked to find the molecular formula.	**GIVEN:** Empirical formula = C_2H_3O molar mass = 86.09 g/mol **FIND:** molecular formula
STRATEGIZE A molecular formula is always a whole-number multiple of the empirical formula. Divide the molar mass by the empirical formula mass to get the whole number.	Molecular formula = empirical formula $\times n$ $n = \dfrac{\text{molar mass}}{\text{empirical formula mass}}$
SOLVE Compute the empirical formula mass.	Empirical formula molar mass $\quad = 2(12.01 \text{ g/mol}) + 3(1.008 \text{ g/mol}) + 16.00 \text{ g/mol} = 43.04 \text{ g/mol}$
Divide the molar mass by the empirical formula mass to find n.	$n = \dfrac{\text{molar mass}}{\text{empirical formula mass}} = \dfrac{86.09 \text{ g/mol}}{43.04 \text{ g/mol}} = 2$
Multiply the empirical formula by n to obtain the molecular formula.	Molecular formula = $C_2H_3O \times 2$ $\quad = C_4H_6O_2$

CHECK Check the answer by computing the molar mass of the computed formula as follows:

$$4(12.01 \text{ g/mol}) + 6(1.008 \text{ g/mol}) + 2(16.00 \text{ g/mol}) = 86.09 \text{ g/mol}$$

The computed molar mass is in agreement with the given molar mass.

FOR PRACTICE 3.18

A compound has the empirical formula CH and a molar mass of 78.11 g/mol. What is its molecular formula?

FOR MORE PRACTICE 3.18

A compound with the percent composition shown below has a molar mass of 60.10 g/mol. Find its molecular formula.

C, 39.97%
H, 13.41%
N, 46.62%

 Conceptual Connection 3.7 Chemical Formula and Mass Percent Composition

Without doing any calculations, order the elements in the following compound in order of decreasing mass percent composition.

$$C_6H_6O$$

ANSWER: C > O > H. Since carbon and oxygen differ in atomic mass by only 4 amu, and since there are 6 carbon atoms in the formula, we can conclude that carbon must constitute the greatest fraction of the mass. Oxygen is next because its mass is 16 times that of hydrogen and there only 6 hydrogen atoms to every 1 oxygen atom.

Combustion Analysis

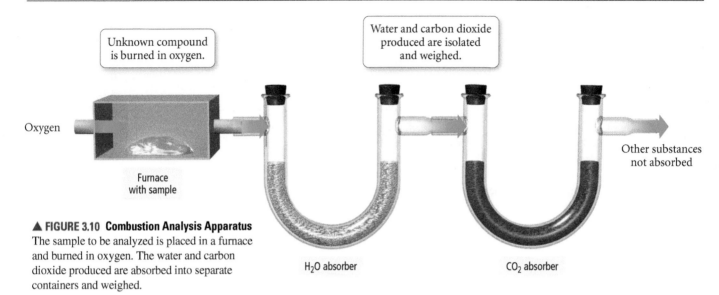

Unknown compound is burned in oxygen.

Water and carbon dioxide produced are isolated and weighed.

Oxygen

Furnace with sample

H_2O absorber

CO_2 absorber

Other substances not absorbed

▲ **FIGURE 3.10 Combustion Analysis Apparatus**
The sample to be analyzed is placed in a furnace and burned in oxygen. The water and carbon dioxide produced are absorbed into separate containers and weighed.

Combustion Analysis

In the previous section, we learned how to compute the empirical formula of a compound from the relative masses of its constituent elements. Another common (and related) way of obtaining empirical formulas for unknown compounds, especially those containing carbon and hydrogen, is **combustion analysis**. In combustion analysis, the unknown compound undergoes combustion (or burning) in the presence of pure oxygen, as shown in Figure 3.10 ▲. When the sample is burned, all of the carbon in the sample is converted to CO_2, and all of the hydrogen is converted to H_2O. The CO_2 and H_2O produced are weighed. With these masses, we can use the numerical relationships between moles inherent in the formulas for CO_2 and H_2O (1 mol CO_2 : 1 mol C and 1 mol H_2O : 2 mol H) to determine the amounts of C and H in the original sample. Any other elemental constituents, such as O, Cl, or N, can be determined by subtracting the original mass of the sample from the sum of the masses of C and H. The examples below show how to perform these calculations for a sample containing only C and H and for a sample containing C, H, and O.

Combustion is a type of *chemical reaction*. We discuss chemical reactions and their representation in Section 3.10.

PROCEDURE FOR... **Obtaining an Empirical Formula from Combustion Analysis**	EXAMPLE 3.19 **Obtaining an Empirical Formula from Combustion Analysis**	EXAMPLE 3.20 **Obtaining an Empirical Formula from Combustion Analysis**
	Upon combustion, a compound containing only carbon and hydrogen produces 1.83 g CO_2 and 0.901 g H_2O. Find the empirical formula of the compound.	Upon combustion, a 0.8233-g sample of a compound containing only carbon, hydrogen, and oxygen produces 2.445 g CO_2, and 0.6003 g H_2O. Find the empirical formula of the compound.
1. Write down as *given* the masses of each combustion product and the mass of the sample (if given).	**GIVEN:** 1.83 g CO_2, 0.901 g H_2O **FIND:** empirical formula	**GIVEN:** 0.8233-g sample, 2.445 g CO_2, 0.6003 g H_2O **FIND:** empirical formula
2. Convert the masses of CO_2 and H_2O from step 1 to moles by using the appropriate molar mass for each compound as a conversion factor.	$1.83 \text{ g } CO_2 \times \dfrac{1 \text{ mol } CO_2}{44.01 \text{ g } CO_2}$ $= 0.0416 \text{ mol } CO_2$ $0.901 \text{ g } H_2O \times \dfrac{1 \text{ mol } H_2O}{18.02 \text{ g } H_2O}$ $= 0.0500 \text{ mol } H_2O$	$2.445 \text{ g } CO_2 \times \dfrac{1 \text{ mol } CO_2}{44.01 \text{ g } CO_2}$ $= 0.05556 \text{ mol } CO_2$ $0.6003 \text{ g } H_2O \times \dfrac{1 \text{ mol } H_2O}{18.01 \text{ g } H_2O}$ $= 0.03331 \text{ mol } H_2O$

3. Convert the moles of CO_2 and moles of H_2O from step 2 to moles of C and moles of H using the conversion factors inherent in the chemical formulas of CO_2 and H_2O.	$0.0416 \text{ mol } CO_2 \times \dfrac{1 \text{ mol C}}{1 \text{ mol } CO_2}$ $= 0.0416 \text{ mol C}$ $0.0500 \text{ mol } H_2O \times \dfrac{2 \text{ mol H}}{1 \text{ mol } H_2O}$ $= 0.100 \text{ mol H}$	$0.05556 \text{ mol } CO_2 \times \dfrac{1 \text{ mol C}}{1 \text{ mol } CO_2}$ $= 0.05556 \text{ mol C}$ $0.03331 \text{ mol } H_2O \times \dfrac{2 \text{ mol H}}{1 \text{ mol } H_2O}$ $= 0.06662 \text{ mol H}$
4. If the compound contains an element other than C and H, find the mass of the other element by subtracting the sum of the masses of C and H (obtained in step 3) from the mass of the sample. Finally, convert the mass of the other element to moles.	No other elements besides C and H, so proceed to next step.	$\text{Mass C} = 0.05556 \text{ mol C} \times \dfrac{12.01 \text{ g C}}{\text{mol C}}$ $= 0.6673 \text{ g C}$ $\text{Mass H} = 0.06662 \text{ mol H} \times \dfrac{1.008 \text{ g H}}{\text{mol H}}$ $= 0.06715 \text{ g H}$ $\text{Mass O} = 0.8233 \text{ g}$ $\quad - (0.6673 \text{ g} + 0.06715 \text{ g})$ $\quad = 0.0889 \text{ g}$ $\text{Mol O} = 0.0889 \text{ g O} \times \dfrac{\text{mol O}}{16.00 \text{ g O}}$ $= 0.00556 \text{ mol O}$
5. Write down a pseudoformula for the compound using the number of moles of each element (from steps 3 and 4) as subscripts.	$C_{0.0416}H_{0.100}$	$C_{0.05556}H_{0.06662}O_{0.00556}$
6. Divide all the subscripts in the formula by the smallest subscript. (Round all subscripts that are within 0.1 of a whole number.)	$C_{\frac{0.0416}{0.0416}} H_{\frac{0.100}{0.0416}} \longrightarrow C_1H_{2.4}$	$C_{\frac{0.05556}{0.00556}} H_{\frac{0.06662}{0.00556}} O_{\frac{0.00556}{0.00556}} \longrightarrow C_{10}H_{12}O_1$
7. If the subscripts are not whole numbers, multiply all the subscripts by a small whole number to get whole-number subscripts.	$C_1H_{2.4} \times 5 \longrightarrow C_5H_{12}$ The correct empirical formula is C_5H_{12}.	The subscripts are whole numbers; no additional multiplication is needed. The correct empirical formula is $C_{10}H_{12}O$.
	FOR PRACTICE 3.19 Upon combustion, a compound containing only carbon and hydrogen produced 1.60 g CO_2 and 0.819 g H_2O. Find the empirical formula of the compound.	**FOR PRACTICE 3.20** Upon combustion, a 0.8009-g sample of a compound containing only carbon, hydrogen, and oxygen produced 1.6004 g CO_2 and 0.6551 g H_2O. Find the empirical formula of the compound.

3.10 Writing and Balancing Chemical Equations

Combustion analysis (which we just examined) employs a **chemical reaction**, a process in which one or more substances are converted into one or more different ones. Compounds form and change through chemical reactions. As we have seen, water can be made by the reaction of hydrogen with oxygen. A **combustion reaction** is a particular type of chemical reaction in which a substance combines with oxygen to form one or more oxygen-containing compounds. Combustion reactions also emit heat. The heat produced in a number of combustion reactions is critical to supplying our society's energy needs. For example, the heat from the combustion of gasoline expands the gaseous combustion

products in a car engine's cylinders, which push the pistons and propel the car. We use the heat released by the combustion of *natural gas* to cook food and to heat our homes.

A chemical reaction is represented by a **chemical equation**. The combustion of natural gas is represented by the following equation:

$$\underset{\text{reactants}}{CH_4 + O_2} \longrightarrow \underset{\text{products}}{CO_2 + H_2O}$$

The substances on the left side of the equation are called the **reactants** and the substances on the right side are called the **products**. We often specify the states of each reactant or product in parentheses next to the formula as follows:

$$CH_4(g) + O_2(g) \longrightarrow CO_2(g) + H_2O(g)$$

The (*g*) indicates that these substances are gases in the reaction. The common states of reactants and products and their symbols used in chemical equations are summarized in Table 3.6.

The equation just presented for the combustion of natural gas is not complete, however. If we look closely, we can see that the left side of the equation has two oxygen atoms while the right side has three.

$$CH_4(g) + O_2(g) \longrightarrow CO_2(g) + H_2O(g)$$

2 O atoms   **2 O atoms + 1 O atom = 3 O atoms**

The reaction as written, therefore, violates the law of conservation of mass because an oxygen atom formed out of nothing. Notice also that the left side has four hydrogen atoms while the right side has only two.

$$CH_4(g) + O_2(g) \longrightarrow CO_2(g) + H_2O(g)$$

4 H atoms   **2 H atoms**

Two hydrogen atoms have vanished, again violating mass conservation. To correct these problems—that is, to write an equation that more closely represents *what actually happens*—we must **balance** the equation. We need to change the coefficients (those numbers *in front of* the chemical formulas), not the subscripts (those numbers within the chemical formulas), to ensure that the number of each type of atom on the left side of the equation is equal to the number on the right side. New atoms do not form during a reaction, nor do atoms vanish—matter must be conserved.

When we add coefficients to the reactants and products to balance an equation, we change the number of molecules in the equation but not the *kind of* molecules. To balance the equation for the combustion of methane, we put the coefficient 2 before O_2 in the reactants, and the coefficient 2 before H_2O in the products.

$$CH_4(g) + 2 O_2(g) \longrightarrow CO_2(g) + 2 H_2O(g)$$

The equation is now balanced because the numbers of each type of atom on either side of the equation are equal. The balanced equation tells us that one CH_4 molecule reacts with 2 O_2 molecules to form 1 CO_2 molecule and 2 H_2O molecules. We verify that the

TABLE 3.6 States of Reactants and Products in Chemical Equations

Abbreviation	State
(*g*)	Gas
(*l*)	Liquid
(*s*)	Solid
(*aq*)	Aqueous (water solution)

The reason that you cannot change the subscripts when balancing a chemical equation is that changing the subscripts changes the substance itself, while changing the coefficients changes the number of molecules of the substance. For example, 2 H_2O is simply two water molecules, but H_2O_2 is hydrogen peroxide, a drastically different compound.

equation is balanced by summing the number of each type of atom on each side of the equation.

$$CH_4(g) + 2\,O_2(g) \longrightarrow CO_2(g) + 2\,H_2O(g)$$

Reactants	Products
1 C atom (1 × $\underline{C}H_4$)	1 C atom (1 × $\underline{C}O_2$)
4 H atoms (1 × $C\underline{H}_4$)	4 H atoms (2 × $\underline{H}_2O$)
4 O atoms (2 × $\underline{O}_2$)	4 O atoms (1 × $C\underline{O}_2$ + 2 × $H_2\underline{O}$)

The number of each type of atom on both sides of the equation is now equal—the equation is balanced.

How to Write Balanced Chemical Equations

We can balance many chemical equations simply by trial and error. However, some guidelines are useful. For example, balancing the atoms in the most complex substances first and the atoms in the simplest substances (such as pure elements) last often makes the process shorter. The following illustrations of how to balance chemical equations are presented in a three-column format. The general guidelines are shown on the left, with two examples of how to apply them on the right. This procedure is meant only as a flexible guide, not a rigid set of steps.

PROCEDURE FOR... **Balancing Chemical Equations**	EXAMPLE 3.21 **Balancing Chemical Equations** Write a balanced equation for the reaction between solid cobalt(III) oxide and solid carbon to produce solid cobalt and carbon dioxide gas.	EXAMPLE 3.22 **Balancing Chemical Equations** Write a balanced equation for the combustion of gaseous butane (C_4H_{10}), a fuel used in portable stoves and grills, in which it combines with gaseous oxygen to form gaseous carbon dioxide and gaseous water.
1. Write a skeletal equation by writing chemical formulas for each of the reactants and products. Review Sections 3.5 and 3.6 for nomenclature rules. (If a skeletal equation is provided, go to step 2.)	$Co_2O_3(s) + C(s) \longrightarrow Co(s) + CO_2(g)$	$C_4H_{10}(g) + O_2(g) \longrightarrow CO_2(g) + H_2O(g)$
2. Balance atoms that occur in more complex substances first. Always balance atoms in compounds before atoms in pure elements.	**Begin with O:** $Co_2O_3(s) + C(s) \longrightarrow Co(s) + CO_2(g)$ 3 O atoms → 2 O atoms To balance O, put a 2 before $Co_2O_3(s)$ and a 3 before $CO_2(g)$. $\textbf{2}\,Co_2O_3(s) + C(s) \longrightarrow Co(s) + \textbf{3}\,CO_2(g)$ 6 O atoms → 6 O atoms	**Begin with C:** $C_4H_{10}(g) + O_2(g) \longrightarrow CO_2(g) + H_2O(g)$ 4 C atoms → 1 C atom To balance C, put a 4 before $CO_2(g)$. $C_4H_{10}(g) + O_2(g) \longrightarrow \textbf{4}\,CO_2(g) + H_2O(g)$ 4 C atoms → 4 C atoms **Balance H:** $C_4H_{10}(g) + O_2(g) \longrightarrow 4\,CO_2(g) + H_2O(g)$ 10 H atoms → 2 H atoms To balance H, put a 5 before $H_2O(g)$: $C_4H_{10}(g) + O_2(g) \longrightarrow 4\,CO_2(g) + \textbf{5}\,H_2O(g)$ 10 H atoms → 10 H atoms

3. Balance atoms that occur as free elements on either side of the equation last. Always balance free elements by adjusting the coefficient on the free element.

Balance Co:

$$2 \, Co_2O_3(s) + C(s) \longrightarrow$$
$$Co(s) + 3 \, CO_2(g)$$

4 Co atoms → 1 Co atom

To balance Co, put a 4 before Co(s).

$$2 \, Co_2O_3(s) + C(s) \longrightarrow$$
$$\mathbf{4} \, Co(s) + 3 \, CO_2(g)$$

4 Co atoms → 4 Co atoms

Balance C:

$$2 \, Co_2O_3(s) + C(s) \longrightarrow$$
$$4 \, Co(s) + 3 \, CO_2(g)$$

1 C atom → 3 C atoms

To balance C, put a 3 before C(s).

$$2 \, Co_2O_3(s) + \mathbf{3} \, C(s) \longrightarrow$$
$$4 \, Co(s) + 3 \, CO_2(g)$$

Balance O:

$$C_4H_{10}(g) + O_2(g) \longrightarrow$$
$$4 \, CO_2(g) + 5 \, H_2O(g)$$

2 O atoms → 8 O + 5 O = 13 O atoms

To balance O, put a 13/2 before $O_2(g)$:

$$C_4H_{10}(g) + \mathbf{13/2} \, O_2(g) \longrightarrow$$
$$4 \, CO_2(g) + 5 \, H_2O(g)$$

13 O atoms → 13 O atoms

---

4. If the balanced equation contains coefficient fractions, clear these by multiplying the entire equation by the denominator of the fraction.

This step is not necessary in this example. Proceed to step 5.

$$[C_4H_{10}(g) + 13/2 \, O_2(g) \longrightarrow$$
$$4 \, CO_2(g) + 5 \, H_2O(g)] \times 2$$

$$2 \, C_4H_{10}(g) + 13 \, O_2(g) \longrightarrow$$
$$8 \, CO_2(g) + 10 \, H_2O(g)$$

---

5. Check to make certain the equation is balanced by summing the total number of each type of atom on both sides of the equation.

$$2 \, Co_2O_3(s) + 3 \, C(s) \longrightarrow$$
$$4 \, Co(s) + 3 \, CO_2(g)$$

Left	Right
4 Co atoms	4 Co atoms
6 O atoms	6 O atoms
3 C atoms	3 C atoms

The equation is balanced.

$$2 \, C_4H_{10}(g) + 13 \, O_2(g) \longrightarrow$$
$$8 \, CO_2(g) + 10 \, H_2O(g)$$

Left	Right
8 C atoms	8 C atoms
20 H atoms	20 H atoms
26 O atoms	26 O atoms

The equation is balanced.

FOR PRACTICE 3.21

Write a balanced equation for the reaction between solid silicon dioxide and solid carbon to produce solid silicon carbide and carbon monoxide gas.

FOR PRACTICE 3.22

Write a balanced equation for the combustion of gaseous ethane (C_2H_6), a minority component of natural gas, in which it combines with gaseous oxygen to form gaseous carbon dioxide and gaseous water.

 Conceptual Connection 3.8 Balanced Chemical Equations

Which quantity must always be the same on both sides of a chemical equation?

(a) the number of atoms of each kind

(b) the number of molecules of each kind

(c) the number of moles of each kind of molecule

(d) the sum of the masses of all substances involved

ANSWER: Both **(a)** and **(d)** are correct. When the number of atoms of each type is balanced, the sum of the masses of the substances involved will be the same on both sides of the equation. Since molecules change during a chemical reaction, their number is not the same on both sides, nor is the number of moles necessarily the same.

3.11 Organic Compounds

Early chemists divided compounds into two types: organic and inorganic. They designated organic compounds as those that originate from living things. Sugar—from sugarcane or the sugar beet—is a common example of an organic compound. Inorganic compounds, on the other hand, originate from the Earth. Salt—mined from the ground or from the ocean—is a common example of an inorganic compound.

Not only did early chemists view organic and inorganic compounds as different in their origin, they also recognized them to be different in their properties. Organic compounds are easily decomposed. Inorganic compounds, however, are typically more difficult to decompose. Eighteenth-century chemists could synthesize inorganic compounds in the laboratory, but not organic compounds so this was considered another great difference between the two different types of compounds. Today, chemists can synthesize both organic and inorganic compounds, and even though organic chemistry is a subfield of chemistry, the differences between organic and inorganic compounds are now viewed as primarily organizational (not fundamental).

Organic compounds are common in everyday substances. Many smells—such as those in perfumes, spices, and foods—are caused by organic compounds. When you sprinkle cinnamon onto your French toast, some cinnamaldehyde—an organic compound present in cinnamon—evaporates into the air. As you inhale some of the cinnamaldehyde molecules, you experience the unique smell of cinnamon. Organic compounds are the major components of living organisms. They are also the main components of most of our fuels, such as gasoline, oil, and natural gas, and they are the active ingredients in most pharmaceuticals, such as aspirin and ibuprofen.

Organic compounds are composed of carbon and hydrogen and a few other elements, including nitrogen, oxygen, and sulfur. The key element in organic chemistry, however, is carbon. In its compounds, carbon always forms four bonds. The simplest organic compound is methane or CH_4.

The chemistry of carbon is unique and complex because carbon frequently bonds to itself to form chain, branched, and ring structures:

▲ The organic compound cinnamaldehyde is largely responsible for the taste and smell of cinnamon.

Structural formula   Space-filling model

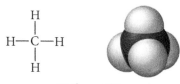

Methane, CH_4

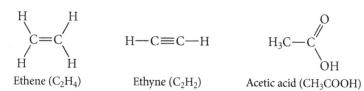

Propane (C_3H_8)   Isobutane (C_4H_{10})   Cyclohexane (C_6H_{12})

Carbon can also form double bonds and triple bonds with itself and with other elements.

Ethene (C_2H_4)   Ethyne (C_2H_2)   Acetic acid (CH_3COOH)

This versatility allows carbon to act as the backbone of millions of different chemical compounds, which is why a general survey of organic chemistry is a yearlong course.

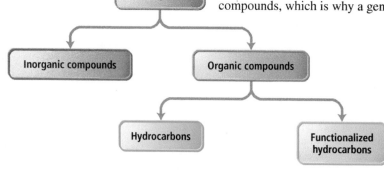

Hydrocarbons

We can begin to scratch the surface of organic chemistry by categorizing organic compounds into types: hydrocarbons and functionalized hydrocarbons.

Hydrocarbons are organic compounds that contain only carbon and hydrogen. Hydrocarbons compose common fuels such as oil, gasoline, liquid propane gas, and natural gas.

Hydrocarbons containing only single bonds are called **alkanes**, while those containing double or triple bonds are called **alkenes** and **alkynes**, respectively. The names of simple, straight-chain hydrocarbons consist of a base name, which is determined by the number of carbon atoms in the chain, and a suffix, determined by whether the hydrocarbon is an alkane (*-ane*), alkene (*-ene*), or alkyne (*-yne*).

| Base name determined by number of C atoms | Suffix determined by presence of multiple bonds |

The base names for a number of hydrocarbons are listed here:

1	meth	2	eth
3	prop	4	but
5	pent	6	hex
7	hept	8	oct
9	non	10	dec

Table 3.7 lists some common hydrocarbons, their names, and their uses.

▲ Gasoline is composed mostly of hydrocarbons.

TABLE 3.7 Common Hydrocarbons

Name	Molecular Formula	Structural Formula	Space-filling Model	Common Uses
Methane	CH_4			Primary component of natural gas
Propane	C_3H_8			LP gas for grills and outdoor stoves
n-Butane*	C_4H_{10}			Common fuel for lighters
n-Pentane*	C_5H_{12}			Component of gasoline
Ethene	C_2H_4			Ripening agent in fruit
Ethyne	C_2H_2			Fuel for welding torches

*The "*n*" in the names of these hydrocarbons stands for normal, which means straight chain.

Functionalized Hydrocarbons

The term *functional group* derives from the functionality or chemical character that a specific atom or group of atoms imparts to an organic compound. Even a carbon–carbon double bond can justifiably be called a "functional group."

Functionalized hydrocarbons can be thought of as hydrocarbons in which a **functional group**—a characteristic atom or group of atoms—is incorporated into the hydrocarbon. For example, **alcohols** are organic compounds that have an –OH functional group. We designate the hydrocarbon portion of the molecule as "R," so the general formula for an alcohol can be written R—OH. Some examples of alcohols include methanol (also known as methyl alcohol or wood alcohol) and isopropanol (also known as isopropyl alcohol or rubbing alcohol):

Hydrocarbon (R) group ⟶ CH_3OH ⟵ OH functional group

Methanol

Hydrocarbon (R) group ⟶ $CH_3\overset{\overset{\displaystyle CH_3}{|}}{CH}OH$ ⟵ OH functional group

Isopropanol
(2-propanol)

A group of organic compounds with the same functional group forms a **family**. Methanol and isopropyl alcohol are both members of the alcohol family of compounds.

The addition of a functional group to a hydrocarbon usually alters the properties of the compound significantly. Take *methanol*—which can be thought of as methane with an –OH group substituted for one of the hydrogen atoms—it is a liquid at room temperature, while *methane* is a gas. While each member of a family is unique, the common functional group bestows some chemical similarities on members of the same family. The names of functional groups have suffixes or endings unique to that functional group. Alcohols, for example, always have names that end in *-ol*. Table 3.8 provides examples of some common functional groups, their general formulas, and their characteristic suffixes or endings.

▲ Rubbing alcohol is isopropyl alcohol.

TABLE 3.8 Families of Organic Compounds

Family	Name Ending	General Formula	Example	Name	Occurrence/Use
Alcohols	-ol	R—OH	CH_3CH_2—OH	Ethanol (ethyl alcohol)	Alcohol in fermented beverages
Ethers	ether	R—O—R′	CH_3H_2C—O—CH_2CH_3	Diethyl ether	Anesthetic; laboratory solvent
Aldehydes	-al	$R-\overset{\overset{\displaystyle O}{\|}}{C}-H$	$H_3C-\overset{\overset{\displaystyle O}{\|}}{C}-H$	Ethanal (acetaldehyde)	Perfumes; flavors
Ketones	-one	$R-\overset{\overset{\displaystyle O}{\|}}{C}-R'$	$H_3C-\overset{\overset{\displaystyle O}{\|}}{C}-CH_3$	Propanone (acetone)	Fingernail polish remover
Carboxylic acids	acid	$R-\overset{\overset{\displaystyle O}{\|}}{C}-OH$	$H_3C-\overset{\overset{\displaystyle O}{\|}}{C}-OH$	Acetic acid	Vinegar
Esters	-ate	$R-\overset{\overset{\displaystyle O}{\|}}{C}-OR'$	$H_3C-\overset{\overset{\displaystyle O}{\|}}{C}-OCH_3$	Methyl acetate	Laboratory solvent
Amines	amine	RNH_2	$CH_3H_2C-\overset{\overset{\displaystyle H}{\|}}{N}-H$	Ethyl amine	Smell of rotten fish

CHAPTER IN REVIEW

Key Terms

Section 3.2
ionic bond (81)
covalent bond (81)

Section 3.3
chemical formula (82)
empirical formula (82)
molecular formula (82)
structural formula (82)
ball-and-stick model (83)
space-filling molecular model (83)

Section 3.4
atomic element (84)
molecular element (85)

molecular compound (85)
ionic compound (86)
formula unit (86)
polyatomic ion (86)

Section 3.5
common name (88)
systematic name (88)
binary compound (89)
oxyanion (92)
hydrate (92)

Section 3.6
acid (94)
binary acid (95)
oxyacid (95)

Section 3.7
formula mass (97)

Section 3.8
mass percent composition (mass percent) (100)

Section 3.9
empirical formula molar mass (107)
combustion analysis (109)

Section 3.10
chemical reaction (110)
combustion reaction (110)
chemical equation (111)

reactants (111)
products (111)
balanced chemical equation (111)

Section 3.11
organic compound (114)
hydrocarbon (114)
alkane (115)
alkene (115)
alkyne (115)
functional group (116)
alcohol (116)
family (116)

Key Concepts

Chemical Bonds (3.2)

Chemical bonds, the forces that hold atoms together in compounds, arise from the interactions between nuclei and electrons in atoms. In an ionic bond, one or more electrons are *transferred* from one atom to another, forming a cation (positively charged) and an anion (negatively charged). The two ions are then drawn together by the attraction between the opposite charges. In a covalent bond, one or more electrons are *shared* between two atoms. The atoms are held together by the attraction between their nuclei and the shared electrons.

Representing Molecules and Compounds (3.3, 3.4)

A compound is represented with a chemical formula, which indicates the elements present and the number of atoms of each. An empirical formula gives only the *relative* number of atoms, while a molecular formula gives the *actual* number of atoms present in the molecule. Structural formulas show how the atoms are bonded together, while molecular models portray the geometry of the molecule.

Compounds can be divided into two types: molecular compounds, formed between two or more covalently bonded nonmetals; and ionic compounds, usually formed between a metal ionically bonded to one or more nonmetals. The smallest identifiable unit of a molecular compound is a molecule, and the smallest identifiable unit of an ionic compound is a formula unit: the smallest electrically neutral collection of ions. Elements can also be divided into two types: molecular elements, which occur as (mostly diatomic) molecules; and atomic elements, which occur as individual atoms.

Naming Inorganic Ionic and Molecular Compounds and Acids (3.5, 3.6)

A flowchart for naming simple inorganic compounds is shown at the end of this section. Refer to this chart when naming inorganic compounds.

Formula Mass and Mole Concept for Compounds (3.7)

The formula mass of a compound is the sum of the atomic masses of all the atoms in the chemical formula. Like the atomic masses of elements, the formula mass characterizes the average mass of a molecule (or a formula unit). The mass of one mole of a compound is called the molar mass and equals its formula mass (in grams).

Chemical Composition (3.8, 3.9)

The mass percent composition of a compound indicates each element's percentage of the total compound's mass. The mass percent composition can be obtained from the compound's chemical formula and the molar masses of its elements. The chemical formula of a compound provides the relative number of atoms (or moles) of each element in a compound, and can therefore be used to determine numerical relationships between moles of the compound and moles of its constituent elements. This relationship can be extended to mass by using the molar masses of the compound and its constituent elements. The calculation can also go the other way—if the mass percent composition and molar mass of a compound are known, its empirical and molecular formulas can be determined.

Writing and Balancing Chemical Equations (3.10)

In chemistry, we represent chemical reactions with chemical equations. The substances on the left hand side of a chemical equation are called the reactants and the substances on the right hand side are called the products. Chemical equations are balanced when the number of each type of atom on the left side of the equation is equal to the number on the right side.

Organic Compounds (3.11)

Organic compounds are composed of carbon, hydrogen, and a few other elements such as nitrogen, oxygen, and sulfur. The simplest organic compounds are hydrocarbons, compounds composed of only carbon and hydrogen. Hydrocarbons can be divided into three types based on the bonds they contain: alkanes contain single bonds, alkenes contain double bonds, and alkynes contain triple bonds. All other organic compounds can be thought of as hydrocarbons with one or more functional groups, characteristic atoms or groups of atoms. Common functionalized hydrocarbons include alcohols, ethers, aldehydes, ketones, carboxylic acids, esters, and amines.

Key Equations and Relationships

Formula Mass (3.7)

$$\left(\begin{array}{c} \text{\# atoms of 1st element} \\ \text{in chemical formula} \end{array} \times \begin{array}{c} \text{atomic mass} \\ \text{of 1st element} \end{array} \right) + \left(\begin{array}{c} \text{\# atoms of 2nd element} \\ \text{in chemical formula} \end{array} \times \begin{array}{c} \text{atomic mass} \\ \text{of 2nd element} \end{array} \right) + \cdots$$

Mass Percent Composition (3.8)

$$\text{Mass \% of element X} = \frac{\text{mass of X in 1 mol compound}}{\text{mass of 1 mol compound}} \times 100\%$$

Empirical Formula Molar Mass (3.9)

$$\text{Molecular formula} = n \times (\text{empirical formula})$$

$$n = \frac{\text{molar mass}}{\text{empirical formula molar mass}}$$

Inorganic Nomenclature Summary Chart

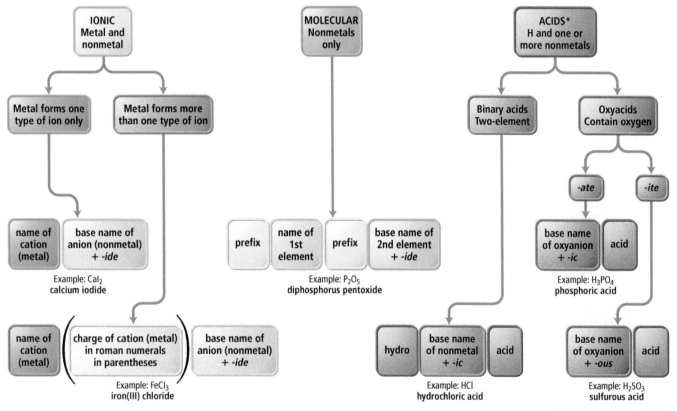

*Acids must be in aqueous solution.

Using the Flowchart

The examples below show how to name compounds using the flowchart. The path through the flowchart is shown below each compound followed by the correct name for the compound.

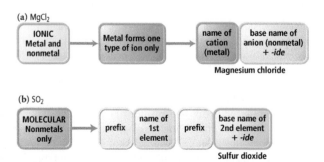

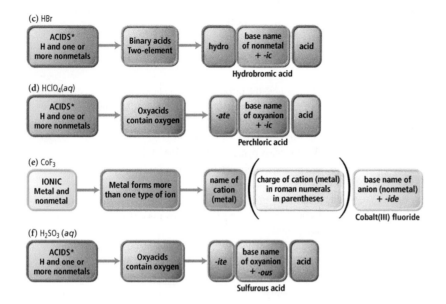

(c) HBr — Hydrobromic acid

(d) HClO₄(aq) — Perchloric acid

(e) CoF₃ — Cobalt(III) fluoride

(f) H₂SO₃ (aq) — Sulfurous acid

Key Skills

Writing Molecular and Empirical Formulas (3.3)
- Example 3.1 • For Practice 3.1 • Exercises 4, 23–26

Classifying Substances as Atomic Elements, Molecular Elements, Molecular Compounds, or Ionic Compounds (3.4)
- Example 3.2 • For Practice 3.2 • Exercises 27–32

Writing Formulas for Ionic Compounds (3.5)
- Examples 3.3, 3.4 • For Practice 3.3, 3.4 • Exercises 33–36, 43, 44

Naming Ionic Compounds (3.5)
- Examples 3.5, 3.6 • For Practice 3.5, 3.6 • For More Practice 3.5, 3.6 • Exercises 37–40

Naming Ionic Compounds Containing Polyatomic Ions (3.5)
- Example 3.7 • For Practice 3.7 • For More Practice 3.7 • Exercises 41–44

Naming Molecular Compounds (3.6)
- Example 3.8 • For Practice 3.8 • For More Practice 3.8 • Exercises 47–50

Naming Acids (3.6)
- Examples 3.9, 3.10 • For Practice 3.9, 3.10 • For More Practice 3.10 • Exercises 51–54

Calculating Formula Mass (3.7)
- Example 3.11 • For Practice 3.11 • Exercises 55, 56

Using Formula Mass to Count Molecules by Weighing (3.7)
- Example 3.12 • For Practice 3.12 • For More Practice 3.12 • Exercises 59–64

Calculating Mass Percent Composition (3.8)
- Example 3.13 • For Practice 3.13 • For More Practice 3.13 • Exercises 65–70

Using Mass Percent Composition as a Conversion Factor (3.8)
- Example 3.14 • For Practice 3.14 • For More Practice 3.14 • Exercises 71, 72

Using Chemical Formulas as Conversion Factors (3.8)
- Example 3.15 • For Practice 3.15 • For More Practice 3.15 • Exercises 77, 78

Obtaining an Empirical Formula from Experimental Data (3.9)
- Examples 3.16, 3.17 • For Practice 3.16, 3.17 • Exercises 79–86

Calculating a Molecular Formula from an Empirical Formula and Molar Mass (3.9)
- Example 3.18 • For Practice 3.18 • For More Practice 3.18 • Exercises 87–88

Obtaining an Empirical Formula from Combustion Analysis (3.9)
- Examples 3.19, 3.20 • For Practice 3.19, 3.20 • Exercises 89–92

Balancing Chemical Equations (3.10)
- Examples 3.21, 3.22 • For Practice 3.21, 3.22 • Exercises 93–102

EXERCISES

Review Questions

1. How do the properties of compounds compare to the properties of the elements from which they are composed?

2. What is a chemical bond? Explain the difference between an ionic bond and a covalent bond.

3. Explain the different ways to represent compounds. Why are there so many?

4. What is the difference between an empirical formula and a molecular formula?

5. Define and provide an example for each of the following: atomic element, molecular element, ionic compound, molecular compound.

6. Explain how to write a formula for an ionic compound given the names of the metal and nonmetal (or polyatomic ion) in the compound.

7. Explain how to name binary ionic compounds. How do you name an ionic compound if it contains a polyatomic ion?

8. Why do the names of some ionic compounds include the charge of the metal ion while others do not?

9. Explain how to name molecular inorganic compounds.

10. How many atoms are specified by these prefixes: mono, di, tri, tetra, penta, hexa?

11. Explain how to name binary and oxy acids.

12. What is the formula mass for a compound? Why is it useful?

13. Explain how the information in a chemical formula can be used to determine how much of a particular element is present in a given amount of a compound. Give some examples demonstrating why this might be important.

14. What is mass percent composition? Why is it useful?

15. What kinds of conversion factors are inherent in chemical formulas? Give an example.

16. What kind of chemical formula can be obtained from experimental data showing the relative masses of the elements in a compound?

17. How can a molecular formula be obtained from an empirical formula? What additional information is required?

18. What is combustion analysis? What is it used for?

19. What elements are normally present in organic compounds?

20. What is the difference between an alkane, an alkene, and an alkyne?

21. What are functionalized hydrocarbons? Give an example of a functionalized hydrocarbon.

22. Write a generic formula for each of the families of organic compounds.
   a. alcohols   b. ethers
   c. aldehydes   d. ketones
   e. carboxylic acids   f. esters
   g. amines

Problems by Topic

Note: Answers to all odd-numbered Problems, numbered in blue, can be found in Appendix III. Exercises in the Problems by Topic section are paired, with each odd-numbered problem followed by a similar even-numbered problem. Exercises in the Cumulative Problems section are also paired, but somewhat more loosely. (Challenge Problems and Conceptual Problems, because of their nature, are unpaired.)

Chemical Formulas and Molecular View of Elements and Compounds

23. Determine the number of each type of atom in each formula:
   a. $Mg_3(PO_4)_2$ b. $BaCl_2$
   c. $Fe(NO_2)_2$ d. $Ca(OH)_2$

24. Determine the number of each type of atom in each formula:
   a. $Ca(NO_2)_2$ b. $CuSO_4$
   c. $Al(NO_3)_3$ d. $Mg(HCO_3)_2$

25. Write a chemical formula for each molecular model. (See Appendix IIA for color codes.)

   (a)   (b)   (c)

26. Write a chemical formula for each molecular model. (See Appendix IIA for color codes.)

   (a)   (b)   (c)

27. Classify each element as atomic or molecular.
   a. neon   b. fluorine
   c. potassium   d. nitrogen

28. Determine whether or not each element has molecules as its basic units.
   a. hydrogen   b. iodine
   c. lead   d. oxygen

29. Classify each compound as ionic or molecular.
   a. CO_2 b. $NiCl_2$ c. NaI d. PCl_3

30. Classify each compound as ionic or molecular.
   a. CF_2Cl_2 b. CCl_4 c. PtO_2 d. SO_3

31. Based on the molecular views, classify each substance as an atomic element, a molecular element, an ionic compound, or a molecular compound.

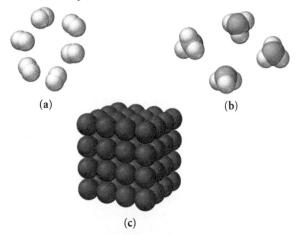

   (a)   (b)

   (c)

32. Based on the molecular views, classify each substance as an atomic element, a molecular element, an ionic compound, or a molecular compound.

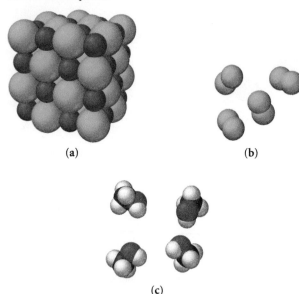

(a) (b)

(c)

Formulas and Names for Ionic Compounds

33. Write a formula for the ionic compound that forms between each pair of elements.
 a. calcium and oxygen **b.** zinc and sulfur
 c. rubidium and bromine **d.** aluminum and oxygen

34. Write a formula for the ionic compound that forms between each pair of elements.
 a. silver and chlorine **b.** sodium and sulfur
 c. aluminum and sulfur **d.** potassium and chlorine

35. Write a formula for the compound that forms between calcium and each polyatomic ion:
 a. hydroxide **b.** chromate
 c. phosphate **d.** cyanide

36. Write a formula for the compound that forms between potassium and each polyatomic ion:
 a. carbonate **b.** phosphate
 c. hydrogen phosphate **d.** acetate

37. Name each ionic compound.
 a. Mg_3N_2 **b.** KF **c.** Na_2O **d.** Li_2S
 e. CsF **f.** KI **g.** $SrCl_2$ **h.** $BaCl_2$

38. Name each ionic compound.
 a. $SnCl_4$ **b.** PbI_2 **c.** Fe_2O_3 **d.** CuI_2
 e. SnO_2 **f.** $HgBr_2$ **g.** $CrCl_2$ **h.** $CrCl_3$

39. Give each ionic compound an appropriate name.
 a. SnO **b.** Cr_2S_3 **c.** RbI **d.** $BaBr_2$

40. Give each ionic compound an appropriate name.
 a. BaS **b.** $FeCl_3$ **c.** PbI_4 **d.** $SrBr_2$

41. Name each ionic compound containing a polyatomic ion.
 a. $CuNO_2$ **b.** $Mg(C_2H_3O_2)_2$ **c.** $Ba(NO_3)_2$
 d. $Pb(C_2H_3O_2)_2$ **e.** $KClO_3$ **f.** $PbSO_4$

42. Name each ionic compound containing a polyatomic ion.
 a. $Ba(OH)_2$ **b.** NH_4I **c.** $NaBrO_4$
 d. $Fe(OH)_3$ **e.** $CoSO_4$ **f.** KClO

43. Write a formula for each ionic compound:
 a. sodium hydrogen sulfite
 b. lithium permanganate
 c. silver nitrate
 d. potassium sulfate

e. rubidium hydrogen sulfate
 f. potassium hydrogen carbonate

44. Write a formula for each ionic compound:
 a. copper(II) chloride **b.** copper(I) iodide
 c. lead(II) chromate **d.** calcium fluoride
 e. potassium hydroxide **f.** iron(II) phosphate

45. Give the name from the formula or the formula from the name for each hydrated ionic compound:
 a. $CoSO_4 \cdot 7H_2O$
 b. iridium(III) bromide tetrahydrate
 c. $Mg(BrO_3)_2 \cdot 6H_2O$
 d. potassium carbonate dihydrate

46. Give the name from the formula or the formula from the name for each hydrated ionic compound:
 a. cobalt(II) phosphate octahydrate
 b. $BeCl_2 \cdot 2H_2O$
 c. chromium(III) phosphate trihydrate
 d. $LiNO_2 \cdot H_2O$

Formulas and Names for Molecular Compounds and Acids

47. Name each molecular compound.
 a. CO **b.** NI_3 **c.** $SiCl_4$
 d. N_4Se_4 **e.** I_2O_5

48. Name each molecular compound.
 a. SO_3 **b.** SO_2 **c.** BrF_5
 d. NO **e.** XeO_3

49. Write a formula for each molecular compound.
 a. phosphorus trichloride **b.** chlorine monoxide
 c. disulfur tetrafluoride **d.** phosphorus pentafluoride
 e. diphosphorus pentasulfide

50. Write a formula for each molecular compound.
 a. boron tribromide **b.** dichlorine monoxide
 c. xenon tetrafluoride **d.** carbon tetrabromide
 e. diboron tetrachloride

51. Name each acid.
 a. HI **b.** HNO_3 **c.** H_2CO_3 **d.** $HC_2H_3O_2$

52. Name each acid.
 a. HCl **b.** $HClO_2$ **c.** H_2SO_4 **d.** HNO_2

53. Write formulas for each acid.
 a. hydrofluoric acid **b.** hydrobromic acid
 c. sulfurous acid

54. Write formulas for each acid.
 a. phosphoric acid **b.** hydrocyanic acid
 c. chlorous acid

Formula Mass and the Mole Concept for Compounds

55. Calculate the formula mass for each compound.
 a. NO_2 **b.** C_4H_{10} **c.** $C_6H_{12}O_6$ **d.** $Cr(NO_3)_3$

56. Calculate the formula mass for each compound.
 a. $MgBr_2$ **b.** HNO_2 **c.** CBr_4 **d.** $Ca(NO_3)_2$

57. How many moles (of molecules or formula units) are in each sample?
 a. 25.5 g NO_2 **b.** 1.25 kg CO_2
 c. 38.2 g KNO_3 **d.** 155.2 kg Na_2SO_4

58. How many moles (of molecules or formula units) are in each sample?
 a. 55.98 g CF_2Cl_2 **b.** 23.6 kg $Fe(NO_3)_2$
 c. 0.1187 g C_8H_{18} **d.** 195 kg CaO

59. How many molecules are in each sample?
 a. 6.5 g H_2O **b.** 389 g CBr_4
 c. 22.1 g O_2 **d.** 19.3 g C_8H_{10}

60. How many molecules (or formula units) are in each sample?
  a. 85.26 g CCl_4
  b. 55.93 kg $NaHCO_3$
  c. 119.78 g C_4H_{10}
  d. 4.59×10^5 g Na_3PO_4

61. Calculate the mass (in g) of each sample.
  a. 5.94×10^{20} SO_3 molecules
  b. 2.8×10^{22} H_2O molecules
  c. 1 glucose molecule ($C_6H_{12}O_6$)

62. Calculate the mass (in g) of each sample.
  a. 4.5×10^{25} O_3 molecules
  b. 9.85×10^{19} CCl_2F_2 molecules
  c. 1 water molecule

63. A sugar crystal contains approximately 1.8×10^{17} sucrose ($C_{12}H_{22}O_{11}$) molecules. What is its mass in mg?

64. A salt crystal has a mass of 0.12 mg. How many NaCl formula units does it contain?

Composition of Compounds

65. Calculate the mass percent composition of carbon in each carbon-containing compound:
  a. CH_4 **b.** C_2H_6 **c.** C_2H_2 **d.** C_2H_5Cl

66. Calculate the mass percent composition of nitrogen in each nitrogen-containing compound:
  a. N_2O **b.** NO **c.** NO_2 **d.** HNO_3

67. Most fertilizers consist of nitrogen-containing compounds such as NH_3, $CO(NH_2)_2$, NH_4NO_3, and $(NH_4)_2SO_4$. The nitrogen content in these compounds is used for protein synthesis by plants. Calculate the mass percent composition of nitrogen in each of the fertilizers named above. Which fertilizer has the highest nitrogen content?

68. Iron from the earth is in the form of iron ore. Common ores include Fe_2O_3 (hematite), Fe_3O_4 (magnetite), and $FeCO_3$ (siderite). Calculate the mass percent composition of iron for each of these iron ores. Which ore has the highest iron content?

69. Copper(II) fluoride contains 37.42% F by mass. Calculate the mass of fluorine (in g) contained in 55.5 g of copper(II) fluoride.

70. Silver chloride, often used in silver plating, contains 75.27% Ag by mass. Calculate the mass of silver chloride required to plate 155 mg of pure silver.

71. The iodide ion is a dietary mineral essential to good nutrition. In countries where potassium iodide is added to salt, iodine deficiency (or goiter) has been almost completely eliminated. The recommended daily allowance (RDA) for iodine is 150 μg/day. How much potassium iodide (76.45% I) should you consume if you want to meet the RDA?

72. The American Dental Association recommends that an adult female should consume 3.0 mg of fluoride (F^-) per day to prevent tooth decay. If the fluoride is consumed in the form of sodium fluoride (45.24% F), what amount of sodium fluoride contains the recommended amount of fluoride?

73. Write a ratio showing the relationship between the amounts of each element for each compound:

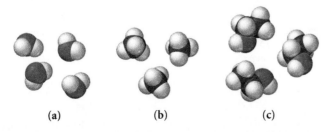

(a)   (b)   (c)

74. Write a ratio showing the relationship between the amounts of each element for each compound:

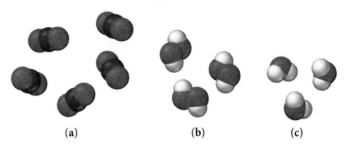

(a)   (b)   (c)

75. Determine the number of moles of hydrogen atoms in each sample:
  a. 0.0885 mol C_4H_{10} **b.** 1.3 mol CH_4
  c. 2.4 mol C_6H_{12} **d.** 1.87 mol C_8H_{18}

76. Determine the number of moles of oxygen atoms in each sample:
  a. 4.88 mol H_2O_2 **b.** 2.15 mol N_2O
  c. 0.0237 mol H_2CO_3 **d.** 24.1 mol CO_2

77. Calculate mass (in grams) of sodium in 8.5 g of each sodium-containing food additive.
  a. NaCl (table salt)
  b. Na_3PO_4 (sodium phosphate)
  c. $NaC_7H_5O_2$ (sodium benzoate)
  d. $Na_2C_6H_6O_7$ (sodium hydrogen citrate)

78. Calculate the mass (in kilograms) of chlorine in 25 kg of each chlorofluorocarbon (CFC).
  a. CF_2Cl_2 **b.** $CFCl_3$ **c.** $C_2F_3Cl_3$ **d.** CF_3Cl

Chemical Formulas from Experimental Data

79. A chemist decomposes samples of several compounds; the masses of their constituent elements are shown below. Calculate the empirical formula for each compound.
  a. 1.651 g Ag, 0.1224 g O
  b. 0.672 g Co, 0.569 g As, 0.486 g O
  c. 1.443 g Se, 5.841 g Br

80. A chemist decomposes samples of several compounds; the masses of their constituent elements are shown below. Calculate the empirical formula for each compound.
  a. 1.245 g Ni, 5.381 g I
  b. 2.677 g Ba, 3.115 g Br
  c. 2.128 g Be, 7.557 g S, 15.107 g O

81. Calculate the empirical formula for each stimulant based on its elemental mass percent composition:
  a. nicotine (found in tobacco leaves): C 74.03%, H 8.70%, N 17.27%
  b. caffeine (found in coffee beans): C 49.48%, H 5.19%, N 28.85%, O 16.48%

82. Calculate the empirical formula for each natural flavor based on its elemental mass percent composition:
  a. methyl butyrate (component of apple taste and smell): C 58.80%, H 9.87%, O 31.33%
  b. vanillin (responsible for the taste and smell of vanilla): C 63.15%, H 5.30%, O 31.55%

83. The elemental mass percent composition of ibuprofen (an aspririn substitute) is 75.69% C, 8.80% H, and 15.51% O. Determine the empirical formula of ibuprofen.

84. The elemental mass percent composition of ascorbic acid (vitamin C) is 40.92% C, 4.58% H, and 54.50% O. Determine the empirical formula of ascorbic acid.

85. A 0.77-mg sample of nitrogen reacts with chlorine to form 6.61 mg of the chloride. Determine the empirical formula of nitrogen chloride.

86. A 45.2-mg sample of phosphorus reacts with selenium to form 131.6 mg of the selenide. Determine the empirical formula of phosphorus selenide.

87. The empirical formula and molar mass of several compounds are listed below. Find the molecular formula of each compound.
a. C_6H_7N, 186.24 g/mol   **b.** C_2HCl, 181.44 g/mol
c. $C_5H_{10}NS_2$, 296.54 g/mol

88. The molar mass and empirical formula of several compounds are listed below. Find the molecular formula of each compound.
a. C_4H_9, 114.22 g/mol   **b.** CCl, 284.77 g/mol
c. C_3H_2N, 312.29 g/mol

89. Combustion analysis of a hydrocarbon produced 33.01 g CO_2 and 13.51 g H_2O. Calculate the empirical formula of the hydrocarbon.

90. Combustion analysis of naphthalene, a hydrocarbon used in mothballs, produced 8.80 g CO_2 and 1.44 g H_2O. Calculate the empirical formula for naphthalene.

91. The foul odor of rancid butter is due largely to butyric acid, a compound containing carbon, hydrogen, and oxygen. Combustion analysis of a 4.30-g sample of butyric acid produced 8.59 g CO_2 and 3.52 g H_2O. Determine the empirical formula for butyric acid.

92. Tartaric acid is the white, powdery substance that coats tart candies such as Sour Patch Kids. Combustion analysis of a 12.01-g sample of tartaric acid—which contains only carbon, hydrogen, and oxygen—produced 14.08 g CO_2 and 4.32 g H_2O. Determine the empirical formula for tartaric acid.

Writing and Balancing Chemical Equations

93. Sulfuric acid is a component of acid rain formed when gaseous sulfur dioxide pollutant reacts with gaseous oxygen and liquid water to form aqueous sulfuric acid. Write a balanced chemical equation for this reaction.

94. Nitric acid is a component of acid rain that forms when gaseous nitrogen dioxide pollutant reacts with gaseous oxygen and liquid water to form aqueous nitric acid. Write a balanced chemical equation for this reaction.

95. In a popular classroom demonstration, solid sodium is added to liquid water and reacts to produce hydrogen gas and aqueous sodium hydroxide. Write a balanced chemical equation for this reaction.

96. When iron rusts, solid iron reacts with gaseous oxygen to form solid iron(III) oxide. Write a balanced chemical equation for this reaction.

97. Write a balanced chemical equation for the fermentation of sucrose ($C_{12}H_{22}O_{11}$) by yeasts in which the aqueous sugar reacts with water to form aqueous ethyl alcohol (C_2H_5OH) and carbon dioxide gas.

98. Write a balanced equation for the photosynthesis reaction in which gaseous carbon dioxide and liquid water react in the presence of chlorophyll to produce aqueous glucose ($C_6H_{12}O_6$) and oxygen gas.

99. Write a balanced chemical equation for each reaction:
a. Solid lead(II) sulfide reacts with aqueous hydrobromic acid to form solid lead(II) bromide and dihydrogen monosulfide gas.
b. Gaseous carbon monoxide reacts with hydrogen gas to form gaseous methane (CH_4) and liquid water.
c. Aqueous hydrochloric acid reacts with solid manganese(IV) oxide to form aqueous manganese(II) chloride, liquid water, and chlorine gas.

d. Liquid pentane (C_5H_{12}) reacts with gaseous oxygen to form carbon dioxide and liquid water.

100. Write a balanced chemical equation for each reaction:
a. Solid copper reacts with solid sulfur to form solid copper(I) sulfide.
b. Solid iron(III) oxide reacts with hydrogen gas to form solid iron and liquid water.
c. Sulfur dioxide gas reacts with oxygen gas to form sulfur trioxide gas.
d. Gaseous ammonia (NH_3) reacts with gaseous oxygen to form gaseous nitrogen monoxide and gaseous water.

101. Balance each chemical equation:
a. $CO_2(g) + CaSiO_3(s) + H_2O(l) \longrightarrow$
$$SiO_2(s) + Ca(HCO_3)_2(aq)$$
b. $Co(NO_3)_3(aq) + (NH_4)_2S(aq) \longrightarrow$
$$Co_2S_3(s) + NH_4NO_3(aq)$$
c. $Cu_2O(s) + C(s) \longrightarrow Cu(s) + CO(g)$
d. $H_2(g) + Cl_2(g) \longrightarrow HCl(g)$

102. Balance each chemical equation:
a. $Na_2S(aq) + Cu(NO_3)_2(aq) \longrightarrow NaNO_3(aq) + CuS(s)$
b. $N_2H_4(l) \longrightarrow NH_3(g) + N_2(g)$
c. $HCl(aq) + O_2(g) \longrightarrow H_2O(l) + Cl_2(g)$
d. $FeS(s) + HCl(aq) \longrightarrow FeCl_2(aq) + H_2S(g)$

Organic Compounds

103. Classify each compound as organic or inorganic:
a. $CaCO_3$ **b.** C_4H_8 **c.** $C_4H_6O_6$ **d.** LiF

104. Classify each compound as organic or inorganic:
a. C_8H_{18} **b.** CH_3NH_2 **c.** CaO **d.** $FeCO_3$

105. Classify each hydrocarbon as an alkane, alkene, or alkyne:
a. $H_2C{=}CH{-}CH_3$ **b.** $H_3C{-}CH_2{-}CH_3$
c. $HC{\equiv}C{-}CH_3$ **d.** $H_3C{-}CH_2{-}CH_2{-}CH_3$

106. Classify each hydrocarbon as an alkane, alkene, or alkyne:
a. $HC{\equiv}CH$ **b.** $H_3C{-}CH{=}C{-}CH_3$

c. $H_3C{-}\underset{\underset{CH_3}{|}}{CH}{-}CH_3$ **d.** $H_3C{-}C{\equiv}C{-}CH_3$

107. Write a formula based on the name, or a name based on the formula, for each hydrocarbon:
a. propane   **b.** $CH_3CH_2CH_3$
c. octane   **d.** $CH_3CH_2CH_2CH_2CH_3$

108. Write a formula based on the name, or a name based on the formula, for each hydrocarbon:
a. CH_3CH_3 **b.** pentane
c. $CH_3CH_2CH_2CH_2CH_2CH_3$ **d.** heptane

109. Classify each organic compound as a hydrocarbon or a functionalized hydrocarbon. For functionalized hydrocarbons, identify the family to which the compound belongs.
a. $H_3C{-}CH_2OH$ **b.** $H_3C{-}CH_3$

c. $H_3C{-}\overset{\overset{O}{\|}}{C}{-}CH_2{-}CH_3$ **d.** $H_3C{-}NH_2$

110. Classify each organic compound as a hydrocarbon or a functionalized hydrocarbon. For functionalized hydrocarbons, identify the family to which the compound belongs.
a. $H_3C{-}CH_2{-}\overset{\overset{O}{\|}}{C}{-}OH$ **b.** $H_3C{-}\overset{\overset{O}{\|}}{C}H$

c. $H_3C{-}\underset{\underset{CH_3}{|}}{\overset{\overset{CH_3}{|}}{C}}{-}CH_3$ **d.** $H_3C{-}CH_2{-}O{-}CH_3$

Cumulative Problems

111. How many molecules of ethanol (C_2H_5OH) (the alcohol in alcoholic beverages) are present in 145 mL of ethanol? The density of ethanol is 0.789 g/cm^3.

112. A drop of water has a volume of approximately 0.05 mL. How many water molecules does it contain? The density of water is 1.0 g/cm^3.

113. Determine the chemical formula of each compound and then use it to calculate the mass percent composition of each constituent element:
   a. potassium chromate
   b. lead(II) phosphate
   c. sulfurous acid
   d. cobalt(II) bromide

114. Determine the chemical formula of each compound and then use it to calculate the mass percent composition of each constituent element:
   a. perchloric acid
   b. phosphorus pentachloride
   c. nitrogen triiodide
   d. carbon dioxide

115. A Freon leak in the air conditioning system of an old car releases 25 g of CF_2Cl_2 per month. What mass of chlorine is emitted into the atmosphere each year by this car?

116. A Freon leak in the air-conditioning system of a large building releases 12 kg of CHF_2Cl per month. If the leak is allowed to continue, how many kilograms of Cl will be emitted into the atmosphere each year?

117. A metal (M) forms a compound with the formula MCl_3. If the compound contains 65.57% Cl by mass, what is the identity of the metal?

118. A metal (M) forms an oxide with the formula M_2O. If the oxide contains 16.99% O by mass, what is the identity of the metal?

119. Estradiol is a female sexual hormone that causes maturation and maintenance of the female reproductive system. Elemental analysis of estradiol gives the following mass percent composition: C 79.37%, H 8.88%, O 11.75%. The molar mass of estradiol is 272.37 g/mol. Find the molecular formula of estradiol.

120. Fructose is a common sugar found in fruit. Elemental analysis of fructose gives the following mass percent composition: C 40.00%, H 6.72%, O 53.28%. The molar mass of fructose is 180.16 g/mol. Find the molecular formula of fructose.

121. Combustion analysis of a 13.42-g sample of equilin (which contains only carbon, hydrogen, and oxygen) produces 39.61 g CO_2 and 9.01 g H_2O. The molar mass of equilin is 268.34 g/mol. Find the molecular formula for equilin.

122. Estrone, which contains only carbon, hydrogen, and oxygen, is a female sexual hormone that occurs in the urine of pregnant women. Combustion analysis of a 1.893-g sample of estrone produces 5.545 g of CO_2 and 1.388 g H_2O. The molar mass of estrone is 270.36 g/mol. Find the molecular formula for estrone.

123. Epsom salts is a hydrated ionic compound with the following formula: $MgSO_4 \cdot xH_2O$. A 4.93-g sample of Epsom salts was heated to drive off the water of hydration. The mass of the sample after complete dehydration was 2.41 g. Find the number of waters of hydration (x) in Epsom salts.

124. A hydrate of copper(II) chloride has the following formula: $CuCl_2 \cdot xH_2O$. The water in a 3.41-g sample of the hydrate was driven off by heating. The remaining sample had a mass of 2.69 g. Find the number of waters of hydration (x) in the hydrate.

125. A compound of molar mass 177 g/mol contains only carbon, hydrogen, bromine, and oxygen. Analysis reveals that the compound contains 8 times as much carbon as hydrogen by mass. Find the molecular formula.

126. Researchers obtained the following data from experiments to find the molecular formula of benzocaine, a local anesthetic, which contains only carbon, hydrogen, nitrogen, and oxygen. Complete combustion of a 3.54-g sample of benzocaine with excess O_2 formed 8.49 g of CO_2 and 2.14 g H_2O. Another sample of mass 2.35 g was found to contain 0.199 g of N. The molar mass of benzocaine was found to be 165 g/mol. Find the molar formula of benzocaine.

127. Find the total number of atoms in a sample of cocaine hydrochloride, $C_{17}H_{22}ClNO_4$, of mass 23.5 mg.

128. Vanadium forms four different oxides in which the percent by mass of vanadium is respectively (a) 76%, (b) 68%, (c) 61%, and (d) 56%. Find the formula and give the name of each one of these oxides.

129. The chloride of an unknown metal is believed to have the formula MCl_3. A 2.395-g sample of the compound is found to contain 3.606×10^{-2} mol Cl. Find the atomic mass of M.

130. Write the structural formulas of three different compounds that each have the molecular formula C_5H_{12}.

131. A chromium-containing compound has the formula $Fe_xCr_yO_4$ and is 28.59% oxygen by mass. Find x and y.

132. A phosphorus compound that contains 34.00% phosphorus by mass has the formula X_3P_2. Identify the element X.

133. A particular brand of beef jerky contains 0.0552% sodium nitrite by mass and is sold in an 8.00-oz bag. What mass of sodium does the sodium nitrite contribute to sodium content of the bag of beef jerky?

134. Phosphorus is obtained primarily from ores containing calcium phosphate. If a particular ore contains 57.8% calcium phosphate, what minimum mass of the ore must be processed to obtain 1.00 kg of phosphorus?

Challenge Problems

135. A mixture of NaCl and NaBr has a mass of 2.00 g and is found to contain 0.75 g of Na. What is the mass of NaBr in the mixture?

136. Three pure compounds form when 1.00-g samples of element X combine with, respectively, 0.472 g, 0.630 g, and 0.789 g of element Z. The first compound has the formula X_2Z_3. Find the empirical formulas of the other two compounds.

137. A mixture of $CaCO_3$ and $(NH_4)_2CO_3$ is 61.9% CO_3 by mass. Find the mass percent of $CaCO_3$ in the mixture.

138. A mixture of 50.0 g of S and 1.00×10^2 g of Cl_2 reacts completely to form S_2Cl_2 and SCl_2. Find the mass of S_2Cl_2 formed.

139. Because of increasing evidence of damage to the ozone layer, chlorofluorocarbon (CFC) production was banned in 1996. However, there are about 100 million auto air conditioners that still use CFC-12 (CF_2Cl_2). These air conditioners are recharged from stockpiled supplies of CFC-12. If each of the 100 million automobiles contains 1.1 kg of CFC-12 and leaks 25% of its CFC-12 into the atmosphere per year, how much chlorine, in kg, is added to the atmosphere each year due to auto air conditioners? (Assume two significant figures in your calculations.)

140. A particular coal contains 2.55% sulfur by mass. When the coal is burned, it produces SO_2 emissions which combine with rainwater to produce sulfuric acid. Use the formula of sulfuric acid to calculate the mass percent of S in sulfuric acid. Then determine how much sulfuric acid (in metric tons) is produced by the combustion of 1.0 metric ton of this coal. (A metric ton is 1000 kg.)

141. Lead is found in Earth's crust as several different lead ores. Suppose a certain rock is 38.0% PbS (galena), 25.0% $PbCO_3$ (cerussite), and 17.4% $PbSO_4$ (anglesite). The remainder of the rock is composed of substances containing no lead. How much of this rock (in kg) must be processed to obtain 5.0 metric tons of lead? (A metric ton is 1000 kg.)

142. A 2.52-g sample of a compound containing only carbon, hydrogen, nitrogen, oxygen, and sulfur was burned in excess O to yield 4.23 g of CO_2 and 1.01 g of H_2O. Another sample of the same compound, of mass 4.14 g, yielded 2.11 g of SO_3. A third sample, of mass 5.66 g, yielded 2.27 g of HNO_3. Calculate the empirical formula of the compound.

143. A compound of molar mass 229 contains only carbon, hydrogen, iodine, and sulfur. Analysis shows that a sample of the compound contains 6 times as much carbon as hydrogen, by mass. Calculate the molecular formula of the compound.

144. The elements X and Y form a compound that is 40% X and 60% Y by mass. The atomic mass of X is twice that of Y. What is the empirical formula of the compound?

145. A compound of X and Y is $\frac{1}{3}$ X by mass. The atomic mass of element X is $\frac{1}{3}$ the atomic mass of element Y. Find the empirical formula of the compound.

146. A mixture of carbon and sulfur has a mass of 9.0 g. Complete combustion with excess O_2 gives 23.3 g of a mixture of CO_2 and SO_2. Find the mass of sulfur in the original mixture.

Conceptual Problems

147. When molecules are represented by molecular models, what does each sphere represent? How big is the nucleus of an atom in comparison to the sphere used to represent an atom in a molecular model?

148. Without doing any calculations, determine which element in each of the compounds will have the highest mass percent composition.

    a. CO   **b.** N_2O **c.** $C_6H_{12}O_6$ **d.** NH_3

149. Explain the problem with the following statement and correct it. "The chemical formula for ammonia (NH_3) indicates that ammonia contains three grams of hydrogen to each gram of nitrogen."

150. Explain the problem with the following statement and correct it. "When a chemical equation is balanced, the number of molecules of each type on both sides of the equation will be equal."

151. Without doing any calculations, arrange the elements in H_2SO_4 in order of decreasing mass percent composition.

4

Chemical Quantities and Aqueous Reactions

I feel sorry for people who don't understand anything about chemistry. They are missing an important source of happiness.
—Linus Pauling (1901–1994)

THE AMOUNT OF PRODUCT FORMED IN A CHEMICAL REACTION is related to the amount of reactant that reacts. This concept makes sense intuitively, but how do we describe and understand this relationship more fully? The first half of this chapter focuses on chemical stoichiometry—the numerical relationships between the amounts of reactants and products in chemical reactions. In Chapter 3, we learned how to write balanced chemical equations for chemical reactions. Here we will examine more closely the meaning of those balanced equations. In the second half of this chapter, we turn to describing chemical reactions that occur in water. You have probably witnessed many of these types of reactions in your daily life because they are so common. Have you ever mixed baking soda with vinegar and observed the subsequent bubbling? Or have you ever noticed the hard water deposits that form on plumbing fixtures? These reactions—and many others, including those that occur within the watery environment of living cells—are aqueous chemical reactions, the subject of the second half of this chapter.

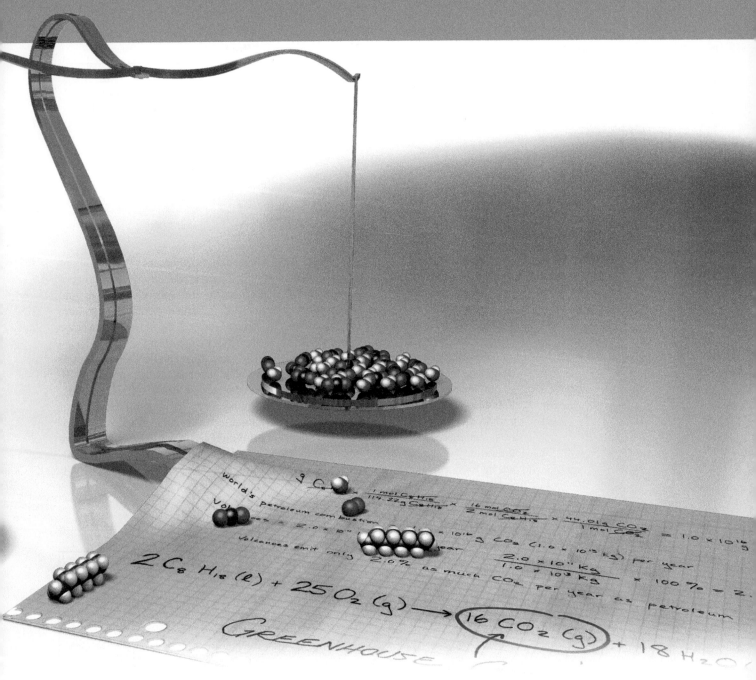

The molecular models on this balance represent the reactants and products in the combustion of octane, a component of petroleum. One of the products, carbon dioxide, is the main greenhouse gas implicated in global warming.

4.1 Global Warming and the Combustion of Fossil Fuels

The temperature outside my office today is a cool 48 °F, lower than normal for this time of year on the California Coast. However, today's "chill" pales in comparison with how cold it would be without the presence of *greenhouse gases* in the atmosphere. These gases act like the glass of a greenhouse, allowing sunlight to enter the atmosphere and warm Earth's surface, but preventing some of the heat generated by the sunlight from escaping, as shown in Figure 4.1 ▶ on the next page. The balance between incoming and outgoing energy from the sun determines Earth's average temperature.

If the greenhouse gases in the atmosphere were not present, more heat energy would escape, and Earth's average temperature would be about 60 °F colder than it is now. The temperature outside of my office today would be below 0 °F, and even the sunniest U.S. cities would most likely be covered with snow. However, if the concentration of greenhouse gases in the atmosphere were to increase, Earth's average temperature would rise.

▶ **FIGURE 4.1 The Greenhouse Effect**
Greenhouse gases in the atmosphere act as a one-way filter. They allow visible light to pass through and warm Earth's surface, but they prevent heat energy from radiating back out into space.

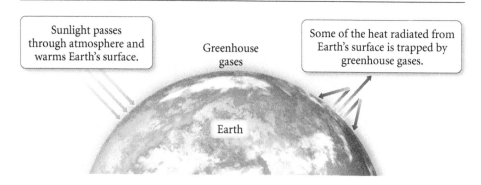

The Greenhouse Effect

Sunlight passes through atmosphere and warms Earth's surface.

Greenhouse gases

Some of the heat radiated from Earth's surface is trapped by greenhouse gases.

Earth

The extremely cold temperatures of Mars are as much a result of its lack of atmosphere as its greater distance from the sun than Earth. Conversely, Venus is an inferno partly because its thick atmosphere is rich in greenhouse gases.

In recent years scientists have become increasingly concerned because the quantity of atmospheric carbon dioxide (CO_2)—Earth's most significant greenhouse gas in terms of its contribution to climate—is rising. More CO_2 enhances the atmosphere's ability to hold heat and is believed to lead to *global warming*, an increase in Earth's average temperature. Since 1860, atmospheric CO_2 levels have risen by 35% (Figure 4.2 ▼), and Earth's average temperature has risen by 0.6 °C (about 1.1 °F), as shown in Figure 4.3 ▼.

Most scientists believe that the primary cause of rising atmospheric CO_2 concentration is the burning of fossil fuels (natural gas, petroleum, and coal), which provide 90% of our society's energy. Some people, however, have suggested that fossil fuel combustion does not significantly contribute to global warming. They argue that the amount of carbon dioxide emitted into the atmosphere by natural sources, such as volcanic eruptions, far exceeds that from fossil fuel combustion. Which group is right? We can judge the validity of the naysayers' argument by calculating how much carbon dioxide is emitted by fossil fuel combustion and comparing that amount to the amount released by volcanic eruptions.

Atmospheric Carbon Dioxide

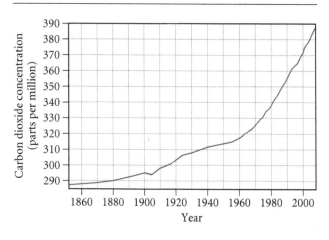

Global Temperature

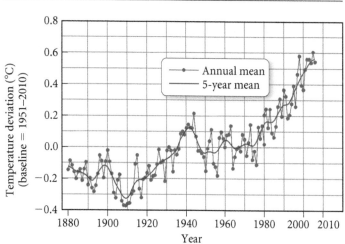

▲ **FIGURE 4.2 Carbon Dioxide Concentrations in the Atmosphere**
The rise in carbon dioxide levels is due largely to fossil fuel combustion.

▲ **FIGURE 4.3 Global Temperature** Average temperatures worldwide have risen by about 0.6 °C since 1880.

4.2 Reaction Stoichiometry: How Much Carbon Dioxide?

The balanced chemical equations for fossil-fuel combustion reactions provide the exact relationships between the amount of fossil fuel burned and the amount of carbon dioxide emitted. In this discussion, we use octane (a component of gasoline) as a representative fossil fuel. The balanced equation for the combustion of octane is

$$2\,C_8H_{18}(l) + 25\,O_2(g) \longrightarrow 16\,CO_2(g) + 18\,H_2O(g)$$

The balanced equation shows that 16 CO_2 molecules are produced for every 2 molecules of octane burned. We can extend this numerical relationship between molecules to the amounts in moles as follows:

> **The coefficients in a chemical reaction specify the relative amounts in moles of each of the substances involved in the reaction.**

In other words, from the equation, we know that 16 *moles* of CO_2 are produced for every 2 *moles* of octane burned. The numerical relationships between chemical amounts in a balanced chemical equation are called reaction **stoichiometry**. Stoichiometry allows us to predict the amounts of products that will form in a chemical reaction based on the amounts of reactants that react. Stoichiometry also allows us to determine the amount of reactants necessary to form a given amount of product. These calculations are central to chemistry, allowing chemists to plan and carry out chemical reactions to obtain products in the desired quantities.

Stoichiometry is pronounced stoy-kee-AHM-e-tree.

Making Pizza: The Relationships among Ingredients

The concepts of stoichiometry are similar to those in a cooking recipe. Calculating the amount of carbon dioxide produced by the combustion of a given amount of a fossil fuel is analogous to calculating the number of pizzas that can be made from a given amount of cheese. For example, suppose we use the following pizza recipe:

$$1 \text{ crust} + 5 \text{ ounces tomato sauce} + 2 \text{ cups cheese} \longrightarrow 1 \text{ pizza}$$

The recipe contains the numerical relationships between the pizza ingredients. It says that if we have 2 cups of cheese—and enough of everything else—we can make 1 pizza. We can write this relationship as a ratio between the cheese and the pizza:

$$2 \text{ cups cheese} : 1 \text{ pizza}$$

What if we have 6 cups of cheese? Assuming that we have enough of everything else, we can use the above ratio as a conversion factor to calculate the number of pizzas:

$$6 \text{ cups cheese} \times \frac{1 \text{ pizza}}{2 \text{ cups cheese}} = 3 \text{ pizzas}$$

Six cups of cheese are sufficient to make 3 pizzas. The pizza recipe contains numerical ratios between other ingredients as well, including the following:

$$1 \text{ crust} : 1 \text{ pizza}$$
$$5 \text{ ounces tomato sauce} : 1 \text{ pizza}$$

Making Molecules: Mole-to-Mole Conversions

In a balanced chemical equation, we have a "recipe" for how reactants combine to form products. From our balanced equation for the combustion of octane, for example, we can write the following stoichiometric ratio:

$$2 \text{ mol } C_8H_{18} : 16 \text{ mol } CO_2$$

We can use this ratio to determine how many moles of CO_2 form when a given number of moles of C_8H_{18} burns. Suppose that we burn 22.0 moles of C_8H_{18}; how many moles of CO_2 form? We use the ratio from the balanced chemical equation in the same way that we used the ratio from the pizza recipe. The ratio acts as a conversion factor between the amount in moles of the reactant (C_8H_{18}) and the amount in moles of the product (CO_2):

$$22.0 \text{ mol } C_8H_{18} \times \frac{16 \text{ mol } CO_2}{2 \text{ mol } C_8H_{18}} = 176 \text{ mol } CO_2$$

The combustion of 22 moles of C_8H_{18} adds 176 moles of CO_2 to the atmosphere.

Making Molecules: Mass-to-Mass Conversions

According to the U.S. Department of Energy, the world burned 3.1×10^{10} barrels of petroleum in 2007, the equivalent of approximately 3.5×10^{15} g of gasoline. Let's estimate the mass of CO_2 emitted into the atmosphere from burning this much gasoline using the combustion of 3.5×10^{15} g octane as the representative reaction. This calculation is similar to the one we just did, except that we are now given the *mass* of octane instead of the *amount* of octane in moles. Consequently, we must first convert the mass (in grams) to the amount (in moles). The general conceptual plan for calculations in which you are given the mass of a reactant or product in a chemical reaction and asked to find the mass of a different reactant or product takes this form:

where A and B are two different substances involved in the reaction. We use the molar mass of A to convert from the mass of A to the amount of A (in moles). We use the appropriate ratio from the balanced chemical equation to convert from the amount of A (in moles) to the amount of B (in moles). And finally, we use the molar mass of B to convert from the amount of B (in moles) to the mass of B. To calculate the mass of CO_2 emitted upon the combustion of 3.5×10^{15} g of octane, therefore, we use the following conceptual plan:

Conceptual Plan

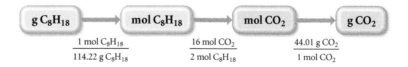

Relationships Used

2 mol C_8H_{18} : 16 mol CO_2 (from the chemical equation)

molar mass C_8H_{18} = 114.22 g/mol

molar mass CO_2 = 44.01 g/mol

Solution

We follow the conceptual plan to solve the problem, beginning with g C_8H_{18} and canceling units to arrive at g CO_2:

$$3.5 \times 10^{15} \ \text{g } C_8H_{18} \times \frac{1 \ \text{mol } C_8H_{18}}{114.22 \ \text{g } C_8H_{18}} \times$$

$$\frac{16 \ \text{mol } CO_2}{2 \ \text{mol } C_8H_{18}} \times \frac{44.01 \ \text{g } CO_2}{1 \ \text{mol } CO_2} = 1.1 \times 10^{16} \ \text{g } CO_2$$

The world's petroleum combustion produces 1.1×10^{16} g CO_2 (1.1×10^{13} kg) per year. In comparison, volcanoes produce about 2×10^{11} kg CO_2 per year.* In other words, volcanoes emit only $\dfrac{2.0 \times 10^{11} \ \text{kg}}{1.1 \times 10^{13} \ \text{kg}} \times 100\% = 1.8\%$ as much CO_2 per year as petroleum combustion. The argument that volcanoes emit more carbon dioxide than fossil fuel combustion is clearly mistaken. Additional examples of stoichiometric calculations follow.

The percentage of CO_2 emitted by volcanoes relative to all fossil fuels is even less than 2% because the combustion of coal and natural gas also emits CO_2.

*Gerlach, T. M., Present-day CO_2 emissions from volcanoes; *Eos, Transactions, American Geophysical Union*, Vol. 72, No. 23, June 4, 1991, pp. 249 and 254–255.

EXAMPLE 4.1 Stoichiometry

In photosynthesis, plants convert carbon dioxide and water into glucose ($C_6H_{12}O_6$) according to the following reaction:

$$6\, CO_2\,(g) + 6\, H_2O\,(l) \xrightarrow{\text{sunlight}} 6\, O_2\,(g) + C_6H_{12}O_6\,(aq)$$

Suppose you determine that a particular plant consumes 37.8 g of CO_2 in one week. Assuming that there is more than enough water present to react with all of the CO_2, what mass of glucose (in grams) can the plant synthesize from the CO_2?

SORT The problem gives the mass of carbon dioxide and asks you to find the mass of glucose that can be produced.	**GIVEN:** 37.8 g CO_2 **FIND:** g $C_6H_{12}O_6$

STRATEGIZE The conceptual plan follows the general pattern of mass A → amount A (in moles) → amount B (in moles) → mass B. From the chemical equation, deduce the relationship between moles of carbon dioxide and moles of glucose. Use the molar masses to convert between grams and moles.

CONCEPTUAL PLAN

g CO_2	mol CO_2	mol $C_6H_{12}O_6$	g $C_6H_{12}O_6$
	$\dfrac{1\ \text{mol } CO_2}{44.01\ \text{g } CO_2}$	$\dfrac{1\ \text{mol } C_6H_{12}O_6}{6\ \text{mol } CO_2}$	$\dfrac{180.2\ \text{g } C_6H_{12}O_6}{1\ \text{mol } C_6H_{12}O_6}$

RELATIONSHIPS USED

molar mass CO_2 = 44.01 g/mol

6 mol CO_2 : 1 mol $C_6H_{12}O_6$

molar mass $C_6H_{12}O_6$ = 180.2 g/mol

SOLVE Follow the conceptual plan to solve the problem. Begin with g CO_2 and use the conversion factors to arrive at g $C_6H_{12}O_6$.

SOLUTION

$$37.8\ \cancel{\text{g } CO_2} \times \frac{1\ \cancel{\text{mol } CO_2}}{44.01\ \cancel{\text{g } CO_2}} \times \frac{1\ \cancel{\text{mol } C_6H_{12}O_6}}{6\ \cancel{\text{mol } CO_2}} \times \frac{180.2\ \text{g } C_6H_{12}O_6}{1\ \cancel{\text{mol } C_6H_{12}O_6}} = 25.8\ \text{g } C_6H_{12}O_6$$

CHECK The units of the answer are correct. The magnitude of the answer (25.8 g) is less than the initial mass of CO_2 (37.8 g). This is reasonable because each carbon in CO_2 has two oxygen atoms associated with it, while in $C_6H_{12}O_6$ each carbon has only one oxygen atom associated with it and two hydrogen atoms, which are much lighter than oxygen. Therefore the mass of glucose produced should be less than the mass of carbon dioxide for this reaction.

FOR PRACTICE 4.1

Magnesium hydroxide, the active ingredient in milk of magnesia, neutralizes stomach acid, primarily HCl, according to the following reaction:

$$Mg(OH)_2(aq) + 2\, HCl(aq) \longrightarrow 2\, H_2O(l) + MgCl_2(aq)$$

What mass of HCl, in grams, can be neutralized by a dose of milk of magnesia containing 3.26 g $Mg(OH)_2$?

EXAMPLE 4.2 Stoichiometry

Sulfuric acid (H_2SO_4) is a component of acid rain that forms when SO_2, a pollutant, reacts with oxygen and water according to the following simplified reaction:

$$2\,SO_2\,(g) + O_2\,(g) + 2\,H_2O\,(l) \longrightarrow 2\,H_2SO_4\,(aq)$$

The generation of the electricity used by a medium-sized home produces about 25 kg of SO_2 per year. Assuming that there is more than enough O_2 and H_2O, what mass of H_2SO_4, in kg, can form from this much SO_2?

SORT The problem gives the mass of sulfur dioxide and asks you to find the mass of sulfuric acid.	**GIVEN:** 25 kg SO_2 **FIND:** kg H_2SO_4

STRATEGIZE The conceptual plan follows the standard format of mass → amount (in moles) → amount (in moles) → mass. Since the original quantity of SO_2 is given in kg, you must first convert to grams. You can deduce the relationship between moles of sulfur dioxide and moles of sulfuric acid from the chemical equation. Since the final quantity is requested in kg, convert to kg at the end.

CONCEPTUAL PLAN

$$\boxed{\text{kg SO}_2} \longrightarrow \boxed{\text{g SO}_2} \longrightarrow \boxed{\text{mol SO}_2} \longrightarrow$$

$$\frac{1000\text{ g}}{1\text{ kg}} \qquad \frac{1\text{ mol SO}_2}{64.07\text{ g SO}_2} \qquad \frac{2\text{ mol H}_2\text{SO}_4}{2\text{ mol SO}_2}$$

$$\boxed{\text{mol H}_2\text{SO}_4} \longrightarrow \boxed{\text{g H}_2\text{SO}_4} \longrightarrow \boxed{\text{kg H}_2\text{SO}_4}$$

$$\frac{98.09\text{ g H}_2\text{SO}_4}{1\text{ mol H}_2\text{SO}_4} \qquad \frac{1\text{ kg}}{1000\text{ g}}$$

RELATIONSHIPS USED

1 kg = 1000 g   2 mol SO_2 : 2 mol H_2SO_4

molar mass SO_2 = 64.07 g/mol   molar mass H_2SO_4 = 98.09 g/mol

SOLVE Follow the conceptual plan to solve the problem. Begin with the given amount of SO_2 in kilograms and use the conversion factors to arrive at kg H_2SO_4.

SOLUTION

$$25\text{ kg SO}_2 \times \frac{1000\text{ g}}{1\text{ kg}} \times \frac{1\text{ mol SO}_2}{64.07\text{ g SO}_2} \times \frac{2\text{ mol H}_2\text{SO}_4}{2\text{ mol SO}_2}$$

$$\times \frac{98.09\text{ g H}_2\text{SO}_4}{1\text{ mol H}_2\text{SO}_4} \times \frac{1\text{ kg}}{1000\text{ g}} = 38\text{ kg H}_2\text{SO}_4$$

CHECK The units of the final answer are correct. The magnitude of the final answer (38 kg H_2SO_4) is larger than the amount of SO_2 given (25 kg). This is reasonable because in the reaction each SO_2 molecule "gains weight" by reacting with O_2 and H_2O.

FOR PRACTICE 4.2

Another component of acid rain is nitric acid, which forms when NO_2, also a pollutant, reacts with oxygen and water according to the following simplified equation:

$$4\,NO_2\,(g) + O_2\,(g) + 2\,H_2O\,(l) \longrightarrow 4\,HNO_3\,(aq)$$

The generation of the electricity used by a medium-sized home produces about 16 kg of NO_2 per year. Assuming that there is adequate O_2 and H_2O, what mass of HNO_3, in kg, can form from this amount of NO_2 pollutant?

 Conceptual Connection 4.1 Stoichiometry

Under certain conditions sodium can react with oxygen to form sodium oxide according to the following reaction:

$$4\,Na(s) + O_2\,(g) \longrightarrow 2\,Na_2O(s)$$

A flask contains the amount of oxygen represented by the diagram on the left ◄.

Which diagram best represents the amount of sodium required to completely react with all of the oxygen in the flask according to the above equation?

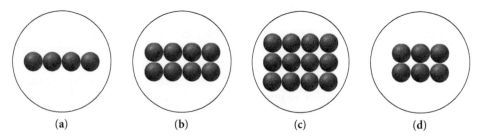

(a)   **(b)**   **(c)**   **(d)**

ANSWER: **(c)** Since each O_2 molecule reacts with 4 Na atoms, 12 Na atoms are required to react with 3 O_2 molecules.

4.3 Limiting Reactant, Theoretical Yield, and Percent Yield

Let's return to our pizza analogy to understand three more important concepts in reaction stoichiometry: *limiting reactant, theoretical yield,* and *percent yield*. Recall our pizza recipe from Section 4.2:

$$1 \text{ crust } + 5 \text{ ounces tomato sauce } + 2 \text{ cups cheese } \longrightarrow 1 \text{ pizza}$$

Suppose that we have 4 crusts, 10 cups of cheese, and 15 ounces of tomato sauce. How many pizzas can we make?

We have enough crusts to make:

$$4 \text{ crusts} \times \frac{1 \text{ pizza}}{1 \text{ crust}} = 4 \text{ pizzas}$$

We have enough cheese to make:

$$10 \text{ cups cheese} \times \frac{1 \text{ pizza}}{2 \text{ cups cheese}} = 5 \text{ pizzas}$$

We have enough tomato sauce to make:

$$15 \text{ ounces tomato sauce} \times \frac{1 \text{ pizza}}{5 \text{ ounces tomato sauce}} = 3 \text{ pizzas}$$

Limiting reactant   Smallest number of pizzas

We have enough crusts for 4 pizzas, enough cheese for 5 pizzas, but enough tomato sauce for only 3 pizzas. Consequently, unless we get more ingredients, we can make only 3 pizzas. The tomato sauce *limits* how many pizzas we can make. If the pizza recipe were a chemical reaction, the tomato sauce would be the **limiting reactant**, the reactant that limits the amount of product in a chemical reaction. Notice that the limiting reactant is the reactant that makes *the least amount of product*. The reactants that *do not* limit the amount of product—such as the crusts and the cheese in this example—are said to be *in excess*. If this were a chemical reaction, 3 pizzas would be the **theoretical yield**, the amount of product that can be made in a chemical reaction based on the amount of limiting reactant.

The term *limiting reagent* is sometimes used in place of *limiting reactant*.

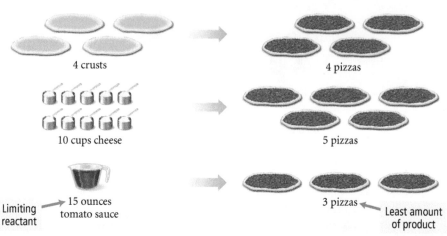

4 crusts → 4 pizzas

10 cups cheese → 5 pizzas

Limiting reactant → 15 ounces tomato sauce → 3 pizzas ← Least amount of product

◀ The ingredient that makes the least amount of pizza determines how many pizzas you can make.

Let us carry this analogy one step further. Suppose we go on to cook our pizzas and accidentally burn one of them. So even though we theoretically have enough ingredients for 3 pizzas, we end up with only 2. If this were a chemical reaction, the 2 pizzas would be our **actual yield**, the amount of product actually produced by a chemical reaction. (The actual yield is always equal to or less than the theoretical yield because a small amount of product is usually lost to other reactions or does not form during a reaction.) Finally, our **percent yield**, the percentage of the theoretical yield that was actually attained, is calculated as the ratio of the actual yield to the theoretical yield:

Actual yield

$$\% \text{ yield} = \frac{2 \text{ pizzas}}{3 \text{ pizzas}} \times 100\% = 67\%$$

Theoretical yield

Since one of our pizzas burned, we obtained only 67% of our theoretical yield.

Summarizing Limiting Reactant and Yield:

▶ **The limiting reactant** (or **limiting reagent**) is the reactant that is completely consumed in a chemical reaction and limits the amount of product.

▶ **The reactant in excess** is any reactant that occurs in a quantity greater than is required to completely react with the limiting reactant.

▶ **The theoretical yield** is the amount of product that can be made in a chemical reaction based on the amount of limiting reactant.

▶ **The actual yield** is the amount of product actually produced by a chemical reaction.

▶ **The percent yield** is calculated as $\dfrac{\text{actual yield}}{\text{theoretical yield}} \times 100\%$.

Now let's apply these concepts to a chemical reaction. Recall from Section 3.10 our balanced equation for the combustion of methane:

$$CH_4(g) + 2\,O_2(g) \longrightarrow CO_2(g) + 2\,H_2O(l)$$

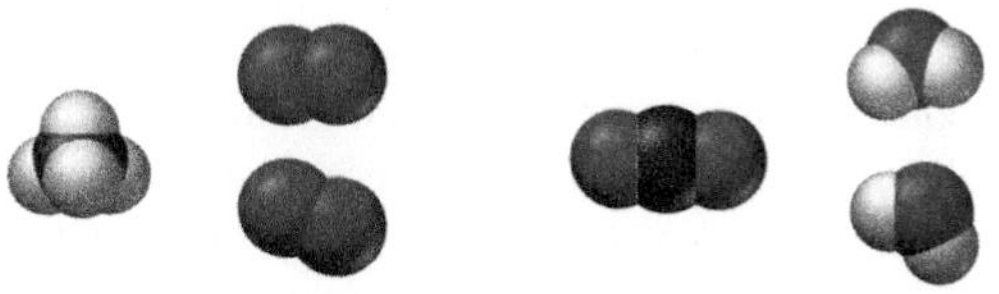

If we start out with 5 CH_4 molecules and 8 O_2 molecules, what is our limiting reactant? What is our theoretical yield of carbon dioxide molecules? We first calculate the number of CO_2 molecules that can be made from 5 CH_4 molecules:

$$5\,CH_4 \times \frac{1\,CO_2}{1\,CH_4} = 5\,CO_2$$

We then calculate the number of CO_2 molecules that can be made from 8 O_2 molecules:

$$8\,O_2 \times \frac{1\,CO_2}{2\,O_2} = 4\,CO_2$$

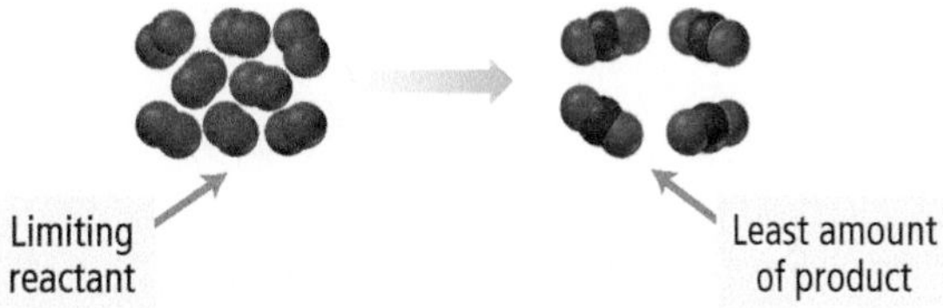

Limiting reactant   Least amount of product

We have enough CH_4 to make 5 CO_2 molecules and enough O_2 to make 4 CO_2 molecules; therefore O_2 is the limiting reactant, and 4 CO_2 molecules is the theoretical yield. The CH_4 is in excess.

An alternative way to calculate the limiting reactant (which we mention here but do not use in this book) is to pick any reactant and determine how much of the *other reactant* is necessary to completely react with it. For the reaction we just examined, we have 5 CH_4 molecules and 8 O_2 molecules. Let's pick the 5 CH_4 molecules and determine how many O_2 molecules are necessary to completely react with them:

$$5 \ \cancel{CH_4} \times \frac{2 \ O_2}{1 \ \cancel{CH_4}} = 10 \ O_2$$

Since we need 10 O_2 molecules to completely react with the 5 CH_4 molecules, and since we have only 8 O_2 molecules, we know that the O_2 is the limiting reactant. The same method can be applied by comparing the amounts of reactants in moles.

 Conceptual Connection 4.2 Limiting Reactant and Theoretical Yield

Nitrogen and hydrogen gas react to form ammonia according to the following reaction:

$$N_2(g) + 3H_2(g) \longrightarrow 2 \ NH_3(g)$$

If a flask contains a mixture of reactants represented by the diagram on the right ▶, which diagram best represents the mixture in the flask after the reactants have reacted as completely as possible? What is the limiting reactant? Which reactant is in excess?

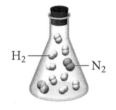

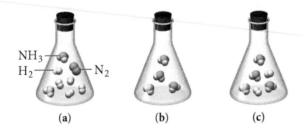

(a)　　　(b)　　　(c)

ANSWER: (c) Nitrogen is the limiting reactant, and there is enough nitrogen to make 4 NH_3 molecules. Hydrogen is in excess, and two hydrogen molecules remain after the reactants have reacted as completely as possible.

Limiting Reactant, Theoretical Yield, and Percent Yield from Initial Reactant Masses

When working in the laboratory, we normally measure the initial quantities of reactants in grams, not in number of molecules. To find the limiting reactant and theoretical yield from initial masses, we must first convert the masses to amounts in moles. Consider the following reaction:

$$2 \ Mg \ (s) + O_2 \ (g) \longrightarrow 2 \ MgO \ (s)$$

A reaction mixture contains 42.5 g Mg and 33.8 g O_2; what is the limiting reactant and theoretical yield?

To solve this problem, we must determine which of the reactants makes the least amount of product.

Conceptual Plan

We can find the limiting reactant by calculating how much product can be made from each reactant. However, since we are given the initial quantities in grams, and stoichiometric relationships are between moles, we must first convert to moles. We then convert

from moles of the reactant to moles of product. The reactant that makes the *least amount of product* is the limiting reactant. The conceptual plan is as follows:

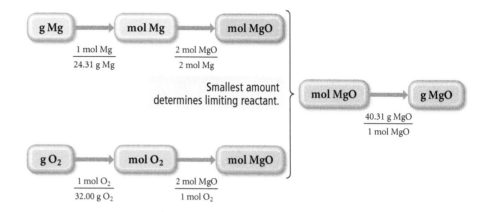

In the plan, we compare the number of moles of MgO made by each reactant and convert only the smaller amount to grams. (Alternatively, you can convert both quantities to grams and determine the limiting reactant based on the mass of the product.)

Relationships Used

molar mass Mg = 24.31 g Mg

molar mass O_2 = 32.00 g O_2

2 mol Mg : 2 mol MgO

1 mol O_2 : 2 mol MgO

molar mass MgO = 40.31 g MgO

Solution

Beginning with the masses of each reactant, we follow the conceptual plan to calculate how much product can be made from each:

$$42.5 \text{ g Mg} \times \frac{1 \text{ mol Mg}}{24.31 \text{ g Mg}} \times \frac{2 \text{ mol MgO}}{2 \text{ mol Mg}} = 1.7483 \text{ mol MgO}$$

Limiting reactant

Least amount of product

$$1.7483 \text{ mol MgO} \times \frac{40.31 \text{ g MgO}}{1 \text{ mol MgO}} = 70.5 \text{ g MgO}$$

$$33.8 \text{ g } O_2 \times \frac{1 \text{ mol } O_2}{32.00 \text{ g } O_2} \times \frac{2 \text{ mol MgO}}{1 \text{ mol } O_2} = 2.1125 \text{ mol MgO}$$

Since Mg makes the least amount of product, it is the limiting reactant, and O_2 is in excess. Notice that the limiting reactant is not necessarily the reactant with the least mass. In this case, the mass of O_2 is less than the mass of Mg, yet Mg is the limiting reactant because it makes the least amount of MgO. The theoretical yield is 70.5 g of MgO, the mass of product possible based on the limiting reactant.

Suppose that after the synthesis, the actual yield of MgO is 55.9 g. What is the percent yield? We compute the percent yield as follows:

$$\% \text{ yield} = \frac{\text{actual yield}}{\text{theoretical yield}} \times 100\% = \frac{55.9 \text{ g}}{70.5 \text{ g}} \times 100\% = 79.3\%$$

EXAMPLE 4.3 Limiting Reactant and Theoretical Yield

Ammonia, NH_3, can be synthesized by the following reaction:

$$2\ NO(g) + 5\ H_2(g) \longrightarrow 2\ NH_3(g) + 2\ H_2O(g)$$

Starting with 86.3 g NO and 25.6 g H_2, find the theoretical yield of ammonia in grams.

SORT You are given the mass of each reactant in grams and asked to find the theoretical yield of a product.

GIVEN: 86.3 g NO, 25.6 g H_2

FIND: theoretical yield of $NH_3(g)$

STRATEGIZE Determine which reactant makes the least amount of product by converting from grams of each reactant to moles of the reactant to moles of the product. Use molar masses to convert between grams and moles and use the stoichiometric relationships (deduced from the chemical equation) to convert between moles of reactant and moles of product. Remember that the reactant that makes *the least amount of product* is the limiting reactant. Convert the number of moles of product obtained using the limiting reactant to grams of product.

CONCEPTUAL PLAN

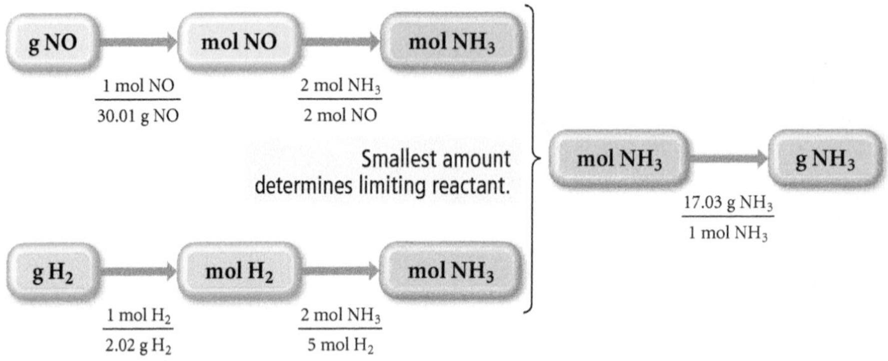

RELATIONSHIPS USED

molar mass NO = 30.01 g/mol

molar mass H_2 = 2.02 g/mol

2 mol NO : 2 mol NH_3 (from chemical equation)

5 mol H_2 : 2 mol NH_3 (from chemical equation)

molar mass NH_3 = 17.03 g/mol

SOLVE Beginning with the given mass of each reactant, calculate the amount of product that can be made in moles. Convert the amount of product made by the limiting reactant to grams—this is the theoretical yield.

SOLUTION

$$86.3\ \text{g NO} \times \frac{1\ \text{mol NO}}{30.01\ \text{g NO}} \times \frac{2\ \text{mol } NH_3}{2\ \text{mol NO}} = 2.8\underline{7}57\ \text{mol } NH_3$$

Limiting reactant — Least amount of product

$$2.8\underline{7}57\ \text{mol } NH_3 \times \frac{17.03\ \text{g } NH_3}{\text{mol } NH_3} = 49.0\ \text{g } NH_3$$

$$25.6\ \text{g } H_2 \times \frac{1\ \text{mol } H_2}{2.02\ \text{g } H_2} \times \frac{2\ \text{mol } NH_3}{5\ \text{mol } H_2} = 5.0\underline{6}93\ \text{mol } NH_3$$

Since NO makes the least amount of product, it is the limiting reactant, and the theoretical yield of ammonia is 49.0 g.

CHECK The units of the answer (g NH_3) are correct. The magnitude (49.0 g) seems reasonable given that 86.3 g NO is the limiting reactant. NO contains one oxygen atom per nitrogen atom and NH_3 contains three hydrogen atoms per nitrogen atom. Since three hydrogen atoms have less mass than one oxygen atom, it is reasonable that the mass of NH_3 obtained is less than the mass of NO.

FOR PRACTICE 4.3

Ammonia can also be synthesized by the following reaction:

$$3\ H_2(g) + N_2(g) \longrightarrow 2\ NH_3(g)$$

What is the theoretical yield of ammonia, in kg, that we can synthesize from 5.22 kg of H_2 and 31.5 kg of N_2?

EXAMPLE 4.4 Limiting Reactant and Theoretical Yield

Titanium metal can be obtained from its oxide according to the following balanced equation:

$$TiO_2(s) + 2\,C(s) \longrightarrow Ti(s) + 2\,CO(g)$$

When 28.6 kg of C reacts with 88.2 kg of TiO_2, 42.8 kg of Ti is produced. Find the limiting reactant, theoretical yield (in kg), and percent yield.

SORT You are given the mass of each reactant and the mass of product formed. You are asked to find the limiting reactant, theoretical yield, and percent yield.	**GIVEN:** 28.6 kg C, 88.2 kg TiO_2, 42.8 kg Ti produced **FIND:** limiting reactant, theoretical yield, % yield

STRATEGIZE Determine which of the reactants makes the least amount of product by converting from kilograms of each reactant to moles of product. Convert between grams and moles using molar mass. Convert between moles of reactant and moles of product using the stoichiometric relationships derived from the chemical equation. Remember that the reactant that makes the *least amount of product* is the limiting reactant.

Determine the theoretical yield (in kg) by converting the number of moles of product obtained with the limiting reactant to kilograms of product.

CONCEPTUAL PLAN

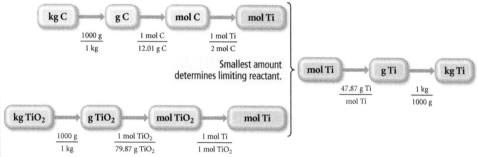

RELATIONSHIPS USED

1000 g = 1 kg   1 mol TiO_2 : 1 mol Ti

molar mass of C = 12.01 g/mol   2 mol C : 1 mol Ti

molar mass of TiO_2 = 79.87 g/mol   molar mass of Ti = 47.87 g/mol

SOLVE Beginning with the actual amount of each reactant, calculate the amount of product that can be made in moles. Convert the amount of product made by the limiting reactant to kilograms—this is the theoretical yield.

SOLUTION

$$28.6\ \text{kg C} \times \frac{1000\ \text{g}}{1\ \text{kg}} \times \frac{1\ \text{mol C}}{12.01\ \text{g C}} \times \frac{1\ \text{mol Ti}}{2\ \text{mol C}} = 1.1907 \times 10^3\ \text{mol Ti}$$

Limiting reactant ↓   Least amount of product ↓

$$88.2\ \text{kg TiO}_2 \times \frac{1000\ \text{g}}{1\ \text{kg}} \times \frac{1\ \text{mol TiO}_2}{79.87\ \text{g TiO}_2} \times \frac{1\ \text{mol Ti}}{1\ \text{mol TiO}_2} = 1.1043 \times 10^3\ \text{mol Ti}$$

$$1.1043 \times 10^3\ \text{mol Ti} \times \frac{47.87\ \text{g Ti}}{1\ \text{mol Ti}} \times \frac{1\ \text{kg}}{1000\ \text{g}} = 52.9\ \text{kg Ti}$$

Since TiO_2 makes the least amount of product, it is the limiting reactant, and 52.9 kg Ti is the theoretical yield.

Calculate the percent yield by dividing the actual yield (42.8 kg Ti) by the theoretical yield.

$$\% \text{ yield} = \frac{\text{actual yield}}{\text{theoretical yield}} \times 100\% = \frac{42.8\ \text{g}}{52.9\ \text{g}} \times 100\% = 80.9\%$$

CHECK The theoretical yield has the correct units (kg Ti) and has a reasonable magnitude compared to the mass of TiO_2. Since Ti has a lower molar mass than TiO_2, the amount of Ti made from TiO_2 should have a lower mass. The percent yield is reasonable (under 100% as it should be).

FOR PRACTICE 4.4

Mining companies use the following reaction to obtain iron from iron ore:

$$Fe_2O_3(s) + 3\,CO(g) \longrightarrow 2\,Fe(s) + 3\,CO_2(g)$$

The reaction of 167 g Fe_2O_3 with 85.8 g CO produces 72.3 g Fe. Find the limiting reactant, theoretical yield, and percent yield.

Conceptual Connection 4.3 Reactant in Excess

Nitrogen dioxide reacts with water to form nitric acid and nitrogen monoxide according to the following equation:

$$3\ NO_2(g)\ +\ H_2O(l)\ \longrightarrow\ 2\ HNO_3(l)\ +\ NO(g)$$

Suppose that 5 mol NO_2 and 1 mol H_2O combine and react completely. How many moles of the reactant in excess is present after the reaction has completed?

ANSWER: The limiting reactant is the 1 mol H_2O, which is completely consumed. The 1 mol of H_2O requires 3 mol of NO_2 to completely react, therefore 2 mol NO_2 remain after the reaction is complete.

 CHEMISTRY IN THE ENVIRONMENT **MTBE in Gasoline**

We have seen that the balanced chemical equation for the combustion of octane, a component of gasoline, is as follows:

$$2\ C_8H_{18}\ (l)\ +\ 25\ O_2\ (g)\ \longrightarrow\ 16\ CO_2\ (g)\ +\ 18\ H_2O(g)$$

The equation shows that 25 moles of O_2 are required to completely react with 2 moles of C_8H_{18}. What if there is not enough O_2 in an automobile cylinder to fully react with the amount of octane that is present? For many reactions, a shortage of one reactant means that less product forms—oxygen would become the limiting reactant. However, for some reactions, a shortage of one reactant causes side reactions to occur along with the desired reaction. In the case of octane and the other major components of gasoline, those side reactions produce pollutants such as carbon monoxide (CO) and unburned hydrocarbon fragments that lead to the formation of ozone (O_3).

In 1990, the U.S. Congress, in efforts to lower air pollution, passed amendments to the Clean Air Act requiring oil companies to add substances to gasoline that prevent these side reactions. Because these additives have the effect of increasing the amount of oxygen present during combustion, the resulting gasoline is called an oxygenated fuel. The additive of choice among oil companies was a compound called MTBE (methyl tertiary butyl ether).

◄ MTBE, a gasoline additive that promotes complete combustion.

The immediate results of adding MTBE to gasoline were positive. Carbon monoxide and ozone levels in many major cities decreased significantly.

Over time, however, MTBE—a compound that does not readily biodegrade (naturally break down in the environment)—began to appear in drinking water supplies across the nation. MTBE entered the drinking water supply via gasoline spills at gas stations, from boat motors, and from leaking underground storage tanks. MTBE, even at low levels, imparts a turpentinelike odor and foul taste to drinking water. It is also a suspected carcinogen.

Public response was swift and dramatic. Several class action lawsuits were filed against the manufacturers of MTBE, against gas stations suspected of leaking it, and against the oil companies that put it into gasoline. Many states banned MTBE from gasoline, and the oil industry stopped adding it to gasoline (because of liability concerns). This raises a question, however. MTBE was added to gasoline as a way to meet the requirements of the 1990 Clean Air Act amendments. If MTBE is no longer an option, and the oil companies are not able to comply with the law, should the government remove the requirements, weakening the Clean Air Act? One potential solution is substituting ethanol for MTBE. Ethanol, made from the fermentation of grains, has many of the same pollution-reducing effects without the associated health hazards.

Question

How many kilograms of oxygen (O_2) are required to completely react with 48 kg of octane (approximate capacity of a 15-gallon automobile gasoline tank)?

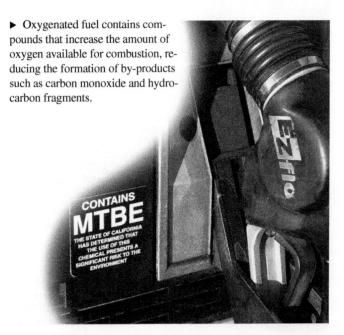

► Oxygenated fuel contains compounds that increase the amount of oxygen available for combustion, reducing the formation of by-products such as carbon monoxide and hydrocarbon fragments.

4.4 Solution Concentration and Solution Stoichiometry

Chemical reactions involving reactants dissolved in water are among the most common and important. The reactions that occur in lakes, streams, and oceans, as well as the reactions that occur in every cell within our bodies, take place in water. A homogeneous mixture of two substances—such as salt and water—is a **solution**. The majority component of the mixture is the **solvent**, and the minority component is the **solute**. An **aqueous solution** is one in which water acts as the solvent. In this section, we first examine how to quantify the concentration of a solution (the amount of solute relative to solvent) and then turn to applying the principles of stoichiometry, which we learned in the previous section, to reactions occurring in solution.

Concentrated and Dilute Solutions

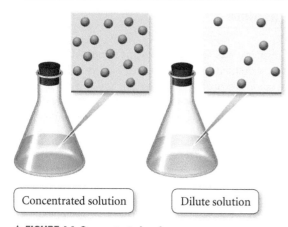

Concentrated solution   Dilute solution

▲ **FIGURE 4.4 Concentrated and Dilute Solutions** A concentrated solution contains a relatively large amount of solute relative to solvent. A dilute solution contains a relatively small amount of solute relative to solvent.

Solution Concentration

The amount of solute in a solution is variable. For example, you can add just a little salt to water to make a **dilute solution**, one that contains a small amount of solute relative to the solvent, or you can add a lot of salt to water to make a **concentrated solution**, one that contains a large amount of solute relative to the solvent (Figure 4.4 ◄). A common way to express solution concentration is **molarity (M)**, the amount of solute (in moles) divided by the volume of solution (in liters).

$$\text{Molarity (M)} = \frac{\text{amount of solute (in mol)}}{\text{volume of solution (in L)}}$$

Notice that molarity is a ratio of the amount of solute per liter of *solution,* not per liter of solvent. To make an aqueous solution of a specified molarity, we usually put the solute into a flask and then add water to reach the desired volume of solution. For example, to make 1 L of a 1 M NaCl solution, we add 1 mol of NaCl to a flask and then add enough water to make 1 L of solution (Figure 4.5 ▼). We *do not* combine 1 mol of NaCl with 1 L of water because the resulting solution would have a total volume exceeding 1 L and therefore a molarity of less than 1 M. To calculate molarity, divide the amount of the solute in moles by the volume of the solution (solute *and* solvent) in liters, as shown in the following example.

Preparing a Solution of Specified Concentration

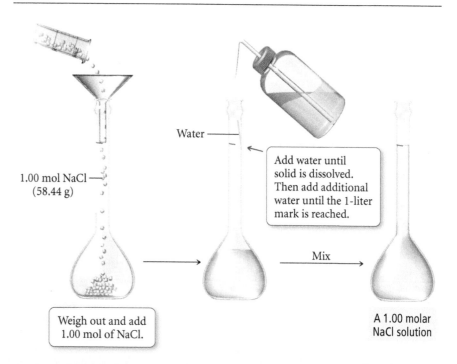

1.00 mol NaCl
(58.44 g)

Weigh out and add
1.00 mol of NaCl.

Water

Add water until
solid is dissolved.
Then add additional
water until the 1-liter
mark is reached.

Mix

A 1.00 molar
NaCl solution

▶ **FIGURE 4.5 Preparing a 1 Molar NaCl Solution**

EXAMPLE 4.5 Calculating Solution Concentration

If 25.5 g KBr is dissolved in enough water to make 1.75 L of solution, what is the molarity of the solution?

SORT You are given the mass of KBr and the volume of a solution and asked to find its molarity.	**GIVEN:** 25.5 g KBr, 1.75 L of solution **FIND:** molarity (M)

STRATEGIZE When formulating the conceptual plan, think about the definition of molarity, the amount of solute *in moles* per liter of solution.

You are given the mass of KBr, so first use the molar mass of KBr to convert from g KBr to mol KBr.

Then use the number of moles of KBr and liters of solution to find the molarity.

CONCEPTUAL PLAN

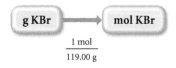

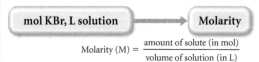

RELATIONSHIPS USED
molar mass of KBr = 119.00 g/mol

SOLVE Follow the conceptual plan. Begin with g KBr and convert to mol KBr; then use mol KBr and L solution to compute molarity.

SOLUTION

$$25.5 \ \cancel{\text{g KBr}} \times \frac{1 \ \text{mol KBr}}{119.00 \ \cancel{\text{g KBr}}} = 0.21\underline{4}29 \ \text{mol KBr}$$

$$\text{molarity (M)} = \frac{\text{amount of solute (in mol)}}{\text{volume of solution (in L)}}$$

$$= \frac{0.21\underline{4}29 \ \text{mol KBr}}{1.75 \ \text{L solution}}$$

$$= 0.122 \ \text{M}$$

CHECK The units of the answer (M) are correct. The magnitude is reasonable since common solutions range in concentration from 0 to about 18 M. Concentrations significantly above 18 M are suspect and should be double-checked.

FOR PRACTICE 4.5
Calculate the molarity of a solution made by adding 45.4 g of $NaNO_3$ to a flask and dissolving it with water to create a total volume of 2.50 L.

FOR MORE PRACTICE 4.5
What mass of KBr (in grams) do you need to make 250.0 mL of a 1.50 M KBr solution?

Using Molarity in Calculations

We can use the molarity of a solution as a conversion factor between moles of the solute and liters of the solution. For example, a 0.500 M NaCl solution contains 0.500 mol NaCl for every liter of solution:

$$\frac{0.500 \ \text{mol NaCl}}{\text{L solution}} \quad converts \quad \boxed{\text{L solution}} \longrightarrow \boxed{\text{mol NaCl}}$$

This conversion factor converts from L solution to mol NaCl. If we want to go the other way, we invert the conversion factor:

$$\frac{\text{L solution}}{0.500 \ \text{mol NaCl}} \quad converts \quad \boxed{\text{mol NaCl}} \longrightarrow \boxed{\text{L solution}}$$

The following example shows how to use molarity in this way.

EXAMPLE 4.6 Using Molarity in Calculations

How many liters of a 0.125 M NaOH solution contains 0.255 mol of NaOH?

SORT You are given the concentration of a NaOH solution. You are asked to find the volume of the solution that contains a given amount (in moles) of NaOH.	**GIVEN:** 0.125 M NaOH solution, 0.255 mol NaOH **FIND:** volume of NaOH solution (in L)
STRATEGIZE The conceptual plan begins with mol NaOH and shows the conversion to L of solution using molarity as a conversion factor.	**CONCEPTUAL PLAN** 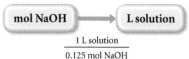 $$\frac{1 \text{ L solution}}{0.125 \text{ mol NaOH}}$$ **RELATIONSHIPS USED** $0.125 \text{ M NaOH} = \dfrac{0.125 \text{ mol NaOH}}{1 \text{ L solution}}$
SOLVE Follow the conceptual plan. Begin with mol NaOH and convert to L solution.	**SOLUTION** $$0.255 \text{ mol NaOH} \times \frac{1 \text{ L solution}}{0.125 \text{ mol NaOH}} = 2.04 \text{ L solution}$$

CHECK The units of the answer (L) are correct. The magnitude seems reasonable because the solution contains 0.125 mol per liter. Therefore, roughly 2 L contains the given amount of moles (0.255 mol).

FOR PRACTICE 4.6

How many grams of sucrose ($C_{12}H_{22}O_{11}$) are in 1.55 L of 0.758 M sucrose solution?

FOR MORE PRACTICE 4.6

How many mL of a 0.155 M KCl solution contains 2.55 g KCl?

 Conceptual Connection 4.4 Solutions

If we dissolve 25 grams of salt in 251 grams of water, what is the mass of the resulting solution?

(a) 251 g   (b) 276 g   (c) 226 g

ANSWER: (b) The mass of a solution is equal to the mass of the solute plus the mass of the solvent. Although the solute seems to disappear, it really does not, and its mass becomes part of the mass of the solution, in accordance with the law of mass conservation.

> When diluting acids, always add the concentrated acid to the water. Never add water to concentrated acid solutions, as the heat generated may cause the concentrated acid to splatter and burn your skin.

Solution Dilution To save space in storerooms, laboratories often store solutions in concentrated forms called **stock solutions**. For example, hydrochloric acid is frequently stored as a 12 M stock solution. However, many lab procedures call for much less concentrated hydrochloric acid solutions, so we must dilute the stock solution to the required concentration. How do we know how much of the stock solution to use? The easiest way to solve dilution problems is to use the following dilution equation:

$$M_1 V_1 = M_2 V_2 \qquad\qquad [4.1]$$

where M_1 and V_1 are the molarity and volume of the initial concentrated solution, and M_2 and V_2 are the molarity and volume of the final diluted solution. This equation works

because the molarity multiplied by the volume gives the number of moles of solute, which is the same in both solutions.

$$M_1V_1 = M_2V_2$$
$$\text{mol}_1 = \text{mol}_2$$

In other words, the number of moles of solute does not change when we dilute a solution.

For example, suppose a laboratory procedure calls for 3.00 L of a 0.500 M $CaCl_2$ solution. How should we prepare this solution from a 10.0 M stock solution? We solve Equation 4.1 for V_1, the volume of the stock solution required for the dilution, and then substitute in the correct values to compute it.

$$M_1V_1 = M_2V_2$$
$$V_1 = \frac{M_2V_2}{M_1}$$
$$= \frac{0.500 \text{ mol/L} \times 3.00 \text{ L}}{10.0 \text{ mol/L}}$$
$$= 0.150 \text{ L}$$

Consequently, we make the solution by diluting 0.150 L of the stock solution to a total volume of 3.00 L (V_2). The resulting solution will be 0.500 M in $CaCl_2$ (Figure 4.6 ▼).

Diluting a Solution

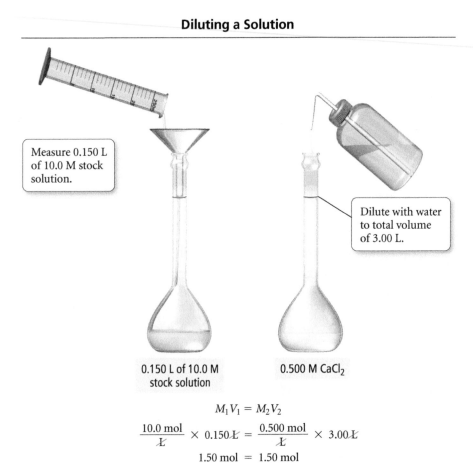

Measure 0.150 L of 10.0 M stock solution.

Dilute with water to total volume of 3.00 L.

0.150 L of 10.0 M stock solution

0.500 M $CaCl_2$

$$M_1V_1 = M_2V_2$$
$$\frac{10.0 \text{ mol}}{\text{L}} \times 0.150 \text{ L} = \frac{0.500 \text{ mol}}{\text{L}} \times 3.00 \text{ L}$$
$$1.50 \text{ mol} = 1.50 \text{ mol}$$

▲ **FIGURE 4.6 Preparing 3.00 L of 0.500 M CaCl$_2$ from a 10.0 M Stock Solution**

EXAMPLE 4.7   Solution Dilution

To what volume should you dilute 0.200 L of a 15.0 M NaOH solution to obtain a 3.00 M NaOH solution?

SORT You are given the initial volume, initial concentration, and final concentration of a solution, and you need to find the final volume.	**GIVEN:** $V_1 = 0.200$ L $M_1 = 15.0$ M $M_2 = 3.00$ M **FIND:** V_2
STRATEGIZE Equation 4.1 relates the initial and final volumes and concentrations for solution dilution problems. You are asked to find V_2. The other quantities (V_1, M_1, and M_2) are all given in the problem.	**CONCEPTUAL PLAN** 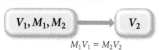 $$M_1V_1 = M_2V_2$$ **RELATIONSHIPS USED** $$M_1V_1 = M_2V_2$$
SOLVE Begin with the solution dilution equation and solve it for V_2. Substitute in the required quantities and compute V_2. Make the solution by diluting 0.200 L of the stock solution to a total volume of 1.00 L (V_2). The resulting solution will have a concentration of 3.00 M.	**SOLUTION** $M_1V_1 = M_2V_2$ $$V_2 = \frac{M_1V_1}{M_2}$$ $$= \frac{15.0 \text{ mol/L} \times 0.200 \text{ L}}{3.00 \text{ mol/L}}$$ $$= 1.00 \text{ L}$$

CHECK The final units (L) are correct. The magnitude of the answer is reasonable because the solution is diluted from 15.0 M to 3.00 M, a factor of five. Therefore the volume should increase by a factor of five.

FOR PRACTICE 4.7

To what volume (in mL) should you dilute 100.0 mL of a 5.00 M $CaCl_2$ solution to obtain a 0.750 M $CaCl_2$ solution?

FOR MORE PRACTICE 4.7

What volume of a 6.00 M $NaNO_3$ solution should you use to make 0.525 L of a 1.20 M $NaNO_3$ solution?

 Conceptual Connection 4.5 Solution Dilution

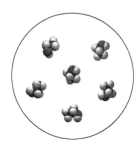

The figure at left represents a small volume within 500 mL of aqueous ethanol (CH_3CH_2OH) solution. (The water molecules have been omitted for clarity.)

Which picture best represents the same volume of the solution after we add an additional 500 mL of water?

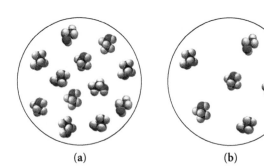

(a)   (b)   (c)

ANSWER: (c) Since the volume has doubled, the concentration is halved, so the same volume should contain half as many solute molecules.

Solution Stoichiometry

In Section 4.2 we learned how the coefficients in chemical equations are used as conversion factors between the amounts of reactants (in moles) and the amounts of products (in moles). In aqueous reactions, quantities of reactants and products are often specified in terms of volumes and concentrations. We can use the volume and concentration of a reactant or product to calculate its amount in moles. We can then use the stoichiometric coefficients in the chemical equation to convert to the amount of another reactant or product in moles. The general conceptual plan for these kinds of calculations begins with the volume of a reactant or product:

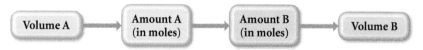

We make the conversions between solution volumes and amounts of solute in moles using the molarities of the solutions. We make the conversions between amounts in moles of A and B using the stoichiometric coefficients from the balanced chemical equation. The following example demonstrates solution stoichiometry.

EXAMPLE 4.8 Solution Stoichiometry

What volume (in L) of 0.150 M KCl solution will completely react with 0.150 L of a 0.175 M $Pb(NO_3)_2$ solution according to the following balanced chemical equation?

$$2 KCl(aq) + Pb(NO_3)_2 (aq) \longrightarrow PbCl_2 (s) + 2 KNO_3 (aq)$$

SORT You are given the volume and concentration of a $Pb(NO_3)_2$ solution. You are asked to find the volume of KCl solution (of a given concentration) required to react with it.

GIVEN: 0.150 L of $Pb(NO_3)_2$ solution, 0.175 M $Pb(NO_3)_2$ solution, 0.150 M KCl solution

FIND: volume KCl solution (in L)

STRATEGIZE The conceptual plan has the following form: volume A → amount A (in moles) → amount B (in moles) → volume B. The molar concentrations of the KCl and $Pb(NO_3)_2$ solutions can be used as conversion factors between the number of moles of reactants in these solutions and their volumes. The stoichiometric coefficients from the balanced equation are used to convert between number of moles of $Pb(NO_3)_2$ and number of moles of KCl.

CONCEPTUAL PLAN

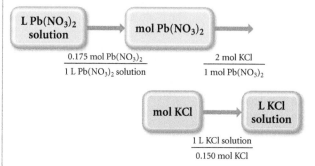

RELATIONSHIPS USED

$$M\left[Pb(NO_3)_2\right] = \frac{0.175 \text{ mol } Pb(NO_3)_2}{1 \text{ L } Pb(NO_3)_2 \text{ solution}}$$

2 mol KCl : 1 mol $Pb(NO_3)_2$

$$M [KCl] = \frac{0.150 \text{ mol } KCl}{1 \text{ L KCl solution}}$$

SOLVE Begin with L $Pb(NO_3)_2$ solution and follow the conceptual plan to arrive at L KCl solution.

SOLUTION

$$0.150 \text{ L } \cancel{Pb(NO_3)_2 \text{ solution}} \times \frac{0.175 \cancel{\text{ mol } Pb(NO_3)_2}}{1 \text{ L } \cancel{Pb(NO_3)_2 \text{ solution}}}$$

$$\times \frac{2 \cancel{\text{ mol KCl}}}{1 \cancel{\text{ mol } Pb(NO_3)_2}} \times \frac{1 \text{ L KCl solution}}{0.150 \cancel{\text{ mol KCl}}} = 0.350 \text{ L KCl solution}$$

CHECK The final units (L KCl solution) are correct. The magnitude (0.350 L) seems reasonable because the reaction stoichiometry requires 2 mol of KCl per mole of $Pb(NO_3)_2$. Since the concentrations of the two solutions are not very different (0.150 M compared to 0.175 M), the volume of KCl required should be roughly two times the 0.150 L of $Pb(NO_3)_2$ given in the problem.

FOR PRACTICE 4.8

What volume (in mL) of a 0.150 M HNO_3 solution will completely react with 35.7 mL of a 0.108 M Na_2CO_3 solution according to the following balanced chemical equation?

$$Na_2CO_3\,(aq) + 2\,HNO_3\,(aq) \longrightarrow 2\,NaNO_3\,(aq) + CO_2\,(g) + H_2O(l)$$

FOR MORE PRACTICE 4.8

In the reaction above, what mass (in grams) of carbon dioxide forms?

Solute and Solvent Interactions

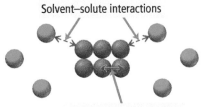

▲ **FIGURE 4.7 Solute and Solvent Interactions** When a solid is put into a solvent, the interactions between solvent and solute particles compete with the interactions among the solute particles themselves.

▲ **FIGURE 4.8 Charge Distribution in a Water Molecule** An uneven distribution of electrons within the water molecule causes the oxygen side of the molecule to have a partial negative charge and the hydrogen side to have a partial positive charge.

4.5 Types of Aqueous Solutions and Solubility

Consider two familiar aqueous solutions: salt water and sugar water. Salt water is a homogeneous mixture of NaCl and H_2O, and sugar water is a homogeneous mixture of $C_{12}H_{22}O_{11}$ and H_2O. You may have made these solutions yourself by adding table salt or sugar to water. As you stir either of these two substances into the water, it seems to disappear. However, you know that the original substance is still present because you can taste saltiness or sweetness in the water. How do solids such as salt and sugar dissolve in water?

When a solid is put into a liquid solvent, the attractive forces that hold the solid together (the solute–solute interactions) come into competition with the attractive forces between the solvent molecules and the particles that compose the solid (the solvent–solute interactions), as shown in Figure 4.7 ◄. For example, when sodium chloride is put into water, there is a competition between the attraction of Na^+ cations and Cl^- anions to each other (due to their opposite charges) and the attraction of Na^+ and Cl^- to water molecules. The attraction of Na^+ and Cl^- to water is based on the *polar nature* of the water molecule. For reasons we discuss later in this book (Section 9.6), the oxygen atom in water is electron-rich, giving it a partial negative charge (δ^-), as shown in Figure 4.8 ◄. The hydrogen atoms, in contrast, are electron-poor, giving them a partial positive charge (δ^+). As a result, the positively charged sodium ions are strongly attracted to the oxygen side of the water molecule (which has a partial negative charge), and the negatively charged chloride ions are attracted to the hydrogen side of the water molecule (which has a partial positive charge), as shown in Figure 4.9 ▼. In the case of NaCl, the attraction between the separated ions and the water molecules overcomes the attraction of sodium and chloride ions to each other, and the sodium chloride dissolves in the water (Figure 4.10 ▼).

Interactions in a Sodium Chloride Solution

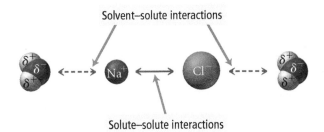

▲ **FIGURE 4.9 Solute and Solvent Interactions in a Sodium Chloride Solution** When sodium chloride is put into water, the attraction of Na^+ and Cl^- ions to water molecules competes with the attraction among the oppositely charged ions themselves.

Dissolution of an Ionic Compound

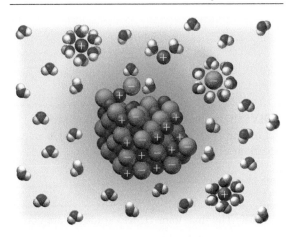

▲ **FIGURE 4.10 Sodium Chloride Dissolving in Water** The attraction between water molecules and the ions of sodium chloride causes NaCl to dissolve in the water.

Electrolyte and Nonelectrolyte Solutions

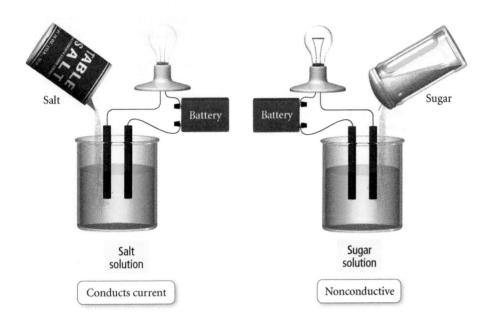

Salt

Battery   Battery

Sugar

Salt
solution

Sugar
solution

Conducts current

Nonconductive

◀ **FIGURE 4.11 Electrolyte and Non-electrolyte Solutions**   A solution of salt (an electrolyte) conducts electrical current. A solution of sugar (a nonelectrolyte) does not.

Electrolyte and Nonelectrolyte Solutions

As Figure 4.11 ▲ shows, a salt solution conducts electricity while a sugar solution does not. The difference between the way that salt (an ionic compound) and sugar (a molecular compound) dissolve in water illustrates a fundamental difference between types of solutions. Ionic compounds such as the sodium chloride in the previous example, dissociate into their component ions when they dissolve in water. An NaCl solution, represented as NaCl(*aq*), does not contain any NaCl units, but rather dissolved Na^+ ions and Cl^- ions. The dissolved ions act as charge carriers, allowing the solution to conduct electricity. Substances that dissolve in water to form solutions that conduct electricity are **electrolytes**. Substances such as sodium chloride that completely dissociate into ions when they dissolve in water are **strong electrolytes**, and the resulting solutions are strong electrolyte solutions.

In contrast to sodium chloride, sugar is a molecular compound. Most molecular compounds—with the important exception of acids, which we discuss shortly—dissolve in water as intact molecules. Sugar dissolves because the attraction between sugar molecules and water molecules shown in Figure 4.12 ▼ overcomes the attraction of sugar molecules

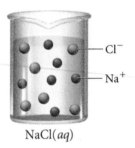

Cl^-

Na^+

NaCl(*aq*)

Interactions between Sugar and Water Molecules

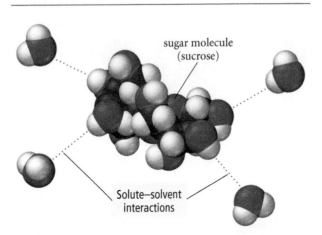

sugar molecule
(sucrose)

Solute–solvent
interactions

◀ **FIGURE 4.12 Sugar and Water Interactions**   Partial charges on sugar molecules and water molecules (discussed more fully in Chapter 11) result in attractions between the sugar molecules and water molecules.

$C_{12}H_{22}O_{11}(aq)$

Unlike soluble ionic compounds, which contain ions and therefore *dissociate* in water, acids are molecular compounds that *ionize* in water.

to each other (Figure 4.13 ▼). So unlike a sodium chloride solution (which is composed of dissociated ions), a sugar solution is composed of intact $C_{12}H_{22}O_{11}$ molecules homogeneously mixed with the water molecules. Compounds such as sugar that do not dissociate into ions when dissolved in water are called **nonelectrolytes**, and the resulting solutions—called *nonelectrolyte solutions*—do not conduct electricity.

Acids, first encountered in Section 3.6, are molecular compounds, but they do ionize—form ions—when they dissolve in water. Hydrochloric acid (HCl) is a molecular compound that ionizes into H^+ and Cl^- when it dissolves in water. HCl is an example of a **strong acid**, one that completely ionizes in solution. Since strong acids completely ionize in solution, they are also strong electrolytes. We represent the complete ionization of a strong acid with a single reaction arrow between the acid and its ionized form:

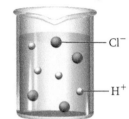

$HCl(aq)$

$$HCl\,(aq) \longrightarrow H^+\,(aq) + Cl^-\,(aq)$$

Many acids are **weak acids**; they do not completely ionize in water. For example, acetic acid ($HC_2H_3O_2$), the acid present in vinegar, is a weak acid. A solution of a weak acid is composed mostly of the nonionized acid—only a small percentage of the acid molecules ionize. We represent the partial ionization of a weak acid with opposing half arrows between the reactants and products:

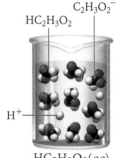

$HC_2H_3O_2$ $C_2H_3O_2^-$

H^+

$HC_2H_3O_2(aq)$

$$HC_2H_3O_2(aq) \rightleftharpoons H^+(aq) + C_2H_3O_2^-(aq)$$

Weak acids are classified as **weak electrolytes** and the resulting solutions—called *weak electrolyte solutions*—conduct electricity only weakly. Figure 4.14 ▼ summarizes the electrolytic properties of solutions.

Sugar Solution

▲ **FIGURE 4.13 A Sugar Solution** Sugar dissolves because the attractions between sugar molecules and water molecules, which both contain a distribution of electrons that results in partial positive and partial negative charges, overcome the attractions between sugar molecules to each other.

Electrolytic Properties of Solutions

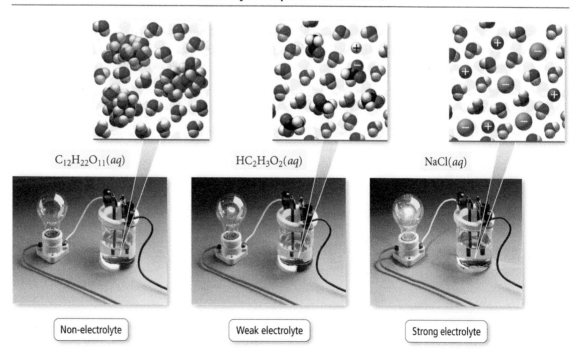

$C_{12}H_{22}O_{11}(aq)$ $HC_2H_3O_2(aq)$ $NaCl(aq)$

Non-electrolyte Weak electrolyte Strong electrolyte

▲ **FIGURE 4.14 Electrolytic Properties of Solutions**

The Solubility of Ionic Compounds

We have just seen that, when an ionic compound dissolves in water, the resulting solution contains, not the intact ionic compound itself, but its component ions dissolved in water. However, not all ionic compounds dissolve in water. If we add AgCl to water, for example, it remains solid and appears as a white powder at the bottom of the water.

In general, a compound is termed **soluble** if it dissolves in water and **insoluble** if it does not. However, these classifications are a bit of an oversimplification. (In reality, solubility is a continuum and even "insoluble" compounds dissolve to some extent, though usually orders of magnitude less than soluble compounds.) For example, silver nitrate is soluble. If we mix solid $AgNO_3$ with water, it dissolves and forms a strong electrolyte solution. Silver chloride, on the other hand, is almost completely insoluble. If we mix solid AgCl with water, virtually all of it remains as a solid within the liquid water.

▲ AgCl does not dissolve in water; it remains as a white powder at the bottom of the beaker.

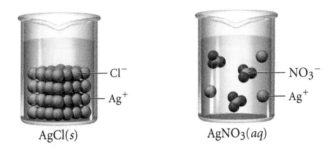

AgCl(s) $AgNO_3$(aq)

There is no easy way to tell whether a particular compound is soluble or insoluble just by looking at its formula. In Section 12.3, we examine more closely the energy changes associated with solution formation. For now, however, we can follow a set of empirical rules that chemists have inferred from observations on many ionic compounds. These are *solubility rules* and are summarized in Table 4.1.

The solubility rules state that compounds containing the sodium ion are soluble. That means that compounds such as NaBr, $NaNO_3$, Na_2SO_4, NaOH, and Na_2CO_3 all dissolve in water to form strong electrolyte solutions. Similarly, the solubility rules state that

TABLE 4.1 Solubility Rules for Ionic Compounds in Water

Compounds Containing the Following Ions Are Generally Soluble	Exceptions
Li^+, Na^+, K^+, and NH_4^+	None x
NO_3^- and $C_2H_3O_2^-$	None
Cl^-, Br^-, and I^-	When these ions pair with Ag^+, Hg_2^{2+} or Pb^{2+}, the resulting compounds are insoluble.
SO_4^{2-}	When SO_4^{2-} pairs with Sr^{2+}, Ba^{2+}, Pb^{2+}, Ag^+, or Ca^{2+}, the resulting compound is insoluble.

Compounds Containing the Following Ions Are Generally Insoluble	Exceptions
OH^- and S^{2-}	When these ions pair with Li^+, Na^+, K^+, or NH_4^+, the resulting compounds are soluble.
	When S^{2-} pairs with Ca^{2+}, Sr^{2+}, or Ba^{2+}, the resulting compound is soluble.
	When OH^- pairs with Ca^{2+}, Sr^{2+}, or Ba^{2+}, the resulting compound is slightly soluble.
CO_3^{2-} and PO_4^{3-}	When these ions pair with Li^+, Na^+, K^+, or NH_4^+, the resulting compounds are soluble.

compounds containing the NO_3^- ion are soluble. That means that compounds such as $AgNO_3$, $Pb(NO_3)_2$, $NaNO_3$, $Ca(NO_3)_2$, and $Sr(NO_3)_2$ all dissolve in water to form strong electrolyte solutions.

Notice that when compounds containing polyatomic ions such as NO_3^- dissolve, the polyatomic ions dissolve as intact units.

The solubility rules also state that, with some exceptions, compounds containing the CO_3^{2-} ion are insoluble. Therefore, compounds such as $CuCO_3$, $CaCO_3$, $SrCO_3$, and $FeCO_3$ do not dissolve in water. Note that the solubility rules contain many exceptions. For example, compounds containing CO_3^{2-} *are* soluble when paired with Li^+, Na^+, K^+, or NH_4^+. Thus Li_2CO_3, Na_2CO_3, K_2CO_3, and $(NH_4)_2CO_3$ are all soluble.

EXAMPLE 4.9 Predicting whether an Ionic Compound Is Soluble

Predict whether each compound is soluble or insoluble.

(a) $PbCl_2$ (b) $CuCl_2$ (c) $Ca(NO_3)_2$ (d) $BaSO_4$

SOLUTION

(a) Insoluble. Compounds containing Cl^- are normally soluble, but Pb^{2+} is an exception.

(b) Soluble. Compounds containing Cl^- are normally soluble and Cu^{2+} is not an exception.

(c) Soluble. Compounds containing NO_3^- are always soluble.

(d) Insoluble. Compounds containing SO_4^{2-} are normally soluble, but Ba^{2+} is an exception.

FOR PRACTICE 4.9

Predict whether each compound is soluble or insoluble.

(a) NiS (b) $Mg_3(PO_4)_2$ (c) Li_2CO_3 (d) NH_4Cl

4.6 Precipitation Reactions

▲ The reaction of ions in hard water with soap produces a gray curd you can see after you drain the bathwater.

Have you ever taken a bath in hard water? Hard water contains dissolved ions such as Ca^{2+} and Mg^{2+} that diminish the effectiveness of soap. These ions react with soap to form a gray curd that may appear as "bathtub ring" when you drain the tub. Hard water is particularly troublesome when washing clothes. Imagine how your white shirt would look covered with the gray curd from the bathtub and you can understand the problem. Consequently, most laundry detergents include substances designed to remove Ca^{2+} and Mg^{2+} from the laundry mixture. The most common substance used for this purpose is sodium carbonate, which dissolves in water to form sodium cations (Na^+) and carbonate (CO_3^{2-}) anions:

$$Na_2CO_3 \ (aq) \longrightarrow 2\,Na^+ \ (aq) + CO_3^{2-} \ (aq)$$

Sodium carbonate is soluble, but calcium carbonate and magnesium carbonate are not (see the solubility rules in Table 4.1). Consequently, the carbonate anions react with dissolved Mg^{2+} and Ca^{2+} ions in hard water to form solids that *precipitate* from (or come out of) solution:

$$Mg^{2+} \ (aq) + CO_3^{2-} \ (aq) \longrightarrow MgCO_3 \ (s)$$
$$Ca^{2+} \ (aq) + CO_3^{2-} \ (aq) \longrightarrow CaCO_3 \ (s)$$

The precipitation of these ions prevents their reaction with the soap, eliminating curd and preventing white shirts from turning gray.

The reactions between CO_3^{2-} and Mg^{2+} and Ca^{2+} are examples of **precipitation reactions**, ones in which a solid or **precipitate** forms when we mix two solutions. Precipitation reactions are common in chemistry. As another example, consider potassium iodide and lead(II) nitrate, which each form colorless, strong electrolyte solutions when dissolved in water. When the two solutions are combined, however, a brilliant yellow pre-

Precipitation Reaction

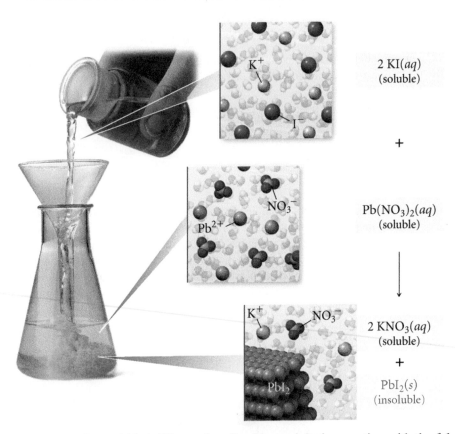

$$2 \, KI(aq) \; + \; Pb(NO_3)_2(aq) \longrightarrow 2 \, KNO_3(aq) \; + \; PbI_2(s)$$

(soluble)   (soluble)   (soluble)   (insoluble)

When a potassium iodide solution is mixed with a lead(II) nitrate solution, a yellow lead(II) iodide precipitate forms.

$2 \, KI(aq)$
(soluble)

+

$Pb(NO_3)_2(aq)$
(soluble)

$2 \, KNO_3(aq)$
(soluble)

+

$PbI_2(s)$
(insoluble)

◀ **FIGURE 4.15 Precipitation of Lead(II) Iodide**   When a potassium iodide solution is mixed with a lead(II) nitrate solution, a yellow lead(II) iodide precipitate forms.

cipitate forms (Figure 4.15 ▲). We can describe this precipitation reaction with the following chemical equation:

$$2 \, KI(aq) + Pb(NO_3)_2 \, (aq) \longrightarrow 2 \, KNO_3 \, (aq) + PbI_2(s)$$

Precipitation reactions do not always occur when two aqueous solutions are mixed. For example, if we combine solutions of $KI(aq)$ and $NaCl(aq)$, nothing happens (Figure 4.16 ▶ on the next page):

$$KI(aq) + NaCl(aq) \longrightarrow NO \; REACTION$$

The key to predicting precipitation reactions is to understand that *only insoluble compounds form precipitates.* In a precipitation reaction, two solutions containing soluble compounds combine and an insoluble compound precipitates. Consider the precipitation reaction described previously:

$$2 \, KI(aq) + Pb(NO_3)_2 \, (aq) \longrightarrow PbI_2(s) + 2 \, KNO_3(aq)$$

   soluble   soluble   insoluble   soluble

KI and $Pb(NO_3)_2$ are both soluble, but the precipitate, PbI_2, is insoluble. Before mixing, $KI(aq)$ and $Pb(NO_3)_2(aq)$ are both dissociated in their respective solutions:

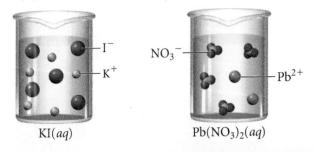

KI(aq)   Pb(NO₃)₂(aq)

The instant that the solutions come into contact, all four ions are present:

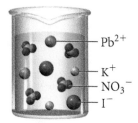

KI(aq) and Pb(NO$_3$)$_2$(aq)

Now, new compounds—one or both of which might be insoluble—are possible. Specifically, the cation from either compound can pair with the anion from the other to form possibly insoluble products:

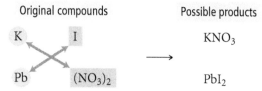

If the possible products are both soluble, no reaction occurs and no precipitate forms. If one or both of the possible products are insoluble, a precipitation reaction occurs. In this case, KNO$_3$ is soluble, but PbI$_2$ is insoluble. Consequently, PbI$_2$ precipitates.

To predict whether a precipitation reaction will occur when two solutions are mixed and to write an equation for the reaction, we use the procedure that follows. The steps are outlined in the left column, and two examples of applying the procedure are shown in the center and right columns.

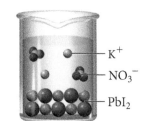

PbI$_2$(s) and KNO$_3$(aq)

No Reaction

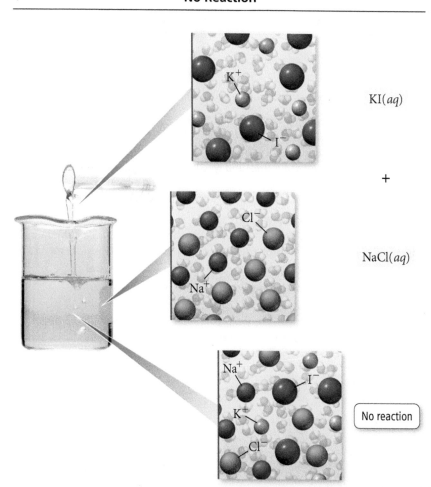

KI(aq)

+

NaCl(aq)

No reaction

▶ **FIGURE 4.16 No Precipitation**
When a potassium iodide solution is mixed with a sodium chloride solution, no reaction occurs.

PROCEDURE FOR... **Writing Equations for Precipitation Reactions**	**EXAMPLE 4.10** **Writing Equations for Precipitation Reactions** Write an equation for the precipitation reaction that occurs (if any) when solutions of potassium carbonate and nickel(II) chloride are mixed.	**EXAMPLE 4.11** **Writing Equations for Precipitation Reactions** Write an equation for the precipitation reaction that occurs (if any) when solutions of sodium nitrate and lithium sulfate are mixed.
1. Write the formulas of the two compounds being mixed as reactants in a chemical equation.	$K_2CO_3(aq) + NiCl_2(aq) \longrightarrow$	$NaNO_3(aq) + Li_2SO_4(aq) \longrightarrow$
2. Below the equation, write the formulas of the products that could form from the reactants. Obtain these by combining the cation from each reactant with the anion from the other. Make sure to write correct formulas for these ionic compounds, as described in Section 3.5.	$K_2CO_3(aq) + NiCl_2(aq) \longrightarrow$ Possible products KCl $NiCO_3$	$NaNO_3(aq) + Li_2SO_4(aq) \longrightarrow$ Possible products $LiNO_3$ Na_2SO_4
3. Use the solubility rules to determine whether any of the possible products are insoluble.	KCl is soluble. (Compounds containing Cl^- are usually soluble and K^+ is not an exception.) $NiCO_3$ is insoluble. (Compounds containing CO_3^{2-} are usually insoluble and Ni^{2+} is not an exception.)	$LiNO_3$ is soluble. (Compounds containing NO_3^- are soluble and Li^+ is not an exception.) Na_2SO_4 is soluble. (Compounds containing SO_4^{2-} are generally soluble and Na^+ is not an exception.)
4. If all of the possible products are soluble, there will be no precipitate. Write NO REACTION after the arrow.	Since this example has an insoluble product, we proceed to the next step.	Since this example has no insoluble product, there is no reaction. $NaNO_3(aq) + Li_2SO_4(aq) \longrightarrow$ NO REACTION
5. If any of the possible products are insoluble, write their formulas as the products of the reaction using (s) to indicate solid. Write any soluble products with (aq) to indicate aqueous.	$K_2CO_3(aq) + NiCl_2(aq) \longrightarrow$ $NiCO_3(s) + KCl(aq)$	
6. Balance the equation. Remember to adjust only coefficients here, not subscripts.	$K_2CO_3(aq) + NiCl_2(aq) \longrightarrow$ $NiCO_3(s) + 2KCl(aq)$ **FOR PRACTICE 4.10** Write an equation for the precipitation reaction that occurs (if any) when solutions of ammonium chloride and iron(III) nitrate are mixed.	**FOR PRACTICE 4.11** Write an equation for the precipitation reaction that occurs (if any) when solutions of sodium hydroxide and copper(II) bromide are mixed.

4.7 Representing Aqueous Reactions: Molecular, Ionic, and Complete Ionic Equations

Consider the following equation for a precipitation reaction:

$$Pb(NO_3)_2\ (aq) + 2\ KCl(aq) \longrightarrow PbCl_2\ (s) + 2\ KNO_3(aq)$$

This equation is a **molecular equation**, an equation showing the complete neutral formulas for each compound in the reaction as if they existed as molecules. However, in actual

solutions of soluble ionic compounds, dissolved substances are present as ions. We can write equations for reactions occurring in aqueous solution in a way that better shows the dissociated nature of dissolved ionic compounds. For example, the above equation can be rewritten as follows:

$$Pb^{2+}\,(aq) + 2\,NO_3^{\,-}\,(aq) + 2\,K^+\,(aq) + 2\,Cl^-(aq) \longrightarrow$$
$$PbCl_2\,(s) + 2\,K^+\,(aq) + 2\,NO_3^{\,-}(aq)$$

Equations such as this, which list all of the ions present as either reactants or products in a chemical reaction, are called **complete ionic equations**.

Notice that in the complete ionic equation, some of the ions in solution appear unchanged on both sides of the equation. These ions are called **spectator ions** because they do not participate in the reaction.

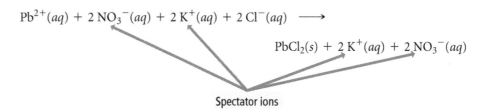

Spectator ions

To simplify the equation, and to show more clearly what is happening, we can omit spectator ions:

$$Pb^{2+}\,(aq) + 2\,Cl^-\,(aq) \longrightarrow PbCl_2\,(s)$$

Equations that show only the species that actually change during the reaction are called **net ionic equations**.

As another example, consider the following reaction between HCl(*aq*) and KOH(*aq*):

$$HCl(aq) + KOH(aq) \longrightarrow H_2O(l) + KCl(aq)$$

Since HCl, KOH, and KCl all exist in solution primarily as independent ions, the complete ionic equation is:

$$H^+\,(aq) + Cl^-\,(aq) + K^+\,(aq) + OH^-(aq) \longrightarrow H_2O(l) + K^+\,(aq) + Cl^-\,(aq)$$

To write the net ionic equation, we remove the spectator ions, those that are unchanged on both sides of the equation:

$$H^+(aq) + Cl^-(aq) + K^+(aq) + OH^-(aq) \longrightarrow H_2O(l) + K^+(aq) + Cl^-(aq)$$

Spectator ions

The net ionic equation is $H^+\,(aq) + OH^-\,(aq) \longrightarrow H_2O(l)$.

Summarizing Aqueous Equations:

▶ A **molecular equation** is a chemical equation showing the complete, neutral formulas for every compound in a reaction.

▶ A **complete ionic equation** is a chemical equation showing all of the species as they are actually present in solution.

▶ A **net ionic equation** is an equation showing only the species that actually change during the reaction.

EXAMPLE 4.12 Writing Complete Ionic and Net Ionic Equations

Consider the following precipitation reaction occurring in aqueous solution:

$$3\ SrCl_2(aq) + 2\ Li_3PO_4(aq) \longrightarrow Sr_3(PO_4)_2(s) + 6\ LiCl(aq)$$

Write the complete ionic equation and net ionic equation for this reaction.

SOLUTION Write the complete ionic equation by separating aqueous ionic compounds into their constituent ions. The $Sr_3(PO_4)_2(s)$, precipitating as a solid, remains as one unit.	**Complete ionic equation:** $3\ Sr^{2+}(aq) + 6\ Cl^-(aq) + 6\ Li^+(aq) + 2\ PO_4{}^{3-}(aq) \longrightarrow$ $Sr_3(PO_4)_2(s) + 6\ Li^+(aq) + 6\ Cl^-(aq)$
Write the net ionic equation by eliminating the spectator ions, those that do not change from one side of the reaction to the other.	**Net ionic equation:** $3\ Sr^{2+}(aq) + 2\ PO_4{}^{3-}(aq) \longrightarrow Sr_3(PO_4)_2(s)$

FOR PRACTICE 4.12

Consider the following reaction occurring in aqueous solution:

$$2\ HI(aq) + Ba(OH)_2(aq) \longrightarrow 2\ H_2O(l) + BaI_2(aq)$$

Write the complete ionic equation and net ionic equation for this reaction.

FOR MORE PRACTICE 4.12

Write complete ionic and net ionic equations for the following reaction occurring in aqueous solution:

$$2\ AgNO_3(aq) + MgCl_2(aq) \longrightarrow 2\ AgCl(s) + Mg(NO_3)_2(aq)$$

4.8 Acid–Base and Gas-Evolution Reactions

Two other important classes of reactions that occur in aqueous solution are acid–base reactions and gas-evolution reactions. In an **acid–base reaction** (also called a **neutralization reaction**), an acid reacts with a base and the two neutralize each other, producing water (or in some cases a weak electrolyte). In a **gas-evolution reaction**, a gas forms, resulting in bubbling. In both cases, as in precipitation reactions, the reactions occur when the anion from one reactant combines with the cation of the other. Many gas-evolution reactions are also acid–base reactions.

Acid–Base Reactions

Our stomachs contain hydrochloric acid, which acts in the digestion of food. Certain foods or stress, however, can increase the stomach's acidity to uncomfortable levels, causing acid stomach or heartburn. Antacids are over-the-counter medicines that work by reacting with and neutralizing stomach acid. Antacids employ different *bases*—substances that produce hydroxide (OH^-) ions in water—as neutralizing agents. Milk of magnesia, for example, contains $Mg(OH)_2$ and Mylanta contains $Al(OH)_3$. All antacids, regardless of the base they employ, have the same effect of neutralizing stomach acid and relieving heartburn through *acid–base reactions*.

We learned in Chapter 3 that an acid forms H^+ ions in solution, and we learned above that a base is a substance that produces OH^- ions in solution:

- Acid: Substance that produces H^+ ions in aqueous solution
- Base: Substance that produces OH^- ions in aqueous solution

These definitions of acids and bases, called the **Arrhenius definitions**, are named after Swedish chemist Svante Arrhenius (1859–1927). In Chapter 15, we will learn more general definitions of acids and bases, but these are sufficient to describe neutralization reactions.

▲ Gas-evolution reactions, such as the reaction of hydrochloric acid with limestone ($CaCO_3$), typically produce CO_2; bubbling occurs as the gas is released.

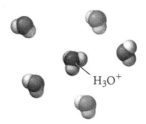

H_3O^+

► **FIGURE 4.17 The Hydronium Ion**
Protons normally associate with water molecules in solution to form H_3O^+ ions, which in turn interact with other water molecules.

▲ Lemons, limes, and vinegar contain acids. Vitamin C and aspirin are acids.

> H^+ and H_3O^+ are used interchangeably because, even though H^+ associates with water to form hydronium, it is the H^+ part that reacts with other substances such as bases.

▲ Many common household products are bases.

According to the Arrhenius definition, HCl is an acid because it produces H^+ ions in solution:

$$HCl(aq) \longrightarrow H^+(aq) + Cl^-(aq)$$

An H^+ ion is a bare proton. In solution bare protons normally associate with water molecules to form **hydronium ions** (Figure 4.17 ▲):

$$H^+(aq) + H_2O \longrightarrow H_3O^+(aq)$$

Chemists often use $H^+(aq)$ and $H_3O^+(aq)$ interchangeably, however, to refer to the same thing—a hydronium ion. The chemical equation for the ionization of HCl and other acids is often written to show the association of the proton with a water molecule to form the hydronium ion:

$$HCl(aq) + H_2O \longrightarrow H_3O^+(aq) + Cl^-(aq)$$

Some acids—called **polyprotic acids**—contain more than one ionizable proton and release them sequentially. For example, sulfuric acid, H_2SO_4, is a **diprotic acid**. It is strong in its first ionizable proton, but weak in its second:

$$H_2SO_4(aq) \longrightarrow H^+(aq) + HSO_4^-(aq)$$
$$HSO_4^-(aq) \rightleftharpoons H^+(aq) + SO_4^{2-}(aq)$$

According to the Arrhenius definition, NaOH is a base because it produces OH^- ions in solution:

$$NaOH(aq) \longrightarrow Na^+(aq) + OH^-(aq)$$

In analogy to diprotic acids, some bases, such as $Sr(OH)_2$, produce two moles of OH^- per mole of the base.

$$Sr(OH)_2(aq) \longrightarrow Sr^{2+}(aq) + 2\,OH^-(aq)$$

Table 4.2 lists common acids and bases. You can find acids and bases in many everyday substances. Foods such as citrus fruits and vinegar contain acids. Soap, baking soda, and milk of magnesia all contain bases.

TABLE 4.2 Some Common Acids and Bases

Name of Acid	Formula	Name of Base	Formula
Hydrochloric acid	HCl	Sodium hydroxide	NaOH
Hydrobromic acid	HBr	Lithium hydroxide	LiOH
Hydroiodic acid	HI	Potassium hydroxide	KOH
Nitric acid	HNO_3	Calcium hydroxide	$Ca(OH)_2$
Sulfuric acid	H_2SO_4	Barium hydroxide	$Ba(OH)_2$
Perchloric acid	$HClO_4$	Ammonia*	NH_3 (weak base)
Acetic acid	$HC_2H_3O_2$ (weak acid)		
Hydrofluoric acid	HF (weak acid)		

*Ammonia does not contain OH^-, but it produces OH^- in a reaction with water that occurs only to a small extent: $NH_3(aq) + H_2O(l) \rightleftharpoons NH_4^+(aq) + OH^-(aq)$.

Acid–Base Reaction

$$HCl(aq) + NaOH(aq) \longrightarrow H_2O(l) + NaCl(aq)$$

The reaction between hydrochloric acid and sodium hydroxide forms water and a salt, sodium chloride, which remains dissolved in the solution.

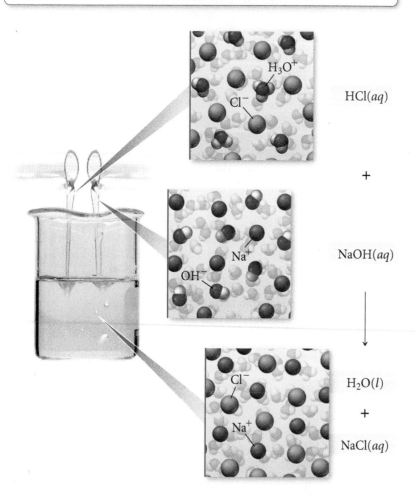

$HCl(aq)$

+

$NaOH(aq)$

$H_2O(l)$

+

$NaCl(aq)$

◀ **FIGURE 4.18 Acid–Base Reaction**
The reaction between hydrochloric acid and sodium hydroxide forms water and a salt, sodium chloride, which remains dissolved in the solution.

When we mix an acid and a base, the $H^+(aq)$ from the acid—whether it is weak or strong—combines with the $OH^-(aq)$ from the base to form $H_2O(l)$ (Figure 4.18 ▲). Consider the reaction between hydrochloric acid and sodium hydroxide:

$$HCl(aq) + NaOH(aq) \longrightarrow H_2O(l) + NaCl(aq)$$

| Acid | Base | | Water | Salt |

Acid–base reactions generally form water and an ionic compound—called a **salt**—that usually remains dissolved in the solution. The net ionic equation for many acid–base reactions is:

$$H^+(aq) + OH^-(aq) \longrightarrow H_2O(l)$$

Another example of an acid–base reaction is the reaction between sulfuric acid and potassium hydroxide:

$$H_2SO_4(aq) + 2\,KOH(aq) \longrightarrow 2\,H_2O(l) + K_2SO_4(aq)$$

acid   base   water   salt

Again, notice the pattern of acid and base reacting to form water and a salt.

$$\textbf{Acid + Base} \longrightarrow \textbf{Water + Salt} \quad \text{(acid–base reactions)}$$

When writing equations for acid–base reactions, write the formula of the salt using the procedure for writing formulas of ionic compounds given in Section 3.5.

The word *salt* in this sense applies to any ionic compound and is therefore more general than the common usage, which refers only to table salt (NaCl).

EXAMPLE 4.13 Writing Equations for Acid–Base Reactions

Write a molecular and net ionic equation for the reaction between aqueous HI and aqueous $Ba(OH)_2$.

SOLUTION You must first identify these substances as an acid and a base. Begin by writing the skeletal reaction in which the acid and the base combine to form water and a salt.	$\underset{\text{acid}}{HI(aq)} + \underset{\text{base}}{Ba(OH)_2(aq)} \longrightarrow \underset{\text{water}}{H_2O(l)} + \underset{\text{salt}}{BaI_2(aq)}$
Next, balance the equation; this is the molecular equation.	$2\ HI(aq) + Ba(OH)_2(aq) \longrightarrow 2\ H_2O(l) + BaI_2(aq)$
Write the net ionic equation by removing the spectator ions.	$2\ H^+(aq) + 2\ OH^-(aq) \longrightarrow 2\ H_2O(l)$ or simply $H^+(aq) + OH^-(aq) \longrightarrow H_2O(l)$

FOR PRACTICE 4.13

Write a molecular and a net ionic equation for the reaction that occurs between aqueous H_2SO_4 and aqueous LiOH.

Acid–Base Titrations We can apply the principles of acid–base neutralization and stoichiometry to a common laboratory procedure called a *titration*. In a **titration**, a substance in a solution of known concentration is reacted with another substance in a solution of unknown concentration. For example, consider the following acid–base reaction:

$$HCl(aq) + NaOH(aq) \longrightarrow H_2O(l) + NaCl(aq)$$

The net ionic equation for this reaction eliminates the spectator ions:

$$H^+(aq) + OH^-(aq) \longrightarrow H_2O$$

Suppose we have an HCl solution represented by the following molecular diagram (we have omitted the Cl^- ions and the H_2O molecules not involved in the reaction from this representation for clarity):

▼ **FIGURE 4.19** **Acid–Base Titration**

Acid–Base Titration

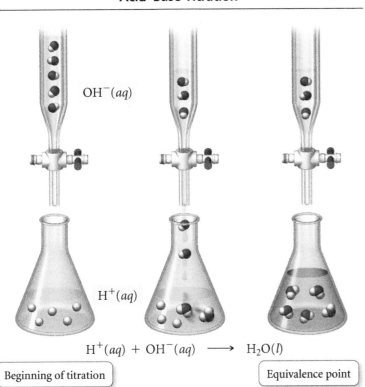

Beginning of titration

$$H^+(aq) + OH^-(aq) \longrightarrow H_2O(l)$$

Equivalence point

In titrating this sample, we slowly add a solution of known OH^- concentration, as shown in the molecular diagrams in Figure 4.19 ◄. As the OH^- is added, it reacts with and neutralizes the H^+, forming water. At the **equivalence point**—the point in the titration when the number of moles of OH^- equals the number of moles of H^+ in solution—the titration is complete. The equivalence point is typically signaled by an **indicator**, a dye whose color depends on the acidity or basicity of the solution (Figure 4.20 ►).

We cover acid–base titrations and indicators in more detail in Chapter 16. In most laboratory titrations, the concentration of one of the reactant solutions is unknown, and the concentration of the other is precisely known. By carefully measuring the volume of each solution required to reach the equivalence point, the concentration of the unknown solution can be determined, as demonstrated in the following example.

Indicator in Titration

◀ **FIGURE 4.20 Titration** In this titration, NaOH is added to a dilute HCl solution. When the NaOH and HCl reach stoichiometric proportions (the equivalence point), the phenolphthalein indicator changes color to pink.

EXAMPLE 4.14 Acid–Base Titration

The titration of a 10.00-mL sample of an HCl solution of unknown concentration requires 12.54 mL of a 0.100 M NaOH solution to reach the equivalence point. What is the concentration of the unknown HCl solution in M?

SORT You are given the volume and concentration of NaOH solution required to titrate a given volume of HCl solution. You are asked to find the concentration of the HCl solution.	**GIVEN:** 12.54 mL of NaOH solution, 0.100 M NaOH solution, 10.00 mL of HCl solution **FIND:** concentration of HCl solution
STRATEGIZE Since this problem involves an acid–base neutralization reaction between HCl and NaOH, you must start by writing the balanced equation, using the techniques covered earlier in this section. The first part of the conceptual plan has the following form: volume A → moles A → moles B. The concentration of the NaOH solution is a conversion factor between moles and volume of NaOH. The balanced equation provides the relationship between number of moles of NaOH and number of moles of HCl. In the second part of the conceptual plan, use the number of moles of HCl (from the first part) and the volume of HCl solution (given) to calculate the molarity of the HCl solution.	$HCl(aq) + NaOH(aq) \longrightarrow H_2O(l) + NaCl(aq)$ **CONCEPTUAL PLAN** 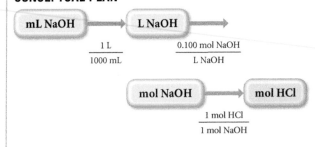 **RELATIONSHIPS USED** $1 L = 1000 mL$ $M (NaOH) = \dfrac{0.100 \text{ mol NaOH}}{\text{L NaOH}}$ 1 mol HCl : 1 mol NaOH $Molarity (M) = \dfrac{\text{moles of solute (mol)}}{\text{volume of solution (L)}}$
SOLVE In the first part of the solution, determine the number of moles of HCl in the unknown solution. In the second part of the solution, divide the number of moles of HCl by the volume of the HCl solution in L. 10.0 mL is equivalent to 0.010 L.	**SOLUTION** $12.54 \text{ mL NaOH} \times \dfrac{1 \text{ L}}{1000 \text{ mL}} \times \dfrac{0.100 \text{ mol NaOH}}{\text{L NaOH}}$ $\times \dfrac{1 \text{ mol HCl}}{1 \text{ mol NaOH}} = 1.25 \times 10^{-3} \text{ mol HCl}$ $Molarity = \dfrac{1.25 \times 10^{-3} \text{ mol HCl}}{0.01000 \text{ L}} = 0.125 \text{ M HCl}$

CHECK The units of the answer (M HCl) are correct. The magnitude of the answer (0.125 M) seems reasonable because it is similar to the molarity of the NaOH solution, as expected from the reaction stoichiometry (1 mol HCl reacts with 1 mol NaOH) and the similar volumes of NaOH and HCl.

FOR PRACTICE 4.14

The titration of a 20.0-mL sample of an H_2SO_4 solution of unknown concentration requires 22.87 mL of a 0.158 M KOH solution to reach the equivalence point. What is the concentration of the unknown H_2SO_4 solution?

FOR MORE PRACTICE 4.14

What volume (in mL) of 0.200 M NaOH do we need to titrate 35.00 mL of 0.140 M HBr to the equivalence point?

Gas-Evolution Reactions

In a *gas-evolution reaction*, two aqueous solutions mix to form a gaseous product that bubbles out of solution. Some gas-evolution reactions form a gaseous product directly when the cation of one reactant combines with the anion of the other. For example, when sulfuric acid reacts with lithium sulfide, dihydrogen sulfide gas is formed:

$$H_2SO_4(aq) + Li_2S(aq) \longrightarrow \underset{\text{gas}}{H_2S(g)} + Li_2SO_4(aq)$$

Other gas-evolution reactions often form an intermediate product that then decomposes (breaks down into simpler substances) to form a gas. For example, when aqueous hydrochloric acid is mixed with aqueous sodium bicarbonate, the following reaction occurs (Figure 4.21 ▶):

Many gas-evolution reactions such as this one are also acid–base reactions. In Chapter 15 we will learn how ions such as CO_3^{2-} act as bases in aqueous solution.

$$HCl(aq) + NaHCO_3(aq) \longrightarrow \underset{\text{intermediate product}}{H_2CO_3(aq)} + NaCl(aq) \longrightarrow H_2O(l) + \underset{\text{gas}}{CO_2(g)} + NaCl(aq)$$

The intermediate product, H_2CO_3, is not stable and decomposes into H_2O and gaseous CO_2. Other important gas-evolution reactions form either H_2SO_3 or NH_4OH as intermediate products:

$$HCl(aq) + NaHSO_3(aq) \longrightarrow \underset{\text{intermediate product}}{H_2SO_3(aq)} + NaCl(aq) \longrightarrow H_2O(l) + \underset{\text{gas}}{SO_2(g)} + NaCl(aq)$$

The intermediate product NH_4OH provides a convenient way to think about this reaction, but the extent to which it actually forms is debatable.

$$NH_4Cl(aq) + NaOH(aq) \longrightarrow \underset{\text{intermediate product}}{NH_4OH(aq)} + NaCl(aq) \longrightarrow H_2O(l) + \underset{\text{gas}}{NH_3(g)} + NaCl(aq)$$

Table 4.3 lists the main types of compounds that form gases in aqueous reactions, as well as the gases formed.

TABLE 4.3 Types of Compounds That Undergo Gas-Evolution Reactions

Reactant Type	Intermediate Product	Gas Evolved	Example
Sulfides	None	H_2S	$2\,HCl(aq) + K_2S(aq) \longrightarrow H_2S(g) + 2\,KCl(aq)$
Carbonates and bicarbonates	H_2CO_3	CO_2	$2\,HCl(aq) + K_2CO_3(aq) \longrightarrow H_2O(l) + CO_2(g) + 2\,KCl(aq)$
Sulfites and bisulfites	H_2SO_3	SO_2	$2\,HCl(aq) + K_2SO_3(aq) \longrightarrow H_2O(l) + SO_2(g) + 2\,KCl(aq)$
Ammonium	NH_4OH	NH_3	$NH_4Cl(aq) + KOH(aq) \longrightarrow H_2O(l) + NH_3(g) + KCl(aq)$

Gas-Evolution Reaction

$$NaHCO_3(aq) + HCl(aq) \longrightarrow H_2O(l) + NaCl(aq) + CO_2(g)$$

When aqueous sodium bicarbonate is mixed with aqueous hydrochloric acid, gaseous CO_2 bubbles are the result of the reaction.

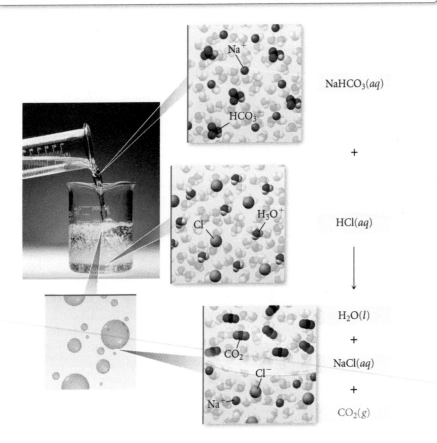

$NaHCO_3(aq)$

+

$HCl(aq)$

$H_2O(l)$

+

$NaCl(aq)$

+

$CO_2(g)$

◄ **FIGURE 4.21 Gas-Evolution Reaction** When aqueous hydrochloric acid is mixed with aqueous sodium bicarbonate, gaseous CO_2 bubbles out of the reaction mixture.

EXAMPLE 4.15 Writing Equations for Gas-Evolution Reactions

Write a molecular equation for the gas-evolution reaction that occurs when you mix aqueous nitric acid and aqueous sodium carbonate.

Begin by writing a skeletal equation in which the cation of each reactant combines with the anion of the other.	$HNO_3(aq) + Na_2CO_3(aq) \longrightarrow$ $\qquad\qquad\qquad H_2CO_3(aq) + NaNO_3(aq)$
You must then recognize that $H_2CO_3(aq)$ decomposes into $H_2O(l)$ and $CO_2(g)$ and write these products into the equation.	$HNO_3(aq) + Na_2CO_3(aq) \longrightarrow H_2O(l) + CO_2(g) + NaNO_3(aq)$
Finally, balance the equation.	$2\,HNO_3(aq) + Na_2CO_3(aq) \longrightarrow H_2O(l) + CO_2(g) + 2\,NaNO_3(aq)$

FOR PRACTICE 4.15

Write a molecular equation for the gas-evolution reaction that occurs when you mix aqueous hydrobromic acid and aqueous potassium sulfite.

FOR MORE PRACTICE 4.15

Write a net ionic equation for the reaction that occurs when you mix hydroiodic acid with calcium sulfide.

4.9 Oxidation–Reduction Reactions

Oxidation–reduction reactions are covered in more detail in Chapter 18.

Oxidation–reduction reactions or **redox reactions** are reactions in which electrons transfer from one reactant to the other. The rusting of iron, the bleaching of hair, and the production of electricity in batteries involve redox reactions. Many redox reactions involve the reaction of a substance with oxygen (Figure 4.22 ▾):

$$4\, Fe(s) + 3\, O_2\,(g) \longrightarrow 2\, Fe_2O_3(s) \qquad \text{(rusting of iron)}$$

$$2\, C_8H_{18}\,(l) + 25\, O_2\,(g) \longrightarrow 16\, CO_2\,(g) + 18\, H_2O(g) \quad \text{(combustion of octane)}$$

$$2\, H_2\,(g) + O_2\,(g) \longrightarrow 2H_2O(g) \qquad \text{(combustion of hydrogen)}$$

However, redox reactions need not involve oxygen. Consider, for example, the reaction between sodium and chlorine to form sodium chloride (NaCl), depicted in Figure 4.23 ▶:

$$2\, Na\,(s) + Cl_2\,(g) \longrightarrow 2\, NaCl(s)$$

This reaction is similar to the reaction between sodium and oxygen which forms sodium oxide:

$$4\, Na(s) + O_2\,(g) \longrightarrow 2\, Na_2O(s)$$

Helpful Mnemonics O I L R I G— **O**xidation **I**s **L**oss; **R**eduction **I**s **G**ain.

In both cases, a metal (which has a tendency to lose electrons) reacts with a nonmetal (which has a tendency to gain electrons). In both cases, metal atoms lose electrons to nonmetal atoms. A fundamental definition of **oxidation** is the loss of electrons, and a fundamental definition of **reduction** is the gain of electrons.

The transfer of electrons need not be a *complete* transfer (as occurs in the formation of an ionic compound) for the reaction to qualify as oxidation–reduction. For example, consider the reaction between hydrogen gas and chlorine gas:

$$H_2\,(g) + Cl_2\,(g) \longrightarrow 2\, HCl(g)$$

Oxidation–Reduction Reaction

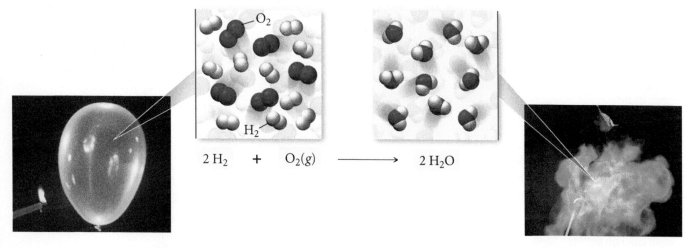

$$2\, H_2(g) + O_2(g) \longrightarrow 2\, H_2O(g)$$

Hydrogen and oxygen react to form gaseous water.

$$2\, H_2 \quad + \quad O_2(g) \longrightarrow 2\, H_2O$$

▲ **FIGURE 4.22 Oxidation–Reduction Reaction**   The hydrogen in the balloon reacts with oxygen upon ignition to form gaseous water (which is dispersed in the flame).

Oxidation–Reduction Reaction without Oxygen

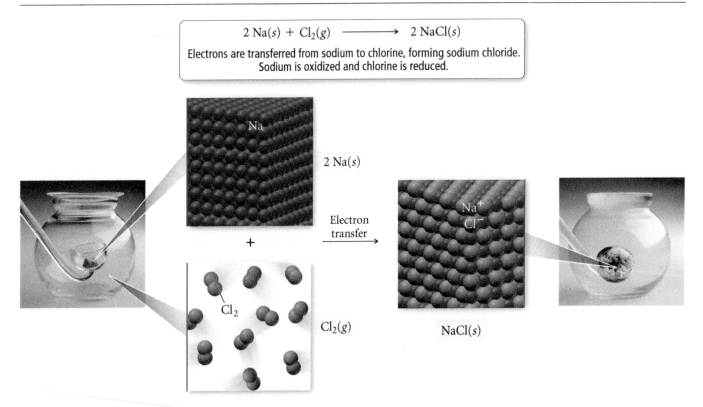

$$2 \, Na(s) + Cl_2(g) \longrightarrow 2 \, NaCl(s)$$

Electrons are transferred from sodium to chlorine, forming sodium chloride. Sodium is oxidized and chlorine is reduced.

Na

$2 \, Na(s)$

+

Cl_2

Electron transfer

Na^+
Cl^-

$Cl_2(g)$ NaCl(s)

▲ **FIGURE 4.23 Oxidation–Reduction without Oxygen**   When sodium reacts with chlorine, electrons transfer from the sodium to the chlorine, resulting in the formation of sodium chloride. In this redox reaction, sodium is oxidized and chlorine is reduced.

Even though hydrogen chloride is a molecular compound with a covalent bond, and even though the hydrogen has not completely transferred its electron to chlorine during the reaction, you can see from the electron density diagrams (Figure 4.24 ▶) that hydrogen has lost some of its electron density—it has *partially* transferred its electron to chlorine. In the reaction, hydrogen is oxidized and chlorine is reduced and, therefore, this is a redox reaction.

The ability of an element to attract electrons in a chemical bond is called electronegativity. We cover electronegativity in more detail in Section 8.6.

Oxidation States

Identifying whether or not a reaction between a metal and a nonmetal is a redox reaction is fairly straightforward because of ion formation. But how do we identify redox reactions that occur between nonmetals? Chemists have devised a scheme to track electrons before and after a chemical reaction. In this scheme—which is like bookkeeping for electrons—each shared electron is assigned to the atom that attracts the electrons most strongly. Then a number, called the **oxidation state** or **oxidation number**, is given to each atom based on the electron assignments. In other words, the oxidation number of an atom in a compound is the "charge" it would have if all shared electrons were assigned to the atom with the greatest attraction for those electrons.

For example, consider HCl. Since chlorine attracts electrons more strongly than hydrogen, we assign the two shared electrons in the bond to chlorine; then H (which has lost an electron in our assignment) has an oxidation state of +1, and Cl (which has gained one electron in our assignment) has an oxidation state of –1. Notice that, in contrast to ionic charges, which are usually written with the sign of the charge *after* the magnitude (1+ and 1–, for example), oxidation states are written with the sign of the charge *before*

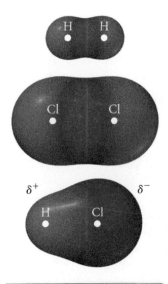

▶ **FIGURE 4.24 Redox with Partial Electron Transfer**
When hydrogen bonds to chlorine, the electrons are unevenly shared, resulting in an increase of electron density (reduction) for chlorine and a decrease in electron density (oxidation) for hydrogen.

H   H

Cl   Cl

δ^+ δ^-

H   Cl

Hydrogen loses electron density (reduction) and chlorine gains electron density (oxidation).

the magnitude (+1 and –1, for example). You can use the following rules to assign oxidation states to atoms in elements and compounds.

Rules for Assigning Oxidation States	Examples

Rules for Assigning Oxidation States
(These rules are hierarchical. If any two rules conflict, follow the rule that is higher on the list.)

Examples

1. The oxidation state of an atom in a free element is 0.

$$Cu \qquad Cl_2$$
0 ox state   0 ox state

2. The oxidation state of a monoatomic ion is equal to its charge. $\quad Ca^{2+} \qquad Cl^-$
+2 ox state   –1 ox state

3. The sum of the oxidation states of all atoms in:
   • A neutral molecule or formula unit is 0.

$$H_2O$$
2(H ox state) + 1(O ox state) = 0

   • An ion is equal to the charge of the ion.

$$NO_3^-$$
1(N ox sate) + 3(O ox state) = –1

4. In their compounds, metals have positive oxidation states.
   • Group 1A metals *always* have an oxidation state of +1.

$$NaCl$$
+1 ox state

   • Group 2A metals *always* have an oxidation state of +2.

$$CaF_2$$
+2 ox state

Nonmetal	Oxidation State	Example
Fluorine	–1	MgF_2 –1 ox state
Hydrogen	+1	H_2O +1 ox state
Oxygen	–2	CO_2 –2 ox state
Group 7A	–1	CCl_4 –1 ox state
Group 6A	–2	H_2S –2 ox state
Group 5A	–3	NH_3 –3 ox state

5. In their compounds, nonmetals are assigned oxidation states according to the table at left. Entries at the top of the table take precedence over entries at the bottom of the table.

When assigning oxidation states, keep these points in mind:

• The oxidation state of any given element generally depends on what other elements are present in the compound. (The exceptions are the group 1A and 2A metals, which are *always* +1 and +2, respectively.)

• Rule 3 must always be followed. Therefore, when following the hierarchy shown in rule 5, give priority to the element(s) highest on the list and then assign the oxidation state of the element lowest on the list using rule 3.

• When assigning oxidation states to elements that are not covered by rules 4 and 5 (such as carbon) use rule 3 to deduce their oxidation state once all other oxidation states have been assigned.

EXAMPLE 4.16 Assigning Oxidation States

Assign an oxidation state to each atom in each element, ion, or compound.

(a) Cl_2 **(b)** Na^+ **(c)** KF   **(d)** CO_2 **(e)** SO_4^{2-} **(f)** K_2O_2

SOLUTION

Since Cl_2 is a free element, the oxidation state of both Cl atoms is 0 (rule 1).	**(a)** Cl_2 ClCl 0 0
Since Na^+ is a monoatomic ion, the oxidation state of the Na^+ ion is +1 (rule 2).	**(b)** Na^+ Na^+ +1
The oxidation state of K is +1 (rule 4). The oxidation state of F is –1 (rule 5). Since this is a neutral compound, the sum of the oxidation states is 0.	**(c)** KF KF +1 –1 sum: +1 –1 = 0

The oxidation state of oxygen is –2 (rule 5). The oxidation state of carbon must be deduced using rule 3, which says that the sum of the oxidation states of all the atoms must be 0.	**(d)** CO_2 (C ox state) + 2(O ox state) = 0 (C ox sate) + 2(−2) = 0 C ox state = +4 $\underset{+4\ -2}{CO_2}$ sum: +4+2(−2)=0
The oxidation state of oxygen is –2 (rule 5). We would ordinarily expect the oxidation state of S to be –2 (rule 5). However, if that were the case, the sum of the oxidation states would not equal the charge of the ion. Since O is higher on the list than S, it takes priority and we compute the oxidation state of sulfur by setting the *sum* of all of the oxidation states equal to –2 (the charge of the ion).	**(e)** $SO_4{}^{2-}$ (S ox state) + 4(O ox state) = −2 (S ox state) + 4(−2) = −2 S ox state = +6 $\underset{+6\ -2}{SO_4{}^{2-}}$ sum: +6+4(−2)=−2
The oxidation state of potassium is +1 (rule 4). We would ordinarily expect the oxidation state of O to be –2 (rule 5), but rule 4 takes priority, and we deduce the oxidation state of O by setting the sum of all of the oxidation states equal to 0.	**(f)** K_2O_2 2(K ox state) + 2(O ox state) = 0 2(+1) + 2(O ox state) = 0 O ox state = −1 $\underset{+1\ -1}{K_2O_2}$ sum: 2(+1)+2(−1)=0

FOR PRACTICE 4.16

Assign an oxidation state to each atom in each element, ion, or compound.

(a) Cr   **(b)** Cr^{3+} **(c)** CCl_4 **(d)** $SrBr_2$ **(e)** SO_3 **(f)** $NO_3{}^-$

In most cases, oxidation states are positive or negative integers; however, on occasion an atom within a compound can have a fractional oxidation state. Consider KO_2. The oxidation states are assigned as follows:

$$\underset{+1\ -\frac{1}{2}}{KO_2}$$
$$\text{sum: } +1+2\left(-\tfrac{1}{2}\right) = 0$$

In KO_2, oxygen has a $-\frac{1}{2}$ oxidation state. Although this seems unusual, it is accepted because oxidation states are merely an imposed electron bookkeeping scheme, not an actual physical quantity.

 Conceptual Connection 4.6 Oxidation Numbers in Polyatomic Ions

Which statement best describes the *difference* between the *charge* of a polyatomic ion and the *oxidation states* of its constituent atoms? (For example, the charge of $NO_3{}^-$ is 1−, and the oxidation states of its atoms are +5 for the nitrogen atom and –2 for each oxygen atom.)

(a) The charge of a polyatomic ion is a property of the entire ion, while the oxidation states are assigned to each individual atom.

(b) The oxidation state of the ion is the same as its charge.

(c) The charge of a polyatomic ion is not a real physical property, while the oxidation states of atoms are actual physical properties.

ANSWER: (a) The charge of a polyatomic ion is the charge associated with the ion *as a whole*. The oxidation states of the individual atoms must sum to the charge of the ion, but they are assigned to *the individual atoms themselves.* Answer **(b)** is false because oxidation state and charge *are not identical,* even though the charge of a *monoatomic* ion is equal to its oxidation state. Answer **(c)** is false because charge *is* a physical property of ions. Conversely, the oxidation states of atoms are *not* real physical properties, but an imposed electron bookkeeping scheme.

The balancing of redox reactions is covered in Section 18.2.

Identifying Redox Reactions

We can use oxidation states to identify redox reactions, even between nonmetals. For example, is the following reaction between carbon and sulfur a redox reaction?

$$C + 2S \longrightarrow CS_2$$

If so, what element is oxidized? What element is reduced? We can use the oxidation state rules to assign oxidation states to all elements on both sides of the equation.

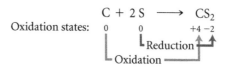

Carbon changes from an oxidation state of 0 to an oxidation state of +4. In terms of our electron bookkeeping scheme (the assigned oxidation state), carbon *loses electrons* and is *oxidized*. Sulfur changes from an oxidation state of 0 to an oxidation state of –2. In terms of our electron bookkeeping scheme, sulfur *gains electrons* and is *reduced*. In terms of oxidation states, oxidation and reduction are defined as follows.

- Oxidation: An increase in oxidation state
- Reduction: A decrease in oxidation state

Remember that a reduction is a *reduction* in oxidation state.

EXAMPLE 4.17 Using Oxidation States to Identify Oxidation and Reduction

Use oxidation states to identify the element that is oxidized and the element that is reduced in the following redox reaction.

$$Mg(s) + 2H_2O(l) \longrightarrow Mg(OH)_2(aq) + H_2(g)$$

SOLUTION

Begin by assigning oxidation states to each atom in the reaction.

$$Mg(s) + 2H_2O(l) \longrightarrow Mg(OH)_2(aq) + H_2(g)$$

Oxidation states: 0   +1 –2   +2 –2 +1   0

Since Mg increased in oxidation state, it was oxidized. Since H decreased in oxidation state, it was reduced.

FOR PRACTICE 4.17

Use oxidation states to identify the element that is oxidized and the element that is reduced in the following redox reaction.

$$Sn(s) + 4HNO_3(aq) \longrightarrow SnO_2(s) + 4NO_2(g) + 2H_2O(g)$$

FOR MORE PRACTICE 4.17

Which reactions are redox reactions? If the reaction is a redox reaction, identify which element is oxidized and which is reduced.

(a) $Hg_2(NO_3)_2(aq) + 2KBr(aq) \longrightarrow Hg_2Br_2(s) + 2KNO_3(aq)$

(b) $4Al(s) + 3O_2(g) \longrightarrow 2Al_2O_3(s)$

(c) $CaO(s) + CO_2(g) \longrightarrow CaCO_3(s)$

Notice that *oxidation and reduction must occur together.* If one substance loses electrons (oxidation) then another substance must gain electrons (reduction). A substance that causes the oxidation of another substance is called an **oxidizing agent**. Oxygen, for

example, is an excellent oxidizing agent because it causes the oxidation of many substances. In a redox reaction, *the oxidizing agent is always reduced.* A substance that causes the reduction of another substance is called a **reducing agent**. Hydrogen, for example, as well as the group 1A and group 2A metals (because of their tendency to lose electrons) are excellent reducing agents. In a redox reaction, *the reducing agent is always oxidized.*

In Section 18.2 you will learn more about redox reactions, including how to balance them. For now, you will want to be able to identify redox reactions, as well as oxidizing and reducing agents, according to the following guidelines.

Redox reactions:
- Any reaction in which there is a change in the oxidation states of atoms in going from reactants to products.

In a redox reaction:
- The oxidizing agent oxidizes another substance (and is itself reduced).
- The reducing agent reduces another substance (and is itself oxidized).

EXAMPLE 4.18 Identifying Redox Reactions, Oxidizing Agents, and Reducing Agents

Determine whether each reaction is an oxidation–reduction reaction. For each oxidation–reduction reaction, identify the oxidizing agent and the reducing agent.

(a) $2 \, \text{Mg}(s) + \text{O}_2 \, (g) \longrightarrow 2 \, \text{MgO}(s)$

(b) $2 \, \text{HBr}(aq) + \text{Ca(OH)}_2 \, (aq) \longrightarrow 2 \, \text{H}_2\text{O}(l) + \text{CaBr}_2(aq)$

(c) $\text{Zn}(s) + \text{Fe}^{2+} \, (aq) \longrightarrow \text{Zn}^{2+} \, (aq) + \text{Fe}(s)$

SOLUTION

This is a redox reaction because magnesium increases in oxidation number (oxidation) and oxygen decreases in oxidation number (reduction).	**(a)** $2 \, \text{Mg}(s) + \text{O}_2(g) \longrightarrow 2 \, \text{MgO}(s)$ Reduction / Oxidation Oxidizing agent: O_2 Reducing agent: Mg
This is not a redox reaction because none of the atoms undergoes a change in oxidation number.	**(b)** $2 \, \text{HBr}(aq) + \text{Ca(OH)}_2(aq) \longrightarrow 2\text{H}_2\text{O}(l) + \text{CaBr}_2(aq)$
This is a redox reaction because zinc increases in oxidation number (oxidation) and iron decreases in oxidation number (reduction).	**(c)** $\text{Zn}(s) + \text{Fe}^{2+}(aq) \longrightarrow \text{Zn}^{2+}(aq) + \text{Fe}(s)$ Reduction / Oxidation Oxidizing agent: Fe^{2+} Reducing agent: Zn

FOR PRACTICE 4.18

Which of the following is a redox reaction? For all redox reactions, identify the oxidizing agent and the reducing agent.

(a) $2 \, \text{Li}(s) + \text{Cl}_2 \, (g) \longrightarrow 2 \, \text{LiCl}(s)$

(b) $2 \, \text{Al}(s) + 3 \, \text{Sn}^{2+} \, (aq) \longrightarrow 2 \, \text{Al}^{3+} \, (aq) + 3 \, \text{Sn}(s)$

(c) $\text{Pb(NO}_3)_2 \, (aq) + 2 \, \text{LiCl}(aq) \longrightarrow \text{PbCl}_2 \, (s) + 2 \, \text{LiNO}_3(aq)$

(d) $\text{C}(s) + \text{O}_2 \, (g) \longrightarrow \text{CO}_2 \, (g)$

Conceptual Connection 4.7 Oxidation and Reduction

Which statement is true?

(a) A redox reaction involves *either* the transfer of an electron *or* a change in the oxidation state of an element.

(b) If any of the reactants or products in a reaction contains oxygen, the reaction is a redox reaction.

(c) In a reaction, oxidation can occur independently of reduction.

(d) In a redox reaction, any increase in the oxidation state of a reactant must be accompanied by a decrease in the oxidation state of a reactant.

ANSWER: (d) Since oxidation and reduction must occur together, an increase in the oxidation state of a reactant will always be accompanied by a decrease in the oxidation state of a reactant.

 CHEMISTRY IN YOUR DAY   Bleached Blonde

Have you ever bleached your hair? Most home kits for hair bleaching contain hydrogen peroxide (H_2O_2), an excellent oxidizing agent. When applied to hair, hydrogen peroxide oxidizes melanin, the dark pigment that gives hair its color. Once melanin is oxidized, it no longer imparts a dark color to hair, leaving the hair with the familiar bleached look. Hydrogen peroxide also oxidizes other components of hair. For example, protein molecules in hair contain —SH groups called thiols. Hydrogen peroxide oxidizes these thiol groups to sulfonic acid groups, —SO_3H. The oxidation of thiol groups to sulfonic acid groups causes changes in the proteins that compose hair, making the hair more brittle and more likely to tangle. Consequently, people with heavily bleached hair generally use conditioners, which contain compounds that form thin, lubricating coatings on individual hair shafts. These coatings prevent tangling and make hair softer and more manageable.

Question

The following is a reaction of hydrogen peroxide with an alkene:

$$H_2O_2 + C_2H_4 \longrightarrow C_2H_4O + H_2O$$

Can you see why this reaction is a redox reaction? Can you identify the oxidizing and reducing agents?

▶ The bleaching of hair involves a redox reaction in which melanin—the main pigment in hair—is oxidized.

Combustion Reactions

We encountered combustion reactions, a type of redox reaction, in the opening section of this chapter. Combustion reactions are important because most of our society's energy is derived from them (Figure 4.25 ▼).

As we learned in Section 4.1, *combustion reactions* are characterized by the reaction of a substance with O_2 to form one or more oxygen-containing compounds, often includ-

▶ **FIGURE 4.25 U.S. Energy Consumption**
Over 85% of the energy the United States uses is produced by combustion reactions.
Source: U.S. Energy Information Administration *Annual Energy Review* (Numbers may not sum to 100% because of Independent Rounding)

U.S. Energy Use by Source, 2007

Fossil fuel combustion
- Coal: 22.8%
- Natural gas: 23.6%
- Petroleum: 39.8%

- Nuclear: 8.4%
- Renewable Energy: 6.8%

ing water. Combustion reactions also emit heat. For example, as we saw earlier in this chapter, natural gas (CH_4) reacts with oxygen to form carbon dioxide and water:

$$CH_4(g) + 2\,O_2(g) \longrightarrow CO_2(g) + 2\,H_2O(g)$$
$$\text{Oxidation state: } -4 +1 \qquad 0 \qquad +4\,-2 \qquad +1\,-2$$

In this reaction, carbon is oxidized and oxygen is reduced. Ethanol, the alcohol in alcoholic beverages, also reacts with oxygen in a combustion reaction to form carbon dioxide and water:

$$C_2H_5OH(l) + 3\,O_2(g) \longrightarrow 2\,CO_2(g) + 3H_2O(g)$$

Compounds containing carbon and hydrogen—or carbon, hydrogen, and oxygen—always form carbon dioxide and water upon complete combustion. Other combustion reactions include the reaction of carbon with oxygen to form carbon dioxide:

$$C(s) + O_2(g) \longrightarrow CO_2(g)$$

and the reaction of hydrogen with oxygen to form water:

$$2\,H_2(g) + O_2(g) \longrightarrow 2\,H_2O(g)$$

EXAMPLE 4.19 Writing Equations for Combustion Reactions

Write a balanced equation for the combustion of liquid methyl alcohol (CH_3OH).

SOLUTION

Begin by writing a skeletal equation showing the reaction of CH_3OH with O_2 to form CO_2 and H_2O.	$CH_3OH(l) + O_2(g) \longrightarrow CO_2(g) + H_2O(g)$
Balance the equation using the guidelines in Section 3.10.	$2\,CH_3OH(l) + 3\,O_2(g) \longrightarrow 2\,CO_2(g) + 4\,H_2O(g)$

FOR PRACTICE 4.19

Write a balanced equation for the complete combustion of liquid C_2H_5SH.

CHAPTER IN REVIEW

Key Terms

Section 4.2
stoichiometry (129)

Section 4.3
limiting reactant (133)
theoretical yield (133)
actual yield (134)
percent yield (134)

Section 4.4
solution (140)
solvent (140)
solute (140)
aqueous solution (140)
dilute solution (140)

concentrated solution (140)
molarity (M) (140)
stock solution (142)

Section 4.5
electrolyte (147)
strong electrolyte (147)
nonelectrolyte (148)
strong acid (148)
weak acid (148)
weak electrolyte (148)
soluble (149)
insoluble (149)

Section 4.6
precipitation reaction (150)

precipitate (150)

Section 4.7
molecular equation (153)
complete ionic equation (154)
spectator ion (154)
net ionic equation (154)

Section 4.8
acid–base reaction
   (neutralization reaction)
   (155)
gas-evolution reaction (155)
Arrhenius definitions (155)
hydronium ion (156)
polyprotic acid (156)

diprotic acid (156)
salt (157)
titration (158)
equivalence point (158)
indicator (158)

Section 4.9
oxidation–reduction (redox)
   reaction (162)
oxidation (162)
reduction (162)
oxidation state (oxidation
   number) (163)
oxidizing agent (166)
reducing agent (167)

Key Concepts

Global Warming and the Combustion of Fossil Fuels (4.1)

Greenhouse gases are not in themselves harmful; they warm Earth by trapping some of the sunlight that penetrates Earth's atmosphere. However, global warming, resulting from rising atmospheric carbon dioxide levels, is potentially harmful. The largest carbon dioxide source is, arguably, the burning of fossil fuels. This can be verified by reaction stoichiometry.

Reaction Stoichiometry (4.2)

Reaction stoichiometry refers to the numerical relationships between the reactants and products in a balanced chemical equation. Reaction stoichiometry allows us to predict, for example, the amount of product that can be formed for a given amount of reactant, or how much of one reactant is required to react with a given amount of another.

Limiting Reactant, Theoretical Yield, and Percent Yield (4.3)

When a chemical reaction actually occurs, the reactants are usually not present in the exact stoichiometric ratios specified by the balanced chemical equation. The limiting reactant is the one that is available in the smallest stoichiometric quantity—it will be completely consumed in the reaction and it limits the amount of product that can be made. Any reactant that does not limit the amount of product is said to be in excess. The amount of product that can be made from the limiting reactant is the theoretical yield. The actual yield—always equal to or less than the theoretical yield—is the amount of product that is actually made when the reaction is carried out. The percentage of the theoretical yield that is actually produced is the percent yield.

Solution Concentration and Stoichiometry (4.4)

An aqueous solution is a homogeneous mixture of water (the solvent) with another substance (the solute). We often express the concentration of a solution in molarity, the number of moles of solute per liter of solution. We can use the molarities and volumes of reactant solutions to predict the amount of product that will form in an aqueous reaction.

Aqueous Solutions and Precipitation Reactions (4.5, 4.6)

Solutes that completely dissociate (or completely ionize in the case of the acids) to ions in solution are strong electrolytes and are good conductors of electricity. Solutes that only partially dissociate (or partially ionize) are weak electrolytes, and solutes that do not dissociate (or ionize) at all are nonelectrolytes. A substance that dissolves in water to form a solution is soluble.

In a precipitation reaction, we mix two aqueous solutions and a solid—or precipitate—forms. The solubility rules are an empirical set of guidelines that help predict the solubilities of ionic compounds; these rules are especially useful when determining whether or not a precipitate will form.

Equations for Aqueous Reactions (4.7)

An aqueous reaction can be represented with a molecular equation, which shows the complete neutral formula for each compound in the reaction. Alternatively, it can be represented with a complete ionic equation, which shows the dissociated nature of the aqueous ionic compounds. A third representation is the net ionic equation, in which the spectator ions—those that do not change in the course of the reaction—are left out of the equation.

Acid–Base and Gas-Evolution Reactions (4.8)

In an acid–base reaction, an acid, a substance which produces H^+ in solution, reacts with a base, a substance which produces OH^- in solution, and the two neutralize each other, producing water (or in some cases a weak electrolyte). An acid–base titration is a laboratory procedure in which a reaction is carried to its equivalence point—the point at which the reactants are in exact stoichiometric proportions; titrations are useful in determining the concentrations of unknown solutions. In gas-evolution reactions, two aqueous solutions combine and a gas is produced.

Oxidation–Reduction Reactions (4.9)

In oxidation–reduction reactions, one substance transfers electrons to another substance. The substance that loses electrons is oxidized and the substance that gains them is reduced. An oxidation state is a fictitious charge given to each atom in a redox reaction by assigning all shared electrons to the atom with the greater attraction for those electrons. Oxidation states are an imposed electronic bookkeeping scheme, not an actual physical state. The oxidation state of an atom increases upon oxidation and decreases upon reduction. A combustion reaction is a specific type of oxidation–reduction reaction in which a substance reacts with oxygen—emitting heat and forming one or more oxygen-containing products.

Key Equations and Relationships

Mass-to-Mass Conversion: Stoichiometry (4.2)

mass A $\rightarrow$ amount A (in moles) $\rightarrow$ amount B (in moles) $\rightarrow$ mass B

Percent Yield (4.3)

$$\% \text{ yield} = \frac{\text{actual yield}}{\text{theoretical yield}} \times 100\%$$

Molarity (M): Solution Concentration (4.4)

$$M = \frac{\text{amount of solute (in mol)}}{\text{volume of solution (in L)}}$$

Solution Dilution (4.4)

$$M_1 V_1 = M_2 V_2$$

Solution Stoichiometry (4.4)

volume A $\rightarrow$ amount A (in moles) $\rightarrow$ amount B (in moles) $\rightarrow$ volume B

Key Skills

Calculations Involving the Stoichiometry of a Reaction (4.2)
   • Examples 4.1, 4.2   • For Practice 4.1, 4.2   • Exercises 31–36

Determining the Limiting Reactant and Calculating Theoretical and Percent Yield (4.3)
   • Examples 4.3, 4.4   • For Practice 4.3, 4.4   • Exercises 41–51

Calculating and Using Molarity as a Conversion Factor (4.4)
   • Examples 4.5, 4.6   • For Practice 4.5, 4.6   • For More Practice 4.5, 4.6   • Exercises 53–58

Determining Solution Dilutions (4.4)
   • Example 4.7   • For Practice 4.7   • For More Practice 4.7   • Exercises 61, 62

Using Solution Stoichiometry to Find Volumes and Amounts (4.4)
   • Example 4.8   • For Practice 4.8   • For More Practice 4.8   • Exercises 63–65

Predicting whether a Compound Is Soluble (4.5)

Writing Equations for Precipitation Reactions (4.6)

Writing Complete Ionic and Net Ionic Equations (4.7)

Writing Equations for Acid–Base Reactions (4.8)

Calculations Involving Acid–Base Titrations (4.8)

Writing Equations for Gas-Evolution Reactions (4.8)

Assigning Oxidation States (4.9)

Identifying Redox Reactions, Oxidizing Agents, and Reducing Agents Using Oxidation States (4.9)

Writing Equations for Combustion Reactions (4.9)

EXERCISES

Review Questions

1. What is reaction stoichiometry? What is the significance of the coefficients in a balanced chemical equation?

2. In a chemical reaction, what is the limiting reactant? The theoretical yield? The percent yield? What do we mean when we say a reactant is in excess?

3. The percent yield is normally calculated using the actual yield and theoretical yield in units of mass (g or kg). Would the percent yield be different if the actual yield and theoretical yield were in units of amount (moles)?

4. What is an aqueous solution? What is the difference between the solute and the solvent?

5. What is molarity? How is it useful?

6. Explain how a strong electrolyte, a weak electrolyte, and a non-electrolyte differ.

7. Explain the difference between a strong acid and a weak acid.

8. What does it mean for a compound to be soluble? Insoluble?

9. What are the solubility rules? How are they useful?

10. What are the cations and anions whose compounds are usually soluble? What are the exceptions? What are the anions whose compounds are mostly insoluble? What are the exceptions?

11. What is a precipitation reaction? Give an example.

12. How can you predict whether a precipitation reaction will occur upon mixing two aqueous solutions?

13. Explain how a molecular equation, a complete ionic equation, and a net ionic equation differ.

14. What are the Arrhenius definitions of an acid and a base?

15. What is an acid–base reaction? Give an example.

16. Explain the principles behind an acid–base titration. What is an indicator?

17. What is a gas-evolution reaction? Give an example.

18. What reactant types give rise to gas-evolution reactions?

19. What is an oxidation–reduction reaction? Give an example.

20. What are oxidation states?

21. How can oxidation states be used to identify redox reactions?

22. What happens to a substance when it becomes oxidized? Reduced?

23. In a redox reaction, which reactant is the oxidizing agent? The reducing agent?

24. What is a combustion reaction? Why are they important? Give an example.

Problems by Topic

Reaction Stoichiometry

25. Consider the unbalanced equation for the combustion of hexane:

$$C_6H_{14}(g) + O_2(g) \longrightarrow CO_2(g) + H_2O(g)$$

Balance the equation and determine how many moles of O_2 are required to react completely with 7.2 moles C_6H_{14}.

26. Consider the unbalanced equation for the neutralization of acetic acid:

$$HC_2H_3O_2(aq) + Ba(OH)_2(aq) \longrightarrow H_2O(l) + Ba(C_2H_3O_2)_2(aq)$$

Balance the equation and determine how many moles of $Ba(OH)_2$ are required to completely neutralize 0.461 mole of $HC_2H_3O_2$.

27. Calculate how many moles of NO_2 form when each quantity of reactant completely reacts.

$$2 N_2O_5(g) \longrightarrow 4 NO_2(g) + O_2(g)$$

a. 2.5 mol N_2O_5
b. 6.8 mol N_2O_5
c. 15.2 g N_2O_5
d. 2.87 kg N_2O_5

28. Calculate how many moles of NH_3 form when each quantity of reactant completely reacts.

$$3 N_2H_4(l) \longrightarrow 4 NH_3(g) + N_2(g)$$

a. 2.6 mol N_2H_4
b. 3.55 mol N_2H_4
c. 65.3 g N_2H_4
d. 4.88 kg N_2H_4

29. Consider the balanced equation:

$$SiO_2(s) + 3 C(s) \longrightarrow SiC(s) + 2 CO(g)$$

Complete the table showing the appropriate number of moles of reactants and products. If the number of moles of a *reactant* is provided, fill in the required amount of the other reactant, as well as the moles of each product formed. If the number of moles of a *product* is provided, fill in the required amount of each reactant to make that amount of product, as well as the amount of the other product that is made.

Mol SiO$_2$	Mol C	Mol SiC	Mol CO
3	___	___	___
___	6	___	___
___	___	___	10
2.8	___	___	___
___	1.55	___	___

30. Consider the balanced equation:

$$2 N_2H_4(g) + N_2O_4(g) \longrightarrow 3 N_2(g) + 4 H_2O(g)$$

Complete the table showing the appropriate number of moles of reactants and products. If the number of moles of a *reactant* is provided, fill in the required amount of the other reactant, as well as the moles of each product formed. If the number of moles of a *product* is provided, fill in the required amount of each reactant to make that amount of product, as well as the amount of the other product that is made.

Mol N$_2$H$_4$	Mol N$_2$O$_4$	Mol N$_2$	Mol H$_2$O
2	___	___	___
___	5	___	___
___	___	___	10
2.5	___	___	___
___	4.2	___	___
___	___	11.8	___

31. Hydrobromic acid dissolves solid iron according to the reaction:

$$Fe(s) + 2 HBr(aq) \longrightarrow FeBr_2(aq) + H_2(g)$$

What mass of HBr (in g) would you need to dissolve a 3.2-g pure iron bar on a padlock? What mass of H_2 would the complete reaction of the iron bar produce?

32. Sulfuric acid dissolves aluminum metal according to the reaction:

$$2 Al(s) + 3 H_2SO_4(aq) \longrightarrow Al_2(SO_4)_3(aq) + 3 H_2(g)$$

Suppose you wanted to dissolve an aluminum block with a mass of 15.2 g. What minimum mass of H_2SO_4 (in g) would you need? What mass of H_2 gas (in g) would the complete reaction of the aluminum block produce?

33. For each of the reactions, calculate the mass (in grams) of the product formed when 3.67 g of the underlined reactant completely reacts. Assume that there is more than enough of the other reactant.

a. $\underline{Ba}(s) + Cl_2(g) \longrightarrow BaCl_2(s)$
b. $\underline{CaO}(s) + CO_2(g) \longrightarrow CaCO_3(s)$
c. $2 \underline{Mg}(s) + O_2(g) \longrightarrow 2 MgO(s)$
d. $4 \underline{Al}(s) + 3 O_2(g) \longrightarrow 2 Al_2O_3(s)$

34. For each of the reactions, calculate the mass (in grams) of the product formed when 15.39 g of the underlined reactant completely reacts. Assume that there is more than enough of the other reactant.

a. $2 K(s) + \underline{Cl_2}(g) \longrightarrow 2 KCl(s)$
b. $2 K(s) + \underline{Br_2}(l) \longrightarrow 2 KBr(s)$
c. $4 Cr(s) + 3 \underline{O_2}(g) \longrightarrow 2 Cr_2O_3(s)$
d. $2 \underline{Sr}(s) + O_2(g) \longrightarrow 2 SrO(s)$

35. For each of the acid–base reactions, calculate the mass (in grams) of each acid necessary to completely react with and neutralize 4.85 g of the base.

a. $HCl(aq) + NaOH(aq) \longrightarrow H_2O(l) + NaCl(aq)$
b. $2 HNO_3(aq) + Ca(OH)_2(aq) \longrightarrow$
$$2 H_2O(l) + Ca(NO_3)_2(aq)$$
c. $H_2SO_4(aq) + 2 KOH(aq) \longrightarrow 2 H_2O(l) + K_2SO_4(aq)$

36. For each precipitation reaction, calculate how many grams of the first reactant are necessary to completely react with 55.8 g of the second reactant.

a. $2 KI(aq) + Pb(NO_3)_2(aq) \longrightarrow PbI_2(s) + 2 KNO_3(aq)$
b. $Na_2CO_3(aq) + CuCl_2(aq) \longrightarrow CuCO_3(s) + 2 NaCl(aq)$
c. $K_2SO_4(aq) + Sr(NO_3)_2(aq) \longrightarrow$
$$SrSO_4(s) + 2 KNO_3(aq)$$

Limiting Reactant, Theoretical Yield, and Percent Yield

37. For the reaction below, find the limiting reactant for each of the initial amounts of reactants.

$$2 Na(s) + Br_2(g) \longrightarrow 2 NaBr(s)$$

a. 2 mol Na, 2 mol Br_2
b. 1.8 mol Na, 1.4 mol Br_2
c. 2.5 mol Na, 1 mol Br_2
d. 12.6 mol Na, 6.9 mol Br_2

38. Find the limiting reactant for each initial amount of reactants.

$$4 Al(s) + 3 O_2(g) \longrightarrow 2 Al_2O_3(s)$$

a. 1 mol Al, 1 mol O_2
b. 4 mol Al, 2.6 mol O_2
c. 16 mol Al, 13 mol O_2
d. 7.4 mol Al, 6.5 mol O_2

39. Consider the reaction:

$$4 HCl(g) + O_2(g) \longrightarrow 2 H_2O(g) + 2 Cl_2(g)$$

Each molecular diagram represents an initial mixture of the reactants. How many molecules of Cl_2 would be formed from the reaction mixture that produces the greatest amount of products?

(a) (b) (c)

40. Consider the reaction:

$$2 CH_3OH(g) + 3 O_2(g) \longrightarrow 2 CO_2(g) + 4 H_2O(g)$$

Each of the molecular diagrams represents an initial mixture of the reactants. How many CO_2 molecules would be formed from the reaction mixture that produces the greatest amount of products?

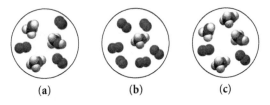

(a)   **(b)**   **(c)**

41. Compute the theoretical yield of the product (in moles) for each initial amount of reactants.

$$Ti(s) + 2 Cl_2(g) \longrightarrow TiCl_4(s)$$

a. 4 mol Ti, 4 mol Cl_2 **b.** 7 mol Ti, 17 mol Cl_2
c. 12.4 mol Ti, 18.8 mol Cl_2

42. Compute the theoretical yield of product (in moles) for each initial amount of reactants.

$$2 Mn(s) + 2 O_2(g) \longrightarrow 2 MnO_2(s)$$

a. 3 mol Mn, 3 mol O_2 **b.** 4 mol Mn, 7 mol O_2
c. 27.5 mol Mn, 43.8 mol O_2

43. Zinc(II) sulfide reacts with oxygen according to the reaction:

$$2 ZnS(s) + 3 O_2(g) \longrightarrow 2 ZnO(s) + 2 SO_2(g)$$

A reaction mixture initially contains 4.2 mol ZnS and 6.8 mol O_2. Once the reaction has occurred as completely as possible, what amount (in moles) of the excess reactant is left?

44. Iron(II) sulfide reacts with hydrochloric acid according to the reaction:

$$FeS(s) + 2 HCl(aq) \longrightarrow FeCl_2(s) + H_2S(g)$$

A reaction mixture initially contains 0.223 mol FeS and 0.652 mol HCl. Once the reaction has occurred as completely as possible, what amount (in moles) of the excess reactant is left?

45. For the reaction shown, compute the theoretical yield of product (in grams) for each initial amount of reactants.

$$2 Al(s) + 3 Cl_2(g) \longrightarrow 2 AlCl_3(s)$$

a. 2.0 g Al, 2.0 g Cl_2 **b.** 7.5 g Al, 24.8 g Cl_2
c. 0.235 g Al, 1.15 g Cl_2

46. For the reaction shown, compute the theoretical yield of the product (in grams) for each initial amount of reactants.

$$Ti(s) + 2 F_2(g) \longrightarrow TiF_4(s)$$

a. 5.0 g Ti, 5.0 g F_2 **b.** 2.4 g Ti, 1.6 g F_2
c. 0.233 g Ti, 0.288 g F_2

47. Iron(III) oxide reacts with carbon monoxide according to the equation:

$$Fe_2O_3(s) + 3 CO(g) \longrightarrow 2 Fe(s) + 3 CO_2(g)$$

A reaction mixture initially contains 22.55 g Fe_2O_3 and 14.78 g CO. Once the reaction has occurred as completely as possible, what mass (in g) of the excess reactant is left?

48. Elemental phosphorus reacts with chlorine gas according to the equation:

$$P_4(s) + 6 Cl_2(g) \longrightarrow 4 PCl_3(l)$$

A reaction mixture initially contains 45.69 g P_4 and 131.3 g Cl_2. Once the reaction has occurred as completely as possible, what mass (in g) of the excess reactant is left?

49. Lead ions can be precipitated from solution with KCl according to the reaction:

$$Pb^{2+}(aq) + 2 KCl(aq) \longrightarrow PbCl_2(s) + 2 K^+(aq)$$

When 28.5 g KCl is added to a solution containing 25.7 g Pb^{2+}, a $PbCl_2$ precipitate forms. The precipitate is filtered and dried and found to have a mass of 29.4 g. Determine the limiting reactant, theoretical yield of $PbCl_2$, and percent yield for the reaction.

50. Magnesium oxide can be made by heating magnesium metal in the presence of oxygen. The balanced equation for the reaction is

$$2 Mg(s) + O_2(g) \longrightarrow 2 MgO(s)$$

When 10.1 g of Mg is allowed to react with 10.5 g O_2, 11.9 g MgO is collected. Determine the limiting reactant, theoretical yield, and percent yield for the reaction.

51. Urea (CH_4N_2O) is a common fertilizer that can be synthesized by the reaction of ammonia (NH_3) with carbon dioxide:

$$2 NH_3(aq) + CO_2(aq) \longrightarrow CH_4N_2O(aq) + H_2O(l)$$

In an industrial synthesis of urea, a chemist combines 136.4 kg of ammonia with 211.4 kg of carbon dioxide and obtains 168.4 kg of urea. Determine the limiting reactant, theoretical yield of urea, and percent yield for the reaction.

52. Many computer chips are manufactured from silicon, which occurs in nature as SiO_2. When SiO_2 is heated to melting, it reacts with solid carbon to form liquid silicon and carbon monoxide gas. In an industrial preparation of silicon, 155.8 kg of SiO_2 reacts with 78.3 kg of carbon to produce 66.1 kg of silicon. Determine the limiting reactant, theoretical yield, and percent yield for the reaction.

Solution Concentration and Solution Stoichiometry

53. Calculate the molarity of each solution.
a. 3.25 mol of LiCl in 2.78 L solution
b. 28.33 g $C_6H_{12}O_6$ in 1.28 L of solution
c. 32.4 mg NaCl in 122.4 mL of solution

54. Calculate the molarity of each solution.
a. 0.38 mol of $LiNO_3$ in 6.14 L of solution
b. 72.8 g C_2H_6O in 2.34 L of solution
c. 12.87 mg KI in 112.4 mL of solution

55. How many moles of KCl are contained in each solution?
a. 0.556 L of a 2.3 M KCl solution
b. 1.8 L of a 0.85 M KCl solution
c. 114 mL of a 1.85 M KCl solution

56. What volume of 0.200 M ethanol solution contains each amount in moles of ethanol?
a. 0.45 mol ethanol   **b.** 1.22 mol ethanol
c. 1.2×10^{-2} mol ethanol

57. A laboratory procedure calls for making 400.0 mL of a 1.1 M $NaNO_3$ solution. What mass of $NaNO_3$ (in g) is needed?

58. A chemist wants to make 5.5 L of a 0.300 M $CaCl_2$ solution. What mass of $CaCl_2$ (in g) should the chemist use?

59. If 123 mL of a 1.1 M glucose solution is diluted to 500.0 mL, what is the molarity of the diluted solution?

60. If 3.5 L of a 4.8 M $SrCl_2$ solution is diluted to 45 L, what is the molarity of the diluted solution?

61. To what volume should you dilute 50.0 mL of a 12 M stock HNO_3 solution to obtain a 0.100 M HNO_3 solution?

62. To what volume should you dilute 25 mL of a 10.0 M H_2SO_4 solution to obtain a 0.150 M H_2SO_4 solution?

63. Consider the precipitation reaction:

$$2\,Na_3PO_4(aq) + 3\,CuCl_2(aq) \longrightarrow Cu_3(PO_4)_2(s) + 6\,NaCl(aq)$$

What volume of 0.175 M Na_3PO_4 solution is necessary to completely react with 95.4 mL of 0.102 M $CuCl_2$?

64. Consider the reaction:

$$Li_2S(aq) + Co(NO_3)_2(aq) \longrightarrow 2\,LiNO_3(aq) + CoS(s)$$

What volume of 0.150 M Li_2S solution is required to completely react with 125 mL of 0.150 M $Co(NO_3)_2$?

65. What is the minimum amount of 6.0 M H_2SO_4 necessary to produce 25.0 g of $H_2\,(g)$ according to the reaction between aluminum and sulfuric acid?

$$2\,Al(s) + 3\,H_2SO_4(aq) \longrightarrow Al_2(SO_4)_3(aq) + 3H_2(g)$$

66. What is the molarity of $ZnCl_2$ that forms when 25.0 g of zinc completely reacts with $CuCl_2$ according to the following reaction? Assume a final volume of 275 mL.

$$Zn(s) + CuCl_2(aq) \longrightarrow ZnCl_2(aq) + Cu(s)$$

Types of Aqueous Solutions and Solubility

67. For each compound (all water soluble), would you expect the resulting aqueous solution to conduct electrical current?
  a. CsCl   **b.** CH_3OH **c.** $Ca(NO_2)_2$ **d.** $C_6H_{12}O_6$

68. Classify each compound as a strong electrolyte or nonelectrolyte.
  a. $MgBr_2$ **b.** $C_{12}H_{22}O_{11}$ **c.** Na_2CO_3 **d.** KOH

69. Determine whether each compound is soluble or insoluble. If the compound is soluble, list the ions present in solution.
  a. $AgNO_3$ **b.** $Pb(C_2H_3O_2)_2$ **c.** KNO_3 **d.** $(NH_4)_2\,S$

70. Determine whether each compound is soluble or insoluble. For the soluble compounds, list the ions present in solution.
  a. AgI   **b.** $Cu_3(PO_4)_2$ **c.** $CoCO_3$ **d.** K_3PO_4

Precipitation Reactions

71. Complete and balance each equation. If no reaction occurs, write NO REACTION.
  a. $LiI(aq) + BaS(aq) \longrightarrow$
  b. $KCl(aq) + CaS(aq) \longrightarrow$
  c. $CrBr_2(aq) + Na_2CO_3(aq) \longrightarrow$
  d. $NaOH(aq) + FeCl_3(aq) \longrightarrow$

72. Complete and balance each equation. If no reaction occurs, write NO REACTION.
  a. $NaNO_3(aq) + KCl(aq) \longrightarrow$
  b. $NaCl(aq) + Hg_2(C_2H_3O_2)_2(aq) \longrightarrow$
  c. $(NH_4)_2SO_4(aq) + SrCl_2(aq) \longrightarrow$
  d. $NH_4Cl(aq) + AgNO_3(aq) \longrightarrow$

73. Write a molecular equation for the precipitation reaction that occurs (if any) when each pair of aqueous solutions is mixed. If no reaction occurs, write NO REACTION.
  a. potassium carbonate and lead(II) nitrate
  b. lithium sulfate and lead(II) acetate
  c. copper(II) nitrate and magnesium sulfide
  d. strontium nitrate and potassium iodide

74. Write a molecular equation for the precipitation reaction that occurs (if any) when each pair of aqueous solutions is mixed. If no reaction occurs, write NO REACTION.

a. sodium chloride and lead(II) acetate
b. potassium sulfate and strontium iodide
c. cesium chloride and calcium sulfide
d. chromium(III) nitrate and sodium phosphate

Ionic and Net Ionic Equations

75. Write balanced complete ionic and net ionic equations for each reaction.
  a. $HCl(aq) + LiOH(aq) \longrightarrow H_2O(l) + LiCl(aq)$
  b. $MgS(aq) + CuCl_2(aq) \longrightarrow CuS(s) + MgCl_2(aq)$
  c. $NaOH(aq) + HNO_3(aq) \longrightarrow H_2O(l) + NaNO_3(aq)$
  d. $Na_3PO_4(aq) + NiCl_2(aq) \longrightarrow$
$$Ni_3(PO_4)_2(s) + NaCl(aq)$$

76. Write balanced complete ionic and net ionic equations for each reaction.
  a. $K_2SO_4(aq) + CaI_2(aq) \longrightarrow CaSO_4(s) + KI(aq)$
  b. $NH_4Cl(aq) + NaOH(aq) \longrightarrow$
$$H_2O(l) + NH_3(g) + NaCl(aq)$$
  c. $AgNO_3(aq) + NaCl(aq) \longrightarrow AgCl(s) + NaNO_3(aq)$
  d. $HC_2H_3O_2(aq) + K_2CO_3(aq) \longrightarrow$
$$H_2O(l) + CO_2(g) + KC_2H_3O_2(aq)$$

77. Mercury ions ($Hg_2{}^{2+}$) can be removed from solution by precipitation with Cl^-. Suppose that a solution contains aqueous $Hg_2(NO_3)_2$. Write complete ionic and net ionic equations to show the reaction of aqueous $Hg_2(NO_3)_2$ with aqueous sodium chloride to form solid Hg_2Cl_2 and aqueous sodium nitrate.

78. Lead ions can be removed from solution by precipitation with sulfate ions. Suppose that a solution contains lead(II) nitrate. Write complete ionic and net ionic equations to show the reaction of aqueous lead(II) nitrate with aqueous potassium sulfate to form solid lead(II) sulfate and aqueous potassium nitrate.

Acid–Base and Gas-Evolution Reactions

79. Write balanced molecular and net ionic equations for the reaction between hydrobromic acid and potassium hydroxide.

80. Write balanced molecular and net ionic equations for the reaction between nitric acid and calcium hydroxide.

81. Complete and balance each acid–base equation:
  a. $H_2SO_4(aq) + Ca(OH)_2(aq) \longrightarrow$
  b. $HClO_4(aq) + KOH(aq) \longrightarrow$
  c. $H_2SO_4(aq) + NaOH(aq) \longrightarrow$

82. Complete and balance each acid–base equation:
  a. $HI(aq) + LiOH(aq) \longrightarrow$
  b. $HC_2H_3O_2(aq) + Ca(OH)_2(aq) \longrightarrow$
  c. $HCl(aq) + Ba(OH)_2(aq) \longrightarrow$

83. A 25.00-mL sample of an unknown $HClO_4$ solution requires titration with 22.62 mL of 0.2000 M NaOH to reach the equivalence point. What is the concentration of the unknown $HClO_4$ solution? The neutralization reaction is

$$HClO_4(aq) + NaOH(aq) \longrightarrow H_2O(l) + NaClO_4(aq)$$

84. A 30.00-mL sample of an unknown H_3PO_4 solution is titrated with a 0.100 M NaOH solution. The equivalence point is reached when 26.38 mL of NaOH solution is added. What is the concentration of the unknown H_3PO_4 solution? The neutralization reaction is

$$H_3PO_4(aq) + 3\,NaOH(aq) \longrightarrow 3\,H_2O(l) + Na_3PO_4(aq)$$

85. Complete and balance each gas-evolution equation:
  a. $HBr(aq) + NiS(s) \longrightarrow$
  b. $NH_4I(aq) + NaOH(aq) \longrightarrow$

c. $HBr(aq) + Na_2S(aq) \longrightarrow$

d. $HClO_4(aq) + Li_2CO_3(aq) \longrightarrow$

86. Complete and balance each gas-evolution equation:

a. $HNO_3(aq) + Na_2SO_3(aq) \longrightarrow$

b. $HCl(aq) + KHCO_3(aq) \longrightarrow$

c. $HC_2H_3O_2(aq) + NaHSO_3(aq) \longrightarrow$

d. $(NH_4)_2SO_4(aq) + Ca(OH)_2(aq) \longrightarrow$

Oxidation–Reduction and Combustion

87. Assign oxidation states to each atom in each element, ion, or compound.

a. Ag   b. Ag^+ c. CaF_2

d. H_2S e. CO_3^{2-} f. CrO_4^{2-}

88. Assign oxidation states to each atom in each element, ion, or compound.

a. Cl_2 b. Fe^{3+} c. $CuCl_2$

d. CH_4 e. $Cr_2O_7^{2-}$ f. HSO_4^-

89. What is the oxidation state of Cr in each compound?

a. CrO   b. CrO_3 c. Cr_2O_3

90. What is the oxidation state of Cl in each ion?

a. ClO^- b. ClO_2^- c. ClO_3^- d. ClO_4^-

91. Determine whether each reaction is a redox reaction. For each redox reaction, identify the oxidizing agent and the reducing agent.

a. $4 Li(s) + O_2(g) \longrightarrow 2 Li_2O(s)$

b. $Mg(s) + Fe^{2+}(aq) \longrightarrow Mg^{2+}(aq) + Fe(s)$

c. $Pb(NO_3)_2(aq) + Na_2SO_4(aq) \longrightarrow$
$PbSO_4(s) + 2 NaNO_3(aq)$

d. $HBr(aq) + KOH(aq) \longrightarrow H_2O(l) + KBr(aq)$

92. Determine whether each reaction is a redox reaction. For each redox reaction, identify the oxidizing agent and the reducing agent.

a. $Al(s) + 3 Ag^+(aq) \longrightarrow Al^{3+}(aq) + 3 Ag(s)$

b. $SO_3(g) + H_2O(l) \longrightarrow H_2SO_4(aq)$

c. $Ba(s) + Cl_2(g) \longrightarrow BaCl_2(s)$

d. $Mg(s) + Br_2(l) \longrightarrow MgBr_2(s)$

93. Complete and balance each combustion reaction equation.

a. $S(s) + O_2(g) \longrightarrow$

b. $C_3H_6(g) + O_2(g) \longrightarrow$

c. $Ca(s) + O_2(g) \longrightarrow$

d. $C_5H_{12}S(l) + O_2(g) \longrightarrow$

94. Complete and balance each combustion reaction equation:

a. $C_4H_6(g) + O_2(g) \longrightarrow$

b. $C(s) + O_2(g) \longrightarrow$

c. $CS_2(s) + O_2(g) \longrightarrow$

d. $C_3H_8O(l) + O_2(g) \longrightarrow$

Cumulative Problems

95. The density of a 20.0% by mass ethylene glycol ($C_2H_6O_2$) solution in water is 1.03 g/mL. Find the molarity of the solution.

96. Find the percent by mass of sodium chloride in a 1.35 M NaCl solution. The density of the solution is 1.05 g/mL.

97. People often use sodium bicarbonate as an antacid to neutralize excess hydrochloric acid in an upset stomach. What mass of hydrochloric acid (in grams) can 2.5 g of sodium bicarbonate neutralize? (Hint: Begin by writing a balanced equation for the reaction between aqueous sodium bicarbonate and aqueous hydrochloric acid.)

98. Toilet bowl cleaners often contain hydrochloric acid, which dissolves the calcium carbonate deposits that accumulate within a toilet bowl. What mass of calcium carbonate (in grams) can 3.8 g of HCl dissolve? (Hint: Begin by writing a balanced equation for the reaction between hydrochloric acid and calcium carbonate.)

99. The combustion of gasoline produces carbon dioxide and water. Assume gasoline to be pure octane (C_8H_{18}) and calculate the mass (in kg) of carbon dioxide that is added to the atmosphere per 1.0 kg of octane burned. (Hint: Begin by writing a balanced equation for the combustion reaction.)

100. Many home barbeques are fueled with propane gas (C_3H_8). What mass of carbon dioxide (in kg) is produced upon the complete combustion of 18.9 L of propane (approximate contents of one 5-gallon tank)? Assume that the density of the liquid propane in the tank is 0.621 g/mL. (Hint: Begin by writing a balanced equation for the combustion reaction.)

101. Aspirin can be made in the laboratory by reacting acetic anhydride ($C_4H_6O_3$) with salicylic acid ($C_7H_6O_3$) to form aspirin ($C_9H_8O_4$) and acetic acid ($C_2H_4O_2$). The balanced equation is

$$C_4H_6O_3 + C_7H_6O_3 \longrightarrow C_9H_8O_4 + C_2H_4O_2$$

In a laboratory synthesis, a student begins with 3.00 mL of acetic anhydride (density = 1.08 g/mL) and 1.25 g of salicylic acid. Once the reaction is complete, the student collects 1.22 g of aspirin. Determine the limiting reactant, theoretical yield of aspirin, and percent yield for the reaction.

102. The combustion of liquid ethanol (C_2H_5OH) produces carbon dioxide and water. After 4.62 mL of ethanol (density = 0.789 g/mL) was allowed to burn in the presence of 15.55 g of oxygen gas, 3.72 mL of water (density = 1.00 g/mL) was collected. Determine the limiting reactant, theoretical yield of H_2O, and percent yield for the reaction. (Hint: Write a balanced equation for the combustion of ethanol.)

103. A loud classroom demonstration involves igniting a hydrogen-filled balloon. The hydrogen within the balloon reacts explosively with oxygen in the air to form water. If the balloon is filled with a mixture of hydrogen and oxygen, the explosion is even louder than if the balloon is filled only with hydrogen—the intensity of the explosion depends on the relative amounts of oxygen and hydrogen within the balloon. Look at the molecular views representing different amounts of hydrogen and oxygen in four different balloons. Based on the balanced chemical equation, which balloon will make the loudest explosion?

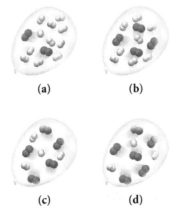

(a)   (b)

(c)   (d)

104. A hydrochloric acid solution will neutralize a sodium hydroxide solution. Look at the molecular views showing one beaker of HCl and four beakers of NaOH. Which NaOH beaker will just neutralize the HCl beaker? Begin by writing a balanced chemical equation for the neutralization reaction.

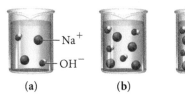

   (a)   (b)   (c)   (d)

105. Predict the products and write a balanced molecular equation for each reaction. If no reaction occurs, write NO REACTION.
   a. $HCl(aq) + Hg_2(NO_3)_2(aq) \longrightarrow$
   b. $KHSO_3(aq) + HNO_3(aq) \longrightarrow$
   c. aqueous ammonium chloride and aqueous lead(II) nitrate
   d. aqueous ammonium chloride and aqueous calcium hydroxide

106. Predict the products and write a balanced molecular equation for each reaction. If no reaction occurs, write NO REACTION.
   a. $H_2SO_4(aq) + HNO_3(aq) \longrightarrow$
   b. $Cr(NO_3)_3(aq) + LiOH(aq) \longrightarrow$
   c. liquid pentanol ($C_5H_{12}O$) and gaseous oxygen
   d. aqueous strontium sulfide and aqueous copper(II) sulfate

107. Hard water often contains dissolved Ca^{2+} and Mg^{2+} ions. One way to soften water is to add phosphates. The phosphate ion forms insoluble precipitates with calcium and magnesium ions, removing them from solution. Suppose that a solution is 0.050 M in calcium chloride and 0.085 M in magnesium nitrate. What mass of sodium phosphate would have to be added to 1.5 L of this solution to completely eliminate the hard water ions? Assume complete reaction.

108. An acid solution is 0.100 M in HCl and 0.200 M in H_2SO_4. What volume of a 0.150 M KOH solution would completely neutralize all the acid in 500.0 mL of this solution?

109. Find the mass of barium metal (in grams) that must react with O_2 to produce enough barium oxide to prepare 1.0 L of a 0.10 M solution of OH^-.

110. A solution contains Cr^{3+} ion and Mg^{2+} ion. The addition of 1.00 L of 1.51 M NaF solution is required to cause the complete precipitation of these ions as $CrF_3(s)$ and $MgF_2(s)$. The total mass of the precipitate is 49.6 g. Find the mass of Cr^{3+} in the original solution.

111. The nitrogen in sodium nitrate and in ammonium sulfate is available to plants as fertilizer. Which is the more economical source of nitrogen, a fertilizer containing 30.0% sodium nitrate by weight and costing $9.00 per 100 lb or one containing 20.0% ammonium sulfate by weight and costing $8.10 per 100 lb?

112. Find the volume of 0.110 M hydrochloric acid necessary to react completely with 1.52 g $Al(OH)_3$.

113. Treatment of gold metal with BrF_3 and KF produces Br_2 and $KAuF_4$, a salt of gold. Identify the oxidizing agent and the reducing agent in this reaction. Find the mass of the gold salt that forms when a 73.5-g mixture of equal masses of all three reactants is prepared.

114. We prepare a solution by mixing 0.10 L of 0.12 M sodium chloride with 0.23 L of a 0.18 M $MgCl_2$ solution. What volume of a 0.20 M silver nitrate solution do we need to precipitate all the Cl^- ion in the solution as AgCl?

115. A solution contains one or more of the following ions: Ag^+, Ca^{2+}, and Cu^{2+}. When you add sodium chloride to the solution, no precipitate forms. When you add sodium sulfate to the solution, a white precipitate forms. You filter off the precipitate and add sodium carbonate to the remaining solution, producing another precipitate. Which ions were present in the original solution? Write net ionic equations for the formation of each of the precipitates observed.

116. A solution contains one or more of the following ions: Hg_2^{2+}, Ba^{2+}, and Fe^{2+}. When potassium chloride is added to the solution, a precipitate forms. The precipitate is filtered off, and potassium sulfate is added to the remaining solution, producing no precipitate. When potassium carbonate is added to the remaining solution, a precipitate forms. Which ions were present in the original solution? Write net ionic equations for the formation of each of the precipitates observed.

117. The reaction of NH_3 and O_2 forms NO and water. The NO can be used to convert P_4 to P_4O_6, forming N_2 in the process. The P_4O_6 can be treated with water to form H_3PO_3, which forms PH_3 and H_3PO_4 when heated. Find the mass of PH_3 that forms from the reaction of 1.00 g NH_3.

118. An important reaction that takes place in a blast furnace during the production of iron is the formation of iron metal and CO_2 from Fe_2O_3 and CO. Find the mass of Fe_2O_3 required to form 910 kg of iron. Find the amount of CO_2 that forms in this process.

119. A liquid fuel mixture contains 30.35% hexane (C_6H_{14}), 15.85% heptane (C_7H_{16}), and the rest octane (C_8H_{18}). What maximum mass of carbon dioxide is produced by the complete combustion of 10.0 kg of this fuel mixture?

120. Titanium occurs in the magnetic mineral ilmenite ($FeTiO_3$), which is often found mixed up with sand. The ilmenite can be separated from the sand with magnets. The titanium can then be extracted from the ilmenite by the following set of reactions:

$$FeTiO_3(s) + 3\,Cl_2(g) + 3\,C(s) \longrightarrow$$
$$3\,CO(g) + FeCl_2(s) + TiCl_4(g)$$
$$TiCl_4(g) + 2\,Mg(s) \longrightarrow 2\,MgCl_2(l) + Ti(s)$$

Suppose that an ilmenite-sand mixture contains 22.8% ilmenite by mass and that the first reaction is carried out with a 90.8% yield. If the second reaction is carried out with an 85.9% yield, what mass of titanium can be obtained from 1.00 kg of the ilmenite-sand mixture?

Challenge Problems

121. A mixture of C_3H_8 and C_2H_2 has a mass of 2.0 g. It is burned in excess O_2 to form a mixture of water and carbon dioxide that contains 1.5 times as many moles of CO_2 as of water. Find the mass of C_2H_2 in the original mixture.

122. A mixture of 20.6 g of P and 79.4 g Cl₂ reacts completely to form PCl_3 and PCl_5 as the only products. Find the mass of PCl_3 formed.

123. A solution contains Ag^+ and Hg^{2+} ions. The addition of 0.100 L of 1.22 M NaI solution is just enough to precipitate all the ions as AgI and HgI_2. The total mass of the precipitate is 28.1 g. Find the mass of AgI in the precipitate.

124. Lakes that have been acidified by acid rain (HNO_3 and H_2SO_4) can be neutralized by a process called liming, in which limestone ($CaCO_3$) is added to the acidified water. What mass of limestone

(in kg) would completely neutralize a 15.2 billion-liter lake that is 1.8×10^{-5} M in H_2SO_4 and 8.7×10^{-6} M in HNO_3?

125. We learned in Section 4.6 that sodium carbonate is often added to laundry detergents to soften hard water and make the detergent more effective. Suppose that a particular detergent mixture is designed to soften hard water that is 3.5×10^{-3} M in Ca^{2+} and 1.1×10^{-3} M in Mg^{2+} and that the average capacity of a washing machine is 19.5 gallons of water. If the detergent requires using 0.65 kg detergent per load of laundry, determine what percentage (by mass) of the detergent should be sodium carbonate in order to completely precipitate all of the calcium and magnesium ions in an average load of laundry water.

126. Lead poisoning is a serious condition resulting from the ingestion of lead in food, water, or other environmental sources. It affects the central nervous system, leading to a variety of symptoms such as distractibility, lethargy, and loss of motor coordination. Lead poisoning is treated with chelating agents, substances that bind to metal ions, allowing it to be eliminated in the urine. A modern chelating agent used for this purpose is succimer ($C_4H_6O_4S_2$). Suppose you are trying to determine the appropriate dose for succimer treatment of lead poisoning. What minimum mass of succimer (in mg) is needed to bind all of the lead in a patient's bloodstream? Assume that patient blood lead levels are 45 $\mu g/dL$, that total blood volume is 5.0 L, and that one mole of succimer binds one mole of lead.

127. A particular kind of emergency breathing apparatus—often placed in mines, caves, or other places where oxygen might become depleted or where the air might become poisoned—works via the following chemical reaction:

$$4 \, KO_2 \, (s) + 2 \, CO_2 \, (g) \longrightarrow 2 \, K_2CO_3 \, (s) + 3 \, O_2(g)$$

Notice that the reaction produces O_2, which can be breathed, and absorbs CO_2, a product of respiration. Suppose you work for a company interested in producing a self-rescue breathing apparatus (based on the above reaction) which would allow the user to survive for 10 minutes in an emergency situation. What are the important chemical considerations in designing such a unit? Estimate how much KO_2 would be required for the apparatus. (Find any necessary additional information—such as human breathing rates—from appropriate sources. Assume that normal air is 20% oxygen.)

128. Metallic aluminum reacts with MnO_2 at elevated temperatures to form manganese metal and aluminum oxide. A mixture of the two reactants is 67.2% mole percent Al. Find the theoretical yield (in grams) of manganese from the reaction of 250 g of this mixture.

129. Hydrolysis of the compound B_5H_9 forms boric acid, H_3BO_3. Fusion of boric acid with sodium oxide forms a borate salt, $Na_2B_4O_7$. Without writing complete equations, find the mass (in grams) of B_5H_9 required to form 151 g of the borate salt by this reaction sequence.

Conceptual Problems

130. Consider the reaction:

$$4 \, K(s) + O_2 \, (g) \longrightarrow 2 \, K_2O(s)$$

The molar mass of K is 39.09 g/mol and that of O_2 is 32.00 g/mol. Without doing any calculations, pick the conditions under which potassium is the limiting reactant and explain your reasoning.

a. 170 g K, 31 g O_2 **b.** 16 g K, 2.5 g O_2
c. 165 kg K, 28 kg O_2 **d.** 1.5 g K, 0.38 g O_2

131. Consider the reaction:

$$2 \, NO(g) + 5 \, H_2 \, (g) \longrightarrow 2 \, NH_3 \, (g) + 2 \, H_2O(g)$$

A reaction mixture initially contains 5 moles of NO and 10 moles of H_2. Without doing any calculations, determine which set of amounts best represents the mixture after the reactants have reacted as completely as possible. Explain your reasoning.

a. 1 mol NO, 0 mol H_2, 4 mol NH_3, 4 mol H_2O
b. 0 mol NO, 1 mol H_2, 5 mol NH_3, 5 mol H_2O
c. 3 mol NO, 5 mol H_2, 2 mol NH_3, 2 mol H_2O
d. 0 mol NO, 0 mol H_2, 4 mol NH_3, 4 mol H_2O

132. The circle below represents 1.0 liter of a solution with a solute concentration of 1 M:

Explain what you would add (the amount of solute or volume of solvent) to the solution to obtain a solution represented by each diagram:

  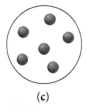

(a)   (b)   (c)

133. Consider the reaction:

$$2 \, N_2H_4(g) + N_2O_4(g) \longrightarrow 3 \, N_2(g) + 4 \, H_2O(g)$$

Consider also this representation of an initial mixture of N_2H_4 and N_2O_4:

Which diagram best represents the reaction mixture after the reactants have reacted as completely as possible?

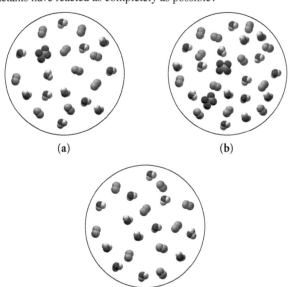

(a)   (b)

(c)

5

Gases

So many of the properties of matter, especially when in the gaseous form, can be deduced from the hypothesis that their minute parts are in rapid motion, the velocity increasing with the temperature, that the precise nature of this motion becomes a subject of rational curiosity.

—James Clerk Maxwell (1831–1879)

WE CAN SURVIVE FOR WEEKS without food, days without water, but only minutes without air. Fortunately, we live at the bottom of a vast ocean of air, held to Earth by gravity. We inhale a lungful of this air every few seconds, keep some of the molecules for our own needs, add some molecules our bodies no longer have a use for, and exhale the mixture back into the surrounding air. The air around us is matter in the gaseous state. What are the fundamental properties of these gases? What laws describe their behavior? What theory explains these properties and laws? Recall that the scientific method (see Section 1.2) proceeds in this way—from observations to laws to theories—exactly the way we will proceed in this chapter. The gaseous state is the simplest and best-understood state of matter. In this chapter, we examine that state.

The buildup of pressure, which results from the constant collisions of gas molecules with the surfaces around them, expels the cork in a bottle of champagne.

5.1 Breathing: Putting Pressure to Work

Every day, without even thinking about it, you move approximately 8500 liters of air into and out of your lungs. The total weight of this air is about 25 pounds. How do you do it? The simple answer is *pressure*. You rely on your body's ability to create pressure differences to move air into and out of your lungs. **Pressure** is the force exerted per unit area by gas molecules as they strike the surfaces around them (Figure 5.1 ▶ on the next page). Just as a ball exerts a force when it bounces against a wall, so a gaseous atom or molecule exerts a force when it collides with a surface. The sum of all these molecular collisions is pressure—a constant force on the surfaces exposed to any gas. The total pressure exerted by a gas depends on several factors, including the concentration of gas molecules in the sample; the higher the concentration, the greater the pressure.

When you inhale, the muscles that surround your chest cavity expand the volume of your lungs. The expanded volume results in a lower concentration of gas molecules (the number of molecules does not change, but since the volume increases, the *concentration*

Gas molecules

Surface

Force

Collisions with surfaces creates pressure.

▲ **FIGURE 5.1 Gas Pressure**
Pressure is the force per unit area exerted by gas molecules colliding with the surfaces around them.

goes down). This in turn results in fewer molecular collisions, which results in lower pressure. The external pressure (the pressure outside of your lungs) remains relatively constant and is now higher than the pressure within your lungs. As a result, gaseous molecules flow into your lungs, from the region of higher pressure to the region of lower pressure. When you exhale, the process is reversed. The chest cavity muscles relax which *decreases* the lung volume, increasing the pressure within the lungs and forcing air back out. In this way, within the course of a normal human lifetime, you will take about half a billion breaths, and move about 250 million liters of air through your lungs. With each breath you create pressure differences that allow you to obtain the oxygen that you need to live.

5.2 Pressure: The Result of Molecular Collisions

Air can hold up a jumbo jet or knock down a building. How? As we just discussed, air contains gaseous atoms and molecules in constant motion. The particles collide with each other and with the surfaces around them. Each collision exerts only a small force, but when the forces of the many particles are summed, they quickly add up. As we have just seen, the result of the constant collisions between the atoms or molecules in a gas and the surfaces around them is *pressure*. Because of pressure, we can drink from straws, inflate basketballs, and move air into and out of our lungs. Variation in pressure in Earth's atmosphere creates wind, and changes in pressure help us to predict weather. Pressure is all around us and even

Pressure and Density

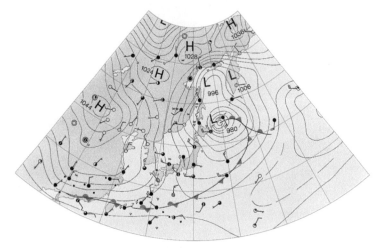

Lower pressure   Higher pressure

▲ **FIGURE 5.2 Pressure and Particle Density**   A low density of gas particles results in low pressure. A high density of gas particles results in high pressure.

▲ Pressure variations in Earth's atmosphere create wind and weather. The H's in this map indicate regions of high pressure, usually associated with clear weather. The L's indicate regions of low pressure, usually associated with unstable weather. The map shows a typhoon off the northeast coast of Japan. The isobars, or lines of constant pressure, are labeled in hectopascals (100 Pa).

inside of us. The pressure that a gas sample exerts, as we have just seen, is the force per unit area that results from the collisions of gas particles with the surrounding surfaces:

$$\text{Pressure} = \frac{\text{force}}{\text{area}} = \frac{F}{A} \qquad [5.1]$$

The pressure of a gas sample depends on several factors, including the number of gas particles in a given volume—the fewer the gas particles, the lower the pressure (Figure 5.2 ◄). Pressure decreases with increasing altitude because there are fewer molecules per unit volume of air. Above 30,000 ft, for example, where most commercial airplanes fly, the pressure is so low that you could pass out due to a lack of oxygen. For this reason, most airplane cabins are artificially pressurized.

You can often feel the effect of a drop in pressure as a brief pain in your ears. This pain arises within the air-containing cavities in your ear (Figure 5.3 ▶). When you ascend a mountain, the external pressure (the pressure that surrounds you) drops, while the pressure within your ear cavities (the internal pressure) remains the same. This creates an imbalance—the greater internal pressure forces your eardrum to bulge outward, causing pain. With time, and with the help of a yawn or two, the excess air within your ear's cavities escapes, equalizing the internal and external pressure and relieving the pain.

Pressure Imbalance

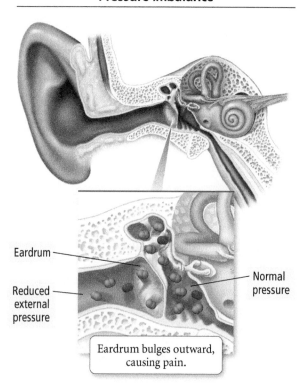

Eardrum

Reduced external pressure

Normal pressure

Eardrum bulges outward, causing pain.

◀ **FIGURE 5.3 Pressure Imbalance**
The discomfort you may feel in your ears upon ascending a mountain is caused by a pressure imbalance between the cavities in your ears and the outside air.

Pressure Units

Pressure can be measured in several different units. A common unit of pressure, the **millimeter of mercury (mmHg)**, originates from how pressure is measured with a **barometer** (Figure 5.4 ▶). A barometer is an evacuated glass tube, the tip of which is submerged in a pool of mercury. Liquid in an evacuated tube is forced upward by atmospheric gas pressure on the liquid's surface. Because mercury is so dense (13.5 times more dense than water), atmospheric pressure can support a column of Hg that is only about 0.760 m or 760 mm (about 30 in) tall. This makes a column of mercury a convenient way to measure pressure.

In a barometer, when the atmospheric pressure rises, the height of the mercury column rises as well. Similarly, when atmospheric pressure falls, the height of the column falls. The unit *millimeter of mercury* is often called a **torr**, after the Italian physicist Evangelista Torricelli (1608–1647) who invented the barometer.

$$1 \text{ mmHg} = 1 \text{ torr}$$

A second unit of pressure is the **atmosphere (atm)**, the average pressure at sea level. Since one atmosphere of pressure pushes a column of mercury to a height of 760 mm, 1 atm and 760 mmHg are equal:

$$1 \text{ atm} = 760 \text{ mmHg}$$

A fully inflated mountain bike tire has a pressure of about 6 atm, and the pressure at the top of Mt. Everest is about 0.31 atm.

The SI unit of pressure is the **pascal (Pa)**, defined as 1 newton (N) per square meter.

$$1 \text{ Pa} = 1 \text{ N/m}^2$$

The pascal is a much smaller unit of pressure than the atmosphere:

$$1 \text{ atm} = 101{,}325 \text{ Pa}$$

Other common units of pressure include inches of mercury (in Hg) and pounds per square inch (psi).

$$1 \text{ atm} = 29.92 \text{ in Hg} \qquad 1 \text{ atm} = 14.7 \text{ psi}$$

Table 5.1 contains a summary of these units.

The Mercury Barometer

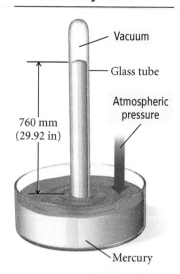

Vacuum

Glass tube

Atmospheric pressure

760 mm (29.92 in)

Mercury

▲ **FIGURE 5.4 The Mercury Barometer**
Average atmospheric pressure at sea level can support a column of mercury 760 mm in height.

TABLE 5.1 Common Units of Pressure

Unit	Abbreviation	Average Air Pressure at Sea Level
Pascal (1 N/m²)	Pa	101,325 Pa
Pounds per square inch	psi	14.7 psi
Torr (1 mmHg)	torr	760 torr (exact)
Inches of mercury	in Hg	29.92 in Hg
Atmosphere	atm	1 atm

EXAMPLE 5.1 Converting between Pressure Units

A high-performance road bicycle tire is inflated to a total pressure of 132 psi. What is this pressure in mmHg?

SORT The problem gives a pressure in psi and asks you to convert the units to mmHg.	**GIVEN:** 132 psi **FIND:** mmHg
STRATEGIZE Since Table 5.1 does not have a direct conversion factor between psi and mmHg, but does provide relationships between both of these units and atmospheres, you can convert to atm as an intermediate step.	**CONCEPTUAL PLAN** 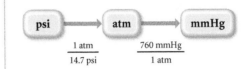 **RELATIONSHIPS USED** 1 atm = 14.7 psi 760 mmHg = 1 atm (both from Table 5.1)
SOLVE Follow the conceptual plan to solve the problem. Begin with 132 psi and use the conversion factors to arrive at the pressure in mmHg.	**SOLUTION** $132 \text{ psi} \times \dfrac{1 \text{ atm}}{14.7 \text{ psi}} \times \dfrac{760 \text{ mmHg}}{1 \text{ atm}} = 6.82 \times 10^3 \text{ mmHg}$

CHECK The units of the answer are correct. The magnitude of the answer (6.82×10^3 mmHg) is greater than the given pressure in psi. This is reasonable since mmHg is a much smaller unit than psi.

FOR PRACTICE 5.1

Your local weather report announces that the barometric pressure is 30.44 in Hg. Convert this pressure to psi.

FOR MORE PRACTICE 5.1

Convert a pressure of 23.8 in Hg to kPa.

The Manometer

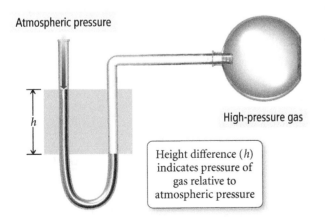

▲ **FIGURE 5.5 The Manometer**
A manometer measures the pressure exerted by a sample of gas.

The Manometer: A Way to Measure Pressure in the Laboratory

We can measure the pressure of a gas sample in the laboratory with a **manometer**. A manometer is a U-shaped tube containing a dense liquid, usually mercury, as shown in Figure 5.5 ◄. In this manometer, one end of the tube is open to atmospheric pressure and the other is attached to a flask containing the gas sample. If the pressure of the gas sample is exactly equal to atmospheric pressure, then the mercury levels on both sides of the tube are the same. If the pressure of the sample is *greater than* atmospheric pressure, the mercury level on the left side of the tube is *higher than* the level on the right. If the pressure of the sample is *less than* atmospheric pressure, the mercury level on the left side is *lower than* the level on the right. This type of manometer always measures the pressure of the gas sample relative to atmospheric pressure. The difference in height between the two levels is equal to the difference between the sample's pressure and atmospheric pressure. To accurately calculate the absolute pressure of the sample, you also need a barometer to measure atmospheric pressure (which can vary from day to day).

CHEMISTRY AND MEDICINE Blood Pressure

Blood pressure is the force within arteries that drives the circulation of blood throughout the body. Blood pressure in the body is analogous to water pressure in a plumbing system. Just as water pressure pushes water through the pipes to faucets and fixtures throughout a house, blood pressure pushes blood to muscles and other tissues throughout the body. However, unlike the water pressure in a plumbing system—which is typically nearly constant—our blood pressure varies with each heartbeat. When the heart muscle contracts, blood pressure increases; between contractions it decreases. Systolic blood pressure is the peak pressure during a contraction, and diastolic blood pressure is the lowest pressure between contractions. Just as excessively high water pressure in a plumbing system can damage pipes, so too high blood pressure in a circulatory system can damage the heart and arteries, resulting in increased risk of stroke and heart attack.

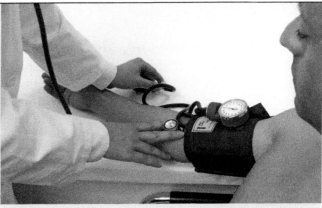

▲ A doctor or a nurse typically measures blood pressure with an inflatable cuff that compresses the main artery in the arm. A stethoscope is used to listen for blood flowing through the artery with each heartbeat.

Medical professionals usually measure blood pressure with an instrument called a sphygmomanometer—an inflatable cuff equipped with a pressure gauge—and a stethoscope. The cuff is wrapped around the patient's arm and inflated with air. As air is pumped into the cuff, the pressure in the cuff increases. The cuff tightens around the arm and compresses the artery, momentarily stopping blood flow. The person measuring the blood pressure listens to the artery through the stethoscope while slowly releasing the pressure in the cuff. When the pressure in the cuff equals the systolic blood pressure (the peak pressure), a pulse is heard through the stethoscope. The pulse is the sound of blood getting through the compressed artery during a contraction of the heart. The pressure reading at that exact moment is the systolic blood pressure. As the pressure in the cuff continues to decrease, the blood can flow through the compressed artery even between contractions, so the pulsing sound stops. The pressure reading when the pulsing sound stops is the diastolic blood pressure (the lowest pressure).

A blood pressure measurement is usually reported as two pressures, in mmHg, separated by a slash. For example, a blood pressure measurement of 122/84 indicates that the systolic blood pressure is 122 mmHg and the diastolic blood pressure is 84 mmHg. Although the value of blood pressure can vary throughout the day, a healthy (or normal) value is usually considered to be below 120 mmHg for systolic and below 80 mmHg for diastolic (Table 5.2). High blood pressure, also called hypertension, entails the health risks mentioned previously.

Risk factors for hypertension include obesity, high salt (sodium) intake, high alcohol intake, lack of exercise, stress, a family history of high blood pressure, and age (blood pressure tends to increase as we get older). Mild hypertension can be managed with diet and exercise. Moderate to severe cases require doctor-prescribed medication.

TABLE 5.2 Blood Pressure Ranges

Blood Pressure	Systolic (mmHg)	Diastolic (mmHg)
Hypotension	<100	<60
Normal	100–119	60–79
Prehypertension	120–139	80–89
Hypertension Stage 1	140–159	90–99
Hypertension Stage 2	>160	>100

5.3 The Simple Gas Laws: Boyle's Law, Charles's Law, and Avogadro's Law

We have learned about pressure and its characteristics. We now broaden our discussion to include the four basic properties of a gas sample: pressure (P), volume (V), temperature (T), and amount in moles (n). These properties are interrelated—when one changes, it affects the others. The simple gas laws describe the relationships between pairs of these properties. For example, how does *volume* vary with *pressure* at constant temperature and amount of gas, or with *temperature* at constant pressure and amount of gas? We can

elucidate these relationships by conducting experiments in which two of the four basic properties are held constant in order to determine the relationship between the other two. We can then express the results of the experiments as laws, called the simple gas laws.

Boyle's Law: Volume and Pressure

In the early 1660s, the pioneering English scientist Robert Boyle (1627–1691) and his assistant Robert Hooke (1635–1703) used a J-tube (Figure 5.6 ▼) to measure the volume of a sample of gas at different pressures. They trapped a sample of air in the J-tube and added mercury to increase the pressure on the gas. Boyle and Hook observed an *inverse relationship* between volume and pressure—an increase in one results in a decrease in the other—as shown in Figure 5.7 ▼. This relationship is now known as **Boyle's law**.

> Boyle's law assumes constant temperature and constant amount of gas.

$$\text{Boyle's law:}\quad V \propto \frac{1}{P}\quad\text{(constant } T \text{ and } n)$$

Boyle's law follows from the idea that pressure results from the collisions of the gas particles with the walls of their container. If the volume of a gas sample is decreased, the same number of gas particles is crowded into a smaller volume, resulting in more collisions with the walls and therefore an increase in the pressure (Figure 5.8 ▶).

Scuba divers learn about Boyle's law during certification because it explains why they should not ascend toward the surface without continuous breathing. For every 10 m of depth that a diver descends in water, she experiences an additional 1 atm of pressure due to the weight of the water above her (Figure 5.9 ▶). The pressure regulator used in scuba diving delivers air into the diver's lungs at a pressure that matches the external pressure; otherwise the diver could not inhale the air (see *Chemistry in Your Day: Extralong Snorkels* on page 187). For example, when a diver is 20 m below the surface, the regulator delivers air at a pressure of 3 atm to match the 3 atm of pressure around the diver (1 atm due to normal atmospheric pressure and 2 additional atmospheres due to the weight of the water at 20 m). Suppose that a diver inhaled a lungful of air at a pressure of 3 atm and swam quickly to the surface (where the pressure is 1 atm) while holding her breath. What would happen to the volume of air in her lungs? Since the pressure decreases by a factor of 3, the volume of the air in her lungs would increase by a factor of 3—a dangerous situation. Of course, the volume increase in the diver's lungs would be so great that she would not be able to hold her breath all the way to the surface—the air would

The J-Tube

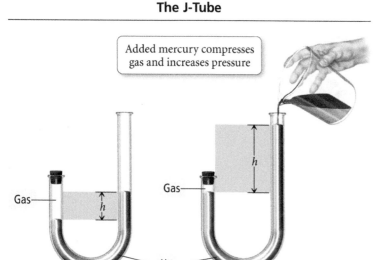

▲ **FIGURE 5.6 The J-Tube**   In a J-tube, a column of mercury traps a sample of gas. The pressure on the gas can be increased by increasing the height (*h*) of mercury in the column.

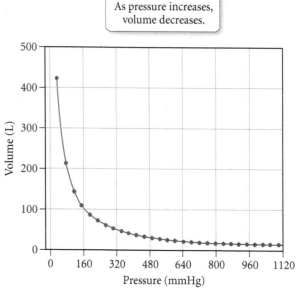

▲ **FIGURE 5.7 Volume versus Pressure**   A plot of the volume of a gas sample—as measured in a J-tube—versus pressure. The plot shows that volume and pressure are inversely related.

Volume versus Pressure: A Molecular View

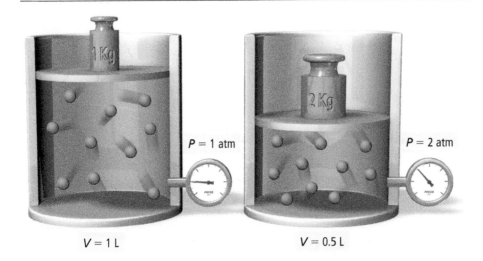

◀ **FIGURE 5.8 Molecular Interpretation of Boyle's Law**   As the volume of a gas sample is decreased, gas molecules collide with surrounding surfaces more frequently, resulting in greater pressure.

force itself out of her mouth but probably not before the expanded air severely damaged her lungs, possibly killing her. Consequently, the most important rule in diving is *never hold your breath*. To avoid such catastrophic results, divers must ascend slowly and breathe continuously, allowing the regulator to bring the air pressure in their lungs back to 1 atm by the time they reach the surface.

We can use Boyle's law to calculate the volume of a gas following a pressure change or the pressure of a gas following a volume change *as long as the temperature and the amount of gas remain constant*. For these types of calculations, we write Boyle's law in a slightly different way.

$$\text{Since } V \propto \frac{1}{P}, \quad \text{then} \quad V = (\text{constant}) \times \frac{1}{P} \quad \text{or} \quad V = \frac{(\text{constant})}{P}$$

If two quantities are proportional, then one is equal to the other multiplied by a constant.

If we multiply both sides by P, we get

$$PV = \text{constant}$$

Depth = 0 m
P = 1 atm

Depth = 20 m
P = 3 atm

◀ **FIGURE 5.9 Increase in Pressure with Depth**   For every 10 m of depth, a diver experiences approximately one additional atmosphere of pressure due to the weight of the surrounding water. At 20 m, for example, the diver experiences approximately 3 atm of pressure (1 atm of normal atmospheric pressure plus an additional 2 atm due to the weight of the water).

This relationship indicates that if the pressure increases, the volume decreases, but the product $P \times V$ always equals the same constant. For two different sets of conditions, we can say that

$$P_1 V_1 = \text{constant} = P_2 V_2$$

or

$$P_1 V_1 = P_2 V_2 \qquad [5.2]$$

where P_1 and V_1 are the initial pressure and volume of the gas and P_2 and V_2 are the final volume and pressure.

EXAMPLE 5.2 Boyle's Law

A cylinder equipped with a movable piston has a volume of 7.25 L under an applied pressure of 4.52 atm. What is the volume of the cylinder if we decrease the applied pressure to 1.21 atm?

To solve the problem, first solve Boyle's law (Equation 5.2) for V_2 and then substitute the given quantities to calculate V_2.	**SOLUTION** $P_1 V_1 = P_2 V_2$ $V_2 = \dfrac{P_1}{P_2} V_1$ $= \dfrac{4.52 \text{ atm}}{1.21 \text{ atm}} 7.25 \text{ L}$ $= 27.1 \text{ L}$

FOR PRACTICE 5.2

A snorkeler takes a syringe filled with 16 mL of air from the surface, where the pressure is 1.0 atm, to an unknown depth. The volume of the air in the syringe at this depth is 7.5 mL. What is the pressure at this depth? If the pressure increases by 1 atm for every additional 10 m of depth, how deep is the snorkeler?

Charles's Law: Volume and Temperature

Suppose we keep the pressure of a gas sample constant and measure its volume at a number of different temperatures. Figure 5.10 ▼ shows the results of several such measurements. From the plot we can see a relationship between volume and temperature: the volume of

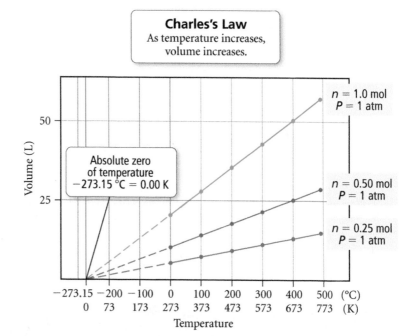

▶ FIGURE 5.10 **Volume versus Temperature** The volume of a fixed amount of gas at a constant pressure increases linearly with increasing temperature in kelvins. (The extrapolated lines could not be measured experimentally because all gases condense into liquids before −273.15 °C is reached.)

CHEMISTRY IN YOUR DAY **Extra-long Snorkels**

Several episodes of *The Flintstones* cartoon featured Fred Flintstone and Barney Rubble snorkeling. Their snorkels, however, were not the modern kind, but long reeds that stretched from the surface of the water down to many meters of depth. Fred and Barney swam around in deep water while breathing air provided to them by these extra-long snorkels. Would this work? Why do people bother with scuba diving equipment if they could instead simply use 10-m snorkels as Fred and Barney did?

As we saw in Section 5.1, when we breathe, we expand the volume of our chest cavity, reducing the pressure on the outer surface of the lungs to less than 1 atm (Boyle's law). Because of this pressure differential, the lungs expand, the pressure in them falls, and air from outside of our lungs then flows into them. Extra-long snorkels do not work because of the pressure exerted by water at depth. A diver at 10 m experiences an external pressure of 2 atm. This is more than the muscles of the chest cavity can overcome—the chest cavity and lungs are compressed, resulting in an air pressure within them of more than 1 atm. If the diver had a snorkel that went to the surface— where the air pressure is 1 atm—air would flow out of his lungs (*from* greater pressure *to* less pressure), not into them. It would be impossible to breathe.

▲ In the popular cartoon *The Flintstones*, cavemen used long reeds to breathe surface air while swimming at depth. This would not work because the increased pressure at depth would force air out of their lungs; the pressure would not allow them to inhale.

▲ If two balloons were joined by a long tube and one end was submerged in water, what would happen to the volumes of the two balloons?

Question

A diver takes a balloon with a volume of 2.5 L from the surface, where the pressure is 1.0 atm, to a depth of 20 m, where the pressure is 3.0 atm. What happens to the volume of the balloon? What if the end of the submerged balloon were on a long pipe that went to the surface and was attached to another balloon? Which way would air flow as the diver descended?

a gas increases with increasing temperature. Looking at the plot more closely, however, reveals more—volume and temperature are *linearly related*. If two variables are linearly related, then plotting one against the other produces a straight line.

Another interesting feature emerges if we extend or *extrapolate* the line in the plot backwards from the lowest measured temperature. The dotted extrapolated line shows that the gas should have a zero volume at –273.15 °C. Recall from Chapter 1 that –273.15 °C corresponds to 0 K (zero on the Kelvin scale), the coldest possible temperature. The extrapolated line shows that below –273.15 °C, the gas would have a negative volume, which is physically impossible. For this reason, we refer to 0 K as *absolute zero*—colder temperatures do not exist.

The first person to carefully quantify the relationship between the volume of a gas and its temperature was J. A. C. Charles (1746–1823), a French mathematician and physicist. Charles was interested in gases and was among the first people to ascend in a hydrogen-filled balloon. The direct proportionality between volume and temperature is named **Charles's law** after him.

$$\text{Charles's law:} \quad V \propto T \quad (\text{constant } P \text{ and } n)$$

Charles's law assumes constant pressure and constant amount of gas.

When the temperature of a gas sample is increased, the gas particles move faster; collisions with the walls are more frequent, and the force exerted with each collision is greater. The only way for the pressure (the force per unit area) to remain constant is for

▲ A hot-air balloon floats because the hot air is less dense than the surrounding cold air.

▲ If we place a balloon into liquid nitrogen (77 K), it shrivels up as the air within it cools and occupies less volume at the same external pressure.

Volume versus Temperature: A Molecular View

Low kinetic energy   High kinetic energy

Ice water   Boiling water

▲ **FIGURE 5.11 Molecular Interpretation of Charles's Law** If we move a balloon from an ice water bath to a boiling water bath, its volume expands as the gas particles within the balloon move faster (due to the increased temperature) and collectively occupy more space.

the gas to occupy a larger volume, so that collisions become less frequent and occur over a larger area (Figure 5.11 ▲).

Charles's law explains why the second floor of a house is usually warmer than the ground floor. According to Charles's law, when air is heated, its volume increases, resulting in a lower density. The warm, less dense air tends to rise in a room filled with colder, denser air. Similarly, Charles's law explains why a hot-air balloon can take flight. The gas that fills a hot-air balloon is warmed with a burner, increasing its volume and lowering its density, and causing it to float in the colder, denser surrounding air.

You can experience Charles's law directly by holding a partially inflated balloon over a warm toaster. As the air in the balloon warms, you can feel the balloon expanding. Alternatively, you can a put an inflated balloon into liquid nitrogen and see that it becomes smaller as it cools.

We can use Charles's law to calculate the volume of a gas following a temperature change or the temperature of a gas following a volume change *as long as the pressure and the amount of gas are constant*. For these calculations, we rearrange Charles's law as follows:

$$\text{Since } V \propto T, \text{ then } V = \text{constant} \times T$$

If we divide both sides by T, we get

$$V/T = \text{constant}$$

If the temperature increases, the volume increases in direct proportion so that the quotient, V/T, is always equal to the same constant. So, for two different measurements, we can say that

$$V_1/T_1 = \text{constant} = V_2/T_2,$$

or

$$\frac{V_1}{T_1} = \frac{V_2}{T_2} \qquad [5.3]$$

where V_1 and T_1 are the initial volume and temperature of the gas and V_2 and T_2 are the final volume and temperature. *The temperatures must always be expressed in kelvins (K)*, because, as you can see in Figure 5.10, the volume of a gas is directly proportional to its absolute temperature, not its temperature in °C. For example, doubling the temperature of a gas sample from 1 °C to 2 °C does not double its volume, but doubling the temperature from 200 K to 400 K does.

EXAMPLE 5.3 Charles's Law

A sample of gas has a volume of 2.80 L at an unknown temperature. When the sample is submerged in ice water at $T = 0.00\ °C$, its volume decreases to 2.57 L. What was its initial temperature (in K and in °C)?

To solve the problem, first solve Charles's law for T_1.	**SOLUTION** $$\frac{V_1}{T_1} = \frac{V_2}{T_2}$$ $$T_1 = \frac{V_1}{V_2} T_2$$
Before you substitute the numerical values to calculate T_1, you must convert the temperature to kelvins (K). *Remember, gas law problems must always be worked with Kelvin temperatures.*	$T_2\ (K) = 0.00 + 273.15 = 273.15\ K$
Substitute T_2 and the other given quantities to calculate T_1.	$$T_1 = \frac{V_1}{V_2} T_2$$ $$= \frac{2.80\ \cancel{L}}{2.57\ \cancel{L}}\ 273.15\ K$$ $$= 297.6\ K$$
Calculate T_1 in °C by subtracting 273 from the value in kelvins.	$T_1\ (°C) = 297.6 - 273.15 = 24\ °C$

FOR PRACTICE 5.3

A gas in a cylinder with a moveable piston has an initial volume of 88.2 mL. If we heat the gas from 35 °C to 155 °C, what is its final volume (in mL)?

Avogadro's Law: Volume and Amount (in Moles)

So far, we have learned the relationships between volume and pressure, and volume and temperature, but we have considered only a constant amount of a gas. What happens when the amount of gas changes? The volume of a gas sample (at constant temperature and pressure) as a function of the amount of gas (in moles) in the sample is shown in Figure 5.12 ▶. We can see that the relationship between volume and amount is linear. As we might expect, extrapolation to zero moles shows zero volume. This relationship, first stated formally by Amadeo Avogadro, is called **Avogadro's law**:

> Avogadro's law assumes constant temperature and constant pressure and is independent of the nature of the gas.

$$\text{Avogadro's law:} \quad V \propto n \quad \text{(constant } T \text{ and } P\text{)}$$

When the amount of gas in a sample increases at constant temperature and pressure, its volume increases in direct proportion because the greater number of gas particles fill more space.

You experience Avogadro's law when you inflate a balloon. With each exhaled breath, you add more gas particles to the inside of the balloon, increasing its volume. We can use Avogadro's law to calculate the volume of a gas following a change in the amount of the gas *as long as the pressure and temperature of the gas are constant.* For these types of calculations, we express Avogadro's law as

$$\frac{V_1}{n_1} = \frac{V_2}{n_2} \qquad [5.4]$$

where V_1 and n_1 are the initial volume and number of moles of the gas and V_2 and n_2 are the final volume and number of moles. In calculations, we use Avogadro's law in a manner similar to the other gas laws, as demonstrated in the following example.

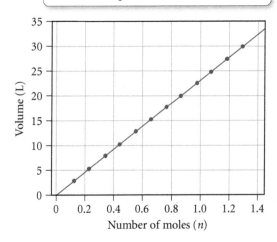

▲ **FIGURE 5.12 Volume versus Number of Moles** The volume of a gas sample increases linearly with the number of moles of gas in the sample.

EXAMPLE 5.4 Avogadro's Law

A 4.65-L sample of helium gas contains 0.225 mol of helium. How many additional moles of helium gas must we add to the sample to obtain a volume of 6.48 L? Assume constant temperature and pressure.

To solve the problem, first solve Avogadro's law for n_2. Then substitute the given quantities to calculate n_2.	**SOLUTION** $$\frac{V_1}{n_1} = \frac{V_2}{n_2}$$ $$n_2 = \frac{V_2}{V_1} n_1$$
Since the balloon already contains 0.225 mol of gas, calculate the amount of gas to add by subtracting 0.225 mol from the value you calculated for n_2. (In Chapter 1, we introduced the practice of underlining the least (rightmost) significant digit of intermediate answers, but not rounding the final answer until the very end of the calculation. We continue that practice in this chapter. However, in order to avoid unnecessary notation, we will not carry additional digits in cases, such as this one, where doing so would not affect the final answer.)	$$= \frac{6.48 \text{ L}}{4.65 \text{ L}} 0.225 \text{ mol}$$ $$= 0.314 \text{ mol}$$ moles to add $= 0.314 \text{ mol} - 0.225 \text{ mol}$ $$= 0.089 \text{ mol}$$

FOR PRACTICE 5.4

A chemical reaction occurring in a cylinder equipped with a moveable piston produces 0.621 mol of a gaseous product. If the cylinder contained 0.120 mol of gas before the reaction and had an initial volume of 2.18 L, what was its volume after the reaction? (Assume constant pressure and temperature and that the initial amount of gas completely reacts.)

5.4 The Ideal Gas Law

The relationships that we have learned so far can be combined into a single law that encompasses all of them. So far, we know that

$$V \propto \frac{1}{P} \qquad \text{(Boyle's law)}$$

$$V \propto T \qquad \text{(Charles's law)}$$

$$V \propto n \qquad \text{(Avogadro's law)}$$

Combining these three expressions, we get

$$V \propto \frac{nT}{P}$$

The volume of a gas is directly proportional to the number of moles of gas and to the temperature of the gas, but is inversely proportional to the pressure of the gas. We can replace the proportionality sign with an equals sign by incorporating R, a proportionality constant called the *ideal gas constant*:

$$V = \frac{RnT}{P}$$

Rearranging, we get

$$PV = nRT \qquad [5.5]$$

This equation is the **ideal gas law**, and a hypothetical gas that exactly follows this law is an **ideal gas**. The value of R, the **ideal gas constant**, is the same for all gases and has the following value:

$$R = 0.08206 \frac{L \cdot atm}{mol \cdot K}$$

| L = liters
| atm = atmospheres
| mol = moles
| K = kelvins

The ideal gas law contains within it the simple gas laws that we have learned. For example, recall that Boyle's law states that $V \propto 1/P$ when the amount of gas (n) and the temperature of the gas (T) are kept constant. We can rearrange the ideal gas law as follows:

$$PV = nRT$$

First, divide both sides by P:

$$V = \frac{nRT}{P}$$

Then put the variables that are constant, along with R, in parentheses:

$$V = (nRT)\frac{1}{P}$$

Since n and T are constant in this case, and since R is always a constant, we can write

$$V \propto (constant) \times \frac{1}{P}$$

which means that $V \propto 1/P$.

The ideal gas law also shows how other pairs of variables are related. For example, from Charles's law we know that $V \propto T$ at constant pressure and constant number of moles. But what if we heat a sample of gas at constant *volume* and constant number of moles? This question applies to the warning labels on aerosol cans such as hair spray or deodorants. These labels warn against excessive heating or incineration of the can, even after the contents are used up. Why? An "empty" aerosol can is not really empty but contains a fixed amount of gas trapped in a fixed volume. What would happen if you were to heat the can? Let's rearrange the ideal gas law to clearly see the relationship between pressure and temperature at constant volume and constant number of moles:

$$PV = nRT$$

$$P = \frac{nRT}{V} = \left(\frac{nR}{V}\right)T$$

| Divide both sides by V.

Since n and V are constant and since R is always a constant:

$$P = (constant) \times T$$

This relationship between pressure and temperature is also known as *Gay-Lussac's law*. As the temperature of a fixed amount of gas in a fixed volume increases, the pressure increases. In an aerosol can, this pressure increase can blow the can apart, which is why aerosol cans should not be heated or incinerated. They might explode.

The ideal gas law can also be used to determine the value of any one of the four variables (P, V, n, or T) given the other three. To do so, each of the quantities in the ideal gas law *must be expressed* in the units within R:

- pressure (P) in atm
- volume (V) in L
- moles (n) in mol
- temperature (T) in K

Ideal Gas Law

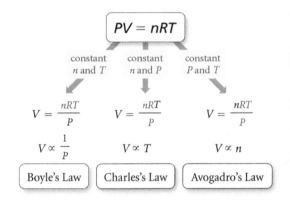

▲ The ideal gas law contains the simple gas laws within it.

▲ The labels on most aerosol cans warn against incineration. Since the volume of the can is constant, an increase in temperature causes an increase in pressure and possibly an explosion.

EXAMPLE 5.5 Ideal Gas Law I

Calculate the volume occupied by 0.845 mol of nitrogen gas at a pressure of 1.37 atm and a temperature of 315 K.

SORT The problem gives you the number of moles of nitrogen gas, the pressure, and the temperature. You are asked to find the volume.	**GIVEN:** $n = 0.845$ mol, $P = 1.37$ atm, $T = 315$ K **FIND:** V
STRATEGIZE You are given three of the four variables (P, T, and n) in the ideal gas law and asked to find the fourth (V). The conceptual plan shows how the ideal gas law provides the relationship between the known quantities and the unknown quantity.	**CONCEPTUAL PLAN** 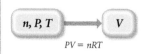 $PV = nRT$ **RELATIONSHIP USED** $PV = nRT$ (ideal gas law)
SOLVE To solve the problem, first solve the ideal gas law for V. Then substitute the given quantities to calculate V.	**SOLUTION** $$PV = nRT$$ $$V = \frac{nRT}{P}$$ $$V = \frac{0.845 \text{ mol} \times 0.08206 \frac{\text{L} \cdot \text{atm}}{\text{mol} \cdot \text{K}} \times 315 \text{ K}}{1.37 \text{ atm}}$$ $$= 15.9 \text{ L}$$

CHECK The units of the answer are correct. The magnitude of the answer (15.9 L) makes sense because, as you will see in the next section, one mole of an ideal gas under standard conditions (273 K and 1 atm) occupies 22.4 L. Although these are not standard conditions, they are close enough for a ballpark check of the answer. Since this gas sample contains 0.845 mol, a volume of 15.9 L is reasonable.

FOR PRACTICE 5.5

An 8.50-L tire contains 0.552 mol of gas at a temperature of 305 K. What is the pressure (in atm and psi) of the gas in the tire?

EXAMPLE 5.6 Ideal Gas Law II

Calculate the number of moles of gas in a 3.24-L basketball inflated to a *total pressure* of 24.3 psi at 25 °C. (Note: The *total pressure* is not the same as the pressure read on a pressure gauge such as the kind used for checking a car or bicycle tire. That pressure, called the *gauge pressure*, is the *difference* between the total pressure and atmospheric pressure. In this case, if atmospheric pressure is 14.7 psi, the gauge pressure would be 9.6 psi. However, for calculations involving the ideal gas law, you must use the *total pressure* of 24.3 psi.)

SORT The problem gives you the pressure, the volume, and the temperature. You are asked to find the number of moles of gas.	**GIVEN:** $P = 24.3$ psi, $V = 3.24$ L, T (°C) = 25 °C **FIND:** n
STRATEGIZE The conceptual plan shows how the ideal gas law provides the relationship between the given quantities and the quantity to be found.	**CONCEPTUAL PLAN** 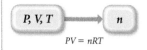 $PV = nRT$ **RELATIONSHIP USED** $PV = nRT$ (ideal gas law)

SOLVE To solve the problem, first solve the ideal gas law for n.	**SOLUTION** $$PV = nRT$$ $$n = \frac{PV}{RT}$$
Before substituting into the equation, convert P and T into the correct units.	$P = 24.3 \text{ psi} \times \dfrac{1 \text{ atm}}{14.7 \text{ psi}} = 1.6\underline{5}31 \text{ atm}$ (Since rounding the intermediate answer would result in a slightly different final answer, we mark the least significant digit in the intermediate answer, but don't round until the end.)
Finally, substitute into the equation and calculate n.	$T \text{ (K)} = 25 + 273 = 298 \text{ K}$ $n = \dfrac{1.6\underline{5}31 \text{ atm} \times 3.24 \text{ L}}{0.08206 \dfrac{\text{L} \cdot \text{atm}}{\text{mol} \cdot \text{K}} \times 298 \text{ K}} = 0.219 \text{ mol}$

CHECK The units of the answer are correct. The magnitude of the answer (0.219 mol) makes sense because, as you will see in the next section, one mole of an ideal gas under standard conditions (273 K and 1 atm) occupies 22.4 L. At a pressure that is 65% higher than standard conditions, the volume of 1 mol of gas would be proportionally lower. Since this gas sample occupies 3.24 L, the answer of 0.219 mol is reasonable.

FOR PRACTICE 5.6

What volume does 0.556 mol of gas occupy at a pressure of 715 mmHg and a temperature of 58 °C?

FOR MORE PRACTICE 5.6

Find the pressure in mmHg of a 0.133-g sample of helium gas in a 648-mL container at a temperature of 32 °C.

5.5 Applications of the Ideal Gas Law: Molar Volume, Density, and Molar Mass of a Gas

We just examined how we can use the ideal gas law to calculate one of the variables (P, V, T, or n) given the other three. We now turn to three other applications of the ideal gas law: molar volume, density, and molar mass.

Molar Volume at Standard Temperature and Pressure

The volume occupied by one mole of a substance is its **molar volume**. For gases, we often specify the molar volume under conditions known as **standard temperature** ($T = 0 \text{ °C}$ or 273 K) **and pressure** ($P = 1.00$ atm), abbreviated as **STP**. Using the ideal gas law, we can determine that the molar volume of ideal gas at STP is

$$V = \frac{nRT}{P}$$

$$= \frac{1.00 \text{ mol} \times 0.08206 \dfrac{\text{L} \cdot \text{atm}}{\text{mol} \cdot \text{K}} \times 273 \text{ K}}{1.00 \text{ atm}}$$

$$= 22.4 \text{ L}$$

The molar volume of 22.4 L only applies at STP.

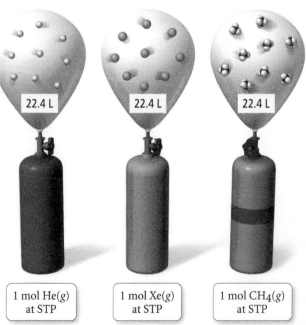

| 1 mol He(g) at STP | 1 mol Xe(g) at STP | 1 mol CH₄(g) at STP |

▲ One mole of any gas occupies approximately 22.4 L at standard temperature (273 K) and pressure (1.0 atm).

The molar volume of an ideal gas at STP is useful because—as we saw in the *Check* sections of Examples 5.5 and 5.6—it gives us a way to approximate the volume of an ideal gas under conditions that are close to STP.

Conceptual Connection 5.1 **Molar Volume**

Assuming ideal behavior, which of the following gas samples will have the greatest volume at STP?

(a) 1 g of H_2 **(b)** 1 g of O_2 **(c)** 1 g of Ar

ANSWER: (a) Since 1 g of H_2 contains the greatest number of moles (due to H_2 having the lowest molar mass of the listed gases), and since one mole of *any* ideal gas occupies the same volume, the H_2 will occupy the greatest volume.

Density of a Gas

If we know the molar volume of an ideal gas under standard conditions, we can readily calculate the density of the gas under these conditions. Since density is mass/volume, and since the mass of one mole of a gas is simply its molar mass, the *density of a gas under standard conditions* is given by the following relationship:

$$\text{Density} = \frac{\text{molar mass}}{\text{molar volume}}$$

For example, we calculate the densities of helium and nitrogen gas at STP as follows:

$$d_{He} = \frac{4.00 \text{ g/mol}}{22.4 \text{ L/mol}} = 0.179 \text{ g/L} \qquad d_{N_2} = \frac{28.02 \text{ g/mol}}{22.4 \text{ L/mol}} = 1.25 \text{ g/L}$$

Notice that *the density of a gas is directly proportional to its molar mass*. The greater the molar mass of a gas, the more dense the gas. For this reason, a gas with a molar mass lower than that of air tends to rise in air. For example, both helium and hydrogen gas (molar masses of 4.00 and 2.01 g/mol, respectively) have molar masses that are lower than the average molar mass of air (approximately 28.8 g/mol). Therefore a balloon filled with either helium or hydrogen gas floats in air.

> The detailed composition of air is covered in Section 5.6. The primary components of air are nitrogen (about four-fifths) and oxygen (about one-fifth).

We can calculate the density of a gas more generally (under any conditions) by using the ideal gas law. To do so, we can arrange the ideal gas law as follows:

$$PV = nRT$$

$$\frac{n}{V} = \frac{P}{RT}$$

Since the left-hand side of this equation has units of moles/liter, it represents the *molar density*. We can obtain the density in grams/liter from the molar density by multiplying by the molar mass ($\mathcal{M}$):

$$\underbrace{\frac{\text{moles}}{\text{liter}}}_{\text{Molar density}} \times \underbrace{\frac{\text{grams}}{\text{mole}}}_{\text{Molar mass}} = \underbrace{\frac{\text{grams}}{\text{liter}}}_{\substack{\text{Density in} \\ \text{grams/liter}}}$$

Therefore,

$$d = \frac{P\mathcal{M}}{RT} \qquad\qquad [5.6]$$

Notice that, as expected, density increases with increasing molar mass. Notice also that as we learned in Section 5.3, density decreases with increasing temperature.

$$\text{Density}$$
$$\underbrace{\frac{n}{V}}_{\text{Molar density}} \, \mathcal{M} = \underbrace{\frac{P\mathcal{M}}{RT}}_{\text{Molar mass}}$$

$$d = \frac{P\mathcal{M}}{RT}$$

EXAMPLE 5.7 Density

Calculate the density of nitrogen gas at 125 °C and a pressure of 755 mmHg.

SORT The problem gives you the temperature and pressure of a gas and asks you to find its density. The problem also states that the gas is nitrogen.	**GIVEN:** $T(°C) = 125 °C$, $P = 755$ mmHg **FIND:** d
STRATEGIZE Equation 5.6 provides the relationship between the density of a gas and its temperature, pressure, and molar mass. The temperature and pressure are given. You can calculate the molar mass from the formula of the gas, which we know is N_2.	**CONCEPTUAL PLAN** 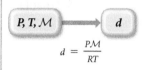 $d = \dfrac{P\mathcal{M}}{RT}$ **RELATIONSHIPS USED** $d = \dfrac{P\mathcal{M}}{RT}$ (density of a gas) Molar mass $N_2 = 28.02$ g/mol
SOLVE To solve the problem, gather each of the required quantities in the correct units. Convert the temperature to kelvins and the pressure to atmospheres.	**SOLUTION** $T(K) = 125 + 273 = 398$ K $P = 755 \text{ mmHg} \times \dfrac{1 \text{ atm}}{760 \text{ mmHg}} = 0.99342$ atm
Now substitute the quantities into the equation to calculate density.	$d = \dfrac{P\mathcal{M}}{RT}$ $= \dfrac{0.99342 \text{ atm} \left(28.02 \dfrac{\text{g}}{\text{mol}}\right)}{0.08206 \dfrac{\text{L} \cdot \text{atm}}{\text{mol} \cdot \text{K}} \left(398 \text{ K}\right)}$ $= 0.852$ g/L

CHECK The units of the answer are correct. The magnitude of the answer (0.852 g/L) makes sense because earlier we calculated the density of nitrogen gas at STP as 1.25 g/L. Since the temperature is higher than standard conditions, it follows that the density is lower.

FOR PRACTICE 5.7

Calculate the density of xenon gas at a pressure of 742 mmHg and a temperature of 45 °C.

FOR MORE PRACTICE 5.7

A gas has a density of 1.43 g/L at a temperature of 23 °C and a pressure of 0.789 atm. Calculate its molar mass.

Molar Mass of a Gas

We can use the ideal gas law in combination with mass measurements to calculate the molar mass of an unknown gas. First we measure the mass and volume of an unknown gas under conditions of known pressure and temperature. Then, we determine the amount of the gas in moles from the ideal gas law. Finally, we calculate the molar mass by dividing the mass (in grams) by the amount (in moles) as shown in the following example.

EXAMPLE 5.8 Molar Mass of a Gas

A sample of gas has a mass of 0.311 g. Its volume is 0.225 L at a temperature of 55 °C and a pressure of 886 mmHg. Find its molar mass.

SORT The problem gives you the mass of a gas sample, along with its volume, temperature, and pressure. You are asked to find the molar mass.	**GIVEN:** $m = 0.331$ g, $V = 0.225$ L, T (°C) $= 55$ °C, $P = 886$ mmHg **FIND:** molar mass (g/mol)
STRATEGIZE The conceptual plan has two parts. In the first part, use the ideal gas law to find the number of moles of gas. In the second part, use the definition of molar mass to find the molar mass.	**CONCEPTUAL PLAN** 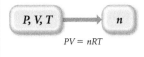 $PV = nRT$ 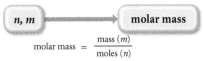 molar mass $= \dfrac{\text{mass } (m)}{\text{moles } (n)}$ **RELATIONSHIPS USED** $PV = nRT$ Molar mass $= \dfrac{\text{mass } (m)}{\text{moles } (n)}$
SOLVE To find the number of moles, first solve the ideal gas law for n. Before substituting into the equation for n, convert the pressure to atm and the temperature to K. Now, substitute into the equation and calculate n, the number of moles. Finally, use the number of moles (n) and the given mass (m) to find the molar mass.	**SOLUTION** $PV = nRT$ $n = \dfrac{PV}{RT}$ $P = 886 \ \text{mmHg} \times \dfrac{1 \ \text{atm}}{760 \ \text{mmHg}} = 1.1658 \ \text{atm}$ $T(\text{K}) = 55 + 273 = 328 \ \text{K}$ $n = \dfrac{1.1658 \ \text{atm} \times 0.225 \ \text{L}}{0.08206 \ \dfrac{\text{L} \cdot \text{atm}}{\text{mol} \cdot \text{K}} \times 328 \ \text{K}}$ $= 9.7454 \times 10^{-3} \ \text{mol}$ molar mass $= \dfrac{\text{mass } (m)}{\text{moles } (n)}$ $= \dfrac{0.311 \ \text{g}}{9.7454 \times 10^{-3} \ \text{mol}}$ $= 31.9 \ \text{g/mol}$

CHECK The units of the answer are correct. The magnitude of the answer (31.9 g/mol) is a reasonable number for a molar mass. If you calculated some very small number (such as any number smaller than 1) or a very large number, you probably made some mistake. Most gases have molar masses between one and several hundred grams per mole.

FOR PRACTICE 5.8

A sample of gas has a mass of 827 mg. Its volume is 0.270 L at a temperature of 88 °C and a pressure of 975 mmHg. Find its molar mass.

5.6 Mixtures of Gases and Partial Pressures

Many gas samples are not pure, but are mixtures of gases. Dry air, for example, is a mixture containing nitrogen, oxygen, argon, carbon dioxide, and a few other gases in trace amounts (Table 5.3).

Because the molecules in an ideal gas do not interact (as we will discuss further in Section 5.8), each of the components in an ideal gas mixture acts independently of the others. For example, the nitrogen molecules in air exert a certain pressure—78% of the total pressure—that is independent of the other gases in the mixture. Likewise, the oxygen molecules in air exert a certain pressure—21% of the total pressure—that is also independent of the other gases in the mixture. The pressure due to any individual component in a gas mixture is the **partial pressure (P_n)** of that component and can be calculated from the ideal gas law by assuming that each gas component acts independently. For a multicomponent gas mixture, we can calculate the partial pressure of each component from the ideal gas law and the number of moles of that component (n_n) as follows:

$$P_a = n_a \frac{RT}{V}; \quad P_b = n_b \frac{RT}{V}; \quad P_c = n_c \frac{RT}{V}; \quad \cdots \qquad [5.7]$$

The sum of the partial pressures of the components in a gas mixture must equal the total pressure:

$$P_{total} = P_a + P_b + P_c + \cdots \qquad [5.8]$$

where P_{total} is the total pressure and P_a, P_b, P_c,..., are the partial pressures of the components. This relationship is known as **Dalton's law of partial pressures**.

Combining Equations 5.7 and 5.8, we get

$$P_{total} = P_a + P_b + P_c + \cdots$$
$$= n_a \frac{RT}{V} + n_b \frac{RT}{V} + n_c \frac{RT}{V} + \cdots \qquad [5.9]$$
$$= (n_a + n_b + n_c + \cdots) \frac{RT}{V}$$
$$= (n_{total}) \frac{RT}{V}$$

The total number of moles in the mixture, when substituted into the ideal gas law, indicates the total pressure of the sample.

If we divide Equation 5.7 by Equation 5.9, we get the following result:

$$\frac{P_a}{P_{total}} = \frac{n_a (RT/V)}{n_{total} (RT/V)} = \frac{n_a}{n_{total}} \qquad [5.10]$$

The quantity n_a/n_{total}, the number of moles of a component in a mixture divided by the total number of moles in the mixture, is called the **mole fraction (χ_a)**:

$$\chi_a = \frac{n_a}{n_{total}} \qquad [5.11]$$

Rearranging Equation 5.10 and substituting the definition of mole fraction gives the following:

$$\frac{P_a}{P_{total}} = \frac{n_a}{n_{total}}$$
$$P_a = \frac{n_a}{n_{total}} P_{total} = \chi_a P_{total}$$

or simply

$$P_a = \chi_a P_{total} \qquad [5.12]$$

TABLE 5.3 Composition of Dry Air

Gas	Percent by Volume (%)
Nitrogen (N_2)	78
Oxygen (O_2)	21
Argon (Ar)	0.9
Carbon dioxide (CO_2)	0.04

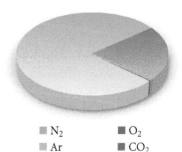

■ N_2 ■ O_2
■ Ar   ■ CO_2

The partial pressure of a component in a gaseous mixture is its mole fraction multiplied by the total pressure. For gases, the mole fraction of a component is equivalent to its percent by volume divided by 100%. Therefore, based on Table 5.3, we calculate the partial pressure of nitrogen (P_{N_2}) in air at 1.00 atm as follows:

$$P_{N_2} = 0.78 \times 1.00 \text{ atm}$$
$$= 0.78 \text{ atm}$$

Likewise, the partial pressure of oxygen in air at 1.00 atm is 0.21 atm and the partial pressure of Ar in air is 0.01 atm. Applying Dalton's law of partial pressures to air at 1.00 atm:

For these purposes, we can ignore the contribution of the CO_2 and other trace gases because they are so small.

$$P_{total} = P_{N_2} + P_{O_2} + P_{Ar}$$
$$P_{total} = 0.78 \text{ atm} + 0.21 \text{ atm} + 0.01 \text{ atm}$$
$$= 1.00 \text{ atm}$$

EXAMPLE 5.9 Total Pressure and Partial Pressures

A 1.00-L mixture of helium, neon, and argon has a total pressure of 662 mmHg at 298 K. If the partial pressure of helium is 341 mmHg and the partial pressure of neon is 112 mmHg, what mass of argon is present in the mixture?

SORT The problem gives you the partial pressures of two of the three components in a gas mixture, along with the total pressure, the volume, and the temperature, and asks you to find the mass of the third component.	**GIVEN:** $P_{He} = 341$ mmHg, $P_{Ne} = 112$ mmHg, $P_{total} = 662$ mmHg, $V = 1.00$ L, $T = 298$ K **FIND:** m_{Ar}
STRATEGIZE You can find the mass of argon from the number of moles of argon, which you can calculate from the partial pressure of argon and the ideal gas law. Begin by using Dalton's law to determine the partial pressure of argon. Then use the partial pressure of argon together with the volume of the sample and the temperature to find the number of moles of argon. Finally, use the molar mass of argon to calculate the mass of argon from the number of moles of argon.	**CONCEPTUAL PLAN** 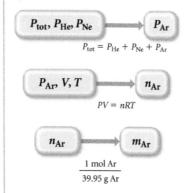 **RELATIONSHIPS USED** $P_{total} = P_{He} + P_{Ne} + P_{Ar}$ (Dalton's law) $PV = nRT$ (ideal gas law) molar mass Ar = 39.95 g/mol
SOLVE Follow the conceptual plan. To find the partial pressure of argon, solve the equation for P_{Ar} and substitute the values of the other partial pressures to calculate P_{Ar}.	**SOLUTION** $P_{total} = P_{He} + P_{Ne} + P_{Ar}$ $P_{Ar} = P_{total} - P_{He} - P_{Ne}$ $\quad = 662 \text{ mmHg} - 341 \text{ mmHg} - 112 \text{ mmHg}$ $\quad = 209 \text{ mmHg}$
Convert the partial pressure from mmHg to atm and use it in the ideal gas law to calculate the amount of argon in moles.	$209 \text{ mmHg} \times \dfrac{1 \text{ atm}}{760 \text{ mm Hg}} = 0.275 \text{ atm}$ $n = \dfrac{PV}{RT} = \dfrac{0.275 \text{ atm} \left(1.00 \text{ L}\right)}{0.08206 \dfrac{\text{L} \cdot \text{atm}}{\text{mol} \cdot \text{K}} \left(298 \text{ K}\right)} = 1.125 \times 10^{-2} \text{ mol Ar}$
Use the molar mass of argon to convert from amount of argon in moles to mass of argon.	$1.125 \times 10^{-2} \text{ mol Ar} \times \dfrac{39.95 \text{ g Ar}}{1 \text{ mol Ar}} = 0.449 \text{ g Ar}$

CHECK The units of the answer are correct. The magnitude of the answer makes sense because the volume is 1.0 L, which at STP would contain about 1/22 mol. Since the partial pressure of argon in the mixture is about 1/3 of the total pressure, we roughly estimate about 1/66 of one molar mass of argon, which is fairly close to the answer we got.

FOR PRACTICE 5.9

A sample of hydrogen gas is mixed with water vapor. The mixture has a total pressure of 755 torr and the water vapor has a partial pressure of 24 torr. What amount (in moles) of hydrogen gas is contained in 1.55 L of this mixture at 298 K?

Deep-Sea Diving and Partial Pressures

Our lungs have evolved to breathe oxygen at a partial pressure of $P_{O_2} = 0.21$ atm. If the total pressure decreases—when we climb a mountain, for example—the partial pressure of oxygen also decreases. On top of Mt. Everest, where the total pressure is 0.311 atm, the partial pressure of oxygen is only 0.065 atm. Low oxygen levels produce a physiological condition called **hypoxia** or oxygen starvation (Figure 5.13 ▶). Mild hypoxia causes dizziness, headache, and shortness of breath. Severe hypoxia, which occurs when (P_{O_2}) drops below 0.1 atm, may result in unconsciousness or even death. For this reason, climbers hoping to make the summit of Mt. Everest usually carry oxygen to breathe.

While not as dangerous as a lack of oxygen, too much oxygen can also cause physiological problems. Scuba divers, as we have learned, breathe pressurized air. At 30 m, a scuba diver breathes air at a total pressure of 4.0 atm, making P_{O_2} about 0.84 atm. This elevated partial pressure of oxygen raises the density of oxygen molecules in the lungs, resulting in a higher concentration of oxygen in body tissues. When P_{O_2} increases beyond 1.4 atm, the increased oxygen concentration in body tissues causes a condition called **oxygen toxicity**, which results in muscle twitching, tunnel vision, and convulsions. Divers who venture too deep without proper precautions have drowned because of oxygen toxicity. A second problem associated with breathing pressurized air is the increase of nitrogen in the lungs. At 30 m, a scuba diver breathes nitrogen at $P_{N_2} = 3.12$ atm, which increases the nitrogen concentration in body tissues and fluids. When P_{N_2} increases beyond about 4 atm, a condition called **nitrogen narcosis** or *rapture of the deep* results. Divers describe this condition as feeling inebriated or drunk. A diver breathing compressed air at 60 m feels as if he has consumed too much wine.

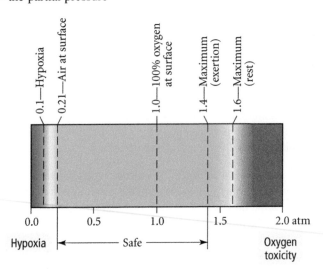

▲ FIGURE 5.13 **Oxygen Partial Pressure Limits** The partial pressure of oxygen in air at sea level is 0.21 atm. Partial pressures of oxygen below 0.1 atm and above 1.4 atm are dangerous to humans.

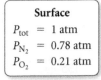

Surface	
P_{tot}	= 1 atm
P_{N_2}	= 0.78 atm
P_{O_2}	= 0.21 atm

30 m	
P_{tot}	= 4 atm
P_{N_2}	= 3.12 atm
P_{O_2}	= 0.84 atm

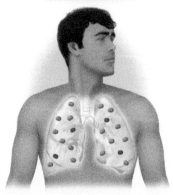
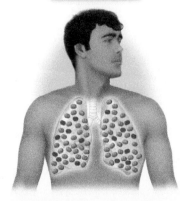

◀ When a diver breathes compressed air, the abnormally high partial pressure of oxygen in the lungs leads to an elevated concentration of oxygen in body tissues.

To avoid oxygen toxicity and nitrogen narcosis, deep-sea divers—those who descend beyond 50 m—breathe specialized mixtures of gases. One common mixture is called heliox, a mixture of helium and oxygen. These mixtures usually contain a smaller percentage of oxygen than would be found in air, thereby lowering the risk of oxygen toxicity. Heliox also contains helium instead of nitrogen, eliminating the risk of nitrogen narcosis.

EXAMPLE 5.10 Partial Pressures and Mole Fractions

A 12.5-L scuba diving tank contains a helium-oxygen (heliox) mixture made up of 24.2 g of He and 4.32 g of O_2 at 298 K. Calculate the mole fraction and partial pressure of each component in the mixture and the total pressure of the mixture.

SORT The problem gives the masses of two gases in a mixture and the volume and temperature of the mixture. You are to find the mole fraction and partial pressure of each component, as well as the total pressure.	**GIVEN:** $m_{He} = 24.2$ g, $m_{O_2} = 4.32$ g, $V = 12.5$ L, $T = 298$ K **FIND:** χ_{He}, χ_{O_2}, P_{He}, P_{O_2}, P_{total}

STRATEGIZE The conceptual plan has several parts. To calculate the mole fraction of each component, you must first find the number of moles of each component. Therefore, in the first part of the conceptual plan, convert the masses to moles using the molar masses. In the second part, calculate the mole fraction of each component using the mole fraction definition. To calculate *partial pressures* calculate the *total pressure* and then use the mole fractions from the previous part to calculate the partial pressures. Calculate the total pressure from the sum of the moles of both components. (Alternatively, you can calculate the partial pressures of the components individually, using the number of moles of each component. Then you can sum them to obtain the total pressure.) Last, use the mole fractions of each component and the total pressure to calculate the partial pressure of each component.	**CONCEPTUAL PLAN** 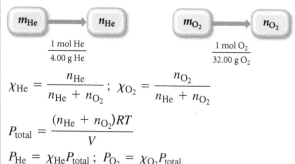 $\chi_{He} = \dfrac{n_{He}}{n_{He} + n_{O_2}}$; $\chi_{O_2} = \dfrac{n_{O_2}}{n_{He} + n_{O_2}}$ $P_{total} = \dfrac{(n_{He} + n_{O_2})RT}{V}$ $P_{He} = \chi_{He} P_{total}$; $P_{O_2} = \chi_{O_2} P_{total}$ **RELATIONSHIPS USED** $\chi_a = n_a/n_{total}$ (mole fraction definition) $P_{total}V = n_{total}RT$ (ideal gas law) $P_a = \chi_a P_{total}$

SOLVE Follow the plan to solve the problem. Begin by converting each of the masses to amounts in moles. Calculate each of the mole fractions. Calculate the total pressure. Finally, calculate the partial pressure of each component.	**SOLUTION** $24.2 \text{ g He} \times \dfrac{1 \text{ mol He}}{4.00 \text{ g He}} = 6.05 \text{ mol He}$ $4.32 \text{ g O}_2 \times \dfrac{1 \text{ mol O}_2}{32.00 \text{ g O}_2} = 0.135 \text{ mol O}_2$ $\chi_{He} = \dfrac{n_{He}}{n_{He} + n_{O_2}} = \dfrac{6.05}{6.05 + 0.135} = 0.97817$ $\chi_{O_2} = \dfrac{n_{O_2}}{n_{He} + n_{O_2}} = \dfrac{0.135}{6.05 + 0.135} = 0.021827$ $P_{total} = \dfrac{(n_{He} + n_{O_2})RT}{V}$ $= \dfrac{(6.05 \text{ mol} + 0.135 \text{ mol})\left(0.08206\dfrac{L \cdot atm}{mol \cdot K}\right)(298 \text{ K})}{12.5 \text{ L}}$ $= 12.099 \text{ atm}$ $P_{He} = \chi_{He} P_{total} = 0.97817 \times 12.099 \text{ atm}$ $\qquad = 11.8 \text{ atm}$ $P_{O_2} = \chi_{O_2} P_{total} = 0.021827 \times 12.099 \text{ atm}$ $\qquad = 0.264 \text{ atm}$

CHECK   The units of the answers are correct and the magnitudes are reasonable.

FOR PRACTICE 5.10
A diver breathes a heliox mixture with an oxygen mole fraction of 0.050. What must the total pressure be for the partial pressure of oxygen to be 0.21 atm?

Collecting Gases over Water

When the desired product of a chemical reaction is a gas, the gas is often collected by the displacement of water. For example, suppose the following reaction is used as a source of hydrogen gas:

$$Zn(s) + 2\,HCl(aq) \longrightarrow ZnCl_2(aq) + H_2(g)$$

As the hydrogen gas forms, it bubbles through the water and gathers in the collection flask (Figure 5.14 ▼). The hydrogen gas collected in this way is not pure, however, but mixed with water vapor because some water molecules evaporate and mix with the hydrogen molecules.

We cover vapor pressure in detail in Chapter 11.

The partial pressure of water in the mixture, called its **vapor pressure**, depends on temperature (Table 5.4). Vapor pressure increases with increasing temperature because higher temperatures cause more water molecules to evaporate.

Appendix IIE contains a more complete table of the vapor pressure of water versus temperature.

Suppose we collect the hydrogen gas over water at a total pressure of 758.2 mmHg and a temperature of 25 °C. What is the partial pressure of the hydrogen gas? We know that the total pressure is 758.2 mmHg and that the partial pressure of water is 23.78 mmHg (its vapor pressure at 25 °C):

$$P_{total} = P_{H_2} + P_{H_2O}$$
$$758.2\ \text{mmHg} = P_{H_2} + 23.78\ \text{mmHg}$$

Therefore,

$$P_{H_2} = 758.2\ \text{mmHg} - 23.78\ \text{mmHg}$$
$$= 734.4\ \text{mmHg}$$

The partial pressure of the hydrogen in the mixture will be 734.4 mmHg.

TABLE 5.4   Vapor Pressure of Water versus Temperature

Temperature (°C)	Pressure (mmHg)	Temperature (°C)	Pressure (mmHg)
0	4.58	55	118.2
5	6.54	60	149.6
10	9.21	65	187.5
15	12.79	70	233.7
20	17.55	75	289.1
25	23.78	80	355.1
30	31.86	85	433.6
35	42.23	90	525.8
40	55.40	95	633.9
45	71.97	100	760.0
50	92.6		

Collecting a Gas Over Water

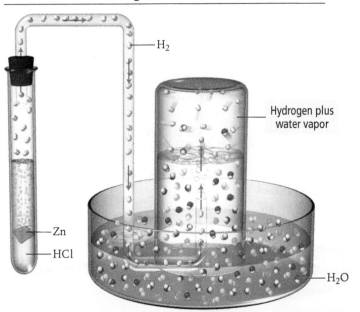

H$_2$

Hydrogen plus water vapor

Zn

HCl

H$_2$O

EXAMPLE 5.11 Collecting Gases over Water

In order to determine the rate of photosynthesis, the oxygen gas emitted by an aquatic plant was collected over water at a temperature of 293 K and a total pressure of 755.2 mmHg. Over a specific time period, a total of 1.02 L of gas was collected. What mass of oxygen gas (in grams) was formed?

SORT The problem gives the volume of gas collected over water as well as the temperature and the pressure. You are to find the mass in grams of oxygen formed.	**GIVEN:** $V = 1.02$ L, $P_{total} = 755.2$ mmHg, $T = 293$ K **FIND:** g O_2

STRATEGIZE You can determine the mass of oxygen from the amount of oxygen in moles, which you can calculate from the ideal gas law if you know the partial pressure of oxygen. Since the oxygen is mixed with water vapor, you can find the partial pressure of oxygen in the mixture by subtracting the partial pressure of water at 293 K (20 °C) from the total pressure. Next, use the ideal gas law to determine the number of moles of oxygen from its partial pressure, volume, and temperature. Finally, use the molar mass of oxygen to convert the number of moles to grams.	**CONCEPTUAL PLAN** $P_{O_2} = P_{total} - P_{H_2O}$ (20 °C) 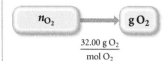 $n_{O_2} \quad\longrightarrow\quad$ g O_2 $\dfrac{32.00 \text{ g } O_2}{\text{mol } O_2}$ **RELATIONSHIPS USED** $P_{total} = P_a + P_b + P_c + \cdots$ (Dalton's law) $PV = nRT$ (ideal gas law)

SOLVE Follow the conceptual plan to solve the problem. Begin by calculating the partial pressure of oxygen in the oxygen/water mixture. You can find the partial pressure of water at 20 °C in Table 5.4. Next, solve the ideal gas law for number of moles. Before substituting into the ideal gas law, you must convert the partial pressure of oxygen from mmHg to atm. Next, substitute into the ideal gas law to find the number of moles of oxygen. Finally, use the molar mass of oxygen to convert to grams of oxygen.	**SOLUTION** $P_{O_2} = P_{total} - P_{H_2O}$ (20 °C) $\quad = 755.2$ mmHg $- 17.55$ mmHg $\quad = 737.\underline{6}5$ mmHg $n_{O_2} = \dfrac{P_{O_2}V}{RT}$ $737.\underline{6}5 \text{ mmHg} \times \dfrac{1 \text{ atm}}{760 \text{ mmHg}} = 0.9705\underline{9}$ atm $n_{O_2} = \dfrac{P_{O_2}V}{RT} = \dfrac{0.9705\underline{9} \text{ atm } (1.02 \text{ L})}{0.08206 \dfrac{\text{L} \cdot \text{atm}}{\text{mol} \cdot \text{K}} (293 \text{ K})}$ $\quad = 4.1\underline{1}75 \times 10^{-2}$ mol $4.1\underline{1}75 \times 10^{-2} \text{ mol } O_2 \times \dfrac{32.00 \text{ g } O_2}{1 \text{ mol } O_2} = 1.32$ g O_2

CHECK The answer is in the correct units. We can quickly check the magnitude of the answer by using molar volume. Under STP one liter is about 1/22 of one mole. Therefore the answer should be about 1/22 the molar mass of oxygen (1/22 × 32 = 1.45). The magnitude of our answer seems reasonable.

FOR PRACTICE 5.11

A common way to make hydrogen gas in the laboratory is to place a metal such as zinc in hydrochloric acid. The hydrochloric acid reacts with the metal to produce hydrogen gas, which is then collected over water. Suppose a student carries out this reaction and collects a total of 154.4 mL of gas at a pressure of 742 mmHg and a temperature of 25 °C. What mass of hydrogen gas (in mg) did the student collect?

5.7 Gases in Chemical Reactions: Stoichiometry Revisited

In Chapter 4, we learned how we can use the coefficients in chemical equations as conversion factors between number of moles of reactants and number of moles of products in a chemical reaction. We used these conversion factors to determine, for example, the mass of product obtained in a chemical reaction based on a given mass of reactant, or the mass of one reactant needed to react completely with a given mass of another reactant. The general conceptual plan for these kinds of calculations is

where A and B are two different substances involved in the reaction and the conversion factor between amounts (in moles) of each comes from the stoichiometric coefficients in the balanced chemical equation.

   In reactions involving *gaseous* reactant or products, we often specify the quantity of a gas in terms of its volume at a given temperature and pressure. As we have seen, stoichiometric relationships always express relative amounts in moles. However, we can use the ideal gas law to determine the amounts in moles from the volumes, or to determine the volumes from the amounts in moles.

$$n = \frac{PV}{RT} \qquad V = \frac{nRT}{P}$$

| The pressures here could also be partial pressures.

The general conceptual plan for these kinds of calculations is

The following examples demonstrate this kind of calculation.

EXAMPLE 5.12 Gases in Chemical Reactions

Methanol (CH_3OH) can be synthesized by the following reaction:

$$CO(g) + 2\,H_2(g) \longrightarrow CH_3OH(g)$$

What volume (in liters) of hydrogen gas, at a temperature of 355 K and a pressure of 738 mmHg, is required to synthesize 35.7 g of methanol?

SORT You are given the mass of methanol, the product of a chemical reaction. You are asked to find the required volume of one of the reactants (hydrogen gas) at a specified temperature and pressure.	**GIVEN:** 35.7 g CH_3OH, $T = 355$ K, $P = 738$ mmHg **FIND:** V_{H_2}

STRATEGIZE You can calculate the required volume of hydrogen gas from the number of moles of hydrogen gas, which you can obtain from the number of moles of methanol via the stoichiometry of the reaction.

First, find the number of moles of methanol from its mass by using the molar mass.

Then use the stoichiometric relationship from the balanced chemical equation to find the number of moles of hydrogen you need to form that quantity of methanol.

Finally, substitute the number of moles of hydrogen together with the pressure and temperature into the ideal gas law to find the volume of hydrogen.

CONCEPTUAL PLAN

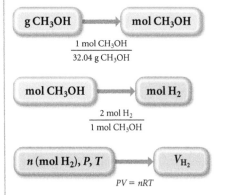

$$g\ CH_3OH \longrightarrow mol\ CH_3OH$$
$$\frac{1\ mol\ CH_3OH}{32.04\ g\ CH_3OH}$$

$$mol\ CH_3OH \longrightarrow mol\ H_2$$
$$\frac{2\ mol\ H_2}{1\ mol\ CH_3OH}$$

$$n\ (mol\ H_2),\ P,\ T \longrightarrow V_{H_2}$$
$$PV = nRT$$

RELATIONSHIPS USED

$PV = nRT$ (ideal gas law)

$2\ mol\ H_2 : 1\ mol\ CH_3OH$ (from balanced chemical equation)

molar mass $CH_3OH = 32.04$ g/mol

SOLVE Follow the conceptual plan to solve the problem. Begin by using the mass of methanol to determine the number of moles of methanol.

Next, convert the number of moles of methanol to moles of hydrogen.

Finally, use the ideal gas law to find the volume of hydrogen. Before substituting into the equation, you must convert the pressure to atmospheres.

SOLUTION

$$35.7\ \cancel{g\ CH_3OH} \times \frac{1\ mol\ CH_3OH}{32.04\ \cancel{g\ CH_3OH}} = 1.1142\ mol\ CH_3OH$$

$$1.1142\ \cancel{mol\ CH_3OH} \times \frac{2\ mol\ H_2}{1\ \cancel{mol\ CH_3OH}} = 2.2284\ mol\ H_2$$

$$V_{H_2} = \frac{n_{H_2}\ RT}{P}$$

$$P = 738\ \cancel{mmHg} \times \frac{1\ atm}{760\ \cancel{mmHg}} = 0.97105\ atm$$

$$V_{H_2} = \frac{(2.2284\ \cancel{mol})\left(0.08206\dfrac{L\cdot atm}{\cancel{mol}\cdot\cancel{K}}\right)(355\ \cancel{K})}{0.97105\ atm}$$

$$= 66.9\ L$$

CHECK The units of the answer are correct. The magnitude of the answer (66.9 L) seems reasonable. You are given slightly more than one molar mass of methanol, which is therefore slightly more than one mole of methanol. From the equation you can see that you need 2 mol hydrogen to make 1 mol methanol so the answer must be slightly greater than 2 mol hydrogen. Under standard conditions, slightly more than two mol hydrogen occupies slightly more than $2 \times 22.4\ L = 44.8\ L$. At a temperature greater than standard temperature, the volume would be even greater; therefore, this answer is reasonable.

FOR PRACTICE 5.12

In the following reaction, 4.58 L of O_2 was formed at $P = 745$ mmHg and $T = 308$ K. How many grams of Ag_2O must have decomposed?

$$2\ Ag_2O(s) \longrightarrow 4\ Ag(s) + O_2(g)$$

FOR MORE PRACTICE 5.12

In the above reaction, what mass of $Ag_2O(s)$ (in grams) is required to form 388 mL of oxygen gas at $P = 734$ mmHg and 25.0 °C?

Molar Volume and Stoichiometry

In Section 5.5, we saw that, under standard conditions, 1 mol of an ideal gas occupies 22.4 L. Consequently, if a reaction is occurring at or near standard conditions, we can use 1 mol = 22.4 L as a conversion factor in stoichiometric calculations, as shown in the following example.

EXAMPLE 5.13 Using Molar Volume in Gas Stoichiometric Calculations

How many grams of water form when 1.24 L of H_2 gas at STP completely reacts with O_2?

$$2 H_2(g) + O_2(g) \longrightarrow 2 H_2O(g)$$

SORT You are given the volume of hydrogen gas (a reactant) at STP and asked to determine the mass of water that forms upon complete reaction.	**GIVEN:** 1.24 L H_2 **FIND:** g H_2O
STRATEGIZE Since the reaction occurs under standard conditions, you can convert directly from the volume (in L) of hydrogen gas to the amount in moles. Then use the stoichiometric relationship from the balanced equation to find the number of moles of water formed. Finally, use the molar mass of water to obtain the mass of water formed.	**CONCEPTUAL PLAN** L H_2 $\rightarrow$ mol H_2 $\rightarrow$ mol H_2O $\rightarrow$ g H_2O $\dfrac{1 \text{ mol } H_2}{22.4 \text{ L } H_2}$ $\dfrac{2 \text{ mol } H_2O}{2 \text{ mol } H_2}$ $\dfrac{18.02 \text{ g}}{1 \text{ mol}}$ **RELATIONSHIPS USED** 1 mol = 22.4 L (at STP) 2 mol H_2 : 2 mol H_2O (from balanced equation) molar mass H_2O = 18.02 g/mol
SOLVE Follow the conceptual plan to solve the problem.	**SOLUTION** $1.24 \text{ L } H_2 \times \dfrac{1 \text{ mol } H_2}{22.4 \text{ L } H_2} \times \dfrac{2 \text{ mol } H_2O}{2 \text{ mol } H_2} \times \dfrac{18.02 \text{ g } H_2O}{1 \text{ mol } H_2O} = 0.998 \text{ g } H_2O$

CHECK The units of the answer are correct. The magnitude of the answer (0.998 g) is about 1/18 of the molar mass of water, roughly equivalent to the approximately 1/22 of a mole of hydrogen gas given, as expected for the 1:1 stoichiometric relationship between number of moles of hydrogen and number of moles of water.

FOR PRACTICE 5.13

How many liters of oxygen (at STP) are required to form 10.5 g of H_2O?

$$2 H_2(g) + O_2(g) \longrightarrow 2 H_2O(g)$$

⬭ Conceptual Connection 5.2 Pressure and Number of Moles

Nitrogen and hydrogen react to form ammonia according to the following equation:

$$N_2(g) + 3 H_2(g) \rightleftharpoons 2 NH_3(g)$$

Consider the following representations of the initial mixture of reactants and the resulting mixture after the reaction has been allowed to react for some time:

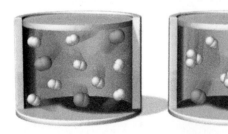

If the volume is kept constant, and nothing is added to the reaction mixture, what happens to the total pressure during the course of the reaction?

(a) the pressure increases

(b) the pressure decreases

(c) the pressure does not change

ANSWER: (b) Since the total number of gas molecules decreases, the total pressure—the sum of all the partial pressures—must also decrease.

5.8 Kinetic Molecular Theory: A Model for Gases

In Chapter 1, we learned how the scientific method proceeds from observations to laws and eventually to theories. Remember that laws summarize behavior—for example, Charles's law summarizes *how* the volume of a gas depends on temperature—while theories give the underlying reasons for the behavior. A theory of gas behavior explains, for example, *why* the volume of a gas increases with increasing temperature.

The simplest model for the behavior of gases is the **kinetic molecular theory**. In this theory, a gas is modeled as a collection of particles (either molecules or atoms, depending on the gas) in constant motion (Figure 5.15 ◄). A single particle moves in a straight line until it collides with another particle (or with the wall of the container). The basic postulates (or assumptions) of kinetic molecular theory are as follows:

1. **The size of a particle is negligibly small.** Kinetic molecular theory assumes that the particles themselves occupy no volume, even though they have mass. This postulate is justified because, under normal pressures, the space between atoms or molecules in a gas is very large compared to the size of an atom or molecule itself. For example, in a sample of argon gas at STP, only about 0.01% of the volume is occupied by atoms, and the average distance from one argon atom to another is 3.3 nm. In comparison, the atomic radius of argon is 97 pm. If an argon atom were the size of a golf ball, its nearest neighbor would be, on average, just over 4 ft away at STP.

2. **The average kinetic energy of a particle is proportional to the temperature in kelvins.** The motion of atoms or molecules in a gas is due to thermal energy, which distributes itself among the particles in the gas. At any given moment, some particles are moving faster than others—there is a distribution of velocities—but the higher the temperature, the faster the overall motion, and the greater the average kinetic energy. Notice that *kinetic energy* ($\frac{1}{2} mv^2$)—not *velocity*—is proportional to temperature. The atoms in a sample of helium and a sample of argon at the same temperature have the same average *kinetic energy*, but not the same average *velocity*. Since the helium atoms are lighter, they must move faster to have the same kinetic energy as argon atoms.

3. **The collision of one particle with another (or with the walls of its container) is completely elastic.** This means that when two particles collide, they may *exchange energy*, but there is no overall *loss of energy*. Any kinetic energy lost by one particle is completely gained by the other. In other words, the particles have no "stickiness," and they are not deformed by the collision. An encounter between two particles in kinetic molecular theory is more like the collision between two billiard balls than the collision between two lumps of clay (Figure 5.16 ▶). Between collisions, the particles do not exert any forces on one another.

If you start with the postulates of kinetic molecular theory, you can mathematically derive the ideal gas law (as we will show later). In other words, the ideal gas law follows directly from kinetic molecular theory, which gives us confidence that the assumptions of the theory are valid, at least under conditions where the ideal gas law applies. Let's see how the concept of pressure as well as each of the gas laws we have examined follow conceptually from kinetic molecular theory.

The Nature of Pressure In Section 5.2, we defined pressure as force divided by area:

$$P = \frac{F}{A}$$

Kinetic Molecular Theory

▲ **FIGURE 5.15 A Model for Gas Behavior** In the kinetic molecular theory of gases, a gas sample is modeled as a collection of particles in constant straight-line motion. The size of the particles is negligibly small and their collisions are elastic.

Elastic collision

Inelastic collision

▲ **FIGURE 5.16 Elastic versus Inelastic Collisions** When two billiard balls collide, the collision is elastic—the total kinetic energy of the colliding bodies is the same before and after the collision. When two lumps of clay collide, the collision is inelastic—the kinetic energy of the colliding bodies dissipates in the form of heat during the collision.

According to kinetic molecular theory, a gas is a collection of particles in constant motion. The motion results in collisions between the particles and the surfaces around them. As each particle collides with a surface, it exerts a force upon that surface. The result of many particles in a gas sample exerting forces on the surfaces around them is a constant pressure.

> The force (F) associated with an individual collision is given by $F = ma$, where m is the mass of the particle and a is its acceleration as it changes its direction of travel due to the collision.

Boyle's Law Boyle's law states that, for a constant number of particles at constant temperature, the volume of a gas is inversely proportional to its pressure. According to kinetic molecular theory, if you decrease the volume of a gas, you force the gas particles to occupy a smaller space. As long as the temperature remains the same, the number of collisions with the surrounding surfaces (per unit surface area) must necessarily increase, resulting in a greater pressure.

Charles's Law Charles's law states that, for a constant number of particles at constant pressure, the volume of a gas is proportional to its temperature. According to kinetic molecular theory, when you increase the temperature of a gas, the average speed, and thus the average kinetic energy, of the particles increases. Since this greater kinetic energy results in more frequent collisions and more force per collision, the pressure of the gas increases if its volume is held constant (Gay-Lussac's law). The only way for the pressure to remain constant is for the volume to increase. The greater volume spreads the collisions out over a greater surface area, so that the pressure (defined as force per unit area) is unchanged.

Avogadro's Law Avogadro's law states that, at constant temperature and pressure, the volume of a gas is proportional to the number of particles. According to kinetic molecular theory, when you increase the number of particles in a gas sample, the number of collisions with the surrounding surfaces increases. The greater number of collisions results in a greater overall force on surrounding surfaces; the only way for the pressure to remain constant is for the volume to increase so that the number of particles per unit volume (and thus the number of collisions) remains constant.

Dalton's Law Dalton's law states that the total pressure of a gas mixture is the sum of the partial pressures of its components. In other words, according to Dalton's law, the components in a gas mixture act identically to, and independently of, one another. According to kinetic molecular theory, the particles have negligible size and they do not interact. Consequently, the only property that would distinguish one type of particle from another is its mass. However, even particles of different masses have the same average kinetic energy at a given temperature, so they exert the same force upon collision with a surface. Consequently, adding components to a gas mixture—even different *kinds* of gases—has the same effect as simply adding more particles. The partial pressures of all the components sum to the overall pressure.

Calculating Gas Pressure: A Molecular View

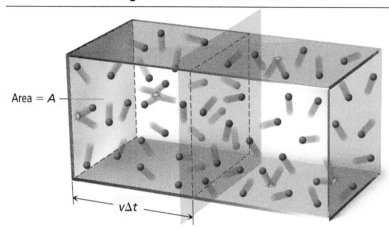

Area = A

$v\Delta t$

▶ **FIGURE 5.17 The Pressure on the Wall of a Container** The pressure on the wall of a container can be calculated by determining the total force due to collisions of the particles with the wall.

Kinetic Molecular Theory and the Ideal Gas Law

We have just seen how each of the gas laws conceptually follows from kinetic molecular theory. We can also *derive* the ideal gas law from the postulates of kinetic molecular theory. In other words, the kinetic molecular theory is a quantitative model that *implies* $PV = nRT$. We now explore this derivation.

The pressure on a wall of a container (Figure 5.17 ▲) occupied by particles in constant motion is the total force on the wall (due to the collisions) divided by the area of the wall.

$$P = \frac{F_{total}}{A} \qquad [5.13]$$

From Newton's second law, the force (F) associated with an individual collision is given by $F = ma$, where m is the mass of the particle and a is its acceleration as it changes its direction of travel due to the collision. The acceleration for each collision is the change in velocity (Δv) divided by the time interval (Δt), so the force imparted for each collision is

$$F_{collision} = m\frac{\Delta v}{\Delta t} \qquad [5.14]$$

If a particle collides elastically with the wall, it bounces off the wall with no loss of energy. For a straight-line collision, the change in velocity is $2v$ (the particle's velocity was v before the collision and $-v$ after the collision; therefore, the change is $2v$). The force per collision is given by the following:

$$F_{collision} = m\frac{2v}{\Delta t} \qquad [5.15]$$

The total number of collisions in the time interval Δt on a wall of surface area A is proportional to the number of particles that can reach the wall in this time interval—in other words, all particles within a distance of $v\,\Delta t$ of the wall. These particles occupy a volume given by $v\,\Delta t \times A$, and their total number is equal to this volume multiplied by the density of particles in the container (n/V):

Number of collisions $\propto$ number of particles within $v\,\Delta t$

$$\propto\ \underset{\substack{\uparrow \\ \text{Volume}}}{v\,\Delta t \times A} \times \underset{\substack{\uparrow \\ \text{Density of} \\ \text{particles}}}{\frac{n}{V}} \qquad [5.16]$$

The *total force* on the wall is equal to the force per collision multiplied by the number of collisions:

$$F_{\text{total}} = F_{\text{collision}} \times \text{number of collisions}$$

$$\propto m\frac{2v}{\Delta t} \times v\,\Delta t \times A \times \frac{n}{V}$$

$$\propto mv^2 \times A \times \frac{n}{V} \qquad [5.17]$$

The pressure on the wall is equal to the total force divided by the surface area of the wall:

$$P = \frac{F_{\text{total}}}{A}$$

$$\propto \frac{mv^2 \times A \times \dfrac{n}{V}}{A}$$

$$P \propto mv^2 \times \frac{n}{V} \qquad [5.18]$$

Notice that Equation 5.18 contains within it Boyle's law ($P \propto 1/V$) and Avogadro's law ($V \propto n$). We can get the complete ideal gas law from postulate 2 of the kinetic molecular theory, which states that the average kinetic energy ($\frac{1}{2}mv^2$) is proportional to the temperature in kelvins (T):

$$mv^2 \propto T \qquad [5.19]$$

By combining Equations 5.18 and 5.19, we get the following:

$$P \propto \frac{T \times n}{V}$$

$$PV \propto nT \qquad [5.20]$$

The proportionality can be replaced by an equals sign if we provide the correct constant, R:

$$PV = nRT \qquad [5.21]$$

In other words, the kinetic molecular theory (a model for how gases behave) predicts behavior that is consistent with our observations and measurements of gases—the theory agrees with the experiment. Recall from Chapter 1 that a scientific theory is the most powerful kind of scientific knowledge. In the kinetic molecular theory, we have a model for what a gas is like. Although the model is not perfect—indeed, it breaks down under certain conditions, as we shall see later in this chapter—it predicts a great deal about the behavior of gases. Therefore, the model is a good approximation of what a gas is actually like. A careful examination of the conditions under which the model breaks down (see Section 5.10) gives us even more insight into the behavior of gases.

Temperature and Molecular Velocities

According to kinetic molecular theory, particles of different masses have the same average kinetic energy at a given temperature. The kinetic energy of a particle depends on its mass and velocity according to the following equation:

$$KE = \tfrac{1}{2}mv^2$$

The only way for particles of different masses to have the same kinetic energy is if they are traveling at different velocities.

In a gas at a given temperature, lighter particles travel faster (on average) than heavier ones.

In kinetic molecular theory, we define the root mean square velocity (u_{rms}) of a particle as follows:

$$u_{\text{rms}} = \sqrt{\overline{u^2}} \qquad [5.22]$$

where $\overline{u^2}$ is the average of the squares of the particle velocities. Even though the root mean square velocity of a collection of particles is not identical to the average velocity, the two are close in value and conceptually similar. Root mean square velocity is just a special *type* of average. The average kinetic energy of one mole of gas particles is then given by

$$KE_{avg} = \tfrac{1}{2} N_A \, m\overline{u^2} \qquad [5.23]$$

where N_A is Avogadro's number.

Postulate 2 of the kinetic molecular theory states that the average kinetic energy is proportional to the temperature in kelvins. The constant of proportionality in this relationship is $(3/2) R$:

$$KE_{avg} = (3/2) RT \qquad [5.24]$$

where R is the gas constant, but in different units ($R = 8.314 \text{ J/mol} \cdot \text{K}$) than those we use in the ideal gas law. If we combine Equations 5.23 and 5.24, and solve for $\overline{u^2}$, we get the following:

$$(1/2) \, N_A m\overline{u^2} = (3/2) \, RT$$

$$\overline{u^2} = \frac{(3/2) \, RT}{(1/2) \, N_A m} = \frac{3RT}{N_A m}$$

Taking the square root of both sides we get

$$\sqrt{\overline{u^2}} = u_{rms} = \sqrt{\frac{3RT}{N_A m}} \qquad [5.25]$$

In Equation 5.25, m is the mass of a particle in kg and N_A is Avogadro's number. The product $N_A m$, then, is the molar mass in kg/mol. If we call this quantity $\mathcal{M}$, then the expression for mean square velocity as a function of temperature becomes the following important result:

$$u_{rms} = \sqrt{\frac{3RT}{\mathcal{M}}} \qquad [5.26]$$

The root mean square velocity of a collection of gas particles is proportional to the square root of the temperature in kelvins and inversely proportional to the square root of the molar mass of the particles (which because of the units of R must be in kilograms per mole). The root mean square velocity of nitrogen molecules at 25 °C, for example, is 515 m/s (1152 mi/hr). The root mean square velocity of hydrogen molecules at room temperature is 1920 m/s (4295 mi/hr). Notice that the lighter molecules move much faster at a given temperature.

The root mean square velocity, as we have seen, is a kind of average velocity. Some particles are moving faster and some are moving slower than this average. The velocities of all the particles in a gas sample form distributions like those shown in Figure 5.18 ▼.

> The $(3/2) R$ proportionality constant comes from a derivation that is beyond our current scope.

> The joule (J) is a unit of energy which we discuss in more detail in Section 6.1.
>
> $$\left(1 \, \text{J} = 1 \, \text{kg} \, \frac{m^2}{s^2} \right)$$

▶ FIGURE 5.18 **Velocity Distribution for Several Gases at 25 °C** At a given temperature, there is a distribution of velocities among the particles in a sample of gas. The exact shape and peak of the distribution varies with the molar mass of the gas.

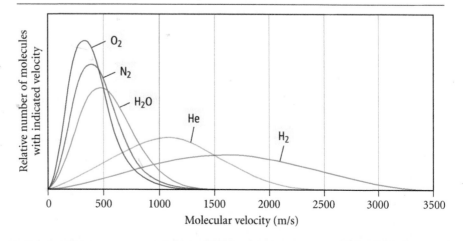

Variation of Velocity Distribution with Molar Mass

We can see from these distributions that some particles are indeed traveling at the root mean square velocity. However, many particles are traveling faster and many slower than the root mean square velocity. For lighter particles, such as helium and hydrogen, the velocity distribution is shifted toward higher velocities and the curve becomes broader, indicating a wider range of velocities. The velocity distribution for nitrogen at different temperatures is shown in Figure 5.19 ▶. As the temperature increases, the root mean square velocity increases and the distribution becomes broader.

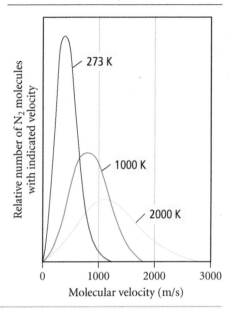

Variation of Velocity Distribution with Temperature

273 K

1000 K

2000 K

Relative number of N_2 molecules with indicated velocity

Molecular velocity (m/s)

▶ **FIGURE 5.19 Velocity Distribution for Nitrogen at Several Temperatures**
As the temperature of a gas sample increases, the velocity distribution of the molecules shifts toward higher velocity and becomes less sharply peaked.

EXAMPLE 5.14 Root Mean Square Velocity

Calculate the root mean square velocity of oxygen molecules at 25 °C.

SORT You are given the kind of molecule and the temperature and asked to find the root mean square velocity.

GIVEN: O_2, $t = 25\ °C$
FIND: u_{rms}

STRATEGIZE The conceptual plan for this problem shows how the molar mass of oxygen and the temperature (in kelvins) can be used with the equation that defines the root mean square velocity to calculate root mean square velocity.

CONCEPTUAL PLAN

$$M, T \longrightarrow u_{rms}$$

$$u_{rms} = \sqrt{\frac{3RT}{M}}$$

RELATIONSHIP USED

$$u_{rms} = \sqrt{\frac{3RT}{M}} \text{ (Equation 5.26)}$$

SOLVE First gather the required quantities in the correct units. Note that molar mass must be in kg/mol.

SOLUTION

$T = 25 + 273 = 298\ K$

$$M = \frac{32.00\ \text{g}\ O_2}{1\ \text{mol}\ O_2} \times \frac{1\ \text{kg}}{1000\ \text{g}} = \frac{32.00 \times 10^{-3}\ \text{kg}\ O_2}{1\ \text{mol}\ O_2}$$

Substitute the quantities into the equation to calculate root mean square velocity. Note that $1\ J = 1\ \text{kg} \cdot \text{m}^2/\text{s}^2$.

$$u_{rms} = \sqrt{\frac{3RT}{M}}$$

$$= \sqrt{\frac{3\left(8.314\ \dfrac{J}{\text{mol} \cdot K}\right)(298\ K)}{\dfrac{32.00 \times 10^{-3}\ \text{kg}\ O_2}{1\ \text{mol}\ O_2}}}$$

$$= \sqrt{2.32 \times 10^5\ \frac{J}{\text{kg}}}$$

$$= \sqrt{2.32 \times 10^5\ \frac{\dfrac{\text{kg} \cdot \text{m}^2}{\text{s}^2}}{\text{kg}}} = 482\ \text{m/s}$$

CHECK The units of the answer (m/s) are correct. The magnitude of the answer seems reasonable because oxygen is slightly heavier than nitrogen and should therefore have a slightly lower root mean square velocity at the same temperature. Recall that earlier we stated that the root mean square velocity of nitrogen is 515 m/s at 25 °C.

FOR PRACTICE 5.14

Calculate the root mean square velocity of gaseous xenon atoms at 25 °C.

Conceptual Connection 5.3 **Kinetic Molecular Theory**

Which sample of an ideal gas has the greatest pressure? Assume that the mass of each particle is proportional to its size and that all the gas samples are at the same temperature.

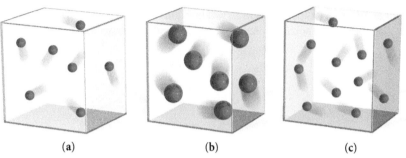

(a)   (b)   (c)

ANSWER: (c) Since the temperature and the volume are both constant, the ideal gas law tells us that the pressure depends solely on the number of particles. Sample (c) has the greatest number of particles per unit volume, and therefore has the greatest pressure. The pressures of (a) and (b) at a given temperature are identical. Even though the particles in (b) are more massive than those in (a), they have the same average kinetic energy at a given temperature. The particles in (b) move more slowly than those in (a), and so exert the same pressure as the particles in (a).

5.9 Mean Free Path, Diffusion, and Effusion of Gases

In a ventilated room, air currents also enhance the transport of gas molecules.

We have just learned that the root mean square velocity of gas molecules at room temperature is measured in hundreds of meters per second. However, suppose that your roommate just put on too much perfume in the bathroom only 2 m away. Why does it take a minute or two before you can smell the fragrance? Although most molecules in a perfume bottle have higher molar masses than nitrogen, their velocities are still hundreds of meters per second, so why the delay? The answer is that, even though gaseous particles travel at tremendous speeds, they also travel in haphazard paths (Figure 5.20 ◄). To a perfume molecule, the path from the perfume bottle in the bathroom to your nose 2 m away is much like a bargain hunter's path through a busy shopping mall during a clearance sale. The molecule travels only a short distance before it collides with another molecule, changes direction, only to collide again, and so on. In fact, at room temperature and atmospheric pressure, a molecule in the air experiences several billion collisions per second. The average distance that a molecule travels between collisions is called its **mean free path**. At room temperature and atmospheric pressure, the mean free path of a nitrogen molecule with a molecular diameter of 300 pm (four times the covalent radius) is 93 nm, or about 310 molecular diameters. If the nitrogen molecule were the size of a golf ball, it would travel about 40 ft between collisions. Mean free path increases with *decreasing* pressure. Under conditions of ultrahigh vacuum (10^{-10} torr), the mean free path of a nitrogen molecule is hundreds of kilometers.

Typical Gas Molecule Path

The average distance between collisions is the mean free path.

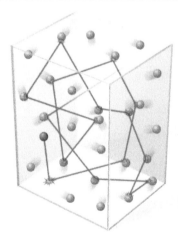

▲ **FIGURE 5.20 Mean Free Path**
A molecule in a volume of gas follows a haphazard path, involving many collisions with other molecules.

The process by which gas molecules spread out in response to a concentration gradient is called **diffusion**, and even though the particles undergo many collisions, the root mean square velocity still influences the rate of diffusion. Heavier molecules diffuse more slowly than lighter ones, so the first molecules you would smell from a perfume mixture (in a room with no air currents) are the lighter ones.

A process related to diffusion is **effusion**, the process by which a gas escapes from a container into a vacuum through a small hole (Figure 5.21 ►). The rate of effusion is also related to root mean square velocity—heavier molecules effuse more slowly than lighter ones. The rate of effusion—the amount of gas that effuses in a given time—is inversely proportional to the square root of the molar mass of the gas as follows:

$$\text{rate} \propto \frac{1}{\sqrt{\mathcal{M}}}$$

The ratio of effusion rates of two different gases is given by **Graham's law of effusion**, named after Thomas Graham (1805–1869):

Effusion

$$\frac{\text{rate}_A}{\text{rate}_B} = \sqrt{\frac{\mathcal{M}_B}{\mathcal{M}_A}} \qquad [5.27]$$

In this expression, rate_A and rate_B are the effusion rates of gases A and B and $\mathcal{M}_A$ and $\mathcal{M}_B$ are their molar masses.

Graham's law explains, in part, why helium balloons only float for a day or so. Since helium has a such a low molar mass, it escapes from the balloon quite quickly. A balloon filled with air, by contrast, remains inflated longer.

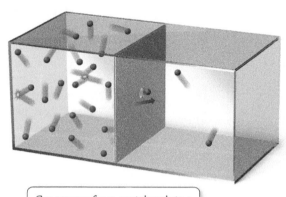

Gas escapes from container into a vacuum through a small hole

▲ **FIGURE 5.21 Effusion** Effusion is the escape of a gas from a container into a vacuum through a small hole.

EXAMPLE 5.15 Graham's Law of Effusion

An unknown gas effuses at a rate that is 0.462 times that of nitrogen gas (at the same temperature). Calculate the molar mass of the unknown gas in g/mol.

SORT You are given the ratio of effusion rates for the unknown gas and nitrogen and asked to find the molar mass of the unknown gas.	**GIVEN:** $\dfrac{\text{Rate}_{unk}}{\text{Rate}_{N_2}} = 0.462$ **FIND:** $\mathcal{M}_{unk}$
STRATEGIZE The conceptual plan uses Graham's law of effusion. You are given the ratio of rates and you know the molar mass of the nitrogen. You can use Graham's law to find the molar mass of the unknown gas.	**CONCEPTUAL PLAN** $\boxed{\dfrac{\text{Rate}_{unk}}{\text{Rate}_{N_2}}, \mathcal{M}_{N_2}} \longrightarrow \boxed{\mathcal{M}_{unk}}$ $\dfrac{\text{Rate}_{unk}}{\text{Rate}_{N_2}} = \sqrt{\dfrac{\mathcal{M}_{N_2}}{\mathcal{M}_{unk}}}$ **RELATIONSHIP USED** $\dfrac{\text{rate}_A}{\text{rate}_B} = \sqrt{\dfrac{\mathcal{M}_B}{\mathcal{M}_A}}$ (Graham's law)
SOLVE Solve the equation for $\mathcal{M}_{unk}$ and substitute the correct values to calculate it.	**SOLUTION** $\dfrac{\text{rate}_{unk}}{\text{rate}_{N_2}} = \sqrt{\dfrac{\mathcal{M}_{N_2}}{\mathcal{M}_{unk}}}$ $\mathcal{M}_{unk} = \dfrac{\mathcal{M}_{N_2}}{\left(\dfrac{\text{rate}_{unk}}{\text{rate}_{N_2}}\right)^2}$ $= \dfrac{28.02 \text{ g/mol}}{(0.462)^2}$ $= 131 \text{ g/mol}$

CHECK The units of the answer are correct. The magnitude of the answer seems reasonable for the molar mass of a gas. In fact, from the answer, we can even conclude that the gas is probably xenon, which has a molar mass of 131.29 g/mol.

FOR PRACTICE 5.15

Find the ratio of effusion rates of hydrogen gas and krypton gas.

5.10 Real Gases: The Effects of Size and Intermolecular Forces

One mole of an ideal gas has a volume of 22.41 L at STP. Figure 5.22 ▼ shows the molar volume of several real gases at STP. As you can see, most of these gases have a volume that is very close to 22.41 L, meaning that they are acting very nearly as ideal gases. Gases behave ideally when both of the following are true: (a) the volume of the gas particles is small compared to the space between them; and (b) the forces between the gas particles are not significant. At STP, these assumptions are valid for most common gases. However, these assumptions break down at higher pressures or lower temperatures.

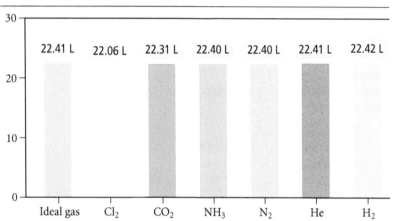

Molar Volume

▶ **FIGURE 5.22 Molar Volumes of Real Gases** The molar volumes of several gases at STP are all close to 22.414 L, indicating that their departures from ideal behavior are small.

The Effect of the Finite Volume of Gas Particles

The finite volume of gas particles—that is, their actual *size*—becomes important at high pressure because the volume of the particles themselves occupies a significant portion of the total gas volume (Figure 5.23 ▼). We can see the effect of particle volume by comparing the molar volume of argon to the molar volume of an ideal gas as a function of pressure at 500 K as shown in Figure 5.24 ▼. At low pressures, the molar volume of argon is nearly identical to that of an ideal gas. But as the pressure increases, the molar volume of

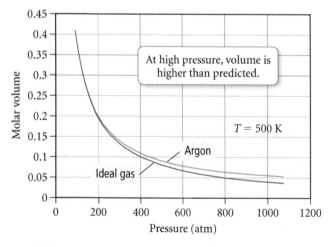

Nonideal Behavior: The effect of particle volume

At high pressure, volume is higher than predicted.

$T = 500$ K

Argon

Ideal gas

▲ **FIGURE 5.23 Particle Volume and Ideal Behavior** As a gas is compressed the gas particles themselves begin to occupy a significant portion of the total gas volume, leading to deviations from ideal behavior.

▲ **FIGURE 5.24 The Effect of Particle Volume** At high pressures, 1 mol of argon occupies a larger volume than 1 mol of an ideal gas because of the volume of the argon atoms themselves. (This example was chosen to minimize the effects of intermolecular forces, which are very small in argon at 500 K, thereby isolating the effect of particle volume.)

argon becomes *greater than* that of an ideal gas. At the higher pressures, the argon atoms themselves occupy a significant portion of the gas volume, making the actual volume greater than that predicted by the ideal gas law.

In 1873, Johannes van der Waals (1837–1923) modified the ideal gas equation to fit the behavior of real gases. From the graph for argon in Figure 5.24 we can see that the ideal gas law predicts a volume that is too small. Van der Waals suggested a small correction factor that accounts for the volume of the gas particles themselves:

Ideal behavior $$V = \frac{nRT}{P}$$

Corrected for volume of gas particles $$V = \frac{nRT}{P} + nb \qquad [5.28]$$

The correction adds the quantity nb to the volume, where n is the number of moles and b is a constant that depends on the gas (see Table 5.5). We can rearrange the corrected equation as follows:

$$(V - nb) = \frac{nRT}{P} \qquad [5.29]$$

The Effect of Intermolecular Forces

Intermolecular forces, covered in more detail in Chapter 11, are attractions between the atoms or molecules that compose any substance. These attractions are typically small in gases and therefore do not matter much at low pressure because the molecules are too far apart to "feel" the attractions. They also do not matter much at high temperatures because the molecules have a lot of kinetic energy and when two particles with high kinetic energies collide, a weak attraction between them does not affect the collision much. At lower temperatures, however, the collisions occur with less kinetic energy, and weak attractions can affect the collisions. We can understand this difference with an analogy to billiard balls. Imagine two billiard balls that are coated with a substance that makes them slightly sticky. If they collide when moving at high velocities, the stickiness will not have much of an effect—the balls bounce off one another as if the sticky substance was not even there. However, if the two billiard balls collide when moving very slowly (say barely rolling) the sticky substance would have an effect—the billiard balls might even stick together and not bounce off one another.

The effect of these weak attractions between particles is a lower number of collisions with the surfaces of the container, thereby lowering the pressure compared to that of an ideal gas. We can see the effect of intermolecular forces by comparing the pressure of 1.0 mol of xenon gas to the pressure of 1.0 mol of an ideal gas as a function of temperature and at a fixed volume of 1.0 L, as shown in Figure 5.25 ▼. At high temperature, the pressure of the xenon gas is nearly identical to that of an ideal gas. But at lower temperatures,

TABLE 5.5 Van der Waals Constants for Common Gases		
Gas	a ($L^2 \cdot$ atm/mol^2)	b (L/mol)
He	0.0342	0.02370
Ne	0.211	0.0171
Ar	1.35	0.0322
Kr	2.32	0.0398
Xe	4.19	0.0511
H_2	0.244	0.0266
N_2	1.39	0.0391
O_2	1.36	0.0318
Cl_2	6.49	0.0562
H_2O	5.46	0.0305
CH_4	2.25	0.0428
CO_2	3.59	0.0427
CCl_4	20.4	0.1383

Nonideal Behavior: The effect of intermolecular forces

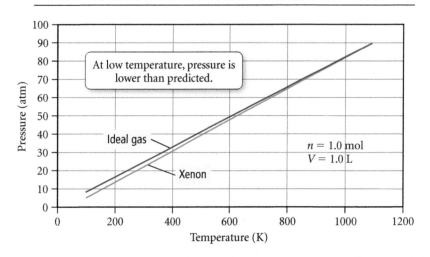

At low temperature, pressure is lower than predicted.

Ideal gas

Xenon

$n = 1.0$ mol
$V = 1.0$ L

◀ **FIGURE 5.25 The Effect of Intermolecular Forces**   At low temperatures, the pressure of xenon is less than an ideal gas exerts because interactions among xenon molecules reduce the number of collisions with the walls of the container.

the pressure of xenon is *less than* that of an ideal gas. At the lower temperatures, the xenon atoms spend more time interacting with each other and less time colliding with the walls, making the actual pressure less than that predicted by the ideal gas law.

From the graph for xenon shown in Figure 5.25 we can see that the ideal gas law predicts a pressure that is too large at low temperatures. Van der Waals suggested a small correction factor that accounts for the intermolecular forces between gas particles:

Ideal behavior $$P = \frac{nRT}{V}$$

Corrected for intermolecular forces $$P = \frac{nRT}{V} - a\left(\frac{n}{V}\right)^2 \qquad [5.30]$$

The correction subtracts the quantity $a(n/V)^2$ from the pressure, where n is the number of moles, V is the volume, and a is a constant that depends on the gas (see Table 5.5). Notice that the correction factor increases as n/V (the number of moles of particles per unit volume) increases because a greater concentration of particles makes it more likely that they will interact with one another. We can rearrange the corrected equation as follows:

$$P + a\left(\frac{n}{V}\right)^2 = \frac{nRT}{V} \qquad [5.31]$$

Van der Waals Equation

We can now combine the effects of particle volume (Equation 5.29) and particle intermolecular forces (Equation 5.31) into one equation that describes nonideal gas behavior:

$$[P + a(\tfrac{n}{V})^2] \times [V - nb] = nRT \qquad [5.32]$$

Correction for intermolecular forces

Correction for particle volume

The above equation is called the **van der Waals equation** and can be used to calculate the properties of a gas under nonideal conditions.

Real Gases

We can see the combined effects of particle volume and intermolecular forces by examining a plot of PV/RT versus P for 1 mol of a number of real gases (Figure 5.26 ▼). For

The Behavior of Real Gases

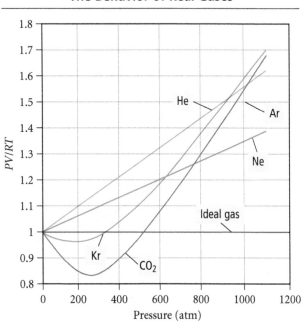

▶ **FIGURE 5.26 Real versus Ideal Behavior** For 1 mol of an ideal gas, PV/RT would be equal to 1. The combined effects of the volume of gas particles and the interactions among them cause each real gas to deviate from ideal behavior in a slightly different way. These curves were calculated at a temperature of 500 K.

an ideal gas, $PV/RT = n$, the number of moles of gas. Therefore, for 1 mol of an ideal gas, PV/RT is equal to 1, as shown in the plot. For real gases, PV/RT deviates from 1, but the deviations are not uniform. For example, water displays a large negative deviation from PV/RT because, for water, the effect of intermolecular forces on lowering the pressure (relative to an ideal gas) is far greater than the effect of particle size on increasing the volume. Notice from Table 5.5 that water has a high value of a, the constant that corrects for intermolecular forces, but a moderate value of b, the constant that corrects for particle size. Therefore PV/RT is lower than predicted from the ideal gas law for water.

By contrast, consider the behavior of helium, which displays a positive deviation from the ideal behavior. This is because helium has very weak intermolecular forces and their effect on lowering the pressure (relative to ideal gas) is small compared to the effect of particle size on increasing the volume. Therefore PV/RT is greater than predicted from the ideal gas law for helium.

Conceptual Connection 5.4 Real Gases

The graph below shows *PV/RT* for carbon dioxide at three different temperatures. Rank the curves in order of increasing temperature.

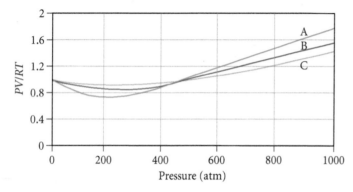

ANSWER: $A < B < C$. Curve A is the lowest temperature curve because it deviates the most from ideality. The tendency for the intermolecular forces in carbon dioxide to lower the pressure (relative to that of an ideal gas) is greatest at low temperature (because the molecules are moving more slowly and are therefore less able to overcome the intermolecular forces). As a result, the curve that dips the lowest must correspond to the lowest temperature.

5.11 Chemistry of the Atmosphere: Air Pollution and Ozone Depletion

In Section 5.6, we learned that our atmosphere is composed primarily of nitrogen and oxygen, with a few other minor components. Human activities have polluted the air with other substances as well. In this section, we take a brief look at two major environmental problems associated with the atmosphere: air pollution and ozone depletion. Air pollution is a problem that occurs primarily in the troposphere, the part of our atmosphere that is closest to Earth and ranges from ground level to about 10 km. Most of the gases emitted into the atmosphere from Earth end up in the troposphere. Ozone depletion occurs primarily in the stratosphere, the region of atmosphere above the troposphere, ranging from 10 km to 50 km (Figure 5.27 ► on the next page).

Air Pollution

The air in all major cities in the world is polluted. Pollution comes from a number of sources including electricity generation, motor vehicle emissions, and industrial waste. There are many different kinds of air pollutants. We briefly examine each of the *major gaseous air pollutants* in the following section.

Sulfur Oxides (SO_x) Sulfur oxides include SO_2 and SO_3, produced primarily during coal-fired electricity generation and industrial metal refining. The sulfur oxides are lung and eye

▶ FIGURE 5.27 **The Structure of the Atmosphere** Earth's atmosphere contains several different regions, including the troposphere and stratosphere.

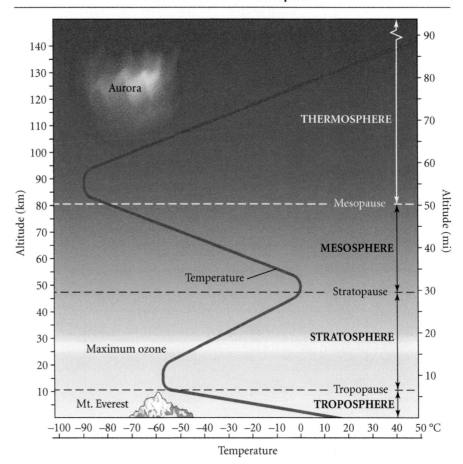

Structure of the Atmosphere

▶ FIGURE 5.27 **The Structure of the Atmosphere** Earth's atmosphere contains several different regions, including the troposphere and stratosphere.

irritants that affect the respiratory system and are the main precursors of acid rain (see Section 3.6).

Carbon Monoxide (CO) Carbon monoxide is formed during the incomplete combustion of fossil fuels (petroleum, natural gas, and coal). It is emitted mainly by motor vehicles. In humans and other animals, carbon monoxide displaces oxygen in the blood, forcing the heart and lungs to work harder. At high levels, CO can cause sensory impairment, decreased thinking ability, unconsciousness, and even death.

Nitrogen Oxides (NO$_x$) The nitrogen oxides include NO and NO$_2$, emitted by motor vehicles, fossil fuel-based electricity generation plants, and any high-temperature combustion process occurring in air. Nitrogen dioxide is an orange-brown gas that causes the dark haze over polluted cities. Nitrogen oxides are eye and lung irritants and precursors of acid rain.

Ozone (O$_3$) Ozone is produced when some of the products of fossil fuel combustion, especially nitrogen oxides and unburned volatile organic compounds (VOCs), react in the presence of sunlight. The products of this reaction, which include ozone, are called *photochemical smog.* Ozone produced in this way—sometimes called ground-level ozone—should not be confused with upper atmospheric or *stratospheric* ozone. Although ozone is always the same molecule (O$_3$), stratospheric ozone is a natural part of our environment that protects Earth from harmful ultraviolet light. Stratospheric ozone does not harm us because we are not directly exposed to it. Ground-level ozone, on the other hand, is a pollutant to which we are directly exposed; it is an eye and lung irritant, and prolonged exposure can cause permanent lung damage.

In the United States, the U.S. Environmental Protection Agency (EPA) has established limits on these pollutants. Beginning in the 1970s, the U.S. Congress passed the Clean Air Act and its amendments, requiring U.S. cities to reduce their pollution and maintain levels below the standards set by the EPA. As a result of this legislation, pollutant levels in U.S. cities have decreased over the last 30 years, even as the number of

vehicles has increased. For example, according to the EPA's 2008 National Air Quality and Emissions Trends Report, the levels of the major pollutants in the air of U.S. cities have decreased significantly during the period 1980–2007 as shown in Table 5.6.

Although the levels of pollutants (especially ozone) in some cities are still above what the EPA considers safe, real progress has been made. These trends demonstrate that legislation can improve our environment.

Ozone Depletion

As we have just seen, ozone in the troposphere is a pollutant. Ozone in the stratosphere, however, is a natural and essential part of our atmosphere. The stratospheric ozone layer absorbs the sun's ultraviolet (UV) light (see Section 7.2). Excessive exposure to UV light increases our risk of skin cancer and cataracts, weakens the immune system, and causes premature wrinkling of the skin. Consequently, stratospheric ozone helps to prevent these conditions. Stratospheric ozone absorbs UV light through the following reaction:

$$O_3 + UV \text{ light} \longrightarrow O_2 + O$$

Under normal conditions, O_2 and O recombine in the stratosphere to re-form O_3.

$$O_2 + O \longrightarrow O_3 + \text{heat}$$

Through these two reactions, ozone transforms UV light into heat and is regenerated to go through the cycle again.

In the 1970s, scientists began to worry that a class of compounds known as chlorofluorocarbons (CFCs) might be destroying stratospheric ozone. These compounds had become important as aerosols, foam-blowing agents, refrigerants (Freons), and industrial solvents. One of the reasons manufacturers used CFCs for these applications is their relative chemical inertness—they do not react with most substances. Consequently, they were seen as stable, trouble-free compounds. But this apparent advantage turned out to be a major problem.

Unlike more reactive pollutants, which are decomposed via natural chemical reactions in the troposphere, CFCs linger in the atmosphere—the Freon that leaks out of your refrigerator can stay in the atmosphere for over 20 years. Consequently, CFCs diffuse into the stratosphere and ozone layer. Once they reach this part of the atmosphere, UV light (which is less abundant below the ozone layer because the ozone absorbs it) breaks a carbon–chlorine bond in the CFC. Consider the reaction of CF_2Cl_2 with UV light:

$$CF_2Cl_2 + UV \text{ light} \longrightarrow CF_2Cl + Cl$$

The newly released chlorine atom then reacts with ozone in the following cycle:

$$Cl + O_3 \longrightarrow ClO + O_2$$
$$O_3 + UV \text{ light} \longrightarrow O_2 + O$$
$$ClO + O \longrightarrow Cl + O_2$$

Notice what happens here. In the first reaction, a chlorine atom destroys an ozone molecule. In the third reaction, the product of the first reaction reacts with an oxygen atom that would normally react with O_2 to re-form ozone. In other words, a single chlorine atom destroys two ozone molecules and regenerates itself to repeat the process. In this way, any given chlorine atom can destroy hundreds of ozone molecules. Since the chlorine is not consumed in the process, it acts as a *catalyst*—a substance that enhances the rate of a chemical reaction without being consumed itself in the reaction. The overall process is called the *catalytic destruction of ozone*.

The first evidence of ozone depletion came from the South Pole in the mid-1980s. At that time, scientists discovered a transitory "hole" in the ozone layer directly over the pole. The amount of ozone depletion within the hole, which appears during the Antarctic spring and generally peaks during the months of September and October, was a startling 50%. Analysis of previous years' data revealed that the hole had been forming every spring since 1977, getting larger each year (Figure 5.28 ▶ on the next page).

For a number of years, scientists wondered why the ozone hole existed only over the South Pole and only in the spring. Over time, they discovered that special conditions exacerbated ozone depletion there. The South Pole has a cold, dark winter, which allows the formation of unique clouds called polar stratospheric clouds (PSCs). Unlike normal clouds, which form in the troposphere and are composed of water droplets, PSCs form in

TABLE 5.6 Changes in National Average Pollutant Levels, 1980–2007

Pollutant	Change (%) in Average Level
SO_2	−68
CO	−76
NO_2	−43
O_3	−21

*Source: EPA's 2008 National Air Quality and Emissions Trends Report

▶ **FIGURE 5.28 Spring in the Antarctic** Maps of the ozone layer in the spring of four different years reveal a startling decline in Antarctic ozone levels. (The darkest blue color represents the greatest ozone depletion.)

The Antarctic Ozone Hole

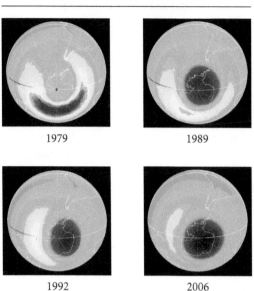

1979   1989

1992   2006

the stratosphere and are composed of ice crystals. During the Antarctic winter, the ice crystals act as catalysts that release molecular chlorine (Cl_2) from atmospheric chemical reservoirs (such as $ClONO_2$). When the sun rises in the Antarctic spring, sunlight breaks the relatively weak Cl—Cl bond in the recently released molecular chlorine, unleashing chlorine atoms into the stratosphere. The chlorine atoms then deplete ozone through the catalytic cycle discussed previously. The degree of ozone depletion observed over the South Pole does not happen all over the world because much of the chlorine that enters our atmosphere from chlorofluorocarbons is neutralized in atmospheric chemical reservoirs. But conditions at the South Pole in the spring months happen to be just right for releasing that chlorine from its reservoirs. Once the sun melts the PSCs, however, the chlorine returns to its reservoirs and the ozone hole recovers . . . until the next Antarctic spring.

Although to a lesser extent than over Antarctica, ozone depletion has occurred over the entire globe. The amount of depletion depends primarily on latitude. The clear scientific data demonstrating the ozone-depleting capability of chlorofluorocarbons, coupled with the immense depletion of ozone over Antarctica, forced lawmakers to take action. In 1992, President George H. W. Bush called for a complete ban on CFC production beginning in 1996. Many nations followed suit. Because of this legislation, atmospheric chlorine levels are projected to level out and eventually drop in coming years. The ozone hole is expected to recover by the year 2050.

CHAPTER IN REVIEW

Key Terms

Section 5.1
pressure (179)

Section 5.2
millimeter of mercury
   (mmHg) (181)
barometer (181)
torr (181)
atmosphere (atm) (181)
pascal (Pa) (181)
manometer (182)

Section 5.3
Boyle's law (184)

Charles's law (187)
Avogadro's law (189)

Section 5.4
ideal gas law (191)
ideal gas (191)
ideal gas constant (191)

Section 5.5
molar volume (193)
standard temperature and
   pressure (STP) (193)

Section 5.6
partial pressure (P_n) (197)
Dalton's law of partial
   pressures (197)
mole fraction (χ_a) (197)
hypoxia (199)
oxygen toxicity (199)
nitrogen narcosis (199)
vapor pressure (201)

Section 5.8
kinetic molecular
   theory (206)

Section 5.9
mean free path (212)
diffusion (212)
effusion (212)
Graham's law of
   effusion (213)

Section 5.10
van der Waals equation
   (216)

Key Concepts

Pressure (5.1, 5.2)

Gas pressure is the force per unit area that results from gas particles colliding with the surfaces around them. Pressure is measured in a number of units including mmHg, torr, Pa, psi, in Hg, and atm.

The Simple Gas Laws (5.3)

The simple gas laws express relationships between pairs of variables when the other variables are held constant. Boyle's law states that the volume of a gas is inversely proportional to its pressure. Charles's law states that the volume of a gas is directly proportional to its temperature. Avogadro's law states that the volume of a gas is directly proportional to the amount (in moles).

The Ideal Gas Law and Its Applications (5.4, 5.5)

The ideal gas law, $PV = nRT$, gives the relationship among all four gas variables and contains the simple gas laws within it. We can use the ideal gas law to find one of the four variables given the other three. We can use it to calculate the molar volume of an ideal gas, which is 22.4 L at STP, and to calculate the density and molar mass of a gas.

Mixtures of Gases and Partial Pressures (5.6)

In a mixture of gases, each gas acts independently of the others so that any overall property of the mixture is the sum of the properties of the individual components. The pressure of any individual component is its partial pressure.

Gas Stoichiometry (5.7)

In reactions involving gaseous reactants and products, quantities are often reported in volumes at specified pressures and temperatures. We can convert these quantities to amounts (in moles) using the ideal gas law. Then we can use the stoichiometric coefficients from the balanced equation to determine the stoichiometric amounts of other reactants or products. The general form for these types of calculations is often as follows: volume A → amount A (in moles) → amount B (in moles) → quantity of B (in desired units). In cases where the reaction is carried out at STP, the molar volume at STP (22.4 L = 1 mol) can be used to convert between volume in liters and amount in moles.

Kinetic Molecular Theory and Its Applications (5.8, 5.9)

Kinetic molecular theory is a quantitative model for gases. The theory has three main assumptions: (1) the gas particles are negligibly small; (2) the average kinetic energy of a gas particle is proportional to the temperature in kelvins; and (3) the collision of one gas particle with another is completely elastic (the particles do not stick together). The gas laws all follow from the kinetic molecular theory.

We can also use the theory to derive the expression for the root mean square velocity of gas particles. This velocity is inversely proportional to the molar mass of the gas, and therefore—at a given temperature—smaller gas particles are (on average) moving more quickly than larger ones. The kinetic molecular theory also allows us to predict the mean free path of a gas particle (the distance it travels between collisions) and relative rates of diffusion or effusion.

Real Gases (5.10)

Real gases differ from ideal gases to the extent that they do not always fit the assumptions of kinetic molecular theory. These assumptions tend to break down at high pressures, where the volume is higher than predicted for an ideal gas because the particles are no longer negligibly small compared to the space between them. The assumptions also break down at low temperatures where the pressure is lower than predicted because the attraction between molecules combined with low kinetic energies causes partially inelastic collisions. The Van der Waals equation predicts gas properties under nonideal conditions.

The Atmosphere (5.11)

Our atmosphere is primarily nitrogen (78%) and oxygen (21%). Common gaseous pollutants in our atmosphere include sulfur dioxide, carbon monoxide, ozone, and nitrogen dioxide. These pollutants affect exposed organs, such as the eyes and lungs, and force our cardiovascular system to work harder. Other pollutants include chlorofluorocarbons that contribute to the depletion of upper atmospheric ozone, which results in higher levels of ultraviolet radiation and an increase in our risk of skin cancer and cataracts.

Key Equations and Relationships

Relationship between Pressure (*P*), Force (*F*), and Area (*A*) (5.2)

$$P = \frac{F}{A}$$

Boyle's Law: Relationship between Pressure (*P*) and Volume (*V*) (5.3)

$$V \propto \frac{1}{P}$$

$$P_1 V_1 = P_2 V_2$$

Charles's Law: Relationship between Volume (*V*) and Temperature (*T*) (5.3)

$$V \propto T \quad \text{(in K)}$$

$$\frac{V_1}{T_1} = \frac{V_2}{T_2}$$

Avogadro's Law: Relationship between Volume (*V*) and Amount in Moles (*n*) (5.3)

$$V \propto n$$

$$\frac{V_1}{n_1} = \frac{V_2}{n_2}$$

Ideal Gas Law: Relationship between Volume (*V*), Pressure (*P*), Temperature (*T*), and Amount (*n*) (5.4)

$$PV = nRT$$

Dalton's Law: Relationship between Partial Pressures (P_n) in Mixture of Gases and Total Pressure (P_{total}) (5.6)

$$P_{total} = P_a + P_b + P_c + \cdots$$

$$P_a = \frac{n_a RT}{V} \qquad P_b = \frac{n_b RT}{V} \qquad P_c = \frac{n_c RT}{V}$$

Mole Fraction (χ_a) (5.6)

$$\chi_a = \frac{n_a}{n_{total}}$$

$$P_a = \chi_a P_{total}$$

Average Kinetic Energy (KE_{avg}) (5.8)

$$KE_{avg} = \frac{3}{2} RT$$

Relationship between Root Mean Square Velocity (u_{rms}) and Temperature (T) (5.8)

$$u_{rms} = \sqrt{\frac{3\,RT}{M}}$$

Relationship of Effusion Rates of Two Different Gases (5.9)

$$\frac{\text{rate A}}{\text{rate B}} = \sqrt{\frac{M_B}{M_A}}$$

Van der Waals Equation: The Effects of Volume and Intermolecular Forces on Nonideal Gas Behavior (5.10)

$$[P + a(n/V)^2] \times (V - nb) = nRT$$

Key Skills

Converting between Pressure Units (5.2)
- Example 5.1 • For Practice 5.1 • For More Practice 5.1 • Exercises 29–32

Relating Volume and Pressure: Boyle's Law (5.3)
- Example 5.2 • For Practice 5.2 • Exercises 35, 36

Relating Volume and Temperature: Charles's Law (5.3)
- Example 5.3 • For Practice 5.3 • Exercises 37, 38

Relating Volume and Moles: Avogadro's Law (5.3)
- Example 5.4 • For Practice 5.4 • Exercises 39, 40

Determining *P*, *V*, *n*, or *T* using the Ideal Gas Law (5.4)
- Examples 5.5, 5.6 • For Practice 5.5, 5.6 • For More Practice 5.6 • Exercises 41–50, 55, 56

Relating the Density of a Gas to Its Molar Mass (5.5)
- Example 5.7 • For Practice 5.7 • For More Practice 5.7 • Exercises 59, 60

Calculating the Molar Mass of a Gas with the Ideal Gas Law (5.5)
- Example 5.8 • For Practice 5.8 • Exercises 61–64

Calculating Total Pressure, Partial Pressures, and Mole Fractions of Gases in a Mixture (5.6)
- Examples 5.9, 5.10, 5.11 • For Practice 5.9, 5.10, 5.11 • Exercises 65, 66, 69, 71, 72, 74

Relating the Amounts of Reactants and Products in Gaseous Reactions: Stoichiometry (5.7)
- Examples 5.12, 5.13 • For Practice 5.12, 5.13 • For More Practice 5.12 • Exercises 75–81

Calculating the Root Mean Square Velocity of a Gas (5.8)
- Example 5.14 • For Practice 5.14 • Exercises 85, 86

Calculating the Effusion Rate or the Ratio of Effusion Rates of Two Gases (5.9)
- Example 5.15 • For Practice 5.15 • Exercises 87–90

EXERCISES

Review Questions

1. What is pressure? What causes pressure?

2. Explain what happens when you inhale. What forces air into your lungs?

3. Explain what happens when you exhale. What forces air out of your lungs?

4. What are some common units of pressure? List these in order of smallest to largest unit.

5. What is a manometer? How does it measure the pressure of a sample of gas?

6. Summarize each of the simple gas laws (Boyle's law, Charles's law, and Avogadro's law). For each law, explain the relationship between the two variables and also state which variables must be kept constant.

7. Explain the source of ear pain that is often experienced due to a rapid change in altitude.

8. Explain why scuba divers should never hold their breath as they ascend to the surface.

9. Why is it impossible to breathe air through an extralong snorkel (greater than a couple of meters) while swimming under water?

10. Explain why hot air balloons float above the ground, and why the second story of a two-story home is often warmer than the ground story.

11. What is the ideal gas law? Why is it useful?

12. Explain how the ideal gas law contains within it the simple gas laws (show an example).

13. Define molar volume and give its value for a gas at STP.

14. How does the density of a gas depend on temperature? Pressure? How does it depend on the molar mass of the gas?

15. What is partial pressure? What is the relationship between the partial pressures of each gas in a sample and the total pressure of gas in the sample?

16. Why do deep-sea divers breathe a mixture of helium and oxygen?

17. When a gas is collected over water, is the gas pure? Why or why not? How can the partial pressure of the collected gas be determined?

18. If a reaction occurs in the gas phase at STP, the mass of a product can be determined from the volumes of reactants. Explain.

19. What are the basic postulates of kinetic molecular theory? How does the concept of pressure follow from kinetic molecular theory?

20. Explain how Boyle's law, Charles's law, Avogadro's law, and Dalton's law all follow from kinetic molecular theory.

21. How is the kinetic energy of a gas related to temperature? How is the root mean square velocity of a gas related to its molar mass?

22. Describe how the molecules in a perfume bottle travel from the bottle to your nose. What is mean free path?

23. Explain the difference between diffusion and effusion. How is the effusion rate of a gas related to its molar mass?

24. Deviations from the ideal gas law are often observed at high pressure and low temperature. Explain why in light of kinetic molecular theory.

25. What are the main atmospheric pollutants and their sources? What are the trends in the levels of these pollutants over U.S. cities?

26. Explain why ozone is a pollutant in the lower atmosphere but a necessary component of our upper atmosphere.

27. What compounds are blamed for the depletion of stratospheric ozone? How do these compounds deplete ozone, and what is being done to prevent further depletion?

28. Why does an ozone hole form over the South Pole every October?

Problems by Topic

Converting between Pressure Units

29. The pressure in Denver, Colorado (elevation 5280 ft), averages about 24.9 in Hg. Convert this pressure to
   a. atm   **b.** mmHg   **c.** psi   **d.** Pa

30. The pressure on top of Mt. Everest averages about 235 mmHg. Convert this pressure to
   a. torr   **b.** psi   **c.** in Hg   **d.** atm

31. The North American record for highest recorded barometric pressure is 31.85 in Hg, set in 1989 in Northway, Alaska. Convert this pressure to
   a. mmHg   **b.** atm   **c.** torr   **d.** kPa (kilopascals)

32. The world record for lowest pressure (at sea level) was 652.5 mmHg recorded inside Typhoon Tip on October 12, 1979, in the Western Pacific Ocean. Convert this pressure to
   a. torr   **b.** atm   **c.** in Hg   **d.** psi

33. Given a barometric pressure of 762.4 mmHg, calculate the pressure of each gas sample as indicated by the manometer.

34. Given a barometric pressure of 751.5 mmHg, calculate the pressure of each gas sample as indicated by the manometer.

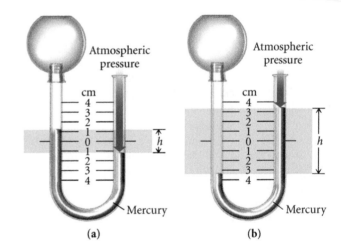

(a)   (b)

Simple Gas Laws

35. A sample of gas has an initial volume of 5.6 L at a pressure of 735 mmHg. If the volume of the gas is increased to 9.4 L, what will the pressure be?

36. A sample of gas has an initial volume of 13.9 L at a pressure of 1.22 atm. If the sample is compressed to a volume of 10.3 L, what will its pressure be?

37. A 48.3-mL sample of gas in a cylinder is warmed from 22 °C to 87 °C. What is its volume at the final temperature?

38. A syringe containing 1.55 mL of oxygen gas is cooled from 95.3 °C to 0.0 °C. What is the final volume of oxygen gas?

39. A balloon contains 0.158 mol of gas and has a volume of 2.46 L. If an additional 0.113 mol of gas is added to the balloon

(at the same temperature and pressure), what will its final volume be?

40. A cylinder with a moveable piston contains 0.553 mol of gas and has a volume of 253 mL. What will its volume be if an additional 0.365 mol of gas is added to the cylinder? (Assume constant temperature and pressure.)

Ideal Gas Law

41. What is the volume occupied by 0.118 mol of helium gas at a pressure of 0.97 atm and a temperature of 305 K? Would the volume be different if the gas was argon (under the same conditions)?

42. What is the volume occupied by 12.5 g of argon gas at a pressure of 1.05 atm and a temperature of 322 K? Would the volume be different if the sample were 12.5 g of helium (under identical conditions)?

43. What is the pressure in a 10.0-L cylinder filled with 0.448 mol of nitrogen gas at a temperature of 315 K?

44. What is the pressure in a 15.0-L cylinder filled with 32.7 g of oxygen gas at a temperature of 302 K?

45. A cylinder contains 28.5 L of oxygen gas at a pressure of 1.8 atm and a temperature of 298 K. How much gas (in moles) is in the cylinder?

46. What is the temperature of 0.52 mol of gas at a pressure of 1.3 atm and a volume of 11.8 L?

47. An automobile tire has a maximum rating of 38.0 psi (gauge pressure). The tire is inflated (while cold) to a volume of 11.8 L and a gauge pressure of 36.0 psi at a temperature of 12.0 °C. Driving on a hot day, the tire warms to 65.0 °C and its volume expands to 12.2 L. Does the pressure in the tire exceed its maximum rating? (Note: The *gauge pressure* is the *difference* between the total pressure and atmospheric pressure. In this case, assume that atmospheric pressure is 14.7 psi.)

48. A weather balloon is inflated to a volume of 28.5 L at a pressure of 748 mmHg and a temperature of 28.0 °C. The balloon rises in the atmosphere to an altitude of approximately 25,000 feet, where the pressure is 385 mmHg and the temperature is –15.0 °C. Assuming the balloon can freely expand, calculate the volume of the balloon at this altitude.

49. A piece of dry ice (solid carbon dioxide) with a mass of 28.8 g sublimes (converts from solid to gas) into a large balloon. Assuming that all of the carbon dioxide ends up in the balloon, what is the volume of the balloon at a temperature of 22 °C and a pressure of 742 mmHg?

50. A 1.0-L container of liquid nitrogen is kept in a closet measuring 1.0 m by 1.0 m by 2.0 m. Assuming that the container is completely full, that the temperature is 25.0 °C, and that the atmospheric pressure is 1.0 atm, calculate the percent (by volume) of air that is displaced if all of the liquid nitrogen evaporates. (Liquid nitrogen has a density of 0.807 g/mL.)

51. A wine-dispensing system uses argon canisters to pressurize and preserve wine in the bottle. An argon canister for the system has a volume of 55.0 mL and contains 26.0 g of argon. Assuming ideal gas behavior, what is the pressure in the canister at 295 K? When the argon is released from the canister it expands to fill the wine bottle. How many 750.0-mL wine bottles can be purged with the argon in the canister at a pressure of 1.20 atm and a temperature of 295 K?

52. Pressurized carbon dioxide inflators can be used to inflate a bicycle tire in the event of a flat. These inflators use metal cartridges that contain 16.0 g of carbon dioxide. At 298 K, to what pressure (in psi) can the carbon dioxide in the cartridge inflate a 3.45-L mountain bike tire? (Note: The *gauge pressure* is the *difference* between the total pressure and atmospheric pressure. In this case, assume that atmospheric pressure is 14.7 psi.)

53. Which gas sample representation has the greatest pressure? Assume that all the samples are at the same temperature. Explain.

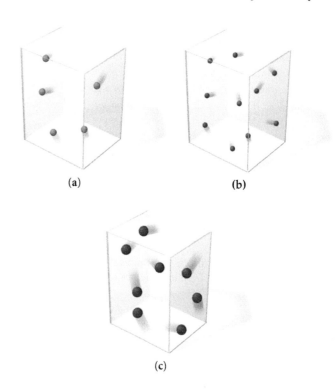

(a)   **(b)**

(c)

54. This picture represents a sample of gas at a pressure of 1 atm, a volume of 1 L, and a temperature of 25 °C. Draw a similar picture showing what would happen to the sample if the volume were reduced to 0.5 L and the temperature increased to 250 °C. What would happen to the pressure?

55. Aerosol cans carry clear warnings against incineration because of the high pressures that can develop upon heating. Suppose that a can contains a residual amount of gas at a pressure of 755 mmHg and a temperature of 25 °C. What would the pressure be if the can were heated to 1155 °C?

56. A sample of nitrogen gas in a 1.75-L container exerts a pressure of 1.35 atm at 25 °C. What is the pressure if the volume of the container is maintained constant and the temperature is raised to 355 °C?

Molar Volume, Density, and Molar Mass of a Gas

57. Use the molar volume of a gas at STP to determine the volume (in L) occupied by 33.6 g of neon at STP.

58. Use the molar volume of a gas at STP to calculate the density (in g/L) of nitrogen gas at STP.

59. What is the density (in g/L) of hydrogen gas at 20.0 °C and a pressure of 1655 psi?

60. A sample of N_2O gas has a density of 2.85 g/L at 298 K. What is the pressure of the gas (in mmHg)?

61. An experiment shows that a 248-mL gas sample has a mass of 0.433 g at a pressure of 745 mmHg and a temperature of 28 °C. What is the molar mass of the gas?

62. An experiment shows that a 113-mL gas sample has a mass of 0.171 g at a pressure of 721 mmHg and a temperature of 32 °C. What is the molar mass of the gas?

63. A sample of gas has a mass of 38.8 mg. Its volume is 224 mL at a temperature of 55 °C and a pressure of 886 torr. Find the molar mass of the gas.

64. A sample of gas has a mass of 0.555 g. Its volume is 117 mL at a temperature of 85 °C and a pressure of 753 mmHg. Find the molar mass of the gas.

Partial Pressure

65. A gas mixture contains each of the following gases at the indicated partial pressures: N_2, 215 torr; O_2, 102 torr; and He, 117 torr. What is the total pressure of the mixture? What mass of each gas is present in a 1.35-L sample of this mixture at 25.0 °C?

66. A gas mixture with a total pressure of 745 mmHg contains each of the following gases at the indicated partial pressures: CO_2, 125 mmHg; Ar, 214 mmHg; and O_2, 187 mmHg. The mixture also contains helium gas. What is the partial pressure of the helium gas? What mass of helium gas is present in a 12.0-L sample of this mixture at 273 K?

67. A 1.20-g sample of dry ice is added to a 755-mL flask containing nitrogen gas at a temperature of 25.0 °C and a pressure of 725 mmHg. The dry ice sublimes (converts from solid to gas) and the mixture returns to 25.0 °C. What is the total pressure in the flask?

68. A 275-mL flask contains pure helium at a pressure of 752 torr. A second flask with a volume of 475 mL contains pure argon at a pressure of 722 torr. If the two flasks are connected through a stopcock and the stopcock is opened, what are the partial pressures of each gas and the total pressure?

69. A gas mixture contains 1.25 g N_2 and 0.85 g O_2 in a 1.55-L container at 18 °C. Calculate the mole fraction and partial pressure of each component in the gas mixture.

70. What is the mole fraction of oxygen gas in air (see Table 5.3)? What volume of air contains 10.0 g of oxygen gas at 273 K and 1.00 atm?

71. The hydrogen gas formed in a chemical reaction is collected over water at 30.0 °C at a total pressure of 732 mmHg. What is the partial pressure of the hydrogen gas collected in this way? If the total volume of gas collected is 722 mL, what mass of hydrogen gas is collected?

72. The air in a bicycle tire is bubbled through water and collected at 25 °C. If the total volume of gas collected is 5.45 L at a temperature of 25 °C and a pressure of 745 torr, how many moles of gas were in the bicycle tire?

73. The zinc within a copper-plated penny will dissolve in hydrochloric acid if the copper coating is filed down in several spots (so that the hydrochloric acid can get to the zinc). The reaction between the acid and the zinc is $2\ H^+(aq) + Zn(s) \longrightarrow H_2(g) + Zn^{2+}(aq)$. When the zinc in a certain penny dissolves, the total volume of gas collected over water at 25 °C was 0.951

L at a total pressure of 748 mmHg. What mass of hydrogen gas was collected?

74. A heliox deep-sea diving mixture contains 2.0 g of oxygen to every 98.0 g of helium. What is the partial pressure of oxygen when this mixture is delivered at a total pressure of 8.5 atm?

Reaction Stoichiometry Involving Gases

75. Consider the chemical reaction:

$$C(s) + H_2O(g) \longrightarrow CO(g) + H_2(g)$$

How many liters of hydrogen gas are formed from the complete reaction of 15.7 g C? Assume that the hydrogen gas is collected at a pressure of 1.0 atm and a temperature of 355 K.

76. Consider the chemical reaction:

$$2\ H_2O(l) \longrightarrow 2\ H_2(g) + O_2(g)$$

What mass of H_2O is required to form 1.4 L of O_2 at a temperature of 315 K and a pressure of 0.957 atm?

77. CH_3OH can be synthesized by the reaction:

$$CO(g) + 2\ H_2(g) \longrightarrow CH_3OH(g)$$

What volume of H_2 gas (in L), at 748 mmHg and 86 °C, is required to synthesize 25.8 g CH_3OH? How many liters of CO gas, measured under the same conditions, is required?

78. Oxygen gas reacts with powdered aluminum according to the reaction:

$$4\ Al(s) + 3\ O_2(g) \longrightarrow 2\ Al_2O_3(s)$$

What volume of O_2 gas (in L), measured at 782 mmHg and 25 °C, completely reacts with 53.2 g Al?

79. Automobile air bags inflate following a serious impact. The impact triggers the chemical reaction:

$$2\ NaN_3(s) \longrightarrow 2\ Na(s) + 3\ N_2(g)$$

If an automobile air bag has a volume of 11.8 L, what mass of NaN_3 (in g) is required to fully inflate the air bag upon impact? Assume STP conditions.

80. Lithium reacts with nitrogen gas according to the reaction:

$$6\ Li(s) + N_2(g) \longrightarrow 2\ Li_3N(s)$$

What mass of lithium (in g) reacts completely with 58.5 mL of N_2 gas at STP?

81. Hydrogen gas (a potential future fuel) can be formed by the reaction of methane with water according to the equation:

$$CH_4(g) + H_2O(g) \longrightarrow CO(g) + 3\ H_2(g)$$

In a particular reaction, 25.5 L of methane gas (measured at a pressure of 732 torr and a temperature of 25 °C) mixes with 22.8 L of water vapor (measured at a pressure of 702 torr and a temperature of 125 °C). The reaction produces 26.2 L of hydrogen gas at STP. What is the percent yield of the reaction?

82. Ozone is depleted in the stratosphere by chlorine from CF_3Cl according to the set of equations:

$$CF_3Cl + UV\ light \longrightarrow CF_3 + Cl$$
$$Cl + O_3 \longrightarrow ClO + O_2$$
$$O_3 + UV\ light \longrightarrow O_2 + O$$
$$ClO + O \longrightarrow Cl + O_2$$

What total volume of ozone at a pressure of 25.0 mmHg and a temperature of 225 K is destroyed when all of the chlorine from 15.0 g of CF_3Cl goes through ten cycles of the above reactions?

Kinetic Molecular Theory

83. Consider a 1.0-L sample of helium gas and a 1.0-L sample of argon gas, both at room temperature and atmospheric pressure.
    a. Do the atoms in the helium sample have the same *average kinetic energy* as the atoms in the argon sample?
    b. Do the atoms in the helium sample have the same *average velocity* as the atoms in the argon sample?
    c. Do the argon atoms, because they are more massive, exert a greater pressure on the walls of the container? Explain.
    d. Which gas sample would have the faster rate of effusion?

84. A flask at room temperature contains exactly equal amounts (in moles) of nitrogen and xenon.
    a. Which of the two gases exerts the greater partial pressure?
    b. The molecules or atoms of which gas have the greater average velocity?
    c. The molecules of which gas have the greater average kinetic energy?
    d. If a small hole were opened in the flask, which gas would effuse more quickly?

85. Calculate the root mean square velocity and kinetic energy of F_2, Cl_2, and Br_2 at 298 K. Rank the three halogens with respect to their rate of effusion.

86. Calculate the root mean square velocity and kinetic energy of CO, CO_2, and SO_3 at 298 K. Which gas has the greatest velocity? The greatest kinetic energy? The greatest effusion rate?

87. We obtain uranium-235 from U-238 by fluorinating the uranium to form UF_6 (which is a gas) and then taking advantage of the different rates of effusion and diffusion for compounds containing the two isotopes. Calculate the ratio of effusion rates for $^{238}UF_6$ and $^{235}UF_6$. The atomic mass of U-235 is 235.054 amu and that of U-238 is 238.051 amu.

88. Calculate the ratio of effusion rates for Ar and Kr.

89. A sample of neon effuses from a container in 76 seconds. The same amount of an unknown noble gas requires 155 seconds. Identify the gas.

90. A sample of N_2O effuses from a container in 42 seconds. How long would it take the same amount of gaseous I_2 to effuse from the same container under identical conditions?

91. The graph shows the distribution of molecular velocities for two different molecules (A and B) at the same temperature. Which molecule has the higher molar mass? Which molecule would have the higher rate of effusion?

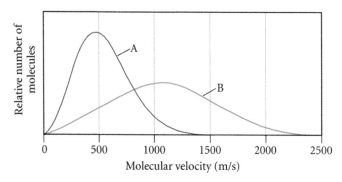

92. The graph shows the distribution of molecular velocities for the same molecule at two different temperatures (T_1 and T_2). Which temperature is greater? Explain.

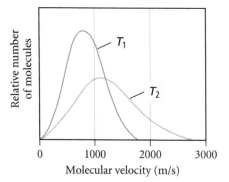

Real Gases

93. Which postulate of the kinetic molecular theory breaks down under conditions of high pressure? Explain.

94. Which postulate of the kinetic molecular theory breaks down under conditions of low temperature? Explain.

95. Use the van der Waals equation and the ideal gas equation to calculate the volume of 1.000 mol of neon at a pressure of 500.0 atm and a temperature of 355.0 K. Explain why the two values are different. (Hint: One way to solve the van der Waals equation for V is to use successive approximations. Use the ideal gas law to get a preliminary estimate for V.)

96. Use the van der Waals equation and the ideal gas equation to calculate the pressure exerted by 1.000 mol of Cl_2 in a volume of 5.000 L at a temperature of 273.0 K. Explain why the two values are different.

Cumulative Problems

97. Modern pennies are composed of zinc coated with copper. A student determines the mass of a penny to be 2.482 g and then makes several scratches in the copper coating (to expose the underlying zinc). The student puts the scratched penny in hydrochloric acid, where the following reaction occurs between the zinc and the HCl (the copper remains undissolved):

    $$Zn(s) + 2\,HCl(aq) \longrightarrow H_2(g) + ZnCl_2(aq)$$

    The student collects the hydrogen produced over water at 25 °C. The collected gas occupies a volume of 0.899 L at a total pressure of 791 mmHg. Calculate the percent zinc (by mass) in the penny. (Assume that all the Zn in the penny dissolves.)

98. A 2.85-g sample of an unknown chlorofluorocarbon decomposes and produces 564 mL of chlorine gas at a pressure of 752 mmHg and a temperature of 298 K. What is the percent chlorine (by mass) in the unknown chlorofluorocarbon?

99. The mass of an evacuated 255-mL flask is 143.187 g. The mass of the flask filled with 267 torr of an unknown gas at 25 °C is 143.289 g. Calculate the molar mass of the unknown gas.

100. A 118-mL flask is evacuated and found to have a mass of 97.129 g. When the flask is filled with 768 torr of helium gas at 35 °C, it has a mass of 97.171 g. Was the helium gas pure?

101. A gaseous hydrogen and carbon containing compound is decomposed and found to contain 82.66% carbon and 17.34% hy-

drogen by mass. The mass of 158 mL of the gas, measured at 556 mmHg and 25 °C, was 0.275 g. What is the molecular formula of the compound?

102. A gaseous hydrogen and carbon containing compound is decomposed and found to contain 85.63% C and 14.37% H by mass. The mass of 258 mL of the gas, measured at STP, was 0.646 g. What is the molecular formula of the compound?

103. Consider the reaction:

$$2 NiO(s) \longrightarrow 2 Ni(s) + O_2(g)$$

If O_2 is collected over water at 40.0 °C and a total pressure of 745 mmHg, what volume of gas will be collected for the complete reaction of 24.78 g of NiO?

104. Consider the reaction:

$$2 Ag_2O(s) \longrightarrow 4 Ag(s) + O_2(g)$$

If this reaction produces 15.8 g of Ag(s), what total volume of gas can be collected over water at a temperature of 25 °C and a total pressure of 752 mmHg?

105. When hydrochloric acid is poured over potassium sulfide, 42.9 mL of hydrogen sulfide gas is produced at a pressure of 752 torr and 25.8 °C. Write an equation for the gas-evolution reaction and determine how much potassium sulfide (in grams) reacted.

106. Consider the reaction:

$$2 SO_2(g) + O_2(g) \longrightarrow 2 SO_3(g)$$

a. If 285.5 mL of SO_2 reacts with 158.9 mL of O_2 (both measured at 315 K and 50.0 mmHg), what is the limiting reactant and the theoretical yield of SO_3?

b. If 187.2 mL of SO_3 is collected (measured at 315 K and 50.0 mmHg), what is the percent yield for the reaction?

107. Ammonium carbonate decomposes upon heating according to the balanced equation:

$$(NH_4)_2 CO_3(s) \longrightarrow 2 NH_3(g) + CO_2(g) + H_2O(g)$$

Calculate the total volume of gas produced at 22 °C and 1.02 atm by the complete decomposition of 11.83 g of ammonium carbonate.

108. Ammonium nitrate decomposes explosively upon heating according to the balanced equation:

$$2 NH_4NO_3(s) \longrightarrow 2 N_2(g) + O_2(g) + 4 H_2O(g)$$

Calculate the total volume of gas (at 125 °C and 748 mmHg) produced by the complete decomposition of 1.55 kg of ammonium nitrate.

109. Olympic cyclists fill their tires with helium to make them lighter. Calculate the mass of air in an air-filled tire and the mass of helium in a helium-filled tire. What is the mass difference between the two? Assume that the volume of the tire is 855 mL, that it is filled to a total pressure of 125 psi, and that the temperature is 25 °C. Also, assume an average molar mass for air of 28.8 g/mol.

110. In a common classroom demonstration, a balloon is filled with air and submerged in liquid nitrogen. The balloon contracts as the gases within the balloon cool. Suppose the balloon initially contains 2.95 L of air at a temperature of 25.0 °C and a pressure of 0.998 atm. Calculate the expected volume of the balloon upon cooling to −196 °C (the boiling point of liquid nitrogen). When the demonstration is carried out, the actual volume of the balloon decreases to 0.61 L. How does the observed volume of the balloon compare to your calculated value? Can you explain the difference?

111. Gaseous ammonia can be injected into the exhaust stream of a coal-burning power plant to reduce the pollutant NO to N_2 according to the reaction:

$$4 NH_3(g) + 4 NO(g) + O_2(g) \longrightarrow 4 N_2(g) + 6 H_2O(g)$$

Suppose that the exhaust stream of a power plant has a flow rate of 335 L/s at a temperature of 955 K, and that the exhaust contains a partial pressure of NO of 22.4 torr. What should be the flow rate of ammonia delivered at 755 torr and 298 K into the stream to react completely with the NO if the ammonia is 65.2% pure (by volume)?

112. The emission of NO_2 by fossil fuel combustion can be prevented by injecting gaseous urea into the combustion mixture. The urea reduces NO (which oxidizes in air to form NO_2) according to the reaction:

$$2 CO(NH_2)_2(g) + 4 NO(g) + O_2(g) \longrightarrow 4 N_2(g)$$
$$+ 2 CO_2(g) + 4 H_2O(g)$$

Suppose that the exhaust stream of an automobile has a flow rate of 2.55 L/s at 655 K and contains a partial pressure of NO of 12.4 torr. What total mass of urea is necessary to react completely with the NO formed during 8.0 hours of driving?

113. An ordinary gasoline can measuring 30.0 cm by 20.0 cm by 15.0 cm is evacuated with a vacuum pump. Assuming that virtually all of the air can be removed from inside the can, and that atmospheric pressure is 14.7 psi, what is the total force (in pounds) on the surface of the can? Do you think that the can could withstand the force?

114. Twenty-five milliliters of liquid nitrogen (density = 0.807 g/mL) is poured into a cylindrical container with a radius of 10.0 cm and a length of 20.0 cm. The container initially contains only air at a pressure of 760.0 mmHg (atmospheric pressure) and a temperature of 298 K. If the liquid nitrogen completely vaporizes, what is the total force (in lb) on the interior of the container at 298 K?

115. A 160.0-L helium tank contains pure helium at a pressure of 1855 psi and a temperature of 298 K. How many 3.5-L helium balloons will the helium in the tank fill? (Assume an atmospheric pressure of 1.0 atm and a temperature of 298 K.)

116. An 11.5-mL sample of liquid butane (density = 0.573 g/mL) is evaporated in an otherwise empty container at a temperature of 28.5 °C. The pressure in the container following evaporation is 892 torr. What is the volume of the container?

117. A scuba diver creates a spherical bubble with a radius of 2.5 cm at a depth of 30.0 m where the total pressure (including atmospheric pressure) is 4.00 atm. What is the radius of the bubble when it reaches the surface of the water? (Assume that the atmospheric pressure is 1.00 atm and the temperature is 298 K.)

118. A particular balloon can be stretched to a maximum surface area of 1257 cm². The balloon is filled with 3.0 L of helium gas at a pressure of 755 torr and a temperature of 298 K. The balloon is then allowed to rise in the atmosphere. If the atmospheric temperature is 273 K, at what pressure will the balloon burst? (Assume the balloon to be in the shape of a sphere.)

119. A catalytic converter in an automobile uses a palladium or platinum catalyst (a substance that increases the rate of a reaction without being consumed by the reaction) to convert carbon monoxide gas to carbon dioxide according to the reaction:

$$2\, CO(g) + O_2(g) \longrightarrow 2\, CO_2(g)$$

A chemist researching the effectiveness of a new catalyst combines a 2.0 : 1.0 mole ratio mixture of carbon monoxide and oxygen gas (respectively) over the catalyst in a 2.45-L flask at a total pressure of 745 torr and a temperature of 552 °C. When the reaction is complete, the pressure in the flask has dropped to 552 torr. What percentage of the carbon monoxide was converted to carbon dioxide?

120. A quantity of N_2 occupies a volume of 1.0 L at 300 K and 1.0 atm. The gas expands to a volume of 3.0 L as the result of a change in both temperature and pressure. Find the density of the gas at these new conditions.

121. A mixture of $CO(g)$ and $O_2(g)$ in a 1.0-L container at 1.0×10^3 K has a total pressure of 2.2 atm. After some time the total pressure falls to 1.9 atm as the result of the formation of CO_2. Find the mass (in grams) of CO_2 that forms.

122. The radius of a xenon atom is 1.3×10^{-8} cm. A 100-mL flask is filled with Xe at a pressure of 1.0 atm and a temperature of 273 K. Calculate the fraction of the volume that is occupied by Xe atoms. (Hint: The atoms are spheres.)

123. A natural gas storage tank is a cylinder with a moveable top whose volume can change only as its height changes. Its radius remains fixed. The height of the cylinder is 22.6 m on a day when the temperature is 22 °C. The next day the height of the cylinder increases to 23.8 m when the gas expands because of a heat wave. Find the temperature on the second day, assuming that the pressure and amount of gas in the storage tank have not changed.

124. A mixture of 8.0 g CH_4 and 8.0 g Xe is placed in a container and the total pressure is found to be 0.44 atm. Find the partial pressure of CH_4.

125. A steel container of volume 0.35 L can withstand pressures up to 88 atm before exploding. What mass of helium can be stored in this container at 299 K?

126. Binary compounds of alkali metals and hydrogen react with water to liberate $H_2(g)$. The H_2 from the reaction of a sample of NaH with an excess of water fills a volume of 0.490 L above the water. The temperature of the gas is 35 °C and the total pressure is 758 mmHg. Determine the mass of H_2 liberated and the mass of NaH that reacted.

127. In a given diffusion apparatus, 15.0 mL of HBr gas diffused in 1.0 min. In the same apparatus and under the same conditions, 20.3 mL of an unknown gas diffused in 1.0 min. The unknown gas is a hydrocarbon. Find its molecular formula.

128. A sample of $N_2O_3(g)$ has a pressure of 0.017 atm. The temperature (in K) is then doubled and the N_2O_3 undergoes complete decomposition to $NO_2(g)$ and $NO(g)$. Find the total pressure of the mixture of gases assuming constant volume and no additional temperature change.

129. When 0.583 g of neon is added to an 800-cm³ bulb containing a sample of argon, the total pressure of the gases is found to be 1.17 atm at a temperature of 295 K. Find the mass of the argon in the bulb.

130. A gas mixture composed of helium and argon has a density of 0.670 g/L at a 755 mm Hg and 298 K. What is the composition of the mixture by volume?

131. A gas mixture contains 75.2% nitrogen and 24.8% krypton by mass. What is the partial pressure of krypton in the mixture if the total pressure is 745 mm Hg?

Challenge Problems

132. A 10-liter container is filled with 0.10 mol of $H_2(g)$ and heated to 3000 K causing some of the $H_2(g)$ to decompose into H(g). The pressure is found to be 3.0 atm. Find the partial pressure of the H(g) that forms from H_2 at this temperature. (Assume two significant figures for the temperature.)

133. A mixture of $NH_3(g)$ and $N_2H_4(g)$ is placed in a sealed container at 300 K. The total pressure is 0.50 atm. The container is heated to 1200 K at which time both substances decompose completely according to the equations $2\, NH_3(g) \longrightarrow N_2(g) + 3\, H_2(g)$; $N_2H_4(g) \longrightarrow N_2(g) + 2\, H_2(g)$. After decomposition is complete the total pressure at 1200 K is found to be 4.5 atm. Find the percent of $N_2H_4(g)$ in the original mixture. (Assume two significant figures for the temperature.)

134. A quantity of CO gas occupies a volume of 0.48 L at 1.0 atm and 275 K. The pressure of the gas is lowered and its temperature is raised until its volume is 1.3 L. Find the density of the CO under the new conditions.

135. When $CO_2(g)$ is put in a sealed container at 701 K and a pressure of 10.0 atm and is heated to 1401 K, the pressure rises to 22.5 atm. Some of the CO_2 decomposes to CO and O_2. Calculate the mole percent of CO_2 that decomposes.

136. The world burns approximately 9.0×10^{12} kg of fossil fuel per year. Use the combustion of octane as the representative reaction and determine the mass of carbon dioxide (the most significant greenhouse gas) formed per year. The current concentration of carbon dioxide in the atmosphere is approximately 387 ppm (by volume). By what percentage does the concentration increase each year due to fossil fuel combustion? Approximate the average properties of the entire atmosphere by assuming that the atmosphere extends from sea level to 15 km and that it has an average pressure of 381 torr and average temperature of 275 K. Assume Earth is a perfect sphere with a radius of 6371 km.

137. The atmosphere slowly oxidizes hydrocarbons in a number of steps that eventually convert the hydrocarbon into carbon dioxide and water. The overall reaction of a number of such steps for methane gas is

$$CH_4(g) + 5\, O_2(g) + 5\, NO(g) \longrightarrow CO_2(g) + H_2O(g) \\ + 5\, NO_2(g) + 2\, OH(g)$$

Suppose that an atmospheric chemist combines 155 mL of methane at STP, 885 mL of oxygen at STP, and 55.5 mL of NO

at STP in a 2.0-L flask. The flask is allowed to stand for several weeks at 275 K. If the reaction reaches 90.0% of completion (90.0% of the limiting reactant is consumed), what is the partial pressure of each of the reactants and products in the flask at 275 K? What is the total pressure in the flask?

138. Two identical balloons are filled to the same volume, one with air and one with helium. The next day, the volume of the air-filled balloon has decreased by 5.0%. By what percent has the volume of the helium-filled balloon decreased? (Assume that the air is four-fifths nitrogen and one-fifth oxygen, and that the temperature did not change.)

139. A mixture of $CH_4(g)$ and $C_2H_6(g)$ has a total pressure of 0.53 atm. Just enough $O_2(g)$ is added to the mixture to bring about its complete combustion to $CO_2(g)$ and $H_2O(g)$. The total pressure of the two product gases is found to be 2.2 atm. Assuming constant volume and temperature, find the mole fraction of CH_4 in the mixture.

140. A sample of $C_2H_2(g)$ has a pressure of 7.8 kPa. After some time a portion of it reacts to form $C_6H_6(g)$. The total pressure of the mixture of gases is then 3.9 kPa. Assume the volume and the temperature do not change. What fraction of $C_2H_2(g)$ has undergone reaction?

Conceptual Problems

141. When the driver of an automobile applies the brakes, the passengers are pushed toward the front of the car, but a helium balloon is pushed toward the back of the car. Upon forward acceleration, the passengers are pushed toward the back of the car, but the helium balloon is pushed toward the front of the car. Why?

142. Suppose that a liquid is 10 times denser than water. If you were to sip this liquid at sea level using a straw, what would be the maximum length of the straw?

143. The reaction occurs in a closed container:

$$A(g) + 2 B(g) \longrightarrow 2 C(g)$$

A reaction mixture initially contains 1.5 L of A and 2.0 L of B. Assuming that the volume and temperature of the reaction mixture remain constant, what is the percent change in pressure if the reaction goes to completion?

144. One mole of nitrogen and one mole of neon are combined in a closed container at STP. How big is the container?

145. Exactly equal amounts (in moles) of gas A and gas B are combined in a 1-L container at room temperature. Gas B has a molar mass that is twice that of gas A. Which statement is true for the mixture of gases and why?
  a. The molecules of gas B have greater kinetic energy than those of gas A.
  b. Gas B has a greater partial pressure than gas A.
  c. The molecules of gas B have a greater average velocity than those of gas A.
  d. Gas B makes a greater contribution to the average density of the mixture than gas A.

146. Which gas would you expect to deviate most from ideal behavior under conditions of low temperature: F_2, Cl_2, or Br_2? Explain.

6

Thermochemistry

There is a fact, or if you wish, a law, governing all natural phenomena that are known to date. There is no exception to this law—it is exact as far as we know. The law is called the conservation of energy. It states that there is a certain quantity, which we call energy, that does not change in the manifold changes which nature undergoes.

—Richard P. Feynman (1918–1988)

WE HAVE SPENT THE FIRST FEW CHAPTERS of this book examining one of the two major components of our universe—matter. We now turn our attention to the other major component—energy. As far as we know, matter and energy—which can be interchanged but not destroyed—make up the physical universe. Unlike matter, energy is not something we can touch or hold in our hand, but we experience it in many ways. The warmth of sunlight, the feel of wind on our faces, and the force that presses us back when a car accelerates are all manifestations of energy and its interconversions. And of course energy is critical to society and to the world. The standard of living around the globe is strongly correlated with the access to and use of energy resources. Most of those resources, as we shall see, are chemical ones, and we can understand their advantages as well as their drawbacks in terms of chemistry.

A chemical hand warmer contains substances that react to emit heat.

6.1 Chemical Hand Warmers

My family loves to snowboard. However, my wife hates being cold (with a passion), especially in her hands and toes. Her solution is the chemical hand warmer, a small pouch that comes sealed in a plastic package. She opens the package and places the pouch in her glove or boot. The pouch slowly warms up and keeps her hand (or foot) warm all day long.

Warming your hands with chemical hand warmers involves many of the principles of **thermochemistry**, the study of the relationships between chemistry and energy. When you open the package that contains the hand warmer, the contents are exposed to air, and an *exothermic reaction* occurs. The most commonly available hand warmers use the oxidation of iron as the exothermic reaction:

$$4 \, Fe(s) + 3 \, O_2(g) \longrightarrow 2 \, Fe_2O_3(s)$$

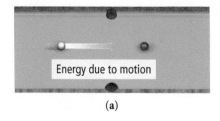

(a)

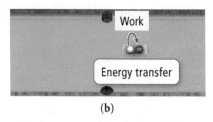

(b)

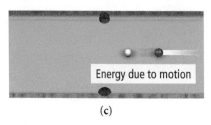

(c)

▲ **(a)** A rolling billiard ball has energy due to its motion. **(b)** When the ball collides with a second ball it does work, transferring energy to the second ball. **(c)** The second ball now has energy as it rolls away from the collision.

▼ **FIGURE 6.1 The Different Manifestations of Energy**

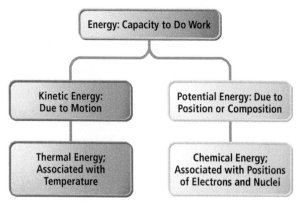

Einstein showed that it is mass–energy that is conserved; one can be converted into the other. This equivalence becomes important in nuclear reactions, discussed in Chapter 19. In ordinary chemical reactions, however, the interconversion of mass and energy is not a significant factor, and we can regard mass and energy as independently conserved.

The most important product of this reaction is not a substance—it is *heat*. We'll define heat more carefully later, but in general heat is what you feel when you touch something that is warmer than your hand (in this case, the hot hand warmer). Although some of the heat is lost through the minute openings in your gloves (which is why my wife prefers mittens) most of it is transferred to your hands and to the pocket of air surrounding your hands, resulting in a temperature increase. The magnitude of the temperature increase depends on the size of the hand warmer and the size of your glove (as well as some other details). But in general, the size of the temperature increase is proportional to the amount of heat released by the reaction.

In this chapter, we examine the relationship between chemical reactions and energy. Specifically, we look at how chemical reactions can *exchange* energy with their surroundings and how to quantify the magnitude of those exchanges. These kinds of calculations are important, not only for chemical hand warmers, but also to many other important processes such as the heating of homes and the production of energy for our society.

6.2 The Nature of Energy: Key Definitions

Recall that we briefly examined energy in Section 1.5. At that point, we defined **energy** as the capacity to do work and defined **work** as the result of a force acting through a distance. When you push a box across the floor, you have done work. Consider another example of work: a billiard ball rolling across a billiard table and colliding straight on with a second, stationary billiard ball. The rolling ball has *energy* due to its motion. When it collides with another ball it does *work,* resulting in the *transfer* of energy from one ball to the other. The second billiard ball absorbs the energy and begins to roll across the table.

As we just saw with chemical hand warmers, energy can also be transferred through **heat**, the flow of energy caused by a temperature difference. For example, if you hold a cup of coffee in your hand, energy is transferred, in the form of heat, from the hot coffee to your cooler hand. Think of *energy* as something that an object or set of objects possesses. Think of *heat* and *work* as ways that objects or sets of objects *exchange* energy.

The energy contained in a rolling billiard ball is an example of **kinetic energy**, the energy associated with the *motion* of an object. The energy contained in a hot cup of coffee is **thermal energy**, the energy associated with the *temperature* of an object. Thermal energy is actually a type of kinetic energy because it arises from the motions of atoms or molecules within a substance. If you raise a billiard ball off the table, you increase its **potential energy**, the energy associated with the *position* or *composition* of an object. The potential energy of the billiard ball, for example, is a result of its position in Earth's gravitational field. Raising the ball off the table, against Earth's gravitational pull, gives it more potential energy. Another example of potential energy is the energy contained in a compressed spring. When you compress a spring, you push against the forces that tend to maintain the spring's uncompressed shape, storing energy as potential energy. **Chemical energy**, the energy associated with the relative positions of electrons and nuclei in atoms and molecules, is also a form of potential energy. Some chemical compounds, such as the methane in natural gas or the iron in a chemical hand warmer, are like a compressed spring—they contain potential energy, and a chemical reaction can release that potential energy. Figure 6.1 ◄ summarizes the different kinds of energy just discussed.

The **law of conservation of energy** states that *energy can be neither created nor destroyed*. However, energy can be transferred from one object to another, and it can assume different forms. For example, if you drop a raised billiard ball, some of its potential energy becomes kinetic energy as the ball falls toward the table, as shown in Figure 6.2 ►. If you release a compressed spring, the potential energy becomes kinetic energy as the spring expands outward, as shown in Figure 6.3 ►. When iron reacts with oxygen

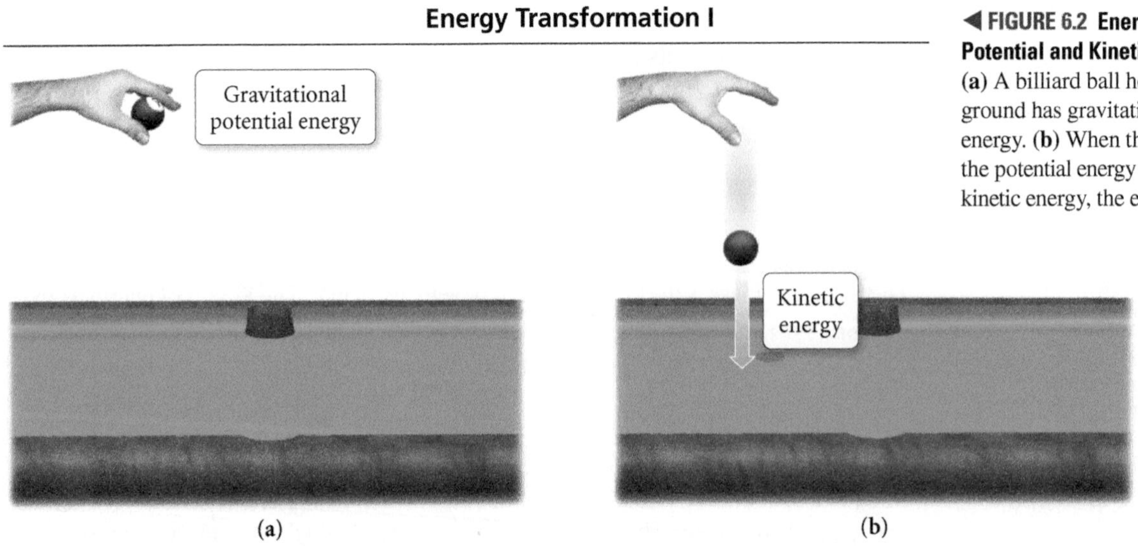

Energy Transformation I

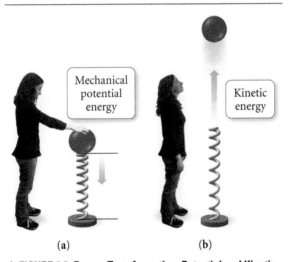

◀ **FIGURE 6.2 Energy Transformation:**
Potential and Kinetic Energy I
(a) A billiard ball held above the ground has gravitational potential energy. **(b)** When the ball is released, the potential energy is transformed into kinetic energy, the energy of motion.

within a chemical hand warmer, the chemical energy of the iron and oxygen becomes thermal energy that increases the temperature of your hand and glove.

A good way to understand and track energy changes is to define the **system** under investigation. For example, the system may be a beaker of chemicals in the lab, or it may be the iron reacting in a hand warmer. The system's **surroundings** are everything with which the system can exchange energy. If we define the chemicals in a beaker as the system, the surroundings may include the water that the chemicals are dissolved in (for aqueous solutions), the beaker itself, the lab bench on which the beaker sits, the air in the room, and so on. For the iron in the hand warmer, the surroundings include your hand, your glove, the air in the glove, and even the air outside of the glove.

In an energy exchange, energy is transferred between the system and the surroundings, as shown in Figure 6.4 ▼. If the system loses energy, the surroundings gain the same exact amount of energy, and vice versa. When the iron within the chemical hand warmer reacts, the system loses energy to the surroundings, producing the desired temperature increase within your gloves.

Energy Transformation II

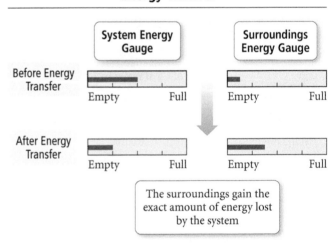

Energy Transfer

▲ **FIGURE 6.3 Energy Transformation: Potential and Kinetic Energy II** **(a)** A compressed spring has potential energy. **(b)** When the spring is released, the potential energy is transformed into kinetic energy.

▲ **FIGURE 6.4 Energy Transfer** If a system and surroundings had energy gauges (which would measure energy content in the way a fuel gauge measures fuel content), an energy transfer in which the system transfers energy to the surroundings would result in a decrease in the energy content of the system and an increase in the energy content of the surroundings. The total amount of energy, however, must be conserved.

Units of Energy

We can deduce the units of energy from the definition of kinetic energy. An object of mass m, moving at velocity v, has a kinetic energy KE given by

$$KE = \frac{1}{2}mv^2 \qquad [6.1]$$

$$\underset{\text{kg} \quad \text{m/s}}{}$$

The SI unit of mass is the kg and the unit of velocity is m/s. The SI unit of energy is therefore $kg \cdot m^2/s^2$, defined as the **joule (J)**, named after the English scientist James Joule (1818–1889).

$$1 \text{ kg} \frac{m^2}{s^2} = 1 \text{ J}$$

One joule is a relatively small amount of energy—for example, a 100-watt lightbulb uses 3.6×10^5 J in 1 hour. Therefore, we often use the kilojoule (kJ) in our energy discussions and calculations $\left(1 \text{ kJ} = 1000 \text{ J}\right)$. A second commonly used unit of energy is the **calorie (cal)**, originally defined as the amount of energy required to raise the temperature of 1 g of water by 1 °C. The current definition is 1 cal = 4.184 J (exact); a calorie is a larger unit than a joule. A related energy unit is the nutritional, or uppercase "C" **Calorie (Cal)**, equivalent to 1000 lowercase "c" calories. The Calorie is the same as a kilocalorie (kcal): 1 Cal = 1 kcal = 1000 cal. Electricity bills typically are based on another, even larger, energy unit, the **kilowatt-hour (kWh)**: 1 kWh = 3.60×10^6 J. Electricity costs $0.08–$0.15 per kWh. Table 6.1 shows various energy units and their conversion factors. Table 6.2 shows the amount of energy required for various processes.

3.6×10^5 J or 0.10 kWh used in 1 hour

▲ A watt (W) is 1 J/s, so a 100-W lightbulb uses 100 J every second or 3.6×10^5 J every hour.

The "calorie" referred to on all nutritional labels (regardless of the capitalization) is always the capital *C* Calorie.

TABLE 6.1 Energy Conversion Factors*

1 calorie (cal)	= 4.184 joules (J)
1 Calorie (Cal) or kilocalorie (kcal)	= 1000 cal = 4184 J
1 kilowatt-hour (kWh)	= 3.60×10^6 J

*All conversion factors in this table are exact.

TABLE 6.2 Energy Uses in Various Units

Unit	Amount Required to Raise Temperature of 1 g of Water by 1 °C	Amount Required to Light 100-W Bulb for 1 Hour	Amount Used by Human Body in Running 1 Mile (Approximate)	Amount Used by Average U.S. Citizen in 1 Day
joule (J)	4.18	3.60×10^5	4.2×10^5	9.0×10^8
calorie (cal)	1.00	8.60×10^4	1.0×10^5	2.2×10^8
Calorie (Cal)	0.00100	86.0	100	2.2×10^5
kilowatt-hour (KWh)	1.16×10^{-6}	0.100	0.12	2.5×10^2

6.3 The First Law of Thermodynamics: There Is No Free Lunch

We call the general study of energy and its interconversions **thermodynamics**. The laws of thermodynamics are among the most fundamental in all of science, governing virtually every process that involves change. The **first law of thermodynamics** is the law of energy conservation, which we can state as follows:

The total energy of the universe is constant.

In other words, since energy is neither created nor destroyed, and since the universe does not exchange energy with anything else, its energy content does not change. The first law

CHEMISTRY IN YOUR DAY **Redheffer's Perpetual Motion Machine**

In 1812, a man named Charles Redheffer appeared in Philadelphia with a machine that he claimed could run forever without any energy input—a perpetual motion machine. He set up the machine on the edge of town and charged admission to view it. He also appealed to the city for money to build a larger version of the machine. When city commissioners came out to inspect the machine, Redheffer did his best to keep them from viewing it too closely. Nonetheless, one of the commissioners noticed something suspicious: the gears that supposedly ran to an external driveshaft were cut in the wrong direction. The driveshaft that the machine was allegedly powering was instead powering the machine. The city commissioners hired a local engineer and clockmaker named Isaiah Lukens to make a similar machine to expose Redheffer's deception. Lukens's machine was even more ingenious than Redheffer's, and Redheffer left Philadelphia exposed as a fraud.

Redheffer was persistent, however, and took his machine to New York. In 1813, during a public display of the machine, the famous mechanical engineer Robert Fulton—who 6 years earlier had demonstrated the first successful steamboat—noticed a rhythm to the machine's motion. It seemed to speed up and slow down at regular intervals. Fulton knew that such rhythmic motion is indicative of motion generated by a manual crank. He knocked away some boards in a wall next to the machine and discovered a long belt that led to an enclosed room where, indeed, an old man sat turning a crank. Redheffer's machine—like many other perpetual motion machines throughout history—was again exposed as a hoax.

Question

Can you think of any recent claims of perpetual motion or limitless free energy?

has many implications: the most important one is that, with energy, you do not get something for nothing. The best you can do with energy is break even—there is no free lunch. According to the first law, a device that would continually produce energy with no energy input, sometimes known as a *perpetual motion machine*, cannot exist. Occasionally, the media report or speculate on the discovery of a machine that can produce energy without the need for energy input. For example, you may have heard someone propose an electric car that recharges itself while driving, or a new motor that can create additional usable electricity as well as the electricity to power itself. Although some hybrid (electric and gasoline powered) vehicles can capture energy from braking and use that energy to recharge their batteries, they could never run indefinitely without additional fuel. As for the motor that powers an external load as well as itself—no such thing exists. Our society has a continual need for energy, and as our current energy resources dwindle, new energy sources will be required. And those sources, whatever they may be, will follow the first law of thermodynamics—energy must be conserved.

Internal Energy

The **internal energy** (*E*) of a system is *the sum of the kinetic and potential energies of all of the particles that compose the system*. Internal energy is a **state function**, which means that its value depends *only on the state of the system*, not on how the system arrived at that state. The state of a chemical system is specified by parameters such as temperature, pressure, concentration, and physical state (solid, liquid, or gas). We can understand state functions with the mountain-climbing analogy depicted in Figure 6.5 ▸ on the next page. The elevation at any point during a mountain climb is analogous to a state function. For example, when you reach 10,000 ft, your elevation is 10,000 ft, no matter how you got there. The distance you traveled to get there, by contrast, is not a state function; you could have climbed the mountain by any number of routes, each requiring you to cover a different distance.

Since state functions depend only on the state of the system, the value of a *change* in a state function is always the difference between its final and initial values. If you start climbing a mountain at an elevation of 3000 ft, and reach the summit at 10,000 feet, then your elevation change is 7000 ft (10,000 ft – 3000 ft), regardless of what path you took.

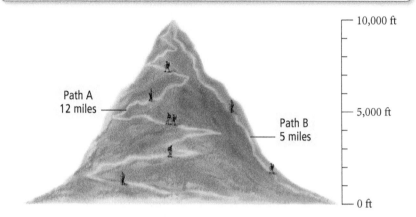

A State Function
Change in altitude depends only on the difference between the initial and final values, not on the path taken.

▶ **FIGURE 6.5 Altitude as a State Function** The change in altitude during a climb depends only on the difference between the final and initial altitudes, not on the route traveled.

Like an altitude change, an internal energy change (ΔE) is determined by the difference in internal energy between the final and initial states:

$$\Delta E = E_{final} - E_{initial}$$

In a chemical system, the reactants constitute the initial state and the products constitute the final state. So ΔE is the difference in internal energy between the products and the reactants.

$$\Delta E = E_{products} - E_{reactants} \qquad [6.2]$$

For example, consider the reaction between carbon and oxygen to form carbon dioxide:

$$C(s) + O_2(g) \longrightarrow CO_2(g)$$

Just as we can portray the changes that occur when climbing a mountain with an *altitude* diagram which depicts the *altitude* before and after the climb (see Figure 6.5), so we can portray the energy changes that occur during a reaction with an *energy* diagram, which compares the *internal energy* of the reactants and the products:

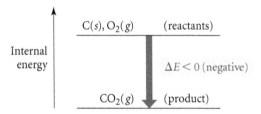

The vertical axis of the diagram is internal *energy*, which increases as you move up on the diagram. For this reaction, the reactants are *higher* on the diagram than the products because they have higher internal energy. As the reaction occurs, the reactants become products, which have lower internal energy. Therefore, energy is given off by the reaction and ΔE (that is, $E_{products} - E_{reactants}$) is *negative*.

Where does the energy lost by the reactants (as they transform to products) go? If we define the thermodynamic *system* as the reactants and products of the reaction, then energy flows *out of the system* and *into the surroundings*.

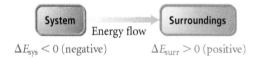

According to the first law, energy must be conserved. Therefore, the amount of energy lost by the system must exactly equal the amount gained by the surroundings.

$$\Delta E_{sys} = -\Delta E_{surr} \qquad [6.3]$$

Now, suppose the reaction is reversed:

$$CO_2(g) \longrightarrow C(s) + O_2(g)$$

The energy level diagram is nearly identical, with one important difference: $CO_2(g)$ is now the reactant and $C(s)$ and $O_2(g)$ are the products. Instead of decreasing in energy as the reaction occurs, the system increases in energy:

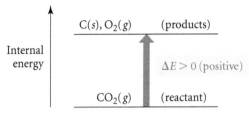

In this reversed reaction ΔE is *positive* and energy flows *into the system* and *out of the surroundings*.

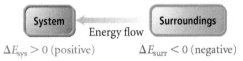

Summarizing Energy Flow:

▶ If the reactants have a higher internal energy than the products, ΔE_{sys} is negative and energy flows out of the system into the surroundings.

▶ If the reactants have a lower internal energy than the products, ΔE_{sys} is positive and energy flows into the system from the surroundings.

You can think of the internal energy of the system in the same way you think about the balance in a checking account. Energy flowing *out of* the system is like a withdrawal and therefore carries a negative sign. Energy flowing *into* the system is like a deposit and carries a positive sign.

Conceptual Connection 6.1   System and Surroundings

Consider these fictitious internal energy gauges for a chemical system and its surroundings:

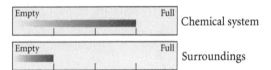

Which of the following best represents the energy gauges for the same system and surroundings following an energy exchange in which ΔE_{sys} is negative?

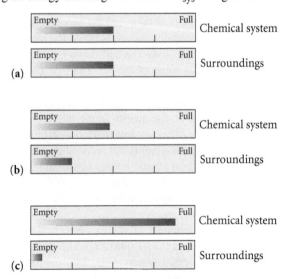

ANSWER: The correct answer is **(a)**. When ΔE_{sys} is negative, energy flows out of the system and into the surroundings. The energy increase in the surroundings must exactly match the decrease in the system.

TABLE 6.3 Sign Conventions for *q*, *w*, and ΔE

q (heat)	+ system *gains* thermal energy	– system *loses* thermal energy
w (work)	+ work done *on* the system	– work done *by* the system
ΔE (change in internal energy)	+ energy flows *into* the system	– energy flows *out* of the system

As we saw earlier, a system can exchange energy with its surroundings through *heat* and *work*:

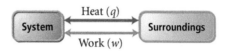

According to the first law of thermodynamics, the change in the internal energy of the system (ΔE) is the sum of the heat transferred (q) and the work done (w):

$$\Delta E = q + w \qquad [6.4]$$

In the above equation, and from this point forward, we follow the standard convention that ΔE (with no subscript) refers to the internal energy change of the *system*. As shown in Table 6.3, energy entering the system through heat or work carries a positive sign, and energy leaving the system through heat or work carries a negative sign. Again, recall the checking account analogy. The system is like the checking account—withdrawals are negative and deposits are positive.

Let's define our system as the previously discussed billiard ball rolling across a pool table. The rolling ball has a certain initial amount of kinetic energy. When it reaches the other end of the table, the rolling ball collides head-on with a second ball. Let's assume that the first ball loses all of its kinetic energy, so that it remains completely still (it has no kinetic energy) at the point of collision. The total change in internal energy (ΔE) for the first ball is the difference between its initial kinetic energy and its final kinetic energy (which is zero); the first billiard ball lost all of its energy. What happened to that energy? According to the first law, it must have been transferred to the surroundings. In fact, the energy lost by the system must *exactly equal* the amount gained by the surroundings.

$$\Delta E_{sys} = -\Delta E_{surr}$$

↑   ↖

Energy lost   Energy gained
by first ball   by surroundings

The surroundings include both the pool table and the second ball. The pool table absorbs some of the ball's kinetic energy as the ball rolls down the table. Minute bumps on the table surface cause friction, which slows the ball down by converting kinetic energy to heat (q). The second ball absorbs some of the ball's kinetic energy in the form of work (w) upon collision.

Although it is always the case that $\Delta E_{sys} = -\Delta E_{surr}$, the exact amount of *work* done on the second ball depends on the quality of the billiard table. On a smooth, high-quality billiard table, the amount of energy lost to friction is relatively small, as shown in Figure 6.6(a) ▸. The speed of the first ball is not reduced by much as it travels across the table and a great deal of its original kinetic energy is available to perform work when it collides with the second ball. In contrast, on a rough, poor-quality table, the ball loses much of its initial kinetic energy as heat, leaving only a relatively small amount available for work, as shown in Figure 6.6(b) ▸.

Notice that the respective amounts of energy converted to heat and work depend on the details of the pool table and the path taken, while the change in internal energy of the rolling ball does not. In other words, since internal energy is a state function, the value of ΔE for the process in which the ball moves across the table and collides with another ball depends only on the ball's initial and final kinetic energy. Work and

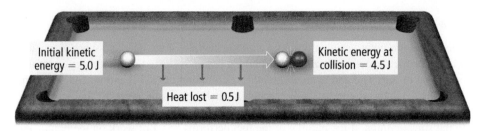

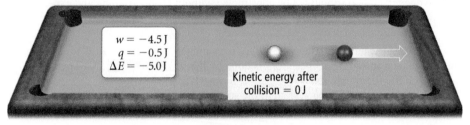

(a) Smooth table

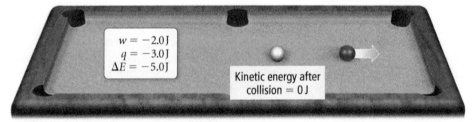

(b) Rough table

heat, however, are *not* state functions; therefore, the values of q and w depend on the details of the ball's journey across the table. On the smooth table, w is greater in magnitude than q; on the rough table, q is greater in magnitude than w. However, ΔE (the sum of q and w) is constant.

Conceptual Connection 6.2 **Heat and Work**

Identify each of the following energy exchanges as heat or work and determine whether the sign of heat or work (relative to the system) is positive or negative.

(a) An ice cube melts and cools the surrounding beverage. (The ice cube is the system.)

(b) A metal cylinder is rolled up a ramp. (The metal cylinder is the system.)

(c) Steam condenses on skin, causing a burn. (The condensing steam is the system.)

ANSWER: **(a)** heat, sign is positive **(b)** work, sign is positive **(c)** heat, sign is negative

EXAMPLE 6.1 Internal Energy, Heat, and Work

The firing of a potato cannon provides a good example of the heat and work associated with a chemical reaction. In a potato cannon, a potato is stuffed into a long cylinder that is capped on one end and open at the other. Some kind of fuel is introduced under the potato at the capped end—usually through a small hole—and ignited. The potato then shoots out of the cannon, sometimes flying hundreds of feet, and the cannon emits heat to the surroundings. If the burning of the fuel performs 855 J of work on the potato and produces 1422 J of heat, what is ΔE for the burning of the fuel? (Note: A potato cannon can be dangerous and should not be constructed without proper training and experience.)

SOLUTION

To solve the problem, substitute the values of q and w into the equation for ΔE. Since work is done by the system on the surroundings, w is negative. Similarly, since heat is released by the system to the surroundings, q is also negative.	$\Delta E = q + w$ $\quad = -1422\ \text{J} - 855\ \text{J}$ $\quad = -2277\ \text{J}$

FOR PRACTICE 6.1

A cylinder and piston assembly (defined as the system) is warmed by an external flame. The contents of the cylinder expand, doing work on the surroundings by pushing the piston outward against the external pressure. If the system absorbs 559 J of heat and does 488 J of work during the expansion, what is the value of ΔE?

6.4 Quantifying Heat and Work

In the previous section, we calculated ΔE based on *given values of q and w*. We now turn to *calculating q (heat) and w (work)* based on changes in temperature and volume.

Heat

As we saw in Section 6.2, *heat* is the exchange of thermal energy between a system and its surroundings caused by a temperature difference. Notice the distinction between heat and temperature. Temperature is a *measure* of the thermal energy within a sample of matter. Heat is the *transfer* of thermal energy. Thermal energy always flows from matter at higher temperatures to matter at lower temperatures. For example, a hot cup of coffee transfers thermal energy—as heat—to the lower temperature surroundings as it cools down. Imagine a world where the cooler surroundings actually got colder as they transferred thermal energy to the hot coffee, which got hotter. Such a world exists only in our imaginations (or in the minds of science fiction writers), because the spontaneous transfer of heat from a hotter object to a colder one is a fundamental principle of our universe—no exception has ever been observed. The thermal energy in the molecules that compose the hot coffee distributes itself to the molecules in the surroundings. The heat transfer from the coffee to the surroundings stops when the two reach the same temperature, a condition called **thermal equilibrium**. At thermal equilibrium, there is no additional net transfer of heat.

The reason for this one-way transfer is related to the second law of thermodynamics, which we discuss in Chapter 17.

Temperature Changes and Heat Capacity When a system absorbs heat (q) its temperature changes by ΔT:

Heat (q) → System

ΔT

Experiments show that the heat absorbed by a system and its corresponding temperature change are directly proportional: $q \propto \Delta T$. The constant of proportionality between q and ΔT is the system's *heat capacity* (C), a measure of the system's ability to absorb thermal energy without undergoing a large change in temperature.

$$q = C \times \Delta T \qquad\qquad [6.5]$$

Heat capacity

Notice that the higher the heat capacity of a system, the smaller the change in temperature for a given amount of absorbed heat. We define the **heat capacity (*C*)** of a system as the quantity of heat required to change its temperature by 1 °C. As we can see by solving Equation 6.5 for heat capacity, the units of heat capacity are those of heat (typically J) divided by those of temperature (typically °C).

$$C = \frac{q}{\Delta T} = \frac{J}{°C}$$

In order to understand two important concepts related to heat capacity, consider putting a steel saucepan on a kitchen flame. The saucepan's temperature rises rapidly as it absorbs heat from the flame. However, if you add some water to the saucepan, the temperature rises more slowly. Why? The first reason is that, when you add the water, the same amount of heat must now warm more matter, so the temperature rises more slowly. In other words, heat capacity is an extensive property—*it depends on the amount of matter being heated* (see Section 1.6). The second (and more fundamental) reason is that *water is more resistant to temperature change than steel*—water has an intrinsically higher capacity to absorb heat without undergoing a large temperature change. The measure of the *intrinsic capacity* of a substance to absorb heat is its **specific heat capacity (*C*ₛ)**, the amount of heat required to raise the temperature of *1 gram* of the substance by 1 °C. The units of specific heat capacity (also called *specific heat*) are $J/g \cdot °C$. Table 6.4 shows the values of the specific heat capacity for several substances. Heat capacity is sometimes reported as **molar heat capacity**, the amount of heat required to raise the temperature of *1 mole* of a substance by 1 °C. The units of molar heat capacity are $J/mol \cdot °C$. You can see from these definitions that *specific* heat capacity and *molar* heat capacity are intensive properties—they depend on the *kind* of substance being heated, not on the amount.

Notice that water has the highest specific heat capacity of all the substances in Table 6.4—changing the temperature of water requires a lot of heat. If you have ever experienced the drop in temperature that occurs when traveling from an inland region to the coast during the summer, you have experienced the effects of water's high specific heat capacity. On a summer's day in California, for example, the temperature difference between Sacramento (an inland city) and San Francisco (a coastal city) can be 18 °C (30 °F)—San Francisco enjoys a cool 20°C (68 °F), while Sacramento bakes at nearly 38 °C (100 °F). Yet the intensity of sunlight falling on these two cities is the same. Why the large temperature difference? San Francisco sits on a peninsula, surrounded by the water of the Pacific Ocean. Water, with its high heat capacity, absorbs much of the sun's heat without undergoing a large increase in temperature, keeping San Francisco cool. Sacramento, by contrast, is about 160 km (100 mi) inland. The land surrounding Sacramento, with its low heat capacity, undergoes a large increase in temperature as it absorbs a similar amount of heat.

Similarly, only two U.S. states have never recorded a temperature above 100 °F. One of them is obvious: Alaska. It is too far north to get that hot. The other one, however, may come as a surprise. It is Hawaii. The high heat capacity of the water that surrounds the only island state moderates the temperature, preventing Hawaii from ever getting too hot.

The specific heat capacity of a substance can be used to quantify the relationship between the amount of heat added to a given amount of the substance and the corresponding temperature increase. The equation that relates these quantities is

$$\text{Heat (J)} \longrightarrow q = m \times C_s \times \Delta T \longleftarrow \begin{array}{l}\text{Temperature}\\ \text{change (°C)}\end{array} \qquad [6.6]$$

$$\underset{\text{Mass (g)}}{\uparrow} \qquad \underset{\substack{\text{Specific heat}\\ \text{capacity } J/g \cdot °C}}{\uparrow}$$

where *q* is the amount of heat in J, *m* is the mass of the substance in g, C_s is the specific heat capacity in $J/g \cdot °C$, and ΔT is the temperature change in °C. The following example demonstrates the use of this equation.

TABLE 6.4 Specific Heat Capacities of Some Common Substances

Substance	Specific Heat Capacity, C_s (J/g · °C)*
Elements	
Lead	0.128
Gold	0.128
Silver	0.235
Copper	0.385
Iron	0.449
Aluminum	0.903
Compounds	
Ethanol	2.42
Water	4.18
Materials	
Glass (Pyrex)	0.75
Granite	0.79
Sand	0.84

*At 298 K.

▲ The high heat capacity of the water surrounding San Francisco results in relatively cool summer temperatures.

ΔT in °C is equal to ΔT in K, but not equal to ΔT in °F (Section 1.6).

EXAMPLE 6.2 Temperature Changes and Heat Capacity

Suppose you find a copper penny (minted before 1982, when pennies were almost entirely copper) in the snow. How much heat is absorbed by the penny as it warms from the temperature of the snow, which is $-8.0\ °C$, to the temperature of your body, $37.0\ °C$? Assume the penny is pure copper and has a mass of 3.10 g.

SORT You are given the mass of copper as well as its initial and final temperature. You are asked to find the heat required for the given temperature change.	**GIVEN:** $m = 3.10$ g copper $T_i = -8.0\ °C$ $T_f = 37.0\ °C$ **FIND:** q
STRATEGIZE The equation $q = m \times C_s \times \Delta T$ gives the relationship between the amount of heat (q) and the temperature change (ΔT).	**CONCEPTUAL PLAN** 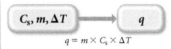 $q = m \times C_s \times \Delta T$ **RELATIONSHIPS USED** $q = m \times C_s \times \Delta T$ (Equation 6.6) $C_s = 0.385\ J/g \cdot °C$ (Table 6.4)
SOLVE Gather the necessary quantities for the equation in the correct units and substitute these into the equation to compute q.	**SOLUTION** $\Delta T = T_f - T_i = 37.0\ °C - (-8.0\ °C) = 45.0\ °C$ $q = m \times C_s \times \Delta T$ $= 3.10\ \text{g} \times 0.385\ \dfrac{J}{g \cdot °C} \times 45.0\ °C = 53.7\ J$

CHECK The units (J) are correct for heat. The sign of q is *positive*, as it should be since the penny *absorbed* heat from the surroundings.

FOR PRACTICE 6.2

To determine whether a shiny gold-colored rock is actually gold, a chemistry student decides to measure its heat capacity. She first weighs the rock and finds it has a mass of 4.7 g. She then finds that upon absorption of 57.2 J of heat, the temperature of the rock rises from 25 °C to 57 °C. Find the specific heat capacity of the substance composing the rock and determine whether the value is consistent with the rock being pure gold.

FOR MORE PRACTICE 6.2

A 55.0-g aluminum block initially at 27.5 °C absorbs 725 J of heat. What is the final temperature of the aluminum?

 Conceptual Connection 6.3 The Heat Capacity of Water

Suppose you are cold-weather camping and decide to heat some objects to bring into your sleeping bag for added warmth. You place a large water jug and a rock of equal mass near the fire. Over time, both the rock and the water jug warm to about 38 °C (100 °F). If you could bring only one into your sleeping bag, which one should you choose to keep you the warmest? Why?

ANSWER: Bring the water; it has the higher heat capacity and will therefore release more heat as it cools.

Thermal Energy Transfer As we noted earlier, when two substances of different temperature are combined, thermal energy flows as heat from the hotter substance to the cooler one. If we assume that the two substances are thermally isolated from everything else, then the heat lost by one substance exactly equals the heat gained by the other (according to the law of energy conservation). If we define one substance as the system and the other as the surroundings, we can quantify the heat exchange as follows:

$$q_{sys} = -q_{surr}$$

Suppose a block of metal initially at 55 °C is submerged into water initially at 25 °C. Thermal energy transfers as heat from the metal to the water:

$$q_{metal} = -q_{water}$$

The metal will get colder and the water will get warmer until the two substances reach the same temperature (thermal equilibrium). The exact temperature change that occurs depends on the masses of the metal and the water and on their specific heat capacities. Since $q = m \times C_s \times \Delta T$ we can arrive at the following relationship:

$$q_{metal} = -q_{water}$$
$$m_{metal} \times C_{s, metal} \times \Delta T_{metal} = -m_{water} \times C_{s, water} \times \Delta T_{water}$$

The following example shows how to work with thermal energy transfer.

EXAMPLE 6.3 Thermal Energy Transfer

A 32.5-g cube of aluminum initially at 45.8 °C is submerged into 105.3 g of water at 15.4 °C. What is the final temperature of both substances at thermal equilibrium? (Assume that the aluminum and the water are thermally isolated from everything else.)

SORT You are given the masses of aluminum and water and their initial temperatures. You are asked to find the final temperature.	**GIVEN:** $m_{Al} = 32.5$ g $m_{H_2O} = 105.3$ g $T_{i, Al} = 45.8$ °C; $T_{i, H_2O} = 15.4$ °C **FIND:** T_f
STRATEGIZE The heat lost by the aluminum (q_{Al}) equals the heat gained by the water (q_{H_2O}). Use the relationship beween q and ΔT and the given variables to find a relationship between ΔT_{Al} and ΔT_{H_2O}. Use the relationship between ΔT_{Al} and ΔT_{H_2O} (that you just found in the previous step) along with the initial temperatures of the aluminum and the water to determine the final temperature. Note that at thermal equilibrium, the final temperature of the aluminum and the water is the same, that is, $T_{f, Al} = T_{f, H_2O} = T_f$	**CONCEPTUAL PLAN** $q_{Al} = -q_{H_2O}$ $m_{Al}, C_{s, Al}, m_{H_2O} C_{s, H_2O} \longrightarrow \Delta T_{Al} = \text{constant} \times \Delta T_{H_2O}$ $m_{Al} \times C_{s, Al} \times \Delta T_{Al} = -m_{H_2O} \times C_{s, H_2O} \times \Delta T_{H_2O}$ $T_{i, Al}; T_{i, H_2O} \longrightarrow T_f$ $\Delta T_{Al} = \text{constant} \times \Delta T_{H_2O}$ **RELATIONSHIPS USED** $C_{s, H_2O} = 4.18$ J/g · °C; $C_{s, Al} = 0.903$ J/g · °C (Table 6.4) $q = m \times C_s \times \Delta T$ (Equation 6.6)
SOLVE Write the equation for the relationship between the heat lost by the aluminum (q_{Al}) and the heat gained by the water (q_{H_2O}) and substitute $q = m \times C_s \times \Delta T$ for each substance. Substitute the values of m (given) and C_s (from Table 6.4) for each substance and solve the equation for ΔT_{Al}. (Alternatively, you can solve the equation for ΔT_{H_2O}.) Substitute the initial temperatures of aluminum and water into the relationship from the previous step and solve the expression for the final temperature (T_f). Remember that the final temperature for both substances will be the same.	**SOLUTION** $q_{Al} = -q_{H_2O}$ $m_{Al} \times C_{s, Al} \times \Delta T_{Al} = -m_{H_2O} \times C_{s, H_2O} \times \Delta T_{H_2O}$ $32.5 \text{ g} \times \dfrac{0.903 \text{ J}}{\text{g} \cdot °C} \cdot \Delta T_{Al} = -105.3 \text{ g} \times \dfrac{4.18 \text{ J}}{\text{g} \cdot °C} \cdot \Delta T_{H_2O}$ $29.3\underline{4}7 \cdot \Delta T_{Al} = -440.1\underline{5} \cdot \Delta T_{H_2O}$ $\Delta T_{Al} = -14.9\underline{9}8 \cdot \Delta T_{H_2O}$ $T_f - T_{i, Al} = -14.9\underline{9}8(T_f - T_{i, H_2O})$ $T_f = -14.9\underline{9}8 \cdot T_f + 14.9\underline{9}8 \cdot T_{i, H_2O} + T_{i, Al}$ $15.9\underline{9}8 \cdot T_f = 14.9\underline{9}8 \cdot T_{i, H_2O} + T_{i, Al}$ $T_f = \dfrac{14.9\underline{9}8 \cdot T_{i, H_2O} + T_{i, Al}}{15.9\underline{9}8} = \dfrac{14.9\underline{9}8 \cdot 15.4 \text{ °C} + 45.8 \text{ °C}}{15.9\underline{9}8}$ $= 17.3$ °C

CHECK The units °C are correct. The final temperature of the mixture is closer to the initial temperature of the *water* than the *aluminum*. This makes sense for two reasons: (1) water has a higher specific heat capacity than aluminum; and (2) there is more water than aluminum. Since the aluminum loses the same amount of heat that is gained by the water, the greater mass and specific heat capacity of the water make the temperature change in the water *less than* the temperature change in the aluminum.

FOR PRACTICE 6.3

A block of copper of unknown mass has an initial temperature of 65.4 °C. The copper is immersed in a beaker containing 95.7 g of water at 22.7 °C. When the two substances reach thermal equilibrium, the final temperature is 24.2 °C. What is the mass of the copper block?

 Conceptual Connection 6.4 Thermal Energy Transfer

Substances A and B, initially at different temperatures, come in contact with each other and reach thermal equilibrium. The mass of substance A is twice the mass of substance B. The specific heat capacity of substance B is twice the specific heat capacity of substance A. Which statement is true about the final temperature of the two substances once thermal equilibrium is reached?

(a) The final temperature will be closer to the initial temperature of substance A than substance B.

(b) The final temperature will be closer to the initial temperature of substance B than substance A.

(c) The final temperature will be exactly midway between the initial temperatures of substance A and B.

ANSWER: **(c)** The specific heat capacity of substance B is twice that of A, but since the mass of B is half that of A, the quantity $m \times C_s$ will be identical for both substances so that the final temperature is exactly midway between the two initial temperatures.

Work: Pressure–Volume Work

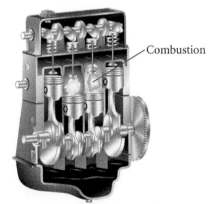

▲ The combustion of gasoline within an engine's cylinders does pressure–volume work that ultimately results in the motion of the car.

Energy transfer between a system and its surroundings can occur via heat (q) or work (w). We just saw how to calculate the *heat* associated with an observed *temperature* change. We now turn to calculating the *work* associated with an observed *volume* change. Although a chemical reaction can do several different types of work, for now we will limit our discussion to **pressure–volume work**. We have already defined work as a force acting through a distance. Pressure–volume work occurs when the force is caused by a volume change against an external pressure. For example, pressure–volume work occurs in the cylinder of an automobile engine. The combustion of gasoline causes gases within the cylinders to expand, pushing the piston outward and ultimately moving the wheels of the car.

We derive an equation for the value of pressure–volume work from the definition of work as a force (F) acting through a distance (D)

$$w = F \times D \qquad [6.7]$$

When the volume of a cylinder increases (Figure 6.7 ▶), it pushes against an external force. That external force is pressure (P), which is defined as force (F) divided by area (A):

> The force in this equation must be a constant force.

$$P = \frac{F}{A} \quad \text{or} \quad F = P \times A$$

If we substitute this expression for force into the definition of work given by Equation 6.7, we arrive at the following:

$$
\begin{aligned}
w &= F \times D \\
&= P \times A \times D
\end{aligned}
$$

The distance through which the force acts is the change in the height of the piston as it moves during the expansion (Δh). Substituting Δh for D, we get

$$w = P \times A \times \Delta h$$

Since the volume of a cylinder is the area of its base times its height, then $A \times \Delta h$ is actually the change in volume (ΔV) that occurs during the expansion. Thus, the expression for work becomes the following:

$$w = P \, \Delta V$$

Still missing from the equation is the *sign* of the work done by the expanding gases. As the volume of the cylinder increases, work is done *on* the surroundings by the system, so w should be negative. However, upon expansion, V_2 (the final volume) is greater than V_1 (the initial volume) so ΔV is positive. In order for w to be negative for a positive expansion, we need to add a negative sign to our equation. In other words, w and ΔV must be opposite in sign.

$$w = -P \, \Delta V \qquad\qquad [6.8]$$

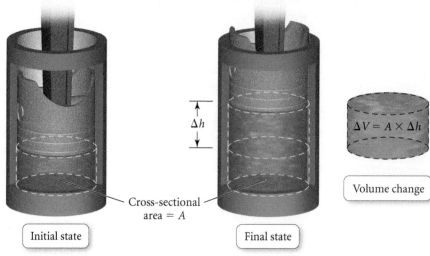

▲ FIGURE 6.7 **Piston Moving within a Cylinder against an External Pressure**

So the work caused by an expansion of volume is the negative of the pressure that the volume expands against multiplied by the change in volume that occurs during the expansion. The units of the work obtained by using this equation are those of pressure (usually atm) multiplied by those of volume (usually L). To convert between L · atm and J, use the conversion factor 101.3 J = 1 L · atm.

EXAMPLE 6.4 Pressure–Volume Work

To inflate a balloon you must do pressure–volume work on the surroundings. If you inflate a balloon from a volume of 0.100 L to 1.85 L against an external pressure of 1.00 atm, how much work is done (in joules)?

SORT You know the initial and final volumes of the balloon and the pressure against which it expands. The balloon and its contents are the system.	**GIVEN:** $V_1 = 0.100$ L, $V_2 = 1.85$ L, $P = 1.00$ atm **FIND:** w
STRATEGIZE The equation $w = -P \, \Delta V$ specifies the amount of work done during a volume change against an external pressure.	**CONCEPTUAL PLAN** $\boxed{P, \Delta V} \longrightarrow \boxed{w}$ $w = -P\,\Delta V$
SOLVE To solve the problem, compute the value of ΔV and substitute it, together with P, into the equation.	**SOLUTION** $\Delta V = V_2 - V_1$ $\quad = 1.85 \text{ L} - 0.100 \text{ L}$ $\quad = 1.75 \text{ L}$ $w = -P \, \Delta V$ $\quad = -1.00 \text{ atm} \times 1.75 \text{ L}$ $\quad = -1.75 \text{ L} \cdot \text{atm}$
Convert the units of the answer (L · atm) to joules using 101.3 J = 1 L · atm.	$-1.75 \text{ L} \cdot \text{atm} \times \dfrac{101.3 \text{ J}}{1 \text{ L} \cdot \text{atm}} = -177 \text{ J}$

CHECK The units (J) are correct for work. The sign of the work is negative, as it should be for an expansion: work is done on the surroundings by the expanding balloon.

FOR PRACTICE 6.4

A cylinder equipped with a piston expands against an external pressure of 1.58 atm. If the initial volume is 0.485 L and the final volume is 1.245 L, how much work (in J) is done?

FOR MORE PRACTICE 6.4

When fuel is burned in a cylinder equipped with a piston, the volume expands from 0.255 L to 1.45 L against an external pressure of 1.02 atm. In addition, 875 J is emitted as heat. What is ΔE for the burning of the fuel?

6.5 Measuring ΔE for Chemical Reactions: Constant-Volume Calorimetry

We now have a complete picture of how a system exchanges energy with its surroundings via heat and pressure–volume work:

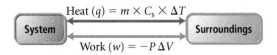

From Section 6.3, we know that the change in internal energy that occurs during a chemical reaction (ΔE) is a measure of *all of the energy* (heat and work) exchanged with the surroundings ($\Delta E = q + w$). Therefore, we can measure the changes in temperature (to calculate heat) and the changes in volume (to calculate work) that occur during a chemical reaction, and then sum them together to calculate ΔE. However, an easier way to obtain the value of ΔE for a chemical reaction is to force all of the energy change associated with a reaction to manifest itself as heat rather than work. We can then measure the temperature change caused by the heat flow.

Recall that $\Delta E = q + w$ and that $w = -P \, \Delta V$. If a reaction is carried out at constant volume, then $\Delta V = 0$ and $w = 0$. The heat evolved (or given off), called the *heat at constant volume* (q_v), is then equal to ΔE_{rxn}.

$$\Delta E_{rxn} = q_v + w \quad \overset{\text{Equals zero}}{\underset{\text{at constant volume}}{}}$$

$$\Delta E_{rxn} = q_v$$

[6.9]

We can measure the heat evolved in a chemical reaction using *calorimetry*. In **calorimetry**, we measure the thermal energy the reaction (defined as the system) and the surroundings exchange by observing the change in temperature of the surroundings.

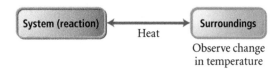

The magnitude of the temperature change in the surroundings depends on the magnitude of ΔE for the reaction and on the heat capacity of the surroundings.

Figure 6.8 ▶ shows a **bomb calorimeter**, a piece of equipment designed to measure ΔE for combustion reactions. In a bomb calorimeter, the reaction occurs in a sealed

The Bomb Calorimeter

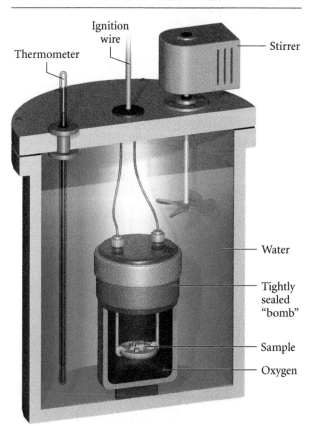

Thermometer

Ignition wire

Stirrer

Water

Tightly sealed "bomb"

Sample

Oxygen

◀ **FIGURE 6.8 The Bomb Calorimeter**
A bomb calorimeter measures changes in internal energy for combustion reactions.

container called a *bomb*, which ensures that the reaction occurs at constant volume. To use a bomb calorimeter, you put the sample to be burned (of known mass) into a cup equipped with an ignition wire. You then seal the cup into the bomb, which is filled with oxygen gas, and place the bomb in a water-filled, insulated container. The container is equipped with a stirrer and a thermometer. Finally, you ignite the sample with a wire coil, and monitor the temperature with the thermometer. The temperature change (ΔT) is related to the heat absorbed by the entire calorimeter assembly (q_{cal}) by the following equation:

$$q_{cal} = C_{cal} \times \Delta T \qquad [6.10]$$

where C_{cal} is the heat capacity of the entire calorimeter assembly (which is usually determined in a separate measurement involving the burning of a substance that gives off a known amount of heat). If no heat escapes from the calorimeter, the amount of heat *gained by* the calorimeter exactly equals that *released by* the reaction (the two are equal in magnitude but opposite in sign):

$$q_{cal} = -q_{rxn} \qquad [6.11]$$

Since the reaction occurs under conditions of constant volume, $q_{rxn} = q_v = \Delta E_{rxn}$. This measured quantity is the change in the internal energy of the reaction for the specific amount of reactant burned. To get ΔE_{rxn} per mole of a particular reactant—a more general quantity—you divide by the number of moles that actually reacted, as shown in the following example.

The heat capacity of the calorimeter, C_{cal}, has units of energy over temperature; its value accounts for all of the heat absorbed by all of the components within the calorimeter (including the water).

EXAMPLE 6.5   Measuring ΔE_{rxn} in a Bomb Calorimeter

When 1.010 g of sucrose ($C_{12}H_{22}O_{11}$) undergoes combustion in a bomb calorimeter, the temperature rises from 24.92 °C to 28.33 °C. Find ΔE_{rxn} for the combustion of sucrose in kJ/mol sucrose. The heat capacity of the bomb calorimeter, determined in a separate experiment, is 4.90 kJ/°C. (You can ignore the heat capacity of the small sample of sucrose because it is negligible compared to the heat capacity of the calorimeter.)

SORT You are given the mass of sucrose, the heat capacity of the calorimeter, and the initial and final temperatures. You are asked to find the change in internal energy for the reaction.	**GIVEN:** 1.010 g $C_{12}H_{22}O_{11}$, T_i = 24.92 °C, T_f = 28.33 °C, C_{cal} = 4.90 kJ/°C **FIND:** ΔE_{rxn}
STRATEGIZE The conceptual plan has three parts. In the first part, use the temperature change and the heat capacity of the calorimeter to find q_{cal}. In the second part, use q_{cal} to get q_{rxn} (which just involves changing the sign). Since the bomb calorimeter ensures constant volume, q_{rxn} is equivalent to ΔE_{rxn} for the amount of sucrose burned. In the third part, divide q_{rxn} by the number of moles of sucrose to get ΔE_{rxn} per mole of sucrose.	**CONCEPTUAL PLAN** 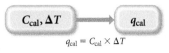 $q_{cal} = C_{cal} \times \Delta T$ q_{cal} → q_{rxn} $q_{rxn} = -q_{cal}$ $\Delta E_{rxn} = \dfrac{q_{rxn}}{\text{mol } C_{12}H_{22}O_{11}}$ **RELATIONSHIPS USED** $q_{cal} = C_{cal} \times \Delta T = -q_{rxn}$ molar mass $C_{12}H_{22}O_{11}$ = 342.3 g/mol
SOLVE Gather the necessary quantities in the correct units and substitute these into the equation to calculate q_{cal}. Find q_{rxn} by taking the negative of q_{cal}. Find ΔE_{rxn} per mole of sucrose by dividing q_{rxn} by the number of moles of sucrose (calculated from the given mass of sucrose and its molar mass).	**SOLUTION** $\Delta T = T_f - T_i$ $= 28.33\ °C - 24.92\ °C = 3.41\ °C$ $q_{cal} = C_{cal} \times \Delta T$ $q_{cal} = 4.90\ \dfrac{kJ}{°C} \times 3.41\ °C = 16.7\ kJ$ $q_{rxn} = -q_{cal} = -16.7\ kJ$ $\Delta E_{rxn} = \dfrac{q_{rxn}}{\text{mol } C_{12}H_{22}O_{11}}$ $= \dfrac{-16.7\ kJ}{1.010\ \text{g } C_{12}H_{22}O_{11} \times \dfrac{1\ \text{mol } C_{12}H_{22}O_{11}}{342.3\ \text{g } C_{12}H_{22}O_{11}}}$ $= -5.66 \times 10^3\ kJ/\text{mol } C_{12}H_{22}O_{11}$

CHECK The units of the answer (kJ) are correct for a change in internal energy. The
~ of ΔE_{rxn} is negative, as it should be for a combustion reaction that gives off energy.

~CE 6.5

~uid hexane (C_6H_{14}) undergoes combustion in a bomb calorimeter,
~m 25.87 °C to 38.13 °C. Find ΔE_{rxn} for the reaction in kJ/mol
~f the bomb calorimeter, determined in a separate experi-

has a ΔE_{rxn} of -3.91×10^3 kJ/mol. When 1.55 g of
combustion in a bomb calorimeter, the temperature rises
C. Find the heat capacity of the bomb calorimeter.

6.6 Enthalpy: The Heat Evolved in a Chemical Reaction at Constant Pressure

We have just seen that when a chemical reaction occurs in a sealed container under conditions of constant volume, the energy evolves only as heat. However, when a chemical reaction occurs open to the atmosphere under conditions of constant pressure—for example, a reaction occurring in an open beaker or the burning of natural gas on a stove—the energy can evolve as both heat and work. As we have also seen, ΔE_{rxn} is a measure of the *total energy change* (both heat and work) that occurs during the reaction. However, in many cases, we are interested only in the heat exchanged, not the work done. For example, when we burn natural gas on a stove to cook food, we do not really care how much work the combustion reaction does on the atmosphere by expanding against it—we just want to know how much heat is given off to cook the food. Under conditions of constant pressure, a thermodynamic quantity called *enthalpy* represents exactly this.

We define the **enthalpy (H)** of a system as the sum of its internal energy and the product of its pressure and volume:

$$H = E + PV \qquad [6.12]$$

Since internal energy, pressure, and volume are all state functions, enthalpy is also a state function. The *change in enthalpy (ΔH)* for any process occurring under constant pressure is given by the following expression:

$$\Delta H = \Delta E + P \, \Delta V \qquad [6.13]$$

To better understand this expression, we can interpret the two terms on the right with the help of relationships already familiar to us. We saw previously that $\Delta E = q + w$. If we represent the heat at constant pressure as q_p, then the change in internal energy at constant pressure is $\Delta E = q_p + w$. In addition, from our definition of pressure–volume work, we know that $P \, \Delta V = -w$. Substituting these expressions into the expression for ΔH gives us

$$\begin{aligned}
\Delta H &= \Delta E + P \, \Delta V \\
&= (q_p + w) + P \, \Delta V \qquad [6.14] \\
&= q_p + w - w \\
\Delta H &= q_p
\end{aligned}$$

We can see that ΔH is equal to q_p, the heat at constant pressure.

Conceptually (and often numerically), ΔH and ΔE are similar: they both represent changes in a state function for the system. However, ΔE is a measure of *all of the energy* (heat and work) exchanged with the surroundings, while ΔH is a measure of only the heat exchanged under conditions of constant pressure. For chemical reactions that do not exchange much work with the surroundings—that is, those that do not cause a large change in reaction volume as they occur—ΔH and ΔE are nearly identical in value. For chemical reactions that produce or consume large amounts of gas, and therefore result in large volume changes, ΔH and ΔE can be slightly different in value.

Conceptual Connection 6.5 The Difference between ΔH and ΔE

Lighters are usually fueled by butane (C_4H_{10}). When 1 mole of butane burns at constant pressure, it produces 2658 kJ of heat and does 3 kJ of work. What are the values of ΔH and ΔE for the combustion of one mole of butane?

ANSWER: ΔH represents only the heat exchanged; therefore $\Delta H = -2658$ kJ. ΔE represents the heat *and work* exchanged; therefore $\Delta E = -2661$ kJ. The signs of both ΔH and ΔE are negative because heat and work are flowing out of the system and into the surroundings. Notice that the values of ΔH and ΔE are similar in magnitude, as is the case for many chemical reactions.

The signs of ΔH and ΔE follow the same conventions. A positive ΔH indicates that heat flows into the system as the reaction occurs. A chemical reaction with a positive ΔH, called an **endothermic reaction**, absorbs heat from its surroundings. A chemical cold pack is a good example of an endothermic reaction. When a barrier separating the

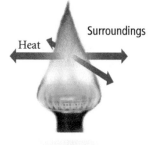

Surroundings   Heat   Heat   Surroundings

Endothermic   Exothermic

▲ The reaction that occurs in a chemical cold pack is endothermic—it absorbs energy from the surroundings. The combustion of natural gas is an exothermic reaction—it releases energy to the surroundings.

reactants in a chemical cold pack is broken, the substances mix, react, and absorb heat from the surroundings. The surroundings—including, say, your bruised wrist—get *colder* because they *lose* energy as the cold pack absorbs it.

A chemical reaction with a negative ΔH, called an **exothermic reaction**, gives off heat to its surroundings. The reaction occurring in the chemical hand warmer discussed in Section 6.1 is a good example of an exothermic reaction. As the reaction occurs, heat is given off into the surroundings (including your hand and glove) making them warmer. The burning of natural gas is another example of an exothermic reaction. As the gas burns, it gives off energy, raising the temperature of its surroundings.

Summarizing Enthalpy:

▶ The value of ΔH for a chemical reaction is the amount of heat absorbed or evolved in the reaction under conditions of constant pressure.

▶ An endothermic reaction has a *positive* ΔH and absorbs heat from the surroundings. An endothermic reaction feels cold to the touch.

▶ An exothermic reaction has a *negative* ΔH and gives off heat to the surroundings. An exothermic reaction feels warm to the touch.

EXAMPLE 6.6   Exothermic and Endothermic Processes

Identify each process as endothermic or exothermic and indicate the sign of ΔH.

(a) sweat evaporating from skin

(b) water freezing in a freezer

(c) wood burning in a fire

SOLUTION

(a) Sweat evaporating from skin cools the skin and is therefore endothermic, with a positive ΔH. The skin must supply heat to the perspiration in order for it to continue to evaporate.

(b) Water freezing in a freezer releases heat and is therefore exothermic, with a negative ΔH. The refrigeration system in the freezer must remove this heat for the water to continue to freeze.

(c) Wood burning in a fire releases heat and is therefore exothermic, with a negative ΔH.

FOR PRACTICE 6.6

Identify each process as endothermic or exothermic and indicate the sign of ΔH.

(a) an ice cube melting

(b) nail polish remover quickly evaporating after it is accidentally spilled on the skin

(c) gasoline burning within the cylinder of an automobile engine

Exothermic and Endothermic Processes: A Molecular View

When a chemical system undergoes a change in enthalpy, where does the energy come from or go to? For example, we just learned that an exothermic chemical reaction gives off *thermal energy*—what is the source of that energy?

First, we know that the emitted thermal energy *does not* come from the original thermal energy of the system. Recall from Section 6.2 that the thermal energy of a system is the composite kinetic energy of the atoms and molecules that compose the system. This kinetic energy *cannot* be the source of the energy given off in an exothermic reaction because, if the atoms and molecules that compose the system were to lose kinetic energy, their temperature would necessarily fall—the system would get colder. Yet, we know that in exothermic reactions, the temperature of the system and the surroundings rises. So there must be some other source of energy.

Recall also from Section 6.2 that the internal energy of a chemical system is the sum of its kinetic energy and its *potential energy*. This potential energy is the source in an exothermic chemical reaction. Under normal circumstances, chemical potential energy (or simply chemical energy) arises primarily from the electrostatic forces between the protons and electrons that compose the atoms and molecules within the system. In an exothermic reaction, some bonds break and new ones form, and the nuclei and electrons reorganize into an arrangement with lower potential energy. As the molecules rearrange, their potential energy converts into thermal energy, the heat emitted in the reaction. In an endothermic reaction, the opposite happens: as some bonds break and others form, the nuclei and electrons reorganize into an arrangement with higher potential energy, absorbing thermal energy in the process.

 Conceptual Connection 6.6 Exothermic and Endothermic Reactions

If an endothermic reaction absorbs heat, then why does it feel cold to the touch?

ANSWER: An endothermic reaction feels cold to the touch because the reaction (acting here as the system) absorbs heat from the surroundings. When you touch the vessel in which the reaction occurs, you, being part of the surroundings, lose heat to the system (the reaction), which makes you feel cold. The heat absorbed by the reaction (from your body, in this case) does not go to increasing its temperature, but rather becomes potential energy stored in chemical bonds.

Stoichiometry Involving ΔH: Thermochemical Equations

The enthalpy change for a chemical reaction, abbreviated ΔH_{rxn}, is also called the **enthalpy of reaction** or **heat of reaction** and is an extensive property, one that depends on the amount of material undergoing the reaction. In other words, the amount of heat generated or absorbed when a chemical reaction occurs depends on the *amounts* of reactants that actually react. We usually specify ΔH_{rxn} in combination with the balanced chemical equation for the reaction. *The magnitude of ΔH_{rxn} is for the stoichiometric amounts of reactants and products for the reaction as written.* For example, the balanced equation and ΔH_{rxn} for the combustion of propane (the main component of LP gas) are as follows:

$$C_3H_8(g) + 5\,O_2(g) \longrightarrow 3\,CO_2(g) + 4\,H_2O(g) \qquad \Delta H_{rxn} = -2044\ \text{kJ}$$

This means that when 1 mol of C_3H_8 reacts with 5 mol of O_2 to form 3 moles of CO_2 and 4 mol of H_2O, 2044 kJ of heat is emitted. We can write these relationships in the same way that we expressed stoichiometric relationships in Chapter 4, as ratios between two quantities. For example, for the reactants, we write:

$$1\ \text{mol}\ C_3H_8 : -2044\ \text{kJ} \qquad \text{or} \qquad 5\ \text{mol}\ O_2 : -2044\ \text{kJ}$$

The ratios indicate that 2044 kJ of heat evolves when 1 mol of C_3H_8 and 5 mol of O_2 completely react. We can use these ratios to construct conversion factors between amounts of

reactants or products and the quantity of heat emitted (for exothermic reactions) or absorbed (for endothermic reactions). To find out how much heat is emitted upon the combustion of a certain mass in grams of C_3H_8, we would use the following conceptual plan:

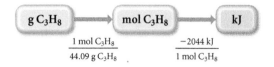

We use the molar mass to convert between grams and moles, and the stoichiometric relationship between moles of C_3H_8 and the heat of reaction to convert between moles and kilojoules, as shown in the following example.

EXAMPLE 6.7 Stoichiometry Involving ΔH

An LP gas tank in a home barbeque contains 13.2 kg of propane, C_3H_8. Calculate the heat (in kJ) associated with the complete combustion of all of the propane in the tank.

$$C_3H_8(g) + 5\,O_2(g) \longrightarrow 3\,CO_2(g) + 4\,H_2O(g) \qquad \Delta H_{rxn} = -2044 \text{ kJ}$$

SORT You are given the mass of propane and asked to find the heat evolved in its combustion.	**GIVEN:** 13.2 kg C_3H_8 **FIND:** q
STRATEGIZE Starting with kg C_3H_8, convert to g C_3H_8 and then use the molar mass of C_3H_8 to find the number of moles. Next, use the stoichiometric relationship between mol C_3H_8 and kJ to find the heat evolved.	**CONCEPTUAL PLAN** 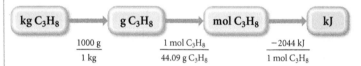 **RELATIONSHIPS USED** 1000 g = 1 kg molar mass C_3H_8 = 44.09 g/mol 1 mol C_3H_8 : −2044 kJ (from balanced equation)
SOLVE Follow the conceptual plan to solve the problem. Begin with 13.2 kg C_3H_8 and multiply by the appropriate conversion factors to arrive at kJ.	**SOLUTION** $13.2 \text{ kg } C_3H_8 \times \dfrac{1000 \text{ g}}{1 \text{ kg}} \times \dfrac{1 \text{ mol } C_3H_8}{44.09 \text{ g } C_3H_8} \times \dfrac{-2044 \text{ kJ}}{1 \text{ mol } C_3H_8}$ $\qquad = -6.12 \times 10^5 \text{ kJ}$

CHECK The units of the answer (kJ) are correct for energy. The answer is negative, as it should be for heat evolved by the reaction.

FOR PRACTICE 6.7

Ammonia reacts with oxygen according to the following equation:

$$4\,NH_3(g) + 5\,O_2(g) \longrightarrow 4\,NO(g) + 6\,H_2O(g) \qquad \Delta H_{rxn} = -906 \text{ kJ}$$

Calculate the heat (in kJ) associated with the complete reaction of 155 g of NH_3.

FOR MORE PRACTICE 6.7

What mass of butane in grams is necessary to produce 1.5×10^3 kJ of heat? What mass of CO_2 is produced?

$$C_4H_{10}(g) + 13/2\,O_2(g) \longrightarrow 4\,CO_2(g) + 5\,H_2O(g) \qquad \Delta H_{rxn} = -2658 \text{ kJ}$$

6.7 Constant-Pressure Calorimetry: Measuring ΔH_{rxn}

For many aqueous reactions, we can measure ΔH_{rxn} fairly simply using a **coffee-cup calorimeter** shown in Figure 6.9 ▶. The calorimeter consists of two Styrofoam coffee cups, one inserted into the other, to provide insulation from the laboratory environment. The calorimeter is equipped with a thermometer and a stirrer. The reaction occurs in a specifically measured quantity of solution within the calorimeter, so that the mass of the solution is known. During the reaction, the heat evolved (or absorbed) causes a temperature change in the solution, which the thermometer measures. If we know the specific heat capacity of the solution, normally assumed to be that of water, we can calculate q_{soln}, the heat absorbed by or lost from the solution (which is acting as the surroundings) using the following equation:

$$q_{soln} = m_{soln} \times C_{s,\,soln} \times \Delta T$$

The insulated calorimeter prevents heat from escaping, so we assume that the heat gained by the solution equals that lost by the reaction (or vice versa):

$$q_{rxn} = -q_{soln}$$

Since the reaction happens under conditions of constant pressure (open to the atmosphere), $q_{rxn} = q_p = \Delta H_{rxn}$. This measured quantity is the heat of reaction for the specific amount (which is measured ahead of time) of reactants that reacted. To get ΔH_{rxn} per mole of a particular reactant—a more general quantity—we divide by the number of moles that actually reacted, as shown in Example 6.8.

Summarizing Calorimetry:

▶ Bomb calorimetry occurs at constant *volume* and measures ΔE for a reaction.

▶ Coffee-cup calorimetry occurs at constant *pressure* and measures ΔH for a reaction.

The Coffee-Cup Calorimeter

— Thermometer

— Glass stirrer

— Cork lid (loose fitting)

— Two nested Styrofoam® cups containing reactants in solution

▲ **FIGURE 6.9 The Coffee-Cup Calorimeter**   A coffee-cup calorimeter measures enthalpy changes for chemical reactions in solution.

This equation assumes that no heat is lost to the calorimeter itself. If heat absorbed by the calorimeter is accounted for, the equation becomes $q_{rxn} = -(q_{soln} + q_{cal})$.

EXAMPLE 6.8 Measuring ΔH_{rxn} in a Coffee-Cup Calorimeter

Magnesium metal reacts with hydrochloric acid according to the following balanced equation:

$$Mg(s) + 2\,HCl(aq) \longrightarrow MgCl_2(aq) + H_2(g)$$

In an experiment to determine the enthalpy change for this reaction, we combine 0.158 g of Mg metal with enough HCl to make 100.0 mL of solution in a coffee-cup calorimeter. The HCl is sufficiently concentrated so that the Mg completely reacts. The temperature of the solution rises from 25.6 °C to 32.8 °C as a result of the reaction. Find ΔH_{rxn} for the reaction as written. Use 1.00 g/mL as the density of the solution and $C_{s,\,soln} = 4.18$ J/g · °C as the specific heat capacity of the solution.

SORT You are given the mass of magnesium, the volume of solution, the initial and final temperatures, the density of the solution, and the heat capacity of the solution. You are asked to find the change in enthalpy for the reaction.	**GIVEN:** 0.158 g Mg 100.0 mL soln $T_i = 25.6$ °C $T_f = 32.8$ °C $d = 1.00$ g/mL, $C_{s,\,soln} = 4.18$ J/g · °C **FIND:** ΔH_{rxn}

STRATEGIZE The conceptual plan has three parts. In the first part, use the temperature change and the other given quantities, together with the equation $q = m \times C_s \times \Delta T$, to find q_{soln}.

In the second part, use q_{soln} to get q_{rxn} (which simply involves changing the sign). Because the pressure is constant, q_{rxn} is equivalent to ΔH_{rxn} for the amount of magnesium that reacted.

In the third part, divide q_{rxn} by the number of moles of magnesium to get ΔH_{rxn} per mole of magnesium.

CONCEPTUAL PLAN

$$q = m \times C_s \times \Delta T$$

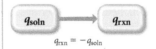

$$q_{rxn} = -q_{soln}$$

$$\Delta H_{rxn} = \frac{q_{rxn}}{\text{mol Mg}}$$

RELATIONSHIPS USED

$$q = m \times C_s \times \Delta T$$
$$q_{rxn} = -q_{soln}$$

SOLVE Gather the necessary quantities in the correct units for the equation $q = m \times C_s \times \Delta T$ and substitute these into the equation to compute q_{soln}. Notice that the sign of q_{soln} is *positive*, meaning that the solution *absorbed heat* from the reaction.

SOLUTION

$$C_{s,\,soln} = 4.18 \text{ J/g} \cdot \degree\text{C}$$

$$m_{soln} = 100.0 \text{ mL soln} \times \frac{1.00 \text{ g}}{1 \text{ mL soln}} = 1.00 \times 10^2 \text{ g}$$

$$\Delta T = T_f - T_i$$
$$= 32.8\,\degree\text{C} - 25.6\,\degree\text{C} = 7.2\,\degree\text{C}$$

$$q_{soln} = m_{soln} \times C_{s,\,soln} \times \Delta T$$

$$= 1.00 \times 10^2 \text{ g} \times 4.18 \frac{\text{J}}{\text{g} \cdot \degree\text{C}} \times 7.2\,\degree\text{C} = 3.0 \times 10^3 \text{ J}$$

Find q_{rxn} by taking the negative of q_{soln}. Notice that q_{rxn} is negative, as expected for an *exothermic* reaction.

$$q_{rxn} = -q_{soln} = -3.0 \times 10^3 \text{ J}$$

Finally, find ΔH_{rxn} per mole of magnesium by dividing q_{rxn} by the number of moles of magnesium that reacted. Find the number of moles of magnesium from the given mass of magnesium and its molar mass.

$$\Delta H_{rxn} = \frac{q_{rxn}}{\text{mol Mg}}$$

$$= \frac{-3.0 \times 10^3 \text{ J}}{0.158 \text{ g Mg} \times \frac{1 \text{ mol Mg}}{24.31 \text{ g Mg}}}$$

$$= -4.6 \times 10^5 \text{ J/mol Mg}$$

Since the stoichiometric coefficient for magnesium in the balanced chemical equation is 1, the computed value represents ΔH_{rxn} for the reaction as written.

$$\text{Mg}(s) + 2\,\text{HCl}(aq) \longrightarrow \text{MgCl}_2(aq) + \text{H}_2(g)$$

$$\Delta H_{rxn} = -4.6 \times 10^5 \text{ J}$$

CHECK The units of the answer (J) are correct for the change in enthalpy of a reaction. The sign is negative, as expected for an exothermic reaction.

FOR PRACTICE 6.8

The addition of hydrochloric acid to a silver nitrate solution precipitates silver chloride according to the following reaction:

$$\text{AgNO}_3(aq) + \text{HCl}(aq) \longrightarrow \text{AgCl}(s) + \text{HNO}_3(aq)$$

When 50.0 mL of 0.100 M AgNO_3 is combined with 50.0 mL of 0.100 M HCl in a coffee-cup calorimeter, the temperature changes from 23.40 °C to 24.21 °C. Calculate ΔH_{rxn} for the reaction as written. Use 1.00 g/mL as the density of the solution and $C = 4.18$ J/g · °C as the specific heat capacity.

Conceptual Connection 6.7 Constant-Pressure versus Constant-Volume Calorimetry

The same reaction, with exactly the same amount of reactant, is conducted in a bomb calorimeter and in a coffee-cup calorimeter. In one of the measurements, $q_{rxn} = -12.5$ kJ and in the other $q_{rxn} = -11.8$ kJ. Which value was obtained in the bomb calorimeter? (Assume that the reaction has a positive ΔV in the coffee-cup calorimeter.)

ANSWER: The value of q_{rxn} with the greater magnitude (–12.5 kJ) must have come from the bomb calorimeter. Recall that $\Delta E_{rxn} = q_{rxn} + w_{rxn}$. In a bomb calorimeter, the energy change that occurs in the course of the reaction all takes the form of heat (q). In a coffee-cup calorimeter, the amount of energy released as heat may be smaller because some of the energy may be used to do work (w).

6.8 Relationships Involving ΔH_{rxn}

The change in enthalpy for a reaction is always associated with a *particular* reaction. If we change the reaction in well-defined ways, then ΔH_{rxn} also changes in well-defined ways. We now turn our attention to three quantitative relationships between a chemical equation and ΔH_{rxn}.

1. **If a chemical equation is multiplied by some factor, then ΔH_{rxn} is also multiplied by the same factor.**

We learned in Section 6.6 that ΔH_{rxn} is an extensive property; it depends on the quantity of reactants undergoing reaction. Recall also that ΔH_{rxn} is usually reported for a reaction involving stoichiometric amounts of reactants. For example, for a reaction $A + 2B \longrightarrow C$, ΔH_{rxn} is typically reported as the amount of heat emitted or absorbed when 1 mol A reacts with 2 mol B to form 1 mol C. Therefore, if a chemical equation is multiplied by a factor, then ΔH_{rxn} is also multiplied by the same factor. For example,

$$A + 2B \longrightarrow C \qquad \Delta H_1$$
$$2A + 4B \longrightarrow 2C \qquad \Delta H_2 = 2 \times \Delta H_1$$

2. **If a chemical equation is reversed, then ΔH_{rxn} changes sign.**

We learned in Section 6.6 that ΔH_{rxn} is a state function, which means that its value depends only on the initial and final states of the system.

$$\Delta H = H_{final} - H_{initial}$$

When a reaction is reversed, the final state becomes the initial state and vice versa. Consequently, ΔH_{rxn} changes sign, as exemplified by the following:

$$A + 2B \longrightarrow C \quad \Delta H_1$$
$$C \longrightarrow A + 2B \quad \Delta H_2 = -\Delta H_1$$

3. **If a chemical equation can be expressed as the sum of a series of steps, then ΔH_{rxn} for the overall equation is the sum of the heats of reactions for each step.**

This last relationship, known as **Hess's law** also follows from the enthalpy of reaction being a state function. Since ΔH_{rxn} is dependent only on the initial and final states, and not on the pathway the reaction follows, then ΔH obtained from summing the individual steps that lead to an overall reaction must be the same as ΔH for that overall reaction. For example,

$$A + 2B \longrightarrow \cancel{C} \qquad \Delta H_1$$
$$\underline{\cancel{C} \longrightarrow 2D \qquad \Delta H_2}$$
$$A + 2B \longrightarrow 2D \qquad \Delta H_3 = \Delta H_1 + \Delta H_2$$

Hess's Law
The change in enthalpy for a stepwise process is the sum of the enthalpy changes of the steps.

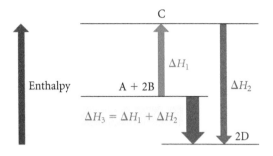

▲ FIGURE 6.10 **Hess's Law**   The change in enthalpy for a stepwise process is the sum of the enthalpy changes of the steps.

We illustrate Hess's law with the energy level diagram shown in Figure 6.10 ◄.

These three quantitative relationships make it possible to determine ΔH for a reaction without directly measuring it in the laboratory. (For some reactions, direct measurement can be difficult.) If we can find related reactions (with known ΔH's) that sum to the reaction of interest, we can find ΔH for the reaction of interest. For example, the following reaction between $C(s)$ and $H_2O(g)$ is an industrially important method of generating hydrogen gas:

$$C(s) + H_2O(g) \longrightarrow CO(g) + H_2(g) \qquad \Delta H_{rxn} = ?$$

We can find ΔH_{rxn} from the following reactions with known ΔH's:

$$C(s) + O_2(g) \longrightarrow CO_2(g) \qquad \Delta H = -393.5 \text{ kJ}$$
$$2\, CO(g) + O_2(g) \longrightarrow 2\, CO_2(g) \qquad \Delta H = -566.0 \text{ kJ}$$
$$2\, H_2(g) + O_2(g) \longrightarrow 2\, H_2O(g) \qquad \Delta H = -483.6 \text{ kJ}$$

We just have to determine how to sum these reactions to get the overall reaction of interest. We do this by manipulating the reactions with known ΔH's in such a way as to get the reactants of interest on the left, the products of interest on the right, and other species to cancel.

Since the first reaction has $C(s)$ as a reactant, and the reaction of interest also has $C(s)$ as a reactant, we write the first reaction unchanged.

$$C(s) + O_2(g) \longrightarrow CO_2(g) \quad \Delta H = -393.5 \text{ kJ}$$

The second reaction has 2 mol of $CO(g)$ as a reactant. However, the reaction of interest has 1 mol of $CO(g)$ as a product. Therefore, we reverse the second reaction, change the sign of ΔH, and multiply the reaction and ΔH by $\frac{1}{2}$.

$$\tfrac{1}{2} \times [2\, CO_2(g) \longrightarrow 2\, CO(g) + O_2(g)]$$
$$\Delta H = \tfrac{1}{2} \times (+566.0 \text{ kJ})$$

The third reaction has $H_2(g)$ as a reactant. In the reaction of interest, however, $H_2(g)$ is a product. Therefore, we reverse the equation and change the sign of ΔH. In addition, to obtain coefficients that match the reaction of interest, and to cancel O_2, we must multiply the reaction and ΔH by $\frac{1}{2}$.

$$\tfrac{1}{2} \times [2\, H_2O(g) \longrightarrow 2\, H_2(g) + O_2(g)]$$
$$\Delta H = \tfrac{1}{2} \times (+483.6 \text{ kJ})$$

Lastly, we rewrite the three reactions after multiplying through by the indicated factors and show how they sum to the reaction of interest. ΔH for the reaction of interest is then just the sum of the ΔH's for the steps.

$$C(s) + \cancel{O_2(g)} \longrightarrow \cancel{CO_2(g)} \qquad\qquad \Delta H = -393.5 \text{ kJ}$$
$$\cancel{CO_2(g)} \longrightarrow CO(g) + \cancel{\tfrac{1}{2} O_2(g)} \qquad \Delta H = +283.0 \text{ kJ}$$
$$H_2O(g) \longrightarrow H_2(g) + \cancel{\tfrac{1}{2} O_2(g)} \qquad \Delta H = +241.8 \text{ kJ}$$
$$\overline{C(s) + H_2O(g) \longrightarrow CO(g) + H_2(g) \qquad \Delta H_{rxn} = +131.3 \text{ kJ}}$$

EXAMPLE 6.9 Hess's Law

Find ΔH_{rxn} for the reaction:

$$3\, C(s) + 4\, H_2(g) \longrightarrow C_3H_8(g)$$

Use these reactions with known ΔH's:

$$C_3H_8(g) + 5\, O_2(g) \longrightarrow 3\, CO_2(g) + 4\, H_2O(g) \qquad \Delta H = -2043 \text{ kJ}$$
$$C(s) + O_2(g) \longrightarrow CO_2(g) \qquad \Delta H = -393.5 \text{ kJ}$$
$$2\, H_2(g) + O_2(g) \longrightarrow 2\, H_2O(g) \qquad \Delta H = -483.6 \text{ kJ}$$

SOLUTION

To work this and other Hess's law problems, manipulate the reactions with known ΔH's in such a way as to get the reactants of interest on the left, the products of interest on the right, and other species to cancel.

The first reaction has C_3H_8 as a reactant, and the reaction of interest has C_3H_8 as a product, so you can reverse the first reaction and change the sign of ΔH.	$3\,CO_2(g) + 4\,H_2O(g) \longrightarrow C_3H_8(g) + 5\,O_2(g) \quad \Delta H = +2043\ kJ$
The second reaction has C as a reactant and CO_2 as a product, just as required in the reaction of interest. However, the coefficient for C is 1, and in the reaction of interest, the coefficient for C is 3. You need to multiply this equation and its ΔH by 3.	$3 \times [C(s) + O_2(g) \longrightarrow CO_2(g)] \quad \Delta H = 3 \times (-393.5\ kJ)$
The third reaction has $H_2(g)$ as a reactant, as required. However, the coefficient for H_2 is 2, and in the reaction of interest, the coefficient for H_2 is 4. Multiply this reaction and its ΔH by 2.	$2 \times [2\,H_2(g) + O_2(g) \longrightarrow 2\,H_2O(g)] \quad \Delta H = 2 \times (-483.6\ kJ)$
Lastly, rewrite the three reactions after multiplying through by the indicated factors and show how they sum to the reaction of interest. ΔH for the reaction of interest is the sum of the ΔH's for the steps.	$3\,CO_2(g) + 4\,H_2O(g) \longrightarrow C_3H_8(g) + 5\,O_2(g) \quad \Delta H = +2043\ kJ$ $3\,C(s) + 3\,O_2(g) \longrightarrow 3\,CO_2(g) \qquad\qquad \Delta H = -1181\ kJ$ $4\,H_2(g) + 2\,O_2(g) \longrightarrow 4\,H_2O(g) \qquad\qquad \Delta H = -967.2\ kJ$ $\overline{3\,C(s) + 4\,H_2(g) \longrightarrow C_3H_8(g) \qquad\qquad \Delta H_{rxn} = -105\ kJ}$

FOR PRACTICE 6.9

Find ΔH_{rxn} for the reaction:

$$N_2O(g) + NO_2(g) \longrightarrow 3\,NO(g)$$

Use these reactions with known ΔH's:

$$2\,NO(g) + O_2(g) \longrightarrow 2\,NO_2(g) \quad \Delta H = -113.1\ kJ$$
$$N_2(g) + O_2(g) \longrightarrow 2\,NO(g) \quad \Delta H = +182.6\ kJ$$
$$2\,N_2O(g) \longrightarrow 2\,N_2(g) + O_2(g) \quad \Delta H = -163.2\ kJ$$

FOR MORE PRACTICE 6.9

Find ΔH_{rxn} for the reaction:

$$3\,H_2(g) + O_3(g) \longrightarrow 3\,H_2O(g)$$

Use these reactions with known ΔH's:

$$2\,H_2(g) + O_2(g) \longrightarrow 2\,H_2O(g) \quad \Delta H = -483.6\ kJ$$
$$3\,O_2(g) \longrightarrow 2\,O_3(g) \quad \Delta H = +285.4\ kJ$$

6.9 Determining Enthalpies of Reaction from Standard Enthalpies of Formation

We have examined two ways to determine ΔH for a chemical reaction: experimentally through calorimetry and inferentially through Hess's law. We now turn to a third and more convenient way to determine ΔH for a large number of chemical reactions: from tabulated *standard enthalpies of formation*.

Standard States and Standard Enthalpy Changes

Recall that ΔH is the *change* in enthalpy for a chemical reaction—the difference in enthalpy between the products and the reactants. Since we are interested in changes in enthalpy (and not in absolute values of enthalpy itself), we are free to define the *zero* of enthalpy as conveniently as possible. Returning to our mountain-climbing analogy, a change in altitude (like a change in enthalpy) is an absolute quantity. Altitude itself (like enthalpy), however, is a relative quantity, defined relative to some standard (such as sea level in the case of altitude). We must define a similar, albeit slightly more complex, standard for

enthalpy. This standard has three parts: the **standard state**, the **standard enthalpy change** ($\Delta H°$), and the **standard enthalpy of formation** ($\Delta H_f°$).

1. **Standard State**
   - *For a Gas:* The standard state for a gas is the pure gas at a pressure of exactly 1 atmosphere.
   - *For a Liquid or Solid:* The standard state for a liquid or solid is the pure substance in its most stable form at a pressure of 1 atm and at the temperature of interest (often taken to be 25 °C).
   - *For a Substance in Solution:* The standard state for a substance in solution is a concentration of exactly 1 M.

2. **Standard Enthalpy Change ($\Delta H°$)**
   - The change in enthalpy for a process when all reactants and products are in their standard states. The degree sign indicates standard states.

3. **Standard Enthalpy of Formation ($\Delta H_f°$)**
   - *For a Pure Compound:* The change in enthalpy when 1 mole of the compound forms from its constituent elements in their standard states.
   - *For a Pure Element in Its Standard State:* $\Delta H_f° = 0$.

> The standard state was changed in 1997 to a pressure of 1 bar, which is very close to 1 atm (1 atm = 1.013 bar). Both standards are now in common use.

The standard enthalpy of formation is also called the **standard heat of formation**.

Assigning the value of zero to the standard enthalpy of formation for an element in its standard state is the equivalent of assigning an altitude of zero to sea level. Once we assume sea level is zero, we can then measure all subsequent changes in altitude relative to sea level. Similarly, we can measure all changes in enthalpy relative to those of pure elements in their standard states. For example, consider the standard enthalpy of formation of methane gas at 25 °C:

$$C(s, \text{graphite}) + 2\,H_2(g) \longrightarrow CH_4(g) \quad \Delta H_f° = -74.6 \text{ kJ/mol}$$

> The carbon in this equation must be graphite (the most stable form of carbon at 1 atm and 25 °C).

For methane, as with most compounds, $\Delta H_f°$ is negative. Continuing our analogy, if we think of pure elements in their standard states as being at *sea level*, then most compounds lie *below sea level*. The chemical equation for the enthalpy of formation of a compound is always written to form 1 mole of the compound, so $\Delta H_f°$ has the units of kJ/mol. Table 6.5 shows $\Delta H_f°$ values for some selected compounds. A more complete list can be found in Appendix IIB.

TABLE 6.5 Standard Enthalpies (or Heats) of Formation, $\Delta H_f°$, at 298 K

Formula	$\Delta H_f°$ (kJ/mol)	Formula	$\Delta H_f°$ (kJ/mol)	Formula	$\Delta H_f°$ (kJ/mol)
Bromine		$C_3H_8O(l, \text{isopropanol})$	−318.1	**Oxygen**	
Br(g)	111.9	$C_6H_6(l)$	49.1	$O_2(g)$	0
$Br_2(l)$	0	$C_6H_{12}O_6(s, \text{glucose})$	−1273.3	$O_3(g)$	142.7
HBr(g)	−36.3	$C_{12}H_{22}O_{11}(s, \text{sucrose})$	−2226.1	$H_2O(g)$	−241.8
Calcium		**Chlorine**		$H_2O(l)$	−285.8
Ca(s)	0	Cl(g)	121.3	**Silver**	
CaO(s)	−634.9	$Cl_2(g)$	0	Ag(s)	0
$CaCO_3(s)$	−1207.6	HCl(g)	−92.3	AgCl(s)	−127.0
Carbon		**Fluorine**		**Sodium**	
C(s, graphite)	0	F(g)	79.38	Na(s)	0
C(s, diamond)	1.88	$F_2(g)$	0	Na(g)	107.5
CO(g)	−110.5	HF(g)	−273.3	NaCl(s)	−411.2
$CO_2(g)$	−393.5	**Hydrogen**		$Na_2CO_3(s)$	−1130.7
$CH_4(g)$	−74.6	H(g)	218.0	$NaHCO_3(s)$	−950.8
$CH_3OH(l)$	−238.6	$H_2(g)$	0	**Sulfur**	
$C_2H_2(g)$	227.4	**Nitrogen**		$S_8(s, \text{rhombic})$	0
$C_2H_4(g)$	52.4	$N_2(g)$	0	$S_8(s, \text{monoclinic})$	0.3
$C_2H_6(g)$	−84.68	$NH_3(g)$	−45.9	$SO_2(g)$	−296.8
$C_2H_5OH(l)$	−277.6	$NH_4NO_3(s)$	−365.6	$SO_3(g)$	−395.7
$C_3H_8(g)$	−103.85	NO(g)	91.3	$H_2SO_4(l)$	−814.0
$C_3H_6O(l, \text{acetone})$	−248.4	$N_2O(g)$	81.6		

EXAMPLE 6.10 Standard Enthalpies of Formation

Write equations for the formation of (a) $MgCO_3(s)$ and (b) $C_6H_{12}O_6(s)$ from their respective elements in their standard states. Include the value of ΔH_f° for each equation.

SOLUTION

(a) $MgCO_3(s)$

Write the equation with the elements in $MgCO_3$ in their standard states as the reactants and 1 mol of $MgCO_3$ as the product.

$$Mg(s) + C(s, \text{graphite}) + O_2(g) \longrightarrow MgCO_3(s)$$

Balance the equation and look up ΔH_f° in Appendix IIB. (Use fractional coefficients so that the product of the reaction is 1 mol of $MgCO_3$.)

$$Mg(s) + C(s, \text{graphite}) + \frac{3}{2} O_2(g) \longrightarrow MgCO_3(s)$$
$$\Delta H_f^\circ = -1095.8 \text{ kJ/mol}$$

(b) $C_6H_{12}O_6(s)$

Write the equation with the elements in $C_6H_{12}O_6$ in their standard states as the reactants and 1 mol of $C_6H_{12}O_6$ as the product.

$$C(s, \text{graphite}) + H_2(g) + O_2(g) \longrightarrow C_6H_{12}O_6(s)$$

Balance the equation and look up ΔH_f° in Appendix IIB.

$$6\,C(s, \text{graphite}) + 6\,H_2(g) + 3\,O_2(g) \longrightarrow C_6H_{12}O_6(s)$$
$$\Delta H_f^\circ = -1273.3 \text{ kJ/mol}$$

FOR PRACTICE 6.10

Write equations for the formation of (a) $NaCl(s)$ and (b) $Pb(NO_3)_2(s)$ from their respective elements in their standard states. Include the value of ΔH_f° for each equation.

Calculating the Standard Enthalpy Change for a Reaction

We have just seen that the standard enthalpy of formation corresponds to the *formation* of a compound from its constituent elements in their standard states:

$$\text{elements} \longrightarrow \text{compound} \quad \Delta H_f^\circ$$

Therefore, the *negative* of the standard enthalpy of formation corresponds to the *decomposition* of a compound into its constituent elements in their standard states.

$$\text{compound} \longrightarrow \text{elements} \quad -\Delta H_f^\circ$$

We can use these two concepts—the decomposing of a compound into its elements and the forming of a compound from its elements—to calculate the enthalpy change of any reaction by mentally taking the reactants through two steps. In the first step we *decompose the reactants* into their constituent elements in their standard states; in the second step we *form the products* from the constituent elements in their standard states.

$$\text{reactants} \longrightarrow \text{elements} \qquad \Delta H_1 = -\Sigma\,\Delta H_f^\circ \text{ (reactants)}$$
$$\underline{\text{elements} \longrightarrow \text{products} \qquad \Delta H_2 = +\Sigma\,\Delta H_f^\circ \text{ (products)}}$$
$$\text{reactants} \longrightarrow \text{products} \qquad \Delta H_{rxn}^\circ = \Delta H_1 + \Delta H_2$$

In these equations, Σ means "the sum of" so that ΔH_1 is the sum of the negatives of the heats of formation of the reactants and ΔH_2 is the sum of the heats of formation of the products.

We can demonstrate this procedure by calculating the standard enthalpy change (ΔH_{rxn}°) for the combustion of methane:

$$CH_4(g) + 2\,O_2(g) \longrightarrow CO_2(g) + 2\,H_2O(g) \quad \Delta H_{rxn}^\circ = ?$$

The energy changes associated with the decomposition of the reactants and the formation of the products are shown in Figure 6.11 ▶ on the next page. The first step (1) is the decomposition of 1 mol of methane into its constituent elements in their standard states. We

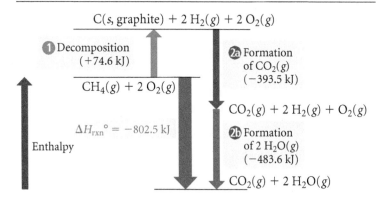

**Calculating the Enthalpy Change
for the Combustion of Methane**

$C(s, \text{graphite}) + 2\,H_2(g) + 2\,O_2(g)$

① Decomposition
(+74.6 kJ)

②a Formation
of $CO_2(g)$
(−393.5 kJ)

$CH_4(g) + 2\,O_2(g)$

$CO_2(g) + 2\,H_2(g) + O_2(g)$

$\Delta H_{rxn}° = -802.5$ kJ

Enthalpy

②b Formation
of 2 $H_2O(g)$
(−483.6 kJ)

$CO_2(g) + 2\,H_2O(g)$

► FIGURE 6.11 **Calculating the
Enthalpy Change for the Combustion of Methane**

can obtain the change in enthalpy for this step by reversing the enthalpy of formation equation for methane and changing the sign of $\Delta H_f°$:

$$(1)\ CH_4(g) \longrightarrow C(s, \text{graphite}) + 2\,H_2(g) \qquad -\Delta H_f° = +74.6\ \text{kJ/mol}$$

The second step, the formation of the products from their constituent elements, has two parts: (a) the formation of 1 mol CO_2 and (b) the formation of 2 mol H_2O. Since part (b) forms 2 mol H_2O, we multiply the $\Delta H_f°$ for that step by 2.

$$(2a)\ C(s, \text{graphite}) + O_2(g) \longrightarrow CO_2(g) \qquad \Delta H_f° = -393.5\ \text{kJ/mol}$$

$$(2b)\ 2 \times [H_2(g) + \tfrac{1}{2}\,O_2(g) \longrightarrow H_2O(g)] \quad 2 \times \Delta H_f° = 2 \times (-241.8\ \text{kJ/mol})$$

As we know from Hess's law, the enthalpy of reaction for the overall reaction is the sum of the enthalpies of reaction of the individual steps:

$$
\begin{aligned}
(1)\ &CH_4(g) \longrightarrow \cancel{C(s,\text{graphite})} + \cancel{2\,H_2(g)} & -\Delta H_f° &= +74.6\ \text{kJ/mol}\\
(2a)\ &\cancel{C(s,\text{graphite})} + O_2(g) \longrightarrow CO_2(g) & \Delta H_f° &= -393.5\ \text{kJ/mol}\\
(2b)\ &\cancel{2\,H_2(g)} + O_2(g) \longrightarrow 2\,H_2O(g) & 2 \times \Delta H_f° &= -483.6\ \text{kJ/mol}\\
\hline
&CH_4(g) + 2\,O_2(g) \longrightarrow CO_2(g) + 2\,H_2O(g) & \Delta H_{rxn}° &= -802.5\ \text{kJ/mol}
\end{aligned}
$$

We can streamline and generalize this process as follows:

To calculate $\Delta H_{rxn}°$, subtract the enthalpies of formation of the reactants multiplied by their stoichiometric coefficients from the enthalpies of formation of the products multiplied by their stoichiometric coefficients.

In the form of an equation,

$$\Delta H_{rxn}° = \Sigma\, n_p \Delta H_f° \text{ (products)} - \Sigma\, n_r \Delta H_f° \text{ (reactants)} \qquad [6.15]$$

In this equation, n_p represents the stoichiometric coefficients of the products, n_r represents the stoichiometric coefficients of the reactants, and $\Delta H_f°$ represents the standard enthalpies of formation. Keep in mind when using this equation that elements in their standard states have $\Delta H_f° = 0$. The following examples demonstrate this process.

EXAMPLE 6.11 ΔH°_{rxn} and Standard Enthalpies of Formation

Use the standard enthalpies of formation to determine ΔH°_{rxn} for the reaction:

$$4\ NH_3(g) + 5\ O_2(g) \longrightarrow 4\ NO(g) + 6\ H_2O(g)$$

SORT You are given the balanced equation and asked to find the enthalpy of reaction.	**GIVEN:** $4\ NH_3(g) + 5\ O_2(g) \longrightarrow 4\ NO(g) + 6\ H_2O(g)$ **FIND:** ΔH°_{rxn}
STRATEGIZE To calculate ΔH°_{rxn} from standard enthalpies of formation, subtract the heats of formation of the reactants multiplied by their stoichiometric coefficients from the heats of formation of the products multiplied by their stoichiometric coefficients.	**CONCEPTUAL PLAN** $\Delta H^\circ_{rxn} = \Sigma\ n_p\ \Delta H^\circ_f\ (\text{products}) - \Sigma\ n_r \Delta H^\circ_f\ (\text{reactants})$

SOLVE Begin by looking up (in Appendix IIB) the standard enthalpy of formation for each reactant and product. Remember that the standard enthalpy of formation of pure elements in their standard state is zero. Compute ΔH°_{rxn} by substituting into the equation.

SOLUTION

Reactant or product	ΔH°_f (kJ/mol, from Appendix IIB)
$NH_3(g)$	−45.9
$O_2(g)$	0.0
$NO(g)$	+91.3
$H_2O(g)$	−241.8

$\Delta H^\circ_{rxn} = \Sigma\ n_p \Delta H^\circ_f\ (\text{products}) - \Sigma\ n_r \Delta H^\circ_f\ (\text{reactants})$

$\quad = [4(\Delta H^\circ_{f,\ NO(g)}) + 6(\Delta H^\circ_{f,\ H_2O(g)})] - [4(\Delta H^\circ_{f,\ NH_3(g)}) + 5(\Delta H^\circ_{f,\ O_2(g)})]$

$\quad = [4(+91.3\ kJ) + 6(-241.8\ kJ)] - [4(-45.9\ kJ) + 5(0.0\ kJ)]$

$\quad = -1085.6\ kJ - (-183.6\ kJ)$

$\quad = -902.0\ kJ$

CHECK The units of the answer (kJ) are correct. The answer is negative, which means that the reaction is exothermic.

FOR PRACTICE 6.11

The thermite reaction, in which powdered aluminum reacts with iron oxide, is highly exothermic.

$$2\ Al(s) + Fe_2O_3(s) \longrightarrow Al_2O_3(s) + 2\ Fe(s)$$

Use standard enthalpies of formation to find ΔH°_{rxn} for the thermite reaction.

▶ The reaction of powdered aluminum with iron oxide, known as the thermite reaction, releases a large amount of heat.

EXAMPLE 6.12 ΔH°_{rxn} and Standard Enthalpies of Formation

A city of 100,000 people uses approximately 1.0×10^{11} kJ of energy per day. Suppose all of that energy comes from the combustion of liquid octane (C_8H_{18}) to form gaseous water and gaseous carbon dioxide. Use standard enthalpies of formation to calculate ΔH°_{rxn} for the combustion of octane and then determine how many kilograms of octane would be necessary to provide this amount of energy.

SORT You are given the amount of energy used and asked to find the mass of octane required to produce the energy.

GIVEN: 1.0×10^{11} kJ
FIND: kg C_8H_{18}

STRATEGIZE The conceptual plan has three parts. In the first part, write a balanced equation for the combustion of octane.

In the second part, calculate ΔH°_{rxn} from the ΔH°_f's of the reactants and products.

In the third part, convert from kilojoules of energy to moles of octane using the conversion factor found in step 2, and then convert from moles of octane to mass of octane using the molar mass.

CONCEPTUAL PLAN
(1) Write balanced equation.

(2)

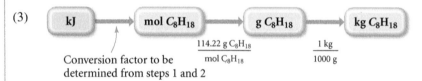

$\Delta H^\circ_{rxn} = \Sigma\, n_p \Delta H^\circ_f \,(\text{products}) - \Sigma\, n_r \Delta H^\circ_f \,(\text{reactants})$

(3)

$$ \boxed{kJ} \longrightarrow \boxed{mol\ C_8H_{18}} \longrightarrow \boxed{g\ C_8H_{18}} \longrightarrow \boxed{kg\ C_8H_{18}} $$

$\dfrac{114.22\ \text{g}\ C_8H_{18}}{\text{mol}\ C_8H_{18}} \qquad \dfrac{1\ \text{kg}}{1000\ \text{g}}$

Conversion factor to be determined from steps 1 and 2

RELATIONSHIPS USED
molar mass C_8H_{18} = 114.22 g/mol
1 kg = 1000 g

SOLVE Begin by writing the balanced equation for the combustion of octane.
For convenience, do not clear the 25/2 fraction in order to keep the coefficient on octane as 1.

SOLUTION STEP 1
$$C_8H_{18}(l) + 25/2\ O_2(g) \longrightarrow 8\ CO_2(g) + 9\ H_2O(g)$$

Look up (in Appendix IIB) the standard enthalpy of formation for each reactant and product and then calculate ΔH°_{rxn}.

SOLUTION STEP 2

Reactant or product	ΔH°_f (kJ/mol from Appendix IIB)
$C_8H_{18}(l)$	−250.1
$O_2(g)$	0.0
$CO_2(g)$	−393.5
$H_2O(g)$	−241.8

$\Delta H^\circ_{rxn} = \Sigma\, n_p \Delta H^\circ_f \,(\text{products}) - \Sigma\, n_r \Delta H^\circ_f \,(\text{reactants})$

$\quad = [8(\Delta H^\circ_{f,\ CO_2(g)}) + 9(\Delta H^\circ_{f,\ H_2O(g)})]$

$\qquad\qquad - \left[1(\Delta H^\circ_{f,\ C_8H_{18}(l)}) + + \dfrac{25}{2}(\Delta H^\circ_{f,\ O_2(g)}) \right]$

$\quad = [8(-393.5\ \text{kJ}) + 9(-241.8\ \text{kJ})] - \left[1(-250.1\ \text{kJ}) + \dfrac{25}{2}(0.0\ \text{kJ}) \right]$

$\quad = -5324.2\ \text{kJ} - (-250.1\ \text{kJ})$

$\quad = -5074.1\ \text{kJ}$

	SOLUTION STEP 3
From steps 1 and 2 build a conversion factor between mol C_8H_{18} and kJ.	1 mol C_8H_{18} : -5074.1 kJ
Follow step 3 of the conceptual plan. Begin with -1.0×10^{11} kJ (since the city uses this much energy, the reaction must emit it, and therefore the sign is negative) and follow the steps to determine kg octane.	-1.0×10^{11} kJ $\times \dfrac{1 \text{ mol } C_8H_{18}}{-5074.1 \text{ kJ}} \times \dfrac{114.22 \text{ g } C_8H_{18}}{1 \text{ mol } C_8H_{18}}$ $\times \dfrac{1 \text{ kg}}{1000 \text{ g}} = 2.3 \times 10^6$ kg C_8H_{18}

CHECK   The units of the answer (kg C_8H_{18}) are correct. The answer is positive, as it should be for mass. The magnitude is fairly large, as you would expect since this amount of octane is supposed to provide the energy for an entire city.

FOR PRACTICE 6.12
The chemical hand warmers described in Section 6.1 produce heat when they are removed from their airtight plastic wrappers. Recall that they utilize the oxidation of iron to form iron oxide according to the reaction: $4 \, Fe(s) + 3 \, O_2(g) \longrightarrow 2 \, Fe_2O_3(s)$. Calculate $\Delta H°_{rxn}$ for this reaction and compute how much heat is produced from a hand warmer containing 15.0 g of iron powder.

6.10 Energy Use and the Environment

In this chapter, we have learned about the relationship between chemical reactions and energy changes. As noted earlier, our society derives the majority of its energy from the energy changes associated with burning fossil fuels. Fossil fuels have traditionally been regarded as convenient sources of energy due to their abundance and portability, and because they undergo combustion reactions that have large negative enthalpies of reaction (the reactions are highly exothermic). However, the burning of fossil fuels also has some serious environmental impacts, to which we now turn our attention.

Energy Consumption

According to the U.S. Department of Energy, the United States currently consumes close to 100 quads (1 quad = 1 quadrillion British thermal units = 1.06×10^{18} J) of energy per year in the categories shown in this chart.

This corresponds to over 100,000 kWh of energy use per person per year. If you used physical laborers to do the equivalent amount of work, you would need about 120 people. In other words, the average American employs the work output of 120 people, day and night, all year long! For this reason, Americans enjoy one of the highest standards of living in the world. As we learned earlier in the chapter, when it comes to energy, there is no free lunch. Our consumption of energy has significant environmental consequences.

■ Residential: 18%
■ Commercial: 18%
  Industrial: 34%
■ Transportation: 30%

Source: U.S. Energy Information Administration, Monthly Energy Review, October 2008.

Most U.S. energy comes from the combustion of fossil fuels, as shown in Figure 6.12 ▶ on the next page. Fossil fuels include petroleum, natural gas, and coal, all of which have been considered convenient fuels because they are relatively abundant in Earth's crust (and therefore relatively inexpensive), they are easily transportable, and their combustion is highly exothermic. The reactions for the combustion of the main or representative components of several fossil fuels, and the associated enthalpies of reaction, are

Coal: $C(s) + O_2(g) \longrightarrow CO_2(g)$ $\Delta H°_{rxn} = -393.5$ kJ

Natural gas: $CH_4(g) + 2 \, O_2(g) \longrightarrow CO_2(g) + 2 \, H_2O(g)$ $\Delta H°_{rxn} = -802.3$ kJ

Petroleum: $C_8H_{18}(l) + 25/2 \, O_2(g) \longrightarrow 8 \, CO_2(g) + 9 \, H_2O(g)$ $\Delta H°_{rxn} = -5074.1$ kJ

▶ **FIGURE 6.12 Energy Consumption by Source**   Source: U.S. Energy Information Administration, Annual Energy Review, 2007.

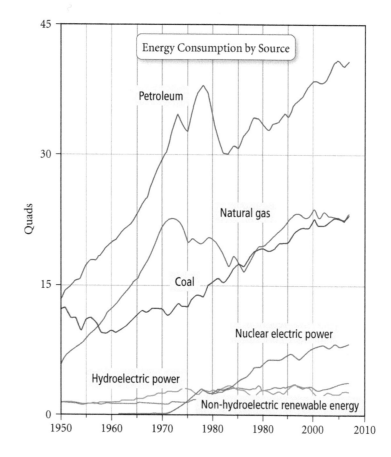

Environmental Problems Associated with Fossil Fuel Use

One of the main problems associated with the burning of fossil fuels is that, even though they are abundant in Earth's crust, they are also finite. Fossil fuels originate from ancient plant and animal life and are a nonrenewable energy source—once they are all burned, they cannot be replenished. At current rates of consumption, oil and natural gas supplies will be depleted in 50 to 100 years. While there is enough coal to last much longer, it is a dirtier fuel and, because it is a solid, is less convenient (more difficult to transport and use) than petroleum and natural gas.

The other major problems associated with fossil fuel use stem from the products of combustion. The chemical equations shown here for fossil fuel combustion all produce carbon dioxide and water. However, these equations represent the reactions under ideal conditions and do not account for impurities in the fuel, side reactions, and incomplete combustion. When these are taken into account, we can identify three major environmental problems associated with the emissions of fossil fuel combustion: air pollution, acid rain, and global climate change. We discussed air pollution in the previous chapter (see Section 5.11), and acid rain in Chapter 3 (see *Chemistry in the Environment: Acid Rain* in Section 3.6). Here we will address global climate change, which we first touched on in Section 4.1.

▼ **FIGURE 6.13 The Rise in Atmospheric Carbon Dioxide**
Atmospheric carbon dioxide levels have been steadily increasing as a result of fossil fuel combustion.

One of the main products of fossil fuel combustion is carbon dioxide (CO_2). Carbon dioxide is a greenhouse gas; it allows visible light from the sun to enter Earth's atmosphere but prevents heat (in the form of infrared light) from escaping. In doing so, carbon dioxide acts as a blanket, keeping Earth warm, which, in moderation, is a very good thing and allows life as we know it to exist on our planet. However, because of fossil fuel combustion, carbon dioxide levels in the atmosphere have been steadily increasing, as shown in Figure 6.13 ◄. This increase is expected to change the global climate and raise Earth's average temperature. Current observations suggest that Earth has already warmed by about 0.6 °C in the last century, due to an approximately 25% increase in atmospheric carbon dioxide. Computer models suggest that the warming

Atmospheric Carbon Dioxide

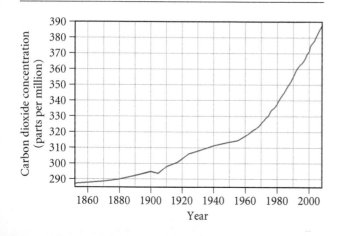

could worsen if carbon dioxide emissions are not curbed. The possible effects of this warming include heightened storm severity, increasing numbers of floods and droughts, major shifts in agricultural zones, rising sea levels and coastal flooding, and profound changes in habitats that could result in the extinction of some plant and animal species.

EXAMPLE 6.13 Fossil Fuels and Climate Change

One way to evaluate fuels with respect to global warming is to determine how much heat they release during combustion relative to how much CO_2 they produce. The greater the heat relative to the amount of CO_2, the better the fuel. Use the combustion reactions of carbon, natural gas, and octane, in combination with the enthalpy of combustion for each reaction (all given earlier), to calculate the heat (in kJ) released by each fuel per 1.00 kg of CO_2 produced.

SORT You are given the mass of CO_2 emitted and asked to find the energy output for three different fuels.	**GIVEN:** 1.00 kg CO_2 **FIND:** kJ
STRATEGIZE You must first write the thermochemical equations for the combustion of each fuel given earlier in the chapter.	$C(s) + O_2(g) \longrightarrow CO_2(g)$ $\Delta H^\circ_{rxn} = -393.5$ kJ $CH_4(g) + 2\,O_2(g) \longrightarrow CO_2(g) + 2\,H_2O(g)$ $\Delta H^\circ_{rxn} = -802.3$ kJ $C_8H_{18}(l) + 25/2\,O_2(g) \longrightarrow 8\,CO_2(g) + 9\,H_2O(g)$ $\Delta H^\circ_{rxn} = -5074.1$ kJ
The conceptual plan has two parts. In the first part, use the molar mass of CO_2 to convert from mass of CO_2 to moles of CO_2. This step is the same for each fuel.	**CONCEPTUAL PLAN** 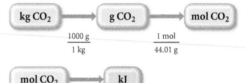
In the second part, use the stoichiometric relationship between moles of CO_2 produced and kilojoules of energy released to calculate the energy output. Repeat the second part for each fuel using the appropriate stoichiometric relationship from the balanced equations.	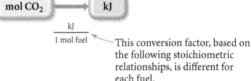 This conversion factor, based on the following stoichiometric relationships, is different for each fuel. **STOICHIOMETRIC RELATIONSHIPS** For C: 1 mol CO_2 : -393.5 kJ For CH_4: 1 mol CO_2 : -802.3 kJ For C_8H_{18}: 8 mol CO_2 : -5074.1 kJ **OTHER RELATIONSHIPS USED** 1 kg = 1000 g molar mass CO_2 = 44.01 g/mol
SOLVE Begin by converting kg CO_2 to mol CO_2. Then, for each fuel, convert mol CO_2 to kJ. As you can see from the heat released in the production of 1 kg CO_2, CH_4 provides the most energy per kg CO_2; therefore, it is the best fuel with respect to climate change.	**SOLUTION** $1.00 \text{ kg } CO_2 \times \dfrac{1000 \text{ g}}{1 \text{ kg}} \times \dfrac{1 \text{ mol } CO_2}{44.01 \text{ g } CO_2} = 22.72 \text{ mol } CO_2$ For C: $22.72 \text{ mol } CO_2 \times \dfrac{-393.5 \text{ kJ}}{1 \text{ mol } CO_2} = -8.94 \times 10^3 \text{ kJ}$ For CH_4: $22.72 \text{ mol } CO_2 \times \dfrac{-802.3 \text{ kJ}}{1 \text{ mol } CO_2} = -1.82 \times 10^4 \text{ kJ}$ For C_8H_{18}: $22.72 \text{ mol } CO_2 \times \dfrac{-5074.1 \text{ kJ}}{8 \text{ mol } CO_2} = -1.44 \times 10^4 \text{ kJ}$

CHECK Each answer is in kJ, as it should be for heat produced. Each answer is negative, as expected for exothermic combustion reactions.

FOR PRACTICE 6.13

What mass of CO_2 (in kg) does the combustion of a 15-gallon tank of gasoline release into the atmosphere? Assume the gasoline is pure octane (C_8H_{18}) and that it has a density of 0.70 g/mL.

CHEMISTRY IN THE ENVIRONMENT **Renewable Energy**

Because of their finite supply and environmental impacts, fossil fuels will not be our major source of energy in the future. What will replace them? Although the answer is not clear, several alternative energy technologies are beginning to emerge. Unlike fossil fuels, these technologies are renewable, and we can use them indefinitely.

Our planet's greatest source of renewable energy is the sun. If we could capture and harness just a small fraction of the total sunlight falling on Earth, we could meet our energy needs several times over. The main problem with solar energy, however, is diffuseness—the sun's energy falls over an enormous area. How do we concentrate and store it? In California, some of the state's electricity is generated by parabolic troughs, solar power towers, and dish/engines.

These devices use reflective surfaces to focus the sun's energy and produce enough heat to generate electricity. Although the direct cost of generating electricity this way is higher than using fossil fuels, the benefits to the environment are obvious. In addition, with time, the costs are expected to fall.

Another way to capture the sun's energy is in chemical bonds. For example, solar energy could be used to drive the decomposition of water:

$$H_2O(l) \longrightarrow H_2(g) + \tfrac{1}{2} O_2(g) \quad \Delta H^\circ_{rxn} = +285.8 \text{ kJ}$$

The hydrogen gas produced could be stored until needed to provide energy by re-forming water in the reverse reaction:

$$H_2(g) + \tfrac{1}{2} O_2(g) \longrightarrow H_2O(l) \quad \Delta H^\circ_{rxn} = -285.8 \text{ kJ}$$

This reaction can be carried out in an electrochemical device called a fuel cell. In a fuel cell, hydrogen and oxygen gas combine to form water and produce electricity. In 2005, General Motors demonstrated the Sequel: a fuel cell SUV with a 300-mile range and quick acceleration (0–60 mph in 10 seconds). According to the company, the Sequel is quicker, easier to handle, easier to build, and safer than gasoline-powered vehicles, and its only emission is water vapor. In 2008, Honda's FCX Clarity, a four-passenger fuel cell vehicle with a 280-mile range, became selectively available for lease in Southern California. The main challenge for these vehicles at

the moment is refueling. The FCX requires hydrogen fuel, which can only be obtained at a small number of refueling stations. Other automakers have similar prototype models in development.

Other renewable energy sources are wind power and hydroelectric

▲ Honda made its 2009 FCX Clarity, a fuel cell vehicle that runs on hydrogen gas and produces only water as exhaust, selectively available for lease in Southern California in the summer of 2008.

power. Hydroelectric power plants—which generate approximately 8% of U.S. electricity—harness the gravitational potential energy of water held behind a dam. Water is released at a controlled rate. As it falls, it acquires kinetic energy that is used to spin a turbine, generating electricity. Wind power plants—which produced about 2.3% of California's electricity in 2007—consist of hundreds of turbines that are spun by the wind to generate electricity. Both of these technologies are cost competitive with fossil fuels, have no emissions, and are completely renewable.

Our energy future will probably involve a combination of these technologies and some new ones, combined with a focus on greater efficiency and conservation. One thing, however, is clear—the future of fossil fuels is limited.

▲ Wind turbines such as these generate about 2.3% of California's electricity.

▼ The sun's energy, concentrated by reflective surfaces in various arrangements, can produce enough heat to generate electricity.

Parabolic troughs

Solar power tower

Dish/engine

CHAPTER IN REVIEW

Key Terms

Section 6.1
thermochemistry (231)

Section 6.2
energy (232)
work (232)
heat (232)
kinetic energy (232)
thermal energy (232)
potential energy (232)
chemical energy (232)
law of conservation of
  energy (232)
system (233)
surroundings (233)

joule (J) (234)
calorie (cal) (234)
Calorie (Cal) (234)
kilowatt-hour (kWh) (234)

Section 6.3
thermodynamics (234)
first law of thermodynamics
  (234)
internal energy (E) (235)
state function (235)

Section 6.4
thermal equilibrium (240)
heat capacity (C) (241)

specific heat capacity (C_s)
  (241)
molar heat capacity (241)
pressure–volume work (244)

Section 6.5
calorimetry (246)
bomb calorimeter (246)

Section 6.6
enthalpy (H) (249)
endothermic reaction (249)
exothermic reaction (250)
enthalpy (heat) of reaction
  (ΔH_{rxn}) (251)

Section 6.7
coffee-cup calorimeter (253)

Section 6.8
Hess's law (255)

Section 6.9
standard state (258)
standard enthalpy change
  ($\Delta H°$) (258)
standard enthalpy of formation
  ($\Delta H_f°$) (258)
standard heat of formation
  (258)

Key Concepts

The Nature of Energy and Thermodynamics (6.2, 6.3)

Energy, which is measured in the SI unit of joules (J), is the capacity to do work. Work is the result of a force acting through a distance. Many different kinds of energy exist, including kinetic energy, thermal energy, potential energy, and chemical energy, a type of potential energy associated with the relative positions of electrons and nuclei in atoms and molecules. According to the first law of thermodynamics, energy can be converted from one form to another, but the total amount of energy is always conserved.

The internal energy (E) of a system is the sum of all of its kinetic and potential energy. Internal energy is a state function, which means that it depends only on the state of the system and not on the pathway by which it got to that state. A chemical system exchanges energy with its surroundings through heat (the transfer of thermal energy caused by a temperature difference) or work. The total change in internal energy is the sum of these two quantities.

Heat and Work (6.4)

Heat can be quantified using the equation $q = m \times C_s \times \Delta T$. In this expression, C_s is the specific heat capacity, the amount of heat required to change the temperature of 1 g of the substance by 1 °C. Compared to most substances, water has a very high heat capacity—it takes a lot of heat to change its temperature.

The type of work most characteristic of chemical reactions is pressure–volume work, which occurs when a gas expands against an external pressure. Pressure–volume work can be quantified with the equation $w = -P\Delta V$. The change in internal energy (ΔE) that occurs during a chemical reaction is the sum of the heat (q) exchanged and the work (w) done: $\Delta E = q + w$.

Enthalpy (6.6)

The heat evolved in a chemical reaction occurring at constant pressure is called the change in enthalpy (ΔH) for the reaction. Like internal energy, enthalpy is a state function. An endothermic reaction has a positive enthalpy of reaction, whereas an exothermic reaction has a negative enthalpy of reaction. The enthalpy of reaction can be used to determine stoichiometrically the heat evolved when a specific amount of reactant reacts.

Calorimetry (6.5, 6.7)

Calorimetry is a method of measuring ΔE or ΔH for a reaction. In bomb calorimetry, the reaction is carried out under conditions of constant volume, so $\Delta E = q_v$. The temperature change of the calorimeter can therefore be used to calculate ΔE for the reaction. When a reaction takes place at constant pressure, energy may be released both as heat and as work. In coffee-cup calorimetry, a reaction is carried out under atmospheric pressure in a solution, so $q = \Delta H$. The temperature change of the solution is then used to calculate ΔH for the reaction.

Calculating ΔH_{rxn} (6.8, 6.9)

The enthalpy of reaction (ΔH_{rxn}) can be calculated from known thermochemical data in two ways. The first method involves using the following relationships: (a) when a reaction is multiplied by a factor, ΔH_{rxn} is multiplied by the same factor; (b) when a reaction is reversed, ΔH_{rxn} changes sign; and (c) if a chemical reaction can be expressed as a sum of two or more steps, ΔH_{rxn} is the sum of the ΔH's for the individual steps (Hess's law). Together, these relationships can be used to determine the enthalpy change of an unknown reaction from reactions with known enthalpy changes. The second method is to calculate ΔH_{rxn} from known thermochemical data by using tabulated standard enthalpies of formation for the reactants and products of the reaction. These are usually tabulated for substances in their standard states, and the enthalpy of reaction is called the standard enthalpy of reaction ($\Delta H_{rxn}°$). For any reaction, $\Delta H_{rxn}°$ is obtained by subtracting the sum of the enthalpies of formation of the reactants multiplied by their stoichiometric coefficients from the sum of the enthalpies of formation of the products multiplied by their stoichiometric coefficients.

Environmental Problems Associated with Fossil Fuel Use (6.10)

Fossil fuels are nonrenewable fuels; once they are consumed, they cannot be replaced. At current rates of consumption, natural gas and petroleum reserves will be depleted in 50–100 years. In addition to their limited supply, the products of the combustion of fossil fuels—directly or indirectly formed—contribute to several environmental problems including air pollution, acid rain, and global climate change, which involves an increase in Earth's average temperature caused by CO_2.

Key Equations and Relationships

Kinetic Energy (6.2)

$$KE = \frac{1}{2}mv^2$$

Change in Internal Energy (ΔE) of a Chemical System (6.3)

$$\Delta E = E_{products} - E_{reactants}$$

Energy Flow between System and Surroundings (6.3)

$$\Delta E_{system} = -\Delta E_{surroundings}$$

Relationship between Internal Energy (ΔE), Heat (q), and Work (w) (6.3)

$$\Delta E = q + w$$

Relationship between Heat (q), Temperature (T), and Heat Capacity (C) (6.4)

$$q = C \times \Delta T$$

Relationship between Heat (q), Mass (m), Temperature (T), and Specific Heat Capacity of a Substance (C_s) (6.4)

$$q = m \times C_s \times \Delta T$$

Relationship between Work (w), Force (F), and Distance (D) (6.4)

$$w = F \times D$$

Relationship between Work (w), Pressure (P), and Change in Volume (ΔV) (6.4)

$$w = -P\,\Delta V$$

Change in Internal Energy (ΔE) of System at Constant Volume (6.5)

$$\Delta E = q_v$$

Heat of a Bomb Calorimeter (q_{cal}) (6.5)

$$q_{cal} = C_{cal} \times \Delta T$$

Heat Exchange between a Calorimeter and a Reaction (6.5)

$$q_{cal} = -q_{rxn}$$

Relationship between Enthalpy (ΔH), Internal Energy (ΔE), Pressure (P), and Volume (V) (6.6)

$$\Delta H = \Delta E + P\,\Delta V$$
$$\Delta H = q_p$$

Relationship between Enthalpy of a Reaction (ΔH_{rxn}°) and the Heats of Formation (ΔH_f°) (6.9)

$$\Delta H_{rxn}^\circ = \Sigma\, n_p \Delta H_f^\circ \text{ (products)} - \Sigma\, n_r \Delta H_f^\circ \text{ (reactants)}$$

Key Skills

Calculating Internal Energy from Heat and Work (6.3)
- Example 6.1 • For Practice 6.1 • Exercises 41–44

Finding Heat from Temperature Changes (6.4)
- Example 6.2 • For Practice 6.2 • For More Practice 6.2 • Exercises 47–50

Thermal Energy Transfer (6.4)
- Example 6.3 • For Practice 6.3 • Exercises 63–68

Finding Work from Volume Changes (6.4)
- Example 6.4 • For Practice 6.4 • For More Practice 6.4 • Exercises 51, 52

Using Bomb Calorimetry to Calculate ΔE_{rxn} (6.5)
- Example 6.5 • For Practice 6.5 • For More Practice 6.5 • Exercises 53, 54

Predicting Endothermic and Exothermic Processes (6.6)
- Example 6.6 • For Practice 6.6 • Exercises 57, 58

Determining Heat from ΔH and Stoichiometry (6.6)
- Examples 6.7, 6.13 • For Practice 6.7, 6.13 • For More Practice 6.7 • Exercises 59–62

Finding ΔH_{rxn} Using Calorimetry (6.7)
- Example 6.8 • For Practice 6.8 • Exercises 73, 74

Finding ΔH_{rxn} Using Hess's Law (6.8)
- Example 6.9 • For Practice 6.9 • For More Practice 6.9 • Exercises 77–80

Finding ΔH_{rxn}° Using Standard Enthalpies of Formation (6.9)
- Examples 6.10, 6.11, 6.12 • For Practice 6.10, 6.11, 6.12 • Exercises 81–90

EXERCISES

Review Questions

1. What is thermochemistry? Why is it important?

2. What is energy? What is work? Give some examples of each.

3. What is kinetic energy? What is potential energy? Give some examples of each.

4. What is the law of conservation of energy? How does it relate to energy exchanges between a thermodynamic system and its surroundings?

5. What is the SI unit of energy? List some other common units of energy.

6. What is the first law of thermodynamics? What are its implications?

7. A friend claims to have constructed a machine that creates electricity, but requires no energy input. Explain why you should be suspicious of your friend's claim.

8. What is a state function? List some examples of state functions.

9. What is internal energy? Is internal energy a state function?

10. If energy flows out of a chemical system and into the surroundings, what is the sign of ΔE_{system}?

11. If the internal energy of the products of a reaction is higher than the internal energy of the reactants, what is the sign of ΔE for the reaction? In which direction does energy flow?

12. What is heat? Explain the difference between heat and temperature.

13. How is the change in internal energy of a system related to heat and work?

14. Explain how the sum of heat and work can be a state function, even though heat and work are themselves not state functions.

15. What is heat capacity? Explain the difference between heat capacity and specific heat capacity.

16. Explain how the high specific heat capacity of water can affect the weather in coastal versus inland regions.

17. If two objects, A and B, of different temperature come into direct contact, what is the relationship between the heat lost by one object and the heat gained by the other? What is the relationship between the temperature changes of the two objects? (Assume that the two objects do not lose any heat to anything else.)

18. What is pressure–volume work? How is it calculated?

19. What is calorimetry? Explain the difference between a coffee-cup calorimeter and a bomb calorimeter. What is each designed to measure?

20. What is the change in enthalpy (ΔH) for a chemical reaction? How is ΔH different from ΔE?

21. Explain the difference between an exothermic and an endothermic reaction. Give the sign of ΔH for each type of reaction.

22. From a molecular viewpoint, where does the energy emitted in an exothermic chemical reaction come from? Why does the reaction mixture undergo an increase in temperature even though energy is emitted?

23. From a molecular viewpoint, where does the energy absorbed in an endothermic chemical reaction go? Why does the reaction mixture undergo a decrease in temperature even though energy is absorbed?

24. Is the change in enthalpy for a reaction an extensive property? Explain the relationship between ΔH for a reaction and the amounts of reactants and products that undergo reaction.

25. Explain how the value of ΔH for a reaction changes upon:
    a. multiplying the reaction by a factor
    b. reversing the reaction

    Why do these relationships hold?

26. What is Hess's law? Why is it useful?

27. What is a standard state? What is the standard enthalpy change for a reaction?

28. What is the standard enthalpy of formation for a compound? For a pure element in its standard state?

29. How can you calculate ΔH_{rxn}° from tabulated standard enthalpies of formation?

30. What are the main sources of the energy consumed in the United States?

31. What are the main environmental problems associated with fossil fuel use?

32. Explain global climate change. What causes global warming? What is the evidence that global warming is occurring?

Problems by Topic

Energy Units

33. Perform each conversion between energy units:
    a. 534 kWh to J
    b. 215 kJ to Cal
    c. 567 Cal to J
    d. 2.85×10^3 J to cal

34. Perform each conversion between energy units:
    a. 231 cal to kJ
    b. 132×10^4 kJ to kcal
    c. 4.99×10^3 kJ to kWh
    d. 2.88×10^4 J to Cal

35. Suppose that a person eats a diet of 2387 Calories per day. Convert this energy into each unit:
    a. J
    b. kJ
    c. kWh

36. A particular frost-free refrigerator uses about 745 kWh of electrical energy per year. Express this amount of energy in each unit:
    a. J
    b. kJ
    c. Cal

Internal Energy, Heat, and Work

37. Which statement is true of the internal energy of a system and its surroundings during an energy exchange with a negative ΔE_{sys}?
    a. The internal energy of the system increases and the internal energy of the surroundings decreases.
    b. The internal energy of both the system and the surroundings increases.
    c. The internal energy of both the system and the surroundings decreases.
    d. The internal energy of the system decreases and the internal energy of the surroundings increases.

38. During an energy exchange, a chemical system absorbs energy from its surroundings. What is the sign of ΔE_{sys} for this process? Explain.

39. Identify each energy exchange as primarily heat or work and determine whether the sign of ΔE is positive or negative for the system.
    a. Sweat evaporates from skin, cooling the skin. (The evaporating sweat is the system.)
    b. A balloon expands against an external pressure. (The contents of the balloon is the system.)
    c. An aqueous chemical reaction mixture is warmed with an external flame. (The reaction mixture is the system.)

40. Identify each energy exchange as primarily heat or work and determine whether the sign of ΔE is positive or negative for the system.
    a. A rolling billiard ball collides with another billiard ball. The first billiard ball (defined as the system) stops rolling after the collision.
    b. A book is dropped to the floor (the book is the system).
    c. A father pushes his daughter on a swing (the daughter and the swing are the system).

41. A system releases 622 kJ of heat and does 105 kJ of work on the surroundings. What is the change in internal energy of the system?

42. A system absorbs 196 kJ of heat and the surroundings do 117 kJ of work on the system. What is the change in internal energy of the system?

43. The gas in a piston (defined as the system) warms and absorbs 655 J of heat. The expansion performs 344 J of work on the surroundings. What is the change in internal energy for the system?

44. The air in an inflated balloon (defined as the system) warms over a toaster and absorbs 115 J of heat. As it expands, it does 77 kJ of work. What is the change in internal energy for the system?

Heat, Heat Capacity, and Work

45. We pack two identical coolers for a picnic, placing twenty-four 12-ounce soft drinks and 5 pounds of ice in each. However, the drinks that we put into cooler A were refrigerated for several hours before they were packed in the cooler, while the drinks that we put into cooler B were at room temperature. When we open the two coolers 3 hours later, most of the ice in cooler A is still present, while nearly all of the ice in cooler B has melted. Explain this difference.

46. A kilogram of aluminum metal and a kilogram of water are each warmed to 75 °C and placed in two identical insulated containers. One hour later, the two containers are opened and the temperature of each substance is measured. The aluminum has cooled to 35 °C while the water has cooled only to 66 °C. Explain this difference.

47. How much heat is required to warm 1.50 L of water from 25.0 °C to 100.0 °C? (Assume a density of 1.0 g/mL for the water.)

48. How much heat is required to warm 1.50 kg of sand from 25.0 °C to 100.0 °C?

49. Suppose that 25 g of each substance is initially at 27.0 °C. What is the final temperature of each substance upon absorbing 2.35 kJ of heat?
    a. gold   b. silver
    c. aluminum   d. water

50. An unknown mass of each substance, initially at 23.0 °C, absorbs 1.95×10^3 J of heat. The final temperature is recorded as indicated. Find the mass of each substance.
    a. Pyrex glass ($T_f = 55.4$ °C)
    b. sand ($T_f = 62.1$ °C)
    c. ethanol ($T_f = 44.2$ °C)
    d. water ($T_f = 32.4$ °C)

51. How much work (in J) is required to expand the volume of a pump from 0.0 L to 2.5 L against an external pressure of 1.1 atm?

52. The average human lung expands by about 0.50 L during each breath. If this expansion occurs against an external pressure of 1.0 atm, how much work (in J) is done during the expansion?

53. The air within a piston equipped with a cylinder absorbs 565 J of heat and expands from an initial volume of 0.10 L to a final volume of 0.85 L against an external pressure of 1.0 atm. What is the change in internal energy of the air within the piston?

54. A gas is compressed from an initial volume of 5.55 L to a final volume of 1.22 L by an external pressure of 1.00 atm. During the compression the gas releases 124 J of heat. What is the change in internal energy of the gas?

Enthalpy and Thermochemical Stoichiometry

55. When 1 mol of a fuel burns at constant pressure, it produces 3452 kJ of heat and does 11 kJ of work. What are the values of ΔE and ΔH for the combustion of the fuel?

56. The change in internal energy for the combustion of 1.0 mol of octane at a pressure of 1.0 atm is 5084.3 kJ. If the change in enthalpy is 5074.1 kJ, how much work is done during the combustion?

57. Determine whether each process is exothermic or endothermic and indicate the sign of ΔH.
    a. natural gas burning on a stove
    b. isopropyl alcohol evaporating from skin
    c. water condensing from steam

58. Determine whether each process is exothermic or endothermic and indicate the sign of ΔH.
    a. dry ice evaporating
    b. a sparkler burning
    c. the reaction that occurs in a chemical cold pack used to ice athletic injuries

59. Consider the thermochemical equation for the combustion of acetone (C_3H_6O), the main ingredient in nail polish remover.

$$C_3H_6O(l) + 4\,O_2(g) \longrightarrow 3\,CO_2(g) + 3\,H_2O(g)$$
$$\Delta H^\circ_{rxn} = -1790 \text{ kJ}$$

If a bottle of nail polish remover contains 177 mL of acetone, how much heat is released by its complete combustion? The density of acetone is 0.788 g/mL.

60. What mass of natural gas (CH_4) must burn to emit 267 kJ of heat?

$$CH_4(g) + 2\,O_2(g) \longrightarrow CO_2(g) + 2\,H_2O(g)$$
$$\Delta H^\circ_{rxn} = -802.3\text{ kJ}$$

61. The propane fuel (C_3H_8) used in gas barbeques burns according to the thermochemical equation:

$$C_3H_8(g) + 5\,O_2(g) \longrightarrow 3\,CO_2(g) + 4\,H_2O(g)$$
$$\Delta H^\circ_{rxn} = -2217\text{ kJ}$$

If a pork roast must absorb 1.6×10^3 kJ to fully cook, and if only 10% of the heat produced by the barbeque is actually absorbed by the roast, what mass of CO_2 is emitted into the atmosphere during the grilling of the pork roast?

62. Charcoal is primarily carbon. Determine the mass of CO_2 produced by burning enough carbon (in the form of charcoal) to produce 5.00×10^2 kJ of heat.

$$C(s) + O_2(g) \longrightarrow CO_2(g) \qquad \Delta H^\circ_{rxn} = -393.5\text{ kJ}$$

Thermal Energy Transfer

63. A silver block, initially at 58.5 °C, is submerged into 100.0 g of water at 24.8 °C, in an insulated container. The final temperature of the mixture upon reaching thermal equilibrium is 26.2 °C. What is the mass of the silver block?

64. A 32.5-g iron rod, initially at 22.7 °C, is submerged into an unknown mass of water at 63.2 °C, in an insulated container. The final temperature of the mixture upon reaching thermal equilibrium is 59.5 °C. What is the mass of the water?

65. A 31.1-g wafer of pure gold initially at 69.3 °C is submerged into 64.2 g of water at 27.8 °C in an insulated container. What is the final temperature of both substances at thermal equilibrium?

66. A 2.85-g lead weight, initially at 10.3 °C, is submerged in 7.55 g of water at 52.3 °C in an insulated container. What is the final temperature of both substances at thermal equilibrium?

67. Two substances, A and B, initially at different temperatures, come into contact and reach thermal equilibrium. The mass of substance A is 6.15 g and its initial temperature is 20.5 °C. The mass of substance B is 25.2 g and its initial temperature is 52.7 °C. The final temperature of both substances at thermal equilibrium is 46.7 °C. If the specific heat capacity of substance B is 1.17 J/g·°C, what is the specific heat capacity of substance A?

68. A 2.74-g sample of a substance suspected of being pure gold is warmed to 72.1 °C and submerged into 15.2 g of water initially at 24.7 °C. The final temperature of the mixture is 26.3 °C. What is the heat capacity of the unknown substance? Could the substance be pure gold?

Calorimetry

69. Exactly 1.5 g of a fuel burns under conditions of constant pressure and then again under conditions of constant volume. In measurement A the reaction produces 25.9 kJ of heat, and in measurement B the reaction produces 23.3 kJ of heat. Which measurement (A or B) corresponds to conditions of constant pressure? Which one corresponds to conditions of constant volume? Explain.

70. In order to obtain the largest possible amount of heat from a chemical reaction in which there is a large increase in the number of moles of gas, should you carry out the reaction under conditions of constant volume or constant pressure? Explain.

71. When 0.514 g of biphenyl ($C_{12}H_{10}$) undergoes combustion in a bomb calorimeter, the temperature rises from 25.8 °C to 29.4 °C. Find ΔE_{rxn} for the combustion of biphenyl in kJ/mol biphenyl. The heat capacity of the bomb calorimeter, determined in a separate experiment, is 5.86 kJ/°C.

72. Mothballs are composed primarily of the hydrocarbon naphthalene ($C_{10}H_8$). When 1.025 g of naphthalene burns in a bomb calorimeter, the temperature rises from 24.25 °C to 32.33 °C. Find ΔE_{rxn} for the combustion of naphthalene. The heat capacity of the calorimeter, determined in a separate experiment, is 5.11 kJ/°C.

73. Zinc metal reacts with hydrochloric acid according to the following balanced equation.

$$Zn(s) + 2\,HCl(aq) \longrightarrow ZnCl_2(aq) + H_2(g)$$

When 0.103 g of $Zn(s)$ is combined with enough HCl to make 50.0 mL of solution in a coffee-cup calorimeter, all of the zinc reacts, raising the temperature of the solution from 22.5 °C to 23.7 °C. Find ΔH_{rxn} for this reaction as written. (Use 1.0 g/mL for the density of the solution and 4.18 J/g·°C as the specific heat capacity.)

74. Instant cold packs, often used to ice athletic injuries on the field, contain ammonium nitrate and water separated by a thin plastic divider. When the divider is broken, the ammonium nitrate dissolves according to the following endothermic reaction:

$$NH_4NO_3(s) \longrightarrow NH_4^+(aq) + NO_3^-(aq)$$

In order to measure the enthalpy change for this reaction, 1.25 g of NH_4NO_3 is dissolved in enough water to make 25.0 mL of solution. The initial temperature is 25.8 °C and the final temperature (after the solid dissolves) is 21.9 °C. Calculate the change in enthalpy for the reaction in kJ. (Use 1.0 g/mL as the density of the solution and 4.18 J/g·°C as the specific heat capacity.)

Quantitative Relationships Involving ΔH and Hess's Law

75. For each generic reaction, determine the value of ΔH_2 in terms of ΔH_1.

a. $A + B \longrightarrow 2\,C$ $\qquad\qquad \Delta H_1$
  $2\,C \longrightarrow A + B$ $\qquad\qquad \Delta H_2 = ?$
b. $A + \frac{1}{2}\,B \longrightarrow C$ $\qquad\quad \Delta H_1$
  $2\,A + B \longrightarrow 2\,C$ $\qquad\quad \Delta H_2 = ?$
c. $A \longrightarrow B + 2\,C$ $\qquad\qquad \Delta H_1$
  $\frac{1}{2}\,B + C \longrightarrow \frac{1}{2}\,A$ $\qquad \Delta H_2 = ?$

76. Consider the generic reaction:

$$A + 2\,B \longrightarrow C + 3\,D \quad \Delta H = 155\text{ kJ}$$

Determine the value of ΔH for each related reaction:
a. $3\,A + 6\,B \longrightarrow 3\,C + 9\,D$
b. $C + 3\,D \longrightarrow A + 2\,B$
c. $\frac{1}{2}\,C + \frac{3}{2}\,D \longrightarrow \frac{1}{2}\,A + B$

77. Calculate ΔH_{rxn} for the reaction:

$$Fe_2O_3(s) + 3\,CO(g) \longrightarrow 2\,Fe(s) + 3\,CO_2(g)$$

Use the following reactions and given ΔH's.

$$2\,Fe(s) + \tfrac{3}{2}\,O_2(g) \longrightarrow Fe_2O_3(s) \quad \Delta H = -824.2\text{ kJ}$$
$$CO(g) + \tfrac{1}{2}\,O_2(g) \longrightarrow CO_2(g) \quad \Delta H = -282.7\text{ kJ}$$

78. Calculate ΔH_{rxn} for the reaction:

$$CaO(s) + CO_2(g) \longrightarrow CaCO_3(s)$$

Use the following reactions and given ΔH's.

$$Ca(s) + CO_2(g) + \tfrac{1}{2}\,O_2(g) \longrightarrow CaCO_3(s) \quad \Delta H = -812.8\text{ kJ}$$
$$2\,Ca(s) + O_2(g) \longrightarrow 2\,CaO(s) \quad \Delta H = -1269.8\text{ kJ}$$

79. Calculate ΔH_{rxn} for the reaction:

$$5\,C(s) + 6\,H_2(g) \longrightarrow C_5H_{12}(l)$$

Use the following reactions and given ΔH's.

$$C_5H_{12}(l) + 8\,O_2(g) \longrightarrow 5\,CO_2(g) + 6\,H_2O(g) \quad \Delta H = -3505.8 \text{ kJ}$$
$$C(s) + O_2(g) \longrightarrow CO_2(g) \qquad\qquad \Delta H = -393.5 \text{ kJ}$$
$$2\,H_2(g) + O_2(g) \longrightarrow 2\,H_2O(g) \qquad \Delta H = -483.5 \text{ kJ}$$

80. Calculate ΔH_{rxn} for the reaction:

$$CH_4(g) + 4\,Cl_2(g) \longrightarrow CCl_4(g) + 4\,HCl(g)$$

Use the following reactions and given ΔH's.

$$C(s) + 2\,H_2(g) \longrightarrow CH_4(g) \qquad \Delta H = -74.6 \text{ kJ}$$
$$C(s) + 2\,Cl_2(g) \longrightarrow CCl_4(g) \qquad \Delta H = -95.7 \text{ kJ}$$
$$H_2(g) + Cl_2(g) \longrightarrow 2\,HCl(g) \qquad \Delta H = -92.3 \text{ kJ}$$

Enthalpies of Formation and ΔH

81. Write an equation for the formation of each compound from its elements in their standard states, and find ΔH_f° for each from Appendix IIB.
a. $NH_3(g)$ b. $CO_2(g)$ c. $Fe_2O_3(s)$ d. $CH_4(g)$

82. Write an equation for the formation of each compound from its elements in their standard states, and find ΔH_f° for each from Appendix IIB.
a. $NO_2(g)$ b. $MgCO_3(s)$ c. $C_2H_4(g)$ d. $CH_3OH(l)$

83. Hydrazine (N_2H_4) is a fuel used by some spacecraft. It is normally oxidized by N_2O_4 according to the equation:

$$N_2H_4(l) + N_2O_4(g) \longrightarrow 2\,N_2O(g) + 2\,H_2O(g)$$

Calculate ΔH_{rxn}° for this reaction using standard enthalpies of formation.

84. Pentane (C_5H_{12}) is a component of gasoline that burns according to the following balanced equation:

$$C_5H_{12}(l) + 8\,O_2(g) \longrightarrow 5\,CO_2(g) + 6\,H_2O(g)$$

Calculate ΔH_{rxn}° for this reaction using standard enthalpies of formation. (The standard enthalpy of formation of liquid pentane is –146.8 kJ/mol.)

85. Use standard enthalpies of formation to calculate ΔH_{rxn}° for each reaction:
a. $C_2H_4(g) + H_2(g) \longrightarrow C_2H_6(g)$
b. $CO(g) + H_2O(g) \longrightarrow H_2(g) + CO_2(g)$
c. $3\,NO_2(g) + H_2O(l) \longrightarrow 2\,HNO_3(aq) + NO(g)$
d. $Cr_2O_3(s) + 3\,CO(g) \longrightarrow 2\,Cr(s) + 3\,CO_2(g)$

86. Use standard enthalpies of formation to calculate ΔH_{rxn}° for each reaction:
a. $2\,H_2S(g) + 3\,O_2(g) \longrightarrow 2\,H_2O(l) + 2\,SO_2(g)$
b. $SO_2(g) + \frac{1}{2}\,O_2(g) \longrightarrow SO_3(g)$
c. $C(s) + H_2O(g) \longrightarrow CO(g) + H_2(g)$
d. $N_2O_4(g) + 4\,H_2(g) \longrightarrow N_2(g) + 4\,H_2O(g)$

87. During photosynthesis, plants use energy from sunlight to form glucose ($C_6H_{12}O_6$) and oxygen from carbon dioxide and water. Write a balanced equation for photosynthesis and calculate ΔH_{rxn}°.

88. Ethanol can be made from the fermentation of crops and has been used as a fuel additive to gasoline. Write a balanced equation for the combustion of ethanol and calculate ΔH_{rxn}°.

89. Top fuel dragsters and funny cars burn nitromethane as fuel according to the balanced combustion equation:

$$2\,CH_3NO_2(l) + \tfrac{3}{2}\,O_2(g) \longrightarrow 2\,CO_2(g) + 3\,H_2O(l) + N_2(g)$$

The standard enthalpy of combustion for nitromethane is –709.2 kJ/mol. Calculate the standard enthalpy of formation (ΔH_f°) for nitromethane.

90. The explosive nitroglycerin ($C_3H_5N_3O_9$) decomposes rapidly upon ignition or sudden impact according to the balanced equation:

$$4\,C_3H_5N_3O_9(l) \longrightarrow 12\,CO_2(g) + 10\,H_2O(g) + 6\,N_2(g) + O_2(g)$$
$$\Delta H_{rxn}^\circ = -5678 \text{ kJ}$$

Calculate the standard enthalpy of formation (ΔH_f°) for nitroglycerin.

Energy Use and the Environment

91. Determine the mass of CO_2 produced by burning enough of each of the following fuels to produce 1.00×10^2 kJ of heat. Which fuel contributes least to global warming per kJ of heat produced?
a. $CH_4(g) + 2\,O_2(g) \longrightarrow CO_2(g) + 2\,H_2O(g)$
$$\Delta H_{rxn}^\circ = -802.3 \text{ kJ}$$
b. $C_3H_8(g) + 5\,O_2(g) \longrightarrow 3\,CO_2(g) + 4\,H_2O(g)$
$$\Delta H_{rxn}^\circ = -2217 \text{ kJ}$$
c. $C_8H_{18}(l) + \tfrac{25}{2}\,O_2(g) \longrightarrow 8\,CO_2(g) + 9\,H_2O(g)$
$$\Delta H_{rxn}^\circ = -5074.1 \text{ kJ}$$

92. Methanol (CH_3OH) has been suggested as a fuel to replace gasoline. Write a balanced equation for the combustion of methanol, find ΔH_{rxn}° and determine the mass of carbon dioxide emitted per kJ of heat produced. Use the information from the previous exercise to calculate the same quantity for octane, C_8H_{18}. How does methanol compare to octane with respect to global warming?

93. The citizens of the world burn the fossil fuel equivalent of 7×10^{12} kg of petroleum per year. Assume that all of this petroleum is in the form of octane (C_8H_{18}) and calculate how much CO_2 (in kg) is produced by world fossil fuel combustion per year. (Hint: Begin by writing a balanced equation for the combustion of octane.) If the atmosphere currently contains approximately 3×10^{15} kg of CO_2, how long will it take for the world's fossil fuel combustion to double the amount of atmospheric carbon dioxide?

94. In a sunny location, sunlight has a power density of about 1 kW/m^2. Photovoltaic solar cells can convert this power into electricity with 15% efficiency. If a typical home uses 385 kWh of electricity per month, how many square meters of solar cells would be required to meet its energy requirements? Assume that electricity can be generated from the sunlight for 8 hours per day.

▲ What area of solar cells do you need to power a home?

Cumulative Problems

95. The kinetic energy of a rolling billiard ball is given by $KE = \frac{1}{2} mv^2$. Suppose a 0.17-kg billiard ball is rolling down a pool table with an initial speed of 4.5 m/s. As it travels, it loses some of its energy as heat. The ball slows down to 3.8 m/s and then collides head-on with a second billiard ball of equal mass. The first billiard ball completely stops and the second one rolls away with a velocity of 3.8 m/s. Assume the first billiard ball is the system and calculate w, q, and ΔE for the process.

96. A 100-W lightbulb is placed in a cylinder equipped with a moveable piston. The lightbulb is turned on for 0.015 hour, and the assembly expands from an initial volume of 0.85 L to a final volume of 5.88 L against an external pressure of 1.0 atm. Use the wattage of the lightbulb and the time it is on to calculate ΔE in joules (assume that the cylinder and lightbulb assembly is the system and assume two significant figures). Calculate w and q.

97. Evaporating sweat cools the body because evaporation is an endothermic process:

$$H_2O(l) \longrightarrow H_2O(g) \quad \Delta H^{\circ}_{rxn} = +44.01 \text{ kJ}$$

Estimate the mass of water that must evaporate from the skin to cool the body by 0.50 °C. Assume a body mass of 95 kg and assume that the specific heat capacity of the body is 4.0 J/g · °C.

98. LP gas burns according to the exothermic reaction:

$$C_3H_8(g) + 5 O_2(g) \longrightarrow 3 CO_2(g) + 4 H_2O(g)$$
$$\Delta H^{\circ}_{rxn} = -2044 \text{ kJ}$$

What mass of LP gas is necessary to heat 1.5 L of water from room temperature (25.0 °C) to boiling (100.0 °C)? Assume that during heating, 15% of the heat emitted by the LP gas combustion goes to heat the water. The rest is lost as heat to the surroundings.

99. Use standard enthalpies of formation to calculate the standard change in enthalpy for the melting of ice. (The ΔH°_{f} for H$_2$O(s) is −291.8 kJ/mol.) Use this value to calculate the mass of ice required to cool 355 mL of a beverage from room temperature (25.0 °C) to 0.0 °C. Assume that the specific heat capacity and density of the beverage are the same as those of water.

100. Dry ice is solid carbon dioxide. Instead of melting, solid carbon dioxide sublimes according to the equation:

$$CO_2(s) \longrightarrow CO_2(g)$$

When dry ice is added to warm water, heat from the water causes the dry ice to sublime more quickly. The evaporating carbon dioxide produces a dense fog often used to create special effects. In a simple dry ice fog machine, dry ice is added to warm water in a Styrofoam cooler. The dry ice produces fog until it evaporates away, or until the water gets too cold to sublime the dry ice quickly enough. Suppose that a small Styrofoam cooler holds 15.0 liters of water heated to 85 °C. Use standard enthalpies of formation to calculate the change in enthalpy for dry ice sublimation, and calculate the mass of dry ice that should be added to the water so that the dry ice completely sublimes away when the water reaches 25 °C. Assume no heat loss to the surroundings. (The ΔH°_{f} for CO$_2$(s) is −427.4 kJ/mol.)

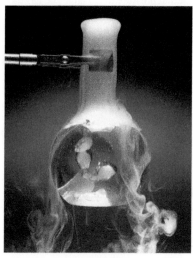

◀ When carbon dioxide sublimes, the gaseous CO$_2$ is cold enough to cause water vapor in the air to condense, forming fog.

101. A 25.5-g aluminum block is warmed to 65.4 °C and plunged into an insulated beaker containing 55.2 g water initially at 22.2 °C. The aluminum and the water are allowed to come to thermal equilibrium. Assuming that no heat is lost, what is the final temperature of the water and aluminum?

102. If 50.0 mL of ethanol (density = 0.789 g/mL) initially at 7.0 °C is mixed with 50.0 mL of water (density = 1.0 g/mL) initially at 28.4 °C in an insulated beaker, and assuming that no heat is lost, what is the final temperature of the mixture?

103. Palmitic acid (C$_{16}$H$_{32}$O$_2$) is a dietary fat found in beef and butter. The caloric content of palmitic acid is typical of fats in general. Write a balanced equation for the complete combustion of palmitic acid and calculate the standard enthalpy of combustion. What is the caloric content of palmitic acid in Cal/g? Do the same calculation for table sugar (sucrose, C$_{12}$H$_{22}$O$_{11}$). Which dietary substance (sugar or fat) contains more Calories per gram? The standard enthalpy of formation of palmitic acid is −208 kJ/mol and that of sucrose is −2226.1 kJ/mol. (Use H$_2$O(l) in the balanced chemical equations because the metabolism of these compounds produces liquid water.)

104. Hydrogen and methanol have both been proposed as alternatives to hydrocarbon fuels. Write balanced reactions for the complete combustion of hydrogen and methanol and use standard enthalpies of formation to calculate the amount of heat released per kilogram of the fuel. Which fuel contains the most energy in the least mass? How does the energy of these fuels compare to that of octane (C$_8$H$_{18}$)?

105. Derive a relationship between ΔH and ΔE for a process in which the temperature of a fixed amount of an ideal gas changes.

106. Under certain nonstandard conditions, oxidation by O$_2$(g) of 1 mol of SO$_2$(g) to SO$_3$(g) absorbs 89.5 kJ. The enthalpy of formation of SO$_3$(g) is −204.2 kJ under these conditions. Find the enthalpy of formation of SO$_2$(g).

107. One tablespoon of peanut butter has a mass of 16 g. It is combusted in a calorimeter whose heat capacity is 120.0 kJ/°C. The temperature of the calorimeter rises from 22.2 °C to 25.4 °C. Find the food caloric content of peanut butter.

108. A mixture of 2.0 mol of H$_2$(g) and 1.0 mol of O$_2$(g) is placed in a sealed evacuated container made of a perfect insulating material at 25 °C. The mixture is ignited with a spark and it reacts to form liquid water. Find the temperature of the water.

109. A 20.0-L volume of an ideal gas in a cylinder with a piston is at a pressure of 3.0 atm. Enough weight is suddenly removed from the piston to lower the external pressure to 1.5 atm. The gas then expands at constant temperature until its pressure is 1.5 atm. Find ΔE, ΔH, q, and w for this change in state.

110. When 10.00 g of phosphorus is burned in $O_2(g)$ to form $P_4O_{10}(s)$, enough heat is generated to raise the temperature of 2950 g of water from 18.0 °C to 38.0 °C. Calculate the enthalpy of formation of $P_4O_{10}(s)$ under these conditions.

111. The ΔH for the oxidation of S in the gas phase to SO_3 is −204 kJ/mol and for the oxidation of SO_2 to SO_3 is 89.5 kJ/mol. Find the enthalpy of formation of SO_2 under these conditions.

112. The ΔH_f° of $TiI_3(s)$ is −328 kJ/mol and the ΔH° for the reaction $2\,Ti(s) + 3\,I_2(g) \longrightarrow 2\,TiI_3(s)$ is −839 kJ. Calculate the ΔH of sublimation of $I_2(s)$, which is a solid at 25 °C.

113. A gaseous fuel mixture contains 25.3% methane (CH_4), 38.2% ethane (C_2H_6) and the rest propane (C_3H_8) by volume. When the fuel mixture contained in a 1.55 L tank, stored at 755 mm Hg and 298 K, undergoes complete combustion, how much heat is emitted? (Assume that the water produced by the combustion is in the gaseous state.)

114. A gaseous fuel mixture stored at 745 mm Hg and 298 K contains only methane (CH_4) and propane (C_3H_8). When 11.7 L of this fuel mixture is burned, it produces 769 kJ of heat. What is the mole fraction of methane in the mixture? (Assume that the water produced by the combustion is in the gaseous state.)

115. A copper cube measuring 1.55 cm on edge and an aluminum cube measuring 1.62 cm on edge are both heated to 55.0 °C and submerged in 100.0 mL of water at 22.2 °C. What is the final temperature of the water when equilibrium is reached? (Assume a density of 0.998 g/mL for water.)

116. A pure gold ring and pure silver ring have a total mass of 14.9 g. The two rings are heated to 62.0 °C and dropped into a 15.0 mL of water at 23.5 °C. When equilibrium is reached, the temperature of the water is 25.0°C. What is the mass of each ring? (Assume a density of 0.998 g/mL for water.)

Challenge Problems

117. A typical frostless refrigerator uses 655 kWh of energy per year in the form of electricity. Suppose that all of this electricity is generated at a power plant that burns coal containing 3.2% sulfur by mass and that all of the sulfur is emitted as SO_2 when the coal is burned. If all of the SO_2 goes on to react with rainwater to form H_2SO_4, what mass of H_2SO_4 does the annual operation of the refrigerator produce? (Hint: Assume that the remaining percentage of the coal is carbon and begin by calculating ΔH_{rxn}° for the combustion of carbon.)

118. A large sport utility vehicle has a mass of 2.5×10^3 kg. Calculate the mass of CO_2 emitted into the atmosphere upon accelerating the SUV from 0.0 mph to 65.0 mph. Assume that the required energy comes from the combustion of octane with 30% efficiency. (Hint: Use KE = $\frac{1}{2}\,mv^2$ to calculate the kinetic energy required for the acceleration.)

119. Combustion of natural gas (primarily methane) occurs in most household heaters. The heat given off in this reaction is used to raise the temperature of the air in the house. Assuming that all the energy given off in the reaction goes to heating up only the air in the house, determine the mass of methane required to heat the air in a house by 10.0 °C. Assume each of the following: house dimensions are 30.0 m × 30.0 m × 3.0 m; specific heat capacity of air is 30 J/K · mol; 1.00 mol of air occupies 22.4 L for all temperatures concerned.

120. When backpacking in the wilderness, hikers often boil water to sterilize it for drinking. Suppose that you are planning a backpacking trip and will need to boil 35 L of water for your group. What volume of fuel should you bring? Assume each of the following: the fuel has an average formula of C_7H_{16}; 15% of the heat generated from combustion goes to heat the water (the rest is lost to the surroundings); the density of the fuel is 0.78 g/mL; the initial temperature of the water is 25.0 °C; and the standard enthalpy of formation of C_7H_{16} is −224.4 kJ/mol.

121. An ice cube of mass 9.0 g is added to a cup of coffee. The coffee's initial temperature is 90.0 °C and the cup contains 120.0 g of liquid. Assume the specific heat capacity of the coffee is the same as that of water. The heat of fusion of ice (the heat associated with ice melting) is 6.0 kJ/mol. Find the temperature of the coffee after the ice melts.

122. Find ΔH, ΔE, q, and w for the freezing of water at −10.0 °C. The specific heat capacity of ice is 2.04 J/g · °C and its heat of fusion (the quantity of heat associated with melting) is −332 J/g.

123. Starting from the relationship between temperature and kinetic energy for an ideal gas, find the value of the molar heat capacity of an ideal gas when its temperature is changed at constant volume. Find its molar heat capacity when its temperature is changed at constant pressure.

124. An amount of an ideal gas expands from 12.0 L to 24.0 L at a constant pressure of 1.0 atm. Then the gas is cooled at a constant volume of 24.0 L back to its original temperature. Then it contracts back to its original volume. Find the total heat flow for the entire process.

125. The heat of vaporization of water at 373 K is 40.7 kJ/mol. Find q, w, ΔE, and ΔH for the evaporation of 454 g of water at this temperature at 1 atm.

126. Find ΔE, ΔH, q, and w for the change in state of 1.0 mol $H_2O(l)$ at 80 °C to $H_2O(g)$ at 110 °C. The heat capacity of $H_2O(l)$ = 75.3 J/mol K, heat capacity of $H_2O(g)$ = 25.0 J/mol K, and the heat of vaporization of H_2O is 40.7×10^3 J/mol at 100 °C.

127. The heat of combustion of liquid octane (C_8H_{18}) to carbon dioxide and liquid water at 298 K is −1303 kJ/mol. Find ΔE for this reaction.

128. Find ΔH for the combustion of ethanol (C_2H_6O) to carbon dioxide and liquid water from the following data. The heat capacity of the bomb calorimeter is 34.65 kJ/K and the combustion of 1.765 g of ethanol raises the temperature of the calorimeter from 294.33 K to 295.84 K.

Conceptual Problems

129. Which statement is true of the internal energy of the system and its surroundings following a process in which $\Delta E_{sys} = +65$ kJ? Explain.

   a. The system and the surroundings both lose 65 kJ of energy.

   b. The system and the surroundings both gain 65 kJ of energy.

   c. The system loses 65 kJ of energy and the surroundings gain 65 kJ of energy.

   d. The system gains 65 kJ of energy and the surroundings lose 65 kJ of energy.

130. The internal energy of an ideal gas depends only on its temperature. Which statement is true of an isothermal (constant-temperature) expansion of an ideal gas against a constant external pressure? Explain.

   a. ΔE is positive   **b.** w is positive

   c. q is positive   **d.** ΔE is negative

131. Which expression describes the heat evolved in a chemical reaction when the reaction is carried out at constant pressure? Explain.

   a. $\Delta E - w$ **b.** ΔE **c.** $\Delta E - q$

132. Two identical refrigerators are plugged in for the first time. Refrigerator A is empty (except for air) and refrigerator B is filled with jugs of water. The compressors of both refrigerators immediately turn on and begin cooling the interiors of the refrigerators. After two hours, the compressor of refrigerator A turns off while the compressor of refrigerator B continues to run. The next day, the compressor of refrigerator A can be heard turning on and off every few minutes, while the compressor of refrigerator B turns off and on every hour or so (and stays on longer each time). Explain these observations.

133. A 1-kg cylinder of aluminum and 1-kg jug of water, both at room temperature, are put into a refrigerator. After one hour, the temperature of each object is measured. One of the objects is much cooler than the other. Which one is cooler and why?

134. Two substances A and B, initially at different temperatures, are thermally isolated from their surroundings and allowed to come into thermal contact. The mass of substance A is twice the mass of substance B, but the specific heat capacity of substance B is four times the specific heat capacity of substance A. Which substance will undergo a larger change in temperature?

135. When 1 mol of a gas burns at constant pressure, it produces 2418 J of heat and does 5 J of work. Identify ΔE, ΔH, q, and w for the process.

136. In an exothermic reaction, the reactants lose energy and the reaction feels hot to the touch. Explain why the reaction feels hot even though the reactants are losing energy. Where does the energy come from?

137. Which statement is true of a reaction in which ΔV is positive? Explain.

   a. $\Delta H = \Delta E$ **b.** $\Delta H > \Delta E$

   c. $\Delta H < \Delta E$

7

The Quantum-Mechanical Model of the Atom

Anyone who is not shocked by quantum mechanics has not understood it.

—Neils Bohr (1885–1962)

T HE EARLY PART OF THE TWENTIETH century brought changes that revolutionized how we think about physical reality, especially in the atomic realm. Before that time, all descriptions of the behavior of matter had been deterministic—the present set of conditions completely determining the future. Quantum mechanics changed that. This new theory suggested that for subatomic particles—electrons, neutrons, and protons—the present does NOT completely determine the future. For example, if you shoot one electron down a path and measure where it lands, a second electron shot down the same path under the same conditions will most likely land in a different place! Quantum-mechanical theory was developed by several unusually gifted scientists including Albert Einstein, Neils Bohr, Louis de Broglie, Max Planck, Werner Heisenberg, P. A. M. Dirac, and Erwin Schrödinger. These scientists did not necessarily feel comfortable with their own theory. Bohr said, "Anyone who is not shocked by quantum mechanics has not understood it." Schrödinger wrote, "I don't like it, and I'm sorry I ever had anything to do with it." Albert Einstein disbelieved the very theory he helped create, stating, "God does not play dice with the universe." In fact, Einstein attempted to disprove quantum mechanics—without success—until he died. But quantum mechanics was able to account for fundamental observations, including the very stability of atoms, which could not be understood within the framework of classical physics. Today, quantum mechanics forms the foundation of chemistry—explaining the periodic table and the behavior of the elements in chemical bonding—as well as providing the practical basis for lasers, computers, and countless other applications.

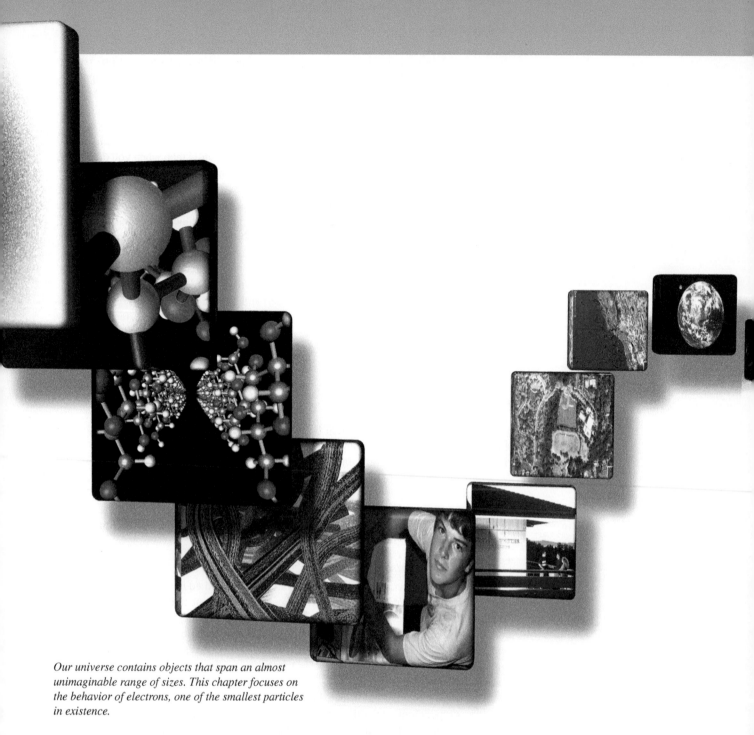

Our universe contains objects that span an almost unimaginable range of sizes. This chapter focuses on the behavior of electrons, one of the smallest particles in existence.

7.1 Quantum Mechanics: The Theory That Explains the Behavior of the Absolutely Small

In everyday language, small is a relative term: something is small relative to something else. A car is smaller than a house, and a person is smaller than a car. But smallness has limits. For example, a house cannot be smaller than the bricks from which it is made.

Atoms and the particles that compose them are unimaginably small. As we have learned, electrons have a mass of less than a trillionth of a trillionth of a gram, and a size so small that it is immeasurable. A single speck of dust contains more electrons than the number of people that have existed on Earth over all the centuries of time. Electrons are *small* in the absolute sense of the word—they are among the smallest particles that make up matter. And yet, an atom's electrons determine many of its chemical and physical properties. If we are to understand these properties, we must try to understand electrons.

The absolute smallness of electrons makes it a challenge to understand them through observation. Consider the difference between observing a baseball, for example, and observing an electron. You can measure the position of a baseball by observing the light that

strikes the ball, bounces off it, and enters your eye. The baseball is large in comparison to the disturbance caused by the light, so the baseball is virtually unaffected by your observation. By contrast, imagine observing the position of an electron. If you attempt to measure its position using light, the light itself disturbs the electron. The interaction of the light with the electron actually changes its position, the very thing you are trying to measure.

The inability to observe electrons without disturbing them has significant implications. It means that when you observe an electron, it behaves differently than when you do not observe it—the act of observation changes what the electron does. It means that our knowledge of electron behavior has limits. It means that the *absolutely small* world of the electron is different from the *large* world that we normally experience. Therefore, we need to think about subatomic particles in a different way than we think about the macroscopic world.

In this chapter, we examine the **quantum-mechanical model** of the atom, a model that explains how electrons exist in atoms and how those electrons determine the chemical and physical properties of elements. We have already learned much about those properties. We know, for example, that some elements are metals and that others are nonmetals. We know that the noble gases are chemically inert and that the alkali metals are chemically reactive. We know that sodium tends to form 1+ ions and that fluorine tends to form 1− ions. But we do not know *why*. The quantum-mechanical model explains why. In doing so, it explains the modern periodic table and provides the basis for our understanding of chemical bonding.

7.2 The Nature of Light

Before we explore electrons and their behavior within the atom, we must understand some of the properties of light. As quantum mechanics developed, light was (surprisingly) found to have many characteristics in common with electrons. Chief among these is the *wave–particle duality* of light. Certain properties of light are best described by thinking of it as a wave, while other properties are best described by thinking of it as a particle. In this section, we will first explore the wave behavior of light, and then its particle behavior. We will then turn to electrons to see how they also display the same wave–particle duality.

The Wave Nature of Light

Light is **electromagnetic radiation**, a type of energy embodied in oscillating electric and magnetic fields. An *electric field* is a region of space where an electrically charged particle experiences a force. A proton, for example, has an electric field around it. If you bring another charged particle into that field, that particle will experience a force. A *magnetic field* is a region of space where a magnetic particle experiences a force. A magnet, for example, has a magnetic field around it. If you bring another magnet into that field, that magnet will experience a force.

Electromagnetic radiation can be described as a wave composed of oscillating, mutually perpendicular electric and magnetic fields propagating through space, as shown in Figure 7.1 ▼. In a vacuum, these waves move at a constant speed of 3.00×10^8 m/s (186,000 mi/s)—fast enough to circle the Earth in one-seventh of a second. This great speed is the reason for the delay between the moment when you see a firework in the sky and the moment when you hear the sound of its explosion. The light from

Electromagnetic Radiation

▶ **FIGURE 7.1 Electromagnetic Radiation** Electromagnetic radiation can be described as a wave composed of oscillating electric and magnetic fields. The fields oscillate in perpendicular planes.

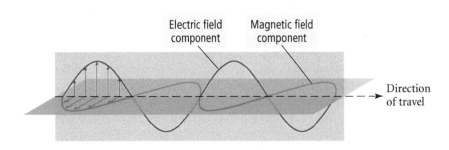

Electric field component

Magnetic field component

Direction of travel

Because light travels nearly a million times faster than sound, the flash of lightning reaches your eyes before the roll of thunder reaches your ears.

the exploding firework reaches your eye almost instantaneously. The sound, traveling much more slowly (340 m/s), takes longer. The same thing happens in a thunderstorm—you see the flash immediately, but the sound takes a few seconds to reach you (The sound of thunder is delayed by five seconds for each mile between you and its origin.)

We can characterize a wave by its *amplitude* and its *wavelength*. In the graphical representation shown here, the **amplitude** of the wave is the vertical height of a crest (or depth of a trough). The amplitude of the electric and magnetic field waves in light determines the light's *intensity* or brightness—the greater the amplitude, the greater the intensity. The **wavelength (λ)** of the wave is the distance between adjacent crests (or any two analogous points) and is measured in units such as meters, micrometers, or nanometers.

The symbol λ is the Greek letter lambda, pronounced "lamb-duh."

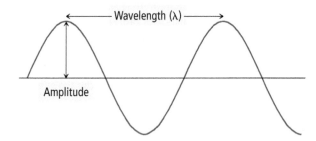

Wavelength and amplitude are both related to the quantity of energy carried by a wave. Imagine trying to swim out from a shore pounded by waves. Waves of greater amplitude (higher waves) or shorter wavelength (more closely spaced, and thus steeper, waves) will make the swim more difficult. Notice also that amplitude and wavelength can vary independently of one another, as shown in Figure 7.2 ▶ on the next page. A wave can have a large amplitude and a long wavelength, or a small amplitude and a short wavelength. The most energetic waves have large amplitudes and short wavelengths.

Like all waves, light is also characterized by its **frequency (ν)**, the number of cycles (or wave crests) that pass through a stationary point in a given period of time. The units of frequency are cycles per second (cycle/s) or simply s^{-1}. An equivalent unit of frequency is the hertz (Hz), defined as 1 cycle/s. The frequency of a wave is directly proportional to the speed at which the wave is traveling—the faster the wave, the more crests will pass a fixed location per unit time. Frequency is also *inversely* proportional to the wavelength

The symbol ν is the Greek letter nu, pronounced "noo."

▶ **FIGURE 7.2 Wavelength and Amplitude**   Wavelength and amplitude are independent properties. The wavelength of light determines its color. The amplitude, or intensity, determines its brightness.

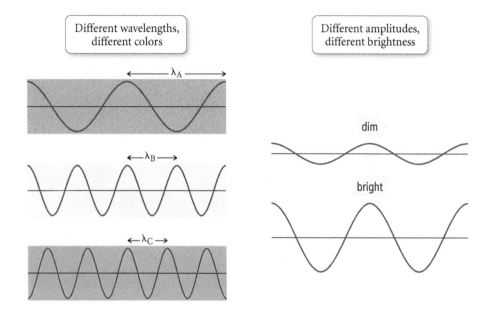

(λ)—the farther apart the crests, the fewer will pass a fixed location per unit time. For light, therefore, we can write

$$\nu = \frac{c}{\lambda} \qquad [7.1]$$

where the speed of light, c, and the wavelength, λ, are both expressed in the same unit of distance. Therefore, wavelength and frequency represent different ways of specifying the same information—if we know one, we can readily calculate the other.

For *visible light*—light that can be seen by the human eye—wavelength (or, alternatively, frequency) determines color. White light, produced by the sun or by a lightbulb, contains a spectrum of wavelengths and therefore a spectrum of colors. We can see these colors—red, orange, yellow, green, blue, indigo, and violet—in a rainbow or when white light is passed through a prism (Figure 7.3 ▼). Red light, with a wavelength of about 750 nanometers (nm), has the longest wavelength of visible light; violet light, with a wavelength of about 400 nm, has the shortest. The presence of a variety of wavelengths in white light is responsible for the way we perceive colors in objects. When a substance absorbs some colors while reflecting others, it appears colored. For example, a red shirt appears red because it reflects predominantly red light while absorbing most other colors (Figure 7.4 ▼). Our eyes see only the reflected light, making the shirt appear red.

nano $= 10^{-9}$

▲ **FIGURE 7.3 Components of White Light** We can pass white light through a prism and decompose it into its constituent colors, each with a different wavelength. The array of colors makes up the spectrum of visible light.

▲ **FIGURE 7.4 The Color of an Object** A red shirt is red because it reflects predominantly red light while absorbing most other colors.

EXAMPLE 7.1 Wavelength and Frequency

Calculate the wavelength (in nm) of the red light emitted by a barcode scanner that has a frequency of $4.62 \times 10^{14}\,\text{s}^{-1}$.

SOLUTION

You are given the frequency of the light and asked to find its wavelength. Use Equation 7.1, which relates frequency to wavelength. You can convert the wavelength from meters to nanometers by using the conversion factor between the two (1 nm = 10^{-9} m)	$\nu = \dfrac{c}{\lambda}$ $\lambda = \dfrac{c}{\nu} = \dfrac{3.00 \times 10^8 \text{ m/s}}{4.62 \times 10^{14}/\text{s}}$ $= 6.49 \times 10^{-7} \text{ m}$ $= 6.49 \times 10^{-7} \text{ m} \times \dfrac{1 \text{ nm}}{10^{-9} \text{ m}} = 649 \text{ nm}$

FOR PRACTICE 7.1

A laser dazzles the audience in a rock concert by emitting green light with a wavelength of 515 nm. Calculate the frequency of the light.

The Electromagnetic Spectrum

Visible light makes up only a tiny portion of the entire **electromagnetic spectrum**, which includes all wavelengths of electromagnetic radiation. Figure 7.5 ▼ shows the main regions of the electromagnetic spectrum, ranging in wavelength from 10^{-15} m (gamma rays) to 10^5 m (radio waves). In Figure 7.5, short-wavelength, high-frequency radiation is on the right and long-wavelength, low-frequency radiation on the left. As you can see, visible light constitutes only a small region in the middle.

As we saw previously, short-wavelength light inherently has greater energy than long-wavelength light. The most energetic forms of electromagnetic radiation have the shortest wavelengths. The form of electromagnetic radiation with the shortest wavelength is the **gamma (γ) ray**. Gamma rays are produced by the sun, other stars, and certain unstable atomic nuclei on Earth. Excessive exposure to gamma rays is dangerous to humans because the high energy of gamma rays can damage biological molecules.

Gamma rays are discussed in more detail in Chapter 19.

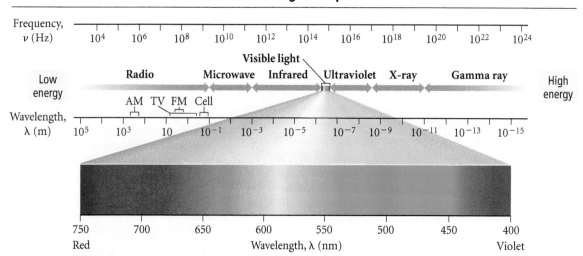

The Electromagnetic Spectrum

▲ FIGURE 7.5 **The Electromagnetic Spectrum**   The right side of the spectrum consists of high-energy, high-frequency, short-wavelength radiation. The left side consists of low-energy, low-frequency, long-wavelength radiation. Visible light constitutes a small segment in the middle.

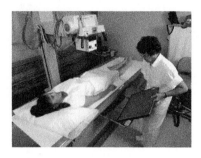

▲ To produce a medical X-ray, the patient is exposed to short-wavelength electromagnetic radiation that can pass through the skin to create an image of bones and internal organs.

High-intensity visible light, such as that emitted by a laser, can damage biological tissue by burning it.

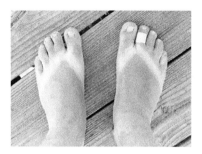

▲ Ultraviolet light from the sun produces suntans and sunburns.

Next on the electromagnetic spectrum, with longer wavelengths than gamma rays, are **X-rays**, familiar to us from their medical use. X-rays pass through many substances that block visible light and are therefore used to image bones and internal organs. Like gamma rays, X-rays are sufficiently energetic to damage biological molecules. While several yearly exposures to X-rays are relatively harmless, too much exposure to X-rays increases cancer risk.

Sandwiched between X-rays and visible light in the electromagnetic spectrum is **ultraviolet (UV) radiation**, most familiar to us as the component of sunlight that produces a sunburn or suntan. While not as energetic as gamma rays or X-rays, ultraviolet light still carries enough energy to damage biological molecules. Excessive exposure to ultraviolet light increases the risk of skin cancer and cataracts and causes premature wrinkling of the skin.

Next on the spectrum is **visible light**, ranging from violet (shorter wavelength, higher energy) to red (longer wavelength, lower energy). Visible light—at low to moderate intensity—does not carry enough energy to damage biological molecules. It does, however, cause certain molecules in our eyes to change their shape, sending a signal to our brains that results in our ability to see.

CHEMISTRY AND MEDICINE Radiation Treatment for Cancer

X-rays and gamma rays are sometimes called *ionizing radiation* because their short wavelengths correspond to high energies that can ionize atoms and molecules. When ionizing radiation interacts with biological molecules, it can permanently change or even destroy them. Consequently, we normally try to limit our exposure to ionizing radiation. However, doctors use ionizing radiation to destroy molecules within unwanted cells such as cancer cells.

In radiation therapy (or radiotherapy) doctors aim X-ray or gamma-ray beams at cancerous tumors (groups of cells that divide uncontrollably and invade surrounding healthy tissue). The ionizing radiation damages the molecules within the tumor's cells that carry genetic information—information necessary for the cell to grow and divide. Consequently, the cell dies or stops dividing. Ionizing radiation also damages molecules in healthy cells, but cancerous cells divide more quickly than normal cells, making them more susceptible to genetic damage. Nonetheless, harm to healthy tissues during treatments can result in side effects such as fatigue, skin lesions, hair loss, and organ damage. Medical workers try to reduce such effects by appropriate shielding (of healthy tissue) and by targeting the tumor from multiple directions, minimizing the exposure of healthy cells while maximizing the exposure of cancerous cells.

Another side effect of exposing healthy cells to radiation is that they too may become cancerous. If a treatment for cancer may cause cancer, why do we continue to use it? In radiation therapy, as in most other disease therapies, there is an associated risk. We take risks all the time, many of them for lesser reasons. For example, every time we fly in an airplane or drive in a car, we risk injury or even death. Why? Because we perceive the benefit—the convenience of being able to travel a significant distance in a short time—to be worth the relatively small risk. The situation is similar in cancer therapy, or any other therapy for that matter. The benefit of cancer therapy (possibly curing a cancer that might otherwise kill you) is worth the risk (a slight increase in the chance of developing a future cancer).

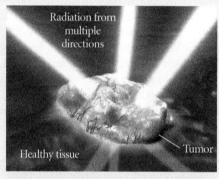

▲ During radiation therapy, a tumor is targeted from multiple directions in order to minimize the exposure of healthy cells while maximizing the exposure of cancerous cells.

▼ In radiation therapy, highly energetic gamma rays are aimed at cancerous tumors.

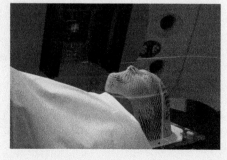

Question

Why is visible light (by itself) not used to destroy cancerous tumors?

Beyond visible light lies **infrared (IR) radiation**. The heat you feel when you place your hand near a hot object is infrared radiation. All warm objects, including human bodies, emit infrared light. Although infrared light is invisible to our eyes, infrared sensors can detect it and are often employed in night vision technology to "see" in the dark.

Beyond infrared light, at longer wavelengths still, are **microwaves**, used for radar and in microwave ovens. Although microwave radiation has longer wavelengths and therefore lower energies than visible or infrared light, it is efficiently absorbed by water and can therefore heat substances that contain water. The longest wavelengths are those of **radio waves**, which are used to transmit the signals responsible for AM and FM radio, cellular telephone, television, and other forms of communication.

Interference and Diffraction

Waves, including electromagnetic waves, interact with each other in a characteristic way called **interference**: they can cancel each other out or build each other up, depending on their alignment upon interaction. For example, if two waves of equal amplitude are *in phase* when they interact—that is, they align with overlapping crests—a wave with twice the amplitude results. This is called **constructive interference**.

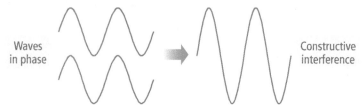

On the other hand, if two waves are completely *out of phase* when they interact—that is, they align so that the crest from one source overlaps with the trough from the other source—the waves cancel by **destructive interference**.

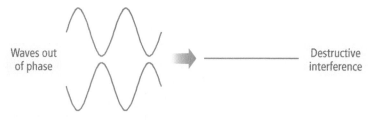

Waves also exhibit a characteristic behavior called **diffraction** (Figure 7.6 ▼). When a wave encounters an obstacle or a slit that is comparable in size to its wavelength, it bends (or *diffracts*) around it. The diffraction of light through two slits separated by a distance comparable to the wavelength of the light, coupled with interference, results in an

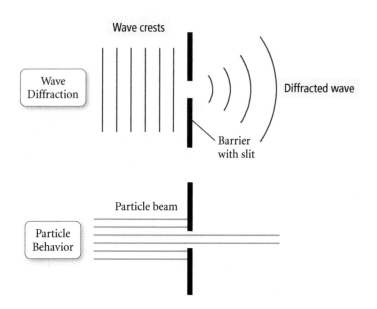

▲ Warm objects emit infrared light, which is invisible to the eye but can be captured on film or by detectors to produce an infrared photograph.

Understanding interference in waves is critical to understanding the wave nature of the electron, as we will soon see.

▲ When a reflected wave meets an incoming wave near the shore, the two waves interfere constructively for an instant, producing a large amplitude spike.

◀ **FIGURE 7.6 Diffraction** In this view from above, we can see how waves bend, or diffract, when they encounter an obstacle or slit with a size comparable to their wavelength. When a wave passes through a small opening, it spreads out. Particles, by contrast, do not diffract; they simply pass through the opening.

Interference from Two Slits

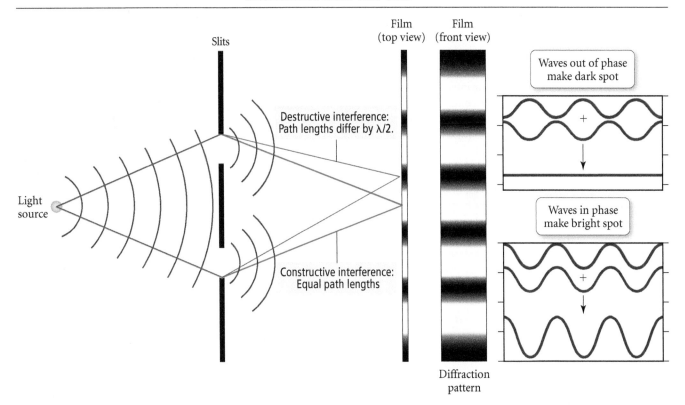

▲ **FIGURE 7.7 Interference from Two Slits**   When a beam of light passes through two small slits, the two resulting waves interfere with each other. Whether the interference is constructive or destructive at any given point depends on the difference in the path lengths traveled by the waves. The resulting interference pattern appears as a series of bright and dark lines on a screen.

interference pattern, as shown in Figure 7.7 ▲. Each slit acts as a new wave source, and the two new waves interfere with each other. The resulting pattern consists of a series of bright and dark lines that can be viewed on a screen (or recorded on a film) placed at a short distance behind the slits. At the center of the screen, the two waves travel equal distances and interfere constructively to produce a bright line. A small distance away from the center in either direction, the two waves travel slightly different distances, so that they are out of phase. At the point where the difference in distance is one-half of one wavelength, the interference is destructive and a dark line appears on the screen. Moving a bit further away from the center produces constructive interference again because the difference between the paths is one whole wavelength. The end result is the interference pattern shown by the light and dark bars in Figure 7.7. Notice that interference is a result of the ability of a wave to diffract through two slits—this is an inherent property of waves.

The Particle Nature of Light

The term *classical*, as in classical electromagnetic theory or classical mechanics, refers to descriptions of matter and energy before the advent of quantum mechanics.

Prior to the early 1900s, and especially after the discovery of the diffraction of light, light was thought to be purely a wave phenomenon. Its behavior was described adequately by classical electromagnetic theory, which treated the electric and magnetic fields that constitute light as waves propagating through space. However, a number of discoveries brought the classical view into question. Chief among these was the *photoelectric effect*.

The **photoelectric effect** is the observation that many metals emit electrons when light shines upon them, as shown in Figure 7.8 ▶. Classical electromagnetic theory attributed this effect to the transfer of energy from the light to an electron in the metal, which resulted in the dislodgment of the electron. If this explanation were correct, changing *either* the wavelength (color) or the amplitude (intensity) of the light would affect the emission of electrons. In other words, according to the classical description, the rate at

The Photoelectric Effect

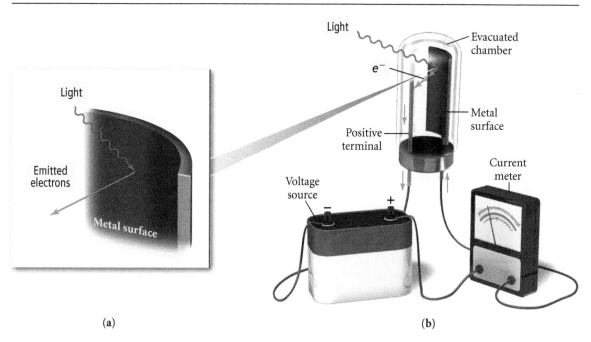

▲ FIGURE 7.8 The Photoelectric Effect (a) When sufficiently energetic light shines on a metal surface, the surface emits electrons. (b) The emitted electrons can be measured as an electrical current.

which electrons leave the metal due to the photoelectric effect would increase if either light of shorter wavelength or light of higher intensity (brighter light) was used. In addition, a dim light would be expected to result in a *lag time* between the initial shining of the light and the subsequent emission of an electron. The lag time would be the minimum amount of time required for the dim light to transfer sufficient energy to the electron to dislodge it.

The experimental results did not, however, follow the classical prediction. Scientists found that a high-frequency, low-intensity light produced electrons *without* the predicted lag time. Furthermore, the light used to dislodge electrons in the photoelectric effect exhibited a *threshold frequency*, below which no electrons were emitted from the metal, no matter how long the light shone on the metal. In other words, low-frequency (long-wavelength) light *would not* eject electrons from a metal regardless of its intensity or its duration. But high-frequency (short-wavelength) light *would* eject electrons, even if its intensity was low. What could explain this odd behavior?

In 1905, Albert Einstein proposed a bold explanation: *light energy must come in packets*. According to Einstein, the amount of energy (E) in a light packet depends on its frequency (ν) according to the following equation:

$$E = h\nu \qquad [7.2]$$

where h, called *Planck's constant*, has the value $h = 6.626 \times 10^{-34}$ J·s. A *packet* of light is called a **photon** or a **quantum** of light. Since $\nu = c/\lambda$, the energy of a photon can also be expressed in terms of wavelength as follows:

$$E = \frac{hc}{\lambda} \qquad [7.3]$$

Unlike classical electromagnetic theory, in which light was viewed purely as a wave whose intensity was *continuously variable*, Einstein suggested that light was *lumpy*. From this perspective, a beam of light is *not* a wave propagating through space, but a shower of particles (photons), each with energy $h\nu$.

> Einstein was not the first to suggest that energy was quantized. Max Planck used the idea in 1900 to account for certain characteristics of radiation from hot bodies. However, he did not suggest that light actually traveled in discrete packets.

> The energy of a photon is directly proportional to its frequency.

> The energy of a photon is inversely proportional to its wavelength.

EXAMPLE 7.2 Photon Energy

A nitrogen gas laser pulse with a wavelength of 337 nm contains 3.83 mJ of energy. How many photons does it contain?

SORT You are given the wavelength and total energy of a light pulse and asked to find the number of photons it contains.	**GIVEN:** $E_{pulse} = 3.83$ mJ $\lambda = 337$ nm **FIND:** number of photons
STRATEGIZE In the first part of the conceptual plan, calculate the energy of an individual photon from its wavelength. In the second part, divide the total energy of the pulse by the energy of a photon to get the number of photons in the pulse.	**CONCEPTUAL PLAN** $$E = \frac{hc}{\lambda}$$ $$\frac{E_{pulse}}{E_{photon}} = \text{number of photons}$$ **RELATIONSHIPS USED** $E = hc/\lambda$ (Equation 7.3)
SOLVE To execute the first part of the conceptual plan, convert the wavelength to meters and substitute it into the equation to compute the energy of a 337-nm photon. To execute the second part of the conceptual plan, convert the energy of the pulse from mJ to J. Then divide the energy of the pulse by the energy of a photon to obtain the number of photons.	**SOLUTION** $\lambda = 337 \text{ nm} \times \dfrac{10^{-9} \text{ m}}{1 \text{ nm}} = 3.37 \times 10^{-7}$ m $E_{photon} = \dfrac{hc}{\lambda} = \dfrac{\left(6.626 \times 10^{-34} \text{ J} \cdot \text{s}\right)\left(3.00 \times 10^{8} \frac{\text{m}}{\text{s}}\right)}{3.37 \times 10^{-7} \text{ m}}$ $\qquad = 5.8\underline{9}85 \times 10^{-19}$ J $3.83 \text{ mJ} \times \dfrac{10^{-3} \text{ J}}{1 \text{ mJ}} = 3.83 \times 10^{-3}$ J number of photons $= \dfrac{E_{pulse}}{E_{photon}} = \dfrac{3.83 \times 10^{-3} \text{ J}}{5.8\underline{9}85 \times 10^{-19} \text{ J}}$ $\qquad = 6.49 \times 10^{15}$ photons

CHECK The units of the answer, photons, are correct. The magnitude of the answer (10^{15}) is reasonable. Photons are small particles and any macroscopic collection should contain a large number of them.

FOR PRACTICE 7.2

A 100-watt lightbulb radiates energy at a rate of 100 J/s. (The watt, a unit of power, or energy over time, is defined as 1 J/s.) If all of the light emitted has a wavelength of 525 nm, how many photons are emitted per second? (Assume three significant figures in this calculation.)

FOR MORE PRACTICE 7.2

The energy required to dislodge electrons from sodium metal via the photoelectric effect is 275 kJ/mol. What wavelength in nm of light has sufficient energy per photon to dislodge an electron from the surface of sodium?

EXAMPLE 7.3 Wavelength, Energy, and Frequency

Arrange the three types of electromagnetic radiation—visible light, X-rays, and microwaves—in order of increasing:

(a) wavelength   **(b)** frequency   **(c)** energy per photon

SOLUTION

Examine Figure 7.5 and note that X-rays have the shortest wavelength, followed by visible light and then microwaves.	**(a)** wavelength X-rays < visible < microwaves
Since frequency and wavelength are inversely proportional—the longer the wavelength the shorter the frequency—the ordering with respect to frequency is the reverse of the order with respect to wavelength.	**(b)** frequency microwaves < visible < X-rays
Energy per photon decreases with increasing wavelength, but increases with increasing frequency; therefore the ordering with respect to energy per photon is the same as for frequency.	**(c)** energy per photon microwaves < visible < X-rays

FOR PRACTICE 7.3

Arrange the following colors of visible light—green, red, and blue—in order of increasing:

(a) wavelength   **(b)** frequency   **(c)** energy per photon

---

Einstein's idea that light is quantized elegantly explains the photoelectric effect. The emission of electrons from the metal depends on whether or not a single photon has sufficient energy (as given by $h\nu$) to dislodge a single electron. For an electron bound to the metal with binding energy ϕ, the threshold frequency is reached when the energy of the photon is equal to ϕ.

The symbol ϕ is the Greek letter phi, pronounced "fi."

Threshold frequency condition

$$h\nu = \phi$$

Energy of photon   Binding energy of emitted electron

Low-frequency light does not eject electrons because no single photon has the minimum energy necessary to dislodge the electron. Increasing the *intensity* of low-frequency light simply increases the number of low-energy photons, but does not produce any single photon with sufficient energy. In contrast, increasing the *frequency* of the light, even at low intensity, increases the energy of each photon, allowing the photons to dislodge electrons with no lag time.

As the frequency of the light is increased past the threshold frequency, the excess energy of the photon (beyond what is needed to dislodge the electron) is transferred to the electron in the form of kinetic energy. The kinetic energy (KE) of the ejected electron, therefore, is the difference between the energy of the photon ($h\nu$) and the binding energy of the electron, as given by the equation

$$\text{KE} = h\nu - \phi$$

Although the quantization of light explained the photoelectric effect, the wave explanation of light continued to have explanatory power as well, depending on the circumstances of the particular observation. So the principle that slowly emerged (albeit with some measure of resistance) is what we now call the *wave–particle duality of light*. Sometimes light appears to behave like a wave, at other times like a particle. Which behavior you observe depends on the particular experiment.

Conceptual Connection 7.1 **The Photoelectric Effect**

Light of three different wavelengths—325 nm, 455 nm, and 632 nm—was shined on a metal surface. The observations for each wavelength, labeled A, B, and C, were as follows:

Observation A: No photoelectrons were observed.

Observation B: Photoelectrons with a kinetic energy of 155 kJ/mol were observed.

Observation C: Photoelectrons with a kinetic energy of 51 kJ/mol were observed.

Which observation corresponds to which wavelength of light?

ANSWER: Observation A corresponds to 632 nm; observation B corresponds to 325 nm; and observation C corresponds to 455 nm. The shortest wavelength of light (highest energy per photon) must correspond to the photoelectrons with the greatest kinetic energy. The longest wavelength of light (lowest energy per photon) must correspond to the instance where no photoelectrons were observed.

7.3 Atomic Spectroscopy and the Bohr Model

The discovery of the particle nature of light began to break down the division that existed in nineteenth century physics between electromagnetic radiation, which was thought of as a wave phenomenon, and the small particles (protons, neutrons, and electrons) that compose atoms, which were thought to follow Newton's laws of motion. Just as the photoelectric effect suggested the particle nature of light, so certain observations within atoms began to suggest a wave nature for particles. The most important of these came from *atomic spectroscopy*, the study of the electromagnetic radiation absorbed and emitted by atoms.

When an atom absorbs energy—in the form of heat, light, or electricity—it often reemits that energy as light. For example, a neon sign is composed of one or more glass tubes filled with neon gas. When an electric current is passed through the tube, the neon atoms absorb some of the electrical energy and reemit it as the familiar red light of a neon sign. If the atoms in the tube are different (that is, not neon), they emit light of a different color. In other words, atoms of each element emit light of a characteristic color. Mercury atoms, for example, emit light that appears blue, helium atoms emit light that appears violet, and hydrogen atoms emit light that appears reddish (Figure 7.9 ◄).

Closer inspection of the light emitted by various atoms reveals that the light contains several distinct wavelengths. We can separate the light emitted by a single element in a glass tube into its constituent wavelengths by passing it through a prism (just like we separate the white light from a lightbulb), as shown in Figure 7.10 ►. The result is a series of bright lines called an **emission spectrum**. The emission spectrum of a particular element is always the same and can be used to identify the element. For example, light arriving from a distant star contains the emission spectra of the elements that compose the star. Analysis of the light allows us to identify the elements present in the star.

Notice the differences between a white light spectrum and the emission spectra of hydrogen, helium, and barium (as shown in Figure 7.10). The white light spectrum is *continuous*, meaning that there are no sudden interruptions in the intensity of the light as a function of wavelength—the spectrum consists of light of all wavelengths. The emission spectra of hydrogen, helium, and barium, however, are not continuous—they consist of bright lines at specific wavelengths, with complete darkness in between. That is, only certain discrete wavelengths of light are present. Classical physics could not explain why these spectra consisted of discrete lines. In fact, according to classical physics, an atom composed of an electron orbiting a nucleus should emit a continuous white light spectrum. Even more problematic, the electron should lose energy as it emitted the light and spiral into the nucleus. According to classical physics, an atom should not even be stable.

Johannes Rydberg, a Swedish mathematician, analyzed many atomic spectra and developed a simple equation that predicted the wavelengths of the hydrogen emission spec-

▲ The familiar red light from a neon sign is emitted by neon atoms that have absorbed electrical energy, which they reemit as visible radiation.

Remember that the color of visible light is determined by its wavelength.

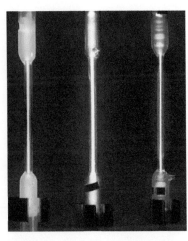

▲ **FIGURE 7.9 Mercury, Helium, and Hydrogen** Each element emits a characteristic color.

Emission Spectra

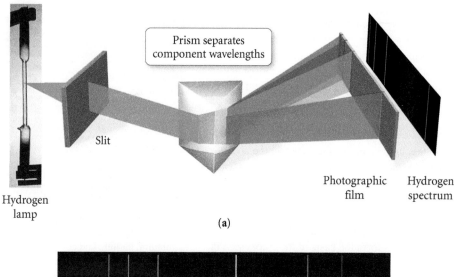

Slit

Prism separates component wavelengths

Photographic film

Hydrogen spectrum

Hydrogen lamp

(a)

◀ **FIGURE 7.10 Emission Spectra**
(a) The light emitted from a hydrogen, helium, or barium lamp consists of specific wavelengths, which can be separated by passing the light through a prism. **(b)** The resulting bright lines constitute an emission spectrum characteristic of the element that produced it.

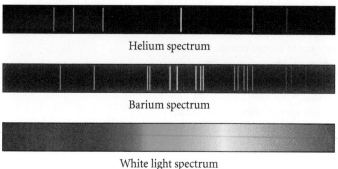

Helium spectrum

Barium spectrum

White light spectrum

(b)

trum. However, his equation (shown in the margin) gave little insight into *why* atomic spectra were discrete, *why* atoms were stable, or *why* his equation worked.

The Danish physicist Neils Bohr (1885–1962) attempted to develop a model for the atom that explained atomic spectra. In his model, electrons travel around the nucleus in circular orbits (analogous to those of the planets around the sun). However, in contrast to planetary orbits—which can theoretically exist at any distance from the sun—Bohr's orbits could exist only at specific, fixed distances from the nucleus. The energy of each Bohr orbit was also fixed, or *quantized*. Bohr called these orbits *stationary states* and suggested that, although they obeyed the laws of classical mechanics, they also possessed "a peculiar, mechanically unexplainable, stability." We now know that the stationary states were really manifestations of the wave nature of the electron, which we will expand upon shortly. Bohr further proposed that, in contradiction to classical electromagnetic theory, no radiation was emitted by an electron orbiting the nucleus in a stationary state. It was only when an electron jumped, or made a *transition*, from one stationary state to another that radiation was emitted or absorbed (Figure 7.11 ▶).

The transitions between stationary states in a hydrogen atom are quite unlike any transitions

The Rydberg equation is $1/\lambda = R(1/m^2 - 1/n^2)$, where R is the Rydberg constant $(1.097 \times 10^7 \, \text{m}^{-1})$, and m and n are integers.

The Bohr Model and Emission Spectra

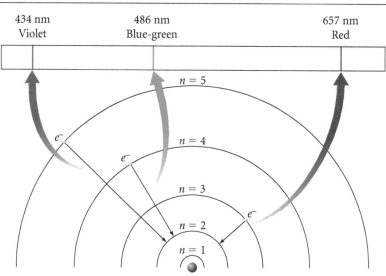

434 nm
Violet

486 nm
Blue-green

657 nm
Red

$n = 5$

e^-

$n = 4$

e^-

$n = 3$

e^-

$n = 2$

$n = 1$

▲ **FIGURE 7.11 The Bohr Model and Emission Spectra** According to the Bohr model, each spectral line is produced when an electron falls from one stable orbit, or stationary state, to another of lower energy.

CHEMISTRY IN YOUR DAY   Atomic Spectroscopy, a Bar Code for Atoms

When you check out of the grocery store, a laser scanner reads the bar code on the items that you buy. Each item has a unique code that identifies it and its price. Similarly, each element in the periodic table has a spectrum unlike that of any other element. For example, Figure 7.12 ▼ shows the emission spectra of oxygen and neon. (In Figure 7.10, we saw the emission spectra of hydrogen, helium, and barium.) Notice that each spectrum is unique and, as such, can be used to identify the substance.

The presence of intense lines in the spectra of a number of metals is the basis for *flame tests*, simple tests used to identify elements in ionic compounds even in the absence of a precise analysis of its spectrum. For example, the emission spectrum of sodium features two closely spaced, bright yellow lines. When a crystal of a sodium salt (or a drop of a solution containing a sodium salt) is put into a flame, the flame glows bright yellow (Figure 7.13 ►). As Figure 7.13 shows, other metals exhibit similarly characteristic colors in flame tests. Each color represents an especially bright spectral emission line (or a combination of two or more such lines). Similar emissions form the basis of the colors seen in fireworks.

Although the *emission* of light from elements is easier to detect, the *absorption* of light by elements is even more commonly used for purposes of identification. Whereas emission spectra consist of bright lines on a dark background, absorption spectra consist of dark lines on a bright background (Figure 7.14 ►). An absorption spectrum is measured by passing white light through a sample and observing what wavelengths are *missing* due to absorption by the sample. Notice that, in the spectra shown here, the absorption lines are at the same wavelengths as the emission lines. This is because the

▲ Fireworks typically contain the salts of such metals as sodium, calcium, strontium, barium, and copper. Emissions from these elements produce the brilliant colors of pyrotechnic displays.

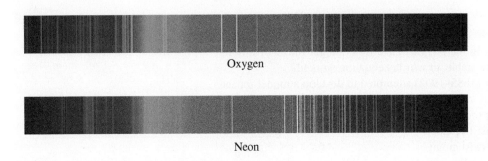

Oxygen

Neon

◄ FIGURE 7.12 **Emission Spectra of Oxygen and Neon**   The emission spectrum of each element is unique and we can use it to identify the element.

that you might be familiar with in the macroscopic world. The electron is *never* observed *between states*, only in one state or the next—the transition between states is instantaneous. The emission spectrum of an atom consists of discrete lines because the stationary states exist only at specific, fixed energies. The energy of the photon created when an electron makes a transition from one stationary state to another is the energy difference between the two stationary states. Transitions between stationary states that are closer together, therefore, produce light of lower energy (longer wavelength) than transitions between stationary states that are farther apart.

In spite of its initial success in explaining the line spectrum of hydrogen, the Bohr model left many unanswered questions. It did, however, serve as an intermediate model between a classical view of the electron and a fully quantum-mechanical view, and therefore has great historical and conceptual importance. Nonetheless, it was ultimately replaced by a more complete quantum-mechanical theory that fully incorporated the wave nature of the electron.

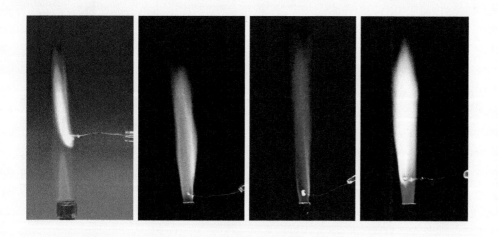

◄ **FIGURE 7.13 Flame Tests for Sodium, Potassium, Lithium, and Barium** We can identify elements by the characteristic color of the light they produce when heated. The colors derive from especially bright lines in their emission spectra.

processes that produce them are mirror images. In emission, an electron makes a transition from a higher energy level to a lower energy one. In absorption, the transition is between the same two energy levels, but from the lower level to the higher one.

Absorption spectrometers, found in most chemistry laboratories, typically plot the intensity of absorption as a function of wavelength. Such plots are useful both for identifying substances (qualitative analysis) and for determining the concentration of substances (quantitative analysis). Quantitative analysis is possible because the amount of light absorbed by a sample depends on the concentration of the absorbing substance within the sample. For example, the concentration of Ca^{2+} in a hard water sample can be determined by measuring the quantity of light absorbed by the calcium ion at its characteristic wavelength.

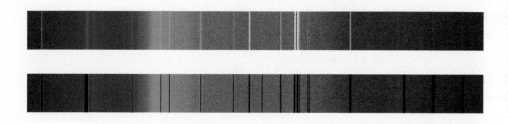

◄ **FIGURE 7.14 Emission and Absorption Spectrum of Mercury** Elements absorb light of the same wavelengths that they radiate when heated. When these wavelengths are subtracted from a beam of white light, the result is a pattern of dark lines called an absorption spectrum.

7.4 The Wave Nature of Matter: The de Broglie Wavelength, the Uncertainty Principle, and Indeterminacy

The heart of the quantum-mechanical theory that replaced Bohr's model is the wave nature of the electron, first proposed by Louis de Broglie (1892–1987) in 1924 and later confirmed by experiments in 1927. It seemed incredible at the time, but electrons—which were thought of as particles and known to have mass—were shown to also have a wave nature. The wave nature of the electron is seen most clearly in its diffraction. If an electron beam is aimed at two closely spaced slits, and a series (or array) of detectors is arranged to detect the electrons after they pass through the slits, an interference pattern similar to that observed for light is recorded behind the slits (Figure 7.15a ► on the next page). The detectors at the center of the array (midway between the two slits) detect a large number of electrons—exactly the opposite of what you would expect for particles

The first evidence of electron wave properties was provided by the Davisson-Germer experiment of 1927, in which electrons were observed to undergo diffraction by a metal crystal.

▶ **FIGURE 7.15 Electron Diffraction**
When a beam of electrons goes through two closely spaced slits **(a)**, an interference pattern is created, as if the electrons were waves. By contrast, a beam of particles passing through two slits **(b)** produces two smaller beams of particles. Notice that for particle beams, there is a dark line directly behind the center of the two slits, in contrast to wave behavior, which produces a bright line.

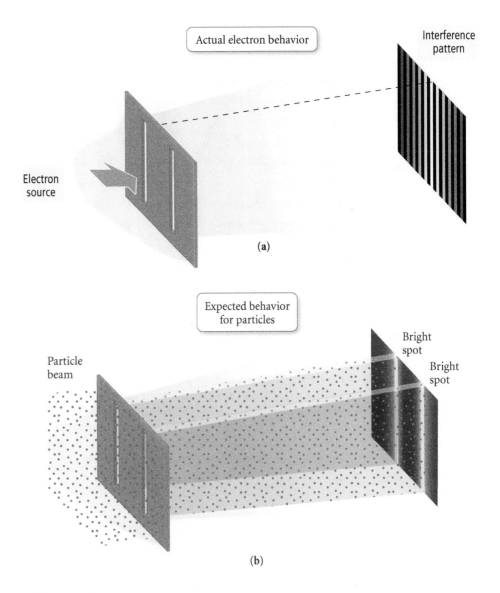

For interference to occur, the spacing of the slits has to be on the order of atomic dimensions.

(Figure 7.15b ▲). Moving outward from this center spot, the detectors alternately detect small numbers of electrons and then large numbers again and so on, forming an interference pattern characteristic of waves.

Counter to what might be our initial intuition about electron interference, the interference pattern is *not caused by pairs of electrons interfering with each other, but rather by single electrons interfering with themselves*. If the electron source is turned down to a very low level, so that electrons come out only one at a time, *the interference pattern remains*. In other words, we can design an experiment in which electrons come out of the source singly. We can then record where each electron strikes the detector after it has passed the slits. If we record the positions of thousands of electrons over a long period of time, we find the same interference pattern shown in Figure 7.15(a). This leads us to an important conclusion: *The wave nature of the electron is an inherent property of individual electrons*. As it turns out, this wave nature is what explains the existence of stationary states (in the Bohr model) and prevents the electrons in an atom from crashing into the nucleus as predicted by classical physics. We now turn to three important manifestations of the electron's wave nature: the de Broglie wavelength, the uncertainty principle, and indeterminacy.

The de Broglie Wavelength

As we have seen, a single electron traveling through space has a wave nature; its wavelength is related to its kinetic energy (the energy associated with its motion). The faster

the electron is moving, the higher its kinetic energy and the shorter its wavelength. The wavelength (λ) of an electron of mass m moving at velocity v is given by the **de Broglie relation**:

$$\lambda = \frac{h}{mv} \qquad \text{de Broglie relation} \qquad [7.4]$$

where h is Planck's constant. *Notice that the velocity of a moving electron is related to its wavelength—knowing one is equivalent to knowing the other.*

> The mass of an object (m) times its velocity (v) is its momentum. Therefore, the wavelength of an electron is inversely proportional to its momentum.

EXAMPLE 7.4 De Broglie Wavelength

Calculate the wavelength of an electron traveling with a speed of 2.65×10^6 m/s.

SORT You are given the speed of an electron and asked to calculate its wavelength.	**GIVEN:** $v = 2.65 \times 10^6$ m/s **FIND:** λ
STRATEGIZE The conceptual plan shows how the de Broglie relation relates the wavelength of an electron to its mass and velocity.	**CONCEPTUAL PLAN** $v \longrightarrow \lambda$ $\lambda = \dfrac{h}{mv}$ **RELATIONSHIPS USED** $\lambda = h/mv$ (de Broglie relation, Equation 7.4)
SOLVE Substitute the velocity, Planck's constant, and the mass of an electron to compute the electron's wavelength. To correctly cancel the units, break down the J in Planck's constant into its SI base units (1 J = 1 kg·m²/s²).	**SOLUTION** $\lambda = \dfrac{h}{mv} = \dfrac{6.626 \times 10^{-34}\, \frac{\text{kg} \cdot \text{m}^2}{\text{s}^2}\, \text{s}}{\left(9.11 \times 10^{-31}\, \text{kg}\right)\left(2.65 \times 10^6\, \frac{\text{m}}{\text{s}}\right)}$ $= 2.74 \times 10^{-10}$ m

CHECK The units of the answer (m) are correct. The magnitude of the answer is very small, as expected for the wavelength of an electron.

FOR PRACTICE 7.4

What is the velocity of an electron having a de Broglie wavelength that is approximately the length of a chemical bond? Assume this length to be 1.2×10^{-10} m.

 Conceptual Connection 7.2 The de Broglie Wavelength of Macroscopic Objects

Since quantum-mechanical theory is universal, it applies to all objects, regardless of size. Therefore, according to the de Broglie relation, a thrown baseball should also exhibit wave properties. Why do we not observe such properties at the ballpark?

ANSWER: Because of the baseball's large mass, its de Broglie wavelength is minuscule. (For a 150-g baseball, λ is on the order of 10^{-34} m.) This minuscule wavelength is insignificant compared to the size of the baseball itself, and therefore its effects are not observable.

The Uncertainty Principle

The wave nature of the electron is difficult to reconcile with its particle nature. How can a single entity behave as both a wave and a particle? We can begin to address this question by returning to the single-electron diffraction experiment. Specifically, we can ask the following question: how does a single electron aimed at a double slit produce an interference pattern? A possible hypothesis is that the electron splits into two, travels through both slits, and interferes with itself. This hypothesis seems testable. To do so, we would simply have to observe the single electron as it travels through the slits. If it travels through both slits simultaneously, we would know our hypothesis is correct.

The following electron diffraction experiment is designed to "watch" which slit the electron travels through by using a laser beam placed directly behind the slits.

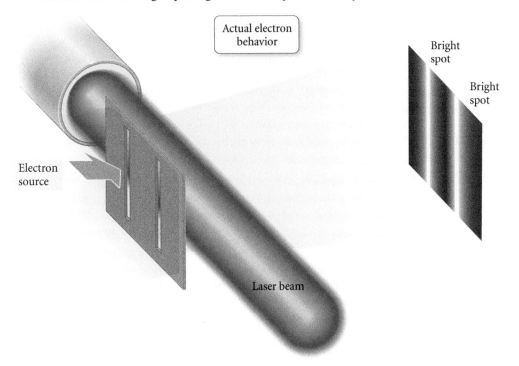

An electron that crosses the laser beam produces a tiny "flash" when a single photon is scattered at the point of crossing. If a flash shows up behind a particular slit, that indicates an electron is passing through that slit. However, when the experiment is performed, the flash always originates either from one slit *or* the other, but *never* from both at once. Furthermore, the interference pattern, which was present without the laser, is now absent. With the laser on, the electrons hit positions directly behind each slit, as if they were ordinary particles; their wave-like behavior is no longer manifested.

Any experiment designed to observe the electron as it travels through the slits results in the detection of an electron "particle" traveling through a single slit and no interference pattern. As it turns out, no matter how hard we try, or whatever method we set up, *we can never see the interference pattern and simultaneously determine which hole the electron goes through*. It has never been done, and most scientists agree that it never will. In the words of P. A. M. Dirac,

> There is a limit to the fineness of our powers of observation and the smallness of the accompanying disturbance—a limit which is inherent in the nature of things and can never be surpassed by improved technique or increased skill on the part of the observer.

We have encountered the absolutely small and have no way of observing its behavior without disturbing it.

The single electron diffraction experiment demonstrates that you cannot simultaneously observe both the wave nature and the particle nature of the electron. When you try to observe which hole the electron goes through (associated with the particle nature of the electron) you lose the interference pattern (associated with the wave nature of the electron). When you try to observe the interference pattern, you cannot determine which

hole the electron goes through. The wave nature and particle nature of the electron are said to be **complementary properties**. Complementary properties exclude one another—the more you know about one, the less you know about the other. Which of two complementary properties you observe depends on the experiment you perform—remember that in quantum mechanics, the observation of an event affects its outcome.

As we just saw in the de Broglie relation, the *velocity* of an electron is related to its *wave nature*. The *position* of an electron, however, is related to its *particle nature*. (Particles have well-defined position, but waves do not.) Consequently, our inability to observe the electron simultaneously as both a particle and a wave means that *we cannot simultaneously measure its position and its velocity*. Werner Heisenberg formalized this idea with the following equation:

$$\Delta x \times m\,\Delta v \geq \frac{h}{4\pi} \quad \text{Heisenberg's uncertainty principle} \qquad [7.5]$$

▲ Werner Heisenberg (1901–1976)

where Δx is the uncertainty in the position, Δv is the uncertainty in the velocity, m is the mass of the particle, and h is Planck's constant. **Heisenberg's uncertainty principle** states that the product of Δx and $m\,\Delta v$ must be greater than or equal to a finite number $(h/4\pi)$. In other words, the more accurately you know the position of an electron (the smaller Δx) the less accurately you can know its velocity (the bigger Δv) and vice versa. The complementarity of the wave nature and particle nature of the electron results in the complementarity of velocity and position.

Although Heisenberg's uncertainty principle may seem puzzling, it actually solves a great puzzle. Without the uncertainty principle, we are left with a paradox: how can something be *both* a particle and a wave? Saying that an object is both a particle and a wave is like saying that an object is both a circle and a square, a contradiction. Heisenberg solved the contradiction by introducing complementarity—an electron is observed as *either* a particle or a wave, but never both at once.

Indeterminacy and Probability Distribution Maps

According to classical physics, and in particular Newton's laws of motion, particles move in a *trajectory* (or path) that is determined by the particle's velocity (the speed and direction of travel), its position, and the forces acting on it. Even if you are not familiar with Newton's laws, you probably have an intuitive sense of them. For example, when you chase a baseball in the outfield, you visually predict where the ball will land by observing its path. You do this by noting its initial position and velocity, watching how these are affected by the forces acting on it (gravity, air resistance, wind), and then inferring its trajectory, as shown in Figure 7.16 ▼. If you knew only the ball's velocity, or only its position (imagine a still photo of the baseball in the air), you could not predict its landing spot. In classical mechanics, both position and velocity are required to predict a trajectory.

Newton's laws of motion are **deterministic**—the present *determines* the future. This means that if two baseballs are hit consecutively with the same velocity from the same

Remember that velocity includes speed as well as direction of travel.

The Classical Concept of Trajectory

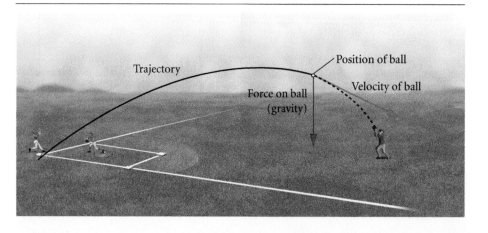

Trajectory

Position of ball

Velocity of ball

Force on ball
(gravity)

◀ **FIGURE 7.16 The Concept of Trajectory** In classical mechanics, the position and velocity of a particle determine its future trajectory, or path. Thus, an outfielder can catch a baseball by observing its position and velocity, allowing for the effects of forces acting on it, such as gravity, and estimating its trajectory. (For simplicity, air resistance and wind are not shown.)

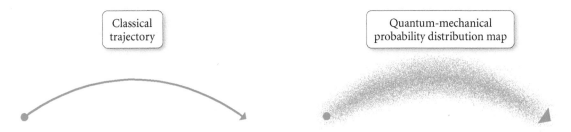

Classical trajectory

Quantum-mechanical probability distribution map

▲ **FIGURE 7.17 Trajectory versus Probability** In quantum mechanics, we cannot calculate deterministic trajectories. Instead, it is necessary to think in terms of probability maps: statistical pictures of where a quantum-mechanical particle, such as an electron, is most likely to be found. In this hypothetical map, darker shading indicates greater probability.

▲ **FIGURE 7.18 Trajectory of a Macroscopic Object** A baseball follows a well-defined trajectory from the hand of the pitcher to the mitt of the catcher.

position under identical conditions, they will land in exactly the same place. The same is not true of electrons. We have just seen that we cannot simultaneously know the position and velocity of an electron; therefore, we cannot know its trajectory. In quantum mechanics, trajectories are replaced with *probability distribution maps*, as shown in Figure 7.17 ▲. A probability distribution map is a statistical map that shows where an electron is likely to be found under a given set of conditions.

To understand the concept of a probability distribution map, let us return to baseball. Imagine a baseball thrown from the pitcher's mound to a catcher behind home plate (Figure 7.18 ◄.) The catcher can watch the baseball's path, predict exactly where it will cross home plate, and place his mitt in the correct place to catch it. As we have seen, the same predictions are impossible for an electron. If an electron were thrown from the pitcher's mound to home plate, it would land in a different place every time, even if it were thrown in exactly the same way. This behavior is called **indeterminacy**. Unlike a baseball, whose future path is *determined* by its position and velocity when it leaves the pitcher's hand, the future path of an electron is indeterminate, and can only be described statistically.

In the quantum-mechanical world of the electron, the catcher could not know exactly where the electron will cross the plate for any given throw. However, if he recorded hundreds of identical electron throws, the catcher would observe a reproducible, *statistical pattern* of where the electron crosses the plate. He could even draw a map of the strike zone showing the probability of an electron crossing a certain area, as shown in Figure 7.19 ▼. This would be a probability distribution map. In the sections that follow, we discuss quantum-mechanical electron *orbitals*, which are essentially probability distribution maps for electrons as they exist within atoms.

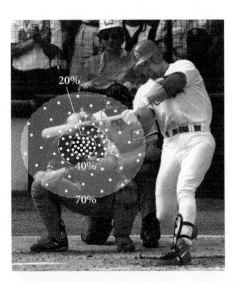

20%

40%

70%

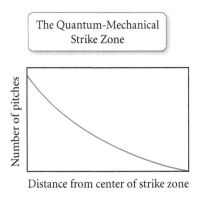

The Quantum-Mechanical Strike Zone

Number of pitches

Distance from center of strike zone

▲ **FIGURE 7.19 The Quantum-Mechanical Strike Zone** An electron does not have a well-defined trajectory. However, we can construct a probability distribution map to show the relative probability of it crossing home plate at different points.

7.5 Quantum Mechanics and the Atom

As we have seen, the position and velocity of the electron are complementary properties—if we know one accurately, the other becomes indeterminate. Since velocity is directly related to energy (we have seen that kinetic energy equals $\frac{1}{2}mv^2$), position and *energy* are also complementary properties—the more you know about one, the less you know about the other. Many of the properties of an element, however, depend on the energies of its electrons. For example, whether an electron is transferred from one atom to another to form an ionic bond depends in part on the relative energies of the electron in the two atoms. In the following paragraphs, we describe the probability distribution maps for electron states in which the electron has well-defined energy, but not well-defined position. In other words, for each state, we can specify the *energy* of the electron precisely, but not its location at a given instant. Instead, the electron's position is described in terms of an **orbital**, a probability distribution map showing where the electron is likely to be found. Since chemical bonding often involves the sharing of electrons between atoms to form covalent bonds, the spatial distribution of atomic electrons is important to bonding.

> These states are known as energy *eigenstates*.

The mathematical derivation of energies and orbitals for electrons in atoms comes from solving the *Schrödinger* equation for the atom of interest. The general form of the Schrödinger equation is as follows:

$$\mathcal{H}\psi = E\psi \qquad [7.6]$$

The symbol $\mathcal{H}$ stands for the Hamiltonian operator, a set of mathematical operations that represent the total energy (kinetic and potential) of the electron within the atom. The symbol E is the actual energy of the electron. The symbol ψ is the **wave function**, a mathematical function that describes the wavelike nature of the electron. A plot of the wave function squared (ψ^2) represents an orbital, a position probability distribution map of the electron.

> An operator is different from a normal algebraic entity. In general, an operator transforms a mathematical function into another mathematical function. For example, d/dx is an operator that means "take the deriviative of." When d/dx operates on a function (such as x^2) it returns another function ($2x$).

> The symbol ψ is the Greek letter psi, pronounced "sigh."

Solutions to the Schrödinger Equation for the Hydrogen Atom

When the Schrödinger equation is solved, it yields many solutions—many possible wave functions. The wave functions themselves are fairly complicated mathematical functions, and we will not examine them in detail in this book. Instead, we will introduce graphical representations (or plots) of the orbitals that correspond to the wave functions. Each orbital is specified by three interrelated **quantum numbers**: n, the **principal quantum number**; l, the **angular momentum quantum number** (sometimes called the *azimuthal quantum number*); and m_l, the **magnetic quantum number**. These quantum numbers all have integer values, as had been hinted at by both the Rydberg equation and Bohr's model. We examine each of these quantum numbers individually.

The Principal Quantum Number (n) The principal quantum number is an integer that determines the overall size and energy of an orbital. Its possible values are $n = 1, 2, 3, \ldots$ and so on. For the hydrogen atom, the energy of an electron in an orbital with quantum number n is given by

$$E_n = -2.18 \times 10^{-18} \text{ J} \left(\frac{1}{n^2}\right) \qquad (n = 1, 2, 3, \ldots) \qquad [7.7]$$

The energy is negative because the electron's energy is lowered (made more negative) by its interaction with the nucleus (as described by Coulomb's law). The constant, 2.18×10^{-18} J, is known as the Rydberg constant for hydrogen (R_H). Notice that orbitals with higher values of n have greater (less negative) energies, as shown in the energy level diagram on the right. Notice also that, as n increases, the spacing between the energy levels becomes smaller.

The Angular Momentum Quantum Number (l) The angular momentum quantum number is an integer that determines the shape of the orbital. We will consider these shapes in Section 7.6. The possible values of l are $0, 1, 2, \ldots, (n - 1)$. In other words, for a given value of n, l can be any integer (including 0) up to $n - 1$.

$n = 4$ ———— $E_4 = -1.36 \times 10^{-19}$ J
$n = 3$ ———— $E_3 = -2.42 \times 10^{-19}$ J

$n = 2$ ———— $E_2 = -5.45 \times 10^{-19}$ J

Energy

$n = 1$ ———— $E_1 = -2.18 \times 10^{-18}$ J

For example, if $n = 1$, then the only possible value of l is 0; if $n = 2$, the possible values of l are 0 and 1. In order to avoid confusion between n and l, values of l are often assigned letters as follows:

The values of l beyond 3 are designated with letters in alphabetical order so that $l = 4$ is designated g, $l = 5$ is designated h, and so on.

Value of l	Letter Designation
$l = 0$	s
$l = 1$	p
$l = 2$	d
$l = 3$	f

The Magnetic Quantum Number (m_l) The magnetic quantum number is an integer that specifies the orientation of the orbital. We will consider these orientations in Section 7.6. The possible values of m_l are the integer values (including zero) ranging from $-l$ to $+l$. For example, if $l = 0$, then the only possible value of m_l is 0; if $l = 1$, the possible values of m_l are -1, 0, and $+1$; if $l = 2$, the possible values of m_l are -2, -1, 0, $+1$, and $+2$, and so on.

Each specific combination of n, l, and m_l specifies one atomic orbital. For example, the orbital with $n = 1$, $l = 0$, and $m_l = 0$ is known as the 1s orbital. The 1 in 1s is the value of n and the s specifies that $l = 0$. There is only one 1s orbital in an atom, and its m_l value is zero. Orbitals with the same value of n are said to be in the same **principal level** (or **principal shell**). Orbitals with the same value of n and l are said to be in the same **sublevel** (or **subshell**). The following diagram shows all of the orbitals in the first three principal levels.

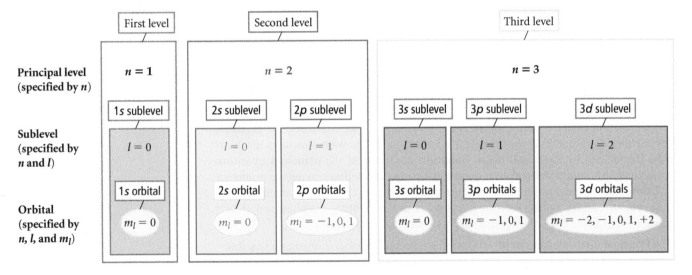

For example, the $n = 2$ level contains the $l = 0$ and $l = 1$ sublevels. Within the $n = 2$ level, the $l = 0$ sublevel—called the 2s sublevel—contains only one orbital (the 2s orbital), with $m_l = 0$. The $l = 1$ sublevel—called the 2p sublevel—contains three 2p orbitals, with $m_l = -1, 0, +1$.

In general, notice the following:

- The number of sublevels in any level is equal to n, the principal quantum number. Therefore, the $n = 1$ level has one sublevel, the $n = 2$ level has two sublevels, etc.

- The number of orbitals in any sublevel is equal to $2l + 1$. Therefore, the s sublevel ($l = 0$) has one orbital, the p sublevel ($l = 1$) has three orbitals, the d sublevel ($l = 2$) has five orbitals, etc.

- The number of orbitals in a level is equal to n^2. Therefore, the $n = 1$ level has one orbital, the $n = 2$ level has four orbitals, the $n = 3$ level has nine orbitals, etc.

EXAMPLE 7.5 Quantum Numbers I

What are the quantum numbers and names (for example, $2s$, $2p$) of the orbitals in the $n = 4$ principal level? How many $n = 4$ orbitals exist?

SOLUTION

First determine the possible values of l (from the given value of n). Then determine the possible values of m_l for each possible value of l. For a given value of n, the possible values of l are $0, 1, 2, \ldots, (n - 1)$.	$n = 4$; therefore $l = 0$, 1, 2, and 3

For a given value of l, the possible values of m_l are the integer values including zero ranging from $-l$ to $+l$. The name of an orbital is its principal quantum number (n) followed by the letter corresponding to the value l. The total number of orbitals is given by n^2.

l	possible m_l Values	Orbital name(s)
0	0	$4s$ (1 orbital)
1	$-1, 0, +1$	$4p$ (3 orbitals)
2	$-2, -1, 0, +1, +2$	$4d$ (5 orbitals)
3	$-3, -2, -1, 0, +1, +2, +3$	$4f$ (7 orbitals)

Total number of orbitals $= 4^2 = 16$

FOR PRACTICE 7.5

List the quantum numbers associated with all of the $5d$ orbitals. How many $5d$ orbitals exist?

EXAMPLE 7.6 Quantum Numbers II

The sets of quantum numbers are each supposed to specify an orbital. One set, however, is erroneous. Which one and why?

(a) $n = 3; l = 0; m_l = 0$ **(b)** $n = 2; l = 1; m_l = -1$

(c) $n = 1; l = 0; m_l = 0$ **(d)** $n = 4; l = 1; m_l = -2$

SOLUTION

Choice **(d)** is erroneous because, for $l = 1$, the possible values of m_l are only -1, 0, and $+1$.

FOR PRACTICE 7.6

Each set of quantum numbers is supposed to specify an orbital. However, each set contains one quantum number that is not allowed. Replace the quantum number that is not allowed with one that is allowed.

(a) $n = 3; l = 3; m_l = +2$

(b) $n = 2; l = 1; m_l = -2$

(c) $n = 1; l = 1; m_l = 0$

Atomic Spectroscopy Explained

Quantum theory explains the atomic spectra of atoms discussed earlier. Each wavelength in the emission spectrum of an atom corresponds to an electron *transition* between quantum-mechanical orbitals. When an atom absorbs energy, an electron in a lower energy

▶ **FIGURE 7.20 Excitation and Radiation** When an atom absorbs energy, an electron can be excited from an orbital in a lower energy level to an orbital in a higher energy level. The electron in this "excited state" is unstable, however, and relaxes to a lower energy level, releasing energy in the form of electromagnetic radiation.

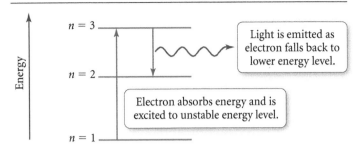

Excitation and Radiation

$n = 3$

$n = 2$

$n = 1$

Energy

Light is emitted as electron falls back to lower energy level.

Electron absorbs energy and is excited to unstable energy level.

level is *excited* or promoted to a higher energy level, as shown in Figure 7.20 ▲. In this new configuration, however, the atom is unstable, and the electron quickly falls back or *relaxes* to a lower energy orbital. As it does so, it releases a photon of light containing an amount of energy precisely equal to the energy difference between the two energy levels. We saw previously (see Equation 7.7) that the energy of an orbital with principal quantum number n is given by $E_n = -2.18 \times 10^{-18}$ J$(1/n^2)$, where $n = 1, 2, 3, \ldots$ Therefore, the *difference* in energy between two levels n_{initial} and n_{final} is given by $\Delta E = E_{\text{final}} - E_{\text{initial}}$. If we substitute the expression for E_n into the expression for ΔE, we get the following important expression for the change in energy that occurs in an atom when an electron changes energy levels:

$$\Delta E = E_{\text{final}} - E_{\text{initial}}$$

$$= -2.18 \times 10^{-18} \text{ J}\left(\frac{1}{n_f^2}\right) - \left[-2.18 \times 10^{-18} \text{ J}\left(\frac{1}{n_i^2}\right)\right]$$

$$\Delta E = -2.18 \times 10^{-18} \text{ J}\left(\frac{1}{n_f^2} - \frac{1}{n_i^2}\right) \qquad [7.8]$$

For example, suppose that an electron in a hydrogen atom relaxes from an orbital in the $n = 3$ level to an orbital in the $n = 2$ level. Then ΔE, the energy difference corresponding to the transition from $n = 3$ to $n = 2$, is determined as follows:

$$\Delta E_{\text{atom}} = E_2 - E_3$$

$$= -2.18 \times 10^{-18} \text{ J}\left(\frac{1}{2^2}\right) - \left[-2.18 \times 10^{-18} \text{ J}\left(\frac{1}{3^2}\right)\right]$$

$$= -2.18 \times 10^{-18} \text{ J}\left(\frac{1}{2^2} - \frac{1}{3^2}\right)$$

$$= -3.03 \times 10^{-19} \text{ J}$$

The energy carries a negative sign because the atom *emits* the energy as it relaxes from $n = 3$ to $n = 2$. Since energy must be conserved, the exact amount of energy emitted by the atom is carried away by the photon:

$$\Delta E_{\text{atom}} = -E_{\text{photon}}$$

This energy then determines the frequency and wavelength of the photon. Since the wavelength of the photon is related to its energy as $E = hc/\lambda$, we calculate the wavelength of the photon as follows:

The Rydberg equation, $1/\lambda = R(1/m^2 - 1/n^2)$, can be derived from the relationships just covered. We leave this derivation to an exercise (see Problem 7.98).

$$\lambda = \frac{hc}{E}$$

$$= \frac{(6.626 \times 10^{-34} \text{ J} \cdot \text{s})(3.00 \times 10^8 \text{ m/s})}{3.03 \times 10^{-19} \text{ J}}$$

$$= 6.56 \times 10^{-7} \text{ m} \quad \text{or} \quad 656 \text{ nm}$$

Hydrogen Energy Transitions and Radiation

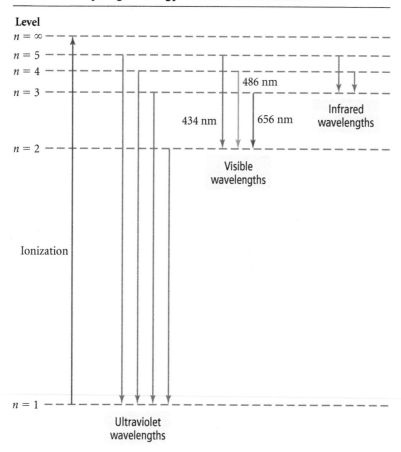

▲ FIGURE 7.21 Hydrogen Energy Transitions and Radiation   An atomic energy level diagram for hydrogen, showing some possible electron transitions between levels and the corresponding wavelengths of emitted light.

Consequently, the light emitted by an excited hydrogen atom as it relaxes from an orbital in the $n = 3$ level to an orbital in the $n = 2$ level has a wavelength of 656 nm (red). Using the same method, we can calculate the light emitted due to a transition from $n = 4$ to $n = 2$ to be 486 nm (green). Notice that transitions between orbitals that are further apart in energy produce light that is higher in energy, and therefore shorter in wavelength, than transitions between orbitals that are closer together. Figure 7.21 ▲ shows several of the transitions in the hydrogen atom and their corresponding wavelengths.

 Conceptual Connection 7.3 Emission Spectra

Which transition will result in emitted light with the shortest wavelength?

(a) $n = 5 \longrightarrow n = 4$

(b) $n = 4 \longrightarrow n = 3$

(c) $n = 3 \longrightarrow n = 2$

ANSWER: (c) The energy difference between $n = 3$ and $n = 2$ is greatest because the energy differences get closer together with increasing n. The greater energy difference results in an emitted photon of greater energy and therefore shorter wavelength.

EXAMPLE 7.7 Wavelength of Light for a Transition in the Hydrogen Atom

Determine the wavelength of light emitted when an electron in a hydrogen atom makes a transition from an orbital in $n = 6$ to an orbital in $n = 5$.

SORT You are given the energy levels of an atomic transition and asked to find the wavelength of emitted light.	**GIVEN:** $n = 6 \longrightarrow n = 5$ **FIND:** λ

STRATEGIZE In the first part of the conceptual plan, calculate the energy of the electron in the $n = 6$ and $n = 5$ orbitals using Equation 7.7 and subtract to find ΔE_{atom}. In the second part, find E_{photon} by taking the negative of ΔE_{atom}, and then calculate the wavelength corresponding to a photon of this energy using Equation 7.3. (The difference in sign between E_{photon} and ΔE_{atom} applies only to emission. *The energy of a photon must always be positive.*)	**CONCEPTUAL PLAN** $\boxed{n = 5, n = 6} \longrightarrow \boxed{\Delta E_{atom}}$ $\Delta E = E_5 - E_6$ $\boxed{\Delta E_{atom}} \longrightarrow \boxed{E_{photon}} \longrightarrow \boxed{\lambda}$ $\Delta E_{atom} = -E_{photon}$ $\qquad E = \dfrac{hc}{\lambda}$ **RELATIONSHIPS USED** $E_n = -2.18 \times 10^{-18} \text{ J}(1/n^2)$ $E = hc/\lambda$

SOLVE Follow the conceptual plan. Begin by computing ΔE_{atom}. Compute E_{photon} by changing the sign of ΔE_{atom}. Solve the equation relating the energy of a photon to its wavelength for λ. Substitute the energy of the photon and compute λ.	**SOLUTION** $\Delta E_{atom} = E_5 - E_6$ $= -2.18 \times 10^{-18} \text{ J}\left(\dfrac{1}{5^2}\right) - \left[-2.18 \times 10^{-18} \text{ J}\left(\dfrac{1}{6^2}\right)\right]$ $= -2.18 \times 10^{-18} \text{ J}\left(\dfrac{1}{5^2} - \dfrac{1}{6^2}\right)$ $= -2.6\underline{6}44 \times 10^{-20} \text{ J}$ $E_{photon} = -\Delta E_{atom} = +2.6\underline{6}44 \times 10^{-20} \text{ J}$ $E = \dfrac{hc}{\lambda}$ $\lambda = \dfrac{hc}{E}$ $= \dfrac{(6.626 \times 10^{-34} \text{ J} \cdot \text{s})(3.00 \times 10^8 \text{ m/s})}{2.6\underline{6}44 \times 10^{-20} \text{ J}}$ $= 7.46 \times 10^{-6} \text{ m}$

CHECK The units of the answer (m) are correct for wavelength. The magnitude seems reasonable because 10^{-6} m is in the infrared region of the electromagnetic spectrum. We know that transitions from $n = 3$ or $n = 4$ to $n = 2$ lie in the visible region, so it makes sense that a transition between levels of higher n value (which are energetically closer to one another) would result in light of longer wavelength.

FOR PRACTICE 7.7

Determine the wavelength of the light absorbed when an electron in a hydrogen atom makes a transition from an orbital in which $n = 2$ to an orbital in which $n = 7$.

FOR MORE PRACTICE 7.7

An electron in the $n = 6$ level of the hydrogen atom relaxes to a lower energy level, emitting light of $\lambda = 93.8$ nm. Find the principal level to which the electron relaxed.

7.6 The Shapes of Atomic Orbitals

As we noted previously, the shapes of atomic orbitals are important because covalent chemical bonds depend on the sharing of the electrons that occupy these orbitals. In one model of chemical bonding, for example, a bond consists of the overlap of atomic orbitals on adjacent atoms. The shapes of the overlapping orbitals determine the shape of the molecule. Although we limit ourselves in this chapter to the orbitals of the hydrogen atom, we will see in Chapter 8 that the orbitals of all atoms can be approximated as being hydrogen-like and therefore have very similar shapes to those of hydrogen.

The shape of an atomic orbital is determined primarily by l, the angular momentum quantum number. As we have seen, each value of l is assigned a letter that therefore corresponds to particular orbitals. For example, the orbitals with $l = 0$ are called s orbitals; those with $l = 1$, p orbitals; those with $l = 2$, d orbitals, etc. We now examine the shape of each of these orbitals.

s Orbitals (*l* = 0)

The lowest energy orbital is the spherically symmetrical $1s$ orbital shown in Figure 7.22(a) ▼. This image is actually a three-dimensional plot of the wave function squared (ψ^2), which represents **probability density**, the probability (per unit volume) of finding the electron at a point in space.

$$\psi^2 = \text{probability density} = \frac{\text{probability}}{\text{unit volume}}$$

The magnitude of ψ^2 in this plot is proportional to the density of the dots shown in the image. The high dot density near the nucleus (at the very center of the plot) indicates a higher probability density for the electron there. As you move away from the nucleus, the probability density decreases. Figure 7.22(b) shows a plot of probability density (ψ^2) versus r, the distance from the nucleus. The plot represents a slice through the three-dimensional plot of ψ^2 and shows how the probability density decreases as r increases.

We can understand probability density with the help of a thought experiment. Imagine an electron in the $1s$ orbital located within the volume surrounding the nucleus. Imagine also taking a photograph of the electron every second for 10 or 15 minutes. In one photograph, the electron is very close to the nucleus, in another it is farther away, and so on. Each photo has a dot showing the electron's position relative to the nucleus when the photo was taken. Remember that you can never predict where the electron will be for any one photo. However, if you took hundreds of photos and superimposed all of them, you would have a plot similar to Figure 7.22(a)—a statistical representation of how likely the electron is to be found at each point.

The thought experiment we just examined can result in a possible misunderstanding: that the electron is moving around (like a moth near a flame) between photographs. However, in the quantum mechanical model, that is not the case. Between photographs, the

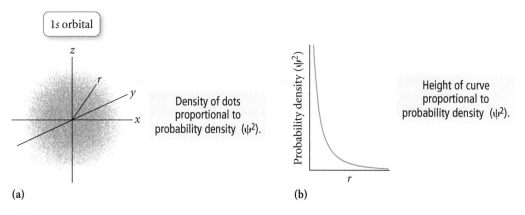

Density of dots proportional to probability density (ψ^2).

Probability density (ψ^2)

r

Height of curve proportional to probability density (ψ^2).

(a) (b)

▲ **FIGURE 7.22 The 1*s* Orbital: Two Representations**   In (a) the dot density is proportional to the electron probability density. In (b), the height of the curve is proportional to the electron probability density. The *x*-axis is *r*, the distance from the nucleus.

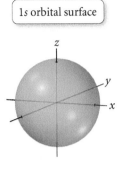

1s orbital surface

▲ **FIGURE 7.23 The 1*s* Orbital Surface**
In this representation, the surface of the sphere encompasses the volume where the electron is found 90% of the time when the electron is in the 1*s* orbital.

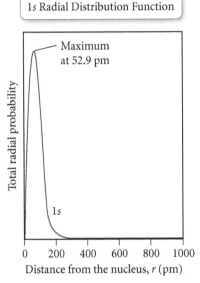

1s Radial Distribution Function

▲ **FIGURE 7.24 The Radial Distribution Function for the 1*s* Orbital**   The curve shows the total probability of finding the electron within a thin shell at a distance *r* from the nucleus.

| 1 pm = 10⁻² m

location of the electron is uncertain—in a sense its location is spread out over the entire volume of the orbital. Only when the photograph is taken (that is, when a measurement of its location is made) does the location of the electron become localized to one spot. Between measurements, the electron has no single location. Remember from Section 7.1, the measurement affects the outcome of any quantum system.

An atomic orbital can also be represented by a geometrical shape that encompasses the volume where the electron is likely to be found most frequently—typically, 90% of the time. For example, the 1*s* orbital can be represented as the three-dimensional sphere shown in Figure 7.23 ◄. If we were to superimpose the dot-density representation of the 1*s* orbital on the shape representation, 90% of the dots would be within the sphere, meaning that when the electron is in the 1*s* orbital it has a 90% chance of being found within the sphere.

The plots we have just seen represent probability *density*. However, they are a bit misleading because they seem to imply that the electron is most likely to be found *at the nucleus*. To get a better idea of where the electron is most likely to be found, we can use a plot called the **radial distribution function**, shown in Figure 7.24 ◄ for the 1*s* orbital. The radial distribution function represents the *total probability of finding the electron within a thin spherical shell at a distance r from the nucleus*.

$$\text{Total radial probability (at a given } r) = \frac{\text{probability}}{\text{unit volume}} \times \text{volume of shell at } r$$

The radial distribution function represents, not probability density *at a point r*, but total probability *at a radius r*. In contrast to probability density, which has a maximum at the nucleus, the radial distribution function has a value of *zero* at the nucleus. It increases to a maximum at 52.9 pm and then decreases again with increasing *r*.

The shape of the radial distribution function is the result of multiplying together two functions with opposite trends in *r*: (1) the probability density function (ψ^2), which is the probability per unit volume and decreases with increasing *r*, and (2) the volume of the thin shell, which increases with increasing *r*. At the nucleus ($r = 0$), for example, the probability *density* is at a maximum; however, the volume of a thin spherical shell is zero, so the radial distribution function is zero. As *r* increases, the volume of the thin spherical shell increases. We can understand this by making an analogy to an onion. A spherical shell at a distance *r* from the nucleus is like a layer in an onion at a distance *r* from its center. If the layers of the onion are all the same thickness, then the volume of any one layer—think of this as the total amount of onion in the layer—is greater as *r* increases. Similarly, the volume of any one spherical shell in the radial distribution function increases with increasing distance from the nucleus, resulting in a greater total probability of finding the electron within that shell. Close to the nucleus, this increase in volume with increasing *r* outpaces the decrease in probability density, producing a maximum at 52.9 pm. Farther out, however, the density tapers off faster than the volume increases.

The maximum in the radial distribution function, 52.9 pm, turns out to be the very same radius that Bohr had predicted for the innermost orbit of the hydrogen atom. However, there is a significant conceptual difference between the two radii. In the Bohr model, every time you probe the atom (in its lowest energy state), you would find the electron at a radius of 52.9 pm. In the quantum-mechanical model, you would generally find the electron at various radii, with 52.9 pm having the greatest probability.

The probability densities and radial distribution functions for the 2*s* and 3*s* orbitals are shown in Figure 7.25 ►. Like the 1*s* orbital, these orbitals are spherically symmetric. These orbitals are larger in size, however, and, unlike the 1*s* orbital, they contain at least one *node*. A **node** is a point where the wave function (ψ), and therefore the probability density (ψ^2) and radial distribution function, all go through zero. A node in a wave function is much like a node in a standing wave on a vibrating string. We can see nodes in an orbital most clearly by looking at a slice through the orbital. Plots of probability density and the radial distribution function as a function of *r* both reveal the presence of nodes. The probability of finding the electron at a node is zero.

► The nodes in quantum-mechanical atomic orbitals are three-dimensional analogs of the nodes on a vibrating string.

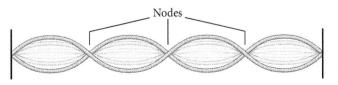

The 2s and 3s Orbitals

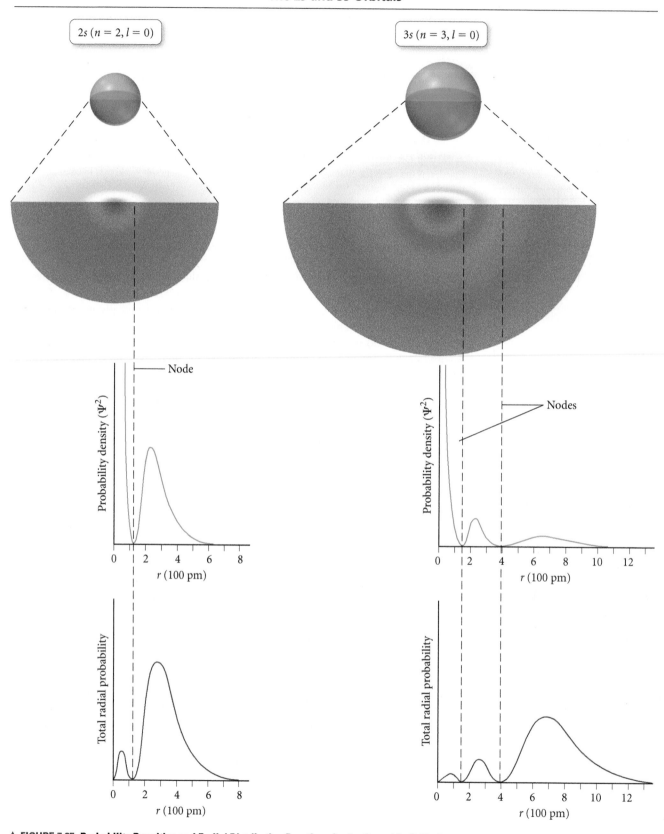

▲ **FIGURE 7.25 Probability Densities and Radial Distribution Functions for the 2s and 3s Orbitals**

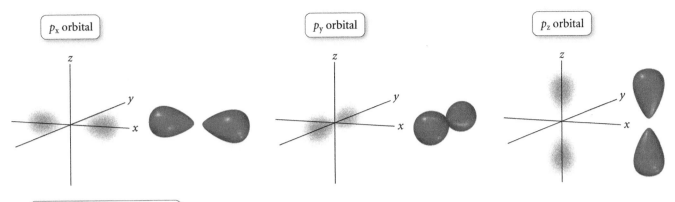

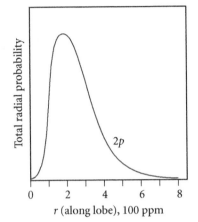

Radial Distribution Function

▲ **FIGURE 7.26 The 2*p* Orbitals and Their Radial Distribution Function** The radial distribution function is the same for all three 2*p* orbitals when the *x*-axis of the graph is taken as the axis containing the lobes of the orbital.

p Orbitals (*l* = 1)

Each principal level with $n = 2$ or greater contains three *p* orbitals ($m_l = -1, 0, +1$). The three 2*p* orbitals and their radial distribution functions are shown in Figure 7.26 ▲. The *p* orbitals are not spherically symmetric like the *s* orbitals, but have two *lobes* of electron density on either side of the nucleus and a node located at the nucleus. The three *p* orbitals differ only in their orientation and are orthogonal (mutually perpendicular) to one another. It is convenient to define an *x*, *y*, and *z* axis system and then label each *p* orbital as p_x, p_y, and p_z. The 3*p*, 4*p*, 5*p*, and higher *p* orbitals are all similar in shape to the 2*p* orbitals, but they contain additional nodes (like the higher *s* orbitals) and are progressively larger in size.

d Orbitals (*l* = 2)

Each principal level with $n = 3$ or greater contains five *d* orbitals ($m_l = -2, -1, 0, +1, +2$). The five 3*d* orbitals are shown in Figure 7.27 ▼. Four of these orbitals have a cloverleaf shape, with four lobes of electron density around the nucleus and two

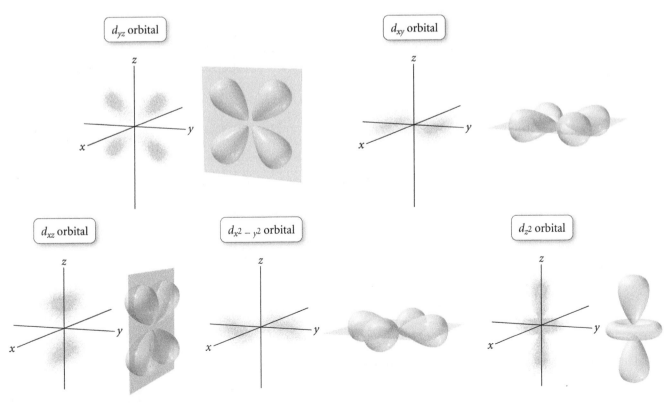

▲ **FIGURE 7.27 The 3*d* Orbitals**

perpendicular nodal planes. The d_{xy}, d_{xz}, and d_{yz} orbitals are oriented along the xy, xz, and yz planes, respectively, and their lobes are oriented *between* the corresponding axes. The four lobes of the $d_{x^2-y^2}$ orbital are oriented along the x- and y-axes. The d_{z^2} orbital is different in shape from the other four, having two lobes oriented along the z-axis and a donut-shaped ring along the xy plane. The $4d$, $5d$, $6d$, etc., orbitals are all similar in shape to the $3d$ orbitals, but they contain additional nodes and are progressively larger in size.

> A nodal plane is a plane where the electron probability density is zero. For example, in the d_{xy} orbitals, the nodal planes lie in the xz and yz planes.

f Orbitals ($l = 3$)

Each principal level with $n = 4$ or greater contains seven f orbitals ($m_l = -3$, -2, -1, 0, $+1$, $+2$, $+3$), as shown in Figure 7.28 ▼. These f orbitals have more lobes and nodes than d orbitals.

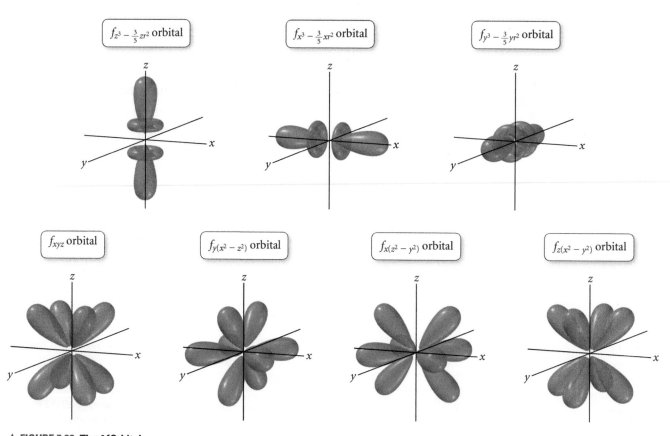

▲ **FIGURE 7.28 The 4f Orbitals**

The Phase of Orbitals

The orbitals we have just seen are three-dimensional waves. We can understand an important property of these orbitals by analogy to one-dimensional waves. Consider the following one-dimensional waves:

The wave on the left has a positive amplitude over its entire length, while the wave on the right has a positive amplitude over half of its length and a negative amplitude over the other half. The sign of the amplitude of a wave—positive or negative—is known as its **phase**. In these images, blue indicates positive phase and red indicates negative phase. The phase of a wave determines how it interferes with another wave as we saw in Section 7.2.

Just as a one-dimensional wave has a phase, so does a three dimensional wave. We often represent the phase of a quantum mechanical orbital with color. For example, the phase of a 1s and 2p orbital can be represented as follows:

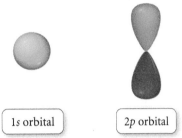

1s orbital   2p orbital

In these depictions, blue represents positive phase and red represents negative phase. The 1s orbital is all one phase, while the 2p orbital exhibits two different phases. The phase of quantum mechanical orbitals is important in bonding, as we shall see in Chapter 10.

Conceptual Connection 7.4 The Shapes of Atoms

If some orbitals are shaped like dumbbells and three-dimensional cloverleafs, and if most of the volume of an atom is empty space diffusely occupied by electrons in these orbitals, then why do we often depict atoms as spheres?

ANSWER: Atoms are usually drawn as spheres because most atoms contain many electrons occupying a number of different orbitals. Therefore, the shape of an atom is obtained by superimposing all of its orbitals. If we superimpose the s, p, and d orbitals we get a spherical shape, as shown in Figure 7.29 ◄.

▲ **FIGURE 7.29 Why Atoms Are Spherical**   Atoms are depicted as roughly spherical because all the orbitals together make up a roughly spherical shape.

CHAPTER IN REVIEW

Key Terms

Section 7.1
quantum-mechanical model (278)

Section 7.2
electromagnetic radiation (278)
amplitude (279)
wavelength (λ) (279)
frequency (ν) (280)
electromagnetic spectrum (281)
gamma rays (281)
X-rays (282)

ultraviolet (UV) radiation (282)
visible light (282)
infrared (IR) radiation (283)
microwaves (283)
radio waves (283)
interference (283)
constructive interference (283)
destructive interference (283)
diffraction (283)
photoelectric effect (284)
photon (quantum) (285)

Section 7.3
emission spectrum (288)

Section 7.4
de Broglie relation (293)
complementary properties (295)
Heisenberg's uncertainty principle (295)
deterministic (295)
indeterminacy (296)

Section 7.5
orbital (297)
wave function (297)
quantum number (297)
principal quantum number (n) (297)

angular momentum quantum number (l) (297)
magnetic quantum number (m_l) (297)
principal level (shell) (298)
sublevel (subshell) (298)

Section 7.6
probability density (303)
radial distribution function (304)
node (304)
phase (307)

Key Concepts

The Realm of Quantum Mechanics (7.1)

The theory of quantum mechanics explains the behavior of particles, such as photons (particles of light) and electrons, in the atomic and subatomic realms. Since the electrons of an atom determine many of its chemical and physical properties, quantum mechanics is foundational to understanding chemistry.

The Nature of Light (7.2)

Light is a type of electromagnetic radiation—a form of energy embodied in oscillating electric and magnetic fields that travels though space at 3.00×10^8 m/s. Light has both a wave nature and a particle nature. The wave nature of light is characterized by its wavelength—the distance between wave crests—and its ability to experience inter-

ference (constructive or destructive) and diffraction. The particle nature of light is characterized by the specific quantity of energy carried in each photon.

The electromagnetic spectrum includes all wavelengths of electromagnetic radiation from gamma rays (high energy per photon, short wavelength) to radio waves (low energy per photon, long wavelength). Visible light is a tiny sliver in the middle of the electromagnetic spectrum.

Atomic Spectroscopy (7.3)

Atomic spectroscopy is the study of the light absorbed and emitted by atoms when an electron makes a transition from one energy level to another. The wavelengths absorbed or emitted depend on the energy differences between the levels involved in the transition; large energy differences result in short wavelengths and small energy differences result in long wavelengths.

The Wave Nature of Matter (7.4)

Electrons have a wave nature with an associated wavelength, as quantified by the de Broglie relation. The wave nature and particle nature of matter are complementary—the more you know of one, the less you know of the other. The wave–particle duality of electrons is quantified in Heisenberg's uncertainty principle, which states that there is a limit to how well we can know both the position of an electron (associated with the electron's particle nature) and the velocity

times the mass of an electron (associated with the electron's wave nature)—the more accurately one is measured, the greater the uncertainty in measurement of the other. The inability to simultaneously know both the position and the velocity of an electron results in indeterminacy, the inability to predict a trajectory for an electron. Consequently electron behavior is described differently than the behavior of everyday-sized particles. The trajectory we normally associate with macroscopic objects is replaced, for electrons, with statistical descriptions that show, not the electron's path, but the region where it is most likely to be found.

The Quantum-Mechanical Model of the Atom (7.5, 7.6)

The most common way to describe electrons in atoms according to quantum mechanics is to solve the Schrödinger equation for the energy states of the electrons within the atom. When the electron is in these states, its energy is well-defined but its position is not. The position of an electron is described by a probability distribution map called an orbital.

The solutions to the Schrödinger equation (including the energies and orbitals) are characterized by three quantum numbers: n, l, and m_l. The principal quantum number (n) determines the energy of the electron and the size of the orbital; the angular momentum quantum number (l) determines the shape of the orbital; and the magnetic quantum number (m_l) determines the orientation of the orbital.

Key Equations and Relationships

Relationship between Frequency (ν), Wavelength (λ), and the Speed of Light (c) (7.2)

$$\nu = \frac{c}{\lambda}$$

Relationship between Energy (E), Frequency (ν), Wavelength (λ), and Planck's Constant (h) (7.2)

$$E = h\nu$$
$$E = \frac{hc}{\lambda}$$

De Broglie Relation: Relationship between Wavelength (λ), Mass (m), and Velocity (ν) of a Particle (7.4)

$$\lambda = \frac{h}{mv}$$

Heisenberg's Uncertainty Principle: Relationship between a Particle's Uncertainty in Position (Δx) and Uncertainty in Velocity (Δv) (7.4)

$$\Delta x \times m\,\Delta v \geq \frac{h}{4\pi}$$

Energy of an Electron in an Orbital with Quantum Number n in a Hydrogen Atom (7.5)

$$E_n = -2.18 \times 10^{-18}\ \text{J} \left(\frac{1}{n^2}\right) \quad (n = 1, 2, 3, \ldots)$$

Change in Energy That Occurs in an Atom When It Undergoes a Transition between Levels n_{initial} and n_{final} (7.5)

$$\Delta E = -2.18 \times 10^{-18}\ \text{J}\left(\frac{1}{n_f^2} - \frac{1}{n_i^2}\right)$$

Key Skills

Calculating the Wavelength and Frequency of Light (7.2)
   • Example 7.1   • For Practice 7.1   • Exercises 41, 42

Calculating the Energy of a Photon (7.2)
   • Example 7.2   • For Practice 7.2   • For More Practice 7.2   • Exercises 43–48

Relating Wavelength, Energy, and Frequency to the Electromagnetic Spectrum (7.2)
   • Example 7.3   • For Practice 7.3   • Exercises 39, 40

Using the de Broglie Relation to Calculate Wavelength (7.4)
   • Example 7.4   • For Practice 7.4   • Exercises 51–56

Relating Quantum Numbers to One Another and to Their Corresponding Orbitals (7.5)
- Examples 7.5, 7.6   • For Practice 7.5, 7.6   • Exercises 61–64

Relating the Wavelength of Light to Transitions in the Hydrogen Atom (7.5)
- Example 7.7   • For Practice 7.7   • For More Practice 7.7   • Exercises 71–74

EXERCISES

Review Questions

1. What does it mean for a particle to be *absolutely* small? What particles fit this description?

2. Explain the difference between observing an object such as a baseball and observing a particle that is absolutely small.

3. Why is the quantum-mechanical model of the atom important for understanding chemistry?

4. What is light? How fast does it travel in a vacuum?

5. Define the wavelength and amplitude of a wave. How are these related to the energy of the wave?

6. Define the frequency of electromagnetic radiation. How is frequency related to wavelength?

7. What determines the color of light? For example, describe the difference between red light and blue light.

8. What determines the color of a colored object? For example, explain why grass appears green.

9. Give an approximate range of wavelengths for each type of electromagnetic radiation and summarize the characteristics and/or the uses of each.
   - **a.** gamma rays
   - **b.** X-rays
   - **c.** ultraviolet radiation
   - **d.** visible light
   - **e.** infrared radiation
   - **f.** microwave radiation
   - **g.** radio waves

10. Explain the wave behavior known as interference. Explain the difference between constructive and destructive interference.

11. Explain the wave behavior known as diffraction. Draw the diffraction pattern that occurs when light travels through two slits comparable in size and separation to the light's wavelength.

12. Describe the photoelectric effect. How did experimental observations of this phenomenon differ from the predictions of classical electromagnetic theory?

13. How did the photoelectric effect lead Einstein to propose that light is quantized?

14. What is a photon? How is the energy of a photon related to its wavelength? Its frequency?

15. What is an emission spectrum? How does an emission spectrum of a gas in a discharge tube differ from a white light spectrum?

16. Describe the Bohr model for the atom. How did the Bohr model account for the emission spectra of atoms?

17. Explain electron diffraction.

18. What is the de Broglie wavelength of an electron? What determines the value of the de Broglie wavelength for an electron?

19. What are complementary properties? How does electron diffraction demonstrate the complementarity of the wave nature and particle nature of the electron?

20. Explain Heisenberg's uncertainty principle. What paradox is at least partially solved by the uncertainty principle?

21. What is a trajectory? What kind of information do you need to predict the trajectory of a particle?

22. Why does the uncertainty principle make it impossible to predict a trajectory for the electron?

23. Newton's laws of motion are *deterministic*. What does this mean?

24. An electron behaves in ways that are at least partially indeterminate. What does this mean?

25. What is a probability distribution map?

26. For each solution to the Schrödinger equation, what can be precisely specified: the electron's energy or its position? Explain.

27. What is a quantum-mechanical orbital?

28. What is the Schrödinger equation? What is a wave function? How is a wave function related to an orbital?

29. What are the possible values of the principal quantum number n? What does the principal quantum number determine?

30. What are the possible values of the angular momentum quantum number l? What does the angular momentum quantum number determine?

31. What are the possible values of the magnetic quantum number m_l? What does the magnetic quantum number determine?

32. List all the orbitals in each principal level. Specify the three quantum numbers for each orbital.
   - **a.** $n = 1$
   - **b.** $n = 2$
   - **c.** $n = 3$
   - **d.** $n = 4$

33. Explain the difference between a plot showing the probability density for an orbital and one showing the radial distribution function.

34. Make sketches of the general shapes of the s, p, and d orbitals.

35. List the four different sublevels. Given that only a maximum of two electrons can occupy an orbital, determine the maximum number of electrons that can exist in each sublevel.

36. Why are atoms usually portrayed as spheres when most orbitals are not spherically shaped?

Problems by Topic

Electromagnetic Radiation

37. The distance from the sun to Earth is 1.496×10^8 km. How long does it take light to travel from the sun to Earth?

38. The nearest star to our sun is Proxima Centauri, at a distance of 4.3 light-years from the sun. A light-year is the distance that light travels in one year (365 days). How far away, in km, is Proxima Centauri from the sun?

39. List these types of electromagnetic radiation in order of (i) increasing wavelength and (ii) increasing energy per photon:
    a. radio waves   b. microwaves
    c. infrared radiation d. ultraviolet radiation

40. List these types of electromagnetic radiation in order of (i) increasing frequency and (ii) decreasing energy per photon:
    a. gamma rays   b. radio waves
    c. microwaves   d. visible light

41. Calculate the frequency of each wavelength of electromagnetic radiation:
    a. 632.8 nm (wavelength of red light from helium–neon laser)
    b. 503 nm (wavelength of maximum solar radiation)
    c. 0.052 nm (a wavelength contained in medical X-rays)

42. Calculate the wavelength of each frequency of electromagnetic radiation:
    a. 100.2 MHz (typical frequency for FM radio broadcasting)
    b. 1070 kHz (typical frequency for AM radio broadcasting) (assume four significant figures)
    c. 835.6 MHz (common frequency used for cell phone communication)

43. Calculate the energy of a photon of electromagnetic radiation at each of the wavelengths indicated in Problem 41.

44. Calculate the energy of a photon of electromagnetic radiation at each of the frequencies indicated in Problem 42.

45. A laser pulse with wavelength 532 nm contains 3.85 mJ of energy. How many photons are in the laser pulse?

46. A heat lamp produces 32.8 watts of power at a wavelength of 6.5 μm. How many photons are emitted per second? (1 watt = 1 J/s)

47. Determine the energy of 1 mol of photons for each kind of light. (Assume three significant figures.)
    a. infrared radiation (1500 nm)
    b. visible light (500 nm)
    c. ultraviolet radiation (150 nm)

48. How much energy is contained in 1 mol of each?
    a. X-ray photons with a wavelength of 0.135 nm
    b. γ-ray photons with a wavelength of 2.15×10^{-5} nm.

The Wave Nature of Matter and the Uncertainty Principle

49. Make a sketch of the interference pattern that results from the diffraction of electrons passing through two closely spaced slits.

50. What happens to the interference pattern described in Problem 49 if the rate of electrons going through the slits is decreased to one electron per hour? What happens to the pattern if we try to determine which slit the electron goes through by using a laser placed directly behind the slits?

51. The resolution limit of a microscope is roughly equal to the wavelength of light used in producing the image. Electron microscopes use an electron beam (in place of photons) to produce much higher resolution images, about 0.20 nm in modern instruments. Assuming that the resolution of an electron microscope is equal to the de Broglie wavelength of the electrons used, to what speed must the electrons be accelerated to obtain a resolution of 0.20 nm?

52. The smallest atoms can themselves exhibit quantum mechanical behavior. Calculate the de Broglie wavelength (in pm) of a hydrogen atom traveling 475 m/s.

53. What is the de Broglie wavelength of an electron traveling at 1.35×10^5 m/s?

54. A proton in a linear accelerator has a de Broglie wavelength of 122 pm. What is the speed of the proton?

55. Calculate the de Broglie wavelength of a 143-g baseball traveling at 95 mph. Why is the wave nature of matter not important for a baseball?

56. A 0.22-caliber handgun fires a 27-g bullet at a velocity of 765 m/s. Calculate the de Broglie wavelength of the bullet. Is the wave nature of matter significant for bullets?

57. An electron has an uncertainty in its position of 552 pm. What is the uncertainty in its velocity?

58. An electron traveling at 3.7×10^5 m/s has an uncertainty in its velocity of 1.88×10^5 m/s. What is the uncertainty in its position?

Orbitals and Quantum Numbers

59. Which electron is, on average, closer to the nucleus: an electron in a 2s orbital or an electron in a 3s orbital?

60. Which electron is, on average, further from the nucleus: an electron in a 3p orbital or an electron in a 4p orbital?

61. What are the possible values of l for each value of n?
    a. 1   b. 2   c. 3   d. 4

62. What are the possible values of m_l for each value of l?
    a. 0   b. 1   c. 2   d. 3

63. Which set of quantum numbers *cannot* occur together to specify an orbital?
    a. $n = 2, l = 1, m_l = -1$ b. $n = 3, l = 2, m_l = 0$
    c. $n = 3, l = 3, m_l = 2$ d. $n = 4, l = 3, m_l = 0$

64. Which combinations of n and l represent real orbitals and which do not exist?
    a. 1s   b. 2p   c. 4s   d. 2d

65. Make a sketch of the 1s and 2p orbitals. How would the 2s and 3p orbitals differ from the 1s and 2p orbitals?

66. Make a sketch of the 3d orbitals. How would the 4d orbitals differ from the 3d orbitals?

Atomic Spectroscopy

67. An electron in a hydrogen atom is excited with electrical energy to an excited state with $n = 2$. The atom then emits a photon. What is the value of n for the electron following the emission?

68. Determine whether each transition in the hydrogen atom corresponds to absorption or emission of energy.
    a. $n = 3 \longrightarrow n = 1$ b. $n = 2 \longrightarrow n = 4$
    c. $n = 4 \longrightarrow n = 3$

69. According to the quantum-mechanical model for the hydrogen atom, which electron transitions would produce light with the longer wavelength: $2p \longrightarrow 1s$ or $3p \longrightarrow 1s$?

70. According to the quantum-mechanical model for the hydrogen atom, which electron transition would produce light with the longer wavelength: $3p \longrightarrow 2s$ or $4p \longrightarrow 3p$?

71. Calculate the wavelength of the light emitted when an electron in a hydrogen atom makes each transition and indicate the region of the electromagnetic spectrum (infrared, visible, ultraviolet, etc.) where the light is found.
   a. $n = 2 \longrightarrow n = 1$ **b.** $n = 3 \longrightarrow n = 1$
   c. $n = 4 \longrightarrow n = 2$ **d.** $n = 5 \longrightarrow n = 2$

72. Calculate the frequency of the light emitted when an electron in a hydrogen atom makes each transition:
   a. $n = 4 \longrightarrow n = 3$ **b.** $n = 5 \longrightarrow n = 1$
   c. $n = 5 \longrightarrow n = 4$ **d.** $n = 6 \longrightarrow n = 5$

73. An electron in the $n = 7$ level of the hydrogen atom relaxes to a lower energy level, emitting light of 397 nm. What is the value of n for the level to which the electron relaxed?

74. An electron in a hydrogen atom relaxes to the $n = 4$ level, emitting light of 114 THz. What is the value of n for the level in which the electron originated?

Cumulative Problems

75. Ultraviolet radiation and radiation of shorter wavelengths can damage biological molecules because they carry enough energy to break bonds within the molecules. A typical carbon–carbon bond requires 348 kJ/mol to break. What is the longest wavelength of radiation with enough energy to break carbon–carbon bonds?

76. The human eye contains a molecule called 11-*cis*-retinal that changes shape when struck with light of sufficient energy. The change in shape triggers a series of events that results in an electrical signal being sent to the brain. The minimum energy required to change the conformation of 11-*cis*-retinal within the eye is about 164 kJ/mol. Calculate the longest wavelength visible to the human eye.

77. An argon ion laser puts out 5.0 W of continuous power at a wavelength of 532 nm. The diameter of the laser beam is 5.5 mm. If the laser is pointed toward a pinhole with a diameter of 1.2 mm, how many photons will travel through the pinhole per second? Assume that the light intensity is equally distributed throughout the entire cross-sectional area of the beam. (1 W = 1 J/s)

78. A green leaf has a surface area of 2.50 cm². If solar radiation is 1000 W/m², how many photons strike the leaf every second? Assume three significant figures and an average wavelength of 504 nm for solar radiation.

79. In a technique used for surface analysis called Auger electron spectroscopy (AES), electrons are accelerated toward a metal surface. These electrons cause the emissions of secondary electrons—called auger electrons—from the metal surface. The kinetic energy of the auger electrons depends on the composition of the surface. The presence of oxygen atoms on the surface results in auger electrons with a kinetic energy of approximately 506 eV. What is the de Broglie wavelength of one of these electrons?
   [KE $= \frac{1}{2}mv^2$; 1 electron volt (eV) $= 1.602 \times 10^{-19}$ J]

80. An X-ray photon of wavelength 0.989 nm strikes a surface. The emitted electron has a kinetic energy of 969 eV. What is the binding energy of the electron in kJ/mol?
   [KE $= \frac{1}{2}mv^2$; 1 electron volt (eV) $= 1.602 \times 10^{-19}$ J]

81. Ionization involves completely removing an electron from an atom. How much energy is required to ionize a hydrogen atom in its ground (or lowest energy) state? What wavelength of light contains enough energy in a single photon to ionize a hydrogen atom?

82. The energy required to ionize sodium is 496 kJ/mol. What minimum frequency of light is required to ionize sodium?

83. Suppose that in an alternate universe, the possible values of l were the integer values from 0 to n (instead of 0 to $n - 1$).

Assuming no other differences between this imaginary universe and ours, how many orbitals would exist in each level?
   a. $n = 1$ **b.** $n = 2$ **c.** $n = 3$

84. Suppose that, in an alternate universe, the possible values of m_l were the integer values including 0 ranging from $-l - 1$ to $l + 1$ (instead of simply $-l$ to $+l$). How many orbitals would exist in each sublevel?
   a. s sublevel   **b.** p sublevel   **c.** d sublevel

85. An atomic emission spectrum of hydrogen shows three wavelengths: 1875 nm, 1282 nm, and 1093 nm. Assign these wavelengths to transitions in the hydrogen atom.

86. An atomic emission spectrum of hydrogen shows three wavelengths: 121.5 nm, 102.6 nm, and 97.23 nm. Assign these wavelengths to transitions in the hydrogen atom.

87. The binding energy of electrons in a metal is 193 kJ/mol. Find the threshold frequency of the metal.

88. In order for a thermonuclear fusion reaction of two deuterons ($^2_1\text{H}^+$) to take place, the deuterons must collide each with a velocity of about 1×10^6 m/s. Find the wavelength of such a deuteron.

89. The speed of sound in air is 344 m/s at room temperature. The lowest frequency of a large organ pipe is 30 s⁻¹ and the highest frequency of a piccolo is 1.5×10^4 s⁻¹. Find the difference in wavelength between these two sounds.

90. The distance from Earth to the sun is 1.5×10^8 km. Find the number of crests in a light wave of frequency 1.0×10^{14} s⁻¹ traveling from the sun to the Earth.

91. The iodine molecule can be photodissociated into iodine atoms in the gas phase with light of wavelengths shorter than about 792 nm. A 100.0 mL glass tube contains 55.7 mtorr of gaseous iodine at 25.0 °C. What minimum amount of light energy must be absorbed by the iodine in the tube to dissociate 15.0% of the molecules?

92. A 5.00 mL ampule of a 0.100 M solution of naphthalene in hexane is excited with a flash of light. The naphthalene emits 15.5 J of energy at an average wavelength of 349 nm. What percentage of the naphthalene molecules emitted a photon?

93. A laser produces 20.0 mW of red light. In 1.00 hr, the laser emits 2.29×10^{20} photons. What is the wavelength of the laser?

94. A particular laser consumes 150.0 Watts of electrical power and produces a stream of 1.33×10^{19} 1064 nm photons per second. What is the percent efficiency of the laser in converting electrical power to light?

Challenge Problems

95. An electron confined to a one-dimensional box has energy levels given by the equation

$$E_n = n^2h^2/8\ mL^2$$

where n is a quantum number with possible values of $1, 2, 3, \ldots$, m is the mass of the particle, and L is the length of the box.

a. Calculate the energies of the $n = 1$, $n = 2$, and $n = 3$ levels for an electron in a box with a length of 155 pm.

b. Calculate the wavelength of light required to make a transition from $n = 1 \longrightarrow n = 2$ and from $n = 2 \longrightarrow n = 3$. In what region of the electromagnetic spectrum do these wavelengths lie?

96. The energy of a vibrating molecule is quantized much like the energy of an electron in the hydrogen atom. The energy levels of a vibrating molecule are given by the equation

$$E_n = \left(n + \frac{1}{2}\right)h\nu$$

where n is a quantum number with possible values of $1, 2, \ldots$, and ν is the frequency of vibration. The vibration frequency of HCl is approximately 8.85×10^{13} s^{-1}. What minimum energy is required to excite a vibration in HCl? What wavelength of light is required to excite this vibration?

97. The wave functions for the $1s$ and $2s$ orbitals are as follows:

$1s$ $\psi = (1/\pi)^{1/2}(1/a_0^{3/2})\ \exp(-r/a_0)$

$2s$ $\psi = (1/32\pi)^{1/2}(1/a_0^{3/2})(2 - r/a_0)\ \exp(-r/a_0)$

where a_0 is a constant ($a_0 = 53$ pm) and r is the distance from the nucleus. Use a spreadsheet to make a plot of each of these wave functions for values of r ranging from 0 pm to 200 pm. Describe the differences in the plots and identify the node in the $2s$ wave function.

98. Before quantum mechanics was developed, Johannes Rydberg developed an equation that predicted the wavelengths (λ) in the atomic spectrum of hydrogen:

$$1/\lambda = R(1/m^2 - 1/n^2)$$

In this equation R is a constant and m and n are integers. Use the quantum-mechanical model for the hydrogen atom to derive the Rydberg equation.

99. Find the velocity of an electron emitted by a metal whose threshold frequency is 2.25×10^{14} s^{-1} when it is exposed to visible light of wavelength 5.00×10^{-7} m.

100. Water is exposed to infrared radiation of wavelength 2.8×10^{-4} cm. Assume that all the radiation is absorbed and converted to heat. How many photons will be required to raise the temperature of 2.0 g of water by 2.0 K?

101. The 2005 Nobel prize in physics was given, in part, to scientists who had made ultrashort pulses of light. These pulses are important in making measurements involving very short time periods. One challenge in making such pulses is the uncertainty principle, which can be stated with respect to energy and time as $\Delta E \cdot \Delta t \geq h/4\pi$. What is the energy uncertainty (ΔE) associated with a short pulse of laser light that lasts for only 5.0 femtoseconds (fs)? Suppose the low energy end of the pulse had a wavelength of 722 nm. What is the wavelength of the high energy end of the pulse that is limited only by the uncertainty principle?

102. A metal whose threshold frequency is 6.71×10^{14} s^{-1} emits an electron with a velocity of 6.95×10^{5} m/s when radiation of 1.01×10^{15} s^{-1} strikes the metal. Use these data to calculate the mass of the electron.

103. Find the longest wavelength of a wave that can travel around in a circular orbit of radius 1.8 m.

104. The heat of fusion of ice is 6.00 kJ/mol. Find the number of photons of wavelength $= 6.42 \times 10^{-6}$ m that must be absorbed to melt 1.00 g of ice.

Conceptual Problems

105. Explain the difference between the Bohr model for the hydrogen atom and the quantum-mechanical model. Is the Bohr model consistent with Heisenberg's uncertainty principle?

106. The light emitted from one of the following electronic transitions ($n = 4 \longrightarrow n = 3$ or $n = 3 \longrightarrow n = 2$) in the hydrogen atom caused the photoelectric effect in a particular metal while light from the other transition did not. Which transition caused the photoelectric effect and why?

107. Determine whether an interference pattern is observed on the other side of the slits in each experiment.

a. An electron beam is aimed at two closely spaced slits. The beam is attenuated to produce only 1 electron per minute.

b. An electron beam is aimed at two closely spaced slits. A light beam is placed at each slit to determine when an electron goes through the slit.

c. A high-intensity light beam is aimed at two closely spaced slits.

d. A gun is fired at a solid wall containing two closely spaced slits. (Will the bullets that pass through the slits form an interference pattern on the other side of the solid wall?)

8 Periodic Properties of the Elements

Beginning students of chemistry often think of the science as a mere collection of disconnected data to be memorized by brute force. Not at all! Just look at it properly and everything hangs together and makes sense.

—Isaac Asimov (1920–1992)

G REAT ADVANCES IN SCIENCE occur not only when a scientist sees something new, but also when a scientist sees what everyone else has seen in a new way. In other words, great scientists often see patterns where others have seen only disjointed facts. Such was the case in 1869 when Dmitri Mendeleev, a Russian chemistry professor, saw a pattern in the properties of elements. Mendeleev's insight led to the periodic table, arguably the single most important tool for the chemist. Recall that scientists devise theories that explain the underlying reasons for observations. If we think of Mendeleev's periodic table as a compact way to summarize a large number of observations, then quantum mechanics (covered in Chapter 7) is the theory that explains the underlying reasons for the periodic table. The concepts of quantum mechanics explain the arrangement of elements in the periodic table by reference to the electrons within the atoms that compose the elements. In this chapter, we see a continuation of the theme we have been developing since page one of this book—the properties of macroscopic substances (in this case, the elements in the periodic table) are explained by the properties of the particles that compose them (in this case, atoms and their electrons).

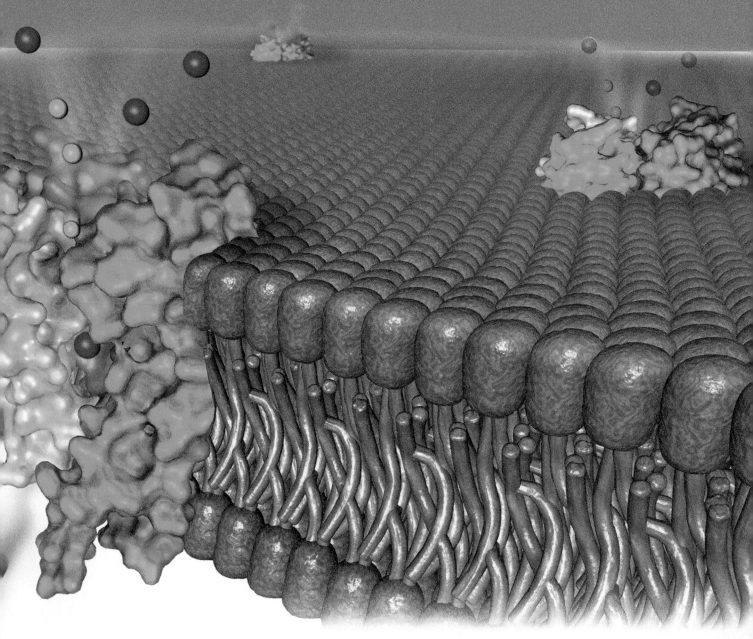

In order for a nerve cell to transmit a signal, sodium and potassium ions must flow in opposite directions through specific ion channels in the cell membrane.

8.1 Nerve Signal Transmission

As you sit reading this book, tiny pumps in the membranes of your cells are working hard to transport ions—especially sodium (Na^+) and potassium (K^+)—through those membranes. Amazingly, the ions are pumped in opposite directions. Sodium ions are pumped *out of cells*, while potassium ions are pumped *into cells*. The result is a *chemical gradient* for each ion: the concentration of sodium is higher outside the cell than within, while just the opposite is true for potassium. These ion pumps are analogous to the water pumps in a high-rise building that pump water against the force of gravity to a tank on the roof. Other structures within the membrane, called ion channels, are like the building's faucets. When these open, sodium and potassium ions flow back down their gradients—sodium flowing in and potassium flowing out. This movement of ions is the basis for the transmission of nerve signals in the brain and throughout the body. Every move you make, every thought you have, and every sensation you experience is mediated by these ion movements.

How do the pumps and channels differentiate between sodium and potassium ions to selectively move one out of the cell and the other into the cell? To answer this question, we must examine the ions more closely. Both are cations of group 1A metals. All group 1A metals tend to lose one electron to form cations with a 1+ charge, so that cannot be

3
Li
6.941

11
Na
22.99

19
K
39.10

37
Rb
85.47

55
Cs
132.91

87
Fr
(223.02)

▲ The group 1A metals. Potassium is directly beneath sodium in the periodic table.

the decisive factor. Potassium (atomic number 19) lies directly below sodium in the periodic table (atomic number 11), indicating that it has more protons, neutrons, and electrons than sodium. How do these additional subatomic particles affect the properties of potassium? As we will see in this chapter, although a higher atomic number does not always result in a larger ion (or atom), it does in the case of potassium (relative to sodium). The potassium ion has a radius of 133 pm while the sodium ion has a radius of 95 pm. (Recall that 1 pm = 10^{-12} m.) The pumps and channels within cell membranes are so sensitive that they can distinguish between the sizes of these two ions and selectively allow only one or the other to pass.

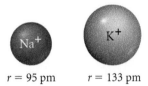

$r = 95$ pm $r = 133$ pm

The size of sodium and potassium ions is an example of a **periodic property**: one that is predictable based on an element's position within the periodic table. In this chapter, we examine several periodic properties of elements, including atomic radius, ionization energy, and electron affinity. We will see that these properties, as well as the overall arrangement of the periodic table, are explained by quantum-mechanical theory, which we examined in Chapter 7. The arrangement of elements in the periodic table—originally based on similarities in the properties of the elements—reflects how electrons fill quantum-mechanical orbitals.

8.2 The Development of the Periodic Table

Prior to the 1700s, the number of known elements was relatively small, consisting mostly of the metals that had long been used for coinage, jewelry, and weapons. From the early 1700s to the mid-1800s, however, chemists discovered over 50 new elements. The first attempt to organize these elements according to similarities in their properties was made by the German chemist Johann Döbereiner (1780–1849), who grouped elements into *triads*: three elements with similar properties. For example, Döbereiner formed a triad out of barium, calcium, and strontium, three fairly reactive metals. About 50 years later, English chemist John Newlands (1837–1898) organized elements into *octaves*, in analogy to musical notes. When arranged this way, the properties of every eighth element were similar, much as every eighth note in the musical scale is similar. Newlands endured some ridicule for drawing an analogy between chemistry and music, including the derisive comments of one colleague who asked Newlands if he had ever tried ordering the elements according to the first letters of their names.

▲ Dmitri Mendeleev is credited with the arrangement of the periodic table.

The modern periodic table is credited primarily to the Russian chemist Dmitri Mendeleev (1834–1907), even though a similar organization had been suggested by the German chemist Julius Lothar Meyer (1830–1895). As we saw in Chapter 2, Mendeleev's table is based on the periodic law, which states that when elements are arranged in order of increasing mass, certain properties recur periodically. Mendeleev arranged the elements in a table in which mass increased from left to right and elements with similar properties fell in the same columns.

Mendeleev's arrangement was a huge success, allowing him to predict the existence and properties of yet undiscovered elements such as eka-aluminum (later discovered and named gallium) and eka-silicon (later discovered and named germanium). The properties of these elements are summarized in Figure 8.1 ▶. (As noted in Chapter 2, *eka* means "the one beyond" or "the next one" in a family of elements.) However, Mendeleev did encounter some difficulties. For example, according to accepted values of atomic masses, tellurium (with higher mass) should come *after* iodine. But based on their properties, Mendeleev placed tellurium *before* iodine and suggested that the mass of tellurium was erroneous. The mass was correct; later work by the English physicist Henry Moseley (1887–1915) showed that listing elements according to *atomic number*, rather than atomic mass, resolved this problem and resulted in even better correlation with elemental properties.

Gallium (eka-aluminum)

Germanium (eka-silicon)

	Mendeleev's predicted properties	Actual properties
Atomic mass	About 68 amu	69.72 amu
Melting point	Low	29.8 °C
Density	5.9 g/cm^3	5.90 g/cm^3
Formula of oxide	X$_2$O$_3$	Ga$_2$O$_3$
Formula of chloride	XCl$_3$	GaCl$_3$

	Mendeleev's predicted properties	Actual properties
Atomic mass	About 72 amu	72.64 amu
Density	5.5 g/cm^3	5.35 g/cm^3
Formula of oxide	XO$_2$	GeO$_2$
Formula of chloride	XCl$_4$	GeCl$_4$

▲ **FIGURE 8.1 Eka-aluminum and Eka-silicon** Mendeleev's arrangement of elements in the periodic table allowed him to predict the existence of these elements, now known as gallium and germanium, and anticipate their properties.

Notice the scientific method in practice in the history of the periodic table. A number of related observations led to a scientific law—the periodic law. Mendeleev's table, which is really just an expression of the periodic law, had predictive power, as laws usually do. However, it did not explain *why* the properties of elements recurred, or *why* certain elements had similar properties. Recall from Chapter 1 that laws *summarize* behavior while theories *explain* behavior. The theory that explains the reasons behind the periodic law is quantum-mechanical theory, which we examined in Chapter 7. In this chapter, we turn to exploring the connection between the periodic table and quantum-mechanical theory.

8.3 Electron Configurations: How Electrons Occupy Orbitals

Quantum-mechanical theory describes the behavior of electrons in atoms. Since chemical bonding involves the transfer or sharing of electrons, quantum-mechanical theory helps us understand and describe chemical behavior. As we saw in Chapter 7, electrons in atoms exist within orbitals. An **electron configuration** for an atom shows the particular orbitals that are occupied for that atom. For example, consider the **ground state**—or lowest energy state—electron configuration for a hydrogen atom:

H   1s^1 ← Number of electrons in orbital

Orbital

The electron configuration indicates that hydrogen's one electron is in the 1s orbital. Electrons generally occupy the lowest energy orbitals available. Since the 1s orbital is the lowest energy orbital in hydrogen (see Section 7.5), hydrogen's electron occupies that orbital. If we could write electron configurations for all the elements, we could see how the arrangements of the electrons within their atoms correlate with the element's chemical properties. However, the solutions to the Schrödinger equation (the atomic orbitals and their energies) that we described in Chapter 7 are for the hydrogen atom. What do the atomic orbitals of *other atoms* look like? What are their relative energies?

The Schrödinger equation for multielectron atoms is so complicated—because of new terms introduced into the equation by the interactions of the electrons with one another—that it cannot be solved exactly. However, approximate solutions indicate that the orbitals in multielectron atoms are hydrogen-like—they are similar to the *s*, *p*, *d*, and *f* orbitals that we examined in Chapter 7. In order to see how the electrons in multielectron atoms occupy these hydrogen-like orbitals, we must examine two additional concepts: *electron spin*, a fundamental property of all electrons that affects the number of electrons

allowed in one orbital; and *sublevel energy splitting*, which determines the order of orbital filling within a level.

Electron Spin and the Pauli Exclusion Principle

The electron configuration of hydrogen ($1s^1$) can be represented in a slightly different way by an **orbital diagram**, which gives similar information, but symbolizes the electron as an arrow and the orbital as a box. The orbital diagram for a hydrogen atom is

H   ↑
     $1s$

A "spinning" electron is something of a metaphor. A more accurate way to express the same idea is to say that an electron has inherent angular momentum.

In orbital diagrams, the direction of the arrow (pointing up or pointing down) represents **electron spin**. Electron spin was demonstrated experimentally in 1922 by the Stern–Gerlach experiment, shown in Figure 8.2 ▼. In this experiment, a beam of silver atoms is directed through a small slit (or hole) and into a magnetic field. As the beam passes through the field, it splits into two separate beams. The splitting of the beam is caused by the spin of the electrons within the silver atoms, which creates a tiny magnetic field (on each atom) that interacts with the external magnetic field. One spin orientation causes the deflection of the beam in one direction, while the other orientation causes a deflection in the opposite direction. This experiment and others that followed it demonstrated two fundamental aspects of electron spin:

1. Spin, like negative electric charge, is a basic property of all electrons. One electron does not have more or less spin than another—all electrons have the same amount of spin.

2. The orientation of the electron's spin is quantized, with only two possibilities that we can call spin up and spin down.

The spin of an electron is specified by a fourth quantum number called the **spin quantum number (m_s)**. The possible values of m_s are $+\frac{1}{2}$ (spin up) and $-\frac{1}{2}$ (spin down).

In an orbital diagram, $m_s = +\frac{1}{2}$ is represented with a half-arrow pointing up (↑) and $m_s = -\frac{1}{2}$ is represented with a half-arrow pointing down (↓). In a collection of hydrogen atoms, the electrons in about half of the atoms are spin up and the electrons in the other half are spin down. Since no additional electrons are present within the hydrogen atom, we conventionally represent the hydrogen atom electron configuration with its one electron as spin up.

Helium is the first element on the periodic table that contains two electrons. The two electrons occupy the $1s$ orbital.

He $1s^2$

Stern–Gerlach Experiment

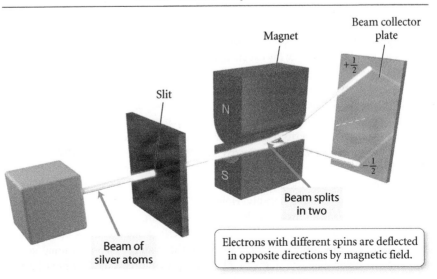

▶ **FIGURE 8.2 The Stern–Gerlach Experiment**

How do the spins of the two electrons in helium align relative to each other? The answer to this question is addressed by the **Pauli exclusion principle**, formulated by Wolfgang Pauli in 1925.

> **Pauli exclusion principle: No two electrons in an atom can have the same four quantum numbers.**

Since two electrons occupying the same orbital have three identical quantum numbers (n, l, and m_l), they must have different spin quantum numbers. Since there are only two possible spin quantum numbers ($+\frac{1}{2}$ and $-\frac{1}{2}$), the Pauli exclusion principle implies that *each orbital can have a maximum of only two electrons, with opposing spins*. By applying the exclusion principle, we can write an electron configuration and orbital diagram for helium as follows:

Electron configuration   Orbital diagram

He $1s^2$ ⇵

                              $1s$

The table below shows the four quantum numbers for each of the two electrons in helium.

n	l	m_l	m_s
1	0	0	$+\dfrac{1}{2}$
1	0	0	$-\dfrac{1}{2}$

The two electrons have three quantum numbers in common (because they are in the same orbital) but have different spin quantum numbers (as indicated by the opposing half-arrows in the orbital diagram).

Sublevel Energy Splitting in Multielectron Atoms

A major difference in the (approximate) solutions to the Schrödinger equation for multi-electron atoms compared to the solutions for the hydrogen atom is the energy ordering of the orbitals. In the hydrogen atom, the energy of an orbital depends only on n, the principal quantum number. For example, the $3s$, $3p$, and $3d$ orbitals (which are empty for hydrogen in its lowest energy state) all have the same energy—they are **degenerate**. The orbitals within a principal level of a *multielectron atom*, in contrast, are not degenerate—their energy depends on the value of l. We say that the energies of the sublevels are *split*. In general, the lower the value of l *within a principal level*, the lower the energy of the corresponding orbital. Thus, for a given value of n:

$$E(s \text{ orbital}) < E(p \text{ orbital}) < E(d \text{ orbital}) < E(f \text{ orbital})$$

In order to understand why the sublevels split in this way, we must examine three key concepts associated with the energy of an electron in the vicinity of a nucleus: (1) Coulomb's law, which describes the interactions between charged particles; (2) Shielding, which describes how one electron can shield another electron from the full charge of the nucleus; and (3) Penetration, which describes how one atomic orbital can overlap spatially with another, thus penetrating into a region that is close to the nucleus (and therefore less shielded from nuclear charge). We will then examine how these concepts, together with the spatial distributions of electron probability for each orbital, result in the above energy ordering.

Coulomb's Law   The attractions and repulsions between charged particles, first introduced in Section 2.4, are described by **Coulomb's law**, which states that the potential energy (E) of two charged particles depends on their charges (q_1 and q_2) and on their separation (r):

$$E = \frac{1}{4\pi\varepsilon_0}\frac{q_1 q_2}{r} \qquad [8.1]$$

In this equation, ε_0 is a constant ($\varepsilon_0 = 8.85 \times 10^{-12}\ \text{C}^2/\text{J}\cdot\text{m}$). The potential energy is positive for charges of the same sign (plus $\times$ plus, or minus $\times$ minus), and negative for

charges of opposite sign (plus × minus, or minus × plus). The *magnitude* of the potential energy depends inversely on the separation between the charged particles. We can draw three important conclusions from Coulomb's law:

- For like charges, the potential energy (*E*) is positive and decreases as the particles get *farther apart* (as *r* increases). Since systems tend toward lower potential energy, like charges repel each other (in much the same way that like poles of two magnets repel each other).

- For opposite charges, the potential energy is negative and becomes more negative as the particles get *closer together* (as *r* decreases). Therefore opposite charges (like opposite poles on a magnet) *attract each other.*

- The *magnitude* of the interaction between charged particles increases as the charges of the particles increases. Consequently, an electron with a charge of 1− is more strongly attracted to a nucleus with a charge of 2+ than it would be to a nucleus with a charge of 1+.

Shielding For multielectron atoms, any one electron experiences both the positive charge of the nucleus (which is attractive) and the negative charges of the other electrons (which are repulsive). We can think of the repulsion of one electron by other electrons as *screening* or **shielding** that electron from the full effects of the nuclear charge. For example, consider a lithium ion (Li⁺). Since the lithium ion contains two electrons, its electron configuration is identical to that of helium:

$$\text{Li}^+ \quad 1s^2$$

Now imagine bringing a third electron toward the lithium ion. When the third electron is far from the nucleus, it experiences the 3+ charge of the nucleus through the *screen or shield* of the 2− charge of the two 1s electrons, as shown in Figure 8.3(a) ▼. In effect, we can think of the third electron as experiencing an **effective nuclear charge** (**Z**_eff) of approximately 1+ (3+ from the nucleus and 2− from the electrons, for a net charge of 1+). We say that the inner electrons *shield* the outer electron from the full nuclear charge.

▶ **FIGURE 8.3 Shielding and Penetration** (a) An electron far from the nucleus is partly shielded by the electrons in the 1s orbital, reducing the effective net nuclear charge that it experiences. (b) An electron that penetrates the electron cloud of the 1s orbital experiences more of the nuclear charge.

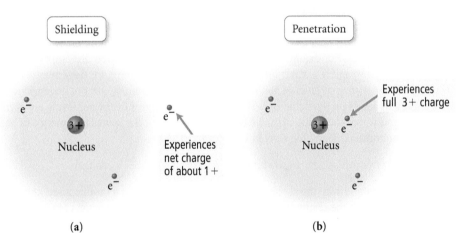

(a)   (b)

Penetration Now imagine allowing this third electron to come closer to the nucleus. As the electron *penetrates* the electron cloud of the 1s electrons it begins to experience the 3+ charge of the nucleus more fully because it is less shielded by the intervening electrons. If the electron could somehow get closer to the nucleus than the 1s electrons, it would experience the full 3+ charge, as shown in Figure 8.3(b) ▲. In other words, as the outer electron undergoes **penetration** into the region occupied by the inner electrons, it experiences a greater nuclear charge and therefore (according to Coulomb's law) a lower energy.

Electron Spatial Distributions and Sublevel Splitting We now have examined the concepts we need to understand the energy splitting of the sublevels within a principal level. The splitting is a result of the spatial distributions of electrons within a sublevel. Recall from Section 7.6 that the radial distribution function for an atomic orbital

shows the total probability of finding the electron within a thin spherical shell at a distance r from the nucleus. Figure 8.4 ▶ shows the radial distribution functions of the 2s and 2p orbitals superimposed on one another (the radial distribution function of the 1s orbital is also shown). Notice that, in general, an electron in a 2p orbital has a greater probability of being found closer to the nucleus than an electron in a 2s orbital. We might initially expect, therefore, that the 2p orbital would be lower in energy. However, exactly the opposite is the case—the 2s orbital is actually lower in energy, *but only when the 1s orbital is occupied.* (When the 1s orbital is empty, the 2s and 2p orbitals are degenerate.) Why? The reason is the bump near $r = 0$ (near the nucleus) for the 2s orbital. This bump represents a significant probability of the electron being found very close to the nucleus. Even more importantly, this area of the probability penetrates into the 1s orbital—it gets into the region where shielding by the 1s electrons is less effective. In contrast, most of the probability in the radial distribution function of the 2p orbital lies *outside* the radial distribution function of the 1s orbital. Consequently, almost all of the 2p orbital is shielded from nuclear charge by the 1s orbital. The end result is that the 2s orbital—since it experiences more of the nuclear charge due to its greater *penetration*—is lower in energy than the 2p orbital. The results are similar when we compare the 3s, 3p, and 3d orbitals. The s orbitals penetrate more fully than the p orbitals, which in turn penetrate more fully than the d orbitals, as shown in Figure 8.5 ▶.

Figure 8.6 ▼, shows the energy ordering of a number of orbitals in multielectron atoms:

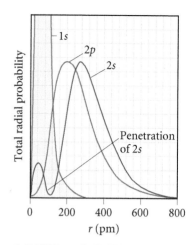

▲ **FIGURE 8.4 Radial Distribution Functions for the 1s, 2s, and 2p Orbitals**

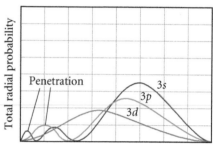

▲ **FIGURE 8.5 Radial Distribution Functions for the 3s, 3p, and 3d Orbitals** The 3s electrons penetrate most deeply into the inner orbitals, are least shielded, and experience the greatest effective nuclear charge. The 3d electrons penetrate least. This accounts for the energy ordering of the sublevels: $s < p < d$.

General Energy Ordering of Orbitals for Multielectron Atoms

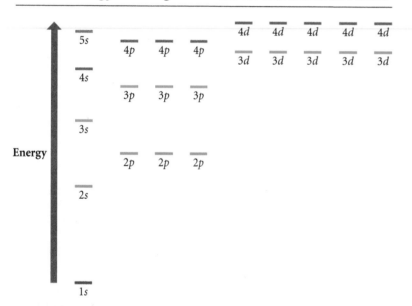

▲ **FIGURE 8.6 General Energy Ordering of Orbitals for Multielectron Atoms**

Notice these features of the diagram:

• Because of penetration, the sublevels of each principal level are *not* degenerate for multielectron atoms.

• In the fourth and fifth principal levels, the effects of penetration become so important that the 4s orbital lies lower in energy than the 3d orbitals and the 5s orbital lies lower in energy than the 4d orbitals.

• The energy separations between one set of orbitals and the next become smaller for 4s orbitals and beyond, and the relative energy ordering of these orbitals can actually vary among elements. These variations result in irregularities in the electron configurations of the transition metals and their ions (as we shall see later).

Conceptual Connection 8.1 Penetration and Shielding

Which statement is true?

(a) An orbital that penetrates into the region occupied by core electrons is more shielded from nuclear charge than an orbital that does not penetrate and will therefore have a higher energy.

(b) An orbital that penetrates into the region occupied by core electrons is less shielded from nuclear charge than an orbital that does not penetrate and will therefore have a higher energy.

(c) An orbital that penetrates into the region occupied by core electrons is less shielded from nuclear charge than an orbital that does not penetrate and will therefore have a lower energy.

(d) An orbital that penetrates into the region occupied by core electrons is more shielded from nuclear charge than an orbital that does not penetrate and will therefore have a lower energy.

ANSWER: (c) Penetration results in less shielding from nuclear charge and therefore lower energy.

Electron Configurations for Multielectron Atoms

| Unless otherwise specified, we will use the term "electron configuration" to mean the ground state (or lowest energy) configuration.

Now that we know the energy ordering of orbitals in multielectron atoms, we can determine ground state electron configurations for the rest of the elements. Since we know that electrons occupy the lowest energy orbitals available when the atom is in its ground state, and that only two electrons (with opposing spins) are allowed in each orbital, we can systematically build up the electron configurations for the elements. The pattern of orbital filling that reflects what you have just learned is known as the **aufbau principle** (the German word *aufbau* means "build up"). For lithium, with three electrons, the electron configuration and orbital diagram are

| Remember that the number of electrons in a neutral atom is equal to its atomic number.

Electron configuration   Orbital diagram

Li $1s^2 2s^1$ [↑↓] [↑]
                           1s   2s

| Electrons with parallel spins have correlated motion that minimizes their mutual repulsion.

For carbon, which has six electrons, the electron configuration and orbital diagram are

Electron configuration   Orbital diagram

C $1s^2 2s^2 2p^2$ [↑↓] [↑↓] [↑] [↑] [ ]
                           1s   2s   2p

Notice that the $2p$ electrons occupy the p orbitals (of equal energy) singly, rather than pairing in one orbital. This way of filling orbitals is in accord with **Hund's rule**, which states that *when filling degenerate orbitals, electrons fill them singly first, with parallel spins*. Hund's rule is a result of an atom's tendency to find the lowest energy state possible. When two electrons occupy separate orbitals of equal energy, the repulsive interaction between them is lower than when they occupy the same orbital because the electrons are spread out over a larger region of space.

Summarizing Orbital Filling:

▶ Electrons occupy orbitals so as to minimize the energy of the atom; therefore, lower energy orbitals fill before higher energy orbitals. Orbitals fill in the following order: $1s\ 2s\ 2p\ 3s\ 3p\ 4s\ 3d\ 4p\ 5s\ 4d\ 5p\ 6s$.

▶ Orbitals can hold no more than two electrons each. When two electrons occupy the same orbital, their spins are opposite. This is another way of expressing the Pauli exclusion principle (no two electrons in one atom can have the same four quantum numbers).

▶ When orbitals of identical energy are available, electrons first occupy these orbitals singly with parallel spins rather than in pairs. Once the orbitals of equal energy are half-full, the electrons start to pair (Hund's rule).

Consider the electron configurations and orbital diagrams for elements with atomic numbers 3–10.

Symbol	Number of electrons	Electron configuration	Orbital diagram
Li	3	$1s^2 2s^1$	$\uparrow\downarrow$ (1s) $\uparrow$ (2s)
Be	4	$1s^2 2s^2$	$\uparrow\downarrow$ (1s) $\uparrow\downarrow$ (2s)
B	5	$1s^2 2s^2 2p^1$	$\uparrow\downarrow$ (1s) $\uparrow\downarrow$ (2s) $\uparrow$ □ □ (2p)
C	6	$1s^2 2s^2 2p^2$	$\uparrow\downarrow$ (1s) $\uparrow\downarrow$ (2s) $\uparrow$ $\uparrow$ □ (2p)

Notice that, as a result of Hund's rule, the *p* orbitals fill with single electrons before the electrons pair.

N	7	$1s^2 2s^2 2p^3$	$\uparrow\downarrow$ (1s) $\uparrow\downarrow$ (2s) $\uparrow$ $\uparrow$ $\uparrow$ (2p)
O	8	$1s^2 2s^2 2p^4$	$\uparrow\downarrow$ (1s) $\uparrow\downarrow$ (2s) $\uparrow\downarrow$ $\uparrow$ $\uparrow$ (2p)
F	9	$1s^2 2s^2 2p^5$	$\uparrow\downarrow$ (1s) $\uparrow\downarrow$ (2s) $\uparrow\downarrow$ $\uparrow\downarrow$ $\uparrow$ (2p)
Ne	10	$1s^2 2s^2 2p^6$	$\uparrow\downarrow$ (1s) $\uparrow\downarrow$ (2s) $\uparrow\downarrow$ $\uparrow\downarrow$ $\uparrow\downarrow$ (2p)

The electron configuration of neon represents the complete filling of the $n = 2$ principal level. When writing electron configurations for elements beyond neon, or beyond any other noble gas, the electron configuration of the previous noble gas—sometimes called the *inner electron configuration*—is often abbreviated by the symbol for the noble gas in square brackets. For example, the electron configuration of sodium is

$$\text{Na} \quad 1s^2 2s^2 2p^6 3s^1$$

This configuration can also be written using [Ne] to represent the inner electrons:

$$\text{Na} \quad [\text{Ne}]\, 3s^1$$

[Ne] represents $1s^2 2s^2 2p^6$, the electron configuration for neon.

To write an electron configuration for an element, first find its atomic number from the periodic table—this number equals the number of electrons. Then use the order of filling to distribute the electrons in the appropriate orbitals. Remember that each orbital can hold a maximum of 2 electrons. Consequently,

- The *s* sublevel has only one orbital and can therefore hold only 2 electrons.
- The *p* sublevel has three orbitals and can hold 6 electrons.
- The *d* sublevel has five orbitals and can hold 10 electrons.
- The *f* sublevel has seven orbitals and can hold 14 electrons.

EXAMPLE 8.1 Electron Configurations

Write electron configurations for each element.

(a) Mg   (b) P   (c) Br   (d) Al

SOLUTION

(a) Mg Magnesium has 12 electrons. Distribute two of these into the $1s$ orbital, two into the $2s$ orbital, six into the $2p$ orbitals, and two into the $3s$ orbital.	Mg $1s^2 2s^2 2p^6 3s^2$ or [Ne] $3s^2$
(b) P Phosphorus has 15 electrons. Distribute two of these into the $1s$ orbital, two into the $2s$ orbital, six into the $2p$ orbitals, two into the $3s$ orbital, and three into the $3p$ orbitals.	P $1s^2 2s^2 2p^6 3s^2 3p^3$ or [Ne] $3s^2 3p^3$

(c) Br
    Bromine has 35 electrons. Distribute two of these into the $1s$ orbital, two into the $2s$ orbital, six into the $2p$ orbitals, two into the $3s$ orbital, six into the $3p$ orbitals, two into the $4s$ orbital, ten into the $3d$ orbitals, and five into the $4p$ orbitals.
	Br $1s^2 2s^2 2p^6 3s^2 3p^6 4s^2 3d^{10} 4p^5$
	    or [Ar] $4s^2 3d^{10} 4p^5$

(d) Al
    Aluminum has 13 electrons. Distribute two of these into the $1s$ orbital, two into the $2s$ orbital, six into the $2p$ orbitals, two into the $3s$ orbital, and one into the $3p$ orbital.
	Al $1s^2 2s^2 2p^6 3s^2 3p^1$
	    or [Ne] $3s^2 3p^1$

FOR PRACTICE 8.1

Write electron configurations for each element.

(a) Cl   (b) Si   (c) Sr   (d) O

EXAMPLE 8.2 Writing Orbital Diagrams

Write an orbital diagram for sulfur and determine the number of unpaired electrons.

SOLUTION

Since sulfur's atomic number is 16, it has 16 electrons and the electron configuration $1s^2 2s^2 2p^6 3s^2 3p^4$. Draw a box for each orbital putting the lowest energy orbital ($1s$) on the far left and proceeding to orbitals of higher energy to the right.	
Distribute the 16 electrons into the boxes representing the orbitals allowing a maximum of two electrons per orbital and remembering Hund's rule. You can see from the diagram that sulfur has two unpaired electrons.	 Two unpaired electrons

FOR PRACTICE 8.2

Write an orbital diagram for Ar and determine the number of unpaired electrons.

Conceptual Connection 8.2 Electron Configurations and Quantum Numbers

What are the four quantum numbers for each of the two electrons in a $4s$ orbital?

ANSWER: $n = 4, l = 0, m_l = 0, m_s = +\frac{1}{2}$; $n = 4, l = 0, m_l = 0, m_s = -\frac{1}{2}$

8.4 Electron Configurations, Valence Electrons, and the Periodic Table

Mendeleev arranged the periodic table so that elements with similar chemical properties lie in the same column. We can begin to make the connection between an element's properties and its electron configuration by superimposing the electron configurations of the first 18 elements onto a partial periodic table, as shown in Figure 8.7 ▼. As we move to the right across a row, the orbitals are filling in the correct order. With each subsequent row, the highest principal quantum number increases by one. Notice that as we move down a column, *the number of electrons in the outermost principal energy level (highest n value) remains the same.* The key connection between the macroscopic world (an element's chemical properties) and the atomic world (an atom's electronic structure) lies in these outermost electrons.

An atom's **valence electrons** are the electrons important in chemical bonding. *For main-group elements, the valence electrons are those in the outermost principal energy level.* For transition elements, we also count the outermost *d* electrons among the valence electrons (even though they are not in an outermost principal energy level). The chemical properties of an element depend on its valence electrons, which are instrumental in bonding because they are held most loosely (and are therefore the easiest to lose or share). We can now see *why* the elements in a column of the periodic table have similar chemical properties: *they have the same number of valence electrons.*

Valence electrons are distinguished from all the other electrons in an atom, which are called **core electrons**. The core electrons are those in *complete* principal energy levels and those in *complete d* and *f* sublevels. For example, silicon, with the electron configuration $1s^2 2s^2 2p^6 3s^2 3p^2$ has 4 valence electrons (those in the $n = 3$ principal level) and 10 core electrons.

Si $1s^2 2s^2 2p^6 3s^2 3p^2$

Core electrons   Valence electrons

Outer Electron Configurations of Elements 1–18

1A							8A
1 **H** $1s^1$	2A	3A	4A	5A	6A	7A	2 **He** $1s^2$
3 **Li** $2s^1$	4 **Be** $2s^2$	5 **B** $2s^2 2p^1$	6 **C** $2s^2 2p^2$	7 **N** $2s^2 2p^3$	8 **O** $2s^2 2p^4$	9 **F** $2s^2 2p^5$	10 **Ne** $2s^2 2p^6$
11 **Na** $3s^1$	12 **Mg** $3s^2$	13 **Al** $3s^2 3p^1$	14 **Si** $3s^2 3p^2$	15 **P** $3s^2 3p^3$	16 **S** $3s^2 3p^4$	17 **Cl** $3s^2 3p^5$	18 **Ar** $3s^2 3p^6$

▲ **FIGURE 8.7 Outer Electron Configurations of the First 18 Elements in the Periodic Table**

EXAMPLE 8.3 Valence Electrons and Core Electrons

Write an electron configuration for Ge. Identify the valence electrons and the core electrons.

SOLUTION

Write the electron configuration for Ge by determining the total number of electrons from germanium's atomic number (32) and then distributing them into the appropriate orbitals.	Ge $1s^2 2s^2 2p^6 3s^2 3p^6 4s^2 3d^{10} 4p^2$
Since germanium is a main-group element, its valence electrons are those in the outermost principal energy level. For germanium, the $n = 1$, 2, and 3 principal levels are complete (or full) and the $n = 4$ principal level is outermost. Consequently, the $n = 4$ electrons are valence electrons and the rest are core electrons. *Note: In this book, electron configurations are always written with the orbitals in the* order *of filling. However, writing electron configurations in* order of increasing principal quantum number *is also common. The electron configuration of germanium written in order of increasing principal quantum number is* Ge $1s^2 2s^2 2p^6 3s^2 3p^6 3d^{10} 4s^2 4p^2$	4 valence electrons Ge $1s^2 2s^2 2p^6 3s^2 3p^6 4s^2 3d^{10} 4p^2$ 28 core electrons

FOR PRACTICE 8.3

Write an electron configuration for phosphorus. Identify the valence electrons and core electrons.

Orbital Blocks in the Periodic Table

A pattern similar to what we just saw for the first 18 elements exists for the entire periodic table, as shown in Figure 8.8 ▶. Note that, because of the filling order of orbitals, the periodic table can be divided into blocks representing the filling of particular sublevels. The first two columns on the left side of the periodic table comprise the *s* block, with outer electron configurations of ns^1 (the alkali metals) and ns^2 (the alkaline earth metals). The six columns on the right side of the periodic table comprise the *p* block, with outer electron configurations of $ns^2 np^1$, $ns^2 np^2$, $ns^2 np^3$, $ns^2 np^4$, $ns^2 np^5$ (halogens), and $ns^2 np^6$ (noble gases). The transition elements comprise the *d* block, and the lanthanides and actinides (also called the inner transition elements) comprise the *f* block. (For compactness, the *f* block is normally printed below the *d* block instead of being imbedded within it.)

You can see that *the number of columns in a block corresponds to the maximum number of electrons that can occupy the particular sublevel of that block*. The *s* block has 2 columns (corresponding to one *s* orbital holding a maximum of two electrons); the *p* block has 6 columns (corresponding to three *p* orbitals with two electrons each); the *d* block has 10 columns (corresponding to five *d* orbitals with two electrons each); and the *f* block has 14 columns (corresponding to seven *f* orbitals with two electrons each).

Notice also that, except for helium, *the number of valence electrons for any main-group element is equal to its lettered group number*. We can tell that chlorine has 7 valence electrons because it is in group number 7A.

Lastly, note that, for main-group elements, *the row number in the periodic table is equal to the number (or n value) of the highest principal level*. For example, because chlorine is in row 3, its highest principal level is the $n = 3$ level.

Summarizing Periodic Table Organization:

▶ The periodic table is divisible into four blocks corresponding to the filling of the four quantum sublevels (*s*, *p*, *d*, and *f*).

| Helium is an exception. Even though it lies in the column with an outer electron configuration of $ns^2 np^6$, its electron configuration is simply $1s^2$.

| Recall from Chapter 2 that main-group elements are those in the two far left columns (groups 1A, 2A) and the six far right columns (groups 3A–8A) of the periodic table.

Orbital Blocks of the Periodic Table

Groups 1 1A	2 2A	3 3B	4 4B	5 5B	6 6B	7 7B	8	8B 9	10	11 1B	12 2B	13 3A	14 4A	15 5A	16 6A	17 7A	18 8A
1 H $1s^1$																	2 He $1s^2$
3 Li $2s^1$	4 Be $2s^2$											5 B $2s^22p^1$	6 C $2s^22p^2$	7 N $2s^22p^3$	8 O $2s^22p^4$	9 F $2s^22p^5$	10 Ne $2s^22p^6$
11 Na $3s^1$	12 Mg $3s^2$											13 Al $3s^23p^1$	14 Si $3s^23p^2$	15 P $3s^23p^3$	16 S $3s^23p^4$	17 Cl $3s^23p^5$	18 Ar $3s^23p^6$
19 K $4s^1$	20 Ca $4s^2$	21 Sc $4s^23d^1$	22 Ti $4s^23d^2$	23 V $4s^23d^3$	24 Cr $4s^13d^5$	25 Mn $4s^23d^5$	26 Fe $4s^23d^6$	27 Co $4s^23d^7$	28 Ni $4s^23d^8$	29 Cu $4s^13d^{10}$	30 Zn $4s^23d^{10}$	31 Ga $4s^24p^1$	32 Ge $4s^24p^2$	33 As $4s^24p^3$	34 Se $4s^24p^4$	35 Br $4s^24p^5$	36 Kr $4s^24p^6$
37 Rb $5s^1$	38 Sr $5s^2$	39 Y $5s^24d^1$	40 Zr $5s^24d^2$	41 Nb $5s^14d^4$	42 Mo $5s^14d^5$	43 Tc $5s^24d^5$	44 Ru $5s^14d^7$	45 Rh $5s^14d^8$	46 Pd $4d^{10}$	47 Ag $5s^14d^{10}$	48 Cd $5s^24d^{10}$	49 In $5s^25p^1$	50 Sn $5s^25p^2$	51 Sb $5s^25p^3$	52 Te $5s^25p^4$	53 I $5s^25p^5$	54 Xe $5s^25p^6$
55 Cs $6s^1$	56 Ba $6s^2$	57 La $6s^25d^1$	72 Hf $6s^25d^2$	73 Ta $6s^25d^3$	74 W $6s^25d^4$	75 Re $6s^25d^5$	76 Os $6s^25d^6$	77 Ir $6s^25d^7$	78 Pt $6s^15d^9$	79 Au $6s^15d^{10}$	80 Hg $6s^25d^{10}$	81 Tl $6s^26p^1$	82 Pb $6s^26p^2$	83 Bi $6s^26p^3$	84 Po $6s^26p^4$	85 At $6s^26p^5$	86 Rn $6s^26p^6$
87 Fr $7s^1$	88 Ra $7s^2$	89 Ac $7s^26d^1$	104 Rf $7s^26d^2$	105 Db $7s^26d^3$	106 Sg $7s^26d^4$	107 Bh	108 Hs	109 Mt	110 Ds	111 Rg	112	113	114	115	116		

Periods (1–7 labeled on rows)

☐ s-block elements   ☐ p-block elements
☐ d-block elements   ☐ f-block elements

Lanthanides	58 Ce $6s^24f^15d^1$	59 Pr $6s^24f^3$	60 Nd $6s^24f^4$	61 Pm $6s^24f^5$	62 Sm $6s^24f^6$	63 Eu $6s^24f^7$	64 Gd $6s^24f^75d^1$	65 Tb $6s^24f^9$	66 Dy $6s^24f^{10}$	67 Ho $6s^24f^{11}$	68 Er $6s^24f^{12}$	69 Tm $6s^24f^{13}$	70 Yb $6s^24f^{14}$	71 Lu $6s^24f^{14}6d^1$
Actinides	90 Th $7s^26d^2$	91 Pa $7s^25f^26d^1$	92 U $7s^25f^36d^1$	93 Np $7s^25f^46d^1$	94 Pu $7s^25f^6$	95 Am $7s^25f^7$	96 Cm $7s^25f^76d^1$	97 Bk $7s^25f^9$	98 Cf $7s^25f^{10}$	99 Es $7s^25f^{11}$	100 Fm $7s^25f^{12}$	101 Md $7s^25f^{13}$	102 No $7s^25f^{14}$	103 Lr $7s^25f^{14}6d^1$

▲ FIGURE 8.8 The *s*, *p*, *d*, and *f* Blocks of the Periodic Table

▶ The group number of a main-group element is equal to the number of valence electrons for that element.

▶ The row number of a main-group element is equal to the highest principal quantum number of that element.

Writing an Electron Configuration for an Element from Its Position in the Periodic Table

The organization of the periodic table allows us to write the electron configuration for any element based on its position in the periodic table. For example, suppose we want to write an electron configuration for Cl. The *inner electron configuration* of Cl is that of the noble gas that precedes it in the periodic table, Ne. So we can represent the inner electron configuration with [Ne]. The *outer electron configuration*—the configuration of the electrons beyond the previous noble gas—is obtained by tracing the elements between Ne and Cl and assigning electrons to the appropriate orbitals, as shown here. Remember that the highest *n* value is given by the row number (3 for chlorine).

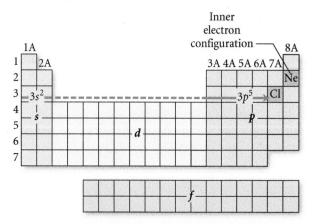

So, we begin with [Ne], then add in the two 3s electrons as we trace across the s block, followed by five 3p electrons as we trace across the p block to Cl, which is in the fifth column of the p block. The electron configuration is

$$\text{Cl}\quad [\text{Ne}]\,3s^2 3p^5$$

Notice that Cl is in column 7A and therefore has 7 valence electrons and an outer electron configuration of $ns^2 np^5$.

EXAMPLE 8.4 Writing Electron Configurations from the Periodic Table

Use the periodic table to write an electron configuration for selenium (Se).

SOLUTION

The atomic number of Se is 34. The noble gas that precedes Se in the periodic table is argon, so the inner electron configuration is [Ar]. Obtain the outer electron configuration by tracing the elements between Ar and Se and assigning electrons to the appropriate orbitals. Begin with [Ar]. Because Se is in row 4, add two 4s electrons as you trace across the s block (n = row number). Next, add ten 3d electrons as you trace across the d block (n = row number − 1). Lastly, add four 4p electrons as you trace across the p block to Se, which is in the fourth column of the p block (n = row number).

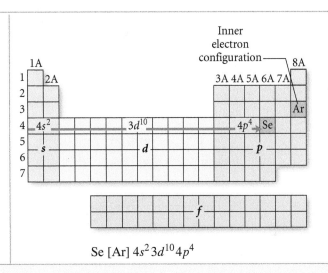

Se [Ar] $4s^2 3d^{10} 4p^4$

FOR PRACTICE 8.4

Use the periodic table to determine the electron configuration of bismuth (Bi).

FOR MORE PRACTICE 8.4

Use the periodic table to write an electron configuration for iodine (I).

The Transition and Inner Transition Elements

The electron configurations of the transition elements (d block) and inner transition elements (f block) exhibit trends that differ somewhat from those of the main-group elements. As we move to the right across a row in the d block, the d orbitals fill as shown here:

21 Sc $4s^2 3d^1$	22 Ti $4s^2 3d^2$	23 V $4s^2 3d^3$	24 Cr $4s^1 3d^5$	25 Mn $4s^2 3d^5$	26 Fe $4s^2 3d^6$	27 Co $4s^2 3d^7$	28 Ni $4s^2 3d^8$	29 Cu $4s^1 3d^{10}$	30 Zn $4s^2 3d^{10}$
39 Y $5s^2 4d^1$	40 Zr $5s^2 4d^2$	41 Nb $5s^1 4d^4$	42 Mo $5s^1 4d^5$	43 Tc $5s^2 4d^5$	44 Ru $5s^1 4d^7$	45 Rh $5s^1 4d^8$	46 Pd $4d^{10}$	47 Ag $5s^1 4d^{10}$	48 Cd $5s^2 4d^{10}$

Notice that *the principal quantum number of the d orbital being filled across each row in the transition series is equal to the row number minus one.* In the fourth row, the 3d orbitals fill, and in the fifth row, the 4d orbitals fill, and so on. This happens because, as we learned in Section 8.3, the 4s orbital is generally lower in energy than the 3d orbital

(because it more efficiently penetrates into the region occupied by the core electrons). The result is that the 4s orbital fills before the 3d orbital, even though its principal quantum number ($n = 4$) is higher.

Keep in mind, however, that the 4s and the 3d orbitals are extremely close to each other in energy and their relative energy ordering depends on the exact species under consideration and the exact electron configuration (first discussed in Section 8.3); this causes some irregular behavior in the transition metals. For example, notice that, in the first transition series of the d block, the outer configuration is $4s^2 3d^x$ with two exceptions: Cr is $4s^1 3d^5$ and Cu is $4s^1 3d^{10}$. This behavior is related to the closely spaced 3d and 4s energy levels and the stability associated with a half-filled (as in Cr) or completely filled (as in Cu) sublevel. Actual electron configurations are definitively determined experimentally (through spectroscopy) and do not always conform to simple patterns. Nonetheless, the patterns we have described allow us to accurately predict electron configurations for most of the elements in the periodic table.

As we move across the f block, the f orbitals fill. Note that, for these elements, the principal quantum number of the f orbital being filled across each row in the inner transition series is the row number *minus two*. (In the sixth row, the 4f orbitals fill, and in the seventh row, the 5f orbitals fill.) In addition, within the inner transition series, the close energy spacing of the 5d and 4f orbitals sometimes causes an electron to enter a 5d orbital instead of the expected 4f orbital. For example, the electron configuration of gadolinium is [Xe] $6s^2 4f^7 5d^1$ (instead of the expected [Xe] $6s^2 4f^8$).

8.5 The Explanatory Power of the Quantum-Mechanical Model

We can now see how the quantum-mechanical model accounts for the chemical properties of the elements, such as the inertness of helium or the reactivity of hydrogen, and (more generally) how it accounts for the periodic law. *The chemical properties of elements are largely determined by the number of valence electrons they contain.* Their properties are periodic because the number of valence electrons is periodic.

Since elements within a column in the periodic table have the same number of valence electrons, they also have similar chemical properties. The noble gases, for example, all have eight valence electrons, except for helium, which has two. Although we do not cover the quantitative (or numerical) aspects of the quantum-mechanical model in this book, calculations of the overall energy of atoms with eight valence electrons (or two, in the case of helium) show that they are particularly stable. In other words, when a quantum level is completely full, the overall energy of the electrons that occupy that level is particularly low. Therefore, those electrons *cannot* lower their energy by reacting with other atoms or molecules, so the corresponding atom is relatively unreactive or inert. The noble gases are the most chemically stable and relatively unreactive family in the periodic table.

Elements with electron configurations *close* to those of the noble gases are the most reactive because they can attain noble gas electron configurations by losing or gaining a small number of electrons. For example, alkali metals (group 1A) are among the most reactive metals because their outer electron configuration (ns^1) is one electron beyond a noble gas configuration. They readily react to lose the ns^1 electron, obtaining a noble gas configuration. This explains why—as we saw in Chapter 2—the group 1A metals tend to form 1+ cations. Similarly, alkaline earth metals, with an outer electron configuration of ns^2, also tend to be reactive metals, losing their ns^2 electrons to form 2+ cations. This does not mean that forming an ion with a noble gas configuration is in itself energetically favorable. In fact, forming cations always *requires energy*. But when the cation formed has a noble gas configuration, the energy cost of forming the cation is often less than the energy payback that occurs when that cation forms ionic bonds with anions, as we shall see in Chapter 9.

8A

| 2 **He** $1s^2$ |
| 10 **Ne** $2s^2 2p^6$ |
| 18 **Ar** $3s^2 3p^6$ |
| 36 **Kr** $4s^2 4p^6$ |
| 54 **Xe** $5s^2 5p^6$ |
| 86 **Rn** $6s^2 6p^6$ |

Noble gases

▲ The noble gases all have eight valence electrons except for helium, which has two. They have full outer energy levels and are particularly stable and unreactive.

► The alkali metals all have one valence electron. Each is one electron beyond a stable electron configuration and they tend to lose that electron in their reactions.

1A

| 3 **Li** $2s^1$ |
| 11 **Na** $3s^1$ |
| 19 **K** $4s^1$ |
| 37 **Rb** $5s^1$ |
| 55 **Cs** $6s^1$ |
| 87 **Fr** $7s^1$ |

Alkali metals

2A

| 4 **Be** $2s^2$ |
| 12 **Mg** $3s^2$ |
| 20 **Ca** $4s^2$ |
| 38 **Sr** $5s^2$ |
| 56 **Ba** $6s^2$ |
| 88 **Ra** $7s^2$ |

Alkaline earth metals

◄ The alkaline earth metals all have two valence electrons. Each is two electrons beyond a stable electron configuration and they tend to lose those electrons in their reactions.

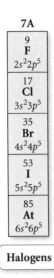

7A

9	**F**
	$2s^2 2p^5$
17	**Cl**
	$3s^2 3p^5$
35	**Br**
	$4s^2 4p^5$
53	**I**
	$5s^2 5p^5$
85	**At**
	$6s^2 6p^5$

Halogens

▲ The halogens all have seven valence electrons. Each is one electron short of a stable electron configuration and they tend to gain one electron in their reactions.

Elements That Form Ions with Predictable Charges

	1A	2A											3A	4A	5A	6A	7A	8A
1	Li⁺														N³⁻	O²⁻	F⁻	
2	Na⁺	Mg²⁺	3B	4B	5B	6B	7B	┌─ 8B ─┐		1B	2B	Al³⁺				S²⁻	Cl⁻	
3	K⁺	Ca²⁺														Se²⁻	Br⁻	
4	Rb⁺	Sr²⁺														Te²⁻	I⁻	
5	Cs⁺	Ba²⁺																

▲ **FIGURE 8.9 Elements That Form Ions with Predictable Charges** Notice that each ion has a noble gas electron configuration.

On the right side of the periodic table, halogens are among the most reactive nonmetals because of their $ns^2 np^5$ electron configurations. They are only one electron short of a noble gas configuration and tend to react to gain that one electron, forming 1− ions. Figure 8.9 ▲, first introduced in Chapter 2, shows the elements that form predictable ions. The charges of these ions reflect their electron configurations—in their reactions, these elements form ions with noble gas electron configurations.

8.6 Periodic Trends in the Size of Atoms and Effective Nuclear Charge

In previous chapters, we saw that the volume of an atom is taken up primarily by its electrons (Chapter 2) occupying quantum-mechanical orbitals (Chapter 7). We also saw that these orbitals do not have a definite boundary, but represent only a statistical probability distribution for where the electron is found. So how do we define the size of an atom? One way to define atomic radii is to consider the distance between *nonbonding* atoms that are in direct contact. For example, krypton can be frozen into a solid in which the krypton atoms are touching each other but are not bonded together. The distance between the centers of adjacent krypton atoms—which can be determined from the solid's density—is then twice the radius of a krypton atom. An atomic radius determined in this way is called the **nonbonding atomic radius** or the **van der Waals radius**. The van der Waals radius represents the radius of an atom when it is not bonded to another atom.

Another way to define the size of an atom, called the **bonding atomic radius** or **covalent radius**, is defined differently for nonmetals and metals, as follows:

Nonmetals: one-half the distance between two of the atoms bonded together

Metals: one-half the distance between two of the atoms next to each other in a crystal of the metal

van der Waals radius

2 × Krypton radius

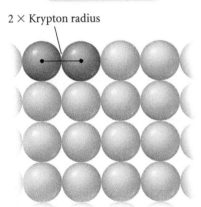

Krypton solid

▲ The van der Waals radius of an atom is one-half the distance between adjacent nuclei in the atomic solid.

Covalent radius

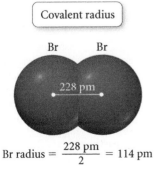

Br Br

228 pm

Br radius = $\dfrac{228 \text{ pm}}{2}$ = 114 pm

▲ The covalent radius of bromine is one-half the distance between two bonded bromine atoms.

For example, the distance between Br atoms in Br_2 is 228 pm; therefore, the Br covalent radius is assigned to be one-half of 228 pm or 114 pm.

Using this method, we can assign radii to all elements in the periodic table that form chemical bonds or form metallic crystals. A more general term, the **atomic radius**, refers to a set of average bonding radii determined from measurements on a large number of elements and compounds. The atomic radius represents the radius of an atom when it is bonded to another atom and is always smaller than the van der Waals radius. The approximate bond length of any two covalently bonded atoms is simply the sum of their atomic radii. For example, the approximate bond length for ICl is iodine's atomic radius (133 pm) plus chlorine's atomic radius (99 pm), for a bond length of 232 pm. (The actual experimentally measured bond length in ICl is 232.07 pm.)

Figure 8.10 ▶ shows the atomic radius plotted as a function of atomic number for the first 57 elements in the periodic table. Notice the periodic trend in the radii. Atomic radii peak with each alkali metal. Figure 8.11 ▶ is a relief map of atomic radii for most of the

Atomic Radii

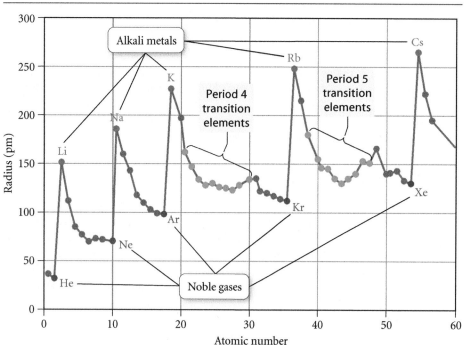

◀ **FIGURE 8.10 Atomic Radius versus Atomic Number**   Notice the periodic trend in atomic radius, starting at a peak with each alkali metal and falling to a minimum with each noble gas.

elements in the periodic table. The general trends in the atomic radii of main-group elements, which are the same as trends observed in van der Waals radii, are stated below.

1. As we move down a column (or family) in the periodic table, atomic radius increases.

2. As we move to the right across a period (or row) in the periodic table, atomic radius decreases.

We can understand the observed trend in radius as we move down a column based on the trends in the sizes of atomic orbitals. The atomic radius is largely determined by the valence electrons, the electrons farthest from the nucleus. As we move down a column in the periodic table, the highest principal quantum number (n) of the valence electrons increases. Consequently, the valence electrons occupy larger orbitals, resulting in larger atoms.

The bonding radii of some elements, such as helium and neon, must be approximated since they do not form either chemical bonds or metallic crystals.

Trends in Atomic Radius

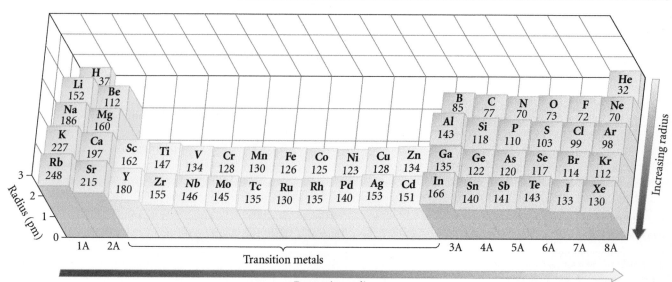

▲ **FIGURE 8.11 Trends in Atomic Radius**   In general, atomic radii increase as we move down a column and decrease as we move to the right across a period in the periodic table.

The observed trend in atomic radius as we move to the right across a row, however, is bit more complex. To understand this trend, we revisit some concepts from Section 8.3, including effective nuclear charge and shielding.

Effective Nuclear Charge

The trend in atomic radius as we move to the right across a row in the periodic table is determined by the inward pull of the nucleus on the electrons in the outermost principal energy level (highest n value). According to Coulomb's law, the attraction between a nucleus and an electron increases with increasing magnitude of nuclear charge. For example, compare the H atom to the He^+ ion.

$$H \quad 1s^1$$
$$He^+ \ 1s^1$$

It takes 1312 kJ/mol of energy to remove the $1s$ electron from hydrogen, but 5251 kJ/mol of energy to remove it from He^+. Why? Although each electron is in a $1s$ orbital, the electron in the helium ion is attracted to the nucleus with a 2+ charge, while the electron in the hydrogen atom is attracted to the nucleus by only a 1+ charge. Therefore, the electron in the helium ion is held more tightly (it has lower potential energy according to Coulomb's law), making it more difficult to remove and making the helium ion smaller than the hydrogen atom.

As we saw in Section 8.3, any one electron in a multielectron atom experiences both the positive charge of the nucleus (which is attractive) and the negative charges of the other electrons (which are repulsive). Consider again the outermost electron in the lithium atom:

$$Li \quad 1s^2 2s^1$$

As shown in Figure 8.12 ▼, even though the $2s$ orbital penetrates into the $1s$ orbital to some degree, the majority of the $2s$ orbital is outside of the $1s$ orbital. Therefore the electron in the $2s$ orbital is partially *screened* or *shielded* from the 3+ charge of the nucleus by the 2− charge of the $1s$ (or core) electrons, reducing the net charge experienced by the $2s$ electron.

As we have seen, we can define the average or net charge experienced by an electron as the *effective nuclear charge*. The effective nuclear charge experienced by a particular electron in an atom is the *actual nuclear charge (Z)* minus *the charge shielded by other electrons (S)*:

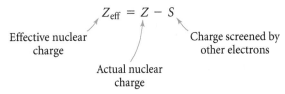

$$Z_{eff} = Z - S$$

Effective nuclear charge

Actual nuclear charge

Charge screened by other electrons

Screening and Effective Nuclear Charge

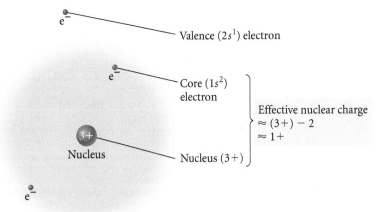

▶ **FIGURE 8.12 Screening and Effective Nuclear Charge** The valence electron in lithium experiences the 3+ charge of the nucleus through the screen of the 2− charge of the core electrons. The effective nuclear charge acting on the valence electron is approximately 1+.

e^-

Valence ($2s^1$) electron

e^-

Core ($1s^2$) electron

Effective nuclear charge
$\approx (3+) - 2$
$\approx 1+$

Nucleus

Nucleus (3+)

e^-

Lithium

For lithium, we estimate that the two core electrons shield the valence electron from the nuclear charge with high efficiency (S is nearly 2). The effective nuclear charge experienced by lithium's valence electron is therefore slightly greater than $1+$.

Now consider the valence electrons in beryllium (Be), with atomic number 4. Its electron configuration is

$$\text{Be} \quad 1s^2 2s^2$$

To estimate the effective nuclear charge experienced by the $2s$ electrons in beryllium, we must distinguish between two different types of shielding: (1) the shielding of the outermost electrons by the core electrons and (2) the shielding of the outermost electrons by *each other*. The key to understanding the trend in atomic radius is the difference between these two types of shielding.

> **Core electrons efficiently shield electrons in the outermost principal energy level from nuclear charge, but outermost electrons do not efficiently shield one another from nuclear charge.**

In other words, the two outermost electrons in beryllium experience the $4+$ charge of the nucleus through the shield of the two $1s$ core electrons without shielding each other from that charge very much. We therefore estimate that the shielding (S) experienced by any one of the outermost electrons due to the core electrons is nearly 2, but that the shielding due to the other outermost electron is nearly zero. The effective nuclear charge experienced by beryllium's outermost electrons is therefore slightly greater than $2+$.

The effective nuclear charge experienced by *beryllium's* outermost electrons is greater than that experienced by *lithium's* outermost electron. Consequently, beryllium's outermost electrons are held more tightly than lithium's, resulting in a smaller atomic radius for beryllium. The effective nuclear charge experienced by an atom's outermost electrons continues to become more positive as we move to the right across the rest of the second row in the periodic table, resulting in successively smaller atomic radii. The same trend is generally observed in all main-group elements.

Summarizing Atomic Radii for Main-Group Elements:

▶ As we move down a column in the periodic table, the principal quantum number (n) of the electrons in the outermost principal energy level increases, resulting in larger orbitals and therefore larger atomic radii.

▶ As we move to the right across a row in the periodic table, the effective nuclear charge (Z_{eff}) experienced by the electrons in the outermost principal energy level increases, resulting in a stronger attraction between the outermost electrons and the nucleus, and smaller atomic radii.

Atomic Radii and the Transition Elements

From Figure 8.11, you can see that as we go down the first two rows of a column within the transition metals, the elements follow the same general trend in atomic radii as the main-group elements (the radii get larger). However, with the exception of the first couple of elements in each transition series, the atomic radii of the transition elements *do not* follow the same trend as the main-group elements as we move to the right across a row. Instead of decreasing in size, *the radii of transition elements stay roughly constant across each row*. Why? The difference is that, across a row of transition elements, the number of electrons in the outermost principal energy level (highest n value) is nearly constant (recall from Section 8.3, for example, that the $4s$ orbital fills before the $3d$). As another proton is added to the nucleus of each successive element, another electron is added as well, but the electron goes into an $n_{highest} - 1$ orbital. The number of outermost electrons stays constant and they experience a roughly constant effective nuclear charge, keeping the radius approximately constant.

EXAMPLE 8.5 Atomic Size

On the basis of periodic trends, choose the larger atom in each pair (if possible). Explain your choices.

(a) N or F **(b)** C or Ge **(c)** N or Al **(d)** Al or Ge

SOLUTION

(a) N atoms are larger than F atoms because, as you trace the path between N and F on the periodic table, you move to the right within the same period. As you move to the right across a period, the effective nuclear charge experienced by the outermost electrons increases, resulting in a smaller radius.

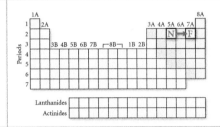

(b) Ge atoms are larger than C atoms because, as you trace the path between C and Ge on the periodic table, you move down a column. Atomic size increases as you move down a column because the outermost electrons occupy orbitals with a higher principal quantum number that are therefore larger, resulting in a larger atom.

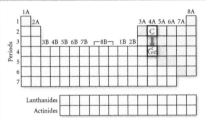

(c) Al atoms are larger than N atoms because, as you trace the path between N and Al on the periodic table, you move down a column (atomic size increases) and then to the left across a period (atomic size increases). These effects add together for an overall increase.

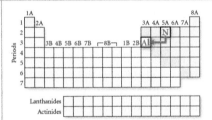

(d) Based on periodic trends alone, you cannot tell which atom is larger, because as you trace the path between Al and Ge you go to the right across a period (atomic size decreases) and then down a column (atomic size increases). These effects tend to oppose each other, and it is not easy to tell which will predominate.

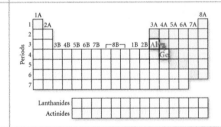

FOR PRACTICE 8.5

On the basis of periodic trends, choose the larger atom in each pair (if possible):

(a) Sn or I **(b)** Ge or Po **(c)** Cr or W **(d)** F or Se

FOR MORE PRACTICE 8.5

Arrange the elements in order of decreasing radius: S, Ca, F, Rb, Si.

8.7 Ions: Electron Configurations, Magnetic Properties, Ionic Radii, and Ionization Energy

As we have seen, ions are simply atoms (or groups of atoms) that have lost or gained electrons. In this section, we examine periodic trends in ionic electron configurations, magnetic properties, ionic radii, and ionization energies.

Electron Configurations and Magnetic Properties of Ions

We can deduce the electron configuration of a main-group monoatomic ion from the electron configuration of the neutral atom and the charge of the ion. For anions, we *add* the number of electrons indicated by the magnitude of the charge of the anion. For example,

the electron configuration of fluorine (F) is $1s^2 2s^2 2p^5$ and that of the fluoride ion (F^-) is $1s^2 2s^2 2p^6$.

We determine the electron configuration of cations by *subtracting* the number of electrons indicated by the magnitude of the charge. For example, the electron configuration of lithium (Li) is $1s^2 2s^1$ and that of the lithium ion (Li^+) is $1s^2 2s^0$ (or simply $1s^2$). For main-group cations, we remove the required number of electrons in the reverse order of filling. However for transition metal cations, the trend is different. When writing the electron configuration of a transition metal cation, *remove the electrons in the highest n-value orbitals first, even if this does not correspond to the reverse order of filling*. For example, the electron configuration of vanadium is as follows:

$$V \quad [Ar]\, 4s^2 3d^3$$

The V^{2+} ion, however, has the following electron configuration:

$$V^{2+} \quad [Ar]\, 4s^0 3d^3$$

In other words, for transition metal cations, the order in which electrons are removed upon ionization is *not* the reverse of the filling order. During filling, the $4s$ orbital normally fills before the $3d$ orbital. When a fourth period transition metal ionizes, however, it normally loses its $4s$ electrons before its $3d$ electrons. Why this unexpected behavior? The full answer to this question is beyond our scope, but the following two factors contribute to this phenomenon.

- As discussed previously, the ns and $(n-1)d$ orbitals are extremely close in energy and, depending on the exact configuration, can vary in relative energy ordering.

- As the $(n-1)d$ orbitals begin to fill in the first transition series, the increasing nuclear charge stabilizes the $(n-1)d$ orbitals relative to the ns orbitals. This happens because the $(n-1)d$ orbitals are not the outermost (or highest n) orbitals and are therefore not effectively shielded from the increasing nuclear charge by the ns orbitals.

The bottom-line experimental observation is that an $ns^0(n-1)d^x$ configuration is lower in energy than an $ns^2(n-1)d^{x-2}$ configuration for transition metal ions. Therefore, remove the ns electrons before the $(n-1)d$ electrons when writing electron configurations for transition metal ions.

The magnetic properties of transition metal ions support these assignments. Recall from Section 8.3 that an unpaired electron generates a magnetic field due to its spin. Consequently, an atom or ion that contains unpaired electrons is attracted to an external magnetic field, and we say that the atom or ion is **paramagnetic**. For example, the magnetic properties of silver—which result in the splitting of a beam of silver atoms in the Stern–Gerlach experiment discussed in Section 8.3—is caused by silver's unpaired $5s$ electron.

$$Ag \quad [Kr]\, 5s^1 4d^{10}$$

An atom or ion in which all electrons are paired is not attracted to an external magnetic field—it is in fact slightly repelled—and we say that the atom or ion is **diamagnetic**. The zinc atom is diamagnetic.

$$Zn \quad [Ar]\, 4s^2 3d^{10}$$

The magnetic properties of the zinc ion provide confirmation that the $4s$ electrons are indeed lost before $3d$ electrons in the ionization of zinc. If zinc lost two $3d$ electrons upon ionization, then the Zn^{2+} would become paramagnetic (because the two electrons would

come out of two different filled d orbitals, leaving each of them with one unpaired electron). But the zinc ion, like the zinc atom, is diamagnetic because the $4s$ electrons are lost instead.

$$Zn^{2+} \quad [Ar] \quad 4s^0 3d^{10}$$

Observations in other transition metals confirm that the ns electrons are lost before the $(n-1)d$ electrons upon ionization.

EXAMPLE 8.6 Electron Configurations and Magnetic Properties for Ions

Write the electron configuration and orbital diagram for each ion and determine whether it is diamagnetic or paramagnetic.

(a) Al^{3+} **(b)** S^{2-} **(c)** Fe^{3+}

SOLUTION

(a) Al^{3+}

Begin by writing the electron configuration of the neutral atom.

Al $[Ne]\, 3s^2 3p^1$

Since this ion has a 3+ charge, remove three electrons to write the electron configuration of the ion. Write the orbital diagram by drawing half-arrows to represent each electron in boxes representing the orbitals. Because there are no unpaired electrons, Al^{3+} is diamagnetic.

Al^{3+} $[Ne]$ or $[He]\, 2s^2 2p^6$

Al^{3+} $[He]$

Diamagnetic

(b) S^{2-}

Begin by writing the electron configuration of the neutral atom.

S $[Ne]\, 3s^2 3p^4$

Since this ion has a 2− charge, add two electrons to write the electron configuration of the ion. Write the orbital diagram by drawing half-arrows to represent each electron in boxes representing the orbitals. Because there are no unpaired electrons, S^{2-} is diamagnetic.

S^{2-} $[Ne]\, 3s^2 3p^6$

S^{2-} $[Ne]$

Diamagnetic

(c) Fe^{3+}

Begin by writing the electron configuration of the neutral atom.

Fe $[Ar]\, 4s^2 3d^6$

Since this ion has a 3+ charge, remove three electrons to write the electron configuration of the ion. Since it is a transition metal, remove the electrons from the $4s$ orbital before removing electrons from the $3d$ orbitals. Write the orbital diagram by drawing half-arrows to represent each electron in boxes representing the orbitals. Because there are unpaired electrons, Fe^{3+} is paramagnetic.

Fe^{3+} $[Ar]\, 4s^0 3d^5$

Fe^{3+} $[Ar]$

Paramagnetic

FOR PRACTICE 8.6

Write the electron configuration and orbital diagram for each ion and predict whether it will be paramagnetic or diamagnetic.

(a) Co^{2+} **(b)** N^{3-} **(c)** Ca^{2+}

Ionic Radii

What happens to the radius of an atom when it becomes a cation? An anion? Consider, for example, the difference between the Na atom and the Na^+ ion. Their electron configurations are as follows:

$$Na \quad [Ne] \, 3s^1$$

$$Na^+ \quad [Ne]$$

The sodium atom has an outer $3s$ electron and a neon core. Since the $3s$ electron is the outermost electron, and since it is shielded from the nuclear charge by the core electrons, it contributes greatly to the size of the sodium atom. The sodium cation, having lost the outermost $3s$ electron, has only the neon core and carries a charge of 1+. Without the $3s$ electron, the sodium cation (ionic radius = 95 pm) becomes much smaller than the sodium atom (covalent radius = 186 pm). The trend is the same with all cations and their atoms, as shown in Figure 8.13 ▼.

Cations are much smaller than their corresponding atoms.

Radii of Atoms and Their Cations (pm)

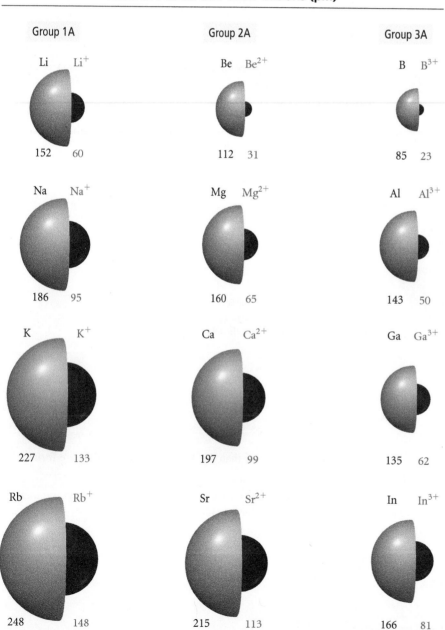

Group 1A	Group 2A	Group 3A
Li Li⁺	Be Be²⁺	B B³⁺
152 60	112 31	85 23
Na Na⁺	Mg Mg²⁺	Al Al³⁺
186 95	160 65	143 50
K K⁺	Ca Ca²⁺	Ga Ga³⁺
227 133	197 99	135 62
Rb Rb⁺	Sr Sr²⁺	In In³⁺
248 148	215 113	166 81

◄ **FIGURE 8.13 Sizes of Atoms and Their Cations** Atomic and ionic radii (pm) for the first three columns of main-group elements.

Radii of Atoms and Their Anions (pm)

Group 6A

O   O^{2-}

73   140

S   S^{2-}

103   184

Se   Se^{2-}

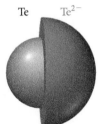

117   198

Te   Te^{2-}

143   221

Group 7A

F   F^{-}

72   136

Cl   Cl^{-}

99   181

Br   Br^{-}

114   195

I   I^{-}

133   216

What about anions? Consider, for example, the difference between Cl and Cl^{-}. Their electron configurations are as follows:

$$Cl \quad [Ne] \, 3s^2 3p^5$$
$$Cl^{-} \quad [Ne] \, 3s^2 3p^6$$

The chlorine anion has one additional outermost electron, but no additional proton to increase the nuclear charge. The extra electron increases the repulsions among the outermost electrons, resulting in a chloride anion that is larger than the chlorine atom. The trend is the same with all anions and their atoms, as shown in Figure 8.14 ◄.

Anions are much larger than their corresponding atoms.

We can observe an interesting trend in ionic size by examining the radii of an *isoelectronic* series of ions—ions with the same number of electrons. Consider the following ions and their radii:

S^{2-} (184 pm)	Cl^{-} (181 pm)	K^{+} (133 pm)	Ca^{2+} (99 pm)
18 electrons	18 electrons	18 electrons	18 electrons
16 protons	17 protons	19 protons	20 protons

All of these ions have 18 electrons in exactly the same orbitals, but the radius of each ion gets successively smaller. Why? The reason is the progressively greater number of protons. The S^{2-} ion has 16 protons, and therefore a charge of 16+ pulling on 18 electrons. The Ca^{2+} ion, however, has 20 protons, and therefore a charge of 20+ pulling on the same 18 electrons. The result is a much smaller radius. For a given number of electrons, a greater nuclear charge results in a smaller atom or ion.

◄ **FIGURE 8.14 Sizes of Atoms and Their Anions** Atomic and ionic radii for groups 6A and 7A in the periodic table.

EXAMPLE 8.7 Ion Size

Choose the larger atom or ion from each pair.

(a) S or S^{2-} **(b)** Ca or Ca^{2+} **(c)** Br^{-} or Kr

SOLUTION

(a) The S^{2-} ion is larger than an S atom because anions are larger than the atoms from which they are formed.

(b) A Ca atom is larger than Ca^{2+} because cations are smaller than the atoms from which they are formed.

(c) A Br^{-} ion is larger than a Kr atom because, although they are isoelectronic, Br^{-} has one fewer proton than Kr, resulting in a lesser pull on the electrons and therefore a larger radius.

FOR PRACTICE 8.7

Choose the larger atom or ion from each pair.

(a) K or K^{+} **(b)** F or F^{-} **(c)** Ca^{2+} or Cl^{-}

FOR MORE PRACTICE 8.7

Arrange the following in order of decreasing radius: Ca^{2+}, Ar, Cl^{-}.

Conceptual Connection 8.3 Ions, Isotopes, and Atomic Size

In the previous sections, we have seen how the number of electrons and the number of protons affects the size of an atom or ion. However, we have not considered how the number of neutrons affects the size of an atom. Why not? Would you expect isotopes—for example, C-12 and C-13—to have different atomic radii?

ANSWER: The isotopes of an element all have the same radii for two reasons: (1) neutrons are negligibly small compared to the size of an atom and therefore extra neutrons do not increase atomic size; and (2) neutrons have no charge and therefore do not attract electrons in the way that protons do.

Ionization Energy

The **ionization energy (IE)** of an atom or ion is the energy required to remove an electron from the atom or ion in the gaseous state. Ionization energy is always positive because removing an electron always takes energy. (The process is similar to an endothermic reaction, which absorbs heat and therefore has a positive ΔH.) The energy required to remove the first electron is called the *first ionization energy* (IE_1). For example, we represent the first ionization of sodium with the following equation:

$$Na(g) \longrightarrow Na^+(g) + 1\,e^- \quad IE_1 = 496 \text{ kJ/mol}$$

The energy required to remove the second electron is called the *second ionization energy* (IE_2), the energy required to remove the third electron is called the *third ionization energy* (IE_3), and so on. We represent the second ionization energy of sodium as follows:

$$Na^+(g) \longrightarrow Na^{2+}(g) + 1\,e^- \quad IE_2 = 4560 \text{ kJ/mol}$$

Notice that the second ionization energy is not the energy required to remove *two* electrons from sodium (that quantity is the sum of IE_1 and IE_2), but rather the energy required to remove one electron from Na^+. We look at trends in IE_1 and IE_2 separately.

Trends in First Ionization Energy

The first ionization energies of the elements through Xe are shown in Figure 8.15 ▼. Notice the periodic trend in ionization energy, peaking at each noble gas and bottoming at each alkali metal. Based on what we have learned about electron configurations and

First Ionization Energies

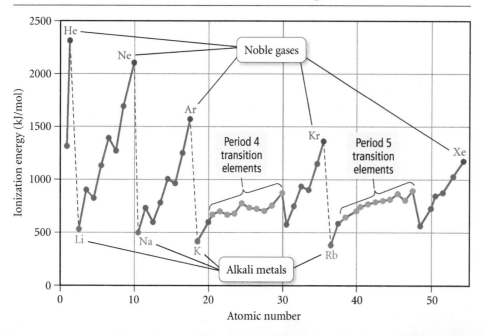

◀ **FIGURE 8.15 First Ionization Energy versus Atomic Number for the Elements through Xenon** Ionization starts at a minimum with each alkali metal and rises to a peak with each noble gas.

▶ FIGURE 8.16 **Trends in Ionization Energy** Ionization energy increases as we move to the right across a period and decreases as we move down a column in the periodic table.

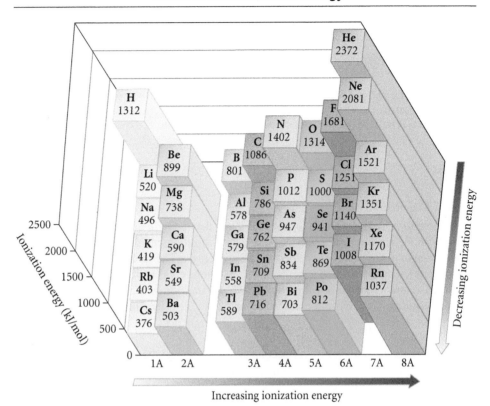

Trends in First Ionization Energy

effective nuclear charge, how can we account for the observed trend? As we have seen, the principal quantum number, n, increases as we move down a column. Within a given sublevel, orbitals with higher principal quantum numbers are larger than orbitals with smaller principal quantum numbers. Consequently, electrons in the outermost principal level are farther away from the positively charged nucleus—and are therefore held less tightly—as we move down a column. This results in a lower ionization energy as we move down a column, as shown in Figure 8.16 ▲.

What about the trend as we move to the right across a row? For example, would it take more energy to remove an electron from Na or from Cl, two elements on either end of the third row in the periodic table? We know that Na has an outer electron configuration of $3s^1$ and Cl has an outer electron configuration of $3s^2 3p^5$. As discussed previously, the outermost electrons in chlorine experience a higher effective nuclear charge than the outermost electrons in sodium (which is why chlorine has a smaller atomic radius than sodium). Consequently, we would expect chlorine to have a higher ionization energy than sodium, which is indeed the case. We can make a similar argument for the other main-group elements: ionization energy generally increases as we move to the right across a row in the periodic table, as shown in Figure 8.16.

Summarizing Ionization Energy for Main-Group Elements:

▶ Ionization energy generally *decreases* as we move down a column (or family) in the periodic table because electrons in the outermost principal level are increasingly farther away from the positively charged nucleus and are therefore held less tightly.

▶ Ionization energy generally *increases* as we move to the right across a period (or row) in the periodic table because electrons in the outermost principal energy level generally experience a greater effective nuclear charge (Z_{eff}).

EXAMPLE 8.8 Ionization Energy

On the basis of periodic trends, choose the element with the higher first ionization energy from each pair (if possible).

(a) Al or S   **(b)** As or Sb   **(c)** N or Si   **(d)** O or Cl

SOLUTION

(a) Al or S

S has a higher ionization energy than Al because, as you trace the path between Al and S on the periodic table, you move to the right within the same period. Ionization energy increases as you go to the right due to increasing effective nuclear charge.

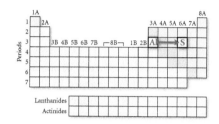

(b) As or Sb

As has a higher ionization energy than Sb because, as you trace the path between As and Sb on the periodic table, you move down a column. Ionization energy decreases as you go down a column as a result of the increasing size of orbitals with increasing n.

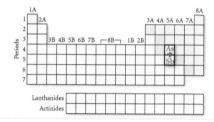

(c) N or Si

N has a higher ionization energy than Si because, as you trace the path between N and Si on the periodic table, you move down a column (ionization energy decreases) and then to the left across a period (ionization energy decreases). These effects sum together for an overall decrease.

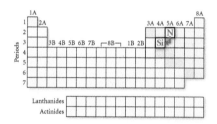

(d) O or Cl

Based on periodic trends alone, it is impossible to tell which has a higher ionization energy because, as you trace the path between O and Cl you go to the right across a period (ionization energy increases) and then down a column (ionization energy decreases). These effects tend to oppose each other, and it is not obvious which will dominate.

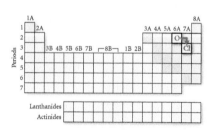

FOR PRACTICE 8.8

On the basis of periodic trends, choose the element with the higher first ionization energy from each pair (if possible).

(a) Sn or I   **(b)** Ca or Sr   **(c)** C or P   **(d)** F or S

FOR MORE PRACTICE 8.8

Arrange the following elements in order of decreasing first ionization energy: S, Ca, F, Rb, Si.

Exceptions to Trends in First Ionization Energy

If you carefully examine Figure 8.16, you can see some exceptions to the trends in first ionization energies. For example, boron has a smaller ionization energy than beryllium, even though it lies to the right of beryllium in the same row. This exception is caused by the change in going from the s block to the p block. Recall from Section 8.3 that the $2p$ orbital penetrates into nuclear region *less than* the $2s$ orbital. Consequently, the $1s$ electrons shield the electron in the $2p$ orbital from nuclear charge more than they shield the electrons in the $2s$ orbital. The result, as we saw in Section 8.3, is that the the $2p$ orbitals are higher in energy, and therefore the electron is easier to remove (it has a lower ionization energy). Similar exceptions occur for aluminum and gallium, both directly below boron in group 3A.

Another exception occurs between nitrogen and oxygen: although oxygen is to the right of nitrogen in the same row, it has a lower ionization energy. This exception is caused by the repulsion between electrons when they must occupy the same orbital. Examine the electron configurations and orbital diagrams of nitrogen and oxygen:

N $1s^2 2s^2 2p^3$ $\boxed{\uparrow\downarrow}$ $\boxed{\uparrow\downarrow}$ $\boxed{\uparrow}\;\boxed{\uparrow}\;\boxed{\uparrow}$
         $1s$ $2s$ $2p$

O $1s^2 2s^2 2p^4$ $\boxed{\uparrow\downarrow}$ $\boxed{\uparrow\downarrow}$ $\boxed{\uparrow\downarrow}\;\boxed{\uparrow}\;\boxed{\uparrow}$
         $1s$ $2s$ $2p$

Nitrogen has three electrons in three p orbitals, while oxygen has four. In nitrogen, the $2p$ orbitals are half-filled (which makes the configuration particularly stable). Oxygen's fourth electron must pair with another electron, making it easier to remove (and less stable). Exceptions for similar reasons occur for S and Se, directly below oxygen in group 6A.

Trends in Second and Successive Ionization Energies

Notice the trends in the first, second, and third ionization energies of sodium (group 1A) and magnesium (group 2A), as shown at left.

For sodium, there is a huge jump between the first and second ionization energies. For magnesium, the ionization energy roughly doubles from the first to the second, but then a huge jump occurs between the second and third ionization energies. What is the reason for these jumps?

We can understand these trends by examining the electron configurations of sodium and magnesium:

$$\text{Na} \quad [\text{Ne}]\, 3s^1$$
$$\text{Mg} \quad [\text{Ne}]\, 3s^2$$

The first ionization of sodium involves removing the valence electron in the $3s$ orbital. Recall that these valence electrons are held more loosely than the core electrons, and that the resulting ion has a noble gas configuration, which is particularly stable. Consequently, the first ionization energy is fairly low. The second ionization of sodium, however, involves removing a core electron from an ion with a noble gas configuration. This requires a tremendous amount of energy, making the value of IE_2 very high.

As with sodium, the first ionization of magnesium involves removing a valence electron in the $3s$ orbital. This requires a bit more energy than the corresponding ionization of sodium because of the trends in Z_{eff} that we discussed earlier (Z_{eff} increases as we move to the right across a row). The second ionization of magnesium also involves removing an outer electron in the $3s$ orbital, but this time from an ion with a $1+$ charge (instead of from a neutral atom). This requires roughly twice the energy as removing the electron from the neutral atom. The third ionization of magnesium is analogous to the

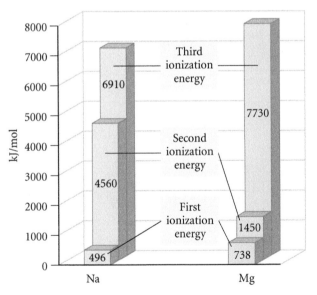

TABLE 8.1 Successive Values of Ionization Energies for the Elements Sodium through Argon (kJ/mol)

Element	IE_1	IE_2	IE_3	IE_4	IE_5	IE_6	IE_7
Na	496	4560			**Core electrons**		
Mg	738	1450	7730				
Al	578	1820	2750	11,600			
Si	786	1580	3230	4360	16,100		
P	1012	1900	2910	4960	6270	22,200	
S	1000	2250	3360	4560	7010	8500	27,100
Cl	1251	2300	3820	5160	6540	9460	11,000
Ar	1521	2670	3930	5770	7240	8780	12,000

second ionization of sodium—it requires removing a core electron from an ion with a noble gas configuration. This requires a tremendous amount of energy, making the value of IE_3 very high.

As shown in Table 8.1, similar trends exist for the successive ionization energies of many elements. The ionization energy increases fairly uniformly with each successive removal of an outermost electron, but then takes a large jump with the removal of the first core electron.

 Conceptual Connection 8.4 Ionization Energies and Chemical Bonding

Based on what you just learned about ionization energies, explain why valence electrons are more important than core electrons in determining the reactivity and bonding in atoms.

ANSWER: As you can see from the successive ionization energies of any element, valence electrons are held most loosely and can therefore be transferred or shared most easily. Core electrons, on the other hand, are held tightly and are not easily transferred or shared. Consequently, valence electrons are most important to chemical bonding.

8.8 Electron Affinities and Metallic Character

Two other properties that exhibit periodic trends are electron affinity and metallic character. Electron affinity is a measure of how easily an atom will accept an additional electron and is crucial to chemical bonding because bonding involves the transfer or sharing of electrons. Metallic character is important because of the high proportion of metals in the periodic table and the large role they play in our lives. Of the roughly 110 elements, 87 are metals. We examine each of these periodic properties individually.

Electron Affinity

The **electron affinity (EA)** of an atom or ion is the energy change associated with the gaining of an electron by the atom in the gaseous state. The electron affinity is usually—though not always—negative because an atom or ion usually releases energy when it gains an electron. (The process is analogous to an exothermic reaction, which releases heat and therefore has a negative ΔH.) In other words, the coulombic attraction between the nucleus of an atom and the incoming electron usually results in the release of energy as the electron is gained. For example, we can represent the electron affinity of chlorine with the following equation:

$$Cl(g) + 1\,e^- \longrightarrow Cl^-(g) \quad EA = -349\ \text{kJ/mol}$$

Electron Affinities (kJ/mol)

1A							8A
H −73	2A	3A	4A	5A	6A	7A	**He** >0
Li −60	**Be** >0	**B** −27	**C** −122	**N** >0	**O** −141	**F** −328	**Ne** >0
Na −53	**Mg** >0	**Al** −43	**Si** −134	**P** −72	**S** −200	**Cl** −349	**Ar** >0
K −48	**Ca** −2	**Ga** −30	**Ge** −119	**As** −78	**Se** −195	**Br** −325	**Kr** >0
Rb −47	**Sr** −5	**In** −30	**Sn** −107	**Sb** −103	**Te** −190	**I** −295	**Xe** >0

▲ **FIGURE 8.17 Electron Affinities of Selected Main-Group Elements**

Figure 8.17 ◄ contains the electron affinities for a number of main-group elements. As you can see from this figure, the trends in electron affinity are not as regular as trends in other properties we have examined. For instance, we might expect electron affinities to become relatively more positive (so that the addition of an electron is less exothermic) as we move down a column because the electron is entering orbitals with successively higher principal quantum numbers, and will therefore be farther from the nucleus. This trend applies to the group 1A metals but does not hold for the other columns in the periodic table.

There is a more regular trend in electron affinity as we move to the right across a row, however. Based on the periodic properties we have learned so far, would you expect more energy to be released when an electron is gained by Na or Cl? We know that Na has an outer electron configuration of $3s^1$ and Cl has an outer electron configuration of $3s^2 3p^5$. Since adding an electron to chlorine gives it a noble gas configuration and adding an electron to sodium does not, and since the outermost electrons in chlorine experience a higher Z_{eff} than the outermost electrons in sodium, we would expect chlorine to have a more negative electron affinity—the process should be more exothermic for chlorine. This is in fact the case. For main-group elements, electron affinity generally becomes more negative (more exothermic) as we move to the right across a row in the periodic table. The halogens (group 7A) therefore have the most negative electron affinities. But exceptions do occur. For example, notice that nitrogen and the other group 5A elements do not follow the general trend. These elements have $ns^2 np^3$ outer electron configurations. When an electron is added to this configuration, it must pair with another electron in an already occupied p orbital. The repulsion between two electrons occupying the same orbital causes the electron affinity to be more positive than for elements in the previous column.

Summarizing Electron Affinity for Main-Group Elements:

▶ Most groups (columns) of the periodic table do not exhibit any definite trend in electron affinity. Among the group 1A metals, however, electron affinity becomes more positive as we move down the column (adding an electron becomes less exothermic).

▶ Electron affinity generally becomes more negative (adding an electron becomes more exothermic) as we move to the right across a period (row) in the periodic table.

Metallic Character

As we learned in Chapter 2, metals are good conductors of heat and electricity; they can be pounded into flat sheets (malleability); they can be drawn into wires (ductility); they are often shiny; and they tend to lose electrons in chemical reactions. Nonmetals, in contrast, have more varied physical properties; some are solids at room temperature, others are gases, but in general they are typically poor conductors of heat and electricity, and they all tend to gain electrons in chemical reactions. As we move to the right across a period in the periodic table, ionization energy increases and electron affinity becomes more negative; therefore, elements on the left side of the periodic table are more likely to lose electrons than elements on the right side of the periodic table (which are more likely to gain them). The other properties associated with metals follow the same general trend (even though we do not quantify them here). Consequently, as shown in Figure 8.18 ▶:

As we move to the right across a period (or row) in the periodic table, metallic character decreases.

As we move down a column in the periodic table, ionization energy decreases, making electrons more likely to be lost in chemical reactions. Consequently:

As we move down a column (or family) in the periodic table, metallic character increases.

Trends in Metallic Character

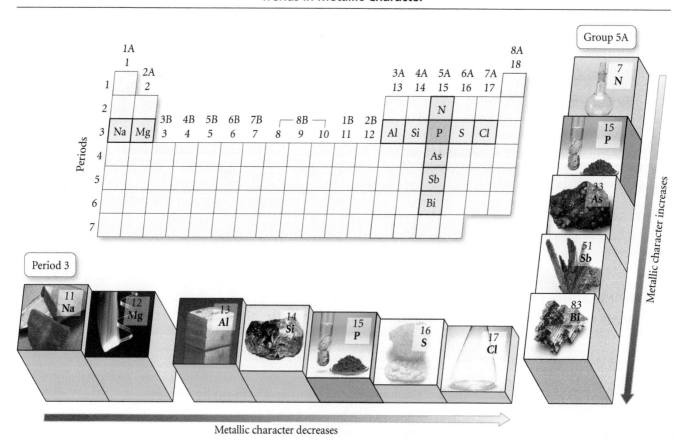

▲ **FIGURE 8.18 Trends in Metallic Character I** Metallic character decreases as we move to the right across a period and increases as we move down a column in the periodic table.

These trends, based on the quantum-mechanical model, explain the distribution of metals and nonmetals in the periodic table that we learned about in Chapter 2. Metals are found on the left side and toward the center and nonmetals on the upper right side. The change in chemical behavior from metallic to nonmetallic can be seen most clearly as you proceed to the right across period 3, or down along group 5A as can be seen in Figure 8.19 ▼.

Trends in Metallic Character

▲ **FIGURE 8.19 Trends in Metallic Character II** As we move down group 5A in the periodic table, metallic character increases. As we move across period 3, metallic character decreases.

EXAMPLE 8.9 Metallic Character

On the basis of periodic trends, choose the more metallic element from each pair (if possible).

(a) Sn or Te   **(b)** P or Sb   **(c)** Ge or In   **(d)** S or Br

SOLUTION

(a) Sn or Te

Sn is more metallic than Te because, as you trace the path between Sn and Te on the periodic table, you move to the right within the same period. Metallic character decreases as we go to the right.

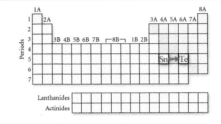

(b) P or Sb

Sb is more metallic than P because, as you trace the path between P and Sb on the periodic table, you move down a column. Metallic character increases as we go down a column.

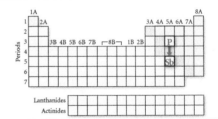

(c) Ge or In

In is more metallic than Ge because, as you trace the path between Ge and In on the periodic table, you move down a column (metallic character increases) and then to the left across a period (metallic character increases). These effects add together for an overall increase.

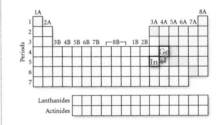

(d) S or Br

Based on periodic trends alone, we cannot tell which is more metallic because as we trace the path between S and Br, we go to the right across a period (metallic character decreases) and then down a column (metallic character increases). These effects tend to oppose each other, and it is not easy to tell which will predominate.

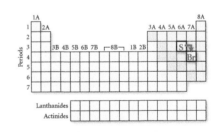

FOR PRACTICE 8.9

On the basis of periodic trends, choose the more metallic element from each pair (if possible).

(a) Ge or Sn   **(b)** Ga or Sn   **(c)** P or Bi   **(d)** B or N

FOR MORE PRACTICE 8.9

Arrange the following elements in order of increasing metallic character: Si, Cl, Na, Rb.

 Conceptual Connection 8.5 Periodic Trends

Use the trends in ionization energy and electron affinity to explain why sodium chloride has the formula NaCl and not Na_2Cl or $NaCl_2$.

ANSWER: The $3s$ electron in sodium has a relatively low ionization energy (496 kJ/mol) because it is a valence electron. The energetic cost for sodium to lose a second electron is extraordinarily

high (4560 kJ/mol) because the next electron to be lost is a core electron ($2p$). Similarly, the electron affinity of chlorine to gain one electron (-349 kJ/mol) is highly exothermic since the added electron completes chlorine's valence shell. The gain of a second electron by the negatively charged chlorine anion would not be so favorable. Therefore, we would expect sodium and chlorine to combine in a 1:1 ratio.

8.9 Some Examples of Periodic Chemical Behavior: The Alkali Metals, the Halogens, and the Noble Gases

In this section, we explore some of the properties and chemical reactions of three families in the periodic table: the alkali metals, the halogens, and the noble gases. These families exemplify the connection between chemical behavior and electron configuration. The alkali metals (group 1A) have ns^1 outer electron configurations. The single valence electron that keeps these metals from having noble gas configurations is easily removed (the metals have low ionization energies), making these elements the most active metals in the periodic table. The halogens (group 7A) have $ns^2 np^5$ outer electron configurations. The one electron needed to attain noble gas configurations is easily acquired (the halogens have highly negative electron affinities), making these elements among the most active nonmetals in the periodic table. The noble gases (group 8A) have electron configurations with full outer principal quantum levels ($ns^2 np^6$), and so are the most chemically inert family in the periodic table. We will examine the properties of each of these groups separately. (Even though hydrogen is often listed in group 1A, it behaves like a nonmetal because of its high ionization energy: 1312 kJ/mol. We therefore do not include hydrogen in our discussion of the group 1A metals.)

The Alkali Metals (Group 1A)

Table 8.2 contains some selected properties of the alkali metals. Notice that, in general, the properties of the alkali metals vary fairly regularly as we proceed down the column. As expected from periodic trends, the atomic radius increases steadily while the first ionization energy decreases steadily.

With the exception of potassium, density increases as we move down the column. This is a general trend that occurs in other columns within the periodic table. As we move down a column, the increase in mass (due to the additional protons and neutrons) outpaces the increase in volume caused by greater atomic radius. The result is successively greater densities. The melting points of the alkali metals as a group are anomalously low for metals, and they steadily decrease as we move down the column. (This is not a general trend for the rest of the periodic table, which shows more irregular patterns in melting points.)

Because of their generally low ionization energies, the alkali metals are excellent reducing agents—they are readily oxidized, losing electrons to other substances. Consequently, the alkali metals exist naturally in their oxidized state, either in compounds or as dissolved ions in seawater. Since ionization energy *decreases* as we go down the column, the relative reactivities of the alkali metals tend to *increase* as we move down the column. In other words, the lower the ionization energy of an alkali metal, the greater tendency it will have to lose its electron and the more reactive it will be.

TABLE 8.2 Properties of the Alkali Metals*

Element	Electron Configuration	Atomic Radius (pm)	IE$_1$ (kJ/mol)	Density at 25 °C (g/cm^3)	Melting Point (°C)
Li	[He] $2s^1$	152	520	0.535	181
Na	[Ne] $3s^1$	186	496	0.968	102
K	[Ar] $4s^1$	227	419	0.856	98
Rb	[Kr] $5s^1$	248	403	1.532	39
Cs	[Xe] $6s^1$	265	376	1.879	29

*Francium is omitted because it has no stable isotopes.

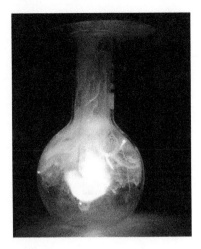

▲ FIGURE 8.20 Reaction of Sodium and Chlorine to Form Sodium Chloride

The reactions of the alkali metals with nonmetals are vigorous. For example, the alkali metals (M) react with halogens (X) according to the following reaction:

$$2\,M + X_2 \longrightarrow 2\,MX$$

The reaction of sodium and chlorine to form sodium chloride is typical:

$$2\,Na(s) + Cl_2(g) \longrightarrow 2\,NaCl(s)$$

This reaction emits heat and sparks as it occurs (Figure 8.20 ◄). Each successive alkali metal reacts even more vigorously with chlorine. The alkali metals also react with water to form the dissolved alkali metal ion, the hydroxide ion, and hydrogen gas:

$$2\,M(s) + 2\,H_2O(l) \longrightarrow 2\,M^+(aq) + 2\,OH^-(aq) + H_2(g)$$

The reaction is highly exothermic and can be explosive because the heat from the reaction can ignite the hydrogen gas. The reaction becomes more explosive as we move down the column from one metal to the next, as shown in Figure 8.21 ▼.*

Reactions of the Alkali Metals with Water

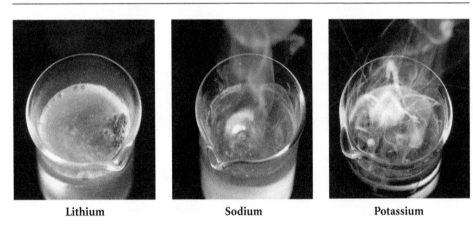

Lithium   Sodium   Potassium

▲ FIGURE 8.21 Reactions of the Alkali Metals with Water   The reaction becomes progressively more vigorous as we move down the group.

The Halogens (Group 7A)

Table 8.3 lists selected properties of the first four halogens. Notice that the properties of the halogens, like those of the alkali metals, vary fairly regularly as you proceed down the column. As expected from periodic trends, the atomic radius and the density increase for each successive halogen. You can see from the melting and boiling points that fluorine and chlorine are both gases at room temperature, bromine is a liquid, and iodine is a solid.

All of the halogens are powerful oxidizing agents—they are readily reduced, gaining electrons from other substances in their reactions. Fluorine is the most powerful oxidizing agent of the group—reacting with almost everything including the heavier noble

TABLE 8.3 Properties of the Halogens*

Element	Electron Configuration	Atomic Radius (pm)	EA (kJ/mol)	Melting Point (°C)	Boiling Point (°C)	Density of Liquid (g/cm^3)
F	[He] $2s^2\,2p^5$	72	−328	−219	−188	1.51
Cl	[Ne] $3s^2\,3p^5$	99	−349	−101	−34	2.03
Br	[Ar] $4s^2\,4p^5$	114	−325	−7	59	3.19
I	[Kr] $5s^2\,5p^5$	133	−295	114	184	3.96

*At is omitted because it is rare and radioactive.

*The rate of the alkali metal reaction with water, and therefore its vigor, is enhanced by the successively lower melting points of the alkali metals as we move down the column. The low melting points of the heavier metals allow the emitted heat to actually melt the metal, increasing the reaction rate.

gases—and iodine is the least. The halogens all react with metals to form *metal halides* according to the following equation:

$$2\,M + n\,X_2 \longrightarrow 2\,MX_n$$

where M is the metal, X is the halogen, and MX_n is the metal halide. For example, chlorine reacts with iron according to the following equation:

$$2\,Fe(s) + 3\,Cl_2(g) \longrightarrow 2\,FeCl_3(s)$$

Since metals tend to lose electrons and the halogens tend to gain them, the metal halides—like all compounds that form between metals and nonmetals—contain ionic bonds.

The halogens also react with hydrogen to form *hydrogen halides* according to the following equation:

$$H_2(g) + X_2 \longrightarrow 2\,HX(g)$$

The hydrogen halides—like all compounds that form between two nonmetals—contain covalent bonds. As we saw in Chapter 3, all of the hydrogen halides form acidic solutions when combined with water.

The halogens also react with each other to form *interhalogen compounds*. For example, bromine reacts with fluorine according to the following equation:

$$Br_2(l) + F_2(g) \longrightarrow 2\,BrF(g)$$

Again, like all compounds that form between two nonmetals, the interhalogen compounds contain covalent bonds.

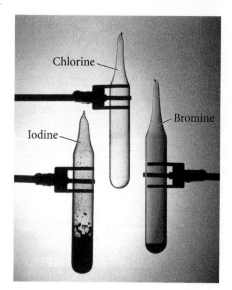

Chlorine

Bromine

Iodine

EXAMPLE 8.10 Alkali Metal and Halogen Reactions

Write a balanced chemical equation for each reaction.

(a) The reaction between potassium metal and bromine gas.

(b) The reaction between rubidium metal and liquid water.

(c) The reaction between gaseous chlorine and solid iodine.

SOLUTION

(a) Alkali metals react with halogens to form metal halides. Write the formulas for the reactants and the metal halide product (making sure to write the correct ionic chemical formula for the metal halide, as outlined in Section 3.5), and then balance the equation.	$2\,K(s) + Br_2(g) \longrightarrow 2\,KBr(s)$
(b) Alkali metals react with water to form the dissolved metal ion, the hydroxide ion, and hydrogen gas. Write the skeletal equation including each of these and then balance it.	$2\,Rb(s) + 2\,H_2O(l) \longrightarrow 2\,Rb^+(aq) + 2\,OH^-(aq) + H_2(g)$
(c) Halogens react with each other to form interhalogen compounds. Write the skeletal equation with each of the halogens as the reactants and the interhalogen compound as the product and balance the equation.	$Cl_2(g) + I_2(s) \longrightarrow 2\,ICl(g)$

FOR PRACTICE 8.10

Write a balanced chemical equation for each reaction.

(a) the reaction between aluminum metal and chlorine gas

(b) the reaction between lithium metal and liquid water

(c) the reaction between gaseous hydrogen and liquid bromine

CHEMISTRY AND MEDICINE Potassium Iodide in Radiation Emergencies

Since the attack on the World Trade Center on September 11, 2001, the United States has been concerned about the threat of additional terrorist strikes, including the possibility of nuclear attack. One danger of such an attack is radiation from the decay of radioisotopes released by a nuclear device—especially a so-called dirty bomb. This radiation can produce elevated rates of many cancers for years following exposure. The risk of developing thyroid cancer after ingesting radioactive isotopes of iodine, for example, is particularly high, especially in children. The number of thyroid cancers among children and adolescents in Belarus and Ukraine (areas affected by the radioactive plume from the 1986 nuclear accident at Chernobyl in the former Soviet Union) is 30–100 times higher than in the normal population.

The U.S. Food and Drug Administration (FDA), in cooperation with other federal agencies, recommends the administration of potassium iodide (KI) to citizens in the event of a nuclear radiation emergency. Although KI does not prevent exposure to radiation, it does decrease the risk of thyroid cancer that follows the intake of radioactive isotopes, particularly I-131. The chief function of the thyroid gland is to synthesize and release the hormone thyroxine, which regulates many aspects of human metabolism. In order to produce thyroxine, which contains iodine, the thyroid normally accumulates iodine in concentrations far greater than those found elsewhere in the body.

When potassium iodide is taken in the recommended doses, it floods the thyroid with nonradioactive iodine, preventing the thyroid from absorbing the cancer-causing radioactive iodine, which is then excreted in the urine.

In the United States, the FDA prioritizes KI treatment in the event of a nuclear emergency based on age. Infants, children, and pregnant females are at highest risk and are therefore treated at the lowest threshold exposure levels. Adults aged 18 to 40 are treated at slightly higher exposure levels, and those over 40 are only treated if the exposure level is actually high enough to destroy the thyroid.

The federal government has purchased stockpiles of potassium iodide for all states with nuclear reactors. Potassium iodide, also available over the counter, works best if taken 3–4 hours after exposure. Because of the increased threat of terrorist attacks after 9/11, potassium iodide pills have been distributed to residents, schools, and businesses within a 10-mile radius of a nuclear reactor. In the event of a terrorist attack on a nuclear reactor, residents are advised to take the potassium iodide pill and evacuate the area as soon as possible.

▲ The U.S. Food and Drug Administration recommends taking potassium iodide pills in the event of a nuclear emergency.

▲ Each molecule of thyroxine, a thyroid hormone that plays a key role in metabolism, contains four iodine atoms.

The Noble Gases (Group 8A)

Table 8.4 lists selected properties of the noble gases. Notice that the properties of the noble gases, like those of the alkali metals and halogens, vary fairly regularly as we proceed down the column. As expected from periodic trends, the atomic radius and the

TABLE 8.4 Properties of the Noble Gases*

Element	Electron Configuration	Atomic Radius (pm)**	IE_1 (kJ/mol)	Boiling Point (K)	Density of Gas (g/L at STP)
He	$1s^2$	32	2372	4.2	0.18
Ne	$[He]2s^2 2p^6$	70	2081	27.1	0.90
Ar	$[Ne]3s^2 3p^6$	98	1521	87.3	1.78
Kr	$[Ar]4s^2 4p^6$	112	1351	119.9	3.74
Xe	$[Kr]5s^2 5p^6$	130	1170	165.1	5.86

*Radon is omitted because it is radioactive.
**Since only the heavier noble gases form compounds, covalent radii for the smaller noble gases are estimated.

density increase for each successive noble gas, and the ionization energy decreases. As you can see from the boiling points, all of the noble gases are gases at room temperature and must be cooled to extremely low temperatures before they liquefy. For this reason some noble gases can be cryogenic liquids—liquids used to cool other substances to low temperatures. For example, researchers often submerse samples of interest in boiling liquid helium to cool them down to 4.2 K and study their properties at this extremely low temperature.

The high ionization energies of the noble gases and their completely full outer quantum levels make them exceptionally unreactive. In fact, before the 1960s, no noble gas compounds were known. Since then, two of the noble gases have been shown to react with fluorine (the most reactive nonmetal on the periodic table) under fairly extreme conditions. Krypton reacts with fluorine to form KrF_2:

$$Kr + F_2 \longrightarrow KrF_2$$

Similarly, Xe reacts with fluorine to form three different xenon fluorides:

$$Xe + F_2 \longrightarrow XeF_2$$
$$Xe + 2 F_2 \longrightarrow XeF_4$$
$$Xe + 3 F_2 \longrightarrow XeF_6$$

The inertness of the noble gases has led to their use in situations where reactions are undesirable. For example, argon is used in lightbulbs to prevent the hot tungsten filament from oxidizing, and helium is part of the mixture breathed by deep-sea divers to prevent the toxicity caused by too much oxygen and nitrogen under high pressures. (The helium replaces some of the oxygen and nitrogen in the tank, lowering the concentrations of oxygen and nitrogen in the blood.)

▲ Liquid helium, a cryogenic liquid, cools substances to temperatures as low as 1.2 K.

Xenon can also be forced to react with oxygen to form XeO_3 and XeO_4.

CHAPTER IN REVIEW

Key Terms

Section 8.1
periodic property (316)

Section 8.3
electron configuration (317)
ground state (317)
orbital diagram (318)
electron spin (318)
spin quantum number
    (m_s) (318)

Pauli exclusion principle (319)
degenerate (319)
Coulomb's law (319)
shielding (320)
effective nuclear charge
    (Z_{eff}) (320)
penetration (320)
aufbau principle (322)
Hund's rule (322)

Section 8.4
valence electrons (325)
core electrons (325)

Section 8.6
van der Waals radius (nonbonding atomic radius) (330)
covalent radius (bonding atomic radius) (330)
atomic radius (330)

Section 8.7
paramagnetic (335)
diamagnetic (335)
ionization energy (IE) (339)

Section 8.8
electron affinity (EA) (343)

Key Concepts

Periodic Properties and the Development of the Periodic Table (8.1, 8.2)

The periodic table was primarily developed by Dmitri Mendeleev in the nineteenth century. Mendeleev arranged the elements in a table so that atomic mass increased from left to right in a row and elements with similar properties fell in the same columns. Periodic properties are those that are predictable based on an element's position within the periodic table. Periodic properties include atomic radius, ionization energy, electron affinity, density, and metallic character.

Electron Configurations (8.3)

An electron configuration for an atom shows which quantum-mechanical orbitals are occupied by the atom's electrons. For example, the electron configuration of helium ($1s^2$) indicates that helium's two

electrons exist within the $1s$ orbital. The order of filling quantum-mechanical orbitals in multielectron atoms is as follows: $1s\ 2s\ 2p\ 3s\ 3p\ 4s\ 3d\ 4p\ 5s\ 4d\ 5p\ 6s$. According to the Pauli exclusion principle, each orbital can hold a maximum of two electrons with opposing spins. According to Hund's rule, orbitals of the same energy first fill singly with electrons with parallel spins, before pairing.

Electron Configurations and the Periodic Table (8.4, 8.5)

Because quantum-mechanical orbitals fill sequentially with increasing atomic number, we can infer the electron configuration of an element from its position in the periodic table. Quantum-mechanical calculations of the relative energies of electron configurations show that the most stable configurations are those with completely full principal energy levels. Therefore, the most stable and unreactive elements—those with the lowest energy electron configurations—

are the noble gases. Elements with one or two valence electrons are among the most active metals, readily losing their valence electrons to attain noble gas configurations. Elements with six or seven valence electrons are among the most active nonmetals, readily gaining enough electrons to attain a noble gas configuration.

Effective Nuclear Charge and Periodic Trends in Atomic Size (8.6)

The size of an atom is largely determined by its outermost electrons. As we move down a column in the periodic table, the principal quantum number (n) of the outermost electrons increases, resulting in successively larger orbitals and therefore larger atomic radii. As we move across a row in the periodic table, atomic radii decrease because the effective nuclear charge—the net or average charge experienced by the atom's outermost electrons—increases. The atomic radii of the transition elements stay roughly constant across each row because, as we move across a row, electrons are added to the $n_{\text{highest}} - 1$ orbitals while the number of highest n electrons stays roughly constant.

Ion Properties (8.7)

We can determine the electron configuration of an ion by adding or subtracting the corresponding number of electrons to the electron configuration of the neutral atom. For main-group ions, the order of removing electrons is the same as the order in which they are added in building up the electron configuration. For transition metal atoms, the ns electrons are removed before the $(n - 1)d$ electrons. The radius of a cation is much *smaller* than that of the corresponding atom, and

the radius of an anion is much *larger* than that of the corresponding atom. The ionization energy—the energy required to remove an electron from an atom in the gaseous state—generally decreases as we move down a column in the periodic table and increases when moving to the right across a row. Successive ionization energies for valence electrons increase smoothly from one to the next, but the ionization energy increases dramatically for the first core electron.

Electron Affinities and Metallic Character (8.8)

Electron affinity—the energy associated with an element in its gaseous state gaining an electron—does not show a general trend as we move down a column in the periodic table, but it generally becomes more negative (more exothermic) to the right across a row. Metallic character—the tendency to lose electrons in a chemical reaction—generally increases down a column in the periodic table and decreases to the right across a row.

The Alkali Metals, Halogens, and Noble Gases (8.9)

The most active metals are the alkali metals (group 1A) and the most active nonmetals are the halogens (group 7A). The alkali metals are powerful reducing agents, reacting with many nonmetals—including the halogens and water—to form ionic compounds. The halogens are powerful oxidizing agents, reacting with many metals to form ionic compounds. The halogens also react with many nonmetals to form covalent compounds. The noble gases are relatively unreactive; only krypton and xenon form compounds, typically only with fluorine, the most reactive element in the periodic table.

Key Equations and Relationships

Order of Filling Quantum-Mechanical Orbitals (8.3)

$$1s\ 2s\ 2p\ 3s\ 3p\ 4s\ 3d\ 4p\ 5s\ 4d\ 5p\ 6s$$

Key Skills

Writing Electron Configurations (8.3)
- Example 8.1 • For Practice 8.1 • Exercises 43, 44

Writing Orbital Diagrams (8.3)
- Example 8.2 • For Practice 8.2 • Exercises 45, 46

Valence Electrons and Core Electrons (8.4)
- Example 8.3 • For Practice 8.3 • Exercises 53, 54

Electron Configurations from the Periodic Table (8.4)
- Example 8.4 • For Practice 8.4 • For More Practice 8.4 • Exercises 47, 48

Using Periodic Trends to Predict Atomic Size (8.6)
- Example 8.5 • For Practice 8.5 • For More Practice 8.5 • Exercises 61–64

Writing Electron Configurations for Ions (8.7)
- Example 8.6 • For Practice 8.6 • Exercises 65, 66

Using Periodic Trends to Predict Ion Size (8.7)
- Example 8.7 • For Practice 8.7 • For More Practice 8.7 • Exercises 69–72

Using Periodic Trends to Predict Relative Ionization Energies (8.7)
- Example 8.8 • For Practice 8.8 • For More Practice 8.8 • Exercises 73–76

Predicting Metallic Character Based on Periodic Trends (8.8)
- Example 8.9 • For Practice 8.9 • For More Practice 8.9 • Exercises 81–84

Writing Reactions for Alkali Metal and Halogen Reactions (8.9)
- Example 8.10 • For Practice 8.10 • Exercises 85–90

EXERCISES

Review Questions

1. What are periodic properties?

2. Which periodic property is particularly important to nerve signal transmission? Why?

3. What were the contributions of Johann Döbereiner and John Newlands to the organization of elements according to their properties?

4. Who is credited with arranging the periodic table? How were elements arranged in this table?

5. Explain the contributions of Meyer and Moseley to the periodic table.

6. The periodic table is a result of the periodic law. What observations led to the periodic law? What theory explains the underlying reasons for the periodic law?

7. What is electron spin? Explain the difference between an electron with $m_s = +\frac{1}{2}$ and $m_s = -\frac{1}{2}$.

8. Describe the Stern–Gerlach experiment. How did the experiment demonstrate that the orientation of electron spin was quantized?

9. What is an electron configuration? Give an example.

10. What is Coulomb's law? Explain how the potential energy of two charged particles depends on the distance between the charged particles and on the magnitude and sign of their charges.

11. What is shielding? In an atom, which electrons tend to do the most shielding (core electrons or valence electrons)?

12. What is penetration? How does the penetration of an orbital into the region occupied by core electrons affect the energy of an electron in that orbital?

13. Why are the sublevels within a principal level split into different energies for multielectron atoms but not for the hydrogen atom?

14. What is an orbital diagram? Give an example.

15. Why is electron spin important when writing electron configurations? Explain in terms of the Pauli exclusion principle.

16. What are degenerate orbitals? According to Hund's rule, how are degenerate orbitals occupied?

17. List all orbitals from $1s$ through $5s$ according to increasing energy for multielectron atoms.

18. What are valence electrons? Why are they important?

19. Copy the following blank periodic table onto a sheet of paper and label each of the blocks within the table: s block, p block, d block, and f block.

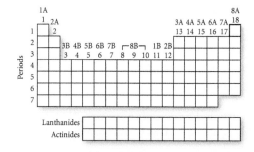

20. Explain why the s block in the periodic table has only two columns while the p block has six.

21. Why do the rows in the periodic table get progressively longer as you move down the table? For example, the first row contains two elements, the second and third rows each contain eight elements, and the fourth and fifth rows each contain eighteen elements. Explain.

22. Explain the relationship between a main-group element's lettered group number (the number of the element's column) and its valence electrons.

23. Explain the relationship between an element's row number in the periodic table and the highest principal quantum number in the element's electron configuration. How does this relationship differ for main-group elements, transition elements, and inner transition elements?

24. Which of the transition elements in the first transition series have anomalous electron configurations?

25. Explain how to write an electron configuration for an element based on its position in the periodic table.

26. Explain the relationship between the properties of an element and the number of valence electrons that it contains.

27. Give the number of valence electrons for each family in the periodic table, and explain the relationship between the number of valence electrons and the resulting chemistry of the elements in the family.
   a. alkali metals   b. alkaline earth metals
   c. halogens   d. oxygen family

28. Define atomic radius. For main-group elements, give the observed trends in atomic radius as you:
   a. move across a period in the periodic table
   b. move down a column in the periodic table

29. What is effective nuclear charge? What is shielding?

30. Use the concepts of effective nuclear charge, shielding, and n value of the valence orbital to explain the trend in atomic radius as you move across a period in the periodic table.

31. For transition elements, give the trends in atomic radius as you:
   a. move across a period in the periodic table
   b. move down a column in the periodic table
   Explain the reasons for the trends in parts a and b.

32. How is the electron configuration of an anion different from that of the corresponding neutral atom? How is the electron configuration of a cation different?

33. Explain how to write an electron configuration for a transition metal cation. Is the order of electron removal upon ionization simply the reverse of electron addition upon filling? Why or why not?

34. Describe the relationship between:
   a. the radius of a cation and that of the atom from which it is formed
   b. the radius of an anion and that of the atom from which it is formed

35. What is ionization energy? What is the difference between first ionization energy and second ionization energy?

36. What is the general trend in ionization energy as you move down a column in the periodic table? As you move across a row?

37. What are the exceptions to the periodic trends in ionization energy? Why do they occur?

38. Examination of the first few successive ionization energies for a given element usually reveals a large jump between two ionization energies. For example, the successive ionization energies of magnesium show a large jump between IE_2 and IE_3. The successive ionization energies of aluminum show a large jump between IE_3 and IE_4. Explain why these jumps occur and how you might predict them.

39. What is electron affinity? What are the observed periodic trends in electron affinity?

40. What is metallic character? What are the observed periodic trends in metallic character?

41. Write a general equation for the reaction of an alkali metal with:
  a. a halogen   **b.** water

42. Write a general equation for the reaction of a halogen with:
  a. a metal   **b.** hydrogen
  c. another halogen

Problems by Topic

Electron Configurations

43. Write full electron configurations for each element:
  a. Si   **b.** O   **c.** K   **d.** Ne

44. Write full electron configurations for each element:
  a. C   **b.** P   **c.** Ar   **d.** Na

45. Write full orbital diagrams for each element:
  a. N   **b.** F   **c.** Mg   **d.** Al

46. Write full orbital diagrams for each element:
  a. S   **b.** Ca   **c.** Ne   **d.** He

47. Use the periodic table to write electron configurations for each element. Represent core electrons with the symbol of the previous noble gas in brackets.
  a. P   **b.** Ge   **c.** Zr   **d.** I

48. Use the periodic table to determine the element corresponding to each electron configuration.
  a. $[Ar]\,4s^2 3d^{10} 4p^6$ **b.** $[Ar]\,4s^2 3d^2$
  c. $[Kr]\,5s^2 4d^{10} 5p^2$ **d.** $[Kr]\,5s^2$

49. Use the periodic table to determine:
  a. The number of $2s$ electrons in Li
  b. The number of $3d$ electrons in Cu
  c. The number of $4p$ electrons in Br
  d. The number of $4d$ electrons in Zr

50. Use the periodic table to determine:
  a. The number of $3s$ electrons in Mg
  b. The number of $3d$ electrons in Cr
  c. The number of $4d$ electrons in Y
  d. The number of $6p$ electrons in Pb

51. Name an element in the fourth period (row) of the periodic table with:
  a. five valence electrons   **b.** four $4p$ electrons
  c. three $3d$ electrons   **d.** a complete outer shell

52. Name an element in the third period (row) of the periodic table with:
  a. three valence electrons
  b. four $3p$ electrons
  c. six $3p$ electrons
  d. two $3s$ electrons and no $3p$ electrons

Valence Electrons and Simple Chemical Behavior from the Periodic Table

53. Determine the number of valence electrons in each element.
  a. Ba   **b.** Cs   **c.** Ni   **d.** S

54. Determine the number of valence electrons in each element. Which elements do you expect to lose electrons in their chemical reactions? Which do you expect to gain electrons?
  a. Al   **b.** Sn   **c.** Br   **d.** Se

55. Which outer electron configuration would you expect to belong to a reactive metal? To a reactive nonmetal?
  a. ns^2 **b.** $ns^2 np^6$ **c.** $ns^2 np^5$ **d.** $ns^2 np^2$

56. Which outer electron configurations would you expect to belong to a noble gas? To a metalloid?
  a. ns^2 **b.** $ns^2 np^6$ **c.** $ns^2 np^5$ **d.** $ns^2 np^2$

Effective Nuclear Charge and Atomic Radius

57. Which electrons experience a greater effective nuclear charge, the valence electrons in beryllium, or the valence electrons in nitrogen? Why?

58. Arrange the atoms according to decreasing effective nuclear charge experienced by their valence electrons: S, Mg, Al, Si.

59. If core electrons completely shielded valence electrons from nuclear charge (i.e., if each core electron reduced nuclear charge by 1 unit) and if valence electrons did not shield one another from nuclear charge at all, what would be the effective nuclear charge experienced by the valence electrons of each atom?
  a. K   **b.** Ca   **c.** O   **d.** C

60. In Section 8.6, we estimated the effective nuclear charge on beryllium's valence electrons to be slightly greater than 2+. What would a similar treatment predict for the effective nuclear charge on boron's valence electrons? Would you expect the effective nuclear charge to be different for boron's $2s$ electrons compared to its $2p$ electron? In what way? (Hint: Consider the shape of the $2p$ orbital compared to that of the $2s$ orbital.)

61. Choose the larger atom from each pair:
  a. Al or In   **b.** Si or N   **c.** P or Pb   **d.** C or F

62. Choose the larger atom from each pair:
  a. Sn or Si   **b.** Br or Ga   **c.** Sn or Bi   **d.** Se or Sn

63. Arrange these elements in order of increasing atomic radius: Ca, Rb, S, Si, Ge, F.

64. Arrange these elements in order of decreasing atomic radius: Cs, Sb, S, Pb, Se.

Ionic Electron Configurations, Ionic Radii, Magnetic Properties, and Ionization Energy

65. Write electron configurations for each ion:
  a. O^{2-} **b.** Br^- **c.** Sr^{2+}
  d. Co^{3+} **e.** Cu^{2+}

66. Write electron configurations for each ion:
  a. Cl^- **b.** P^{3-} **c.** K^+
  d. Mo^{3+} **e.** V^{3+}

67. Write orbital diagrams for each ion and determine if the ion is diamagnetic or paramagnetic.
  a. V^{5+} **b.** Cr^{3+} **c.** Ni^{2+} **d.** Fe^{3+}

68. Write orbital diagrams for each ion and determine if the ion is diamagnetic or paramagnetic.
  a. Cd^{2+} **b.** Au^+ **c.** Mo^{3+} **d.** Zr^{2+}

69. Which is the larger species in each pair?
  a. Li or Li^+ **b.** I^- or Cs^+ **c.** Cr or Cr^{3+} **d.** O or O^{2-}

70. Which is the larger species in each pair?
   a. Sr or Sr^{2+} **b.** N or N^{3-}
   c. Ni or Ni^{2+} **d.** S^{2-} or Ca^{2+}

71. Arrange this isoelectronic series in order of decreasing radius: F^-, Ne, O^{2-}, Mg^{2+}, Na^+.

72. Arrange this isoelectronic series in order of increasing atomic radius: Se^{2-}, Kr, Sr^{2+}, Rb^+, Br^-.

73. Choose the element with the higher first ionization energy from each pair.
   a. Br or Bi   **b.** Na or Rb   **c.** As or At   **d.** P or Sn

74. Choose the element with the higher first ionization energy from each pair.
   a. P or I   **b.** Si or Cl   **c.** P or Sb   **d.** Ga or Ge

75. Arrange these elements in order of increasing first ionization energy: Si, F, In, N.

76. Arrange these elements in order of decreasing first ionization energy: Cl, S, Sn, Pb.

77. For each element, predict where the "jump" occurs for successive ionization energies. (For example, does the jump occur between the first and second ionization energies, the second and third, or the third and fourth?)
   a. Be   **b.** N   **c.** O   **d.** Li

78. Consider this set of successive ionization energies:

$$IE_1 = 578 \text{ kJ/mol}$$
$$IE_2 = 1820 \text{ kJ/mol}$$
$$IE_3 = 2750 \text{ kJ/mol}$$
$$IE_4 = 11{,}600 \text{ kJ/mol}$$

To which third period element do these ionization values belong?

Electron Affinities and Metallic Character

79. Choose the element with the more negative (more exothermic) electron affinity from each pair.
   a. Na or Rb   **b.** B or S   **c.** C or N   **d.** Li or F

80. Choose the element with the more negative (more exothermic) electron affinity from each pair.
   a. Mg or S   **b.** K or Cs   **c.** Si or P   **d.** Ga or Br

81. Choose the more metallic element from each pair.
   a. Sr or Sb   **b.** As or Bi   **c.** Cl or O   **d.** S or As

82. Choose the more metallic element from each pair.
   a. Sb or Pb   **b.** K or Ge   **c.** Ge or Sb   **d.** As or Sn

83. Arrange these elements in order of increasing metallic character: Fr, Sb, In, S, Ba, Se.

84. Arrange these elements in order of decreasing metallic character: Sr, N, Si, P, Ga, Al.

Chemical Behavior of the Alkali Metals and the Halogens

85. Write a balanced chemical equation for the reaction of solid strontium with iodine gas.

86. Based on the ionization energies of the alkali metals, which alkali metal would you expect to undergo the most exothermic reaction with chlorine gas? Write a balanced chemical equation for the reaction.

87. Write a balanced chemical equation for the reaction of solid lithium with liquid water.

88. Write a balanced chemical equation for the reaction of solid potassium with liquid water.

89. Write a balanced equation for the reaction of hydrogen gas with bromine gas.

90. Write a balanced equation for the reaction of chlorine gas with fluorine gas.

Cumulative Problems

91. Bromine is a highly reactive liquid while krypton is an inert gas. Explain the difference based on their electron configurations.

92. Potassium is a highly reactive metal while argon is an inert gas. Explain the difference based on their electron configurations.

93. Both vanadium and its 3+ ion are paramagnetic. Use electron configurations to explain why this is so.

94. Use electron configurations to explain why copper is paramagnetic while its 1+ ion is not.

95. Suppose you were trying to find a substitute for K^+ in nerve signal transmission. Where would you begin your search? What ions would be most like K^+? For each ion you propose, explain the ways in which it would be similar to K^+ and the ways it would be different. Refer to periodic trends in your discussion.

96. Suppose you were trying to find a substitute for Na^+ in nerve signal transmission. Where would you begin your search? What ions would be most like Na^+? For each ion you propose, explain the ways in which it would be similar to Na^+ and the ways it would be different. Use periodic trends in your discussion.

97. Life on Earth evolved around the element carbon. Based on periodic properties, what two or three elements would you expect to be most like carbon?

98. Which pair of elements would you expect to have the most similar atomic radii, and why?
   a. Si and Ga   **b.** Si and Ge   **c.** Si and As

99. Consider these elements: N, Mg, O, F, Al.
   a. Write an electron configuration for each element.
   b. Arrange the elements in order of decreasing atomic radius.
   c. Arrange the elements in order of increasing ionization energy.
   d. Use the electron configurations in part a to explain the differences between your answers to parts b and c.

100. Consider these elements: P, Ca, Si, S, Ga.
   a. Write an electron configuration for each element.
   b. Arrange the elements in order of decreasing atomic radius.
   c. Arrange the elements in order of increasing ionization energy.
   d. Use the electron configurations in part a to explain the differences between your answers to parts b and c.

101. Explain why atomic radius decreases as we move to the right across a period for main-group elements but not for transition elements.

102. Explain why vanadium (radius = 134 pm) and copper (radius = 128 pm) have nearly identical atomic radii, even though the atomic number of copper is about 25% higher than that of vanadium. What would you predict about the relative densities of these two metals? Look up the densities in a reference book, periodic table, or on the Web. Are your predictions correct?

103. The lightest noble gases, such as helium and neon, are completely inert—they do not form any chemical compounds whatsoever. The heavier noble gases, in contrast, do form a limited number of compounds. Explain this difference in terms of trends in fundamental periodic properties.

104. The lightest halogen is also the most chemically reactive, and reactivity generally decreases as we move down the column of halogens in the periodic table. Explain this trend in terms of periodic properties.

105. Write general outer electron configurations ($ns^x np^y$) for groups 6A and 7A in the periodic table. The electron affinity of each group 7A element is more negative than that of each corresponding group 6A element. Use the electron configurations to explain why this is so.

106. The electron affinity of each group 5A element is more positive than that of each corresponding group 4A element. Use the outer electron configurations for these columns to suggest a reason for this behavior.

107. The elements with atomic numbers 35 and 53 have similar chemical properties. Based on their electronic configurations predict the atomic number of a heavier element that also should have these chemical properties.

108. Write the electronic configurations of the six cations that form from sulfur by the loss of one to six electrons. For those cations that have unpaired electrons, write orbital diagrams.

109. You believe you have cracked a secret code that uses elemental symbols to spell words. The code uses numbers to designate the elemental symbols. Each number is the sum of the atomic number and the highest principal quantum number of the highest occupied orbital of the element whose symbol is to be used. The message may be written forward or backward. Decode the following messages:
a. 10, 12, 58, 11, 7, 44, 63, 66
b. 9, 99, 30, 95, 19, 47, 79

110. The electron affinity of sodium is lower than that of lithium, while the electron affinity of chlorine is higher than that of fluorine. Suggest an explanation for this observation.

111. Use Coulomb's law to calculate the ionization energy in kJ/mol of an atom composed of a proton and an electron separated by 100.00 pm. What wavelength of light would have sufficient energy to ionize the atom?

112. The first ionization energy of sodium is 496 kJ/mol. Use Coulomb's law to estimate the average distance between the sodium nucleus and the $3s$ electron. How does this distance compare to the atomic radius of sodium? Why the difference?

Challenge Problems

113. Consider the densities and atomic radii of the noble gases at 25 °C:

Element	Atomic Radius (pm)	Density (g/L)
He	32	0.18
Ne	70	0.90
Ar	98	—
Kr	112	3.75
Xe	130	—
Rn	—	9.73

a. Estimate the densities of argon and xenon by interpolation from the data.
b. Provide an estimate of the density of the yet undiscovered element with atomic number 118 by extrapolation from the data.
c. Use the molar mass of neon to estimate the mass of a neon atom. Then use the atomic radius of neon to calculate the average density of a neon atom. How does this density compare to the density of neon gas? What does this comparison suggest about the nature of neon gas?
d. Use the densities and molar masses of krypton and neon to calculate the number of atoms of each found in a volume of 1.0 L. Use these values to estimate the number of atoms that occur in 1.0 L of Ar. Now use the molar mass of argon to estimate the density of Ar. How does this estimate compare to that in part a?

114. As we have seen, the periodic table is a result of empirical observation (i.e., the periodic law), but quantum-mechanical theory explains *why* the table is so arranged. Suppose that, in another universe, quantum theory was such that there were one *s* orbital but only two *p* orbitals (instead of three) and only three *d* orbitals (instead of five). Draw out the first four periods of the periodic table in this alternative universe. Which elements would be the equivalent of the noble gases? Halogens? Alkali metals?

115. Consider the metals in the first transition series. Use periodic trends to predict a trend in density as you move to the right across the series.

116. Imagine a universe in which the value of m_s can be $+\frac{1}{2}$, 0, and $-\frac{1}{2}$. Assuming that all the other quantum numbers can take only the values possible in our world and that the Pauli exclusion principle applies, determine the following:
a. the new electronic configuration of neon
b. the atomic number of the element with a completed $n = 2$ shell
c. the number of unpaired electrons in fluorine

117. A carbon atom can absorb radiation of various wavelengths with resulting changes in its electronic configuration. Write orbital diagrams for the electronic configuration of carbon that would result from absorption of the three longest wavelengths of radiation it can absorb.

118. Only trace amounts of the synthetic element darmstadtium, atomic number 110, have been obtained. The element is so highly unstable that no observations of its properties have been possible. Based on its position in the periodic table, propose three different reasonable valence electron configurations for this element.

119. What is the atomic number of the as yet undiscovered element in which the $8s$ and $8p$ electron energy levels fill? Predict the chemical behavior of this element.

120. The trend in second ionization energy for the elements from lithium to fluorine is not a regular one. Predict which of these elements has the highest second ionization energy and which has the lowest and explain. Of the elements N, O, and F, O has the highest and N the lowest second ionization energy. Explain.

121. Unlike the elements in groups 1A and 2A, those in group 3A do not show a regular decrease in first ionization energy in going down the column. Explain the irregularities.

122. Using the data in Figures 8.16 and 8.17, calculate ΔE for the reaction

$$Na(g) + Cl(g) \longrightarrow Na^+(g) + Cl^-(g)$$

123. Despite the fact that adding two electrons to O or S forms an ion with a noble gas electron configuration, the second electron affinity of both of these elements is positive. Explain.

124. In Section 2.7 we discussed the metalloids, which form a diagonal band separating the metals from the nonmetals. There are other instances in which elements such as lithium and magnesium that are diagonal to each other have comparable metallic character. Suggest an explanation for this observation.

125. The heaviest known alkaline earth metal is radium, atomic number 88. Find the atomic numbers of the as yet undiscovered next two members of the series.

126. Predict the electronic configurations of the first two excited states (next higher energy states beyond the ground state) of Pd.

127. Table 8.2 does not include francium because none of its isotopes are stable. Predict the values of the entries for Fr in Table 8.2. Predict the nature of the products of the reaction of Fr with (a) water, (b) oxygen, and (c) chlorine.

128. From its electronic configuration, predict which of the first 10 elements would be most similar in chemical behavior to the as yet undiscovered element 165.

Conceptual Problems

129. Imagine that in another universe, atoms and elements are identical to ours, except that atoms with six valence electrons have particular stability (in contrast to our universe where atoms with eight valence electrons have particular stability). Give an example of an element in the alternative universe that corresponds to:
    a. a noble gas   b. a reactive nonmetal
    c. a reactive metal

130. According to Coulomb's law, rank the interactions between charged particles from lowest potential energy to highest potential energy.
    a. A 1+ charge and a 1− charge separated by 100 pm.
    b. A 2+ charge and a 1− charge separated by 100 pm.
    c. A 1+ charge and a 1+ charge separated by 100 pm.
    d. A 1+ charge and a 1− charge separated by 200 pm.

131. Determine whether each statement regarding penetration and shielding is true or false. (Assume that all lower energy orbitals are fully occupied.)

    a. An electron in a $3s$ orbital is more shielded than an electron in a $2s$ orbital.
    b. An electron in a $3s$ orbital penetrates into the region occupied by core electrons more than electrons in a $3p$ orbital.
    c. An electron in an orbital that penetrates closer to the nucleus will always experience more shielding than an electron in an orbital that does not penetrate as far.
    d. An electron in an orbital that penetrates close to the nucleus will tend to experience a higher effective nuclear charge than one that does not.

132. Give a combination of four quantum numbers that could be assigned to an electron occupying a $5p$ orbital. Do the same for an electron occupying a $6d$ orbital.

133. Use the trends in ionization energy and electron affinity to explain why calcium fluoride has the formula CaF_2 and not Ca_2F or CaF.

9 Chemical Bonding I: Lewis Theory

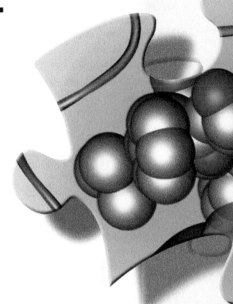

Theories are nets cast to catch what we call 'the world': to rationalize, to explain, and to master it. We endeavor to make the mesh ever finer and finer.
—Karl Popper (1902–1994)

CHEMICAL BONDING IS AT THE HEART of chemistry. The bonding theories that we are about to examine are—as Karl Popper eloquently states in the above quote—nets cast to understand the world. In the next two chapters, we will examine three theories, with successively finer "meshes." The first is Lewis theory, a simple model of chemical bonding, which can be carried out on the back of an envelope. With just a few dots, dashes, and chemical symbols, Lewis theory can help us to understand and predict a myriad of chemical observations. The second is valence bond theory, which treats electrons in a more quantum-mechanical manner, but stops short of viewing them as belonging to the entire molecule. The third is molecular orbital theory, essentially a full quantum-mechanical treatment of the molecule and its electrons as a whole. Molecular orbital theory has great predictive power, but at the expense of great complexity and intensive computational requirements. Which theory is "correct"? Remember that theories are models that help us understand and predict behavior. All three of these theories are extremely useful, depending on exactly what aspect of chemical bonding we want to predict or understand.

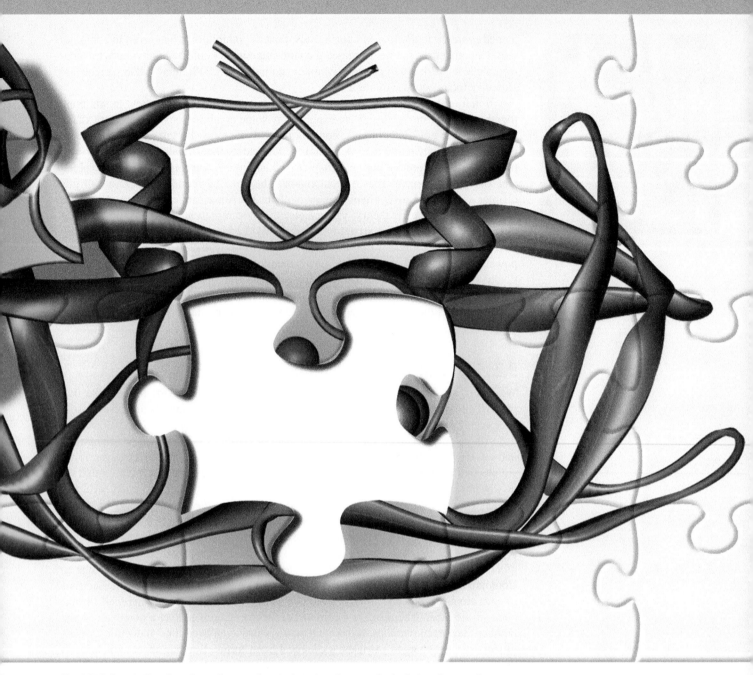

The AIDS drug Indinavir—*shown here as the missing piece in a puzzle depicting the protein HIV-protease—was developed with the help of chemical bonding theories.*

9.1 Bonding Models and AIDS Drugs

In 1989, researchers used X-ray crystallography—a technique in which X-rays are scattered from crystals of the molecule of interest—to determine the structure of a molecule called HIV-protease. HIV-protease is a protein (a class of large biological molecules) synthesized by the human immunodeficiency virus (HIV). This particular protein is crucial to the virus's ability to multiply and cause acquired immune deficiency syndrome, or AIDS. Without HIV-protease, HIV cannot spread in the human body because the virus cannot replicate. In other words, without HIV-protease, AIDS can't develop.

X-ray crystallography is discussed in more detail in Section 11.10.

With knowledge of the HIV-protease structure, pharmaceutical companies set out to create a molecule that would disable HIV-protease by sticking to the working part of the molecule, called the active site. To design such a molecule, researchers used *bonding theories*—models that predict how atoms bond together to form molecules—to simulate the shape of potential drug molecules and how they would interact with the protease molecule. By the early 1990s, these companies had developed several drug molecules that seemed to work. Since these molecules inhibit the action of HIV-protease, they were

Proteins are discussed in more detail in Chapter 21.

359

▲ G. N. Lewis

named *protease inhibitors*. In human trials, protease inhibitors, when given in combination with other drugs, have decreased the viral count in HIV-infected individuals to undetectable levels. Although protease inhibitors do not cure AIDS, many AIDS patients are still alive today because of these drugs.

Bonding theories are central to chemistry because they explain how atoms bond together to form molecules. They explain why some combinations of atoms are stable and others are not. For example, bonding theories explain why table salt is NaCl and not $NaCl_2$ and why water is H_2O and not H_3O. Bonding theories also predict the shapes of molecules—a topic in our next chapter—which in turn determine many of the physical and chemical properties of compounds. The bonding model we examine in this chapter is called **Lewis theory**, named after the American chemist G. N. Lewis (1875–1946). In Lewis theory, valence electrons are represented as dots, and we can draw **Lewis electron-dot structures** (or simply **Lewis structures**) to depict molecules. These structures, which are fairly simple to draw, have tremendous predictive power. With minimal computation, Lewis theory can be used to predict whether a particular set of atoms will form a stable molecule and what that molecule might look like. Although we will also examine more advanced theories in the following chapter, Lewis theory remains the simplest model for making quick, everyday predictions about most molecules.

9.2 Types of Chemical Bonds

We begin our discussion of chemical bonding by asking why bonds form in the first place. This seemingly simple question is vitally important. Imagine our universe without chemical bonding. There would be just 91 different kinds of substances (the 91 naturally occurring elements). With such a poor diversity of substances, life would be impossible, and we would not be around to wonder why. The *answer* to this question, however, is not simple and involves not only quantum mechanics but also some thermodynamics that we do not introduce until Chapter 17. Nonetheless, we can address an important *aspect* of the answer now: *chemical bonds form because they lower the potential energy between the charged particles that compose atoms.*

As we already know, atoms are composed of particles with positive charges (the protons in the nucleus) and negative charges (the electrons). When two atoms approach each other, the electrons of one atom are attracted to the nucleus of the other according to Coulomb's law (see Section 8.3) and vice versa. However, at the same time, the electrons of each atom repel the electrons of the other, and the nucleus of each atom repels the nucleus of the other. The result is a complex set of interactions among a potentially large number of charged particles. If these interactions lead to an overall net reduction of energy between the charged particles, a chemical bond forms. Bonding theories help us to predict the circumstances under which bonds form and also the properties of the resultant molecules.

We can broadly classify chemical bonds into three types depending on the kind of atoms involved in the bonding (Figure 9.1 ▶).

Types of Atoms	Type of Bond	Characteristic of Bond
Metal and nonmetal	Ionic	Electrons transferred
Nonmetal and nonmetal	Covalent	Electrons shared
Metal and metal	Metallic	Electrons pooled

We learned in Chapter 8 that metals tend to have low ionization energies (their electrons are relatively easy to remove) and that nonmetals tend to have negative electron affinities (they readily gain electrons). When a metal bonds with a nonmetal, it transfers one or more electrons to the nonmetal. The metal atom becomes a cation and the nonmetal atom an anion. These oppositely charged ions then attract one another, lowering their overall potential energy as described by Coulomb's law. The resulting bond is an **ionic bond**.

We also learned in Chapter 8 that nonmetals tend to have high ionization energies (their electrons are relatively difficult to remove). Therefore when a nonmetal bonds with

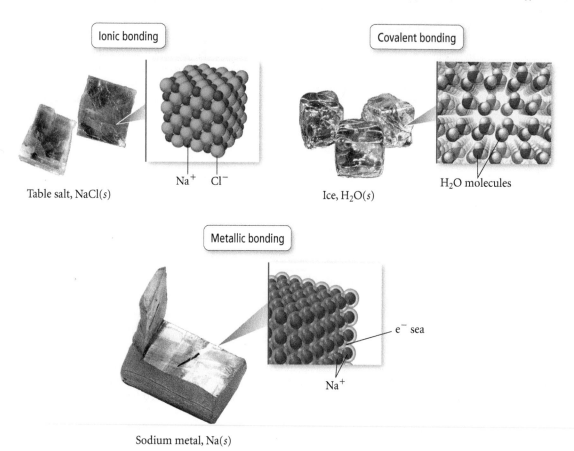

▲ FIGURE 9.1 Ionic, Covalent, and Metallic Bonding

another nonmetal, neither atom transfers electrons to the other. Instead, the two atoms *share* some electrons. The shared electrons interact with the nuclei of both of the bonding atoms, lowering their potential energy in accordance with Coulomb's law. The resulting bond is a **covalent bond**.

Recall from Section 3.2 that we can understand the stability of a covalent bond by considering the most stable arrangement (the one with the lowest potential energy) of two positively charged particles separated by a small distance and a negatively charged particle. As you can see from Figure 9.2 ▼, the arrangement in which the negatively charged particle lies *between* the two positively charged ones has the lowest potential energy because in this arrangement, the negatively charged particle interacts most strongly with *both of the positively charged ones*. In a sense, the negatively charged particle holds the two positively charged ones together. Similarly, shared electrons in a covalent chemical bond *hold* the bonding atoms together by attracting the positive charges of their nuclei.

A third type of bonding, **metallic bonding**, occurs in metals. Since metals have low ionization energies, they tend to lose electrons easily. In the simplest model for metallic bonding—called the *electron sea* model—all of the atoms in a metal lattice pool their valence electrons. These pooled electrons are no longer localized on a single atom, but delocalized over the entire metal. The positively charged metal atoms are then attracted to the sea of electrons, holding the metal together. We discuss metallic bonding in more detail in Section 9.11.

Lowest potential energy
(most stable)

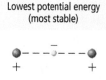
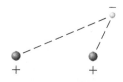

◄ FIGURE 9.2 Possible Configurations of One Negatively Charged Particle and Two Positively Charged Ones

9.3 Representing Valence Electrons with Dots

In Chapter 8, we saw that, for main-group elements, valence electrons are those electrons in the outermost principal energy level. Since valence electrons are held most loosely, and since chemical bonding involves the transfer or sharing of electrons between two or more atoms, valence electrons are most important in bonding, so Lewis theory focuses on these. In a Lewis structure, we represent the valence electrons of main-group elements as dots surrounding the symbol for the element. For example, the electron configuration of O is

$$1s^2 2s^2 2p^4$$
6 valence electrons

And the Lewis structure is

$\cdot \ddot{O} :$ 6 dots representing valence electrons

Each dot represents a valence electron. The dots are placed around the element's symbol with a maximum of two dots per side. The Lewis structures for all of the period 2 elements can be drawn in a similar way:

$$\text{Li}\cdot \quad \cdot \text{Be}\cdot \quad \cdot \dot{\text{B}}\cdot \quad \cdot \dot{\text{C}}\cdot \quad \cdot \ddot{\text{N}}: \quad \cdot \ddot{\text{O}}: \quad :\ddot{\text{F}}: \quad :\ddot{\text{Ne}}:$$

Lewis structures provide a simple way to visualize the number of valence electrons in a main-group atom. Notice that atoms with eight valence electrons—which are particularly stable because they have a full outer level—are easily identified because they have eight dots, an **octet**.

Helium is somewhat of an exception. Its electron configuration and Lewis structure are

$$1s^2 \quad \text{He}:$$

The Lewis structure of helium contains only two dots (a **duet**). For helium, a duet represents a stable electron configuration because the $n = 1$ quantum level fills with only two electrons.

In Lewis theory, a **chemical bond** is the sharing or transfer of electrons to attain stable electron configurations for the bonding atoms. If electrons are transferred, as occurs between a metal and a nonmetal, the bond is an *ionic bond*. If the electrons are shared, as occurs between two nonmetals, the bond is a *covalent bond*. In either case, the bonding atoms obtain stable electron configurations; since the stable configuration is usually eight electrons in the outermost shell, this is known as the **octet rule**. When applying Lewis theory we do not try to calculate the energies associated with the attractions and repulsions between electrons and nuclei on neighboring atoms. The energy changes that occur because of these interactions are central to chemical bonding (as we saw in Section 9.2), yet Lewis theory ignores them because calculating these energy changes is extremely complicated. Instead Lewis theory uses the simple octet rule, a practical approach which accurately predicts what we see in nature for a large number of compounds—hence the success and longevity of Lewis theory.

9.4 Ionic Bonding: Lewis Structures and Lattice Energies

Although Lewis theory's strength is in modeling covalent bonding, it can also be applied to ionic bonding. To represent ionic bonding, we move electron dots from the Lewis structure of the metal to the Lewis structure of the nonmetal and then allow the resultant ions to form a crystalline lattice composed of alternating cations and anions.

Ionic Bonding and Electron Transfer

Consider potassium and chlorine, which have the following Lewis structures:

$$\text{K}\cdot \quad :\ddot{\text{Cl}}:$$

When these atoms bond, potassium transfers its valence electron to chlorine:

$$\text{K}\cdot \; + \; :\ddot{\text{C}}\text{l}: \;\longrightarrow\; \text{K}^{+} \left[:\ddot{\ddot{\text{C}}}\text{l}: \right]^{-}$$

The transfer of the electron gives chlorine an octet (shown as eight dots around chlorine) and leaves potassium without any valence electrons but with an octet in the *previous* principal energy level (which is now the outermost level).

$$\text{K} \qquad 1s^2 2s^2 2p^6 3s^2 3p^6 4s^1$$
$$\text{K}^{+} \quad 1s^2 2s^2 2p^6 \underbrace{3s^2 3p^6}\, 4s^0$$
Octet in previous level

The potassium, because it has lost an electron, becomes positively charged (a cation), while the chlorine, which has gained an electron, becomes negatively charged (an anion). The Lewis structure of an anion is usually written within brackets with the charge in the upper right-hand corner, outside the brackets. The positive and negative charges attract one another, resulting in the compound KCl.

So we can use Lewis structures to predict the correct chemical formulas for ionic compounds. For the compound that forms between K and Cl, for example, the Lewis structures predict a ratio of one potassium cation to every one chloride anion, KCl. In nature, when we examine the compound formed between potassium and chlorine, we indeed find one potassium ion to every chloride ion. As another example, consider the ionic compound formed between sodium and sulfur. The Lewis structures for sodium and sulfur are

$$\text{Na}\cdot \qquad \cdot\ddot{\text{S}}:$$

Sodium must lose its one valence electron in order to have an octet (in the previous principal shell), while sulfur must gain two electrons to get an octet. Consequently, the compound that forms between sodium and sulfur requires a ratio of two sodium atoms to every one sulfur atom. The Lewis structure is

$$2\,\text{Na}^{+} \left[:\ddot{\ddot{\text{S}}}: \right]^{2-}$$

The two sodium atoms each lose their one valence electron while the sulfur atom gains two electrons and gets an octet. The Lewis structures predict that the correct chemical formula is Na_2S, exactly what we see in nature.

> Recall that solid ionic compounds do not contain distinct molecules; they are composed of alternating positive and negative ions in a three-dimensional crystalline array.

EXAMPLE 9.1 Using Lewis Structures to Predict the Chemical Formula of an Ionic Compound

Use Lewis structures to predict the formula for the compound that forms between calcium and chlorine.

SOLUTION

Draw Lewis structures for calcium and chlorine based on their number of valence electrons, obtained from their group number in the periodic table.	$\cdot\text{Ca}\cdot \qquad :\ddot{\text{C}}\text{l}:$
Calcium must lose its two valence electrons (to be left with an octet in its previous principal shell), while chlorine only needs to gain one electron to get an octet. Draw two chlorine anions, each with an octet and a 1− charge, and one calcium cation with a 2+ charge. Place brackets around the chlorine anions and indicate the charges on each ion.	$\text{Ca}^{2+}\; 2\left[:\ddot{\ddot{\text{C}}}\text{l}: \right]^{-}$
Finally, write the formula with subscripts to indicate the number of atoms.	$CaCl_2$

FOR PRACTICE 9.1

Use Lewis structures to predict the formula for the compound that forms between magnesium and nitrogen.

Lattice Energy: The Rest of the Story

The formation of an ionic compound from its constituent elements is usually quite exothermic. For example, when sodium chloride (table salt) forms from elemental sodium and chlorine, 411 kJ of heat is evolved in the following violent reaction:

$$Na(s) + \frac{1}{2}Cl_2(g) \longrightarrow NaCl(s) \qquad \Delta H_f^\circ = -411 \text{ kJ/mol}$$

Where does this energy come from? We may think that it comes solely from the tendency of metals to lose electrons and nonmetals to gain electrons—but it does not. In fact, the transfer of an electron from sodium to chlorine—by itself—actually *absorbs* energy. The first ionization energy of sodium is +496 kJ/mol, and the electron affinity of Cl is only −349 kJ/mol. Based only on these energies, the reaction should be *endothermic* by +147 kJ/mol. So why is the reaction so *exothermic*?

The answer lies in the **lattice energy**—the energy associated with forming a crystalline lattice of alternating cations and anions from the gaseous ions. Since the sodium ions are positively charged and the chlorine ions negatively charged, the potential energy decreases—as prescribed by Coulomb's law—when these ions come together to form a lattice. That energy is emitted as heat when the lattice forms, as shown in Figure 9.3 ▼. The exact value of the lattice energy, however, is not simple to determine because it involves a large number of interactions among many charged particles in a lattice. The easiest way to calculate lattice energy is with the *Born–Haber cycle.*

Lattice Energy of an Ionic Compound

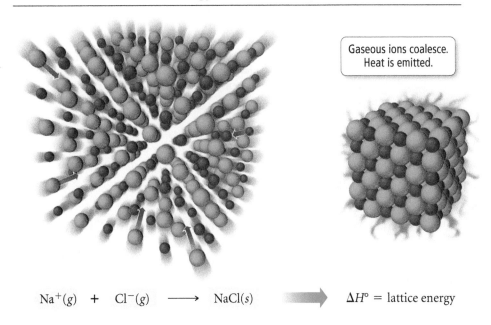

Gaseous ions coalesce. Heat is emitted.

$$Na^+(g) + Cl^-(g) \longrightarrow NaCl(s) \qquad \Delta H^\circ = \text{lattice energy}$$

▶ **FIGURE 9.3 Lattice Energy** The lattice energy of an ionic compound is the energy associated with forming a crystalline lattice of the compound from the gaseous ions.

The Born–Haber Cycle

The **Born–Haber cycle** is a hypothetical series of steps that represents the formation of an ionic compound from its constituent elements. The steps are chosen so that the change in enthalpy of each step is known except for the last one, which is the lattice energy. The change in enthalpy for the overall process is also known. Using Hess's law (see Section 6.7), we can therefore determine the enthalpy change for the unknown last step, the lattice energy.

Consider the formation of NaCl from its constituent elements in their standard states. The enthalpy change for the overall reaction is simply the standard enthalpy of formation of NaCl(s):

$$Na(s) + \frac{1}{2}Cl_2(g) \longrightarrow NaCl(s) \qquad \Delta H_f^\circ = -411 \text{ kJ/mol}$$

Now consider the following set of steps—the Born–Haber cycle—from which NaCl(s) can also be made from Na(s) and Cl₂(g).

Recall that Hess's law states that the change in the overall enthalpy of a stepwise process is the sum of the enthalpy changes of the steps.

- The first step is the formation of gaseous sodium from solid sodium.

$$Na(s) \longrightarrow Na(g) \qquad \Delta H^\circ_{step\ 1} \text{ (sublimation energy of Na)} = +108 \text{ kJ}$$

- The second step is the formation of a chlorine atom from a chlorine molecule.

$$^1/_2\ Cl_2(g) \longrightarrow Cl(g) \qquad \Delta H^\circ_{step\ 2} \text{ (bond energy of } Cl_2 \times {}^1/_2) = +122 \text{ kJ}$$

- The third step is the ionization of gaseous sodium. The enthalpy change for this step is the ionization energy of sodium.

$$Na(g) \longrightarrow Na^+(g) + e^- \qquad \Delta H^\circ_{step\ 3} \text{ (ionization energy of Na)} = +496 \text{ kJ}$$

- The fourth step is the addition of an electron to gaseous chlorine. The enthalpy change for this step is the electron affinity of chlorine.

$$Cl(g) + e^- \longrightarrow Cl^-(g) \qquad \Delta H^\circ_{step\ 4} \text{ (electron affinity of Cl)} = -349 \text{ kJ}$$

- The fifth and final step is the formation of the crystalline solid from the gaseous ions. The enthalpy change for this step is the lattice energy, the unknown quantity.

$$Na^+(g) + Cl^-(g) \longrightarrow NaCl(s) \qquad \Delta H^\circ_{step\ 5} = \Delta H^\circ_{lattice} = ?$$

The entire Born–Haber cycle for NaCl is shown in Figure 9.4 ▼.

Born–Haber Cycle for Production of NaCl from Na(s) and Cl₂(g)

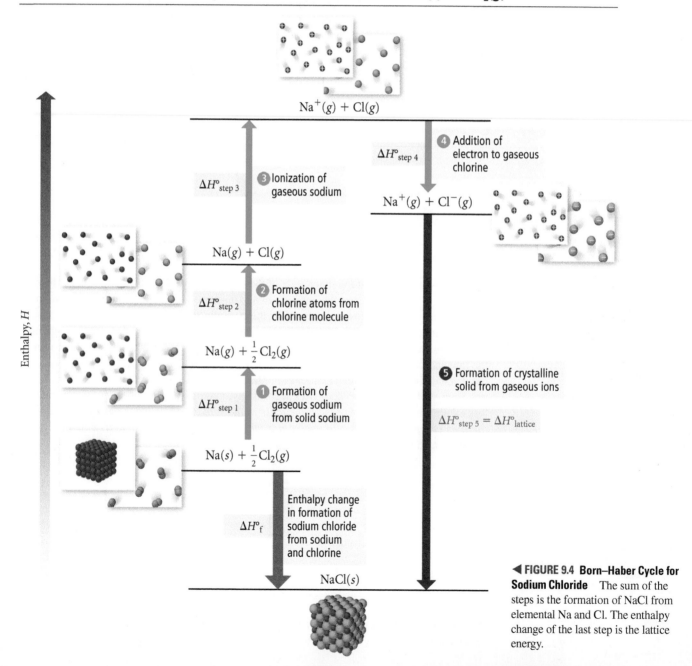

◀ **FIGURE 9.4 Born–Haber Cycle for Sodium Chloride** The sum of the steps is the formation of NaCl from elemental Na and Cl. The enthalpy change of the last step is the lattice energy.

Since the overall reaction obtained by summing the steps in the Born–Haber cycle is equivalent to the formation of NaCl from its constituent elements, we can use Hess's law to set the overall enthalpy of formation for NaCl(*s*) equal to the sum of the steps in the Born–Haber cycle:

Lattice energy

$$\Delta H_f^\circ = \Delta H_{step\,1}^\circ + \Delta H_{step\,2}^\circ + \Delta H_{step\,3}^\circ + \Delta H_{step\,4}^\circ + \Delta H_{step\,5}^\circ$$

We then solve this equation for $\Delta H_{step\,5}^\circ$, which is $\Delta H_{lattice}^\circ$, and substitute the appropriate values to calculate the lattice energy.

$$\Delta H_{lattice}^\circ = \Delta H_{step\,5}^\circ = \Delta H_f^\circ - \left(\Delta H_{step\,1}^\circ + \Delta H_{step\,2}^\circ + \Delta H_{step\,3}^\circ + \Delta H_{step\,4}^\circ\right)$$
$$= -411\ kJ - (+108\ kJ + 122\ kJ + 496\ kJ - 349\ kJ)$$
$$= -788\ kJ$$

The value of the lattice energy is a large negative number. The formation of the crystalline NaCl lattice from sodium cations and chloride anions is highly exothermic and more than compensates for the endothermicity of the electron transfer process. In other words, the formation of ionic compounds is not exothermic because sodium "wants" to lose electrons and chlorine "wants" to gain them; rather, it is exothermic because of the large amount of heat released when sodium and chlorine ions coalesce to form a crystalline lattice.

Trends in Lattice Energies: Ion Size

Consider the lattice energies of the following alkali metal chlorides:

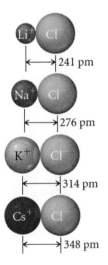

▲ Bond lengths of the group 1A metal chlorides.

Metal Chloride	Lattice Energy (kJ/mol)
LiCl	−834
NaCl	−788
KCl	−701
CsCl	−657

Why do you suppose that the magnitude of the lattice energy decreases as we move down the column? We know from the periodic trends discussed in Chapter 8 that ionic radius increases as we move down a column in the periodic table (see Section 8.7). We also know, from our discussion of Coulomb's law in Section 8.3, that the potential energy of oppositely charged ions becomes less negative (or more positive) as the distance between the ions increases. As the size of the alkali metal ions increases down the column, so does the distance between the metal cations and the chloride anions. The magnitude of the lattice energy of the chlorides decreases accordingly, making the formation of the chlorides less exothermic. In other words, *as the ionic radii increase as we move down the column, the ions cannot get as close to each other and therefore do not release as much energy when the lattice forms.*

Trends in Lattice Energies: Ion Charge

Consider the lattice energies of the following two compounds:

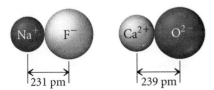

Compound	Lattice Energy (kJ/mol)
NaF	−910
CaO	−3414

Why is the magnitude of the lattice energy of CaO so much greater than the lattice energy of NaF? Na$^+$ has a radius of 95 pm and F$^-$ has a radius of 136 pm, resulting in a

distance between ions of 231 pm. Ca^{2+} has a radius of 99 pm and O^{2-} has a radius of 140 pm, resulting in a distance between ions of 239 pm. Even though the separation between the calcium and oxygen is slightly greater (which would tend to lower the lattice energy), the lattice energy for CaO is almost four times *greater*. The explanation lies in the charges of the ions. Recall from Coulomb's law that the magnitude of the potential energy of two interacting charges depends not only on the distance between the charges, but also on the product of the charges:

$$E = \frac{1}{4\pi\varepsilon_0} \frac{q_1 q_2}{r}$$

For NaF, E is proportional to $(1+)(1-) = 1-$, while for CaO, E is proportional to $(2+)(2-) = 4-$, so the relative stabilization for CaO relative to NaF is roughly four times greater, as observed in the lattice energy.

Summarizing Trends in Lattice Energies:

▶ *Lattice energies become less exothermic (less negative) with increasing ionic radius.*

▶ *Lattice energies become more exothermic (more negative) with increasing magnitude of ionic charge.*

EXAMPLE 9.2 Predicting Relative Lattice Energies

Arrange these ionic compounds in order of increasing *magnitude* of lattice energy: CaO, KBr, KCl, SrO.

SOLUTION

KBr and KCl should have lattice energies of smaller magnitude than CaO and SrO because of their lower ionic charges (1+, 1− compared to 2+, 2−). When we compare KBr and KCl, we expect KBr to have a lattice energy of lower magnitude due to the larger ionic radius of the bromide ion relative to the chloride ion. Between CaO and SrO, we expect SrO to have a lattice energy of lower magnitude due to the larger ionic radius of the strontium ion relative to the calcium ion.

Order of increasing *magnitude* of lattice energy:

KBr < KCl < SrO < CaO

Actual lattice energy values:

Compound	Lattice Energy (kJ/mol)
KBr	−671
KCl	−701
SrO	−3217
CaO	−3414

FOR PRACTICE 9.2

Arrange the following in order of increasing magnitude of lattice energy: LiBr, KI, and CaO.

FOR MORE PRACTICE 9.2

Which compound has a lattice energy of higher magnitude, NaCl or $MgCl_2$?

Ionic Bonding: Models and Reality

In this section, we developed a model for ionic bonding. The value of a model is in how well it accounts for what we see in nature (through experiments). Can the ionic bonding model explain the properties of ionic compounds, including their high melting and boiling points, their tendency *not to conduct* electricity as solids, and their tendency *to conduct* electricity when dissolved in water?

We modeled an ionic solid as a lattice of individual ions held together by coulombic forces which are equal in all directions. To melt the solid, these forces must be overcome, which requires a significant amount of heat. Therefore, our model accounts for the high melting points of ionic solids. In our model, electrons are transferred from the metal to the nonmetal, but the transferred electrons remain localized on one atom. In other words, our model does not include any free electrons that might conduct electricity, and the ions

▶ The melting of solid ionic compounds such as sodium chloride requires enough heat to overcome the electrical forces holding the anions and cations together in a lattice. Thus, the melting points of ionic compounds are relatively high.

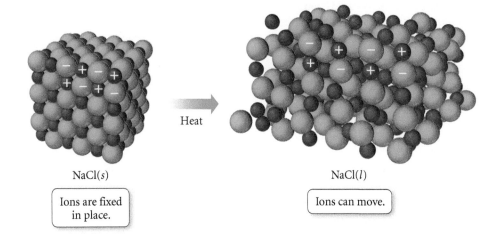

NaCl(*s*)

Ions are fixed
in place.

Heat

NaCl(*l*)

Ions can move.

themselves are fixed in place. Therefore, our model accounts for the nonconductivity of ionic solids. When our idealized ionic solid dissolves in water, however, the cations and anions dissociate, forming free ions in solution. These ions can move in response to electrical forces, creating an electrical current. Thus, our model predicts that solutions of ionic compounds conduct electricity (which in fact they do).

NaCl(*s*)

▲ Solid sodium chloride does not conduct electricity.

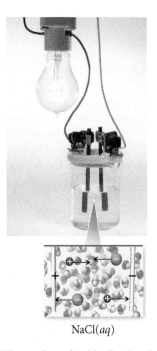

NaCl(*aq*)

▲ When sodium chloride dissolves in water, the resulting solution contains mobile ions that can create an electric current.

Conceptual Connection 9.1   Melting Points of Ionic Solids

Use the ionic bonding model to determine which has the higher melting point, NaCl or MgO. Explain the relative ordering.

ANSWER: We would expect MgO to have the higher melting point because, in our bonding model, the magnesium and oxygen ions are held together in a crystalline lattice by charges of 2+ for magnesium and 2− for oxygen. In contrast, the NaCl lattice is held together by charges of 1+ for sodium and 1− for chlorine. The experimentally measured melting points of these compounds are 801 °C for NaCl and 2852 °C for MgO, in accordance with our model.

CHEMISTRY AND MEDICINE Ionic Compounds in Medicine

Although most drugs are molecular compounds, a number of ionic compounds have medical uses. Consider the following partial list of ionic compounds used in medicine. Notice that many of these compounds contain polyatomic ions. The bonding between a metal and a polyatomic ion is ionic. However, the bonding within a polyatomic ion is covalent, the topic of our next section.

Formula	Name	Medical Use
$AgNO_3$	Silver nitrate	Topical anti-infective agent; in solution, silver nitrate is used to treat and prevent eye infection, especially in newborn infants
$BaSO_4$	Barium sulfate	Given as a contrast medium—or image enhancer—in X-rays
$CaSO_4$	Calcium sulfate	Used to make plaster casts
$KMnO_4$	Potassium permanganate	Topical anti-infective agent; often used to treat fungal infections on the feet
KI	Potassium iodide	Antiseptic and disinfectant; given orally to prevent radiation sickness
Li_2CO_3	Lithium carbonate	Used to treat bipolar (manic-depressive) disorders
$MgSO_4$	Magnesium sulfate	Used to treat eclampsia (a condition that can occur during pregnancy in which elevated blood pressure leads to convulsions)
$Mg(OH)_2$	Magnesium hydroxide	Antacid and mild laxative
$NaHCO_3$	Sodium bicarbonate	Oral antacid used to treat heartburn and acid stomach; injected into blood to treat severe acidosis (acidification of the blood)
NaF	Sodium fluoride	Used to strengthen teeth
ZnO	Zinc oxide	Used as protection from ultraviolet light in sun

9.5 Covalent Bonding: Lewis Structures

Lewis theory provides us with a simple and useful model for covalent bonding. In this model, we represent covalent bonding by depicting neighboring atoms as sharing some (or all) of their valence electrons in order to attain octets (or duets for hydrogen).

Single Covalent Bonds

To see how covalent bonding is conceived in terms of Lewis theory, consider hydrogen and oxygen, which have the following Lewis structures:

$$H\cdot \qquad \cdot\ddot{O}:$$

In water, these atoms share their unpaired valence electrons so that each hydrogen atom gets a duet and the oxygen atom gets an octet:

$$H:\ddot{O}:H$$

The shared electrons—those that appear in the space between the two atoms—count towards the octets (or duets) of *both of the atoms*.

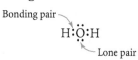

A shared pair of electrons is called a **bonding pair**, while a pair that is associated with only one atom—and therefore not involved in bonding—is called a **lone pair**. Lone pair electrons are also called **nonbonding electrons**.

Bonding pair
$$H:\ddot{O}:H$$
Lone pair

A bonding pair of electrons is often represented by a dash to emphasize that it constitutes a chemical bond.

$$H—\ddot{O}—H$$

Lewis theory also shows why the halogens form diatomic molecules. Consider the Lewis structure of chlorine:

$$:\ddot{C}l:$$

If two Cl atoms pair together, they can each get an octet:

$$:\ddot{C}l:\ddot{C}l:\quad or \quad :\ddot{C}l—\ddot{C}l:$$

Elemental chlorine does indeed exist as a diatomic molecule in nature, just as Lewis theory predicts. The same is true for the other halogens.

Similarly, Lewis theory predicts that hydrogen, which has the Lewis structure

$$H\cdot$$

should exist as H_2. When two hydrogen atoms share their valence electrons, each gets a duet, a stable configuration for hydrogen.

$$H:H \quad or \quad H—H$$

Again, Lewis theory is correct. In nature, elemental hydrogen exists as H_2 molecules.

Double and Triple Covalent Bonds

In Lewis theory, two atoms may share more than one electron pair to get octets. For example, if we pair two oxygen atoms together, they share two electron pairs in order for each oxygen atom to have an octet.

$$\cdot\ddot{O}: + \cdot\ddot{O}:$$
$$\downarrow$$
$$:\ddot{O}::\ddot{O}: \; or \; :\ddot{O}=\ddot{O}:$$

Octet   Octet

| Keep in mind that *one* dash always stands for *two* electrons (a single bonding pair). |

Each oxygen atom now has an octet because *the additional bonding pair counts toward the octet of both oxygen atoms.* When two electron pairs are shared between two atoms, the resulting bond is a **double bond**. In general, double bonds are shorter and stronger than single bonds. Atoms can also share three electron pairs. Consider the Lewis structure of N_2. Since each N atom has five valence electrons, the Lewis structure for N_2 has 10 electrons. Both nitrogen atoms attain octets by sharing three electron pairs:

$$:N:::N: \quad or \quad :N\equiv N:$$

| We will explore the characteristics of multiple bonds more fully in Section 9.10. |

The bond is a **triple bond**. Triple bonds are even shorter and stronger than double bonds. When we examine nitrogen in nature, we find that it exists as a diatomic molecule with a very strong bond between the two nitrogen atoms. The bond is so strong that it is difficult to break, making N_2 a relatively unreactive molecule.

Covalent Bonding: Models and Reality

Lewis theory predicts the properties of molecular compounds in many ways. First, it accounts for why particular combinations of atoms form molecules and others do not. For example, why is water H_2O and not H_3O? We can write a good Lewis structure for H_2O, but not for H_3O.

$$H—\ddot{O}—H \qquad H—\underset{..}{\overset{H}{\underset{|}{O}}}—H$$

Oxygen has nine electrons
(one electron beyond an octet)

In this way, Lewis theory predicts that H_2O should be stable, while H_3O should not be, and that is in fact the case. However, if we remove an electron from H_3O, we get H_3O^+, which should be stable (according to Lewis theory) because, by removing the extra electron, oxygen gets an octet.

$$\begin{bmatrix} & H & \\ & | & \\ H \!-\! \ddot{O} \!-\! H \end{bmatrix}^+$$

This ion, called the hydronium ion, is in fact stable in aqueous solutions (see Section 4.8). Lewis theory predicts other possible combinations for hydrogen and oxygen, as well. For example, we can write a Lewis structure for H_2O_2 as follows:

$$H \!-\! \ddot{O} \!-\! \ddot{O} \!-\! H$$

Indeed, H_2O_2, or hydrogen peroxide, exists and is often used as a disinfectant and a bleach.

Lewis theory also accounts for why covalent bonds are highly *directional*. The attraction between two covalently bonded atoms is due to the sharing of one or more electron pairs in the space between them. Thus, each bond links just one specific pair of atoms—*in contrast to ionic bonds, which are nondirectional and hold together an entire array of ions.* As a result, the fundamental units of covalently bonded compounds are individual molecules. These molecules can interact with one another in a number of different ways that we cover in Chapter 11. However, in covalently bonded molecular compounds the interactions *between* molecules (intermolecular forces) are generally much weaker than the bonding interactions within a molecule (intramolecular forces), as shown in Figure 9.5 ▼. When a molecular compound melts or boils, the molecules themselves remain intact—only the relatively weak interactions between molecules must be overcome. Consequently, molecular compounds tend to have lower melting and boiling points than ionic compounds.

Molecular Compound

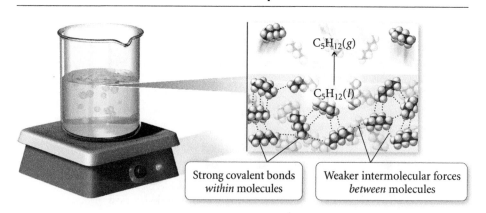

Strong covalent bonds *within* molecules

Weaker intermolecular forces *between* molecules

◀ FIGURE 9.5 **Intermolecular and Intramolecular Forces** The covalent bonds between atoms of a molecule are much stronger than the interactions between molecules. To boil a molecular substance, you simply have to overcome the relatively weak intermolecular forces, so molecular compounds generally have low boiling points.

Conceptual Connection 9.2 Energy and the Octet Rule

What is wrong with the following statement? *Atoms form bonds in order to satisfy the octet rule.*

ANSWER: The reasons that atoms form bonds are complex. One contributing factor is the lowering of their potential energy. The octet rule is just a handy way to predict the combinations of atoms that will have a lower potential energy when they bond together.

9.6 Electronegativity and Bond Polarity

We know from Chapter 7 that representing electrons with dots, as we do in Lewis theory, is a drastic oversimplification. As we have already discussed, this does not invalidate Lewis theory—which is an extremely useful theory—but we must recognize and compensate for its inherent limitations. One limitation of representing electrons as dots, and covalent bonds as two dots shared between two atoms, is that the shared electrons always appear to be *equally* shared. Such is not the case. For example, consider the Lewis structure of hydrogen fluoride.

$$H : \ddot{\underset{\cdot\cdot}{F}} :$$

The two shared electron dots sitting between the H and the F atoms appear to be equally shared between hydrogen and fluorine. However, based on laboratory measurements, we know they are not. When HF is put in an electric field, the molecules orient as shown in Figure 9.6 ▼. From this observation, we know that the hydrogen side of the molecule must have a slight positive charge and the fluorine side of the molecule must have a slight negative charge. We represent this partial separation of charge as follows:

$$\overset{\longrightarrow}{H-F} \quad or \quad \overset{\delta^+ \quad \delta^-}{H-F}$$

The arrow on the left, with a positive sign on the tail, indicates that the left side of the molecule has a partial positive charge and that the right side of the molecule (the side the arrow is pointing *toward*) has a partial negative charge. Similarly, the $\delta+$ (delta plus) represents a partial positive charge and the $\delta-$ (delta minus) represents a partial negative charge. Does this make the bond ionic? No. In an ionic bond, the electron is essentially *transferred* from one atom to another. In HF, the electron is *unequally shared*. In other words, even though the Lewis structure of HF portrays the bonding electrons as residing *between* the two atoms, in reality the electron density is greater on the fluorine atom than on the hydrogen atom (Figure 9.7 ◀). The bond is said to be *polar*—having a positive pole and a negative pole. A **polar covalent bond** is intermediate in nature between a pure covalent bond and an ionic bond. In fact, the categories of pure covalent and ionic are really two extremes within a broad continuum. Most covalent bonds between dissimilar atoms are actually *polar covalent*, somewhere between the two extremes.

▶ **FIGURE 9.6 Orientation of Gaseous Hydrogen Fluoride in an Electric Field** Because one side of the HF molecule has a slight positive charge and the other side a slight negative charge, the molecules will align themselves with an external electric field.

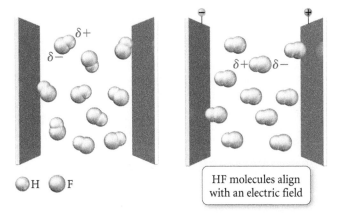

HF molecules align with an electric field

▲ **FIGURE 9.7 Electron Density Plot for the HF Molecule** The F end of the molecule, with its partial negative charge, is pink; the H end, with its partial positive charge, is blue.

Electronegativity

The ability of an atom to attract electrons to itself in a chemical bond (which results in polar and ionic bonds) is called **electronegativity**. We say that fluorine is more *electronegative* than hydrogen because it takes a greater share of the electron density in HF.

Electronegativity was quantified by the American chemist Linus Pauling in his classic book, *The Nature of the Chemical Bond*. Pauling compared the bond energy—the energy required to break a bond—of a heteronuclear diatomic molecule such as HF with the bond energies of its homonuclear counterparts, in this case H_2 and F_2. The bond energies of H_2 and F_2 are 436 kJ/mol and 155 kJ/mol, respectively. Pauling reasoned that if the HF bond were purely covalent—that is, if the electrons were shared exactly equally—the

Trends in Electronegativity

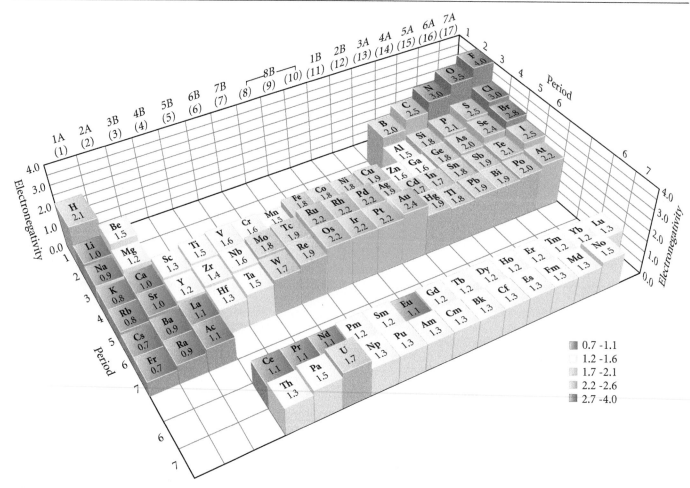

▲ **FIGURE 9.8 Electronegativities of the Elements** Electronegativity generally increases as we move across a row in the periodic table and decreases as we move down a column.

bond energy of HF should simply be an average of the bond energies of H_2 and F_2, which would be 296 kJ/mol. However, the bond energy of HF is experimentally measured to be 565 kJ/mol. Pauling suggested that the additional bond energy was due to the *ionic character* of the bond. Based on many such comparisons of bond energies, and by arbitrarily assigning an electronegativity of 4.0 to fluorine (the most electronegative element on the periodic table), Pauling developed the electronegativity values shown in Figure 9.8 ▲.

For main-group elements, notice the following periodic trends in electronegativity from Figure 9.8:

- Electronegativity generally increases across a period in the periodic table.

- Electronegativity generally decreases down a column in the periodic table.

- Fluorine is the most electronegative element.

- Francium is the least electronegative element (sometimes called the most *electropositive*).

The periodic trends in electronegativity are consistent with other periodic trends we have seen. In general, electronegativity is inversely related to atomic size—the larger the atom, the less ability it has to attract electrons to itself in a chemical bond.

Bond Polarity, Dipole Moment, and Percent Ionic Character

The degree of polarity in a chemical bond depends on the electronegativity difference (sometimes abbreviated ΔEN) between the two bonding elements. The greater the electronegativity difference, the more polar the bond. If two elements with identical electronegativities form a covalent bond, they share the electrons equally, and the bond is

We cover the concept of bond energy in more detail in Section 9.10.

Pauling's "average" bond energy was actually calculated a little bit differently than the normal average shown here. He took the square root of the product of the bond energies of the homologs as the "average."

purely covalent or *nonpolar*. For example, the chlorine molecule, composed of two chlorine atoms (which necessarily have identical electronegativities), has a covalent bond in which electrons are evenly shared.

If there is a large electronegativity difference between the two elements in a bond, such as normally occurs between a metal and a nonmetal, the electron from the metal is almost completely transferred to the nonmetal, and the bond is ionic. For example, sodium and chlorine form an ionic bond.

If there is an intermediate electronegativity difference between the two elements, such as between two different nonmetals, then the bond is polar covalent. For example, HCl has a polar covalent bond.

While all attempts to divide the bond polarity continuum into specific regions are necessarily arbitrary, it is helpful to classify bonds as covalent, polar covalent, and ionic, based on the electronegativity difference between the bonding atoms as shown in Table 9.1 and Figure 9.9 ▼.

TABLE 9.1 The Effect of Electronegativity Difference on Bond Type

Electronegativity Difference (ΔEN)	Bond Type	Example
Small (0–0.4)	Covalent	Cl_2
Intermediate (0.4–2.0)	Polar covalent	HCl
Large (2.0+)	Ionic	NaCl

We can quantify the polarity of a bond by the size of its dipole moment. A **dipole moment (μ)** occurs anytime there is a separation of positive and negative charge. The

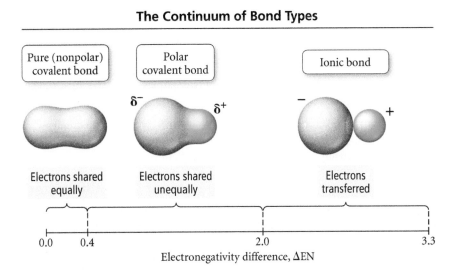

▶ FIGURE 9.9 **Electronegativity Difference (Δ EN) and Bond Type**

magnitude of a dipole moment created by separating two particles of equal but opposite charges of magnitude q by a distance r is given by the following equation:

$$\mu = qr \qquad\qquad [9.1]$$

We can get a sense for the dipole moment of a completely ionic bond by calculating the dipole moment that results from separating a proton and an electron ($q = 1.6 \times 10^{-19}$ C) by a distance of $r = 130$ pm (the approximate length of a short chemical bond)

$$\begin{aligned}
\mu &= qr \\
&= (1.6 \times 10^{-19}\text{ C})(130 \times 10^{-12}\text{ m}) \\
&= 2.1 \times 10^{-29}\text{ C} \cdot \text{m} \\
&= 6.2\text{ D}
\end{aligned}$$

TABLE 9.2 Dipole Moments of Several Molecules in the Gas Phase

Molecule	ΔEN	Dipole Moment (D)
Cl_2	0	0
ClF	1.0	0.88
HF	1.9	1.82
LiF	3.0	6.33

The debye (D) is the unit commonly used for reporting dipole moments ($1\text{ D} = 3.34 \times 10^{-30}$ C·m). Based on this calculation, we would expect the dipole moment of completely ionic bonds with bond lengths close to 130 pm to be about 6 D. The smaller the magnitude of the charge separation, and the smaller the distance the charges are separated by, the smaller the dipole moment. Table 9.2 shows the dipole moments of several molecules along with the electronegativity differences of their atoms.

By comparing the *actual* dipole moment of a bond to what the dipole moment would be if the electron were completely transferred from one atom to the other, we can get a sense of the degree to which the electron is transferred (or the degree to which the bond is ionic). A quantity called the **percent ionic character** is defined as the ratio of a bond's actual dipole moment to the dipole moment it would have if the electron were completely transferred from one atom to the other, multiplied by 100%:

$$\text{Percent ionic character} = \frac{\text{measured dipole moment of bond}}{\text{dipole moment if electron were completely transferred}} \times 100\%$$

For example, suppose a diatomic molecule with a bond length of 130 pm has a dipole moment of 3.5 D. We previously calculated that separating a proton and an electron by 130 pm results in a dipole moment of 6.2 D. Therefore, the percent ionic character of the bond would be:

$$\begin{aligned}
\text{Percent ionic character} &= \frac{3.5\text{ D}}{6.2\text{ D}} \times 100\% \\
&= 56\%
\end{aligned}$$

A bond in which an electron is completely transferred from one atom to another would have 100% ionic character (although even the most ionic bonds do not reach this ideal). Figure 9.10 ▼ shows the percent ionic character of a number of diatomic gas-phase molecules plotted against the electronegativity difference between the bonding atoms. As expected, the percent ionic character generally increases as the electronegativity difference increases. However, as you can see, no bond is 100% ionic. In general, bonds with greater than 50% ionic character are referred to as ionic bonds.

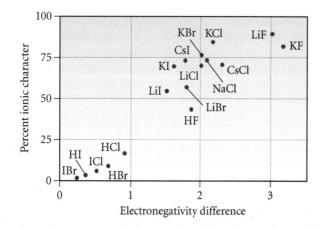

◄ **FIGURE 9.10 Percent Ionic Character versus Electronegativity Difference for Some Compounds**

EXAMPLE 9.3 Classifying Bonds as Pure Covalent, Polar Covalent, or Ionic

Determine whether the bond formed between each pair of atoms is covalent, polar covalent, or ionic.

(a) Sr and F   **(b)** N and Cl   **(c)** N and O

SOLUTION

(a) From Figure 9.8, we find the electronegativity of Sr (1.0) and of F (4.0). The electronegativity difference (ΔEN) is $\Delta EN = 4.0 - 1.0 = 3.0$. Using Table 9.1, we classify this bond as ionic.

(b) From Figure 9.8, we find the electronegativity of N (3.0) and of Cl (3.0). The electronegativity difference (ΔEN) is $\Delta EN = 3.0 - 3.0 = 0$. Using Table 9.1, we classify this bond as covalent.

(c) From Figure 9.8, we find the electronegativity of N (3.0) and of O (3.5). The electronegativity difference (ΔEN) is $\Delta EN = 3.5 - 3.0 = 0.5$. Using Table 9.1, we classify this bond as polar covalent.

FOR PRACTICE 9.3

Determine whether the bond formed between each pair of atoms is pure covalent, polar covalent, or ionic.

(a) I and I   **(b)** Cs and Br   **(c)** P and O

 Conceptual Connection 9.3   Percent Ionic Character

The HCl(g) molecule has a bond length of 127 pm and a dipole moment of 1.08 D. Without doing detailed calculations, determine the best estimate for its percent ionic character.

(a) 5%   **(b)** 15%   **(c)** 50%   **(d)** 80%

ANSWER: (b) We are given that the dipole moment of the HCl bond is about 1 D and that the bond length is 127 pm. Previously we calculated the dipole moment for a 130-pm bond that is 100% ionic to be about 6.2 D. We can therefore estimate the bond's ionic character as $1/6 \times 100\%$, which is closest to 15%.

9.7 Lewis Structures of Molecular Compounds and Polyatomic Ions

Now that we have examined Lewis structures and how they predict chemical bonding in nature, we can address the basic sequence of steps involved in actually writing Lewis structures for given combinations of atoms.

Writing Lewis Structures for Molecular Compounds

To write a Lewis structure for a molecular compound, follow these steps:

> Often, chemical formulas are written in a way that provides clues to how the atoms are bonded together. For example, CH_3OH indicates that three hydrogen atoms and the oxygen atom are bonded to the carbon atom, but the fourth hydrogen atom is bonded to the oxygen atom.

> There are a few exceptions to this rule, such as diborane (B_2H_6), which contains *bridging hydrogens*, but these are rare and cannot be adequately addressed by simple Lewis theory.

1. **Write the correct skeletal structure for the molecule.** The Lewis structure of a molecule must have the atoms in the correct positions. For example, you could not write a Lewis structure for water if you started with the hydrogen atoms next to each other and the oxygen atom at the end (H H O). In nature, oxygen is the central atom and the hydrogen atoms are *terminal* (at the ends). The correct skeletal structure is H O H. The only way to determine the skeletal structure of a molecule with absolute certainty is to examine its structure experimentally. However, you can write likely skeletal structures by remembering two guidelines. First, *hydrogen atoms are always terminal*. Hydrogen does not ordinarily occur as a central atom because central atoms must form at least two bonds, and hydrogen, which has only a single valence electron to share and requires only a duet, can form just one. Second, *put the more electronegative elements in terminal positions* and the less electronegative elements (other than hydrogen) in the central position. Later in this section, you will learn how to distinguish between competing skeletal structures by applying the concept of formal charge.

2. **Calculate the total number of electrons for the Lewis structure by summing the valence electrons of each atom in the molecule.** Remember that the number of valence electrons for any main-group element is equal to its group number in the periodic table.

If you are writing a Lewis structure for a polyatomic ion, the charge of the ion must be considered when calculating the total number of electrons. Add one electron for each negative charge and subtract one electron for each positive charge. Don't worry about which electron comes from which atom—only the total number is important.

3. **Distribute the electrons among the atoms, giving octets (or duets in the case of hydrogen) to as many atoms as possible.** Begin by placing two electrons between every two atoms. These represent the minimum number of bonding electrons. Then distribute the remaining electrons as lone pairs, first to terminal atoms, and then to the central atom, giving octets (or duets for hydrogen) to as many atoms as possible.

4. **If any atoms lack an octet, form double or triple bonds as necessary to give them octets.** Do this by moving lone electron pairs from terminal atoms into the bonding region with the central atom.

The left column that follows contains an abbreviated version of the procedure for writing Lewis structures; the center and right columns contain two examples of applying the procedure.

> Sometimes distributing all the remaining electrons to the central atom results in more than an octet. This is called an expanded octet and is covered in Section 9.9.

PROCEDURE FOR... **Writing Lewis Structures for Covalent Compounds**	**EXAMPLE 9.4** **Writing Lewis Structures** Writing a Lewis Structure for CO_2.	**EXAMPLE 9.5** **Writing Lewis Structures** Writing a Lewis Structure for NH_3.
	SOLUTION	**SOLUTION**
1. Write the correct skeletal structure for the molecule.	Because carbon is the less electronegative atom, we put it in the central position. O C O	Since hydrogen is always terminal, we put nitrogen in the central position. H N H H
2. Calculate the total number of electrons for the Lewis structure by summing the valence electrons of each atom in the molecule.	Total number of electrons for Lewis structure = $\left(\begin{array}{c}\text{number of} \\ \text{valence} \\ e^- \text{ for C}\end{array}\right) + 2\left(\begin{array}{c}\text{number of} \\ \text{valence} \\ e^- \text{ for O}\end{array}\right)$ $= 4 + 2(6) = 16$	Total number of electrons for Lewis structure = $\left(\begin{array}{c}\text{number of} \\ \text{valence} \\ e^- \text{ for N}\end{array}\right) + 3\left(\begin{array}{c}\text{number of} \\ \text{valence} \\ e^- \text{ for H}\end{array}\right)$ $= 5 + 3(1) = 8$

3. Distribute the electrons among the atoms, giving octets (or duets for hydrogen) to as many atoms as possible. Begin with the bonding electrons, and then proceed to lone pairs on terminal atoms, and finally to lone pairs on the central atom.	Bonding electrons are first.
	
	 O:C:O
	
	 (4 of 16 electrons used)
	
	 Lone pairs on terminal atoms are next.
	
	 :Ö:C:Ö:
	
	 (16 of 16 electrons used)
		Bonding electrons are first.
		
		 H:N:H
		    Ḧ
		
		 (6 of 8 electrons used)
		
		 Lone pairs on terminal atoms are next, but none are needed on hydrogen.
		
		 Lone pairs on central atom are last.
		
		 H—N̈—H
		    |
		    H
		
		 (8 of 8 electrons used)

4. If any atom lacks an octet, form double or triple bonds as necessary to give them octets.	Since carbon lacks an octet, move lone pairs from the oxygen atoms to bonding regions to form double bonds. :Ö:C:Ö: ↓ :O̤=C=O̤:	Since all of the atoms have octets (or duets for hydrogen), the Lewis structure for NH_3 is complete as shown above.
	FOR PRACTICE 9.4 Write a Lewis structure for CO.	**FOR PRACTICE 9.5** Write a Lewis structure for H_2CO.

Writing Lewis Structures for Polyatomic Ions

We write Lewis structures for polyatomic ions by following the same procedure, but we pay special attention to the charge of the ion when calculating the number of electrons for the Lewis structure. We add one electron for each negative charge and subtract one electron for each positive charge. The Lewis structure for a polyatomic ion is usually written within brackets with the charge of the ion in the upper right-hand corner, outside the bracket.

EXAMPLE 9.6 Writing Lewis Structures for Polyatomic Ions

Write the Lewis structure for the NH_4^+ ion.

SOLUTION

Begin by writing the skeletal structure. Since hydrogen is always terminal, put the nitrogen atom in the central position.	H H N H H
Calculate the total number of electrons for the Lewis structure by summing the number of valence electrons for each atom and subtracting 1 for the 1+ charge.	Total number of electrons for Lewis structure = (number of valence e⁻ in N) + (number of valence e⁻ in H) − 1 = 5 + 4(1) − 1 = 8 Subtract 1 e⁻ to account for 1⁺ charge of ion.
Place two bonding electrons between every two atoms. Since all of the atoms have complete octets, no double bonds are necessary.	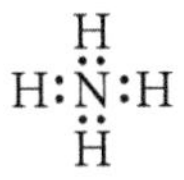 H H:N:H H (8 of 8 electrons used)
Lastly, write the Lewis structure in brackets with the charge of the ion in the upper right-hand corner.	$\left[\begin{array}{c} H \\ | \\ H-N-H \\ | \\ H \end{array}\right]^+$

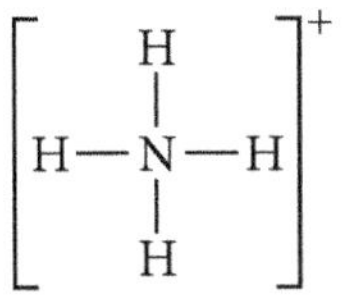

FOR PRACTICE 9.6

Write a Lewis structure for the hypochlorite ion, ClO^-.

9.8 Resonance and Formal Charge

We need two additional concepts to write the best possible Lewis structures for a large number of compounds. The concepts are *resonance*, used when two or more valid Lewis structures can be drawn for the same compound, and *formal charge*, an electron book-keeping system that allows us to discriminate between alternative Lewis structures.

Resonance

When writing Lewis structures, you may find that, for some molecules, you can write more than one valid Lewis structure. For example, consider writing a Lewis structure for O_3. The following two Lewis structures, with the double bond on alternate sides, are equally correct:

$$:\ddot{O}=\ddot{O}-\ddot{O}: \qquad :\ddot{O}-\ddot{O}=\ddot{O}:$$

In cases such as this—where there are two or more valid Lewis structures for the same molecule—we find that, in nature, the molecule exists as an *average* of the two Lewis

structures. Both of the two Lewis structures for O_3 predict that O_3 contains two different bonds (one double bond and one single bond). However, when we experimentally examine the structure of O_3, we find that the bonds in the O_3 molecule are equivalent and each is intermediate in strength and length between a double bond and single bond. We account for this by representing the molecule with both structures, called **resonance structures**, with a double-headed arrow between them:

$$:\ddot{O}=\ddot{O}-\ddot{\underset{\cdot\cdot}{O}}: \quad \longleftrightarrow \quad :\ddot{\underset{\cdot\cdot}{O}}-\ddot{O}=\ddot{O}:$$

A resonance structure is one of two or more Lewis structures that have the same skeletal formula (the atoms are in the same locations), but different electron arrangements. The actual structure of the molecule is intermediate between the two (or more) resonance structures and is called a **resonance hybrid**. The term *hybrid* comes from breeding and means the offspring of two animals or plants of different varieties or breeds. If you breed a Labrador retriever with a German shepherd, you get a *hybrid* that is intermediate between the two breeds (Figure 9.11(a) ▼). Similarly, the actual structure of a resonance hybrid is intermediate between the two resonance structures (Figure 9.11(b)). The only structure that actually exists is the hybrid structure—the individual resonance structures do not exist and are merely a convenient way to describe the actual structure. Notice that the actual structure of ozone has two equivalent bonds and a bent geometry (we discuss molecular geometries in Chapter 10).

The concept of resonance is an adaptation of Lewis theory that helps account for the complexity of actual molecules. In Lewis theory, electrons are *localized* either on one atom (lone pair) or between atoms (bonding pair). However, in nature, the electrons in molecules are often *delocalized* over several atoms or bonds. The delocalization of electrons lowers their energy; it stabilizes them (for reasons beyond the scope of this book). Resonance depicts two or more structures with the electrons in different places in an attempt to more accurately reflect the delocalization of electrons. In the real hybrid structure, an average between the resonance structures, the electrons are more spread out (or delocalized) than in any of the resonance structures. The resulting stabilization of the electrons (that is, the lowering of their potential energy due to delocalization) is sometimes called *resonance stabilization*. Resonance stabilization makes an important contribution to the stability of many molecules.

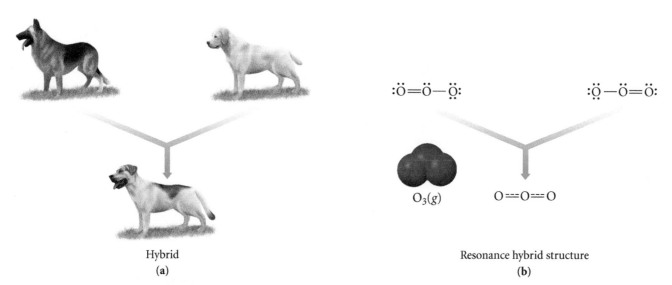

Hybrid
(a)

Resonance hybrid structure
(b)

▲ **FIGURE 9.11 Hybridization** Just as the offspring of two different dog breeds is a hybrid that is intermediate between the two breeds **(a)**, the structure of a resonance hybrid is intermediate between that of the contributing resonance structures **(b)**.

EXAMPLE 9.7 Writing Resonance Structures

Write a Lewis structure for the NO_3^- ion. Include resonance structures.

SOLUTION

Begin by writing the skeletal structure. Since nitrogen is the least electronegative atom, put it in the central position.	O O N O
Calculate the total number of electrons for the Lewis structure by summing the number of valence electrons for each atom and adding 1 for the 1− charge.	Total number of electrons for Lewis structure = (number of valence e⁻ in N) + 3 (number of valence e⁻ in O) + 1 = 5 + 3(6) + 1 = 24 ↑ Add 1 e⁻ to account for 1− charge of ion.
Place two bonding electrons between each pair of atoms.	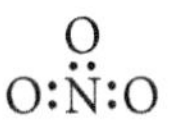 O O:N:O (6 of 24 electrons used)
Distribute the remaining electrons, first to terminal atoms. There are not enough electrons to complete the octet on the central atom.	 :Ö: :Ö:N:Ö: (24 of 24 electrons used)
Form a double bond by moving a lone pair from one of the oxygen atoms into the bonding region with nitrogen. Enclose the structure in brackets and include the charge.	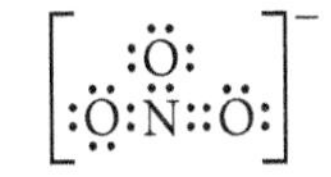 [:Ö: :Ö:N::Ö:]⁻ *or* [:Ö: :Ö—N=Ö:]⁻ 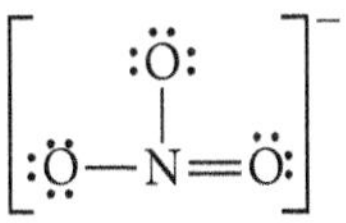
Since the double bond can form equally well with any of the three oxygen atoms, write all three structures as resonance structures. (The actual space filling model of NO_3^- is shown here for comparison. Note that all three bonds are equal in length.)	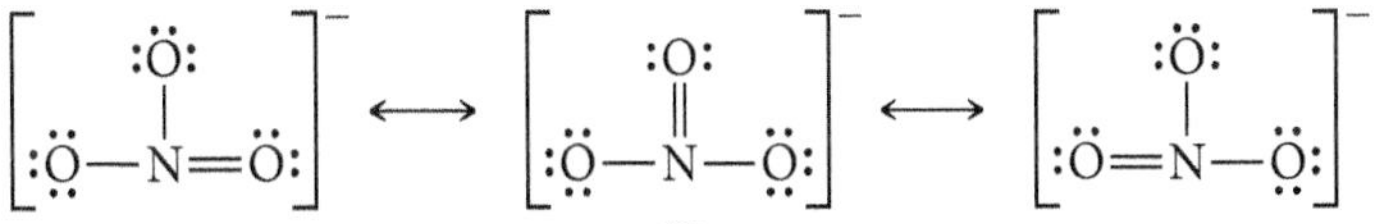  [:Ö: :Ö—N=Ö:]⁻ ⟷ [:O: :Ö—N—Ö:]⁻ ⟷ [:Ö: :Ö=N—Ö:]⁻ NO_3-

FOR PRACTICE 9.7

Write a Lewis structure for the NO_2^- ion. Include resonance structures.

In the examples of resonance hybrids that we have examined so far, the contributing structures have been equivalent (or equally valid) Lewis structures. In these cases, the true structure is an equally weighted average of the resonance structures. In some cases, however, we can write resonance structures that are not equivalent. For reasons we cover below—such as formal charge, for example—one possible resonance structure may be somewhat better than another. In such cases, the true structure is still an average of the resonance structures, but the better resonance structure contributes more to the true structure. In other words, multiple nonequivalent resonance structures may be weighted differently in their contributions to the true overall structure of a molecule (see Example 9.8).

Formal Charge

Formal charge is a fictitious charge assigned to each atom in a Lewis structure that helps us to distinguish among competing Lewis structures. The **formal charge** of an atom in a Lewis structure is *the charge it would have if all bonding electrons were shared equally between the bonded atoms.* In other words, formal charge is the calculated charge for an atom if we completely ignore the effects of electronegativity. For example, we know that because fluorine is more electronegative than hydrogen, HF has a dipole moment—the hydrogen atom has a slight positive charge and the fluorine atom has a slight negative charge. However, the *formal charges* of hydrogen and fluorine in HF (the calculated charges if we ignore their differences in electronegativity) are both zero.

$$H:\ddot{\underset{..}{F}}:$$

Formal charge = 0   Formal charge = 0

We can calculate the formal charge on any atom as the difference between the number of valence electrons in the atom and the number of electrons that it "owns" in a Lewis structure. An atom in a Lewis structure can be thought of as "owning" all of its nonbonding electrons and one-half of its bonding electrons.

Formal charge = number of valence electrons −

(number of nonbonding electrons + $\frac{1}{2}$ number of bonding electrons)

So we calculate the formal charge of hydrogen in HF as follows:

$$\text{Formal charge} = 1 - \left[0 + \tfrac{1}{2}(2)\right] = 0$$

Number of valence electrons for H   Number of electrons that H "owns" in the Lewis structure

Similarly, we calculate the formal charge of fluorine in HF as follows:

$$\text{Formal charge} = 7 - \left[6 + \tfrac{1}{2}(2)\right] = 0$$

Number of valence electrons for F   Number of electrons that F "owns" in the Lewis structure

The concept of formal charge is useful because it can help us distinguish between competing skeletal structures or competing resonance structures. In general, the following rules apply:

1. The sum of all formal charges in a neutral molecule must be zero.
2. The sum of all formal charges in an ion must equal the charge of the ion.
3. Small (or zero) formal charges on individual atoms are better than large ones.
4. When formal charge cannot be avoided, negative formal charge should reside on the most electronegative atom.

We can use formal charge to determine which of the competing skeletal structures for hydrogen cyanide shown here make the biggest contribution to the resonance hybrid. Notice that both skeletal structures equally satisfy the octet rule. The formal charge of each atom in the structure is calculated below it.

	Structure A			Structure B		
	H —	C ≡	N:	H —	N ≡	C:
number of valence e⁻	1	4	5	1	5	4
− number of nonbonding e⁻	−0	−0	−2	−0	−0	−2
− ½ (number of bonding e⁻)	−½(2)	−½(8)	−½(6)	−½(2)	−½(8)	−½(6)
Formal charge	**0**	**0**	**0**	**0**	**+1**	**−1**

As required, the sum of the formal charges for each of these structures is zero (as it always must be for neutral molecules). However, structure B has formal charges on both the N atom and the C atom, while structure A has no formal charges on any atom. Furthermore, in structure B, the negative formal charge is not on the most electronegative element (nitrogen is more electronegative than carbon). Consequently, structure A is the best Lewis structure. Since atoms in the middle of a molecule tend to have more bonding electrons and fewer nonbonding electrons, they also tend to have more positive formal charges. Consequently, the best skeletal structure usually has the least electronegative atom in the central position, as we learned in step 1 of our procedure for writing Lewis structures.

> Both HCN and HNC exist, but—as predicted by formal charge—HCN is more stable than HNC.

EXAMPLE 9.8 Assigning Formal Charges

Assign formal charges to each atom in the resonance forms of the cyanate ion (OCN^-). Which resonance form is likely to contribute most to the correct structure of OCN^-?

$$
\text{A} \qquad\qquad \text{B} \qquad\qquad \text{C}
$$

$$
\left[\ddot{:}\ddot{O}-C\equiv N\ddot{:} \right]^- \quad \left[\ddot{:}\ddot{O}=C=\ddot{N}\ddot{:} \right]^- \quad \left[\ddot{:}O\equiv C-\ddot{\ddot{N}}\ddot{:} \right]^-
$$

SOLUTION

		A $\left[\ddot{:}\ddot{O}-C\equiv N\ddot{:} \right]^-$			B $\left[\ddot{:}\ddot{O}=C=\ddot{N}\ddot{:} \right]^-$			C $\left[\ddot{:}O\equiv C-\ddot{\ddot{N}}\ddot{:} \right]^-$	
Calculate the formal charge on each atom by finding the number of valence electrons and subtracting the number of nonbonding electrons and one-half the number of bonding electrons.	Number of valence e⁻	6	4	5	6	4	5	6	4	5
	− number of nonbonding e⁻	−6	−0	−2	−4	−0	−4	−2	−0	−6
	−$\frac{1}{2}$(number of bond e⁻)	−1	−4	−3	−2	−4	−2	−3	−4	−1
	Formal charge	**−1**	**0**	**0**	**0**	**0**	**−1**	**+1**	**0**	**−2**

The sum of all formal charges for each structure is −1, as it should be for a 1− ion. Structures A and B have the least amount of formal charge and are therefore to be preferred over structure C. Structure A is preferable to B because it has the negative formal charge on the more electronegative atom. We therefore expect structure A to make the biggest contribution to the resonance forms of the cyanate ion.

FOR PRACTICE 9.8

Assign formal charges to each atom in the resonance forms of N_2O. Which resonance form is likely to contribute most to the correct structure of N_2O?

$$
\text{A} \qquad\qquad \text{B} \qquad\qquad \text{C}
$$

$$
\ddot{:}\ddot{N}=N=\ddot{O}\ddot{:} \qquad :N\equiv N-\ddot{\ddot{O}}\ddot{:} \qquad \ddot{\ddot{N}}-N\equiv O\ddot{:}
$$

FOR MORE PRACTICE 9.8

Assign formal charges to each of the atoms in the nitrate ion (NO_3^-). The Lewis structure for the nitrate ion is shown in Example 9.7.

9.9 Exceptions to the Octet Rule: Odd-Electron Species, Incomplete Octets, and Expanded Octets

The octet rule in Lewis theory has some exceptions, which we examine here. They include (1) *odd-electron species,* molecules or ions with an odd number of electrons; (2) *incomplete octets,* molecules or ions with *fewer than eight electrons* around an atom; and (3) *expanded octets,* molecules or ions with *more than eight electrons* around an atom. We examine each of these exceptions individually.

CHEMISTRY IN THE ENVIRONMENT

Free Radicals and the Atmospheric Vacuum Cleaner

Free radicals play a key role in much of the chemistry of the atmosphere. The free radical that is most important to atmospheric reactions is the hydroxyl radical:

$$:\overset{\cdot}{\underset{\cdot\cdot}{O}}-H$$

$NO_2(g)$

▲ $NO_2(g)$ is a pollutant found in urban air.

Many free radical structures are abbreviated by writing a single dot with the formula. Thus, the hydroxyl radical is often abbreviated as follows:

$$\cdot OH$$

In the atmosphere, the hydroxyl radical forms when excited oxygen atoms—formed from the photodecomposition of ozone—react with water vapor.

$$O_3 \xrightarrow{\text{UV light}} O_2 + O*$$
$$O* + H_2O \longrightarrow 2\cdot OH$$

The * next to the O above indicates that the oxygen atom has excess energy.

The resulting hydroxyl radical reacts with a wide variety of molecules from both natural sources and from air pollution that are present in the atmosphere. For example, the hydroxyl radical reacts with carbon monoxide, an atmospheric pollutant that we first encountered in Chapter 1, in the following two-step process:

$$CO + \cdot OH \longrightarrow HOCO\cdot$$
$$HOCO\cdot + O_2 \longrightarrow CO_2 + HOO\cdot$$

You can see from this reaction that the hydroxyl radical converts toxic CO into relatively nontoxic CO_2. The HOO· free radical generated by the second reaction is converted back into the hydroxyl radical when it reacts with other atmospheric substances, and the process repeats itself. Therefore, a single hydroxyl radical can convert a lot of CO into CO_2.

Do you ever wonder what happens to the hydrocarbons you accidentally spill when filling your car's gas tank or to the natural gas that is released into the atmosphere as you light your kitchen stove? Hydrocarbons released into the atmosphere are converted to CO_2 and H_2O in a series of steps initiated by the hydroxyl free radical. Consider the following representative reaction of methane, the main hydrocarbon in natural gas:

$$CH_4 + 5\,O_2 + NO\cdot + 2\cdot OH \xrightarrow{\text{UV light}}$$
$$CO_2 + H_2O + NO_2\cdot + 4\,HOO\cdot$$

Notice the similarity between this reaction and the direct combustion (or burning) of methane:

$$CH_4 + 2\,O_2 \longrightarrow CO_2 + 2\,H_2O$$

As you can see, the free radical reaction initiates a slow "burning" of CH_4 in a series of steps that produce carbon dioxide and water and some additional free radicals. The hydroxyl radical initiates similar reactions with other pollutants as well as undesirable naturally occurring atmospheric gases. Without the hydroxyl free radical—sometimes called *the atmospheric vacuum cleaner*—our atmosphere would be a much dirtier place.

▼ Hydrocarbons such as octane evaporate into the atmosphere when a motor vehicle is fueled. What happens to them?

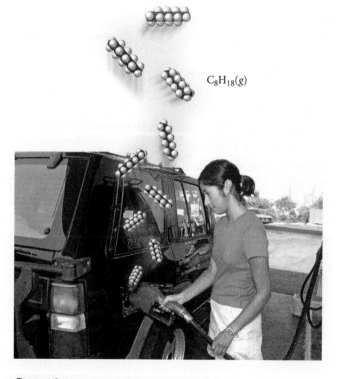

$C_8H_{18}(g)$

Question

Draw the best possible Lewis structures for the free radicals important in atmospheric chemistry: NO, NO_2, HOO, OH, CH_3.

Odd-Electron Species

Molecules and ions with an odd number of electrons in their Lewis structures are called **free radicals** (or simply *radicals*). For example, nitrogen monoxide—a pollutant found in motor vehicle exhaust—has 11 electrons. If we try to write a Lewis structure for nitrogen monoxide the best we can do is as follows:

$$:\overset{..}{\underset{}{N}}::\overset{..}{\underset{}{O}}: \quad or \quad :\overset{.}{N}=\overset{..}{O}:$$

The nitrogen atom does not have an octet, so this Lewis structure does not satisfy the octet rule. Yet, nitrogen monoxide exists, especially in polluted air. Why? As with any simple theory, Lewis theory is not sophisticated enough to model every single case. It is impossible to write good Lewis structures for free radicals, nevertheless some of these molecules exist in nature. Perhaps it is a testament to Lewis theory, however, that *relatively few* such molecules exist and that, in general, they tend to be somewhat unstable and reactive. NO, for example, reacts with oxygen in the air to form NO_2, another odd-electron molecule represented with the following 17-electron resonance structures:

$$:\overset{..}{O}=\overset{.}{N}-\overset{..}{\underset{..}{O}}: \longleftrightarrow :\overset{..}{\underset{..}{O}}-\overset{.}{N}=\overset{..}{O}:$$

In turn, NO_2 reacts with water to form nitric acid (a component of acid rain) and also reacts with other atmospheric pollutants to form peroxyacetylnitrate (PAN), an active component of photochemical smog. For free radicals, such as NO and NO_2, we simply write the best Lewis structure that we can.

Incomplete Octets

Another significant exception to the octet rule involves those elements that tend to form *incomplete octets*. The most important of these is boron, which forms compounds with only six electrons around B, rather than eight. For example, BF_3 and BH_3 lack an octet for B.

$$\overset{\displaystyle :\overset{..}{F}:}{:\overset{..}{F}:\overset{}{B}:\overset{..}{F}:} \qquad \overset{\displaystyle H}{H:\overset{}{B}:H}$$

You might be wondering why we don't just form double bonds to increase the number of electrons around B. For BH_3, of course, we can't, because there are no additional electrons to move into the bonding region. For BF_3, however, we could attempt to give B an octet by moving a lone pair from an F atom into the bonding region with B.

$$\overset{\displaystyle \overset{..}{F}:}{\underset{}{\overset{\|}{:\overset{..}{F}-B-\overset{..}{F}:}}}$$

This Lewis structure has octets for all atoms, including boron. However, when we assign formal charges to this structure, we get the following:

$$\overset{\displaystyle ^{+1}\overset{..}{F}:}{\underset{-1}{\overset{\|}{^{0}:\overset{..}{F}-B-\overset{..}{F}:^{0}}}}$$

In this Lewis structure, fluorine—the most electronegative element in the periodic table—has a positive formal charge, making this an unfavorable structure. This leaves us with the following choice: do we complete the octet on B at the expense of giving fluorine a positive formal charge? Or do we leave B without an octet in order to avoid the positive formal charge on fluorine? The answers to these kinds of questions are not always clear because we are pushing the limits of Lewis theory. In the case of boron, we usually accept the incomplete octet as the better Lewis structure. However, doing so does not rule out the possibility that the doubly bonded Lewis structure might be a minor contributing resonance structure. The ultimate answers to these kinds of issues must be determined from experiments. Experimental measurements of the B—F bond length in BF_3 suggest that the bond may be slightly shorter than expected for a single B—F bond, indicating that it may indeed have a small amount of double-bond character.

The unpaired electron in nitrogen monoxide is put on the nitrogen rather than the oxygen in order to minimize formal charges.

Beryllium compounds, such as BeH_2, also have incomplete octets.

BF_3 can complete its octet in another way—via a chemical reaction. Lewis theory predicts that BF_3 might react in ways that would complete its octet, and indeed it does. For example, BF_3 reacts with NH_3 as follows:

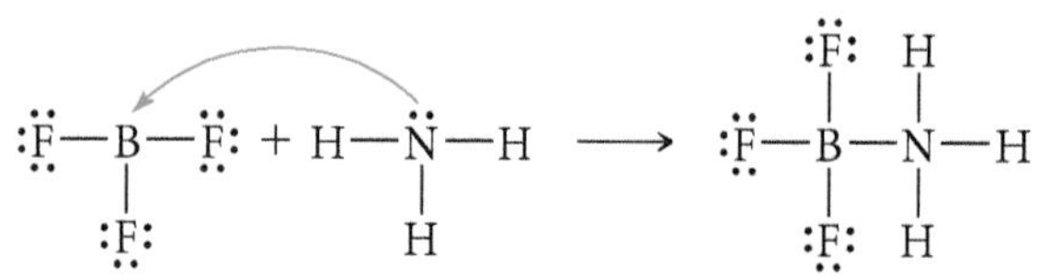

When nitrogen bonds to boron, the nitrogen atom provides both of the electrons. This kind of bond is called a *coordinate covalent bond*, which we discuss in Chapter 24.

The product has complete octets for all atoms in the structure.

Expanded Octets

Elements in the third row of the periodic table and beyond often exhibit *expanded octets* of up to 12 (and occasionally 14) electrons. Consider the Lewis structures of arsenic pentafluoride and sulfur hexafluoride.

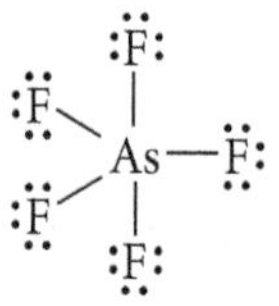

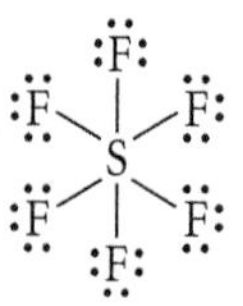

In AsF_5 arsenic has an expanded octet of 10 electrons, and in SF_6 sulfur has an expanded octet of 12 electrons. Both of these compounds exist and are stable. Ten- and twelve-electron expanded octets are common in third-period elements and beyond because the *d* orbitals in these elements are energetically accessible (they are not much higher in energy than the orbitals occupied by the valence electrons) and can accommodate the extra electrons (see Section 8.3). Expanded octets *never* occur in second-period elements.

In some Lewis structures, we must decide whether or not to expand an octet in order to lower formal charge. For example, consider the Lewis structure of H_2SO_4.

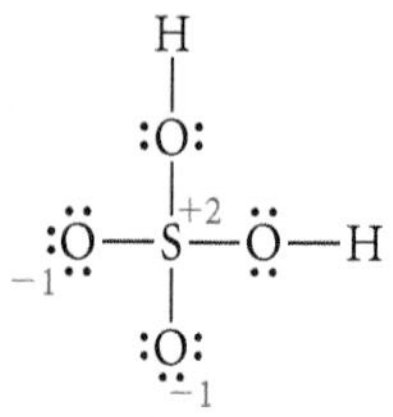

Notice that both of the oxygen atoms have a -1 formal charge and that sulfur has a $+2$ formal charge. While this amount of formal charge is acceptable, especially since the negative formal charge resides on the more electronegative atom, it is possible to eliminate the formal charge by expanding the octet on sulfur.

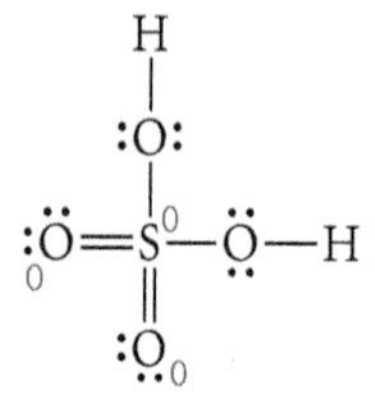

Which of these two Lewis structures for H_2SO_4 is better? Again, the answer is not straightforward. Experiments show that the sulfur–oxygen bond lengths in the two sulfur–oxygen bonds without the hydrogen atoms are shorter than expected for sulfur–oxygen single bonds, indicating that the double-bonded Lewis structure plays an important role in describing the bonding in H_2SO_4. In general, we expand octets in third-row (or beyond) elements in order to lower formal charge. However, we should *never* expand the octets of second-row elements. Second-row elements do not have energetically accessible *d* orbitals and therefore never exhibit expanded octets.

EXAMPLE 9.9 Writing Lewis Structures for Compounds Having Expanded Octets

Write the Lewis structure for XeF_2.

SOLUTION

Begin by writing the skeletal structure. Since xenon is the less electronegative atom, put it in the central position.	F Xe F
Calculate the total number of electrons for the Lewis structure by summing the number of valence electrons for each atom.	Total number of electrons for Lewis structure = (number of valence e⁻ in Xe) + 2(number of valence e⁻ in F) = 8 + 2(7) = 22
Place two bonding electrons between the atoms of each pair of atoms.	F:Xe:F (4 of 22 electrons used)
Distribute the remaining electrons to give octets to as many atoms as possible, beginning with terminal atoms and finishing with the central atom. Arrange additional electrons around the central atom, giving it an expanded octet of up to 12 electrons.	:F̈:Xe :F̈: (16 of 22 electrons used) :F̈:Ẍe:F̈: or :F̈—Ẍe—F̈: (22 of 22 electrons used)

FOR PRACTICE 9.9

Write a Lewis structure for XeF_4.

FOR MORE PRACTICE 9.9

Write a Lewis structure for H_3PO_4. If necessary, expand the octet on any appropriate atoms to lower formal charge.

9.10 Bond Energies and Bond Lengths

In Chapter 6, we learned how to calculate the standard enthalpy change for a chemical reaction (ΔH°_{rxn}) from tabulated standard enthalpies of formation. However, sometimes we may not easily find standard enthalpies of formation for all of the reactants and products of a reaction. In such cases, we can use individual *bond energies* to estimate enthalpy changes of reaction. In this section, we examine the concept of bond energy and how we can use bond energies to calculate enthalpy changes of reaction. We also look at average bond lengths for a number of commonly encountered bonds.

Bond Energy

| Bond energy is also called bond enthalpy or bond dissociation energy.

The **bond energy** of a chemical bond is the energy required to break 1 mole of the bond in the gas phase. For example, the bond energy of the Cl—Cl bond in Cl_2 is 243 kJ/mol.

$$Cl_2(g) \longrightarrow 2\,Cl(g) \qquad \Delta H = 243\ kJ$$

The bond energy of HCl is 431 kJ/mol.

$$HCl(g) \longrightarrow H(g) + Cl(g) \qquad \Delta H = 431\ kJ$$

Bond energies are always positive, because it always takes energy to break a bond. We say that the HCl bond is *stronger* than the Cl_2 bond because it requires more energy to break it. In general, compounds with stronger bonds tend to be more chemically stable, and therefore less chemically reactive, than compounds with weaker bonds. The triple bond in N_2 has a bond energy of 946 kJ/mol.

$$N_2(g) \longrightarrow N(g) + N(g) \qquad \Delta H = 946\ kJ$$

It is a very strong and stable bond, which explains nitrogen's relative inertness.

The bond energy of a particular bond in a polyatomic molecule is a little more difficult to determine because a particular type of bond can have different bond energies in different molecules. For example, consider the C—H bond. In CH_4, the energy required to break one C—H bond is 438 kJ/mol.

$$H_3C—H(g) \longrightarrow H_3C(g) + H(g) \qquad \Delta H = 438 \text{ kJ}$$

However, the energy required to break a C—H bond in other molecules varies slightly, as shown here.

$$F_3C—H(g) \longrightarrow F_3C(g) + H(g) \qquad \Delta H = 446 \text{ kJ}$$
$$Br_3C—H(g) \longrightarrow Br_3C(g) + H(g) \qquad \Delta H = 402 \text{ kJ}$$
$$Cl_3C—H(g) \longrightarrow Cl_3C(g) + H(g) \qquad \Delta H = 401 \text{ kJ}$$

We can calculate an *average bond energy* for a chemical bond, which is an average of the bond energies for that bond in a large number of compounds. For example, for the limited number of compounds listed above, we calculate an average C—H bond energy of 422 kJ/mol. Table 9.3 lists average bond energies for a number of common chemical bonds averaged over a large number of compounds. Notice that the C—H bond energy is listed as 414 kJ/mol, which is not too different from the value we calculated from our limited number of compounds. Notice also that bond energies depend, not only on the kind of atoms involved in the bond, but also on the type of bond: single, double, or triple. In general, for a given pair of atoms, triple bonds are stronger than double bonds, which are, in turn, stronger than single bonds. For example, consider the bond energies of carbon–carbon triple, double, and single bonds listed at right.

Bond	Bond Energy (kJ/mol)
C≡C	837 kJ/mol
C=C	611 kJ/mol
C—C	347 kJ/mol

TABLE 9.3 Average Bond Energies

Bond	Bond Energy (kJ/mol)	Bond	Bond Energy (kJ/mol)	Bond	Bond Energy (kJ/mol)
H—H	436	N—N	163	Br—F	237
H—C	414	N=N	418	Br—Cl	218
H—N	389	N≡N	946	Br—Br	193
H—O	464	N—O	222	I—Cl	208
H—S	368	N=O	590	I—Br	175
H—F	565	N—F	272	I—I	151
H—Cl	431	N—Cl	200	Si—H	323
H—Br	364	N—Br	243	Si—Si	226
H—I	297	N—I	159	Si—C	301
C—C	347	O—O	142	S—O	265
C=C	611	O=O	498	Si=O	368
C≡C	837	O—F	190	S=O	523
C—N	305	O—Cl	203	Si—Cl	464
C=N	615	O—I	234	S=S	418
C≡N	891	F—F	159	S—F	327
C—O	360	Cl—F	253	S—Cl	253
C=O	736*	Cl—Cl	243	S—Br	218
C≡O	1072			S—S	266
C—Cl	339				

*799 in CO_2

Using Average Bond Energies to Estimate Enthalpy Changes for Reactions

We can use average bond energies to *estimate* the enthalpy change of a reaction. For example, consider the following reaction:

$$H_3C—H(g) + Cl—Cl(g) \longrightarrow H_3C—Cl(g) + H—Cl(g)$$

We can imagine this reaction occurring by the breaking of a C—H bond and a Cl—Cl bond and the forming of a C—Cl bond and an H—Cl bond. We know that when bonds

▶ **FIGURE 9.12 Estimating** Δ*H*ₙₓₙ **from Bond Energies** We can approximate the enthalpy change of a reaction by summing up the enthalpy changes involved in breaking old bonds and forming new ones.

Estimating the Enthalpy Change of a Reaction from Bond Energies

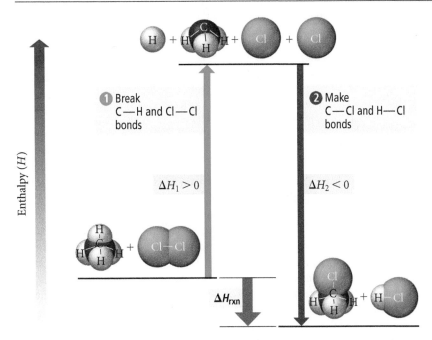

break, the process is endothermic (positive bond energy) and when bonds form, the process is exothermic (negative bond energy). So we can calculate the overall enthalpy change as a sum of the enthalpy changes associated with breaking the required bonds in the reactants and forming the required bonds in the products, as shown in Figure 9.12 ▲.

$$H_3C-H(g) + Cl-Cl(g) \longrightarrow H_3C-Cl(g) + H-Cl(g)$$

Bonds Broken		**Bonds Formed**	
C—H break	+414 kJ	C—Cl form	−339 kJ
Cl—Cl break	+243 kJ	H—Cl form	−431 kJ
Sum (Σ)Δ*H's bonds broken*: +657 kJ		*Sum* (Σ) Δ*H's bonds formed*: −770 kJ	

$$\Delta H_{rxn} = \Sigma(\Delta H's\ bonds\ broken) + \Sigma(\Delta H's\ bonds\ formed)$$
$$= +657\ kJ - 770\ kJ$$
$$= -113\ kJ$$

We find that $\Delta H_{rxn} = -113$ kJ. Calculating ΔH_{rxn}° from tabulated enthalpies of formation—as we learned in Chapter 6—gives $\Delta H_{rxn}^{\circ} = -101$ kJ, fairly close to the value we obtained from average bond energies. In general, you can calculate ΔH_{rxn} from average bond energies by summing the changes in enthalpy for all of the bonds that are broken and adding the sum of the enthalpy changes for all of the bonds that are formed. Remember that ΔH is positive for breaking bonds and negative for forming them:

$$\Delta H_{rxn} = \underbrace{\Sigma(\Delta H's\ bonds\ broken)}_{Positive} + \underbrace{\Sigma(\Delta H's\ bonds\ formed)}_{Negative}$$

As you can see from the above equation:

• A reaction is *exothermic* when weak bonds break and strong bonds form.

• A reaction is *endothermic* when strong bonds break and weak bonds form.

Scientists often say that "energy is stored in chemical bonds or in a chemical compound," which may make it sound as if breaking the bonds in the compound releases energy. For example, we often hear in biology that energy is stored in glucose or in ATP. However, *breaking a chemical bond always requires energy.* When scientists say that

energy is stored in a compound, or that a compound is energy rich, it means that the compound can undergo a reaction in which weak bonds break and strong bonds form, releasing energy. *It is always the forming of chemical bonds that releases energy.*

Conceptual Connection 9.4 Bond Energies and ΔH_{rxn}

The reaction between hydrogen and oxygen to form water is highly exothermic. Which of the following is true of the energies of the bonds that break and form during the reaction?

(a) The energy needed to break the required bonds is greater than the energy released when the new bonds form.

(b) The energy needed to break the required bonds is less than the energy released when the new bonds form.

(c) The energy needed to break the required bonds is about the same as the energy released when the new bonds form.

ANSWER: (b) In a highly exothermic reaction, the energy needed to break bonds is less than the energy released when the new bonds form, resulting in a net release of energy.

EXAMPLE 9.10 Calculating ΔH_{rxn} from Bond Energies

Hydrogen gas, a potential fuel, can be made by the reaction of methane gas and steam.

$$CH_4(g) + 2\,H_2O(g) \longrightarrow 4\,H_2(g) + CO_2(g)$$

Use bond energies to calculate ΔH_{rxn} for this reaction.

SOLUTION

Begin by rewriting the reaction using the Lewis structures of the molecules involved.	$H-\overset{\displaystyle H}{\underset{\displaystyle H}{C}}-H + 2\,H-\ddot{\underset{\cdot\cdot}{O}}-H \longrightarrow 4\,H-H + \ddot{O}=C=\ddot{O}$
Determine which bonds are broken in the reaction and sum the bond energies of these.	$H-\overset{\displaystyle H}{\underset{\displaystyle H}{C}}-H + 2\,H-\ddot{\underset{\cdot\cdot}{O}}-H$ $\Sigma(\Delta H\text{'s bonds broken})$ $= 4(C-H) + 4(O-H)$ $= 4(414\text{ kJ}) + 4(464\text{ kJ})$ $= 3512\text{ kJ}$
Determine which bonds are formed in the reaction and sum the negatives of their bond energies.	$4\,H-H + \ddot{O}=C=\ddot{O}$ $\Sigma(\Delta H\text{'s bonds formed})$ $= -4(H-H) - 2(C=O)$ $= -4(436\text{ kJ}) - 2(799\text{ kJ})$ $= -3342\text{ kJ}$
Find ΔH_{rxn} by summing the results of the previous two steps.	$\Delta H_{rxn} = \Sigma(\Delta H\text{'s bonds broken}) + \Sigma(\Delta H\text{'s bonds formed})$ $= 3512 - 3342$ $= 1.70 \times 10^2\text{ kJ}$

FOR PRACTICE 9.10

Another potential future fuel is methanol (CH_3OH). Write a balanced equation for the combustion of gaseous methanol and use bond energies to calculate the enthalpy of combustion of methanol in kJ/mol.

FOR MORE PRACTICE 9.10

Use bond energies to calculate ΔH_{rxn} for this reaction: $N_2(g) + 3\,H_2(g) \longrightarrow 2\,NH_3(g)$.

TABLE 9.4 Average Bond Lengths

Bond	Bond Length (pm)	Bond	Bond Length (pm)	Bond	Bond Length (pm)
H—H	74	C—C	154	N—N	145
H—C	110	C=C	134	N=N	123
H—N	100	C≡C	120	N≡N	110
H—O	97	C—N	147	N—O	136
H—S	132	C=N	128	N=O	120
H—F	92	C≡N	116	O—O	145
H—Cl	127	C—O	143	O=O	121
H—Br	141	C=O	120	F—F	143
H—I	161	C—Cl	178	Cl—Cl	199
				Br—Br	228
				I—I	266

Bond Lengths

F_2

143 pm

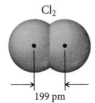

Cl_2

199 pm

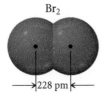

Br_2

228 pm

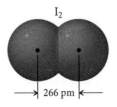

I_2

266 pm

▲ Bond lengths in the diatomic halogen molecules.

Bond Lengths

Just as we can tabulate average bond energies, which represent the average energy of a bond between two particular atoms in a large number of compounds, we can tabulate average bond lengths (Table 9.4). The average **bond length** represents the average length of a bond between two particular atoms in a large number of compounds. Like bond energies, bond lengths depend not only on the kind of atoms involved in the bond, but also on the type of bond: single, double, or triple. In general, for a particular pair of atoms, triple bonds are shorter than double bonds, which are in turn shorter than single bonds. For example, consider the bond lengths (along with bond strengths, repeated from earlier in this section) of carbon–carbon triple, double, and single bonds.

Bond	Bond Length (pm)	Bond Strength (kJ/mol)
C≡C	120 pm	837 kJ/mol
C=C	134 pm	611 kJ/mol
C—C	154 pm	347 kJ/mol

Notice that, as the bond gets longer, it also becomes weaker. This relationship between the length of a bond and the strength of a bond does not necessarily hold for all bonds. Consider the following series of nitrogen–halogen single bonds:

Bond	Bond Length (pm)	Bond Strength (kJ/mol)
N—F	139	272
N—Cl	191	200
N—Br	214	243
N—I	222	159

Although the bonds generally get weaker as they get longer, the trend is not a smooth one.

9.11 Bonding in Metals: The Electron Sea Model

So far, we have developed simple models for bonding between a metal and a nonmetal (ionic bonding) and for bonding between two nonmetals (covalent bonding). We have seen how these models account for and predict the properties of ionic and molecular compounds. The last type of bonding that we examine in this chapter is metallic bonding, which occurs between metals (we will cover this topic in more detail in Chapter 24).

As we know, metals have a tendency to lose electrons, which means that they have relatively low ionization energies. When metal atoms bond together to form a solid, each metal atom donates one or more electrons to an *electron sea*. For example, we can think of sodium metal as an array of positively charged Na^+ ions immersed in a sea of negatively charged electrons (e^-), as shown in Figure 9.13 ◄. Each sodium atom donates its one

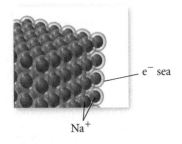

e^- sea

Na^+

▲ **FIGURE 9.13 The Electron Sea Model for Sodium** In this model of metallic bonding, Na^+ ions are immersed in a "sea" of electrons.

CHEMISTRY IN THE ENVIRONMENT The Lewis Structure of Ozone

Ozone is a form of oxygen in which three oxygen atoms bond together. Its Lewis structure consists of the following resonance structures:

$$:\ddot{O}=\ddot{O}-\ddot{\underset{..}{O}}: \longleftrightarrow :\ddot{\underset{..}{O}}-\ddot{O}=\ddot{O}:$$

Compare the Lewis structure of ozone to the Lewis structure of O_2:

$$:\ddot{O}=\ddot{O}:$$

Since double bonds are stronger and shorter than single bonds, O_2 must have a stronger bond because it is a double bond. O_3, on the other hand, has bonds that are intermediate between single and double, which are weaker bonds. The effects of this are significant. As we learned in Section 5.11, O_3 absorbs harmful ultraviolet light entering Earth's atmosphere. Ozone is ideally suited to do this because photons at wavelengths of 280–320 nm (the most harmful components of

sunlight) are just strong enough to break the bonds in the O_3 molecule:

$$:\ddot{\underset{..}{O}}-\ddot{O}=\ddot{O}: + \text{UV light} \longrightarrow :\ddot{O}=\ddot{O}: + \cdot\ddot{\underset{..}{O}}:$$

In this process, the photon is absorbed. O_2 and O then recombine to re-form O_3, which can in turn absorb more UV light. The same wavelengths of UV light, however, do not have sufficient energy to break the stronger double bond of O_2. No other molecules in our atmosphere can do the job that ozone does. Consequently, we should continue, and even strengthen, the ban on ozone-depleting compounds.

Question

Calculate the average bond energy of one O_3 bond. What wavelength of light has just the right amount of energy to break this bond?

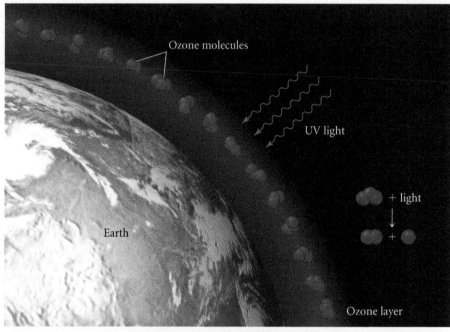

▲ Ozone protects life on Earth from harmful ultraviolet light.

valence electron to the "sea" and becomes a sodium ion. The sodium cations are held together by their attraction to the sea of electrons.

Although this model is simple, it accounts for many of the properties of metals. For example, metals conduct electricity because—in contrast to ionic solids where electrons are localized on an ion—the electrons in a metal are free to move. The movement or flow of electrons in response to an electric potential (or voltage) is an electric current. Metals are also excellent conductors of heat, again because of the highly mobile electrons, which help to disperse thermal energy throughout the metal.

The electron sea model also accounts for the *malleability* of metals (their capacity to be pounded into sheets) and the *ductility* of metals (their capacity to be drawn into wires). Since there are no localized or specific "bonds" in a metal, it can be deformed relatively easily by forcing the metal ions to slide past one another. The electron sea easily accommodates deformations by flowing into the new shape.

▲ Copper can easily be drawn into fine strands like those used in household electrical cords.

CHAPTER IN REVIEW

Key Terms

Section 9.1
Lewis theory (360)
Lewis electron-dot structures (Lewis structures) (360)

Section 9.2
ionic bond (360)
covalent bond (361)
metallic bonding (361)

Section 9.3
octet (362)
duet (362)
chemical bond (362)
octet rule (362)

Section 9.4
lattice energy (364)
Born–Haber cycle (364)

Section 9.5
bonding pair (369)
lone pair (369)
nonbonding electrons (369)
double bond (370)
triple bond (370)

Section 9.6
polar covalent bond (372)
electronegativity (372)
dipole moment (μ) (374)
percent ionic character (375)

Section 9.8
resonance structures (379)
resonance hybrid (379)
formal charge (381)

Section 9.9
free radical (384)

Section 9.10
bond energy (386)
bond length (390)

Key Concepts

Bonding Models and AIDS Drugs (9.1)

Theories that predict how and why atoms bond together are central to chemistry, because they explain compound stability and molecule shape. Bonding theories have been useful in combating HIV because they help in the design of molecules that can bind to the active site of a protein crucial for the development of AIDS.

Types of Chemical Bonds (9.2)

Chemical bonds can be divided into three general types: ionic bonds, which occur between a metal and a nonmetal; covalent bonds, which occur between two nonmetals; and metallic bonds, which occur within metals. In an ionic bond, an electron transfers from the metal to the nonmetal and the resultant ions attract each other by coulombic forces. In a covalent bond, nonmetals share electrons that interact with the nuclei of both atoms via coulombic forces, holding the atoms together. In a metallic bond, the atoms form a lattice in which each metal loses electrons to an "electron sea." The attraction of the positively charged metal ions to the electron sea holds the metal together.

Lewis Theory and Electron Dots (9.3)

In Lewis theory, chemical bonds are formed when atoms transfer (ionic bonding) or share (covalent bonding) valence electrons to attain noble gas electron configurations. Lewis theory represents valence electrons as dots surrounding the symbol for an element. When two or more elements bond together, the dots are transferred or shared so that every atom gets eight dots, an octet (or two dots, a duet, in the case of hydrogen).

Ionic Lewis Structures and Lattice Energy (9.4)

In an ionic Lewis structure involving main-group metals, the metal transfers its valence electrons (dots) to the nonmetal. The formation of most ionic compounds is exothermic because of lattice energy, the energy released when metal cations and nonmetal anions coalesce to form the solid; the smaller the radius of the ions and the greater their charge, the more exothermic the lattice energy.

Covalent Lewis Structures, Electronegativity, and Polarity (9.5, 9.6, 9.7)

In a covalent Lewis structure, neighboring atoms share valence electrons to attain octets (or duets). A single shared electron pair constitutes a single bond, while two or three shared pairs constitute double or triple bonds, respectively. The shared electrons in a covalent bond are not always *equally* shared; when two dissimilar nonmetals form a covalent bond, the electron density is greater on the more electronegative element. The result is a polar bond, with one element carrying a partial positive charge and the other a partial negative charge. Electronegativity—the ability of an atom to attract electrons to itself in chemical bonding—increases as we move to the right across a period in the periodic table and decreases as we move down a column. Elements with very dissimilar electronegativities form ionic bonds; those with very similar electronegativities form nonpolar covalent bonds; and those with intermediate electronegativity differences form polar covalent bonds.

Resonance and Formal Charge (9.8)

Some molecules are best represented not by a single Lewis structure, but by two or more resonance structures. The actual structure of these molecules is a resonance hybrid: a combination or average of the contributing structures. The formal charge of an atom in a Lewis structure is the charge the atom would have if all bonding electrons were shared equally between bonding atoms. In general, the best Lewis structures will have the fewest atoms with formal charge and any negative formal charge will be on the most electronegative atom.

Exceptions to the Octet Rule (9.9)

Although the octet rule is normally used in drawing Lewis structures, some exceptions occur. These exceptions include odd-electron species, which necessarily have Lewis structures with only 7 electrons around an atom. Such molecules, called free radicals, tend to be unstable and chemically reactive. Other exceptions to the octet rule include molecules with incomplete octets—usually totaling 6 electrons (especially important in compounds containing boron)—and molecules with expanded octets—usually 10 or 12 electrons (which can occur in compounds containing elements from the third row of the periodic table and below). Expanded octets never occur in second-period elements.

Bond Energies and Bond Lengths (9.10)

The bond energy of a chemical bond is the energy required to break 1 mole of the bond in the gas phase. Average bond energies for a number of different bonds are tabulated and can be used to calculate enthalpies of reaction. Average bond lengths are also tabulated. In general, triple bonds are shorter and stronger than double bonds, which are in turn shorter and stronger than single bonds.

Bonding in Metals (9.11)

When metal atoms bond together to form a solid, each metal atom donates one or more electrons to an *electron sea*. The metal cations are then held together by their attraction to the sea of electrons. This simple model accounts for the electrical conductivity, thermal conductivity, malleability, and ductility of metals.

Key Equations and Relationships

Coulomb's Law: Potential Energy (E) of Two Charged Particles with Charges q_1 and q_2 Separated by a Distance r (9.2)

$$E = \frac{1}{4\pi\varepsilon_0}\frac{q_1 q_2}{r} \qquad \varepsilon_0 = 8.85 \times 10^{-12}\,\mathrm{C^2/J\cdot m}$$

Dipole Moment (μ): Separation of Two Particles of Equal but Opposite Charges of Magnitude q by a Distance r (9.6)

$$\mu = qr$$

Percent Ionic Character (9.6)

Percent ionic character =

$$\frac{\text{measured dipole moment of bond}}{\text{dipole moment if electron were completely transferred}} \times 100\%$$

Formal Charge (9.8)

Formal charge = number of valence electrons −
(number of nonbonding electrons + $^1/_2$ number of shared electrons)

Enthalpy Change of a Reaction (ΔH_{rxn}): Relationship of Bond Energies (9.10)

$$\Delta H_{rxn} = \Sigma(\Delta H\text{'s bonds broken}) + \Sigma(\Delta H\text{'s bonds formed})$$

Key Skills

Predicting Chemical Formulas of an Ionic Compound (9.4)
  • Example 9.1 • For Practice 9.1 • Exercises 41, 42

Predicting Relative Lattice Energies (9.4)
  • Example 9.2 • For Practice 9.2 • For More Practice 9.2 • Exercise 46

Classifying Bonds: Pure Covalent, Polar Covalent, or Ionic (9.6)
  • Example 9.3 • For Practice 9.3 • Exercises 55, 56

Writing Lewis Structures for Covalent Compounds (9.7)
  • Examples 9.4, 9.5 • For Practice 9.4, 9.5 • Exercises 51, 52

Writing Lewis Structures for Polyatomic Ions (9.7)
  • Example 9.6 • For Practice 9.6 • Exercises 59–64

Writing Resonance Lewis Structures (9.8)
  • Example 9.7 • For Practice 9.7 • Exercises 63, 64

Assigning Formal Charges to Assess Competing Resonance Structures (9.8)
  • Example 9.8 • For Practice 9.8 • For More Practice 9.8 • Exercises 65, 66

Writing Lewis Structures for Compounds Having Expanded Octets (9.9)
  • Example 9.9 • For Practice 9.9 • For More Practice 9.9 • Exercises 73, 74

Calculating ΔH_{rxn} from Bond Energies (9.10)
  • Example 9.10 • For Practice 9.10 • For More Practice 9.10 • Exercises 77–79

EXERCISES

Review Questions

1. Why are bonding theories important? Give some examples of what bonding theories can predict.
2. Why do chemical bonds form? What basic forces are involved in bonding?
3. What are the three basic types of chemical bonds? What happens to electrons in the bonding atoms in each case?
4. How do you determine how many dots to put around the Lewis symbol of an element?
5. Describe the octet rule in Lewis theory.
6. According to Lewis theory, what is a chemical bond?
7. How do you draw an ionic Lewis structure?
8. How can Lewis structures be used to determine the formula of ionic compounds? Give an example.
9. What is lattice energy?
10. Why is the formation of solid sodium chloride from solid sodium and gaseous chlorine exothermic, even though it takes more

energy to form the Na^+ ion than the amount of energy released upon formation of Cl^-?

11. What is the Born–Haber cycle? List each of the steps in the cycle and show how the cycle is used to calculate lattice energy.

12. How does lattice energy relate to ionic radii? To ion charge?

13. How does the ionic bonding model explain the relatively high melting points of ionic compounds?

14. How does the ionic bonding model explain the nonconductivity of ionic solids, and at the same time the conductivity of ionic solutions?

15. Within a covalent Lewis structure, what is the difference between lone pair and bonding pair electrons?

16. In what ways are double and triple covalent bonds different from single covalent bonds?

17. How does the Lewis model for covalent bonding account for why certain combinations of atoms are stable while others are not?

18. How does the Lewis model for covalent bonding account for the relatively low melting and boiling points of molecular compounds (compared to ionic compounds)?

19. What is electronegativity? What are the periodic trends in electronegativity?

20. Explain the difference between a pure covalent bond, a polar covalent bond, and an ionic bond.

21. Explain what is meant by the percent ionic character of a bond. Do any bonds have 100% ionic character?

22. What is a dipole moment?

23. What is the magnitude of the dipole moment formed by separating a proton and an electron by 100 pm? 200 pm?

24. What is the basic procedure for writing a covalent Lewis structure?

25. How do you determine the number of electrons that go into the Lewis structure of a molecule? A polyatomic ion?

26. What are resonance structures? What is a resonance hybrid?

27. Do resonance structures always contribute equally to the overall structure of a molecule? Explain.

28. What is formal charge? How is formal charge calculated? How is it helpful?

29. Why does the octet rule have exceptions? Give the three major categories of exceptions and an example of each.

30. What elements can have expanded octets? What elements should never have expanded octets?

31. What is bond energy? How can average bond energies be used to calculate enthalpies of reaction?

32. Explain the difference between endothermic reactions and exothermic reactions with respect to the bond energies of the bonds broken and formed.

33. What is the electron sea model for bonding in metals?

34. How does the electron sea model explain the conductivity of metals? The malleability and ductility of metals?

Problems by Topic

Valence Electrons and Dot Structures

35. Write an electron configuration for N. Then write a Lewis structure for N and show which electrons from the electron configuration are included in the Lewis structure.

36. Write an electron configuration for Ne. Then write a Lewis structure for Ne and show which electrons from the electron configuration are included in the Lewis structure.

37. Write a Lewis structure for each atom or ion:
    a. Al   b. Na^+ c. Cl   d. Cl^-

38. Write a Lewis structure for each atom or ion:
    a. S^{2-} b. Mg   c. Mg^{2+} d. P

Ionic Lewis Structures and Lattice Energy

39. Write a Lewis structure for each ionic compound.
    a. NaF   b. CaO   c. $SrBr_2$ d. K_2O

40. Write a Lewis structure for each ionic compound.
    a. SrO   b. Li_2S c. CaI_2 d. RbF

41. Use Lewis structures to determine the formula for the compound that forms between each pair of elements:
    a. Sr and Se   b. Ba and Cl   c. Na and S   d. Al and O

42. Use Lewis structures to determine the formula for the compound that forms between each pair of elements:
    a. Ca and N   b. Mg and I   c. Ca and S   d. Cs and F

43. Explain the trend in the lattice energies of the alkaline earth metal oxides.

Metal Oxide	Lattice Energy (kJ/mol)
MgO	−3795
CaO	−3414
SrO	−3217
BaO	−3029

44. Rubidium iodide has a lattice energy of −617 kJ/mol, while potassium bromide has a lattice energy of −671 kJ/mol. Why is the lattice energy of potassium bromide more exothermic than the lattice energy of rubidium iodide?

45. The lattice energy of CsF is −744 kJ/mol, whereas that of BaO is −3029 kJ/mol. Explain this large difference in lattice energy.

46. Arrange these compounds in order of increasing magnitude of lattice energy: KCl, SrO, RbBr, CaO.

47. Use the Born–Haber cycle and data from Appendix IIB and Chapters 8 and 9 to calculate the lattice energy of KCl. (ΔH_{sub} for potassium is 89.0 kJ/mol.)

48. Use the Born–Haber cycle and data from Appendix IIB and Table 9.3 to calculate the lattice energy of CaO. (ΔH_{sub} for calcium is 178 kJ/mol; IE_1 and IE_2 for calcium are 590 kJ/mol and 1145 kJ/mol, respectively; EA_1 and EA_2 for O are −141 kJ/mol and 744 kJ/mol, respectively.)

Simple Covalent Lewis Structures, Electronegativity, and Bond Polarity

49. Use covalent Lewis structures to explain why each element (or family of elements) occurs as diatomic molecules:
    a. hydrogen   b. the halogens
    c. oxygen   d. nitrogen

50. Use covalent Lewis structures to explain why the compound that forms between nitrogen and hydrogen has the formula NH_3. Show why NH_2 and NH_4 are not stable.

51. Write a Lewis structure for each molecule:
    a. PH_3 b. SCl_2 c. HI   d. CH_4

52. Write a Lewis structure for each molecule:
    a. NF_3 b. HBr   c. SBr_2 d. CCl_4

53. Write a Lewis structure for each molecule:
    a. SF_2
    b. SiH_4
    c. HCOOH (both O bonded to C)
    d. CH_3SH (C and S central)

54. Write a Lewis structure for each molecule:
    a. CH_2O **b.** C_2Cl_4
    c. CH_3NH_2 **d.** $CFCl_3$ (C central)

55. Determine whether a bond between each pair of atoms would be pure covalent, polar covalent, or ionic.
    a. Br and Br   **b.** C and Cl   **c.** C and S   **d.** Sr and O

56. Determine whether a bond between each pair of atoms would be pure covalent, polar covalent, or ionic.
    a. C and N   **b.** N and S   **c.** K and F   **d.** N and N

57. Draw a Lewis structure for CO with an arrow representing the dipole moment. Use Figure 9.10 to estimate the percent ionic character of the CO bond.

58. Draw a Lewis structure for BrF with an arrow representing the dipole moment. Use Figure 9.10 to estimate the percent ionic character of the BrF bond.

Covalent Lewis Structures, Resonance, and Formal Charge

59. Write a Lewis structure for each molecule or ion:
    a. CI_4 **b.** N_2O **c.** SiH_4 **d.** Cl_2CO

60. Write a Lewis structure for each molecule or ion:
    a. H_3COH **b.** OH^- **c.** BrO^- **d.** O_2^{2-}

61. Write a Lewis structure for each molecule or ion:
    a. N_2H_2 **b.** N_2H_4 **c.** C_2H_2 **d.** C_2H_4

62. Write a Lewis structure for each molecule or ion
    a. H_3COCH_3 **b.** CN^- **c.** NO_2^- **d.** ClO^-

63. Write a Lewis structure that obeys the octet rule for each molecule or ion. Include resonance structures if necessary and assign formal charges to each atom.
    a. SeO_2 **b.** CO_3^{2-} **c.** ClO^- **d.** NO_2^-

64. Write a Lewis structure that obeys the octet rule for each ion. Include resonance structures if necessary and assign formal charges to each atom.
    a. ClO_3^- **b.** ClO_4^- **c.** NO_3^- **d.** NH_4^+

65. Use formal charge to determine which Lewis structure is better:

66. Use formal charge to determine which Lewis structure is better:

67. How important is this resonance structure to the overall structure of carbon dioxide? Explain.

68. In N_2O, nitrogen is the central atom and the oxygen atom is terminal. In OF_2, however, oxygen is the central atom. Use formal charges to explain why.

Odd-Electron Species, Incomplete Octets, and Expanded Octets

69. Write a Lewis structure for each molecule (octet rule not followed).
    a. BCl_3 **b.** NO_2 **c.** BH_3

70. Write a Lewis structure for each molecule (octet rule not followed).
    a. BBr_3 **b.** NO   **c.** ClO_2

71. Write a Lewis structure for each ion. Include resonance structures if necessary and assign formal charges to all atoms. If necessary, expand the octet on the central atom to lower formal charge.
    a. PO_4^{3-} **b.** CN^- **c.** SO_3^{2-} **d.** ClO_2^-

72. Write Lewis structures for each molecule or ion. Include resonance structures if necessary and assign formal charges to all atoms. If necessary, expand the octet on the central atom to lower formal charge.
    a. SO_4^{2-} **b.** HSO_4^- **c.** SO_3 **d.** BrO_2^-

73. Write Lewis structures for each molecule or ion. Use expanded octets as necessary.
    a. PF_5 **b.** I_3^- **c.** SF_4 **d.** GeF_4

74. Write Lewis structures for each molecule or ion. Use expanded octets as necessary.
    a. ClF_5 **b.** AsF_6^- **c.** Cl_3PO **d.** IF_5

Bond Energies and Bond Lengths

75. Order these compounds in order of increasing carbon–carbon bond *strength* and in order of decreasing carbon–carbon bond *length*: HCCH, H_2CCH_2, H_3CCH_3.

76. Which of these compounds has the stronger nitrogen–nitrogen bond? The shorter nitrogen–nitrogen bond?

$$H_2NNH_2, \; HNNH$$

77. Hydrogenation reactions are used to add hydrogen across double bonds in hydrocarbons and other organic compounds. Use average bond energies to calculate ΔH_{rxn} for the hydrogenation reaction.

$$H_2C\!\!=\!\!CH_2(g) + H_2(g) \longrightarrow H_3C\!-\!CH_3(g)$$

78. Ethanol is a possible fuel. Use average bond energies to calculate ΔH_{rxn} for the combustion of ethanol.

$$CH_3CH_2OH(g) + 3\,O_2(g) \longrightarrow 2\,CO_2(g) + 3\,H_2O(g)$$

79. Hydrogen, a potential future fuel, can be produced from carbon (from coal) and steam by this reaction:

$$C(s) + 2\,H_2O(g) \longrightarrow 2\,H_2(g) + CO_2(g)$$

Use average bond energies to calculate ΔH_{rxn} for the reaction.

80. In the *Chemistry and the Environment* box on free radicals in this chapter, we discussed the importance of the hydroxyl radical in reacting with and eliminating many atmospheric pollutants. However, the hydroxyl radical does not clean up everything. For example, chlorofluorocarbons—which destroy stratospheric ozone—are not attacked by the hydroxyl radical. Consider the hypothetical reaction by which the hydroxyl radical might react with a chlorofluorocarbon:

$$OH(g) + CF_2Cl_2(g) \longrightarrow HOF(g) + CFCl_2(g)$$

Use bond energies to explain why this reaction is improbable.

Cumulative Problems

81. Write an appropriate Lewis structure for each compound. Make certain to distinguish between ionic and molecular compounds.
    a. BI_3 **b.** K_2S **c.** HCFO   **d.** PBr_3

82. Write an appropriate Lewis structure for each compound. Make certain to distinguish between ionic and molecular compounds.
    a. Al_2O_3 **b.** ClF_5 **c.** MgI_2 **d.** XeO_4

83. Each compound contains both ionic and covalent bonds. Write ionic Lewis structures for each of them, including the covalent structure for the ion in brackets. Write resonance structures if necessary.
    a. $BaCO_3$ **b.** $Ca(OH)_2$ **c.** KNO_3 **d.** LiIO

84. Each compound contains both ionic and covalent bonds. Write ionic Lewis structures for each of them, including the covalent structure for the ion in brackets. Write resonance structures if necessary.
    a. $RbIO_2$ **b.** NH_4Cl **c.** KOH   **d.** $Sr(CN)_2$

85. Carbon ring structures are common in organic chemistry. Draw a Lewis structure for each carbon ring structure, including any necessary resonance structures.
    a. C_4H_8 **b.** C_4H_4 **c.** C_6H_{12} **d.** C_6H_6

86. Amino acids are the building blocks of proteins. The simplest amino acid is glycine (H_2NCH_2COOH). Draw a Lewis structure for glycine. (Hint: The central atoms in the skeletal structure are nitrogen bonded to carbon which is bonded to another carbon. The two oxygen atoms are bonded directly to the rightmost carbon atom.)

87. Formic acid is responsible for the sting of ant bites. By mass, formic acid is 26.10% C, 4.38% H, and 69.52% O. The molar mass of formic acid is 46.02 g/mol. Find the molecular formula of formic acid and draw its Lewis structure.

88. Diazomethane is a highly poisonous, explosive compound because it readily evolves N_2. Diazomethane has the following composition by mass: 28.57% C; 4.80% H; and 66.64% N. The molar mass of diazomethane is 42.04 g/mol. Find the molecular formula of diazomethane, draw its Lewis structure, and assign formal charges to each atom. Why is diazomethane not very stable? Explain.

89. The reaction of $Fe_2O_3(s)$ with $Al(s)$ to form $Al_2O_3(s)$ and $Fe(s)$ is called the thermite reaction and is highly exothermic. What role does lattice energy play in the exothermicity of the reaction?

90. NaCl has a lattice energy -787 kJ/mol. Consider a hypothetical salt XY. X^{3+} has the same radius of Na^+ and Y^{3-} has the same radius as Cl^-. Estimate the lattice energy of XY.

91. Draw a Lewis structure for nitric acid (the hydrogen atom is attached to one of the oxygen atoms). Include all three resonance structures by alternating the double bond among the three oxygen atoms. Use formal charge to determine which of the resonance structures is most important to the structure of nitric acid.

92. Phosgene (Cl_2CO) is a poisonous gas used as a chemical weapon during World War I. It is a potential agent for chemical terrorism today. Draw the Lewis structure of phosgene. Include all three resonance forms by alternating the double bond among the three terminal atoms. Which resonance structure is the best?

93. The cyanate ion (OCN^-) and the fulminate ion (CNO^-) share the same three atoms, but have vastly different properties. The cyanate ion is stable, while the fulminate ion is unstable and forms explosive compounds. The resonance structures of the cyanate ion were explored in Example 9.8. Draw Lewis struc-

tures for the fulminate ion—including possible resonance forms—and use formal charge to explain why the fulminate ion is less stable (and therefore more reactive) than the cyanate ion.

94. Use Lewis structures to explain why Br_3^- and I_3^- are stable, while F_3^- is not.

95. Draw a Lewis structure for $HCSNH_2$. (The carbon and nitrogen atoms are bonded together and the sulfur atom is bonded to the carbon atom.) Label each bond in the molecule as polar or nonpolar.

96. Draw a Lewis structure for urea, H_2NCONH_2, one of the compounds responsible for the smell of urine. (The central carbon atom is bonded to both nitrogen atoms and to the oxygen atom.) Does urea contain polar bonds? Which bond in urea is most polar?

97. Some theories of aging suggest that free radicals cause certain diseases and perhaps aging in general. As you know from Lewis theory, such molecules are not chemically stable and will quickly react with other molecules. According to certain theories, free radicals may attack molecules within the cell, such as DNA, changing them and causing cancer or other diseases. Free radicals may also attack molecules on the surfaces of cells, making them appear foreign to the body's immune system. The immune system then attacks the cells and destroys them, weakening the body. Draw Lewis structures for each free radical implicated in this theory of aging.
    a. O_2^-
    b. O^-
    c. OH
    d. CH_3OO (unpaired electron on terminal oxygen)

98. Free radicals are important in many environmentally significant reactions (see the *Chemistry in the Environment* box on free radicals in this chapter). For example, photochemical smog— smog that results from the action of sunlight on air pollutants— forms in part by these two steps:

$$NO_2 \xrightarrow{\text{UV light}} NO + O$$

$$O + O_2 \longrightarrow O_3$$

The product of this reaction, ozone, is a pollutant in the lower atmosphere. (Upper atmospheric ozone is a natural part of the atmosphere that protects life on Earth from ultraviolet light.) Ozone is an eye and lung irritant and also accelerates the weathering of rubber products. Rewrite the above reactions using the Lewis structure of each reactant and product. Identify the free radicals.

99. If hydrogen were used as a fuel, it could be burned according to this reaction:

$$H_2(g) + {}^1/_2 O_2(g) \longrightarrow H_2O(g)$$

Use average bond energies to calculate ΔH_{rxn} for this reaction and also for the combustion of methane (CH_4). Which fuel yields more energy per mole? Per gram?

100. Calculate ΔH_{rxn} for the combustion of octane (C_8H_{18}), a component of gasoline, by using average bond energies and then calculate it using enthalpies of formation from Appendix IIB. What is the percent difference between your results? Which result would you expect to be more accurate?

101. Draw Lewis structures for each compound.
   a. Cl_2O_7 (no Cl—Cl bond)
   b. H_3PO_3 (two OH bonds)
   c. H_3AsO_4

102. The azide ion, N_3^-, is a symmetrical ion, all of whose contributing resonance structures have formal charges. Draw three important contributing structures for this ion.

103. List the following gas-phase ion pairs in order of the quantity of energy released when they form from separated gas-phase ions. Start with the pair that releases the least energy. Na^+F^-, $Mg^{2+}F^-$, Na^+O^{2-}, $Mg^{2+}O^{2-}$, $Al^{3+}O^{2-}$.

104. Calculate $\Delta H°$ for the reaction $H_2(g) + Br_2(g) \longrightarrow 2\ HBr(g)$ using the bond energy values. The $\Delta H_f°$ of $HBr(g)$ is not equal to one-half of the value calculated. Account for the difference.

105. The heat of atomization is the heat required to convert a molecule in the gas phase into its constituent atoms in the gas phase. It is used to calculate average bond energies. Without using any tabulated bond energies, calculate the average C—Cl bond energy from the following data: The heat of atomization of CH_4 is 1660 kJ/mol and of CH_2Cl_2 is 1495 kJ/mol.

106. Calculate the heat of atomization (see previous problem) of C_2H_3Cl, using the average bond energies in Table 9.3.

107. A compound composed of only carbon and hydrogen is 7.743% hydrogen by mass. Propose a Lewis structure for the compound.

108. A compound composed of only carbon and chlorine is 85.5% chlorine by mass. Propose a Lewis structure for the compound.

Challenge Problems

109. The main component of acid rain (H_2SO_4) forms from SO_2 pollutant in the atmosphere via these steps:

$$SO_2 + OH\cdot \longrightarrow HSO_3\cdot$$
$$HSO_3\cdot + O_2 \longrightarrow SO_3 + HOO\cdot$$
$$SO_3 + H_2O \longrightarrow H_2SO_4$$

Draw a Lewis structure for each of the species in these steps and use bond energies and Hess's law to estimate ΔH_{rxn} for the overall process. (Use 265 kJ/mol for the S—O single bond energy.)

110. A 0.167-g sample of an unknown acid requires 27.8 mL of 0.100 M NaOH to titrate to the equivalence point. Elemental analysis of the acid gives the following percentages by mass: 40.00% C; 6.71% H; 53.29% O. Determine the molecular formula, molar mass, and Lewis structure of the unknown acid.

111. Use the dipole moments of HF and HCl (given below) together with the percent ionic character of each bond (Figure 9.10) to estimate the bond length in each molecule. How well does your estimated bond length agree with the bond length given in Table 9.4?

$$HCl \quad \mu = 1.08\ D$$
$$HF \quad \mu = 1.82\ D$$

112. Use average bond energies together with the standard enthalpy of formation of $C(g)$ (718.4 kJ/mol) to estimate the standard enthalpy of formation of gaseous benzene, $C_6H_6(g)$. (Remember that average bond energies apply to the gas phase only.) Compare the value you obtain using average bond energies to the actual standard enthalpy of formation of gaseous benzene,

82.9 kJ/mol. What does the difference between these two values tell you about the stability of benzene?

113. The standard state of phosphorus at 25°C is P_4. This molecule has four equivalent P atoms, no double or triple bonds, and no expanded octets. Draw its Lewis structure.

114. The standard heat of formation of $CaBr_2$ is −675 kJ/mol. The first ionization energy of Ca is 590 kJ/mol and its second ionization energy is 1145 kJ/mol. The heat of sublimation of $Ca[Ca(s) \longrightarrow Ca(g)]$ is 178 kJ/mol. The bond energy of Br_2 is 193 kJ/mol, the heat of vaporization of $Br_2(l)$ is 31 kJ/mol, and the electron affinity of Br is −325 kJ/mol. Calculate the lattice energy of $CaBr_2$.

115. The standard heat of formation of $PI_3(s)$ is −24.7 kJ/mol and the PI bond energy in this molecule is 184 kJ/mol. The standard heat of formation of $P(g)$ is 334 kJ/mol and that of $I_2(g)$ is 62 kJ/mol. The I_2 bond energy is 151 kJ/mol. Calculate the heat of sublimation of $PI_3[PI_3(s) \longrightarrow PI_3(g)]$.

116. A compound has the formula C_8H_8 and does not contain any double or triple bonds. All the carbon atoms are chemically identical and all the hydrogen atoms are chemically identical. Draw a Lewis structure for this molecule.

117. Find the oxidation number of each sulfur in the molecule H_2S_4, which has a linear arrangement of its atoms.

118. Ionic solids of the O^- and O^{3-} anions do not exist, while ionic solids of the O^{2-} anion are common. Explain.

119. The standard state of sulfur is solid rhombic sulfur. Use the appropriate standard heats of formation given in Appendix II to find the average bond energy of the S=O in SO_2.

Conceptual Problems

120. Which statement is true of an endothermic reaction?
   a. Strong bonds break and weak bonds form
   b. Weak bonds break and strong bonds form.
   c. The bonds that break and those that form are of approximately the same strength.

121. When a firecracker explodes, energy is obviously released. The compounds in the firecracker can be viewed as being "energy rich." What does this mean? Explain the source of the energy in terms of chemical bonds.

122. A fundamental difference between compounds containing ionic bonds and those containing covalent bonds is the existence of molecules. Explain why molecules exist in solid covalent compounds but do not exist in solid ionic compounds.

123. In the very first chapter of this book, we described the scientific method and put a special emphasis on scientific models or theories. In this chapter, we looked carefully at a model for chemical bonding (Lewis theory). Why is this theory successful? What are some of the limitations of the theory?

10

Chemical Bonding II: Molecular Shapes, Valence Bond Theory, and Molecular Orbital Theory

No theory ever solves all the puzzles with which it is confronted at a given time; nor are the solutions already achieved often perfect.

—Thomas Kuhn (1922–1996)

I N CHAPTER 9, WE EXAMINED a simple model for chemical bonding called Lewis theory. We saw how this model helps us to explain and predict the combinations of atoms that form stable molecules. When we combine Lewis theory with the idea that valence electron groups repel one another—the basis of an approach known as VSEPR theory—we can predict the general shape of a molecule from its Lewis structure. We address molecular shapes and their importance in the first part of this chapter. We then move on to explore two additional bonding theories—called valence bond theory and molecular orbital theory—that are progressively more sophisticated, but at the cost of being more complex, than Lewis theory. As you work through this chapter, our second on chemical bonding, keep in mind the importance of this topic. In our universe, elements join together to form compounds, and that makes many things possible, including our own existence.

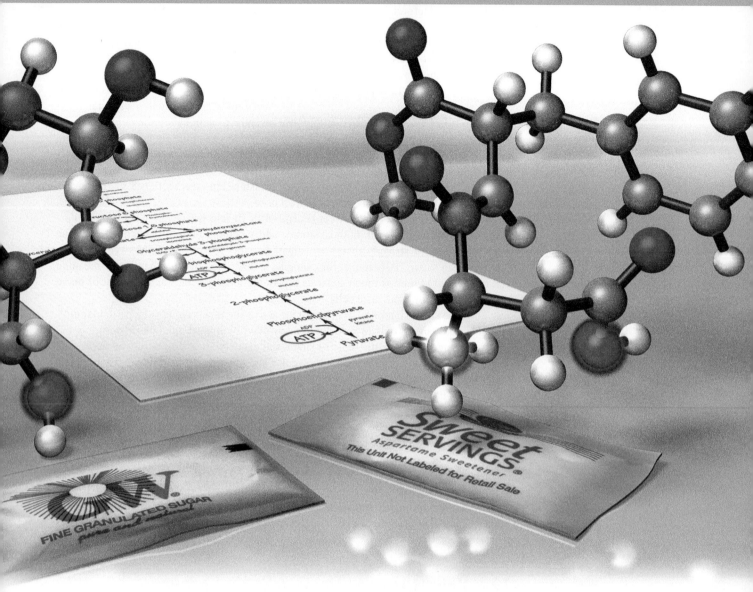

Similarities in the shape of sugar and aspartame give both molecules the ability to stimulate a sweet taste sensation.

10.1 Artificial Sweeteners: Fooled by Molecular Shape

Artificial sweeteners, such as aspartame (Nutrasweet), taste sweet but have few or no calories. Why? *Because taste and caloric value are independent properties of foods.* The caloric value of a food depends on the amount of energy released when the food is metabolized. For example, sucrose (table sugar) is metabolized by oxidation to carbon dioxide and water:

$$C_{12}H_{22}O_{11} + 12\,O_2 \longrightarrow 12\,CO_2 + 11\,H_2O \qquad \Delta H^\circ_{rxn} = -5644 \text{ kJ}$$

When your body metabolizes a mole of sucrose, it obtains 5644 kJ of energy. Some artificial sweeteners, such as saccharin, for example, are not metabolized at all—they just pass through the body unchanged—and therefore have no caloric value. Other artificial sweeteners, such as aspartame, are metabolized but have a much lower caloric content (for a given amount of sweetness) than sucrose.

The *taste* of a food, however, is independent of its metabolism. The sensation of taste originates in the tongue, where specialized cells called taste cells act as highly sensitive and specific molecular detectors. These cells can discern sugar molecules from the thousands of different types of molecules present in a mouthful of food. The main factors for this discrimination are the molecule's shape and charge distribution.

The surface of a taste cell contains specialized protein molecules called taste receptors. A particular *tastant*—a molecule that we can taste—fits snugly into a special pocket (just as a key fits into a lock) on the taste receptor protein called the *active site.* For example, a sugar molecule precisely fits into the active site of the sugar receptor protein called T1r3. When the sugar molecule (the key) enters the active site (the lock), the different subunits of the T1r3 protein split apart. This split causes ion channels in the cell membrane to open, resulting in nerve signal transmission (see Section 8.1). The nerve signal reaches the brain and registers a sweet taste.

Artificial sweeteners taste sweet because they fit into the receptor pocket that normally binds sucrose. In fact, both aspartame and saccharin bind to the active site in the T1r3 protein more strongly than does sugar! For this reason, artificial sweeteners are "sweeter than sugar." Aspartame, for example, is 200 times sweeter than sugar, meaning that it takes 200 times as much sugar as aspartame to trigger the same amount of nerve signal transmission from taste cells.

The type of lock-and-key fit between the active site of a protein and a particular molecule is important not only to taste but to many other biological functions as well. For example, immune response, the sense of smell, and many types of drug action all depend on shape-specific interactions between molecules and proteins. In fact, the ability to determine the shapes of key biological molecules is largely responsible for the revolution in biology that has occurred over the last 50 years.

In this chapter, we look at ways to predict and account for the shapes of molecules. The molecules we examine are much smaller than the protein molecules we just discussed, but the same principles apply to both. The simple model we examine to account for molecular shape is called *valence shell electron pair repulsion* (VSEPR) theory, and we will use it in conjunction with Lewis theory. We will then proceed to explore two additional bonding theories: valence bond theory and molecular orbital theory. These bonding theories are more complex, but also more powerful, than Lewis theory. They also predict and account for molecular shape as well as other properties of molecules.

10.2 VSEPR Theory: The Five Basic Shapes

The first theory that we shall consider, **valence shell electron pair repulsion (VSEPR) theory**, is based on the simple idea that **electron groups**—which we define as lone pairs, single bonds, multiple bonds, and even single electrons—repel one another through coulombic forces. The electron groups, of course, are also attracted to the nucleus (otherwise the molecule would fall apart), but VSEPR theory focuses on the repulsions. According to VSEPR theory, the repulsions between electron groups on *interior atoms* of a molecule determine the geometry of the molecule (Figure 10.1 ◄). The preferred geometry of a molecule is the one in which the electron groups have the maximum separation (and therefore the minimum energy) possible. Consequently, for molecules having just one interior atom (the central atom) molecular geometry depends on (a) the number of electron groups around the central atom and (b) how many of those electron groups are bonding groups and how many are lone pairs. We first look at the molecular geometries associated with two to six electron groups around the central atom when all of those groups are bonding groups (single or multiple bonds). The resulting geometries constitute the five basic shapes of molecules. We will then see how these basic shapes are modified if one or more of the electron groups are lone pairs.

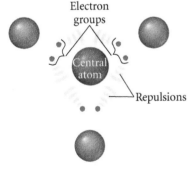

Electron groups

Central atom

Repulsions

▲ FIGURE 10.1 **Repulsion between Electron Groups** The basic idea of VSEPR theory is that repulsions between electron groups determine molecular geometry.

| Beryllium often forms incomplete octets, as it does in this structure.

Two Electron Groups: Linear Geometry

Consider the Lewis structure of $BeCl_2$, which has two electron groups (two single bonds) about the central atom:

According to VSEPR theory, the geometry of $BeCl_2$ is determined by the repulsion between these two electron groups, which can maximize their separation by assuming a 180° bond angle or a **linear geometry**. Experimental measurements of the geometry of $BeCl_2$ indicate that the molecule is indeed linear, as predicted by the theory.

Molecules that form only two single bonds, with no lone pairs, are rare because they do not follow the octet rule. However, the same geometry is observed in all molecules that have two electron groups (and no lone pairs). For example, consider the Lewis structure of CO_2, which has two electron groups (the double bonds) around the central carbon atom:

$$:\ddot{O}=C=\ddot{O}:$$

According to VSEPR theory, the two double bonds repel each other (just as the two single bonds in $BeCl_2$ repel each other), resulting in a linear geometry for CO_2. Experimental observations confirm that CO_2 is indeed a linear molecule.

Three Electron Groups: Trigonal Planar Geometry

The Lewis structure of BF_3 (another molecule with an incomplete octet) has three electron groups around the central atom:

$$\begin{array}{c} :\ddot{F}: \\ :\ddot{F}:\!B\!:\ddot{F}: \end{array}$$

These three electron groups can maximize their separation by assuming 120° bond angles in a plane—a **trigonal planar geometry**. Experimental observations of the structure of BF_3 are again in agreement with the predictions of VSEPR theory.

Another molecule with three electron groups, formaldehyde, has one double bond and two single bonds around the central atom:

$$\begin{array}{c} :O: \\ \| \\ H\!-\!C\!-\!H \end{array}$$

Since formaldehyde has three electron groups around the central atom, we initially predict that the bond angles should also be 120°. However, experimental observations show that the HCO bond angles are 121.9° and that the HCH bond angle is 116.2°. These bond angles are close to the idealized 120° that we originally predicted, but the HCO bond angles are slightly greater than the HCH bond angle because the double bond contains more electron density than the single bond and therefore exerts a slightly greater repulsion on the single bonds. In general, *different types of electron groups exert slightly different repulsions*—the resulting bond angles reflect these differences.

Conceptual Connection 10.1 Electron Groups and Molecular Geometry

In determining electron geometry, why do we consider only the electron groups on the central atom? In other words, why don't we consider electron groups on terminal atoms?

ANSWER: The geometry of a molecule is determined by how the terminal atoms are arranged around the central atom, which is in turn determined by how the electron groups are arranged around the *central* atom. The electron groups on the terminal atoms do not affect this arrangement.

Four Electron Groups: Tetrahedral Geometry

The VSEPR geometries of molecules with two or three electron groups around the central atom are two-dimensional and can therefore easily be visualized and represented on paper. For molecules with four or more electron groups around the central atom, the geometries are three-dimensional and are therefore more difficult to imagine and draw. One common way to help visualize these basic shapes is by analogy to balloons tied together. In this analogy, each electron group around a central atom is like a balloon tied

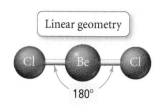

Linear geometry

180°

A double bond counts as one electron group.

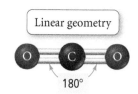

Linear geometry

180°

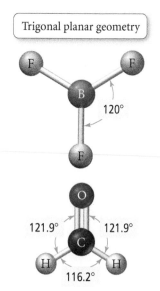

Trigonal planar geometry

120°

121.9°   121.9°

116.2°

▶ **FIGURE 10.2 Representing Electron Geometry with Balloons** **(a)** The bulkiness of balloons causes them to assume a linear arrangement when two of them are tied together. Similarly, the repulsion between two electron groups produces a linear geometry. **(b)** Like three balloons tied together, three electron groups adopt a trigonal planar geometry.

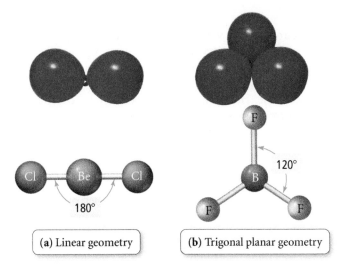

(a) Linear geometry

(b) Trigonal planar geometry

to a central point. The bulkiness of the balloons causes them to spread out as much as possible, much as the repulsion between electron groups causes them to position themselves as far apart as possible. For example, if you tie two balloons together, they assume a roughly linear arrangement, as shown in Figure 10.2a ▲, analogous to the linear geometry of $BeCl_2$ that we just examined. Notice that the balloons do not represent atoms, but *electron groups*. Similarly, if you tie three balloons together—in analogy to three electron groups—they assume a trigonal planar geometry, as shown in Figure 10.2b, much like our BF_3 molecule. If you tie *four* balloons together, however, they assume a three-dimensional **tetrahedral geometry** with 109.5° angles between the balloons. That is, the balloons point toward the vertices of a *tetrahedron*—a geometrical shape with four identical faces, each an equilateral triangle, as shown here.

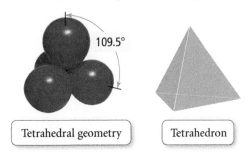

Tetrahedral geometry

Tetrahedron

Methane is an example of a molecule with four electron groups around the central atom:

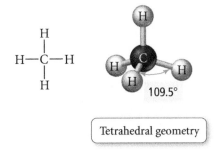

Tetrahedral geometry

For four electron groups, the tetrahedron is the three-dimensional shape that allows the maximum separation among the groups. The repulsions among the four electron groups in the C—H bonds cause the molecule to assume the tetrahedral shape. When we write the Lewis structure of CH_4 on paper, it may seem that the molecule should be square planar, with bond angles of 90°. However, in three dimensions, the electron groups can get farther away from each other by forming the tetrahedral geometry, as shown by our balloon analogy.

Five Electron Groups: Trigonal Bipyramidal Geometry

Five electron groups around a central atom assume a **trigonal bipyramidal geometry**, like that of five balloons tied together. In this structure, three of the groups lie in a single plane, as in the trigonal planar configuration, while the other two are positioned above and below this plane. The angles in the trigonal bipyramidal structure are not all the same. The angles between the *equatorial positions* (the three bonds in the trigonal plane) are 120°, while the angle between the *axial positions* (the two bonds on either side of the trigonal plane) and the trigonal plane is 90°. As an example of a molecule with five electron groups around the central atom, consider PCl_5:

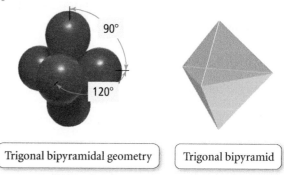

Trigonal bipyramidal geometry

Trigonal bipyramid

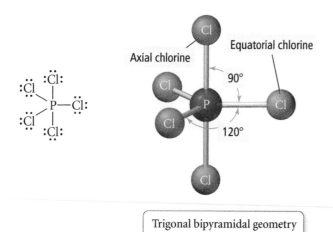

Trigonal bipyramidal geometry

The three equatorial chlorine atoms are separated by 120° bond angles and the two axial chlorine atoms are separated from the equatorial atoms by 90° bond angles.

Six Electron Groups: Octahedral Geometry

Six electron groups around a central atom assume an **octahedral geometry**, like that of six balloons tied together. In this structure—named after the eight-sided geometrical shape called the octahedron—four of the groups lie in a single plane, with a fifth group above the plane and another below it. The angles in this geometry are all 90°. As an example of a molecule with six electron groups around the central atom, consider SF_6:

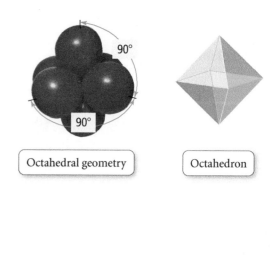

Octahedral geometry

Octahedron

Octahedral geometry

The structure of this molecule is highly symmetrical; all six bonds are equivalent.

EXAMPLE 10.1 VSEPR Theory and the Basic Shapes

Determine the molecular geometry of NO_3^-.

SOLUTION

The molecular geometry of NO_3^- is determined by the number of electron groups around the central atom (N). Begin by drawing a Lewis structure of NO_3^-.	NO_3^- has $5 + 3(6) + 1 = 24$ valence electrons. The Lewis structure is as follows: $$\left[:\ddot{O}-N-\ddot{O}: \atop \quad \overset{\|}{:O:}\right]^- \longleftrightarrow \left[\ddot{O}=N-\ddot{O}: \atop \quad \overset{\|}{:O:}\right]^- \longleftrightarrow \left[:\ddot{O}-N=\ddot{O} \atop \quad \overset{\|}{:O:}\right]^-$$ The hybrid structure is intermediate between these three and has three equivalent bonds.
Use any one of the resonance structures to determine the number of electron groups around the central atom.	$$\left[:\ddot{O}-N-\ddot{O}: \atop \quad \overset{\|}{:O:}\right]^-$$ The nitrogen atom has three electron groups.
Based on the number of electron groups, determine the geometry that minimizes the repulsions between the groups.	The electron geometry that minimizes the repulsions between three electron groups is trigonal planar. 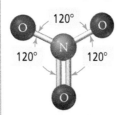 Since the three bonds are equivalent (because of the resonance structures), they each exert the same repulsion on the other two and the molecule has three equal bond angles of $120°$.

FOR PRACTICE 10.1

Determine the molecular geometry of CCl_4.

10.3 VSEPR Theory: The Effect of Lone Pairs

Each of the examples we have just seen has only bonding electron groups around the central atom. What happens in molecules that also have lone pairs around the central atom? The lone pairs also repel other electron groups, as we see in the examples that follow.

Four Electron Groups with Lone Pairs

Consider the Lewis structure of ammonia.

$$\begin{array}{c} H \\ | \\ H-N-H \\ \cdot\cdot \end{array}$$

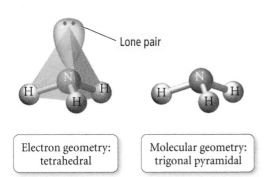

Lone pair

Electron geometry:
tetrahedral

Molecular geometry:
trigonal pyramidal

The central nitrogen atom has four electron groups (one lone pair and three bonding pairs) that repel one another. If we do not distinguish between bonding electron groups and lone pairs, we find that the **electron geometry**—the geometrical arrangement of the *electron groups*—is still tetrahedral, as we expect for four electron groups. However, the **molecular geometry**—the geometrical arrangement of the atoms—is **trigonal pyramidal**, as shown here.

Notice that although the electron geometry and the molecular geometry are different, *the electron geometry is relevant to the molecular geometry*. The lone pair exerts its influence on the bonding pairs.

As we saw previously, different kinds of electron groups generally result in different amounts of repulsion. Lone pair electrons generally exert slightly greater repulsions than bonding electrons. If all four electron groups in NH_3 exerted equal repulsions on one another, the bond angles in the molecule would all be the ideal tetrahedral angle, 109.5°. However, the actual angle between N—H bonds in ammonia is slightly smaller, 107°. A lone electron pair is more spread out in space than a bonding electron pair because a lone pair is attracted to only one nucleus while a bonding pair is attracted to two (Figure 10.3 ▼). The lone pair occupies more of the angular space around a nucleus, exerting a greater repulsive force on neighboring electrons and compressing the N—H bond angles.

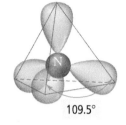

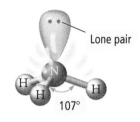

| Ideal tetrahedral geometry | Actual molecular geometry |

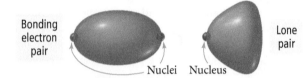

▲ **FIGURE 10.3   Nonbonding versus Bonding Electron Pairs**   A nonbonding electron pair occupies more space than a bonding pair.

A water molecule's Lewis structure is

$$\text{H}-\overset{\cdot\cdot}{\underset{\cdot\cdot}{\text{O}}}-\text{H}$$

Since it has four electron groups (two bonding pairs and two lone pairs), its *electron geometry* is also tetrahedral, but its *molecular geometry* is **bent**, as shown at right. As in NH_3, the bond angles in H_2O are smaller (104.5°) than the ideal tetrahedral bond angles because of the greater repulsion exerted by the lone pair electrons. The bond angle in H_2O is even smaller than in NH_3 because H_2O has *two* lone pairs of electrons on the central oxygen atom. These lone pairs compress the H_2O bond angle to an even greater extent than in NH_3. In general, electron group repulsions vary as follows:

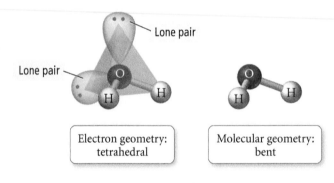

| Electron geometry: tetrahedral | Molecular geometry: bent |

Lone pair–lone pair > Lone pair–bonding pair > Bonding pair–bonding pair

Most repulsive   Least repulsive

We see the effects of this ordering in the progressively smaller bond angles of CH_4, NH_3, and H_2O, as shown in Figure 10.4 ▼. The relative ordering of repulsions also helps to determine the geometry of molecules with five and six electron groups when one or more of those groups are lone pairs, as we shall now see.

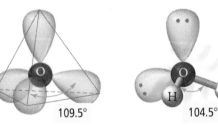

| Ideal tetrahedral geometry | Actual molecular geometry |

Effect of Lone Pairs on Molecular Geometry

| No lone pairs | One lone pair | Two lone pairs |

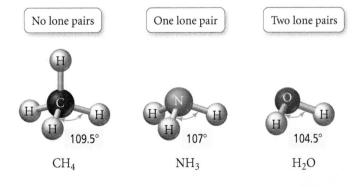

◀ **FIGURE 10.4   The Effect of Lone Pairs on Molecular Geometry**   The bond angles get progressively smaller as the number of lone pairs on the central atom increases from zero in CH_4 to one in NH_3 to two in H_2O.

Five Electron Groups with Lone Pairs

Consider the Lewis structure of SF_4:

$$\ddot{\underset{\displaystyle :\ddot{F}:}{\overset{\displaystyle :\ddot{F}:}{:\ddot{F}-S-\ddot{F}:}}}$$

The central sulfur atom has five electron groups (one lone pair and four bonding pairs). The *electron geometry*, due to the five electron groups, is trigonal bipyramidal. In determining the molecular geometry, notice that the lone pair could occupy either an equatorial position or an axial position within the trigonal bipyramidal electron geometry. Which position is most favorable? To answer this question, we must consider that, as we have just seen, lone pair–bonding pair repulsions are greater than bonding pair–bonding pair repulsions. Consequently, the lone pair should occupy the position that minimizes its interaction with the bonding pairs. If the lone pair were in an axial position, it would have three 90° interactions with bonding pairs. In an equatorial position, however, it has only two 90° interactions. Consequently, the lone pair occupies an equatorial position. The resulting molecular geometry is called **seesaw**, because it resembles a seesaw (or teeter-totter).

> The seesaw molecular geometry is sometimes called an *irregular tetrahedron*.

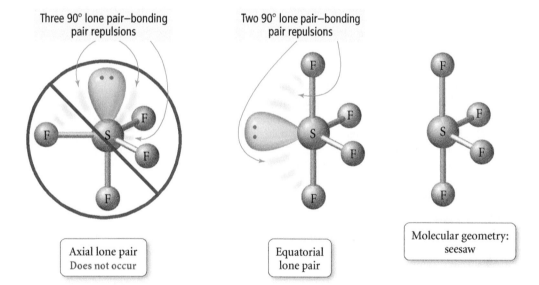

Three 90° lone pair–bonding pair repulsions

Two 90° lone pair–bonding pair repulsions

Axial lone pair
Does not occur

Equatorial lone pair

Molecular geometry: seesaw

When two of the five electron groups around the central atom are lone pairs, as in BrF_3, the lone pairs occupy two of the three equatorial positions—again minimizing 90° interactions with bonding pairs and also avoiding a lone pair–lone pair 90° repulsion. The resulting molecular geometry is **T-shaped**.

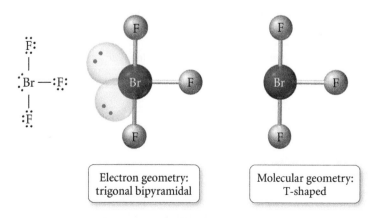

$$\overset{\displaystyle :\ddot{F}:}{\underset{\displaystyle :\ddot{F}:}{:\ddot{B}r-\ddot{F}:}}$$

Electron geometry: trigonal bipyramidal

Molecular geometry: T-shaped

When three of the five electron groups around the central atom are lone pairs, as in XeF_2, the lone pairs occupy all three of the equatorial positions and the resulting molecular geometry is linear.

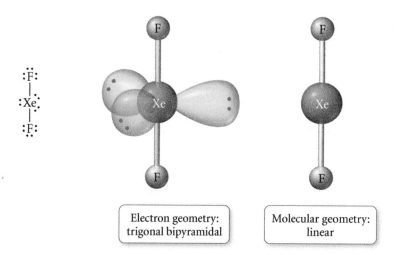

Electron geometry:
trigonal bipyramidal

Molecular geometry:
linear

Six Electron Groups with Lone Pairs

The Lewis structure of BrF_5, is shown below. The central bromine atom has six electron groups (one lone pair and five bonding pairs). The electron geometry, due to the six electron groups, is octahedral. Since all six positions in the octahedral geometry are equivalent, the lone pair can be situated in any one of these positions. The resulting molecular geometry is **square pyramidal**.

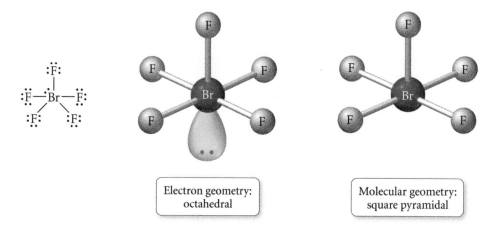

Electron geometry:
octahedral

Molecular geometry:
square pyramidal

When two of the six electron groups around the central atom are lone pairs, as in XeF_4, the lone pairs occupy positions across from one another (to minimize lone pair–lone pair repulsions), and the resulting molecular geometry is **square planar**.

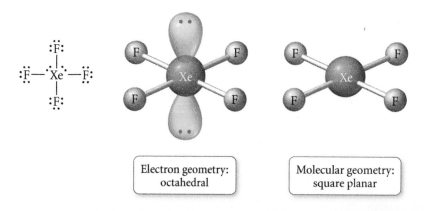

Electron geometry:
octahedral

Molecular geometry:
square planar

TABLE 10.1 Electron and Molecular Geometries

Electron Groups*	Bonding Groups	Lone Pairs	Electron Geometry	Molecular Geometry	Approximate Bond Angles	Example
2	2	0	Linear	Linear	180°	$:\ddot{O}=C=\ddot{O}:$
3	3	0	Trigonal planar	Trigonal planar	120°	
3	2	1	Trigonal planar	Bent	<120°	$:\ddot{O}=\ddot{S}-\ddot{O}:$
4	4	0	Tetrahedral	Tetrahedral	109.5°	
4	3	1	Tetrahedral	Trigonal pyramidal	<109.5°	H—N̈—H
4	2	2	Tetrahedral	Bent	<109.5°	H—$\ddot{O}$—H
5	5	0	Trigonal bipyramidal	Trigonal bipyramidal	120° (equatorial) 90° (axial)	
5	4	1	Trigonal bipyramidal	Seesaw	<120° (equatorial) <90° (axial)	
5	3	2	Trigonal bipyramidal	T-shaped	<90°	
5	2	3	Trigonal bipyramidal	Linear	180°	$:\ddot{F}-Xe-\ddot{F}:$
6	6	0	Octahedral	Octahedral	90°	
6	5	1	Octahedral	Square pyramidal	<90°	
6	4	2	Octahedral	Square planar	90°	

*Count only electron groups around the central atom. Each of the following is considered one electron group: a lone pair, a single bond, a double bond, a triple bond, or a single electron.

Conceptual Connection 10.2 Lone Pair Electrons and Molecular Geometry

Suppose that a molecule with six electron groups were confined to two dimensions and therefore had a hexagonal planar electron geometry. If two of the six groups were lone pairs, where would they be located?

(a) positions 1 and 2   **(b)** positions 1 and 3   **(c)** positions 1 and 4

ANSWER: **(c)** Positions 1 and 4 would put the greatest distance between the lone pairs and minimize lone pair–lone pair repulsions.

Summarizing VSEPR Theory:

▶ The geometry of a molecule is determined by the number of electron groups on the central atom (or on all interior atoms, if there is more than one).

▶ The number of electron groups can be determined from the Lewis structure of the molecule. If the Lewis structure contains resonance structures, use any one of the resonance structures to determine the number of electron groups.

▶ Each of the following counts as a single electron group: a lone pair, a single bond, a double bond, a triple bond, or a single electron.

▶ The geometry of the electron groups is determined by their repulsions as summarized in Table 10.1. In general, electron group repulsions vary as follows:

Lone pair–lone pair > lone pair–bonding pair > bonding pair–bonding pair

▶ Bond angles can vary from the idealized angles because double and triple bonds occupy more space than single bonds (they are bulkier even though they are shorter), and lone pairs occupy more space than bonding groups. The presence of lone pairs will usually make bond angles smaller than the ideal angle for the particular geometry.

 Conceptual Connection 10.3 Molecular Geometry and Electron Groups

Which statement is *always* true according to VSEPR theory?

(a) The shape of a molecule is determined only by repulsions among bonding electron groups.

(b) The shape of a molecule is determined only by repulsions among nonbonding electron groups.

(c) The shape of a molecule is determined by the polarity of its bonds.

(d) The shape of a molecule is determined by repulsions among all electron groups on the central atom (or interior atoms, if there is more than one).

ANSWER: **(d)** All electron groups on the central atom (or interior atoms, if there is more than one) determine the shape of a molecule according to VSEPR theory.

10.4 VSEPR Theory: Predicting Molecular Geometries

To determine the geometry of a molecule, follow the procedure on the next page. As in other examples, we provide the steps in the left column and provide two examples of applying the steps in the center and right columns.

PROCEDURE FOR... **Predicting Molecular Geometries**	EXAMPLE 10.2 **Predicting Molecular Geometries** Predict the geometry and bond angles of PCl_3.	EXAMPLE 10.3 **Predicting Molecular Geometries** Predict the geometry and bond angles of ICl_4^-.
1. *Draw a Lewis structure for the molecule*.	PCl_3 has 26 valence electrons.	ICl_4^- has 36 valence electrons.
2. *Determine the total number of electron groups around the central atom.* Lone pairs, single bonds, double bonds, triple bonds, and single electrons each count as one group.	The central atom (P) has four electron groups.	The central atom (I) has six electron groups.
3. *Determine the number of bonding groups and the number of lone pairs around the central atom.* These should sum to the result from step 2. Bonding groups include single bonds, double bonds, and triple bonds.	Three of the four electron groups around P are bonding groups and one is a lone pair.	Four of the six electron groups around I are bonding groups and two are lone pairs.
4. *Use Table 10.1 to determine the electron geometry and molecular geometry.* If no lone pairs are present around the central atom, the bond angles will be that of the ideal geometry. If lone pairs are present, the bond angles may be smaller than the ideal geometry.	The electron geometry is tetrahedral (four electron groups) and the molecular geometry—the shape of the molecule—is *trigonal pyramidal* (three bonding groups and one lone pair). Because of the presence of a lone pair, the bond angles are less than 109.5°.	The electron geometry is octahedral (six electron groups) and the molecular geometry—the shape of the molecule—is *square planar* (four bonding groups and two lone pairs). Even though lone pairs are present, the bond angles are 90° because the lone pairs are symmetrically arranged and do not compress the I—Cl bond angles.

FOR PRACTICE 10.2
Predict the molecular geometry and bond angle of ClNO.

FOR PRACTICE 10.3
Predict the molecular geometry of I_3^-.

Representing Molecular Geometries on Paper

Since molecular geometries are three-dimensional, they are often difficult to represent on two-dimensional paper. Many chemists use the following notation for bonds to indicate three-dimensional structures on two-dimensional paper.

Straight line
Bond in plane of paper

llllll···

Hatched wedge
Bond going into the page

◄

Solid wedge
Bond coming out of the page

Some examples of the molecular geometries used in this book are shown below using this notation.

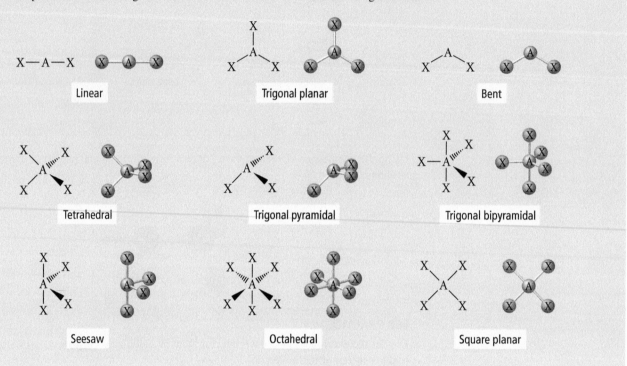

Predicting the Shapes of Larger Molecules

Larger molecules may have two or more *interior* atoms. When predicting the shapes of these molecules, the principles we just covered must be applied to each interior atom. Consider glycine, an amino acid found in many proteins (such as those involved in taste that we discussed in Section 10.1). Glycine, shown here, contains four interior atoms: one nitrogen atom, two carbon atoms, and an oxygen atom. To determine the shape of glycine, we must determine the geometry about each interior atom as follows:

Atom	Number of Electron Groups	Number of Lone Pairs	Molecular Geometry
Nitrogen	4	1	Trigonal pyramidal
Leftmost carbon	4	0	Tetrahedral
Rightmost carbon	3	0	Trigonal planar
Oxygen	4	2	Bent

Using the geometries of each of these, we can determine the entire three-dimensional shape of the molecule as shown here.

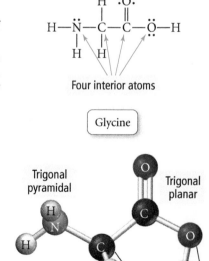

Glycine

EXAMPLE 10.4 Predicting the Shape of Larger Molecules

Predict the geometry about each interior atom in methanol (CH_3OH) and make a sketch of the molecule.

SOLUTION

Begin by drawing the Lewis structure of CH_3OH. CH_3OH contains two interior atoms: one carbon atom and one oxygen atom. To determine the shape of methanol, determine the geometry about each interior atom as follows:

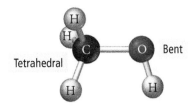

Atom	Number of Electron Groups	Number of Lone Pairs	Molecular Geometry
Carbon	4	0	Tetrahedral
Oxygen	4	2	Bent

Using the geometries of each of these, draw a three-dimensional sketch of the molecule as shown here.

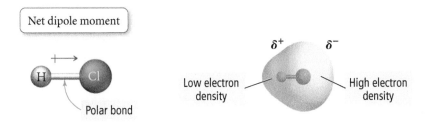

FOR PRACTICE 10.4

Predict the geometry about each interior atom in acetic acid ($H_3C—\overset{\displaystyle O}{\overset{\displaystyle \|}{C}}—OH$) and make a sketch of the molecule.

10.5 Molecular Shape and Polarity

In Chapter 9, we discussed polar bonds. Entire molecules can also be polar, depending on their shape and the nature of their bonds. For example, if a diatomic molecule has a polar bond, the molecule as a whole will be polar.

The figure above is an electron density model of HCl. Yellow indicates moderately high electron density, red indicates very high electron density, and blue indicates low electron density. Notice that the electron density is greater around the more electronegative atom (chlorine). Thus the molecule itself is polar. If the bond in a diatomic molecule is *nonpolar*, the molecule as a whole will be *nonpolar*.

In polyatomic molecules, the presence of polar bonds may or may not result in a polar molecule, depending on the molecular geometry. If the molecular geometry is such

that the dipole moments of individual polar bonds sum together to a net dipole moment, then the molecule will be polar. But, if the molecular geometry is such that the dipole moments of the individual polar bonds cancel each other (that is, sum to zero), then the molecule will be nonpolar. It all depends on the geometry of the molecule. Consider carbon dioxide:

$$:\ddot{O}=C=\ddot{O}:$$

Each $C=O$ bond in CO_2 is polar because oxygen and carbon have significantly different electronegativities (3.5 and 2.5, respectively). However, since CO_2 is a linear molecule, the polar bonds directly oppose one another and the dipole moment of one bond exactly opposes the dipole moment of the other—the two dipole moments sum to zero and the *molecule* is nonpolar. Dipole moments can cancel each other because they are *vector quantities*; they have both a magnitude and a direction. Think of each polar bond as a vector, pointing in the direction of the more electronegative atom. The length of the vector is proportional to the electronegativity difference between the bonding atoms. In CO_2, we have two identical vectors pointing in exactly opposite directions—the vectors sum to zero, much as +1 and −1 sum to zero:

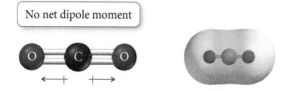

Notice that the electron density model shows regions of moderately high electron density (yellow) positioned symmetrically on either end of the molecule with a region of low electron density (blue) located in the middle.

In contrast, consider water:

$$H-\ddot{O}-H$$

The $O-H$ bonds in water are also polar; oxygen and hydrogen have electronegativities of 3.5 and 2.1, respectively. However, the water molecule is not linear but bent, so the two dipole moments do not sum to zero. If we imagine each bond as a vector pointing toward oxygen (the more electronegative atom) we see that, because of the angle between the vectors, they do not cancel, but sum to an overall vector or a net dipole moment (shown by the dashed arrow).

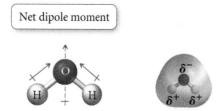

See the box on p. 414 for an explanation of how to add vectors.

The electron density model shows a region of very high electron density at the oxygen end of the molecule. Consequently, water is a polar molecule. Table 10.2 (p. 415) summarizes whether or not various common geometries result in polar molecules.

Summarizing Molecular Shape and Polarity:

▶ *Draw a Lewis structure for the molecule and determine the molecular geometry.*

▶ *Determine whether the molecule contains polar bonds.* A bond is polar if the two bonding atoms have sufficiently different electronegativities (see Figure 9.8). If the molecule contains polar bonds, superimpose a vector, pointing toward the more electronegative atom, on each bond. Make the length of the vector proportional to the electronegativity difference between the bonding atoms.

▶ *Determine whether the polar bonds add together to form a net dipole moment.* Sum the vectors corresponding to the polar bonds together. If the vectors sum to zero, the molecule is nonpolar. If the vectors sum to a net vector, the molecule is polar.

Vector Addition

As discussed previously, we can determine whether a molecule is polar by summing the vectors associated with the dipole moments of all the polar bonds in the molecule. If the vectors sum to zero, the molecule will be nonpolar. If they sum to a net vector, the molecule will be polar. In this box, we show how to add vectors together in one dimension and in two or more dimensions.

Example 3

$$-5 \qquad +5 \qquad\qquad = \qquad\qquad 0$$

$$\vec{A} \qquad \vec{B} \qquad\qquad\qquad\qquad \text{(the vectors exactly cancel)}$$

$$\vec{R} = \vec{A} + \vec{B}$$

One Dimension

To add two vectors that lie on the same line, assign one direction as positive. Vectors pointing in that direction have positive magnitudes. Consider vectors pointing in the opposite direction to have negative magnitudes. Then sum the vectors (always remembering to include their signs), as shown in the following examples.

Two or More Dimensions

To add two vectors, draw a parallelogram in which the two vectors form two adjacent sides. Draw the other two sides of the parallelogram parallel to and the same length as the two original vectors. Draw the resultant vector beginning at the origin and extending to the far corner of the parallelogram.

Example 1

$$+5 \qquad +5 \qquad\qquad = \qquad\qquad +10$$

$$\vec{A} \qquad \vec{B} \qquad\qquad\qquad\qquad \vec{R} = \vec{A} + \vec{B}$$

Example 2

$$-5 \qquad +10 \qquad\qquad = \qquad\qquad +5$$

$$\vec{A} \qquad \vec{B} \qquad\qquad\qquad\qquad \vec{R} = \vec{A} + \vec{B}$$

Example 4

$$\vec{R} = \vec{A} + \vec{B}$$

Example 5

$$\vec{R} = \vec{A} + \vec{B}$$

To add three or more vectors, add two of them together first, and then add the third vector to the result.

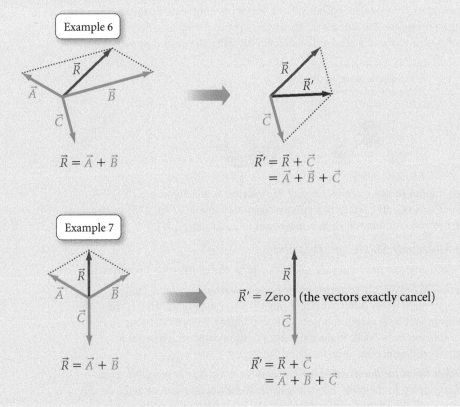

Example 6

$$\vec{R} = \vec{A} + \vec{B}$$

$$\vec{R}' = \vec{R} + \vec{C}$$
$$= \vec{A} + \vec{B} + \vec{C}$$

Example 7

$$\vec{R} = \vec{A} + \vec{B}$$

$$\vec{R}' = \text{Zero} \quad \text{(the vectors exactly cancel)}$$

$$\vec{R}' = \vec{R} + \vec{C}$$
$$= \vec{A} + \vec{B} + \vec{C}$$

TABLE 10.2 Common Cases of Adding Dipole Moments to Determine whether a Molecule Is Polar

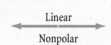

Linear

Nonpolar

The dipole moments of two identical polar bonds pointing in opposite directions will cancel. The molecule is nonpolar.

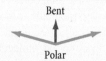

Bent

Polar

The dipole moments of two polar bonds with an angle of less than 180° between them will not cancel. The resultant dipole moment vector is shown in red. The molecule is polar.

Trigonal planar

Nonpolar

The dipole moments of three identical polar bonds at 120° from each other will cancel. The molecule is nonpolar.

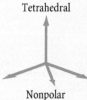

Tetrahedral

Nonpolar

The dipole moments of four identical polar bonds in a tetrahedral arrangement (109.5° from each other) will cancel. The molecule is nonpolar.

Trigonal pyramidal

Polar

The dipole moments of three polar bonds in a trigonal pyramidal arrangement (109.5° from each other) will not cancel. The resultant dipole moment vector is shown in red. The molecule is polar.

Note: In all cases where the dipoles of two or more polar bonds cancel, the bonds are assumed to be identical. If one or more of the bonds are different from the other(s), the dipoles will not cancel and the molecule will be polar.

EXAMPLE 10.5 Determining whether a Molecule Is Polar

Determine whether NH_3 is polar.

SOLUTION

Draw a Lewis structure for the molecule and determine the molecular geometry.	H | H—N—H .. The Lewis structure has three bonding groups and one lone pair about the central atom. Therefore the molecular geometry is trigonal pyramidal.
Determine whether the molecule contains polar bonds. Sketch the molecule and superimpose a vector for each polar bond. The relative length of each vector should be proportional to the electronegativity difference between the atoms forming each bond. The vector should point in the direction of the more electronegative atom.	The electronegativities of nitrogen and hydrogen are 3.0 and 2.1, respectively. Therefore the bonds are polar.
Determine whether the polar bonds add together to form a net dipole moment. Examine the symmetry of the vectors (representing dipole moments) and determine whether they cancel each other or sum to a net dipole moment.	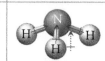 The three dipole moments sum to a net dipole moment. The molecule is polar.

FOR PRACTICE 10.5

Determine whether CF_4 is polar.

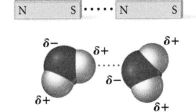

Opposite magnetic poles attract one another.

Opposite partial charges on molecules attract one another.

▲ **FIGURE 10.5 Interaction of Polar Molecules** The north pole of one magnet attracts the south pole of another magnet. In an analogous way, the positively charged end of one molecule attracts the negatively charged end of another (although the forces involved are different). As a result of this electrical attraction, polar molecules interact strongly with one another.

Polar and nonpolar molecules have different properties. Water and oil do not mix, for example, because water molecules are polar and the molecules that compose oil are generally nonpolar. Polar molecules interact strongly with other polar molecules because the positive end of one molecule is attracted to the negative end of another, just as the south pole of a magnet is attracted to the north pole of another magnet (Figure 10.5 ◄). A mixture of polar and nonpolar molecules is similar to a mixture of small magnetic particles and nonmagnetic ones. The magnetic particles (which are like polar molecules) clump together, excluding the nonmagnetic particles (which are like nonpolar molecules) and separating into distinct regions.

Oil is nonpolar.

Water is polar.

▲ Oil and water do not mix because water molecules are polar and the molecules that compose oil are nonpolar.

▲ A mixture of polar and nonpolar molecules is analogous to a mixture of magnetic marbles (opaque) and nonmagnetic marbles (transparent). As with the magnetic marbles, mutual attraction causes polar molecules to clump together, excluding the nonpolar molecules.

 CHEMISTRY IN YOUR DAY How Soap Works

Imagine eating a greasy cheeseburger with both hands and without napkins. By the end of the meal, your hands are coated with grease and oil. If you try to wash them with only water, they remain greasy. However, if you add a little soap, the grease washes away. Why? As we just learned, water molecules are polar and the molecules that compose grease and oil are nonpolar. As a result, water and grease do not mix.

The molecules that compose soap, however, have a special structure that allows them to interact strongly with both water and grease. One end of a soap molecule is polar while the other end is nonpolar.

The nonpolar end is a long hydrocarbon chain. Hydrocarbons are always nonpolar because the electronegativity difference between carbon and hydrogen is small, and because the tetrahedral arrangement about each carbon atom tends to cancel any small dipole moments of individual bonds. The polar head of a soap molecule—usually, though not always, ionic—strongly attracts water molecules, while the nonpolar tail interacts more strongly with grease and oil molecules (we examine the nature of these interactions in Chapter 11). Thus, soap acts as a sort of molecular liaison, one end interacting with water and the other end interacting with grease. Soap allows water and grease to mix, removing the grease from your hands and washing it down the drain.

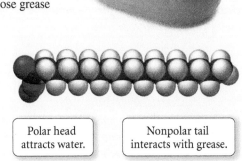

Polar head attracts water.

Nonpolar tail interacts with grease.

$CH_3(CH_2)_{11}OCH_2CH_2OH$

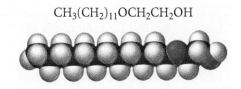

Question

Consider the detergent molecule at right. Which end do you think is polar? Which end is nonpolar?

10.6 Valence Bond Theory: Orbital Overlap as a Chemical Bond

In Lewis theory, we use "dots" to represent electrons as they are transferred or shared between bonding atoms. We know from quantum-mechanical theory, however, that such a treatment is an oversimplification. More advanced bonding theories treat electrons in a quantum-mechanical manner. In fact, these more advanced theories are actually extensions of quantum mechanics, applied to molecules. Although a detailed quantitative treatment of these theories is beyond the scope of this book, we introduce them in a *qualitative* manner in the sections that follow. Keep in mind, however, that modern *quantitative* approaches to chemical bonding using these theories can accurately predict many of the properties of molecules—such as bond lengths, bond strengths, molecular geometries, and dipole moments—that we have been discussing in this book.

The simpler of the two more advanced bonding theories is called **valence bond theory**. In valence bond theory, electrons reside in quantum-mechanical orbitals localized on individual atoms. In many cases, these orbitals are simply the standard *s*, *p*, *d*, and *f* atomic orbitals that we learned about in Chapter 7. In other cases, these orbitals are *hybridized atomic orbitals*, a kind of blend or combination of two or more standard atomic orbitals.

When two atoms approach each other, the electrons and nucleus of one atom interact with the electrons and nucleus of the other atom. In valence bond theory, we calculate the effect of these interactions on the energies of the electrons in the atomic orbitals. If the energy of the system is lowered because of the interactions, then a chemical bond forms. If the energy of the system is raised by the interactions, then a chemical bond does not form.

The interaction energy is usually calculated as a function of the internuclear distance between the two bonding atoms. For example, Figure 10.6 ▼ shows the calculated interaction energy between two hydrogen atoms as a function of the distance between them. The *y*-axis of the graph is the potential energy of the interaction between the electron and nucleus of one hydrogen atom and the electron and nucleus of the other. The *x*-axis is the separation (or internuclear distance) between the two atoms. As you can see from the graph, when the atoms are far apart (right side of the graph), the interaction energy is nearly zero because the two atoms do not interact to any significant extent. As the atoms get closer, the interaction energy becomes negative. This is a net stabilization that attracts

Valence bond theory is an application of a more general quantum-mechanical approximation method called *perturbation theory*. In perturbation theory, a system (for example, an atom) that is simpler than the actual one, is viewed as being slightly altered (or perturbed) by some additional force or interaction.

Interaction Energy of Two Hydrogen Atoms

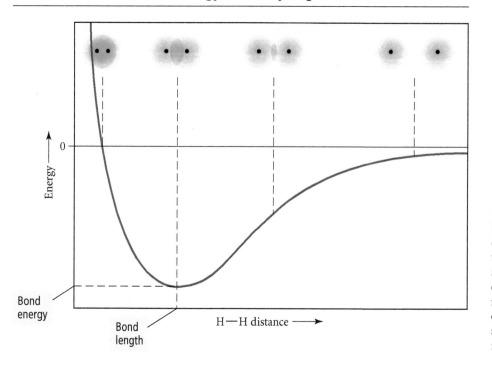

◄ **FIGURE 10.6 Interaction Energy Diagram for H_2**   The potential energy of two hydrogen atoms is lowest when they are separated by a distance that allows their $1s$ orbitals a substantial degree of overlap without too much repulsion between their nuclei. This distance, at which the system is most stable, is the bond length of the H_2 molecule.

one hydrogen atom to the other. If the atoms get too close, however, the interaction energy begins to rise, primarily because of the mutual repulsion of the two positively charged nuclei. The most stable point on the curve occurs at the minimum of the interaction energy—this is the equilibrium bond length. At this distance, the two atomic $1s$ orbitals have a significant amount of overlap and the electrons spend time in the internuclear region where they can interact with both nuclei. The value of the interaction energy at the equilibrium bond distance is the bond energy.

When valence bond theory is applied to a number of atoms and their corresponding molecules, we can make the following general observation: *the interaction energy is usually negative (or stabilizing) when the interacting atomic orbitals contain a total of two electrons that can spin-pair*. Most commonly, the two electrons come from two half-filled orbitals, but in some cases, the two electrons can come from one filled orbital overlapping with a completely empty orbital (this is called a coordinate covalent bond and is covered in more detail in Chapter 24). In other words, when two atoms with half-filled orbitals approach each other, the half-filled orbitals *overlap*—parts of the orbitals occupy the same space—and the electrons occupying them align with opposite spins. This results in a net energy stabilization that constitutes a covalent chemical bond. The resulting geometry of the molecule emerges from the geometry of the overlapping orbitals.

> When *completely filled* orbitals overlap, the interaction energy is positive (or destabilizing) and no bond forms.

Summarizing Valence Bond Theory:

▶ The valence electrons of the atoms in a molecule reside in quantum-mechanical atomic orbitals. The orbitals can be the standard s, p, d, and f orbitals or they may be hybrid combinations of these.

▶ A chemical bond results from the overlap of two half-filled orbitals with spin-pairing of the two valence electrons (or less commonly the overlap of a completely filled orbital with an empty orbital).

▶ The shape of the molecule is determined by the geometry of the overlapping orbitals.

Let's apply the general concepts of valence bond theory to explain bonding in hydrogen sulfide, H_2S. The valence electron configurations of the atoms in the molecule are as follows:

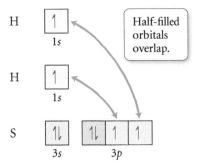

The hydrogen atoms each have one half-filled orbital, and the sulfur atom has two half-filled orbitals. The half-filled orbitals on each hydrogen atom overlap with the two half-filled orbitals on the sulfur atom, forming two chemical bonds:

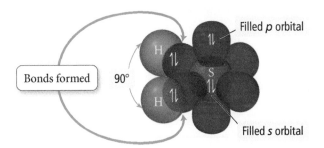

To show the spin-pairing of the electrons in the overlapping orbitals, we superimpose a half-arrow for each electron in each half-filled orbital and show that, within a bond, the electrons are spin-paired (one half-arrow pointing up and the other pointing down). We

also superimpose paired half-arrows in the filled sulfur s and p orbitals to represent the lone pair electrons in those orbitals. (Since those orbitals are full, they are not involved in bonding.)

A quantitative calculation of H_2S using valence bond theory yields bond energies, bond lengths, and bond angles. In our qualitative treatment, we simply show how orbital overlap leads to bonding and make a rough sketch of the molecule based on the overlapping orbitals. Notice that, because the overlapping orbitals on the central atom (sulfur) are p orbitals, and because p orbitals are oriented at 90° to one another, the predicted bond angle is 90°. The actual bond angle in H_2S is 92°. In the case of H_2S, a simple valence bond treatment matches well with the experimentally measured bond angle (in contrast to VSEPR theory, which predicts a bond angle of less than 109.5°).

 Conceptual Connection 10.4   What Is a Chemical Bond, Part I?

The answer to the question, *what is a chemical bond*, depends on the bonding model. Answer these three questions:

(a) What is a covalent chemical bond according to Lewis theory?

(b) What is a covalent chemical bond according to valence bond theory?

(c) Why are the answers different?

ANSWER: (a) In Lewis theory, a covalent chemical bond is the sharing of electrons (represented by dots). **(b)** In valence bond theory, a covalent chemical bond is the overlap of half-filled atomic orbitals. **(c)** The answers are different because Lewis theory and valence bond theory are different *models* for chemical bonding. They both make useful and often similar predictions, but the assumptions of each model are different, and so are their respective descriptions of a chemical bond.

10.7 Valence Bond Theory: Hybridization of Atomic Orbitals

Although the overlap of half-filled *standard* atomic orbitals adequately explains the bonding in H_2S, it cannot adequately explain the bonding in many other molecules. For example, suppose we try to explain the bonding between hydrogen and carbon using the same approach. The valence electron configurations of H and C are as follows:

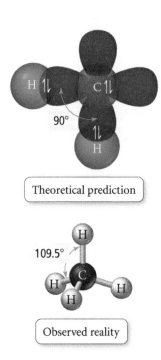

Theoretical prediction

Observed reality

Carbon has only two half-filled orbitals and should therefore form only two bonds with two hydrogen atoms. We would therefore predict that carbon and hydrogen should form a molecule with the formula CH_2 and with a bond angle of 90° (corresponding to the angle between any two p orbitals).

However, from experiments, we know that the stable compound formed from carbon and hydrogen is CH_4 (methane), with bond angles of 109.5°. The experimental reality is different from our simple prediction in two ways. First, carbon forms bonds to four hydrogen atoms, not two. Second, the bond angles are much larger than the angle between two p orbitals. Valence bond theory accounts for the bonding in CH_4 and many other polyatomic molecules by incorporating an additional concept called *orbital hybridization*.

So far, we have assumed that the overlapping orbitals that form chemical bonds are simply the standard s, p, or d atomic orbitals. Valence bond theory treats the electrons in a molecule as if they occupied these standard atomic orbitals, but this is a major oversimplification. The concept of hybridization in valence bond theory is essentially a step toward recognizing that *the orbitals in a molecule are not necessarily the same as the orbitals in an atom*. **Hybridization** is a mathematical procedure in which the standard atomic orbitals are combined to form new atomic orbitals called **hybrid orbitals** that

In Section 10.8, we examine another theory called *molecular orbital theory*, which treats electrons in a molecule as occupying orbitals that belong to the molecule as a whole.

As we saw in Chapter 9, the word *hybrid* comes from breeding. A *hybrid* is an offspring of two animals or plants of different standard races or breeds. Similarly, a hybrid orbital is a product of mixing two or more standard atomic orbitals.

correspond more closely to the actual distribution of electrons in chemically bonded atoms. Hybrid orbitals are still localized on individual atoms, but they have different shapes and energies from those of standard atomic orbitals.

Why do we hypothesize that electrons in some molecules occupy hybrid orbitals? In valence bond theory, a chemical bond is the overlap of two orbitals that together contain two electrons. The greater the overlap, the stronger the bond and the lower the energy. In hybrid orbitals, the electron probability density is more concentrated in a single directional lobe, allowing greater overlap with the orbitals of other atoms. Hybrid orbitals *minimize* the energy of the molecule by *maximizing* the orbital overlap in a bond.

Hybridization, however, is not a free lunch—in most cases it actually costs some energy. So hybridization occurs only to the degree that the energy payback through bond formation is large. In general, therefore, the more bonds that an atom forms, the greater the tendency of its orbitals to hybridize. Central or interior atoms, which form the most bonds, have the greatest tendency to hybridize. Terminal atoms, which form the fewest bonds, have the least tendency to hybridize. *In this book, we focus on the hybridization of interior atoms and assume that all terminal atoms—those bonding to only one other atom—are unhybridized.* Hybridization is particularly important in carbon, which tends to form four bonds in its compounds and therefore always hybridizes.

In a more detailed treatment, hybridization is not an all-or-nothing process—it can occur to varying degrees that are not always easy to predict. We saw earlier, for example, that sulfur does not hybridize very much in forming H_2S.

Although we cannot examine the procedure for obtaining hybrid orbitals in mathematical detail here, we can make the following general statements regarding hybridization:

• The *number of standard atomic orbitals* added together always equals the *number of hybrid orbitals* formed. The total number of orbitals is conserved.

• The *particular combinations* of standard atomic orbitals added together determines the *shapes and energies* of the hybrid orbitals formed.

• The *particular type of hybridization that occurs* is the one that yields the *lowest overall energy for the molecule*. Since actual energy calculations are beyond the scope of this book, we will use electron geometries as determined by VSEPR theory to predict the type of hybridization.

sp^3 Hybridization

We can account for the tetrahedral geometry in CH_4 by the hybridization of the one $2s$ orbital and the three $2p$ orbitals on the carbon atom. The four new orbitals that result, called sp^3 hybrids, are shown in the following energy diagram:

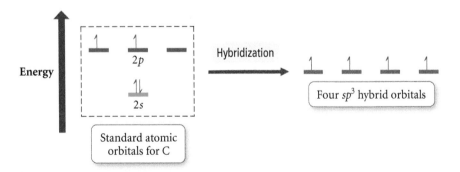

The notation "sp^3" indicates that the hybrid orbitals are mixtures of one s orbital and three p orbitals. Notice that the hybrid orbitals all have the same energy—they are degenerate. The shapes of the sp^3 hybrid orbitals are shown in Figure 10.7 ►. The four hybrid orbitals are arranged in a tetrahedral geometry with 109.5° angles between them.

We can write an orbital diagram for carbon using these hybrid orbitals:

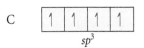

Formation of sp^3 Hybrid Orbitals

One s orbital and three p orbitals combine to form four sp^3 orbitals.

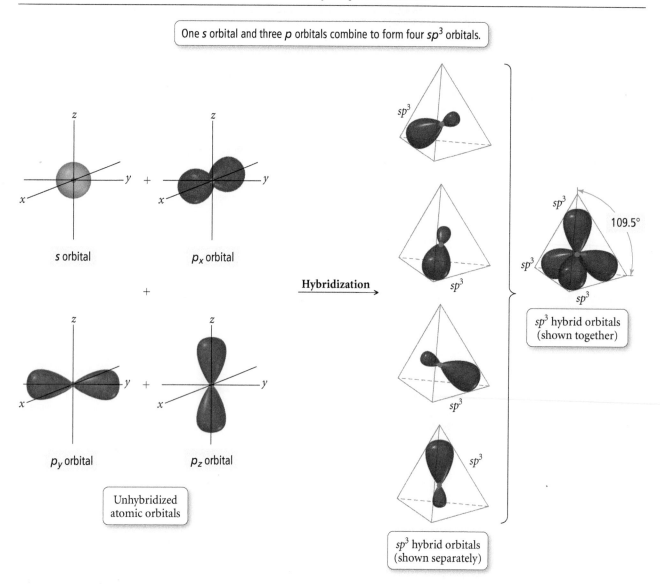

Hybridization

sp^3 hybrid orbitals (shown together)

sp^3 hybrid orbitals (shown separately)

s orbital

p_x orbital

p_y orbital

p_z orbital

Unhybridized atomic orbitals

109.5°

▲ **FIGURE 10.7 sp^3 Hybridization** One s orbital and three p orbitals combine to form four sp^3 hybrid orbitals.

Carbon's four valence electrons occupy the orbitals singly with parallel spins as dictated by Hund's rule. With this electron configuration, carbon has four half-filled orbitals and can form four bonds with four hydrogen atoms:

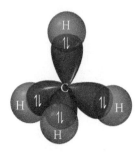

The geometry of the *overlapping orbitals* (the hybrids) is tetrahedral, with angles of 109.5° between the orbitals, so the *resulting geometry of the molecule* is tetrahedral, with 109.5° bond angles, in agreement with the experimentally measured geometry of CH_4 and with the predicted VSEPR geometry.

Hybridized orbitals readily form chemical bonds because they tend to maximize overlap with other orbitals. However, if the central atom of a molecule contains lone pairs, hybrid orbitals can also accommodate them. For example, the nitrogen orbitals in ammonia are sp^3 hybrids. Three of the hybrids are involved in bonding with three hydrogen atoms, but the fourth hybrid contains a lone pair. The presence of the lone pair, however, does lower the tendency of nitrogen's orbitals to hybridize. (Remember that the tendency to hybridize increases with the number of bonds formed.) Therefore the bond angle in NH_3 is 107°, a bit closer to the unhybridized p orbital bond angle of 90°.

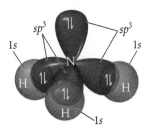

sp^2 Hybridization and Double Bonds

In valence bond theory, the particular hybridization scheme to follow (sp^2 versus sp^3 for example) for a given molecule is determined computationally, which is beyond our scope. In this book, we will determine the particular hybridization scheme from the VSEPR geometry of the molecule, as shown later in this section.

Hybridization of one s and two p orbitals results in three sp^2 hybrids and one leftover unhybridized p orbital.

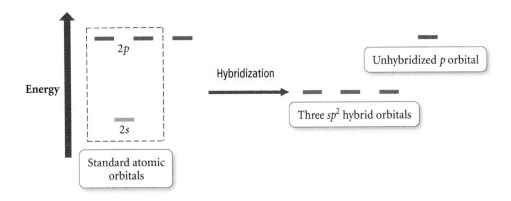

The notation "sp^2" indicates that the hybrids are mixtures of one s orbital and two p orbitals. The shapes of the sp^2 hybrid orbitals are shown in Figure 10.8 ▶. Notice that the three hybrid orbitals have a trigonal planar geometry with 120° angles between them. The unhybridized p orbital is oriented perpendicular to the three hybridized orbitals.

As an example of a molecule with sp^2 hybrid orbitals, consider H_2CO. The unhybridized valence electron configurations of each of the atoms are as follows:

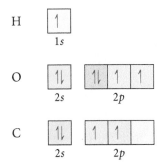

Carbon is the central atom and the hybridization of its orbitals is sp^2:

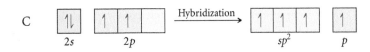

Formation of sp^2 Hybrid Orbitals

One s orbital and two p orbitals combine to form three sp^2 orbitals.

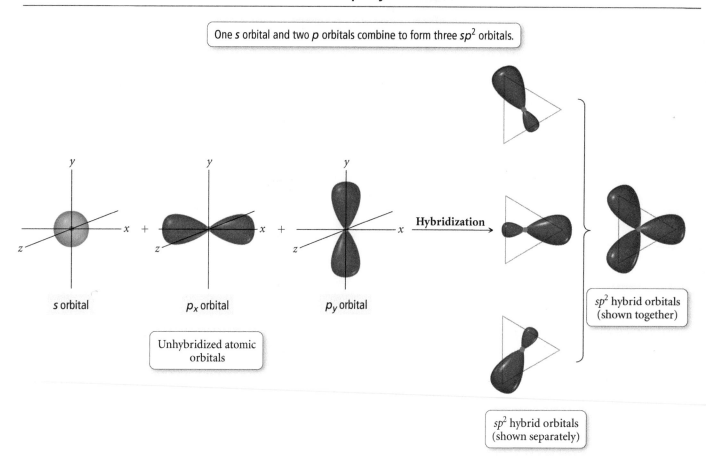

s orbital $\quad+\quad$ p_x orbital $\quad+\quad$ p_y orbital $\quad$ Hybridization $\longrightarrow$

Unhybridized atomic orbitals

sp^2 hybrid orbitals (shown together)

sp^2 hybrid orbitals (shown separately)

▲ **FIGURE 10.8** sp^2 **Hybridization** One s orbital and two p orbitals combine to form three sp^2 hybrid orbitals. One p orbital (not shown) remains unhybridized.

Each of the sp^2 orbitals is half-filled. The remaining electron occupies the leftover p orbital, even though it is slightly higher in energy. We can now see that the carbon atom has four half-filled orbitals and can therefore form four bonds: two with two hydrogen atoms and two (a double bond) with the oxygen atom. We draw the molecule and the overlapping orbitals as follows:

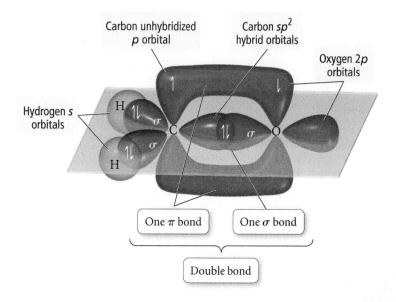

Carbon unhybridized p orbital

Carbon sp^2 hybrid orbitals

Oxygen $2p$ orbitals

Hydrogen s orbitals

One π bond

One σ bond

Double bond

▶ FIGURE 10.9 **Sigma and Pi Bonding**
When orbitals overlap side-by-side, the result is a π bond. When orbitals overlap end-to-end, they form a σ bond. Two atoms can form only one sigma bond. A single bond is a sigma bond; a double bond consists of a sigma bond and a pi bond; a triple bond consists of a sigma bond and two pi bonds.

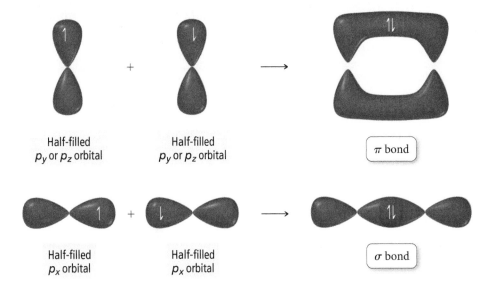

Notice the overlap between the half-filled p orbitals on the carbon and oxygen atoms. When p orbitals overlap this way (side by side) the resulting bond is called a **pi (π) bond**, and the electron density is above and below the internuclear axis. When orbitals overlap end to end, as in all of the rest of the bonds in the molecule, the resulting bond is called a **sigma (σ) bond** (Figure 10.9 ▲). Even though we represent the two electrons in a π bond as two half arrows in the upper lobe, they are actually spread out over both the upper and lower lobes (this is one of the limitations we encounter when we try to represent electrons with arrows). We can now label all the bonds in the molecule using a notation that specifies the type of bond (σ or π) as well as the type of overlapping orbitals. We have included this notation, as well as the Lewis structure of H_2CO for comparison, in the bonding diagram for H_2CO:

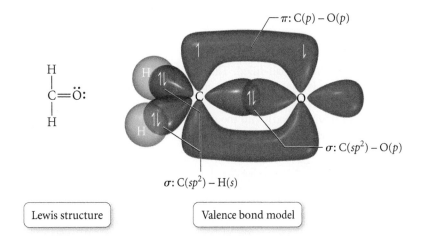

Lewis structure | Valence bond model

Notice the correspondence between valence bond theory and Lewis theory. In both cases, the central carbon atom is forming four bonds: two single bonds and one double bond. However, valence bond theory gives us more insight into the bonds. In the VSEPR model, the double bond between carbon and oxygen consists of two different *kinds* of bonds—one σ and one π—while in Lewis theory the two bonds within the double bond appear identical. *Double bonds in Lewis theory always correspond to one σ and one π bond in valence bond theory.* In general, π bonds are weaker than σ bonds because the side-to-side orbital overlap tends to be less efficient than the end-to-end orbital overlap. Consequently, the π bond in a double bond is generally easier to break than the σ bond. Valence bond theory, as you can see, gives us more insight into the nature of a double bond than Lewis theory.

One—and only one—σ bond forms between any two atoms. Additional bonds must be π bonds.

Valence bond theory also gives us insight into why the rotation about a double bond is severely restricted. Because of the side-by-side overlap of the p orbitals, the π bond must essentially break for rotation to occur (see Chemistry in Your Day: *The Chemistry of Vision* box on the next page). Valence bond theory shows us the types of orbitals involved in the bonding and their shapes. In H_2CO, the sp^2 hybrid orbitals on the central atom are trigonal planar with 120° angles between them, so the resulting predicted geometry of the molecule is trigonal planar with 120° bond angles. The experimentally measured bond angles in H_2CO, as discussed previously, are 121.9° for the HCO bond and 116.2° for the HCH bond angle, close to the predicted values.

Although rotation about a double bond is highly restricted, rotation about a single bond is relatively unrestricted. Consider, for example, the structures of two chlorinated hydrocarbons, 1,2-dichloroethane and 1,2-dichloroethene.

1,2-Dichloroethane

1,2-Dichloroethene

The hybridization of the carbon atoms in 1,2-dichloroethane is sp^3, resulting in relatively free rotation about the sigma single bond. Consequently, there is no difference between the following two structures at room temperature because they quickly interconvert:

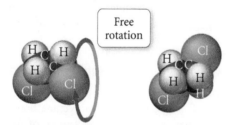

Free rotation

In contrast, rotation about the double bond (sigma + pi) in 1,2-dichloroethene is restricted, so that, at room temperature, 1,2-dichloroethene exists in two forms:

cis-1,2-Dichloroethene   *trans*-1,2-Dichloroethene

CHEMISTRY IN YOUR DAY The Chemistry of Vision

In the human eye, light is detected by a chemical switch involving the breaking and re-forming of a π bond. The back portion of the eye, the retina, is coated with millions of light-sensitive cells called rods and cones. Each of these cells contains proteins that bind a compound called 11-*cis*-retinal, which has the following structure:

11-*cis*-Retinal

When a photon of sufficient energy strikes a rod or cone, it causes the isomerization of 11-*cis*-retinal to all-*trans*-retinal:

all-*trans*-Retinal

The isomerization occurs because visible light contains enough energy to break the π bond between the eleventh and twelfth carbon atom in 11-*cis*-retinal. The σ bond, which is stronger, does not break, allowing the molecule to freely rotate about that bond. The π bond then re-forms with the molecule in the *trans* conformation. The different shape of the resultant all-*trans*-retinal causes conformational changes in the protein to which it is bound. These changes cause an electrical signal to be transmitted to the brain.

Question

What is the hybridization of the eleventh and twelfth carbon atoms in retinal?

These two forms of 1,2-dichloroethene are indeed different compounds with different properties. We distinguish between them with the designations *cis* (meaning "same side") and *trans* (meaning "opposite sides"). Compounds such as these, with the same molecular formula but different structures or different spatial arrangement of atoms, are called *isomers*. Nature can—and does—make different compounds out of the same atoms by arranging the atoms in different ways. Isomerism is common throughout chemistry and especially important in organic chemistry, as we shall see in Chapter 20.

Conceptual Connection 10.5 Single and Double Bonds

In Section 9.10 we learned that double bonds were stronger and shorter than single bonds. For example, a C—C single bond has an average bond energy of 347 kJ/mole while a C=C double bond has an average bond energy of 611 kJ/mole. Use valence bond theory to explain why a double bond is *not* simply twice as strong as a single bond.

ANSWER: Applying valence bond theory, we see that a double bond is actually composed of two different kinds of bonds, one σ and one π. The orbital overlap in the π bond is side-to-side between two *p* orbitals and consequently not as efficient as the end-to-end overlap in a σ bond. Since the strength of the bond depends in part on the degree of overlap between the orbitals and the π bond is weaker than a σ bond, the bond energy of a double bond is less than twice the bond energy of a single σ bond.

sp Hybridization and Triple Bonds

Hybridization of one *s* and one *p* orbital results in two *sp* hybrid orbitals and two leftover unhybridized *p* orbitals.

The shapes of the *sp* hybrid orbitals are shown in Figure 10.10 ▶. Notice that the two *sp* hybrid orbitals are arranged in a linear geometry with a 180° angle between them. The

Formation of *sp* Hybrid Orbitals

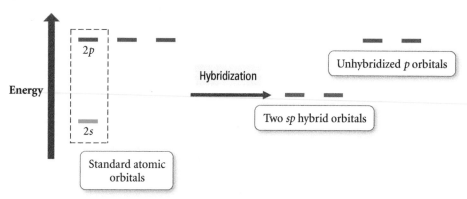

One *s* orbital and one *p* orbital combine to form two *sp* orbitals.

s orbital

p$_x$ orbital

Hybridization

sp hybrid orbitals (shown separately)

sp hybrid orbitals (shown together)

Unhybridized atomic orbitals

◀ **FIGURE 10.10** *sp* **Hybridization** One *s* orbital and one *p* orbital combine to form two *sp* hybrid orbitals. Two *p* orbitals (not shown) remain unhybridized.

unhybridized *p* orbitals are oriented in the plane that is perpendicular to the hybridized *sp* orbitals.

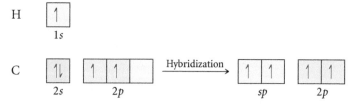

Energy

2*p*

2*s*

Standard atomic orbitals

Hybridization

Unhybridized *p* orbitals

Two *sp* hybrid orbitals

The acetylene molecule, HC≡CH, has *sp* hybrid orbitals. The four valence electrons of carbon can distribute themselves among the two *sp* hybrid oribtals and the two *p* orbitals:

H — 1*s* — ↑

C — 2*s* ↑↓ — 2*p* ↑ ↑ — Hybridization → *sp* ↑ ↑ — 2*p* ↑ ↑

Each carbon atom then has four half-filled orbitals and can form four bonds: one with a hydrogen atom and three (a triple bond) with the other carbon atom. We draw the molecule and the overlapping orbitals as follows:

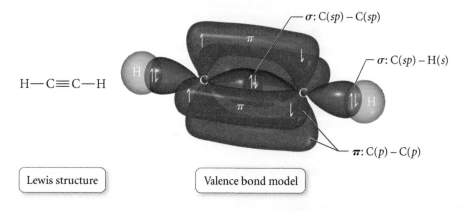

H — C≡C — H

σ: C(*sp*) – C(*sp*)

σ: C(*sp*) – H(*s*)

π: C(*p*) – C(*p*)

Lewis structure

Valence bond model

Notice that the triple bond between the two carbon atoms consists of two π bonds (overlapping p orbitals) and one σ bond (overlapping sp orbitals). The sp orbitals on the carbon atoms are linear with 180° between them, so the resulting geometry of the molecule is linear with 180° bond angles, in agreement with the experimentally measured geometry of HC≡CH, and also in agreement with the prediction of VSEPR theory.

sp^3d and sp^3d^2 Hybridization

Recall that, according to Lewis theory, elements occurring in the third period of the periodic table (or below) can exhibit expanded octets (see Section 9.9). The equivalent concept in valence bond theory is hybridization involving the d orbitals. For third-period elements, the $3d$ orbitals become involved in hybridization because their energies are close to the energies of the $3s$ and $3p$ orbitals. The hybridization of one s orbital, three p orbitals, and one d orbital results in sp^3d hybrid orbitals, as shown in Figure 10.11a ▼. The five sp^3d hybrid orbitals have a trigonal bipyramidal arrangement, as shown in Figure 10.11b ▼. As an example of sp^3d hybridization, consider arsenic pentafluoride, AsF_5. The arsenic atom bonds to five fluorine atoms by overlap between the sp^3d hybrid orbitals on arsenic and p orbitals on the fluorine atoms, as shown here:

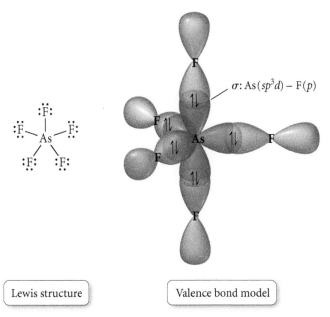

$\sigma: As(sp^3d) - F(p)$

Lewis structure

Valence bond model

The sp^3d orbitals on the arsenic atom are trigonal bipyramidal, so the molecular geometry is trigonal bipyramidal.

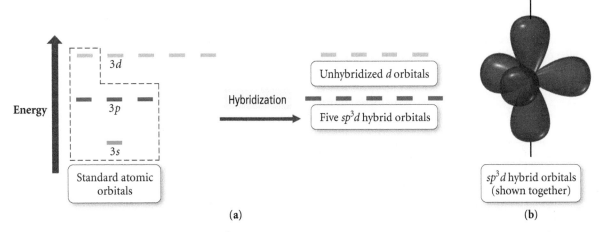

(a)

(b)

▲ **FIGURE 10.11 sp^3d Hybridization**   One s orbital, three p orbitals, and one d orbital combine to form five sp^3d hybrid orbitals.

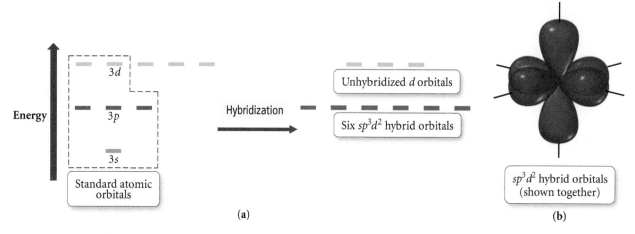

(a)   **(b)**

▲ **FIGURE 10.12 sp^3d^2 Hybridization**   One s orbital, three p orbitals, and two d orbitals combine to form six sp^3d^2 hybrid orbitals.

The hybridization of one s orbital, three p orbitals, and *two d* orbitals results in sp^3d^2 hybrid orbitals, as shown in Figure 10.12a ▲. The six sp^3d^2 hybrid orbitals have an octahedral geometry, shown in Figure 10.12b ▲. As an example of sp^3d^2 hybridization, consider sulfur hexafluoride, SF_6. The sulfur atom bonds to six fluorine atoms by overlap between the sp^3d^2 hybrid orbitals on sulfur and p orbitals on the fluorine atoms:

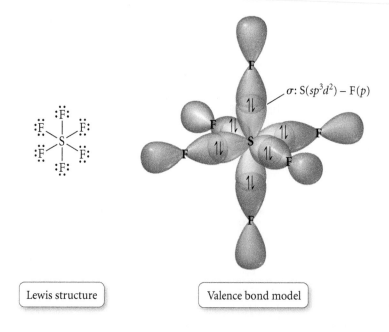

Lewis structure   Valence bond model

The sp^3d^2 orbitals on the sulfur atom are octahedral, so the molecular geometry is octahedral, again in agreement with VSEPR theory and with the experimentally observed geometry.

Writing Hybridization and Bonding Schemes

We have now studied examples of the five main types of atomic orbital hybridization. *But how do we know which hybridization scheme best describes the orbitals of a specific atom in a specific molecule?* In computational valence bond theory, the energy of the molecule is calculated using a computer; the degree of hybridization as well as the type of hybridization are varied to find the combination that gives the molecule the lowest

TABLE 10.3 Hybridization Scheme from Electron Geometry

Number of Electron Groups	Electron Geometry (from VSEPR Theory)	Hybridization Scheme	
2	Linear	sp	
3	Trigonal planar	sp^2	120°
4	Tetrahedral	sp^3	109.5°
5	Trigonal bipyramidal	sp^3d	90° 120°
6	Octahedral	sp^3d^2	90° 90°

overall energy. For our purposes, we can assign a hybridization scheme from the electron geometry—determined using VSEPR theory—of the central atom (or interior atoms) of the molecule. The five VSEPR electron geometries and the corresponding hybridization schemes are shown in Table 10.3. For example, if the electron geometry of the central atom is tetrahedral, then the hybridization is sp^3, and if the electron geometry is octahedral, then the hybridization is sp^3d^2, and so on. Although this method of determining the hybridization scheme is not 100% accurate (for example, it predicts that H_2S should be sp^3 when in fact H_2S is largely unhybridized) it is the best we can do without more complex computer-based calculations.

We are now ready to put Lewis theory and valence bond theory together to describe bonding in molecules. In the procedure and examples that follow, you will learn how to write a *hybridization and bonding scheme* for a molecule. This involves drawing a Lewis structure for the molecule, determining its geometry using VSEPR theory, determining the hybridization of the interior atoms, drawing the molecule with its overlapping orbitals, and labeling each bond with the σ and π notation followed by the type of overlapping orbitals. As you can see, this procedure involves virtually everything you have learned about bonding in this chapter and the previous one. The procedure for writing a hybridization and bonding scheme is shown in the left column on the facing page, with two examples of how to apply the procedure in the columns to the right.

PROCEDURE FOR... Hybridization and Bonding Scheme	**EXAMPLE 10.6** **Hybridization and Bonding Scheme** Write a hybridization and bonding scheme for bromine trifluoride, BrF_3.	**EXAMPLE 10.7** **Hybridization and Bonding Scheme** Write a hybridization and bonding scheme for acetaldehyde, $$H_3C-\overset{\overset{\displaystyle O}{\|}}{C}-H$$
1. **Write a Lewis structure for the molecule.**	**SOLUTION** BrF_3 has 28 valence electrons and the following Lewis structure:	**SOLUTION** Acetaldehyde has 18 valence electrons and the following Lewis structure:
2. **Use VSEPR theory to predict the electron geometry about the central atom (or interior atoms).**	The bromine atom has five electron groups and therefore has a trigonal bipyramidal electron geometry.	The leftmost carbon atom has four electron groups and a tetrahedral electron geometry. The rightmost carbon atom has three electron groups and trigonal planar geometry.
3. **Select the correct hybridization for the central atom (or interior atoms) based on the electron geometry.**	A trigonal bipyramidal electron geometry corresponds to sp^3d hybridization.	The leftmost carbon atom is sp^3 hybridized, and the rightmost carbon atom is sp^2 hybridized.
4. **Sketch the molecule, beginning with the central atom and its orbitals. Show overlap with the appropriate orbitals on the terminal atoms.**	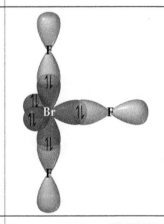	
5. **Label all bonds using the σ or π notation followed by the type of overlapping orbitals.**	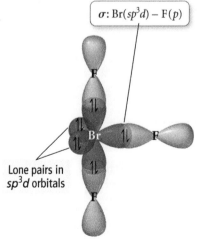 $\sigma: Br(sp^3d) - F(p)$ Lone pairs in sp^3d orbitals	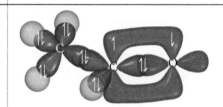 $\sigma: C(sp^3) - H(s)$ $\pi: C(p) - O(p)$ $\sigma: C(sp^2) - H(s)$ $\sigma: C(sp^3) - C(sp^2)$ $\sigma: C(sp^2) - O(p)$
	FOR PRACTICE 10.6 Write a hybridization and bonding scheme for XeF_4.	**FOR PRACTICE 10.7** Write a hybridization and bonding scheme for HCN.

EXAMPLE 10.8 Hybridization and Bonding Scheme

Use valence bond theory to write a hybridization and bonding scheme for ethene, $H_2C = CH_2$.

SOLUTION

1. Write a Lewis structure for the molecule.	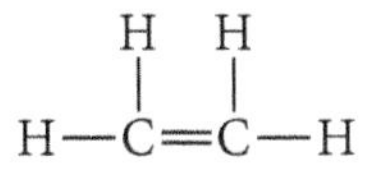 H H | | H — C = C — H
2. Apply VSEPR theory to predict the electron geometry about the central atom (or interior atoms).	The molecule has two interior atoms. Since each atom has three electron groups (one double bond and two single bonds), the electron geometry about each atom is trigonal planar.
3. Refer to Table 10.3 to select the correct hybridization for the central atom (or interior atoms) based on the electron geometry.	A trigonal planar geometry corresponds to sp^2 hybridization.
4. Sketch the molecule, beginning with the central atom and its orbitals. Show overlap with the appropriate orbitals on the terminal atoms.	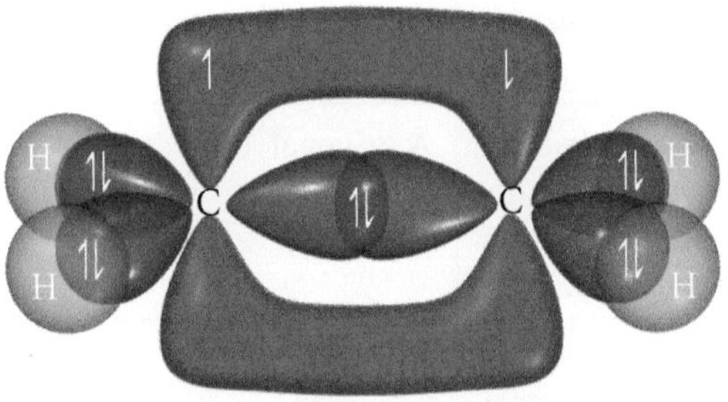
5. Label all bonds using the σ or π notation followed by the type of overlapping orbitals.	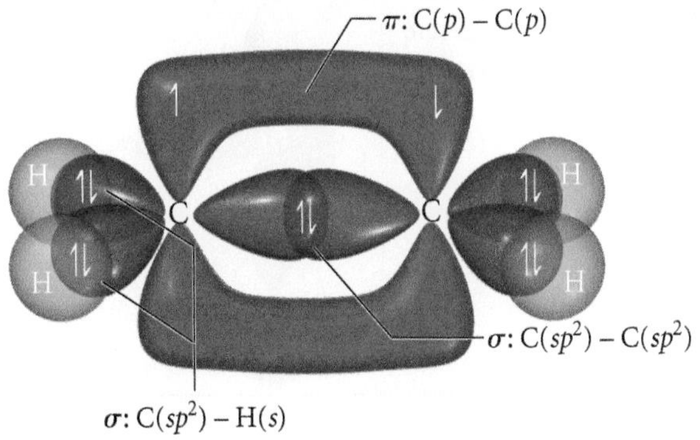

FOR PRACTICE 10.8

Use valence bond theory to write a hybridization and bonding scheme for CO_2.

FOR MORE PRACTICE 10.8

What is the hybridization of the central iodine atom in I_3^-?

10.8 Molecular Orbital Theory: Electron Delocalization

Although we have seen how valence bond theory can explain many aspects of chemical bonding—such as the rigidity of a double bond—it also has limitations. In valence bond theory, we treat electrons as if they reside in the quantum-mechanical orbitals that we calculated *for atoms*. This is a significant oversimplification that we partially compensate for by hybridization. Nevertheless, we can do better.

In Chapter 7, we learned that the mathematical derivation of energies and orbitals for electrons *in atoms* comes from solving the Schrödinger equation for the atom of interest. For a molecule, we can theoretically do the same thing. The resulting orbitals would be the actual *molecular* orbitals of the molecule as a whole (in contrast to valence bond theory, in which the orbitals are those of individual atoms). As it turns out, however, solving the Schrödinger equation exactly for even the simplest molecules is impossible without making some approximations.

In **molecular orbital (MO) theory**, you do not actually solve the Schrödinger equation for a molecule directly. Instead, you use a trial function, an "educated guess" as to what the solution might be. In other words, rather than mathematically solving the Schrödinger equation, which would give you a mathematical function describing an orbital, you start with a trial mathematical function for the orbital. You then test the trial function to see how well it "works."

We can understand this process by analogy to solving an algebraic equation. Suppose you want to know x in the equation $4x + 5 = 70$ without actually solving the equation. For an easy equation like this one, you might first estimate that $x = 16$. You can then determine how well your estimate works by substituting $x = 16$ into the equation. If the estimate did not work, you could try again until you found the right value of x. (In this case, you can quickly see that x must be a little more than 16.)

In molecular orbital theory, the estimating procedure is analogous. However, we need to add one more important concept to get at the heart of molecular orbital theory. In order to determine how well a trial function for an orbital "works" in molecular orbital theory, you calculate its energy. No matter how good your trial function, *you will never do better than nature at minimizing the energy of the orbital*. In other words, devise any trial function that you like for an orbital in a molecule and calculate its energy. The energy you calculate for the devised orbital will always be greater than or (at best) equal to the energy of the actual orbital.

How does this help us? The best possible orbital will therefore be the one with the minimum energy. In modern molecular orbital theory, computer programs are designed to try many different variations of a guessed orbital and compare the energies of each one. The variation with the lowest energy is the best approximation for the actual molecular orbital.

Molecular orbital theory is a specific application of a more general quantum-mechanical approximation technique called the variational method. In the variational method, the energy of a trial function within the Schrödinger equation is minimized.

You calculate the energy of an estimated orbital by substituting it into the Schrödinger equation and solving for the energy.

Linear Combination of Atomic Orbitals (LCAO)

The simplest trial functions that work reasonably well in molecular orbital theory turn out to be linear combinations of atomic orbitals, or LCAOs. An LCAO molecular orbital is a *weighted linear sum—analogous to a weighted average—of the valence atomic orbitals* of the atoms in the molecule. At first glance, this concept might seem very similar to that of hybridization in valence bond theory. However, in valence bond theory, hybrid orbitals are weighted linear sums of the valence atomic orbitals of a *particular atom*, and the hybrid orbitals remain *localized* on that atom. In molecular orbital theory, the molecular orbitals are weighted linear sums of the valence atomic orbitals of *all the atoms* in a molecule, and many of the molecular orbitals are *delocalized* over the entire molecule.

Consider the H_2 molecule. One of the molecular orbitals for H_2 is simply an equally weighted sum of the $1s$ orbital from one atom and the $1s$ orbital from the other. We can represent this pictorially and energetically as follows:

When molecular orbitals are computed mathematically, it is actually the *wave functions* corresponding to the orbitals that are combined.

The name of this molecular orbital is σ_{1s}. The σ comes from the shape of the orbital, which looks like a σ bond in valence bond theory, and the $1s$ comes from its formation by a linear sum of $1s$ orbitals. The σ_{1s} orbital is lower in energy than either of the two $1s$ atomic orbitals from which it was formed. For this reason, this orbital is called a **bonding orbital**. When electrons occupy bonding molecular orbitals, the energy of the electrons is lower than it would be if they were occupying atomic orbitals.

We can think of a molecular orbital in a molecule in much the same way that we think about an atomic orbital in an atom. Electrons will seek the lowest energy molecular orbital available, but just as an atom has more than one atomic orbital (and some may be empty), so a molecule has more than one molecular orbital (and some may be empty). The next molecular orbital of H_2 is approximated by summing the $1s$ orbital on one hydrogen atom with the *negative* (opposite phase) of the $1s$ orbital on the other hydrogen atom.

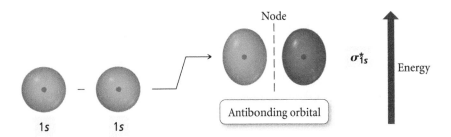

The different phases of the orbitals result in *destructive* interference between them. The resulting molecular orbital therefore has a node between the two atoms. The different colors (red and blue) on either side of the node represent the different phases of the orbital (see Section 7.6). The name of this molecular orbital is σ_{1s}^*. The star indicates that this orbital is an **antibonding orbital**. Electrons in antibonding orbitals have higher energies than they did in their respective atomic orbitals and therefore tend to raise the energy of the system (relative to the unbonded atoms).

In general, when two atomic orbitals are added together to form molecular orbitals, one of the resultant molecular orbitals will be lower in energy (the bonding orbital) than the atomic orbitals and the other will be higher in energy (the antibonding orbital). Remember that electrons in orbitals behave like waves. The bonding molecular orbital arises out of constructive interference between the atomic orbitals because both orbitals have the same phase. The antibonding orbital arises out of destructive interference between the atomic orbitals because *subtracting* one from the other means the two interacting orbitals have opposite phases (Figure 10.13 ▼).

For this reason, the bonding orbital has an increased electron density in the internuclear region while the antibonding orbital has a node in the internuclear region. Bonding orbitals have greater electron density in the internuclear region, thereby lowering their energy compared to the orbitals in nonbonded atoms. Antibonding orbitals have less electron density in the internuclear region, and their energies are generally higher than in the orbitals of nonbonded atoms.

▶ FIGURE 10.13 **Formation of Bonding and Antibonding Orbitals**
Constructive interference between two atomic orbitals gives rise to a molecular orbital that is lower in energy than the atomic orbitals. This is the bonding orbital. Destructive interference between two atomic orbitals gives rise to a molecular orbital that is higher in energy than the atomic orbitals. This is the antibonding orbital.

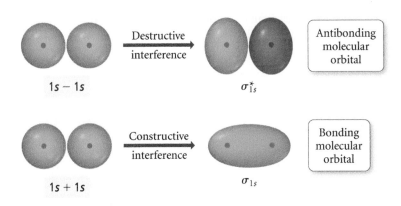

We put all of this together in the molecular orbital energy diagram for H_2:

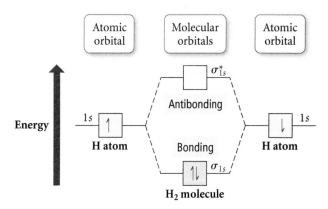

The molecular orbital (MO) diagram shows that two hydrogen atoms can lower their overall energy by forming H_2 because the electrons can move from higher energy atomic orbitals into the lower energy σ_{1s} bonding molecular orbital. In molecular orbital theory, we define the **bond order** of a diatomic molecule such as H_2 as follows:

$$\text{Bond order} = \frac{\text{(number of electrons in bonding MOs)} - \text{(number of electrons in antibonding MOs)}}{2}$$

For H_2, the bond order is:

$$H_2 \text{ bond order} = \frac{2 - 0}{2} = 1$$

A positive bond order means that there are more electrons in bonding molecular orbitals than in antibonding molecular orbitals. The electrons will therefore have lower energy than they did in the orbitals of the isolated atoms and a chemical bond will form. In general, the higher the bond order, the stronger the bond. A negative or zero bond order indicates that a bond will *not* form between the atoms. For example, consider the MO diagram for He_2:

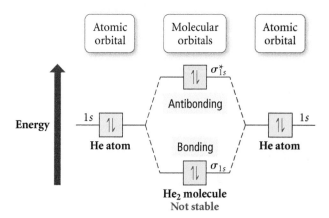

Notice that the two additional electrons must go into the higher energy antibonding orbital. There is no net stabilization by joining two helium atoms to form a helium molecule, as indicated by the bond order:

$$He_2 \text{ bond order} = \frac{2 - 2}{2} = 0$$

So according to MO theory, He_2 should not exist as a stable molecule, and indeed it does not. An interesting case is the helium–helium ion, He_2^+, with the following MO diagram:

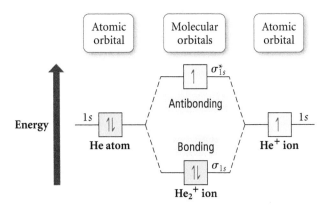

The bond order is $\frac{1}{2}$, indicating that He_2^+ should exist, and indeed it does.

Summarizing LCAO–MO Theory:

▶ We can approximate molecular orbitals (MOs) as a linear combination of atomic orbitals (AOs). The total number of MOs formed from a particular set of AOs will always equal the number of AOs in the set.

▶ When two AOs combine to form two MOs, one MO will be lower in energy (the bonding MO) and the other will be higher in energy (the antibonding MO).

▶ When assigning the electrons of a molecule to MOs, fill the lowest energy MOs first with a maximum of two spin-paired electrons per orbital.

▶ When assigning electrons to two MOs of the same energy, follow Hund's rule—fill the orbitals singly first, with parallel spins, before pairing.

▶ The bond order in a diatomic molecule is the number of electrons in bonding MOs minus the number in antibonding MOs divided by two. Stable bonds require a positive bond order (more electrons in bonding MOs than in antibonding MOs).

Notice the power of the molecular orbital approach. Every electron that enters a bonding MO stabilizes the molecule or polyatomic ion and every electron that enters an antibonding MO destabilizes it. The emphasis on electron pairs has been removed. One electron in a bonding MO stabilizes half as much as two, so a bond order of one-half is nothing mysterious.

EXAMPLE 10.9 Bond Order

Use molecular orbital theory to predict the bond order in H_2^-. Is the H_2^- bond a stronger or weaker bond than the H_2 bond?

SOLUTION

The H_2^- ion has three electrons. Assign the three electrons to the molecular orbitals, filling lower energy orbitals first and proceeding to higher energy orbitals.	
Calculate the bond order by subtracting the number of electrons in antibonding orbitals from the number in bonding orbitals and dividing the result by two.	H_2^- bond order $= \dfrac{2-1}{2} = +\dfrac{1}{2}$

Since the bond order is positive, H_2^- should be stable. However, the bond order of H_2^- is lower than the bond order of H_2 (which is 1); therefore, the bond in H_2^- is weaker than in H_2.

FOR PRACTICE 10.9

Use molecular orbital theory to predict the bond order in H_2^+. Is the H_2^+ bond a stronger or weaker bond than the H_2 bond?

Period Two Homonuclear Diatomic Molecules

The homonuclear diatomic molecules (molecules made up of two atoms of the same kind) formed from second-period elements have between 2 and 16 valence electrons. To explain bonding in these molecules, we must consider the next set of higher energy molecular orbitals, which can be approximated by linear combinations of the valence atomic orbitals of the period 2 elements.

We begin with Li_2. Even though lithium is normally a metal, we can use MO theory to predict whether or not the Li_2 molecule should exist in the gas phase. We approximate the molecular orbitals in Li_2 as linear combinations of the 2s atomic orbitals. The resulting molecular orbitals look much like those of the H_2 molecule. The MO diagram for Li_2 therefore looks a lot like the MO diagram for H_2:

> The core electrons can be ignored because, as with other models for bonding, these electrons do not contribute significantly to chemical bonding.

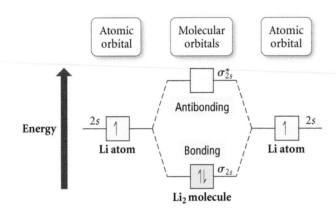

The two valence electrons of Li_2 occupy a bonding molecular orbital. We would predict that the Li_2 molecule is stable with a bond order of 1. Experiments confirm this prediction. In contrast, consider the MO diagram for Be_2:

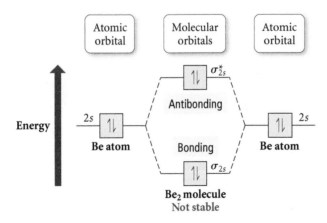

The four valence electrons of Be_2 occupy one bonding MO and one antibonding MO. The bond order is 0 and we predict that Be_2 should not be stable, again consistent with experimental findings.

The next homonuclear molecule composed of second row elements is B_2, which has six total valence electrons to accommodate. We can approximate the next higher energy

molecular orbitals for B_2 and the rest of the period 2 diatomic molecules as linear combinations of the $2p$ orbitals taken pairwise. Since the three $2p$ orbitals orient along three orthogonal axes, we must assign similar axes to the molecule. In this book, we assign the internuclear axis to be the x direction. Then the LCAO–MOs that result from combining the $2p_x$ orbitals—the ones that lie along the internuclear axis—from each atom are represented pictorially as follows:

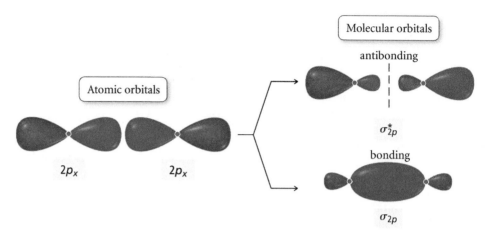

The bonding MO in this pair looks something like candy in a wrapper, with increased electron density in the internuclear region due to constructive interference between the two $2p$ atomic orbitals. It has the characteristic σ shape (it is cylindrically symmetrical about the bond axis) and is therefore called the σ_{2p} bonding orbital. The antibonding orbital, called σ_{2p}^*, has a node between the two nuclei (due to destructive interference between the two $2p$ orbitals) and is higher in energy than either of the $2p_x$ orbitals.

The LCAO–MOs that result from combining the $2p_z$ orbitals from each atom are represented pictorially as follows:

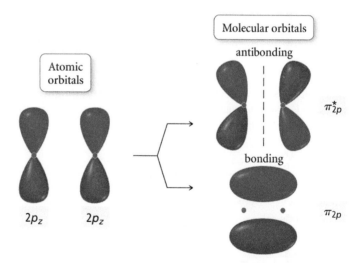

Notice that in this case the p orbitals are added together in a side-by-side orientation (in contrast to the $2p_x$ orbitals which were oriented end to end). The resultant molecular orbitals consequently have a different shape. The electron density in the bonding molecular orbital is above and below the internuclear axis with a nodal plane that includes the internuclear axis. This orbital resembles the electron density distribution of a π bond in valence bond theory. We call this orbital the π_{2p} orbital. The corresponding antibonding orbital has an additional node *between* the nuclei (perpendicular to the internuclear axis) and is called the π_{2p}^* orbital.

The LCAO–MOs that result from combining the $2p_y$ orbitals from each atom are represented pictorially as follows:

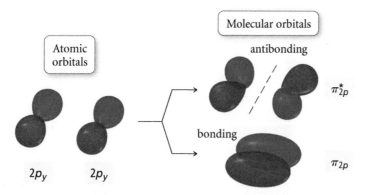

The only difference between the $2p_y$ and the $2p_z$ atomic orbitals is a 90° rotation about the internuclear axis. Consequently, the only difference between the resulting MOs is a 90° rotation about the internuclear axis. The energies and the names of the bonding and antibonding MOs obtained from the combination of the $2p_y$ AOs are identical to those obtained from the combination of the $2p_z$ AOs.

Before we can draw MO diagrams for B_2 and the other second-period diatomic molecules, we must determine the relative energy ordering of the MOs obtained from the $2p$ AO combinations. This is not a simple task. The relative ordering of MOs obtained from LCAO–MO theory is usually determined computationally. There is no single order that works for all molecules. For second-period diatomic molecules, computations reveal that the energy ordering for B_2, C_2, and N_2 is slightly different than that for O_2, F_2, and Ne_2 as follows:

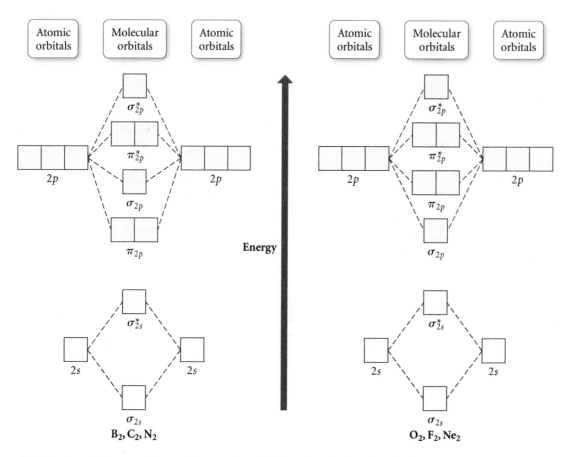

▲ Molecular orbital energy diagrams for second-period diatomic molecules show that the energy ordering of the π_{2p} and σ_{2p} molecular orbitals can vary.

▶ **FIGURE 10.14 The Effects of 2s–2p Mixing** The degree of mixing between two orbitals decreases with increasing energy difference between them. Mixing of the 2s and $2p_x$ orbitals is therefore greater in B_2, C_2, and N_2 than in O_2, F_2, and Ne_2 because in B, C, and N the energy levels of the atomic orbitals are more closely spaced than in O, F, and Ne. This mixing produces a change in energy ordering for the π_{2p} and σ_{2p} molecular orbitals.

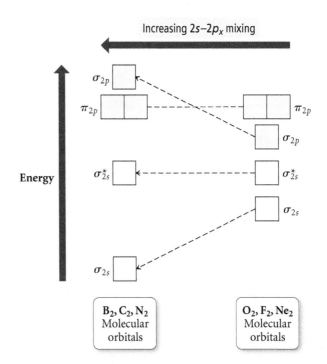

The reason for the difference in energy ordering can only be explained by going back to our LCAO–MO model. In our simplified treatment, we assumed that the MOs that result from the second-period AOs could be calculated pairwise. In other words, we took the linear combination of a 2s from one atom with the 2s from another, a $2p_x$ from one atom with a $2p_x$ from the other and so on. However, in a more detailed treatment, the MOs are formed from linear combinations that include all of the AOs that are relatively close to each other in energy and of the correct symmetry. Specifically, in a more detailed treatment, the two 2s orbitals and the two $2p_x$ orbitals should all be combined to form a total of four molecular orbitals. The extent to which you include this type of mixing affects the energy levels of the corresponding MOs, as shown in Figure 10.14 ▲. The bottom line is that s–p mixing is significant in B_2, C_2, and N_2 but not in O_2, F_2, and Ne_2. The result is a different energy ordering, depending on the specific molecule.

The MO energy diagrams for the rest of the second-period homonuclear diatomic molecules, as well as their bond orders, bond energies, and bond lengths, are shown in

	Large 2s–$2p_x$ interaction				Small 2s–$2p_x$ interaction		
	B_2	**C_2**	**N_2**		**O_2**	**F_2**	**Ne_2**
σ_{2p}^*	☐	☐	☐	σ_{2p}^*	☐	☐	⇅
π_{2p}^*	☐ ☐	☐ ☐	☐ ☐	π_{2p}^*	↑ ↑	⇅ ⇅	⇅ ⇅
σ_{2p}	☐	☐	⇅	π_{2p}	⇅ ⇅	⇅ ⇅	⇅ ⇅
π_{2p}	↑ ↑	⇅ ⇅	⇅ ⇅	σ_{2p}	⇅	⇅	⇅
σ_{2s}^*	⇅	⇅	⇅	σ_{2s}^*	⇅	⇅	⇅
σ_{2s}	⇅	⇅	⇅	σ_{2s}	⇅	⇅	⇅
Bond order	1	2	3		2	1	0
Bond energy (kJ/mol)	290	620	946		498	159	—
Bond length (pm)	159	131	110		121	143	—

▲ **FIGURE 10.15 Molecular Orbital Energy Diagrams for Second-Row p-block Homonuclear Diatomic Molecules**

Figure 10.15 ▼. Notice that as bond order increases, the bond gets stronger (greater bond energy) and shorter (smaller bond length). For B_2, with six electrons, the bond order is 1. For C_2, the bond order is 2, and for N_2, the bond order reaches a maximum with a value of 3. Recall that the Lewis structure of N_2 has a triple bond, so both Lewis theory and molecular orbital theory predict a strong bond for N_2, which is experimentally observed.

In O_2, the two additional electrons occupy antibonding orbitals and the bond order is 2. These two electrons are unpaired—they occupy the π_{2p}^{*} orbitals *singly with parallel spins*, as indicated by Hund's rule. The presence of unpaired electrons in the molecular orbital diagram of oxygen is significant because oxygen is known from experiment to be *paramagnetic* (see Section 8.7)—it is attracted to a magnetic field. The paramagnetism of oxygen can be demonstrated by suspending liquid oxygen between the poles of a magnet. This magnetic property is the direct result of *unpaired electrons*, whose spin and movement around the nucleus (more accurately known as orbital angular momentum) generate tiny magnetic fields. When a paramagnetic substance is placed in an external magnetic field, the magnetic fields of each atom or molecule align with the external field, creating the attraction (much as two magnets attract each other when properly oriented). In contrast, when the electrons in an atom or molecule are all *paired*, the magnetic fields caused by electron spin and orbital angular momentum tend to cancel each other, resulting in diamagnetism. A **diamagnetic** substance is not attracted to a magnetic field (and is, in fact, slightly repelled).

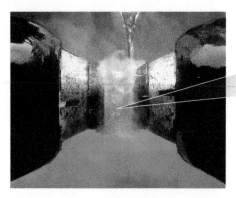

▲ Liquid oxygen can be suspended between the poles of a magnet because it is paramagnetic. It contains unpaired electrons (depicted here in the inset) that generate tiny magnetic fields, which align with and interact with the external field.

In the Lewis structure of O_2, as well as in the valence bond model of O_2, all of its electrons seem to be paired:

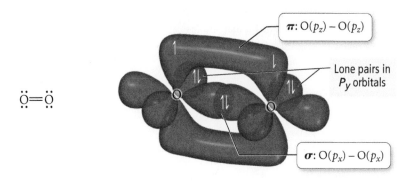

The *s* orbital on each O atom contains two electrons, but for clarity neither the *s* orbitals nor the electrons that occupy them are shown.

In the MO diagram for O_2, however, we can see the unpaired electrons. Molecular orbital theory is the more powerful theory in that it can account for the paramagnetism of O_2—it gives us a picture of bonding that more closely corresponds to what we see in experiment. Continuing along the second-row homonuclear diatomic molecules we see that F_2 has a bond order of 1 and Ne_2 has a bond order of 0, again consistent with experiment since F_2 exists and Ne_2 does not.

EXAMPLE 10.10 Molecular Orbital Theory

Draw an MO energy diagram and determine the bond order for the N_2^- ion. Do you expect the bond to be stronger or weaker than in the N_2 molecule? Is N_2^- diamagnetic or paramagnetic?

SOLUTION

Write an energy level diagram for the molecular orbitals in N_2^-. Use the energy ordering for N_2.	$\square$ σ_{2p}^* $\square\square$ π_{2p}^* $\square$ σ_{2p} $\square\square$ π_{2p} $\square$ σ_{2s}^* $\square$ σ_{2s}
The N_2^- ion has 11 valence electrons (5 for each nitrogen atom plus 1 for the negative charge). Assign the electrons to the molecular orbitals beginning with the lowest energy orbitals and following Hund's rule.	$\square$ σ_{2p}^* $\boxed{\uparrow}\,\square$ π_{2p}^* $\boxed{\uparrow\downarrow}$ σ_{2p} $\boxed{\uparrow\downarrow}\,\boxed{\uparrow\downarrow}$ π_{2p} $\boxed{\uparrow\downarrow}$ σ_{2s}^* $\boxed{\uparrow\downarrow}$ σ_{2s}
Calculate the bond order by subtracting the number of electrons in antibonding orbitals from the number in bonding orbitals and dividing the result by two.	N_2^- bond order $= \dfrac{8 - 3}{2} = +2.5$

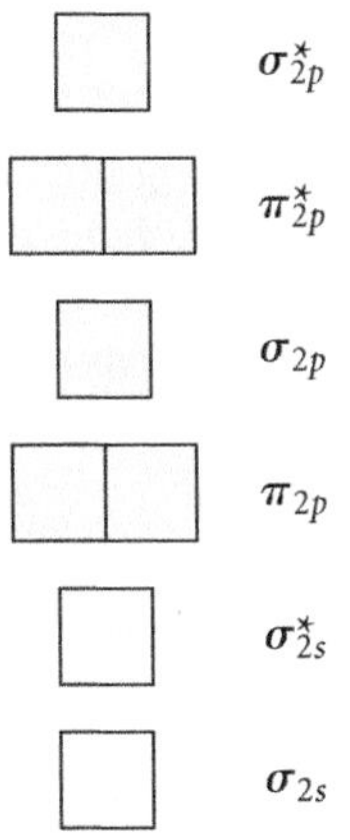

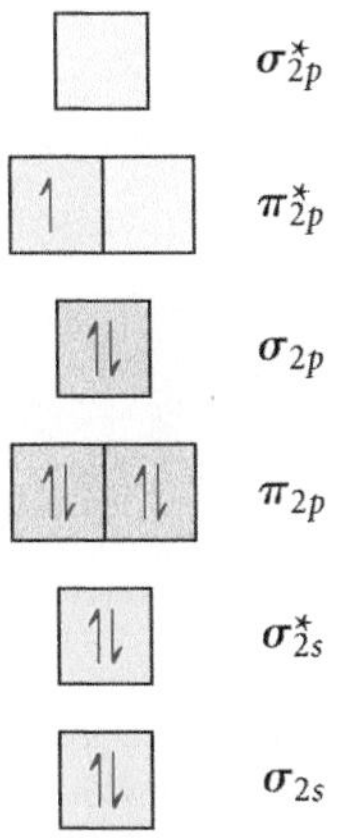

The bond order is 2.5, which is a lower bond order than in the N_2 molecule (bond order = 3); therefore, the bond is weaker. The MO diagram shows that the N_2^- ion has one unpaired electron and is therefore paramagnetic.

FOR PRACTICE 10.10

Draw an MO energy diagram and determine the bond order for the N_2^+ ion. Do you expect the bond to be stronger or weaker than in the N_2 molecule? Is N_2^+ diamagnetic or paramagnetic?

FOR MORE PRACTICE 10.10

Use molecular orbital theory to determine the bond order of Ne_2.

Second-Period Heteronuclear Diatomic Molecules

Molecular orbital theory can also be applied to heteronuclear diatomic molecules (two different atoms). For example, we can draw an MO diagram for NO as follows:

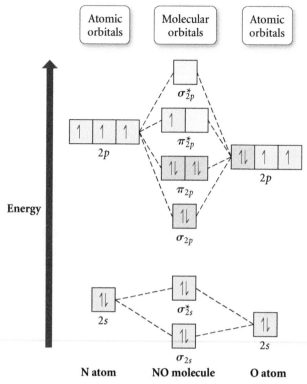

Oxygen is more electronegative than nitrogen, so its atomic orbitals are lower in energy than nitrogen's atomic orbitals. When two atomic orbitals are identical and of equal energy, the weighting of each orbital in forming a molecular orbital is identical. However, when two atomic orbitals are different, the weighting of each orbital in forming a molecular orbital may be different. More specifically, when a molecular orbital is approximated as a linear combination of atomic orbitals of different energies, the lower energy atomic orbital makes a greater contribution to the bonding molecular orbital and the higher energy atomic orbital makes a greater contribution to the antibonding molecular orbital. For example, notice that the σ_{2s} bonding orbital is closer in energy to the oxygen $2s$ orbital than to the nitrogen $2s$ orbital. We can also see this unequal weighting in the shape of the resultant molecular orbital, in which the electron density is concentrated on the oxygen atom, as shown in Figure 10.16 ▶.

As another example of a heteronuclear diatomic molecule, consider the MO diagram for HF:

A given orbital will have lower energy in a more electronegative atom. For this reason, electronegative atoms have the ability to attract electrons to themselves.

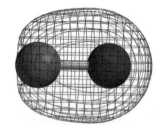

▲ **FIGURE 10.16 Shape of σ_{2s} bonding orbital in NO** The molecular orbital shows more electron density at the oxygen end of the molecule because the atomic orbitals of oxygen, the more electronegative element, are lower in energy than those of nitrogen. They therefore contribute more to the bonding molecular orbital.

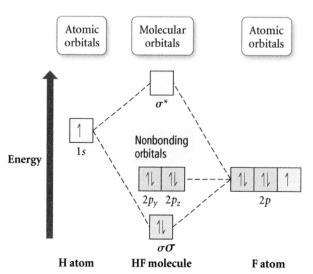

Fluorine is so electronegative that all of its atomic orbitals are lower in energy than hydrogen's atomic orbitals. In fact, fluorine's $2s$ orbital is so low in energy compared to hydrogen's $1s$ orbital that it does not contribute appreciably to the molecular orbitals. The molecular orbitals in HF are approximated by the linear combination of the fluorine $2p_x$ orbital and the hydrogen $1s$ orbital. The other $2p$ orbitals remain localized on the fluorine and appear in the energy diagram as **nonbonding orbitals**. The electrons in the nonbonding orbitals remain localized on the fluorine atom.

EXAMPLE 10.11 Molecular Orbital Theory for Heteronuclear Diatomic Molecules and Ions

Use molecular orbital theory to determine the bond order of the CN^- ion. Is the ion paramagnetic or diamagnetic?

SOLUTION

Determine the number of valence electrons in the molecule or ion.	Number of valence electrons $= 4 \text{ (from C)} + 5 \text{ (from N)} +$ $\qquad 1 \text{ (from negative charge)} = 10$
Write an energy level diagram using Figure 10.15 as a guide. Fill the orbitals beginning with the lowest energy orbital and progressing upward until all electrons have been assigned to an orbital. Remember to allow no more than two electrons (with paired spins) per orbital and to fill degenerate orbitals with single electrons (with parallel spins) before pairing.	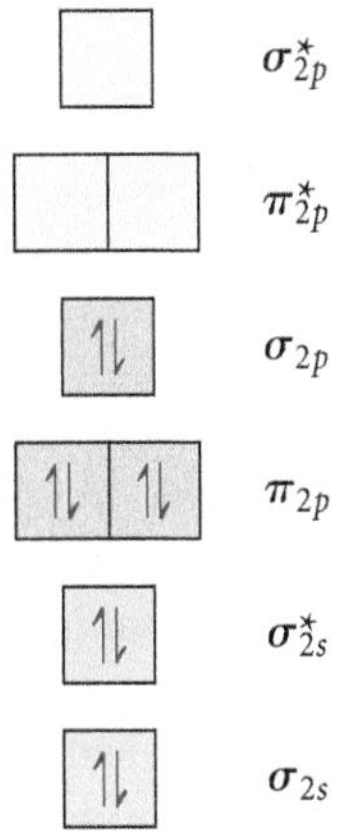 σ_{2p}^* (empty) π_{2p}^* (empty) σ_{2p} $\uparrow\downarrow$ π_{2p} $\uparrow\downarrow$ $\uparrow\downarrow$ σ_{2s}^* $\uparrow\downarrow$ σ_{2s} $\uparrow\downarrow$
Calculate the bond order using the appropriate formula: Bond order = $$\frac{\text{(number of e}^- \text{ in bonding MOs)} - \text{(number of e}^- \text{ in antibonding MOs)}}{2}$$	CN^- bond order $= \dfrac{8 - 2}{2} = +3$
If the MO diagram has unpaired electrons, the molecule or ion is paramagnetic. If the electrons are all paired, the molecule or ion is diamagnetic.	Since the MO diagram has no unpaired electrons, the ion is diamagnetic.

FOR PRACTICE 10.11

Use molecular orbital theory to determine the bond order of NO. (Use the energy ordering of N_2.) Is the molecule paramagnetic or diamagnetic?

Polyatomic Molecules

With the aid of computers, molecular orbital theory can be applied to polyatomic molecules and ions, yielding results that correlate very well with experimental measurements. These applications are beyond the scope of this text. However, the delocalizaton of electrons over an entire molecule is an important contribution of molecular orbital theory to our basic understanding of chemical bonding. For example, consider the Lewis structure and valence bond diagram of ozone:

Lewis structure   Valence bond model

In Lewis theory, we use resonance forms to represent the two equivalent bonds. In valence bond theory, it appears that the two oxygen–oxygen bonds should be different. In molecular orbital theory, however, the π molecular orbitals in ozone are formed from a linear combination of the three oxygen $2p$ orbitals and are delocalized over the entire molecule. The lowest energy π bonding molecular orbital is shown at right.

When we examine ozone in nature, we indeed find two equivalent bonds. A similar situation occurs with benzene (C_6H_6). In Lewis theory, we represent the structure with two resonance forms:

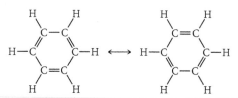
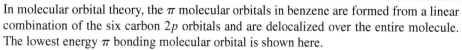

In molecular orbital theory, the π molecular orbitals in benzene are formed from a linear combination of the six carbon $2p$ orbitals and are delocalized over the entire molecule. The lowest energy π bonding molecular orbital is shown here.

Benzene is in fact a highly symmetric molecule with six identical carbon–carbon bonds. The best picture of the π electrons in benzene is one in which the electrons occupy roughly circular shaped orbitals above and below the plane of the molecule, as depicted in the molecular orbital theory approach.

 Conceptual Connection 10.6   What Is a Chemical Bond, Part II?

We have learned that Lewis theory portrays a chemical bond as the transfer or sharing of electrons represented as dots. Valence bond theory portrays a chemical bond as the overlap of two half-filled atomic orbitals. What is a chemical bond according to molecular orbital theory?

ANSWER: In MO theory, atoms will join together (or bond) when the electrons in the atoms can lower their energy by occupying the molecular orbitals of the resultant molecule. Unlike Lewis theory or valence bond theory, the chemical "bonds" in MO theory are not localized between atoms, but spread throughout the entire molecule.

CHAPTER IN REVIEW

Key Terms

Section 10.2
valence shell electron pair repulsion (VSEPR) theory (400)
electron groups (400)
linear geometry (401)
trigonal planar geometry (401)
tetrahedral geometry (402)
trigonal bipyramidal geometry (403)

octahedral geometry (403)

Section 10.3
electron geometry (404)
molecular geometry (404)
trigonal pyramidal geometry (404)
bent geometry (405)
seesaw geometry (406)
T-shaped geometry (406)

square pyramidal geometry (407)
square planar geometry (407)

Section 10.6
valence bond theory (417)

Section 10.7
hybridization (419)
hybrid orbitals (419)

pi (π) bond (424)
sigma (σ) bond (424)

Section 10.8
molecular orbital theory (433)
bonding orbital (434)
antibonding orbital (434)
bond order (435)
diamagnetic (441)
nonbonding orbitals (444)

Key Concepts

Molecular Shape and VSEPR Theory (10.1–10.4)

The properties of molecules are directly related to their shapes. In VSEPR theory, molecular geometries are determined by the repulsions between electron groups on the central atom. An electron group can be a single bond, double bond, triple bond, lone pair, or even a single electron. The five basic shapes are linear (two electron groups), trigonal planar (three electron groups), tetrahedral (four electron groups), trigonal bipyramidal (five electron groups), and octahedral (six electron groups). When lone pairs are present on the central atom, the *electron* geometry is still one of the five basic shapes, but one or more positions are occupied by lone pairs. The *molecular* geometry is therefore different from the electron geometry. Lone pairs are positioned so as to minimize repulsions with other lone pairs and with bonding pairs.

Polarity (10.5)

The polarity of a polyatomic molecule containing polar bonds depends on its geometry. If the dipole moments of the polar bonds are aligned in such a way that they cancel one another, the molecule will not be polar. If they are aligned in such a way as to add together, the molecule will be polar. Highly symmetric molecules tend to be nonpolar, while asymmetric molecules containing polar bonds tend to be polar. The polarity of a molecule dramatically affects its properties.

Valence Bond Theory (10.6, 10.7)

In contrast to Lewis theory, in which a covalent chemical bond is the sharing of electrons represented by dots, in valence bond theory a chemical bond is the overlap of half-filled atomic orbitals (or in some cases the overlap between a completely filled orbital and an empty one). The overlapping orbitals may be the standard atomic orbitals, such as $1s$ or $2p$ or they may be hybridized atomic orbitals, which are mathematical combinations of the standard orbitals on a single atom. The basic hybridized orbitals are sp, sp^2, sp^3, sp^3d, and sp^3d^2. The geometry of the molecule is determined by the geometry of the overlapping orbitals. In our treatment of valence bond theory, we use the molecular geometry determined by VSEPR theory to determine the correct hybridization scheme. In valence bond theory, we distinguish between two types of bonds, σ (sigma) and π (pi). In a σ bond, the orbital overlap occurs in the region that lies directly between the two bonding atoms. In a π bond, formed from the side-by-side overlap of p orbitals, the overlap occurs above and below the region that lies directly between the two bonding atoms. Rotation about a σ bond is relatively free, while rotation about a π bond is restricted.

Molecular Orbital Theory (10.8)

In molecular orbital theory, we approximate solutions to the Schrödinger equation for the molecule *as a whole* by guessing the mathematical form of the orbitals. We differentiate between guesses by calculating the energies of guessed orbitals—the best guesses have the lowest energy. Molecular orbitals obtained in this way are properties of the molecule and are often delocalized over the entire molecule. The simplest guesses that work well are linear combinations of atomic orbitals (LCAOs), weighted averages of the atomic orbitals of the different atoms in the molecule. When two atomic orbitals are combined to form molecular orbitals, they will form one molecular orbital of lower energy (the bonding orbital) and one of higher energy (the antibonding orbital). A set of molecular orbitals are filled in much the same way as atomic orbitals. The stability of the molecule and the strength of the bond depend on the number of electrons in bonding orbitals compared to the number in antibonding orbitals.

Key Equations and Relationships

Bond Order of a Diatomic Molecule (10.8)

$$\text{Bond order} = \frac{\text{(number of electrons in bonding MOs)} - \text{(number of electrons in antibonding MOs)}}{2}$$

Key Skills

Using VSEPR Theory to Predict the Basic Shapes of Molecules (10.2)
• Example 10.1 • For Practice 10.1 • Exercises 31, 32

Predicting Molecular Geometries Using VSEPR Theory and the Effects of Lone Pairs (10.4)
• Examples 10.2, 10.3 • For Practice 10.2, 10.3 • Exercises 35, 36

Predicting the Shapes of Larger Molecules (10.4)
• Example 10.4 • For Practice 10.4 • Exercises 41, 42, 45, 46

Using Molecular Shape to Determine Polarity of a Molecule (10.5)
• Example 10.5 • For Practice 10.5 • Exercises 49–52

Writing Hybridization and Bonding Schemes Using Valence Bond Theory (10.7)
• Examples 10.6, 10.7, 10.8 • For Practice 10.6, 10.7, 10.8 • For More Practice 10.8 • Exercises 61–66

Drawing Molecular Orbital Diagrams to Predict Bond Order and Magnetism of a Diatomic Molecule (10.8)
• Examples 10.9, 10.10, 10.11 • For Practice 10.9, 10.10, 10.11 • For More Practice 10.10 • Exercises 71, 72, 75–78, 81–82

EXERCISES

Review Questions

1. Why is molecular geometry important? Give some examples.

2. According to VSEPR theory, what determines the geometry of a molecule?

3. Name and sketch the five basic electron geometries, and state the number of electron groups corresponding to each. What constitutes an *electron group*?

4. Explain the difference between electron geometry and molecular geometry. Under what circumstances are they not the same?

5. Give the correct electron and molecular geometry that corresponds to each set of electron groups around the central atom of a molecule.
   a. four electron groups overall; three bonding groups and one lone pair
   b. four electron groups overall; two bonding groups and two lone pairs
   c. five electron groups overall; four bonding groups and one lone pair
   d. five electron groups overall; three bonding groups and two lone pairs
   e. five electron groups overall; two bonding groups and three lone pairs
   f. six electron groups overall; five bonding groups and one lone pair
   g. six electron groups overall; four bonding groups and two lone pairs

6. How do you apply VSEPR theory to predict the shape of a molecule with more than one interior atom?

7. How do you determine whether a molecule is polar? Why is polarity important?

8. What is a chemical bond according to valence bond theory?

9. In valence bond theory, what determines the geometry of a molecule?

10. In valence bond theory, the interaction energy between the electrons and nucleus of one atom with the electrons and nucleus of another atom is usually negative (stabilizing) when _____.

11. What is hybridization? Why is hybridization necessary in valence bond theory?

12. How does hybridization of the atomic orbitals in the central atom of a molecule help lower the overall energy of the molecule?

13. How is the *number* of hybrid orbitals related to the number of standard atomic orbitals that are hybridized?

14. Make sketches of each hybrid orbital:
   a. sp b. sp^2 c. sp^3
   d. sp^3d e. sp^3d^2

15. In Lewis theory, the two bonds in a double bond look identical. However, valence bond theory shows that they are not. Describe a double bond according to valence bond theory. Explain why rotation is restricted about a double bond, but not about a single bond.

16. Give the hybridization scheme that corresponds to each electron geometry:
   a. linear   b. trigonal planar
   c. tetrahedral   d. trigonal bipyramidal
   e. octahedral

17. What is a chemical bond according to molecular orbital theory?

18. Explain the difference between hybrid atomic orbitals in valence bond theory and LCAO molecular orbitals in molecular orbital theory.

19. What is a bonding molecular orbital?

20. What is an antibonding molecular orbital?

21. What is the role of wave interference in determining whether a molecular orbital is bonding or antibonding?

22. In molecular orbital theory, what is bond order? Why is it important?

23. How is the number of molecular orbitals approximated by a linear combination of atomic orbitals related to the number of atomic orbitals used in the approximation?

24. Make a sketch of each molecular orbital.
   a. σ_{2s} b. σ_{2s}^* c. σ_{2p}
   d. σ_{2p}^* e. π_{2p} f. π_{2p}^*

25. Draw an energy diagram for the molecular orbitals of period 2 diatomic molecules. Show the difference in ordering for B_2, C_2, and N_2 compared to O_2, F_2, and Ne_2.

26. Why does the energy ordering of the molecular orbitals of the period 2 diatomic molecules change in going from N_2 to O_2?

27. Explain the difference between a paramagnetic species and a diamagnetic one.

28. When applying molecular orbital theory to heteronuclear diatomic molecules, the atomic orbitals used may be of different energies. If two atomic orbitals of different energies make two molecular orbitals, how are the energies of the molecular orbitals related to the energies of the atomic orbitals? How is the shape of the resultant molecular orbitals related to the shapes of the atomic orbitals?

29. In molecular orbital theory, what is a nonbonding orbital?

30. Write a short paragraph describing chemical bonding according to Lewis theory, valence bond theory, and molecular orbital theory. Indicate how the theories differ in their description of a chemical bond and indicate the strengths and weaknesses of each theory. Which theory is correct?

Problems by Topic

VSEPR Theory and Molecular Geometry

31. A molecule with the formula AB_3 has a trigonal pyramidal geometry. How many electron groups are on the central atom (A)?

32. A molecule with the formula AB_3 has a trigonal planar geometry. How many electron groups are on the central atom?

33. For each molecular geometry, give the number of total electron groups, the number of bonding groups, and the number of lone pairs on the central atom.

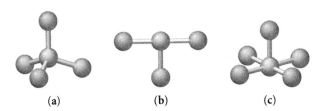

(a)   **(b)**   **(c)**

34. For each molecular geometry, give the number of total electron groups, the number of bonding groups, and the number of lone pairs on the central atom.

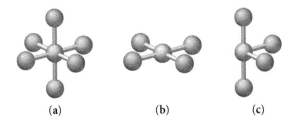

(a)   **(b)**   **(c)**

35. Determine the electron geometry, molecular geometry, and idealized bond angles for each molecule. In which cases do you expect deviations from the idealized bond angle?
    a. PF_3 **b.** SBr_2 **c.** $CHCl_3$ **d.** CS_2

36. Determine the electron geometry, molecular geometry, and idealized bond angles for each molecule. In which cases do you expect deviations from the idealized bond angle?
    a. CF_4 **b.** NF_3 **c.** OF_2 **d.** H_2S

37. Which species has the smaller bond angle, H_3O^+ or H_2O? Explain.

38. Which species has the smaller bond angle, ClO_4^- or ClO_3^-? Explain.

39. Determine the molecular geometry and make a sketch of each molecule or ion using the bond conventions shown in the "Representing Molecular Geometries on Paper" Box in Section 10.4.
    a. SF_4 **b.** ClF_3 **c.** IF_2^- **d.** IBr_4^-

40. Determine the molecular geometry and make a sketch of each molecule or ion, using the bond conventions shown in the "Representing Molecular Geometries on Paper" Box in Section 10.4.
    a. BrF_5 **b.** SCl_6 **c.** PF_5 **d.** IF_4^+

41. Determine the molecular geometry about each interior atom and make a sketch of each molecule.
    a. C_2H_2 (skeletal structure HCCH)
    b. C_2H_4 (skeletal structure H_2CCH_2)
    c. C_2H_6 (skeletal structure H_3CCH_3)

42. Determine the molecular geometry about each interior atom and make a sketch of each molecule.
    a. N_2
    b. N_2H_2 (skeletal structure HNNH)
    c. N_2H_4 (skeletal structure H_2NNH_2)

43. Each ball-and-stick model shows the electron and molecular geometry of a generic molecule. Explain what is wrong with each molecular geometry and provide the correct molecular geometry, given the number of lone pairs and bonding groups on the central atom.

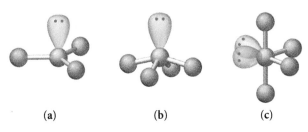

(a)   **(b)**   **(c)**

44. Each ball-and-stick model shows the electron and molecular geometry of a generic molecule. Explain what is wrong with each molecular geometry and provide the correct molecular geometry, given the number of lone pairs and bonding groups on the central atom.

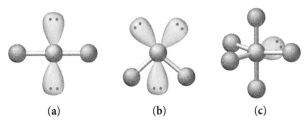

(a)   **(b)**   **(c)**

45. Determine the geometry about each interior atom in each molecule and sketch the molecule. (Skeletal structure is indicated in parentheses.)
    a. CH_3OH (H_3COH)
    b. CH_3OCH_3 (H_3COCH_3)
    c. H_2O_2 (HOOH)

46. Determine the geometry about each interior atom in each molecule and sketch the molecule. (Skeletal structure is indicated in parentheses.)
    a. CH_3NH_2 (H_3CNH_2)
    b. $CH_3CO_2CH_3$ ($H_3CCOOCH_3$ both O atoms attached to second C)
    c. NH_2CO_2H (H_2NCOOH both O atoms attached to C)

Molecular Shape and Polarity

47. Explain why CO_2 and CCl_4 are both nonpolar even though they contain polar bonds.

48. CH_3F is a polar molecule, even though the tetrahedral geometry often leads to nonpolar molecules. Explain.

49. Determine whether each molecule in Exercise 35 is polar or nonpolar.

50. Determine whether each molecule in Exercise 36 is polar or nonpolar.

51. Determine whether each molecule is polar or nonpolar.
    a. ClO_3^- **b.** SCl_2 **c.** SCl_4 **d.** $BrCl_5$

52. Determine whether each molecule is polar or nonpolar.
    a. $SiCl_4$ **b.** CF_2Cl_2 **c.** SeF_6 **d.** IF_5

Valence Bond Theory

53. The valence electron configurations of several atoms are shown below. How many bonds can each atom make without hybridization?
    a. Be $2s^2$ **b.** P $3s^23p^3$ **c.** F $2s^22p^5$

54. The valence electron configurations of several atoms are shown below. How many bonds can each atom make without hybridization?
    a. B $2s^22p^1$ **b.** N $2s^22p^3$ **c.** O $2s^22p^4$

55. Write orbital diagrams (boxes with arrows in them) to represent the electron configurations—without hybridization—for all the atoms in PH_3. Circle the electrons involved in bonding. Draw a three-dimensional sketch of the molecule and show orbital overlap. What bond angle do you expect from the unhybridized orbitals? How well does valence bond theory agree with the experimentally measured bond angle of $93.3°$?

56. Write orbital diagrams (boxes with arrows in them) to represent the electron configurations—without hybridization—for all the atoms in SF_2. Circle the electrons involved in bonding. Draw a three-dimensional sketch of the molecule and show orbital overlap. What bond angle do you expect from the unhybridized orbitals? How well does valence bond theory agree with the experimentally measured bond angle of $98.2°$?

57. Write orbital diagrams (boxes with arrows in them) to represent the electron configuration of carbon before and after sp^3 hybridization.

58. Write orbital diagrams (boxes with arrows in them) to represent the electron configurations of carbon before and after sp hybridization.

59. Which hybridization scheme allows the formation of at least one π bond?

$$sp^3, sp^2, sp^3d^2$$

60. Which hybridization scheme allows the central atom to form more than four bonds?

$$sp^3, sp^3d, sp^2$$

61. Write a hybridization and bonding scheme for each molecule. Sketch the molecule, including overlapping orbitals, and label all bonds using the notation shown in Examples 10.6 and 10.7.
  a. CCl_4 **b.** NH_3 **c.** OF_2 **d.** CO_2

62. Write a hybridization and bonding scheme for each molecule. Sketch the molecule, including overlapping orbitals, and label all bonds using the notation shown in Examples 10.6 and 10.7.
  a. CH_2Br_2 **b.** SO_2 **c.** NF_3 **d.** BF_3

63. Write a hybridization and bonding scheme for each molecule or ion. Sketch the structure, including overlapping orbitals, and label all bonds using the notation shown in Examples 10.6 and 10.7.
  a. $COCl_2$ (carbon is the central atom)
  b. BrF_5
  c. XeF_2
  d. I_3^-

64. Write a hybridization and bonding scheme for each molecule or ion. Sketch the structure, including overlapping orbitals, and label all bonds using the notation shown in Examples 10.6 and 10.7.
  a. SO_3^{2-} **b.** PF_6^- **c.** BrF_3 **d.** HCN

65. Write a hybridization and bonding scheme for each molecule that contains more than one interior atom. Indicate the hybridization about each interior atom. Sketch the structure, including overlapping orbitals, and label all bonds using the notation shown in Examples 10.6 and 10.7.
  a. N_2H_2 (skeletal structure HNNH)
  b. N_2H_4 (skeletal structure H_2NNH_2)
  c. CH_3NH_2 (skeletal structure H_3CNH_2)

66. Write a hybridization and bonding scheme for each molecule that contains more than one interior atom. Indicate the hybridization about each interior atom. Sketch the structure, including overlapping orbitals, and label all bonds using the notation shown in Examples 10.6 and 10.7.

  a. C_2H_2 (skeletal structure HCCH)
  b. C_2H_4 (skeletal structure H_2CCH_2)
  c. C_2H_6 (skeletal structure H_3CCH_3)

67. Consider the structure of the amino acid alanine. Indicate the hybridization about each interior atom.

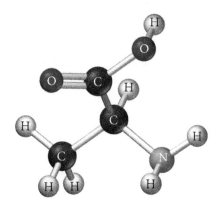

68. Consider the structure of the amino acid aspartic acid. Indicate the hybridization about each interior atom.

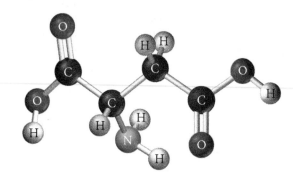

Molecular Orbital Theory

69. Sketch the bonding molecular orbital that results from the linear combination of two $1s$ orbitals. Indicate the region where interference occurs and state the kind of interference (constructive or destructive).

70. Sketch the antibonding molecular orbital that results from the linear combination of two $1s$ orbitals. Indicate the region where interference occurs and state the kind of interference (constructive or destructive).

71. Draw an MO energy diagram and predict the bond order of Be_2^+ and Be_2^-. Do you expect these molecules to exist in the gas phase?

72. Draw an MO energy diagram and predict the bond order of Li_2^+ and Li_2^-. Do you expect these molecules to exist in the gas phase?

73. Sketch the bonding and antibonding molecular orbitals that result from linear combinations of the $2p_x$ atomic orbitals in a homonuclear diatomic molecule. (The $2p_x$ orbitals are those whose lobes are oriented along the bonding axis.)

74. Sketch the bonding and antibonding molecular orbitals that result from linear combinations of the $2p_z$ atomic orbitals in a homonuclear diatomic molecule. (The $2p_z$ orbitals are those whose lobes are oriented perpendicular to the bonding axis.) How do these molecular orbitals differ from those obtained from linear combinations of the $2p_y$ atomic orbitals? (The $2p_y$ orbitals are also oriented perpendicular to the bonding axis, but also perpendicular to the $2p_z$ orbitals.)

75. Using the molecular orbital energy ordering for second-row homonuclear diatomic molecules in which the π_{2p} orbitals lie at *lower* energy than the σ_{2p}, draw MO energy diagrams and predict the bond order in a molecule or ion with each number of total valence electrons. Will the molecule or ion be diamagnetic or paramagnetic?

a. 4 **b.** 6 **c.** 8 **d.** 9

76. Using the molecular orbital energy ordering for second-row homonuclear diatomic molecules in which the π_{2p} orbitals lie at *higher* energy than the σ_{2p}, draw MO energy diagrams and predict the bond order in a molecule or ion with each number of total valence electrons. Will the molecule or ion be diamagnetic or paramagnetic?

a. 10 **b.** 12 **c.** 13 **d.** 14

77. Use molecular orbital theory to predict whether or not each molecule or ion should exist in a relatively stable form.

a. H_2^{2-} **b.** Ne_2 **c.** He_2^{2+} **d.** F_2^{2-}

78. Use molecular orbital theory to predict whether or not each molecule or ion should exist in a relatively stable form.

a. C_2^{2+} **b.** Li_2 **c.** Be_2^{2+} **d.** Li_2^{2-}

79. According to MO theory, which molecule or ion has the highest bond order? Highest bond energy? Shortest bond length?

$$C_2, C_2^+, C_2^-$$

80. According to MO theory, which molecule or ion has the highest bond order? Highest bond energy? Shortest bond length?

$$O_2, O_2^-, O_2^{2-}$$

81. Draw an MO energy diagram for CO. (Use the energy ordering of O_2.) Predict the bond order and make a sketch of the lowest energy bonding molecular orbital.

82. Draw an energy diagram for HCl. Predict the bond order and make a sketch of the lowest energy bonding molecular orbital.

Cumulative Problems

83. For each compound, draw an appropriate Lewis structure, determine the geometry using VSEPR theory, determine whether the molecule is polar, identify the hybridization of all interior atoms, and make a sketch of the molecule, according to valence bond theory, showing orbital overlap.

a. COF_2 (carbon is the central atom)
b. S_2Cl_2 (ClSSCl)
c. SF_4

84. For each compound, draw an appropriate Lewis structure, determine the geometry using VSEPR theory, determine whether the molecule is polar, identify the hybridization of all interior atoms, and make a sketch of the molecule, according to valence bond theory, showing orbital overlap.

a. IF_5 **b.** CH_2CHCH_3 **c.** CH_3SH

85. Amino acids are biological compounds that link together to form proteins, the workhorse molecules in living organisms. The skeletal structures of several simple amino acids are shown here. For each skeletal structure, complete the Lewis structure, determine the geometry and hybridization about each interior atom, and make a sketch of the molecule, using the bond conventions of Section 10.4.

(a) serine

(b) asparagine

(c) cysteine

86. The genetic code is based on four different bases with the structures shown here. Assign a geometry and hybridization to each interior atom in these four bases.

a. cytosine **b.** adenine **c.** thymine **d.** guanine

(a)

(b)

(c)

(d)

87. The structure of caffeine, present in coffee and many soft drinks, is shown here. How many pi bonds are present in caffeine? How many sigma bonds? Insert the lone pairs in the molecule. What kinds of orbitals do the lone pairs occupy?

88. The structure of acetylsalicylic acid (aspirin) is shown here. How many pi bonds are present in acetylsalicylic acid? How many sigma bonds? What parts of the molecule are free to rotate? What parts are rigid?

89. Most vitamins can be classified either as fat soluble, which tend to accumulate in the body (so that taking too much can be harmful), or water soluble, which tend to be quickly eliminated from the body in urine. Examine the structural formulas and space-filling models of these vitamins and determine whether they are fat soluble (mostly nonpolar) or water soluble (mostly polar).

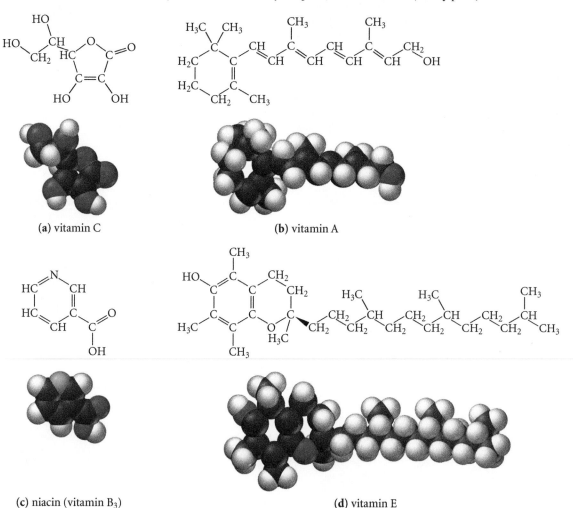

(a) vitamin C   (b) vitamin A

(c) niacin (vitamin B₃)   (d) vitamin E

90. Water does not easily remove grease from dishes or hands because grease is nonpolar and water is polar. The addition of soap to water, however, allows the grease to dissolve. Study the structure of sodium stearate (a soap) and suggest how it works.

$$CH_3(CH_2)_{16}\overset{\displaystyle O}{\overset{\displaystyle \|}{C}}{-}O^-Na^+$$

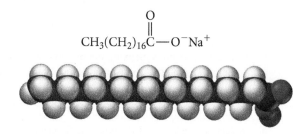

91. Draw a molecular orbital energy diagram for ClF. (Assume that the σ_p orbitals are lower in energy than the π orbitals.) What is the bond order in ClF?

92. Draw Lewis structures and MO diagrams for CN^+, CN, and CN^-. According to Lewis theory, which species is most stable? According to MO theory, which species is most stable? Do the two theories agree?

93. Bromine can form compounds or ions with any number of fluorine atoms from one to five. Write the formulas of all five of these species, assign a hybridization, and describe their electron and molecular geometry.

94. The compound C_3H_4 has two double bonds. Describe its bonding and geometry, using a valence bond approach.

95. Draw the structure of a molecule with the formula $C_4H_6Cl_2$ that has a dipole moment of 0.

96. Draw the structures of two compounds that have the composition CH_3NO_2 and have all three H atoms bonded to the C. Predict which compound has the larger ONO bond angle.

97. How many hybrid orbitals do we use to describe each molecule?
   a. N_2O_5
   b. C_2H_5NO (4 C—H bonds and one O—H bond)
   c. BrCN (no formal charges)

98. Indicate which orbitals overlap to form the σ bonds in:
   a. $BeBr_2$ **b.** $HgCl_2$ **c.** ICN

Challenge Problems

99. In VSEPR theory, which uses Lewis theory to determine molecular geometry, the trend of decreasing bond angle in CH_4, NH_3, and H_2O is accounted for by the greater repulsion of lone pair electrons compared to bonding pair electrons. How would this trend be accounted for in valence bond theory?

100. The results of a molecular orbital calculation for H_2O are shown here. Examine each of the orbitals and classify them as bonding, antibonding, or nonbonding. Assign the correct number of electrons to the energy diagram. According to this energy diagram, is H_2O stable? Explain.

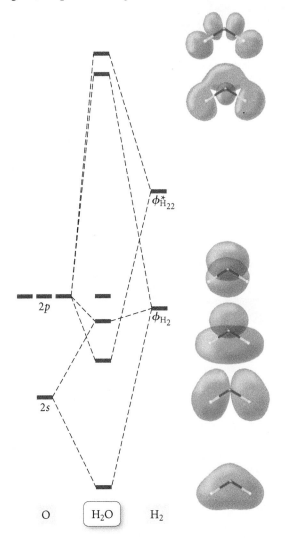

101. The results of a molecular orbital calculation for NH_3 are shown here. Examine each of the orbitals and classify them as bonding, antibonding, or nonbonding. Assign the correct number of electrons to the energy diagram. According to this energy diagram, is NH_3 stable? Explain.

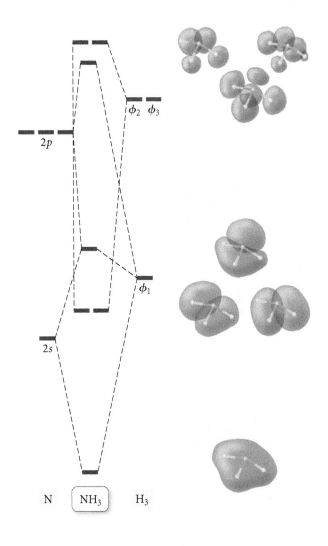

102. *cis*-2-Butene isomerizes to *trans*-2-butene via the reaction:

    a. If isomerization requires breaking the pi bond, what minimum energy is required for isomerization in J/mol? In J/molecule?
    b. If the energy for isomerization came from light, what minimum frequency of light would be required? In what portion of the electromagnetic spectrum does this frequency lie?

103. The species NO_2, NO_2^+, and NO_2^-, in which N is the central atom, have very different bond angles. Predict what these bond angles might be with respect to the ideal angles and justify your prediction.

104. The bond angles increase steadily in the series PF_3, PCl_3, PBr_3, and PI_3. After consulting the data on atomic radii in Chapter 8, provide an explanation for this observation.

105. The ion CH_5^+, can form under very special high-energy conditions in the vapor phase in a mass spectrometer. Propose a hybridization for the carbon atom and predict the geometry.

106. Neither the VSEPR model nor the hybridization model is able to account for the experimental observation that the $F—Ba—F$ bond angle in gaseous BaF_2 is 108° rather than the predicted 180°. Suggest some possible explanations for this observation.

Conceptual Problems

107. Pick the statement that best captures the fundamental idea behind VSEPR theory. Explain what is wrong with each of the other statements.

   a. The angle between two or more bonds is determined primarily by the repulsions between the electrons within those bonds and other (lone pair) electrons on the central atom of a molecule. Each of these electron groups (bonding electrons or lone pair electrons) will lower its potential energy by maximizing its separation from other electron groups, thus determining the geometry of the molecule.

   b. The angle between two or more bonds is determined primarily by the repulsions between the electrons within those bonds. Each of these bonding electrons will lower its potential energy by maximizing its separation from other electron groups, thus determining the geometry of the molecule.

   c. The geometry of a molecule is determined by the shapes of the overlapping orbitals that form the chemical bonds. Therefore, to determine the geometry of a molecule, you must determine the shapes of the orbitals involved in bonding.

108. Suppose that a molecule has four bonding groups and one lone pair on the central atom. Suppose further that the molecule is confined to two dimensions (this is a purely hypothetical assumption for the sake of understanding the principles behind VSEPR theory). Make a sketch of the molecule and estimate the bond angles.

109. How does each of the three major bonding theories (Lewis theory, valence bond theory, and molecular orbital theory) define a single chemical bond? A double bond? A triple bond? How are these definitions similar? How are they different?

110. The most stable forms of the nonmetals in groups 4A, 5A, and 6A of the first period are molecules with multiple bonds. Beginning with the second-period, the most stable forms of the nonmetals of these groups are molecules without multiple bonds. Propose an explanation for this observation based on valence bond theory.

11 Liquids, Solids, and Intermolecular Forces

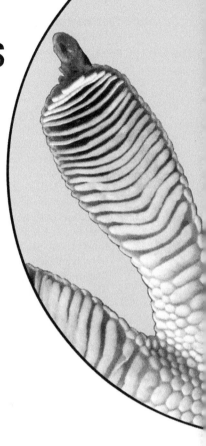

It's a wild dance floor there at the molecular level.
—Roald Hoffmann (1937–)

IN CHAPTER 1, WE SAW that matter exists primarily in three states (or phases): solid, liquid, and gas. In Chapter 5, we examined the gas state. In this chapter we turn to the solid and liquid states, known collectively as the *condensed* states. The solid and liquid states are more similar to each other than they are to the gas state. In the gas state, constituent particles—atoms or molecules—are separated by large distances and do not interact with each other very much. In the condensed states, constituent particles are close together and exert moderate to strong attractive forces on one another. Unlike the gas state, for which we have a good, simple quantitative model (kinetic molecular theory) to describe and predict behavior, we have no such model for the condensed states. In fact, modeling the condensed states is an active area of research. In this chapter, we focus primarily on describing the condensed states and their properties and on providing some qualitative guidelines to help us understand those properties.

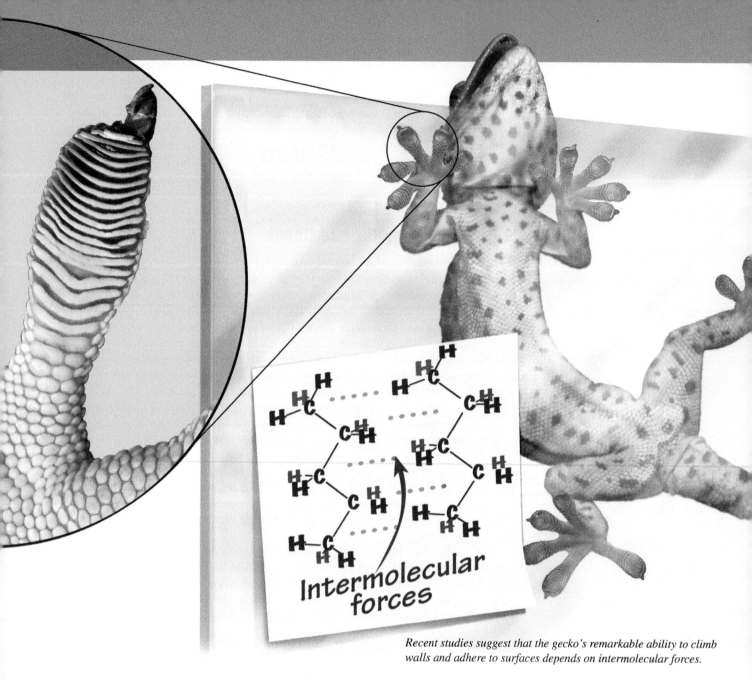

Recent studies suggest that the gecko's remarkable ability to climb walls and adhere to surfaces depends on intermolecular forces.

11.1 Climbing Geckos and Intermolecular Forces

The gecko shown here can run up a polished glass window in seconds or even walk across a ceiling. It can support its entire weight by a single toe in contact with a surface. How? Recent work by several scientists points to *intermolecular forces*—attractive forces that exist *between* all molecules and atoms—as the reason that the gecko can perform its gravity-defying feats. Intermolecular forces are the forces that hold many liquids and solids—such as water and ice, for example—together.

The key to the gecko's sticky feet lies in the millions of microhairs, called *setae*, that line its toes. Each seta is between 30 and 130 μm long and branches out to end in several hundred flattened tips called *spatulae*, as you can see in the photo. This unique structure allows the gecko's toes to have unusually close contact with the surfaces it climbs. The close contact allows intermolecular forces—which are significant only at short distances—to hold the gecko to the wall.

All living organisms depend on intermolecular forces, not for adhesion to walls, but for many physiological processes. For example, in Chapter 21 we examine how intermolecular forces help determine the shapes of protein molecules (the workhorse molecules in living organisms). Later in this chapter, we will discuss how intermolecular forces are central to the structure of DNA, the inheritable molecule that carries the blueprints for life. (See the *Chemistry and Medicine* box in Section 11.3.)

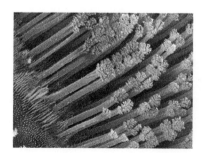

▲ Each of the millions of microhairs on a gecko's feet branches out to end in flattened tips called *spatulae*.

More generally, intermolecular forces are responsible for the very existence of condensed states. The state of a sample of matter—solid, liquid, or gas—depends on magnitude of intermolecular forces between the constituent particles relative to amount of thermal energy in the sample. Recall from Chapter 6 that the molecules and atoms composing matter are in constant random motion that increases with increasing temperature. The energy associated with this motion is called *thermal energy*. When thermal energy is high relative to intermolecular forces, matter tends to be gaseous. When thermal energy is low relative to intermolecular forces, matter tends to be liquid or solid.

11.2 Solids, Liquids, and Gases: A Molecular Comparison

We are all familiar with solids and liquids. Water, gasoline, rubbing alcohol, and nail polish remover are common liquids that you have probably encountered. Ice, dry ice, and diamond are familiar solids. To begin to understand the differences between the three common states of matter, examine Table 11.1, which shows the density and molar volume of water in its three different states, along with molecular representations of each state. Notice that the densities of the solid and liquid states are much greater than the density of the gas state. Notice also that the solid and liquid states are more similar in density and molar volume to one another than they are to the gas state. The molecular representations show the reason for these differences. The molecules in liquid water and ice are in close contact with one another—essentially touching—while those in gaseous water are separated by large distances. The molecular representation of gaseous water in Table 11.1 is actually out of proportion—the water molecules in the figure should be much farther apart for their size. (Only a fraction of a molecule could be included in the figure if it were drawn to scale.) From the molar volumes, we know that 18.0 mL of liquid water (slightly more than a tablespoon) would occupy 30.5 L when converted to gas at 100 °C. The low density of gaseous water is a direct result of this large separation between molecules.

Notice also that, for water, the solid is slightly less dense than the liquid. This is *atypical* behavior. Most solids are slightly denser than their corresponding liquids because the molecules move closer together upon freezing. As we will see in Section 11.9, ice is less dense than liquid water because the unique crystal structure of ice results in water molecules moving slightly further apart upon freezing.

TABLE 11.1 The Three States of Water

Phase	Temperature (°C)	Density (g/cm³, at 1 atm)	Molar Volume	Molecular View
Gas (steam)	100	5.90×10^{-4}	30.5 L	
Liquid (water)	20	0.998	18.0 mL	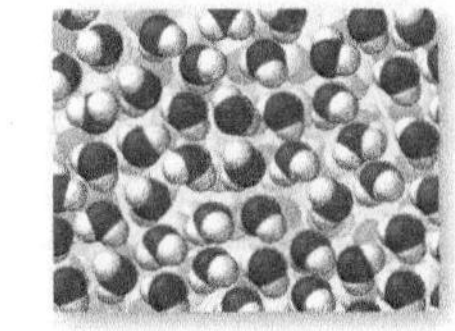
Solid (ice)	0	0.917	19.6 mL	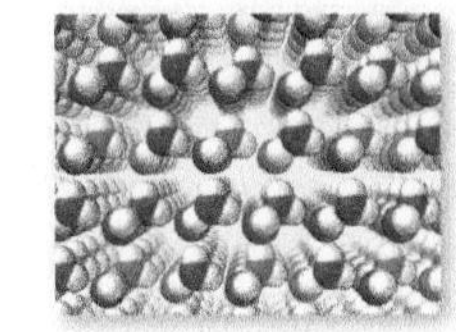

TABLE 11.2 Properties of the States of Matter

State	Density	Shape	Volume	Strength of Intermolecular Forces (Relative to Thermal Energy)
Gas	Low	Indefinite	Indefinite	Weak
Liquid	High	Indefinite	Definite	Moderate
Solid	High	Definite	Definite	Strong

A major difference between liquids and solids is the freedom of movement of the constituent molecules or atoms. Even though the atoms or molecules in a liquid are in close contact, thermal energy partially overcomes the attractions between them, allowing them to move around one another. This is not the case in solids; the atoms or molecules in a solid are virtually locked in their positions, only vibrating back and forth about a fixed point. The properties of liquids and solids, as well as the properties of gases for comparison, are summarized in Table 11.2.

Liquids assume the shape of their containers because the atoms or molecules that compose liquids are free to flow (or move around one another). When you pour water into a beaker, the water flows and assumes the shape of the beaker (Figure 11.1 ▶). Liquids are not easily compressed because the molecules or atoms that compose them are already in close contact—they cannot be pushed much closer together. The molecules in a gas, by contrast, have a great deal of space between them and are easily forced into a smaller volume by an increase in external pressure (Figure 11.2 ▼).

▲ **FIGURE 11.1 Liquids Assume the Shapes of Their Containers** When you pour water into a flask, it assumes the shape of the flask because water molecules are free to flow.

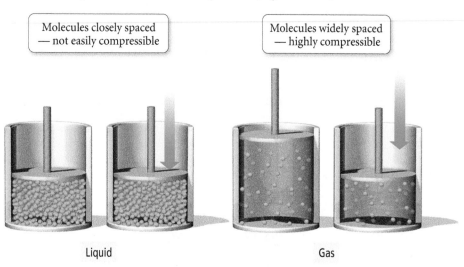

Molecules closely spaced — not easily compressible

Molecules widely spaced — highly compressible

Liquid

Gas

▲ **FIGURE 11.2 Gases Are Compressible** Molecules in a liquid are closely spaced and are not easily compressed. Molecules in a gas have a great deal of space between them, making gases compressible.

Solids have a definite shape because, in contrast to liquids and gases, the molecules or atoms that compose solids are fixed in place—each molecule or atom merely vibrates about a fixed point. Like liquids, solids have a definite volume and generally cannot be compressed because the molecules or atoms composing them are already in close contact. Solids may be **crystalline**, in which case the atoms or molecules that compose them are arranged in a well-ordered three-dimensional array, or they may be **amorphous**, in which case the atoms or molecules that compose them have no long-range order (Figure 11.3 ▶).

According to some definitions, an amorphous solid is considered a unique state, different from the normal solid state because it lacks any long-range order.

Regular ordered structure

No long-range order

▶ **FIGURE 11.3 Crystalline and Amorphous Solids** In a crystalline solid, the arrangement of the particles displays long-range order. In an amorphous solid, the arrangement of the particles has no long-range order.

Crystalline solid

Amorphous solid

Changes between States

We can transform one state of matter to another by changing the temperature, pressure, or both. For example, we can convert solid ice to liquid water by heating, and liquid water to solid ice by cooling. The following diagram shows the three states of matter and the changes in conditions that commonly induce transitions between them.

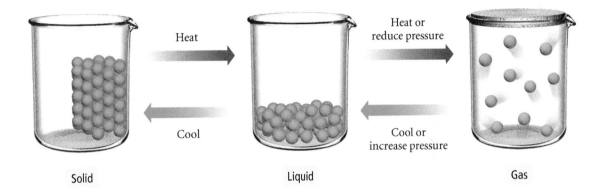

Solid   Liquid   Gas

C_3H_8 (g)

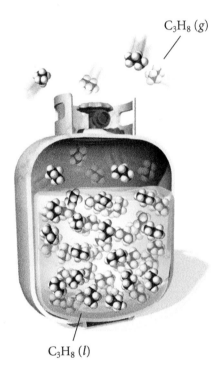

C_3H_8 (l)

▲ The propane in an LP gas tank is in the liquid state. When you open the tank, some propane vaporizes and escapes as a gas.

We can induce a transition between the liquid and gas state, not only by heating and cooling, but also through changing the pressure. In general, increases in pressure favor the denser state, so increasing the pressure of a gas sample results in a transition to the liquid state. The most familiar example of this phenomenon occurs in the LP (liquified petroleum) gas used as a fuel for outdoor grills and lanterns. LP gas is composed primarily of propane, a gas at room temperature and atmospheric pressure. However, it liquefies at pressures exceeding about 2.7 atm. The propane you buy in a tank is under pressure and therefore in the liquid form. When you open the tank, some of the propane escapes as a gas, lowering the pressure in the tank for a brief moment. Immediately, however, some of the liquid propane evaporates, replacing the gas that escaped. Storing gases like propane as liquids is efficient because, in their liquid form, they occupy much less space.

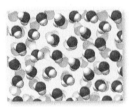 **Conceptual Connection 11.1 State Changes**

The molecular diagram below shows a sample of liquid water.

Which diagram best depicts the vapor emitted from a pot of boiling water?

ANSWER: (a) When water boils, it simply changes state from liquid to gas. Water molecules do not decompose during boiling.

11.3 Intermolecular Forces: The Forces That Hold Condensed States Together

The strength of the intermolecular forces between the molecules or atoms that compose a substance determines its state—solid, liquid, or gas—at a given temperature. At room temperature, moderate to strong intermolecular forces tend to result in liquids and solids (high melting and boiling points) and weak intermolecular forces tend to result in gases (low melting and boiling points).

Intermolecular forces originate from the interactions between charges, partial charges, and temporary charges on molecules (or atoms and ions), much as bonding forces originate from interactions between charged particles in atoms. Recall from Section 8.3 that according to Coulomb's law, the potential energy (E) of two oppositely charged particles (with charges q_1 and q_2) decreases (becomes more negative) with increasing magnitude of charge and with decreasing separation (r):

$$E = \frac{1}{4\pi\varepsilon_0}\frac{q_1 q_2}{r} \quad \text{(When } q_1 \text{ and } q_2 \text{ are opposite in sign, } E \text{ is negative.)}$$

Therefore, as we have seen, protons and electrons are attracted to each other because their potential energy decreases as they get closer together. Similarly, molecules with partial or temporary charges are attracted to each other because *their* potential energy decreases as they get closer together. However, intermolecular forces, even the strongest ones, are generally *much weaker* than bonding forces.

The reason for the relative weakness of intermolecular forces compared to bonding forces is also related to Coulomb's law. Bonding forces are the result of large charges (the charges on protons and electrons) interacting at very close distances. Intermolecular forces are the result of smaller charges (as we shall see in the following discussion) interacting at greater distances. For example, consider the interaction between two water molecules in liquid water:

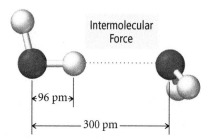

The length of an O—H bond in liquid water is 96 pm; however, the average distance between water molecules in liquid water is about 300 pm. The larger distances between molecules, as well as the smaller charges involved (partial charges on the hydrogen and oxygen atoms), result in weaker forces. To break the O—H bonds in water, you have to heat the water to thousands of degrees Celsius. However, to completely overcome the intermolecular forces *between* water molecules, you have to heat water only to its boiling point, 100 °C (at sea level).

Here we examine several different types of intermolecular forces, including dispersion forces, dipole–dipole forces, hydrogen bonding, and ion–dipole forces. The first three of these can potentially occur in all substances; the last one occurs only in mixtures.

Dispersion Force

The one intermolecular force present in all molecules and atoms is the **dispersion force** (also called the London force). Dispersion forces are the result of fluctuations in the electron distribution within molecules or atoms. Since all atoms and molecules have electrons, they all exhibit dispersion forces. The electrons in an atom or molecule may, *at any*

The nature of dispersion forces was first recognized by Fritz W. London (1900–1954), a German-American physicist.

one instant, be unevenly distributed. Imagine a frame-by-frame movie of a helium atom in which each "frame" captures the position of the helium atom's two electrons.

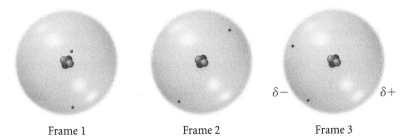

| Frame 1 | Frame 2 | Frame 3 |

In any one frame, the electrons are not symmetrically arranged around the nucleus. In frame 3, for example, helium's two electrons are on the left side of the helium atom. At that instant, the left side will have a slightly negative charge ($\delta-$). The right side of the atom, which temporarily has no electrons, will have a slightly positive charge ($\delta+$) because of the charge of the nucleus. This fleeting charge separation is called an *instantaneous dipole* or a *temporary dipole*. As shown in Figure 11.4 ▼, an instantaneous dipole on one helium atom induces an instantaneous dipole on its neighboring atoms because the positive end of the instantaneous dipole attracts electrons in the neighboring atoms. The neighboring atoms then attract one another—the positive end of one instantaneous dipole attracting the negative end of another. This attraction is the dispersion force.

► **FIGURE 11.4 Dispersion Interactions** The temporary dipole in one helium atom induces a temporary dipole in its neighbor. The resulting attraction between the positive and negative charges creates the dispersion force.

Dispersion Force

An instantaneous dipole on any one helium atom induces instantaneous dipoles on neighboring atoms, which then attract one another.

| To polarize means to form a dipole moment (see Section 9.6).

The *magnitude* of the dispersion force depends on how easily the electrons in the atom or molecule can move or *polarize* in response to an instantaneous dipole, which in turn depends on the size (or volume) of the electron cloud. A larger electron cloud results in a greater dispersion force because the electrons are held less tightly by the nucleus and therefore polarize more easily. If all other variables are constant, the dispersion force increases with increasing molar mass because molecules or atoms of higher molar mass generally have more electrons dispersed over a greater volume. For example, consider the boiling points of the noble gases displayed in Table 11.3. As the molar masses and electron cloud volumes of the noble gases increase, the greater dispersion forces result in increasing boiling points.

Molar mass alone, however, does not determine the magnitude of the dispersion force. Compare the molar masses and boiling points of *n*-pentane and neopentane:

TABLE 11.3 Boiling Points of the Noble Gases

Noble Gas		Molar Mass (g/mol)	Boiling Point (K)
He		4.00	4.2
Ne		20.18	27
Ar		39.95	87
Kr		83.80	120
Xe		131.30	165

n-Pentane
molar mass = 72.15 g/mol
boiling point = 36.1 °C

Neopentane
molar mass = 72.15 g/mol
boiling point = 9.5 °C

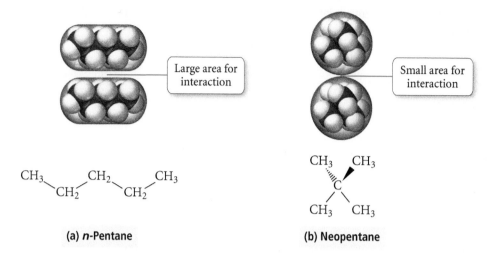

(a) *n*-Pentane   (b) Neopentane

◀ FIGURE 11.5 Dispersion Force and Molecular Shape **(a)** The straight shape of *n*-pentane molecules allows them to interact with one another along the entire length of the molecules. **(b)** The nearly spherical shape of neopentane molecules allows for only a small area of interaction. Thus, dispersion forces are weaker in neopentane than in *n*-pentane, resulting in a lower boiling point.

These molecules have identical molar masses, but *n*-pentane has a higher boiling point than neopentane. Why? Because the two molecules have different shapes. The *n*-pentane molecules are long and can interact with one another along their entire length, as shown in Figure 11.5a ▲. In contrast, the bulky, round shape of neopentane molecules results in a smaller area of interaction between neighboring molecules, as shown in Figure 11.5b. The result is a lower boiling point for neopentane.

Although molecular shape and other factors must always be considered in determining the magnitude of dispersion forces, molar mass can act as a guide when comparing dispersion forces within a family of similar elements or compounds as shown in Figure 11.6 ▼.

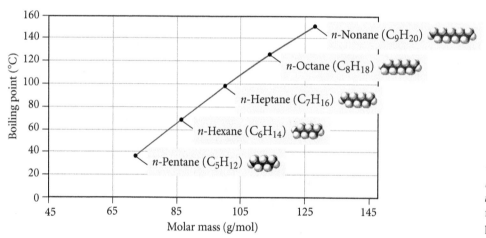

◀ FIGURE 11.6 Boiling Points of the *n*-Alkanes The boiling points of the *n*-alkanes rise with increasing molar mass and the consequent stronger dispersion forces.

Dipole–Dipole Force

The **dipole–dipole force** exists in all molecules that are polar. Polar molecules have **permanent dipoles** that interact with the permanent dipoles of neighboring molecules, as you can see in Figure 11.7 ▶. The positive end of one permanent dipole attracts the negative end of another; this attraction is the dipole–dipole force. Polar molecules, therefore, have higher melting and boiling points than nonpolar molecules of similar molar mass. Remember that all molecules (including polar ones) have dispersion forces. Polar molecules have, *in addition*, dipole–dipole forces. This additional attractive force raises

See Section 9.6 to review how to determine whether a molecule is polar.

Dipole–Dipole Interaction

The positive end of a polar molecule is attracted to the negative end of its neighbor.

▶ **FIGURE 11.7 Dipole–Dipole Interaction** Molecules with permanent dipoles, such as acetone, are attracted to one another via dipole–dipole interactions.

their melting and boiling points relative to nonpolar molecules of similar molar mass. For example, consider formaldehyde and ethane:

Name	Formula	Molar Mass (amu)	Structure		bp (°C)	mp (°C)
Formaldehyde	CH_2O	30.03	O‖H—C—H		−19.5	−92
Ethane	C_2H_6	30.07	H H||H—C—C—H||H H		−88	−172

Formaldehyde is polar, and has a higher melting point and boiling point than nonpolar ethane, even though the two compounds have the same molar mass. Figure 11.8 ▼ shows the boiling points of a series of molecules with similar molar mass but progressively greater dipole moments. Notice that the boiling points increase with increasing dipole moment.

The polarity of molecules composing liquids is also important in determining the **miscibility**—the ability to mix without separating into two states—of liquids. In general, polar liquids are miscible with other polar liquids but are not miscible with nonpolar liquids. For example, water, a polar liquid, is not miscible with pentane (C_5H_{12}) a nonpolar liquid (Figure 11.9 ►). Similarly, water and oil (also nonpolar) do not mix. Consequently, oily hands or oily stains on clothes cannot be washed with plain water (see Chemistry in Your Day: *How Soap Works* in Section 10.5).

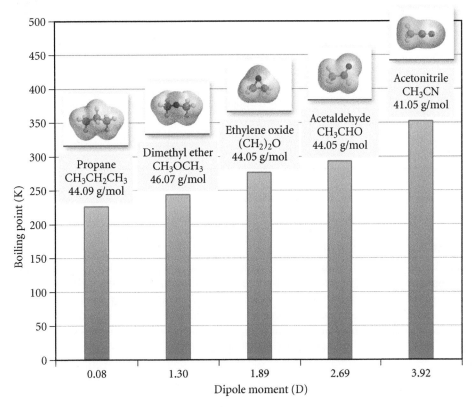

▲ **FIGURE 11.8 Dipole Moment and Boiling Point** The molecules shown here all have similar molar masses but different dipole moments. The boiling points increase with increasing dipole moment.

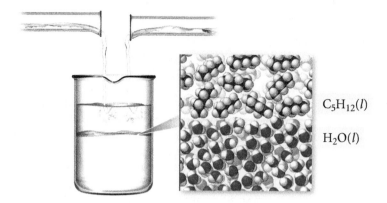

$C_5H_{12}(l)$

$H_2O(l)$

◀ **FIGURE 11.9 Polar and Nonpolar Compounds** Water and pentane do not mix because water molecules are polar and pentane molecules are nonpolar.

EXAMPLE 11.1 Dipole–Dipole Forces

Which of these molecules have dipole–dipole forces?

(a) CO_2 **(b)** CH_2Cl_2 **(c)** CH_4

SOLUTION

A molecule has dipole–dipole forces if it is polar. To determine whether a molecule is polar, (1) *determine whether the molecule contains polar bonds* and (2) *determine whether the polar bonds add together to form a net dipole moment* (Section 9.6).

(a) CO_2 (1) Since the electronegativity of carbon is 2.5 and that of oxygen is 3.5 (Figure 9.8), CO_2 has polar bonds. (2) The geometry of CO_2 is linear. Consequently, the dipoles of the polar bonds cancel, so the molecule is *not polar* and does not have dipole–dipole forces.	(a) O=C=O  No dipole forces present
(b) CH_2Cl_2 (1) The electronegativity of C is 2.5, that of H is 2.1, and that of Cl is 3.0. Consequently, CH_2Cl_2 has two polar bonds (C—Cl) and two bonds that are nearly nonpolar (C—H). (2) The geometry of CH_2Cl_2 is tetrahedral. Since the C—Cl bonds and the C—H bonds are different, their dipoles do not cancel but sum to a net dipole moment. The molecule is polar and has dipole–dipole forces.	CH_2Cl_2 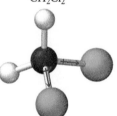 Dipole forces present
(c) CH_4 (1) Since the electronegativity of C is 2.5 and that of hydrogen is 2.1 the C—H bonds are nearly nonpolar. (2) In addition, since the geometry of the molecule is tetrahedral, any slight polarities that the bonds might have will cancel. CH_4 is therefore nonpolar and does not have dipole–dipole forces.	CH_4 No dipole forces present

FOR PRACTICE 11.1

Which molecules have dipole–dipole forces?

(a) CI_4 **(b)** CH_3Cl **(c)** HCl

Hydrogen Bonding

Polar molecules containing hydrogen atoms bonded directly to small electronegative atoms—most importantly fluorine, oxygen, or nitrogen—exhibit an intermolecular force called **hydrogen bonding**. HF, NH_3, and H_2O, for example, all undergo hydrogen bonding. The hydrogen bond is a sort of *super* dipole–dipole force. The large electronegativity difference between hydrogen and any of these electronegative elements causes the hydrogen atom to have a fairly large partial positive charge ($\delta+$) within the bond, while the F, O, or N atom has a fairly large partial negative charge ($\delta-$). In addition, since these atoms are all quite small, the H atom on one molecule can approach the F, O, or N atom on an adjacent molecule very closely. The result is a strong attraction between the H atom on one molecule and the F, O, or N on its neighbor, an attraction called a **hydrogen bond**. For example, in HF, the hydrogen atom in one molecule is strongly attracted to the fluorine atom on a neighboring molecule (Figure 11.10 ◄).

Hydrogen bonds should not be confused with chemical bonds. Chemical bonds occur *between individual atoms within a molecule*, whereas hydrogen bonds—like dispersion forces and dipole–dipole forces—are intermolecular forces that occur *between molecules*. A typical hydrogen bond is only 2–5% as strong as a typical covalent chemical bond. Hydrogen bonds are, however, the strongest of the three *intermolecular* forces we have discussed so far. Substances composed of molecules that form hydrogen bonds have higher melting and boiling points than substances composed of molecules that do not form hydrogen bonds. For example, consider ethanol and dimethyl ether:

Hydrogen Bonding

When H bonds directly to F, O, or N, the bonding atoms acquire relatively large partial charges, giving rise to strong dipole–dipole attractions between neighboring molecules.

▲ **FIGURE 11.10 Hydrogen Bonding in HF** The hydrogen of one HF molecule, with its partial positive charge, is attracted to the fluorine of its neighbor, with its partial negative charge. This dipole–dipole interaction is an example of a hydrogen bond.

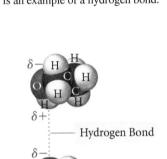

▲ **FIGURE 11.11 Hydrogen Bonding in Ethanol**

Name	Formula	Molar Mass (amu)	Structure	bp (°C)	mp (°C)
Ethanol	C_2H_6O	46.07	CH_3CH_2OH	78.3	−114.1
Dimethyl Ether	C_2H_6O	46.07	CH_3OCH_3	−22.0	−138.5

Since ethanol contains hydrogen bonded directly to oxygen, ethanol molecules form hydrogen bonds with each other as shown in Figure 11.11 ◄. The hydrogen that is directly bonded to oxygen in an individual ethanol molecule is also strongly attracted to the oxygen on neighboring molecules. This strong attraction makes the boiling point of ethanol 78.3 °C. Consequently, ethanol is a liquid at room temperature. In contrast, dimethyl ether has an identical molar mass to ethanol but does not exhibit hydrogen bonding because in the dimethyl ether molecule, the oxygen atom is not bonded directly to hydrogen; this results in lower boiling and melting points and dimethyl ether is a gas at room temperature.

Water is another good example of a molecule with hydrogen bonding (Figure 11.12 ◄). Figure 11.13 ► shows the boiling points of the simple hydrogen compounds of the group 4A and group 6A elements. In general, boiling points increase with increasing molar mass, as expected based on increasing dispersion forces. However, because of hydrogen bonding, the boiling point of water (100 °C) is much higher than expected based on its molar mass (18.0 g/mol). Without hydrogen bonding, all the water on our planet would be gaseous.

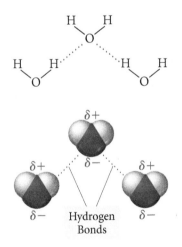

▲ **FIGURE 11.12 Hydrogen Bonding in Water**

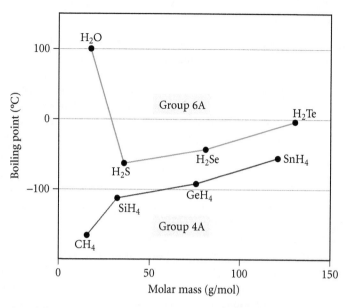

▲ **FIGURE 11.13 Boiling Points of Group 4A and 6A Compounds**
Because of hydrogen bonding, the boiling point of water is anomalous
compared to the boiling points of other hydrogen-containing compounds.

EXAMPLE 11.2 Hydrogen Bonding

One of these compounds is a liquid at room temperature. Which one and why?

Formaldehyde   Fluoromethane   Hydrogen peroxide

SOLUTION

The three compounds have similar molar masses:

Formaldehyde	30.03 g/mol
Fluoromethane	34.03 g/mol
Hydrogen peroxide	34.02 g/mol

So the strengths of their dispersion forces are similar. All three compounds are also
polar, so they have dipole–dipole forces. Hydrogen peroxide, however, is the only one
of these compounds that also contains H bonded directly to F, O, or N. Therefore it also
has hydrogen bonding and is likely to have the highest boiling point of the three. Since
the example stated that only one of the compounds was a liquid, we can safely assume
that hydrogen peroxide is the liquid. Note that, although fluoromethane *contains* both H
and F, H is not *directly bonded* to F, so fluoromethane does not have hydrogen bonding
as an intermolecular force. Similarly, formaldehyde *contains* both H and O, but H is not
directly bonded to O, so formaldehyde does not have hydrogen bonding either.

FOR PRACTICE 11.2

Which has the higher boiling point, HF or HCl? Why?

Ion–Dipole Force

The **ion–dipole force** occurs when an ionic compound is mixed with a polar compound; it is especially important in aqueous solutions of ionic compounds. For example, when sodium chloride is mixed with water, the sodium and chloride ions interact with water molecules via ion–dipole forces, as shown in Figure 11.14 ◄. The positive sodium ions interact with the negative poles of water molecules, while the negative chloride ions interact with the positive poles. Ion–dipole forces are the strongest of the types of intermolecular forces discussed here and are responsible for the ability of ionic substances to form solutions with water. We discuss aqueous solutions more thoroughly in Chapter 12.

Ion–Dipole Forces

The positively charged end of a polar molecule such as H_2O is attracted to negative ions and the negatively charged end of the molecule is attracted to positive ions.

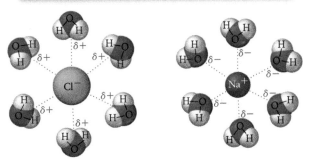

▲ FIGURE 11.14 **Ion–Dipole Forces** Ion–dipole forces exist between Na^+ and the negative ends of H_2O molecules and between Cl^- and the positive ends of H_2O molecules.

Summarizing Intermolecular Forces (as shown in Table 11.4):

▶ Dispersion forces are present in all molecules and atoms and increase with increasing molar mass. These forces are always weak in small molecules but can be significant in molecules with high molar masses.

▶ Dipole–dipole forces are present in polar molecules.

▶ Hydrogen bonds, the strongest of the intermolecular forces that can occur in pure substances (second only to ion–dipole forces in general), are present in molecules containing hydrogen bonded directly to fluorine, oxygen, or nitrogen.

▶ Ion–dipole forces are present in mixtures of ionic compounds and polar compounds. These are very strong and are especially important in aqueous solutions of ionic compounds.

TABLE 11.4 Types of Intermolecular Forces

Type	Present in	Molecular perspective	Strength
Dispersion	All molecules and atoms	$\delta-$ $\delta+\cdots\delta-$ $\delta+$	
Dipole–dipole	Polar molecules	$\delta+$ $\delta-\cdots\delta+$ $\delta-$	
Hydrogen bonding	Molecules containing H bonded to F, O, or N	$\delta+$ $\delta+\cdots\delta-\cdots\delta+$ $\delta-$ $\delta-$	
Ion–dipole	Mixtures of ionic compounds and polar compounds	$\delta-$ $\delta-$ $\delta-$ $+$ $\delta-$ $\delta-$	

CHEMISTRY AND MEDICINE Hydrogen Bonding in DNA

DNA is a long, chainlike molecule that acts as a blueprint for each living organism. Copies of DNA are passed from parent to offspring, which is how we inherit traits from our parents. A DNA molecule is composed of thousands of repeating units called *nucleotides* (Figure 11.15 ▼). Each nucleotide contains one of four different *organic bases*: adenine, thymine, cytosine, and guanine (abbreviated A, T, C, and G). The order of these bases along DNA encodes the information that determines the nature of the proteins that are made in the body (proteins are the molecules that do most of the work in living organisms). Our proteins in turn determine many of our characteristics, including how we look, what diseases we are at risk of developing, and even our behavior.

Thymine
Adenine
Cytosine
Guanine

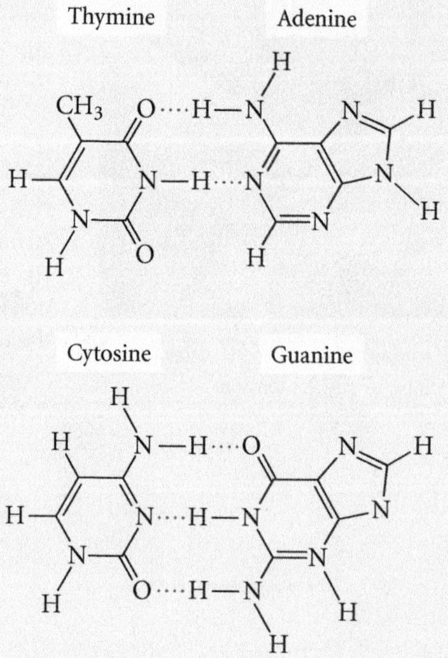

▶ **FIGURE 11.16 Complementary Base Pairing via Hydrogen Bonds** The individual bases in DNA interact with one another via specific hydrogen bonds that form between A and T and between C and G.

Base
Base
Base
Sugar
Sugar
Sugar
Phosphate
Phosphate
Phosphate
Nucleotide

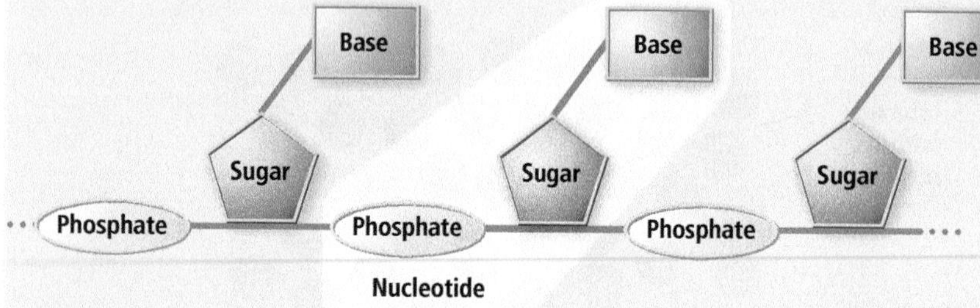

▲ **FIGURE 11.15 Nucleotides** The individual units in a DNA polymer are called nucleotides. Each nucleotide contains one of four bases: adenine, thymine, cytosine, and guanine (abbreviated A, T, C, and G).

The replicating mechanism of DNA is related to its structure, which was discovered in 1953 by James Watson and Francis Crick. DNA consists of two *complementary* strands, wrapped around each other in the now famous double helix and linked by hydrogen bonds between the bases on each strand. Each base (A, T, C, and G) has a complementary partner with which it forms hydrogen bonds (Figure 11.16 ▲): adenine (A) with thymine (T) and cytosine (C) with guanine (G). The hydrogen bonding is so specific that each base will pair only with its complementary partner. When a cell is going to divide, enzymes unzip the DNA molecule across the hydrogen bonds that join its two strands (Figure 11.17 ▼). Then new bases, complementary to the bases in each strand, are added along each of the original strands, forming hydrogen bonds with their complements. The result is two identical copies of the original DNA.

Question

Why would dispersion forces not work as a way to hold the two strands of DNA together? Why would covalent bonds not work?

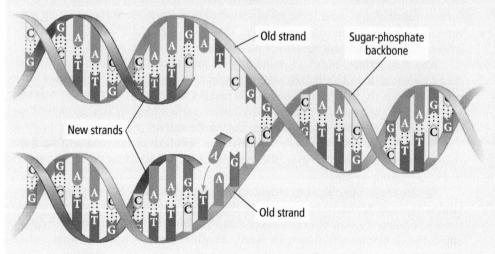

Old strand
Sugar-phosphate backbone
New strands
Old strand

◀ **FIGURE 11.17 Copying DNA** The two strands of the DNA molecule can "unzip" by breaking the hydrogen bonds that join the base pairs. New bases complementary to the bases of each strand are assembled and joined together. The result is two molecules, each identical to the original one.

▲ A trout fly can float on water because of surface tension.

11.4 Intermolecular Forces in Action: Surface Tension, Viscosity, and Capillary Action

The most important manifestation of intermolecular forces is the very existence of liquids and solids. In liquids, we also observe several other manifestations of intermolecular forces including surface tension, viscosity, and capillary action.

Surface Tension

A fly fisherman delicately casts a small fishing fly (a metal hook with a few feathers and strings attached to make it look like an insect) onto the surface of a moving stream. The fly floats on the surface of the water—even though the metal composing the hook is denser than water—and attracts trout. Why? The hook floats because of *surface tension*, the tendency of liquids to minimize their surface area.

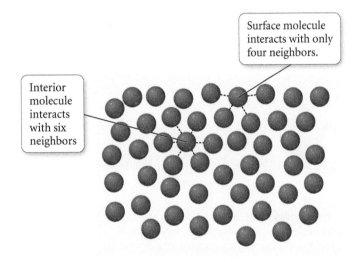

Surface molecule interacts with only four neighbors.

Interior molecule interacts with six neighbors

▶ **FIGURE 11.18 The Origin of Surface Tension** Molecules at the liquid surface have a higher potential energy than those in the interior. As a result, liquids tend to minimize their surface area, and the surface behaves like a membrane or "skin."

Recall from Section 11.3 that the interactions between molecules lower their potential energy in much the same way that the interaction between protons and electrons lowers their potential energy, in accordance with Coulomb's law.

We can understand surface tension by examining Figure 11.18 ▲, which depicts the intermolecular forces experienced by a molecule at the surface of the liquid compared to those experienced by a molecule in the interior. Notice that a molecule at the surface has relatively fewer neighbors with which to interact, and is therefore inherently less stable—it has higher potential energy—than those in the interior. (Remember that the attractive interactions with other molecules lower potential energy.) In order to increase the surface area of the liquid, molecules from the interior have to be moved to the surface, and, since molecules at the surface have a higher potential energy than those in the interior, this movement requires energy. Therefore, liquids tend to minimize their surface area. The **surface tension** of a liquid is the energy required to increase the surface area by a unit amount. For example, at room temperature, water has a surface tension of 72.8 mJ/m^2—it takes 72.8 mJ to increase the surface area of water by one square meter.

Why does surface tension allow the fly fisherman's hook to float on water? The tendency for liquids to minimize their surface creates a kind of skin at the surface that resists penetration. For the fisherman's hook to sink into the water, the water's surface area must increase slightly—an increase that is resisted by the surface tension. You can observe surface tension by carefully placing a paper clip on the surface of water (Figure 11.19 ◀). The paper clip, even though it is denser than water, will float on the surface of the water. A slight tap on the clip will provide the energy necessary to overcome the surface tension and cause the clip to sink.

Surface tension decreases as intermolecular forces decrease. You can't float a paper clip on benzene, for example, because the dispersion forces among the molecules composing benzene are significantly weaker than the hydrogen bonds among water molecules. The surface tension of benzene is only 28 mJ/m^2—just 40% that of water.

Surface tension is also the reason that small water droplets (those not large enough to be distorted by gravity) form nearly perfect spheres. On the Space Shuttle, the complete absence of gravity allows even large samples of water to form nearly perfect spheres

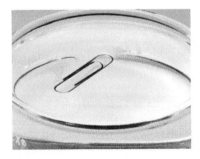

▲ **FIGURE 11.19 Surface Tension in Action** A paper clip floats on water due to surface tension.

(Figure 11.20 ▶). Why? Just as gravity pulls the matter of a planet or star inward to form a sphere, so intermolecular forces among collections of water molecules pull the water into a sphere. A sphere is the geometrical shape with the smallest surface area to volume ratio; therefore, the formation of a sphere minimizes the number of molecules at the surface, thus minimizing the potential energy of the system.

Viscosity

Another manifestation of intermolecular forces is **viscosity**, the resistance of a liquid to flow. Motor oil, for example, is more viscous than gasoline, and maple syrup is more viscous than water. Viscosity is measured in a unit called the poise (P), defined as $1 \text{ g/cm} \cdot \text{s}$. The viscosity of water at room temperature is approximately one centipoise (cP). Viscosity is greater in substances with stronger intermolecular forces because if molecules are more strongly attracted to each other, they do not flow around each other as freely. Viscosity also depends on molecular shape, increasing in longer molecules that can interact over a greater area and possibly become entangled. Table 11.5 lists the viscosity of several hydrocarbons. Notice the increase in viscosity with increasing molar mass (and therefore increasing magnitude of dispersion forces) and with increasing length (and therefore increasing potential for molecular entanglement).

Viscosity also depends on temperature because thermal energy partially overcomes the intermolecular forces, allowing molecules to flow past each other more easily. Table 11.6 lists the viscosity of water as a function of temperature. Nearly all liquids become less viscous as temperature increases.

▲ **FIGURE 11.20 Spherical Water Droplets** On the Space Shuttle in orbit, under weightless conditions, water coalesces into nearly perfect spheres held together by intermolecular forces between water molecules.

TABLE 11.5 Viscosity of Several Hydrocarbons at 20 °C

Hydrocarbon	Molar Mass (g/mol)	Formula	Viscosity (cP)
n-Pentane	72.15	$CH_3CH_2CH_2CH_2CH_3$	0.240
n-Hexane	86.17	$CH_3CH_2CH_2CH_2CH_2CH_3$	0.326
n-Heptane	100.2	$CH_3CH_2CH_2CH_2CH_2CH_2CH_3$	0.409
n-Octane	114.2	$CH_3CH_2CH_2CH_2CH_2CH_2CH_2CH_3$	0.542
n-Nonane	128.3	$CH_3CH_2CH_2CH_2CH_2CH_2CH_2CH_2CH_3$	0.711

TABLE 11.6 Viscosity of Liquid Water at Several Temperatures

Temperature (°C)	Viscosity (cP)
20	1.002
40	0.653
60	0.467
80	0.355
100	0.282

 CHEMISTRY IN YOUR DAY **Viscosity and Motor Oil**

Viscosity is an important property of the motor oil you put into your car. The oil must be thick enough to adequately coat engine surfaces to lubricate them, but also thin enough to be pumped easily into all the required engine compartments. Motor oil viscosity is usually reported on a scale called the SAE scale (named after the Society of Automotive Engineers). The higher the SAE rating, the more viscous the oil. The thinnest motor oils have SAE ratings of 5 or 10, while the thickest have SAE ratings of up to 50. Before the 1950s, most automobile owners changed the oil in their engine to accommodate seasonal changes in weather—a higher SAE rating was required in the summer months and a lower rating in the winter. Today, the advent of multigrade oils allows car owners in many climates to keep the same oil all year long. Multigrade oils, such as the 10W-40 oil shown here, contain polymers (long molecules made up of repeating structural units) that coil at low temperatures but unwind at high temperatures. At low temperatures, the coiled polymers—because of their compact shape—do not contribute very much to the oil's viscosity. As the temperature increases, however, the molecules unwind and their long shape results in intermolecular forces and molecular entanglements that prevent the viscosity from decreasing as much as it would normally. The result is an oil whose viscosity is less temperature dependent than it would be otherwise, allowing the same oil to be used over a wider range of temperatures. The 10W-40 designation indicates that the oil has an SAE rating of 10 at low temperatures and 40 at high temperatures.

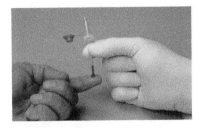

▲ Blood is drawn into a capillary tube by capillary action.

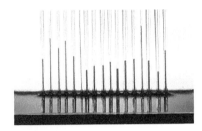

▲ **FIGURE 11.21 Capillary Action**
The attraction of water molecules to the glass surface draws the liquid around the edge of the tube up the walls. The water in the rest of the column is pulled along by the attraction of water molecules to one another. As can be seen above, the narrower the tube, the higher the liquid will rise.

▲ **FIGURE 11.22 Meniscuses of Water and Mercury** The meniscus of water (dyed red for visibility at left) is concave because water molecules are more strongly attracted to the glass wall than to one another. The meniscus of mercury is convex because mercury atoms are more strongly attracted to one another than to the glass walls.

Capillary Action

Medical technicians often take advantage of **capillary action**—the ability of a liquid to flow against gravity up a narrow tube—when taking a blood sample. The technician pokes the patient's finger with a pin, squeezes some blood out of the puncture, and then collects the blood with a thin tube. When the tube's tip comes into contact with the blood, the blood is drawn into the tube by capillary action. The same force plays a role in the way that trees and plants draw water from the soil.

Capillary action results from a combination of two forces: the attraction between molecules in a liquid, called *cohesive forces*, and the attraction between these molecules and the surface of the tube, called *adhesive forces*. The adhesive forces cause the liquid to spread out over the surface of the tube, while the cohesive forces cause the liquid to stay together. If the adhesive forces are greater than the cohesive forces (as is the case for water in a glass tube), the attraction to the surface draws the liquid up the tube and the cohesive forces pull along those molecules not in direct contact with the tube walls (Figure 11.21 ◄). The water rises up the tube until the force of gravity balances the capillary action—the thinner the tube, the higher the rise. If the adhesive forces are smaller than the cohesive forces (as is the case for liquid mercury), the liquid does not rise up the tube at all (and in fact will drop to a level below the level of the surrounding liquid).

The result of the differences in the relative magnitudes of cohesive and adhesive forces can be seen by comparing the meniscus of water to the meniscus of mercury (Figure 11.22 ◄). (The meniscus is the curved shape of a liquid surface within a tube.) The meniscus of water is concave (rounded inward) because the *adhesive forces* are greater than the cohesive forces, causing the edges of the water to creep up the sides of the tube a bit, forming the familiar cupped shape. The meniscus of mercury is convex (rounded outward) because the *cohesive forces*—due to metallic bonding between the atoms—are greater than the adhesive forces. The mercury atoms crowd toward the interior of the liquid to maximize their interactions with each other, resulting in the upward bulge at the center of the surface.

11.5 Vaporization and Vapor Pressure

We now turn our attention to vaporization, the process by which thermal energy can overcome intermolecular forces and produce a state change from liquid to gas. We will first discuss the process of vaporization itself, then the energetics of vaporization, and finally the concepts of vapor pressure, dynamic equilibrium, and critical point. Vaporization is a common occurrence that we experience every day and even depend on to maintain proper body temperature.

The Process of Vaporization

Imagine water molecules in a beaker at room temperature and open to the atmosphere (Figure 11.23 ►). The molecules are in constant motion due to thermal energy. If you could actually see the molecules at the surface, you would witness what Roald Hoffmann described as a "wild dance floor" (see the chapter-opening quote) because of all the vibrating, jostling, and molecular movement. *The higher the temperature, the greater the average energy of the collection of molecules.* However, at any one time, some molecules would have more thermal energy than the average and some would have less.

The distributions of thermal energies for the molecules in a sample of water at two different tem-

$H_2O(g)$

$H_2O(l)$

▶ **FIGURE 11.23 Vaporization of Water** Some molecules in an open beaker have enough kinetic energy to vaporize from the surface of the liquid.

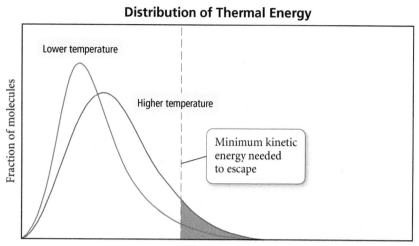

Distribution of Thermal Energy

◀ **FIGURE 11.24 Distribution of Thermal Energy** The thermal energies of the molecules in a liquid are distributed over a range. The peak energy increases with increasing temperature.

peratures are shown in Figure 11.24 ▲. The molecules at the high end of the distribution curve have enough energy to break free from the surface—where molecules are held less tightly than in the interior due to fewer neighbor–neighbor interactions—and into the gas state. This transition, from liquid to gas, is called **vaporization**. Some of the water molecules in the gas state, at the low end of the energy distribution curve for the gaseous molecules, may plunge back into the water and be captured by intermolecular forces. This transition, from gas to liquid, is the opposite of vaporization and is called **condensation**.

Although both evaporation and condensation occur in a beaker open to the atmosphere, under normal conditions evaporation takes place at a greater rate because most of the newly evaporated molecules escape into the surrounding atmosphere and never come back. The result is a noticeable decrease in the water level within the beaker over time (usually several days).

What happens if we increase the temperature of the water within the beaker? Because of the shift in the energy distribution to higher energies (see Figure 11.24), more molecules now have enough energy to break free and evaporate, so vaporization occurs more quickly. What happens if we spill the water on the table or floor? The same amount of water is now spread over a wider area, resulting in more molecules at the surface of the liquid. Since molecules at the surface have the greatest tendency to evaporate—because they are held less tightly—vaporization also occurs more quickly in this case. You probably know from experience that water in a beaker or glass may take many days to evaporate completely, while the same amount of water spilled on a table or floor typically evaporates within a few hours (depending on the exact conditions).

What happens if the liquid in the beaker is not water, but some other substance with weaker intermolecular forces, such as acetone (acetone is the main component in nail polish remover)? The weaker intermolecular forces allow more molecules to evaporate at a given temperature, again increasing the rate of vaporization. We call liquids that vaporize easily **volatile**, and those that do not vaporize easily **nonvolatile**. Acetone is more volatile than water. Motor oil is virtually nonvolatile at room temperature.

Summarizing the Process of Vaporization:

▶ The rate of vaporization increases with increasing temperature.

▶ The rate of vaporization increases with increasing surface area.

▶ The rate of vaporization increases with decreasing strength of intermolecular forces.

The Energetics of Vaporization

To understand the energetics of vaporization, consider again a beaker of water from the molecular point of view, except now let's imagine that the beaker is thermally insulated so that heat from the surroundings cannot enter the beaker. What happens to the temperature of the water left in the beaker as molecules evaporate? To answer this question, think about the energy distribution curve again (see Figure 11.24). The molecules that leave the beaker are the ones at the high end of the energy curve—the most energetic. If

See Chapter 6 to review endothermic and exothermic processes.

▲ When you sweat, water evaporates from the skin. Since evaporation is endothermic, the result is a cooling effect.

no additional heat enters the beaker, the average energy of the entire collection of molecules goes down—much as the class average on an exam goes down if you eliminate the highest-scoring students. So vaporization is an *endothermic* process; it takes energy to vaporize the molecules in a liquid. Another way to understand the endothermicity of vaporization is to remember that vaporization requires overcoming the intermolecular forces that hold liquids together. Since energy is needed to pull the molecules away from one another, the process is endothermic.

Our bodies use the endothermic nature of vaporization for cooling. When you overheat, you sweat, causing your skin to be covered with liquid water. As this water evaporates, it absorbs heat from your body, cooling your skin. A fan makes you feel cooler because it blows newly vaporized water away from your skin, allowing more sweat to vaporize and causing even more cooling. High humidity, on the other hand, slows down the net rate of evaporation, preventing cooling. When the air already contains large amounts of water vapor, the sweat evaporates more slowly, making your body's cooling system less efficient.

Condensation, the opposite of vaporization, is exothermic—heat is released when a gas condenses to a liquid. If you have ever accidentally put your hand above a steaming kettle, or opened a bag of microwaved popcorn too soon, you may have experienced a *steam burn*. As the steam condenses to a liquid on your skin, it releases a lot of heat, causing the burn. The condensation of water vapor is also the reason that winter overnight temperatures in coastal regions, which tend to have water vapor in the air, do not get as low as in deserts, which tend to have dry air. As the air temperature in a coastal area drops, water condenses out of the air, releasing heat and preventing the temperature from dropping further. In deserts, the air contains almost no moisture to condense, so the temperature drop is more extreme.

Heat of Vaporization The amount of heat required to vaporize one mole of a liquid to gas is its **heat of vaporization** (ΔH_{vap}). The heat of vaporization of water at its normal boiling point of 100 °C is +40.7 kJ/mol:

$$H_2O(l) \longrightarrow H_2O(g) \quad \Delta H_{vap} = +40.7 \text{ kJ/mol}$$

The heat of vaporization is always positive because the process is endothermic—energy must be absorbed to vaporize a substance. The heat of vaporization is somewhat temperature dependent. For example, at 25 °C the heat of vaporization of water is +44.0 kJ/mol, slightly more than at 100 °C because the water contains less thermal energy at 25 °C. Table 11.7 lists the heats of vaporization of several liquids at their boiling points and at 25 °C.

When a substance condenses from a gas to a liquid, the same amount of heat is involved, but the heat is emitted rather than absorbed.

$$H_2O(g) \longrightarrow H_2O(l) \quad \Delta H = -\Delta H_{vap} = -40.7 \text{ kJ (at 100 °C)}$$

When one mole of water condenses, it releases 40.7 kJ of heat. The sign of ΔH in this case is negative because the process is exothermic.

The heat of vaporization of a liquid can be used to calculate the amount of energy required to vaporize a given mass of the liquid (or the amount of heat given off by the condensation of a given mass of liquid), using concepts similar to those covered in Section 6.6 (stoichiometry of ΔH). You can use the heat of vaporization as a conversion factor between number of moles of a liquid and the amount of heat required to vaporize it (or the amount of heat emitted when it condenses), as demonstrated in the following example.

The sign conventions of ΔH were introduced in Chapter 6.

TABLE 11.7 Heats of Vaporization of Several Liquids at Their Boiling Points and at 25 °C

Liquid	Chemical Formula	Normal Boiling Point (°C)	ΔH_{vap} (kJ/mol) at Boiling Point	ΔH_{vap} (kJ/mol) at 25 °C
Water	H_2O	100	40.7	44.0
Rubbing alcohol (isopropyl alcohol)	C_3H_8O	82.3	39.9	45.4
Acetone	C_3H_6O	56.1	29.1	31.0
Diethyl ether	$C_4H_{10}O$	34.6	26.5	27.1

EXAMPLE 11.3 Using the Heat of Vaporization in Calculations

Calculate the mass of water (in g) that can be vaporized at its boiling point with 155 kJ of heat.

SORT You are given a certain amount of heat in kilojoules and asked to find the mass of water that can be vaporized.	**GIVEN:** 155 kJ **FIND:** g H_2O
STRATEGIZE The heat of vaporization gives the relationship between heat absorbed and moles of water vaporized. Begin with the given amount of heat (in kJ) and convert to moles of water that can be vaporized. Then use the molar mass as a conversion factor to convert from moles of water to mass of water.	**CONCEPTUAL PLAN** $$\boxed{kJ} \xrightarrow{\dfrac{1\ \text{mol }H_2O}{40.7\ kJ}} \boxed{\text{mol }H_2O} \xrightarrow{\dfrac{18.02\ \text{g }H_2O}{1\ \text{mol }H_2O}} \boxed{\text{g }H_2O}$$ **RELATIONSHIPS USED** $\Delta H_{vap} = 40.7$ kJ/mol (at 100 °C) 18.02 g H_2O = 1 mol H_2O
SOLVE Follow the conceptual plan to solve the problem.	**SOLUTION** $$155\ \text{kJ} \times \frac{1\ \text{mol }H_2O}{40.7\ \text{kJ}} \times \frac{18.02\ \text{g }H_2O}{1\ \text{mol }H_2O} = 68.6\ \text{g }H_2O$$

FOR PRACTICE 11.3

Calculate the amount of heat (in kJ) required to vaporize 2.58 kg of water at its boiling point.

FOR MORE PRACTICE 11.3

Suppose that 0.48 g of water at 25 °C condenses on the surface of a 55-g block of aluminum that is initially at 25 °C. If the heat released during condensation goes only toward heating the metal, what is the final temperature (in °C) of the metal block? (The specific heat capacity of aluminum is 0.903 J/g °C.)

Vapor Pressure and Dynamic Equilibrium

We have already seen that if a container of water is left uncovered at room temperature, the water slowly evaporates away. But what happens if the container is sealed? Imagine a sealed evacuated flask—one from which the air has been removed—containing liquid water, as shown in Figure 11.25 ►. Initially, the water molecules evaporate, as they did in the open beaker. However, because of the seal, the evaporated molecules cannot escape into the atmosphere. As water molecules enter the gas state, some start condensing back into the liquid. As the concentration (or partial pressure) of

> Dynamic equilibrium:
> Rate of evaporation =
> rate of condensation

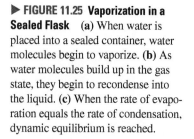 **FIGURE 11.25 Vaporization in a Sealed Flask** **(a)** When water is placed into a sealed container, water molecules begin to vaporize. **(b)** As water molecules build up in the gas state, they begin to recondense into the liquid. **(c)** When the rate of evaporation equals the rate of condensation, dynamic equilibrium is reached.

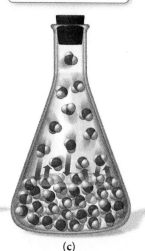

(a)   (b)   (c)

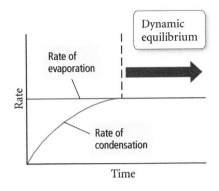

▲ FIGURE 11.26 Dynamic Equilibrium
Dynamic equilibrium occurs when the
rate of condensation is equal to the
rate of evaporation.

| Boyle's law is discussed in Section 5.3.

gaseous water molecules increases, the rate of condensation also increases. However, as
long as the water remains at a constant temperature, the rate of evaporation remains
constant. Eventually the rate of condensation and the rate of vaporization become
equal—**dynamic equilibrium** has been reached (Figure 11.26 ◄). Condensation and
vaporization continue at equal rates and the concentration of water vapor above the liquid
is constant.

The pressure of a gas in dynamic equilibrium with its liquid is called its **vapor pressure**. The vapor pressure of a particular liquid depends on the intermolecular forces present in the liquid and the temperature. Weak intermolecular forces result in volatile
substances with high vapor pressures because the intermolecular forces are easily overcome by thermal energy. Strong intermolecular forces result in nonvolatile substances
with low vapor pressures.

A liquid in dynamic equilibrium with its vapor is a balanced system that tends to
return to equilibrium if disturbed. For example, consider a sample of *n*-pentane (a component of gasoline) at 25 °C in a cylinder equipped with a moveable piston (Figure
11.27a ▼). The cylinder contains no other gases except *n*-pentane vapor in dynamic
equilibrium with the liquid. Since the vapor pressure of *n*-pentane at 25 °C is 510 mmHg,
the pressure in the cylinder is 510 mmHg. Now, what happens when the piston is
moved upward to expand the volume within the cylinder? Initially, the pressure in the
cylinder drops below 510 mmHg, in accordance with Boyle's law. Then, however,
more liquid vaporizes until equilibrium is reached once again (Figure 11.27b). If the
volume of the cylinder is expanded again, the same thing happens—the pressure initially drops and more *n*-pentane vaporizes to bring the system back into equilibrium.
Further expansion will cause the same result *as long as some liquid n-pentane remains
in the cylinder.*

Conversely, what happens if the piston is lowered, decreasing the volume in the
cylinder? Initially, the pressure in the cylinder rises above 510 mmHg, but then some of
the gas condenses into liquid until equilibrium is reached again (Figure 11.27c).

We can describe the tendency of a system in dynamic equilibrium to return to equilibrium with the following general statement:

> **When a system in dynamic equilibrium is disturbed, the system responds so
> as to minimize the disturbance and return to a state of equilibrium.**

If the pressure above a liquid–vapor system in equilibrium is decreased, some of the liquid
evaporates, restoring the equilibrium pressure. If the pressure is increased, some of the
vapor condenses, bringing the pressure back down to the equilibrium pressure. This basic
principle—Le Châtelier's principle—is applicable to any chemical system in equilibrium, as we shall see in Chapter 14.

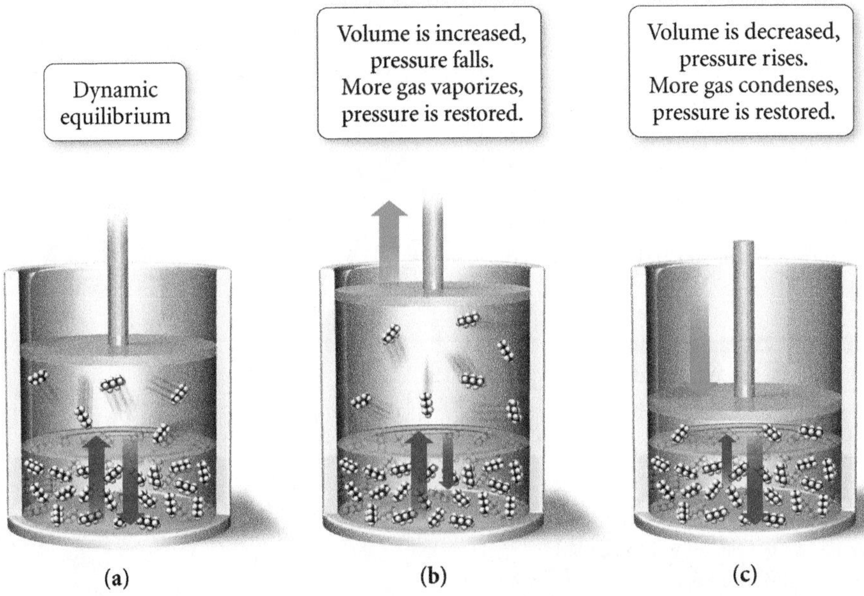

**► FIGURE 11.27 Dynamic Equilibrium
in *n*-Pentane** **(a)** Liquid *n*-pentane is
in dynamic equilibrium with its vapor.
(b) When the volume is increased, the
pressure drops and some liquid is converted to gas to bring the pressure back
up. **(c)** When the volume is decreased,
the pressure increases and some gas is
converted to liquid to bring the pressure back down.

Dynamic
equilibrium

Volume is increased,
pressure falls.
More gas vaporizes,
pressure is restored.

Volume is decreased,
pressure rises.
More gas condenses,
pressure is restored.

(a)   **(b)**   **(c)**

Conceptual Connection 11.2 Vapor Pressure

What happens to the vapor pressure of a substance when its surface area is increased at constant temperature?

(a) The vapor pressure increases.

(b) The vapor pressure remains the same.

(c) The vapor pressure decreases.

ANSWER: (b) Although the *rate of vaporization* increases with increasing surface area, the *vapor pressure* of a liquid is independent of surface area. An increase in surface increases both the rate of vaporization and the rate of condensation—the effects of surface area exactly cancel and the vapor pressure does not change.

Temperature Dependence of Vapor Pressure and Boiling Point

When the temperature of a liquid is increased, its vapor pressure rises because the higher thermal energy increases the number of molecules that have enough energy to vaporize (see Figure 11.24). Because of the shape of the thermal energy distribution curve, a small change in temperature makes a large difference in the number of molecules that have enough energy to vaporize, which results in a large increase in vapor pressure. For example, the vapor pressure of water at 25 °C is 23.3 torr, while at 60 °C the vapor pressure is 149.4 torr. Figure 11.28 ▶ shows the vapor pressure of water and several other liquids as a function of temperature.

The **boiling point** of a liquid is *the temperature at which its vapor pressure equals the external pressure*. When a liquid reaches its boiling point, the thermal energy is enough for molecules in the interior of the liquid (not just those at the surface) to break free of their neighbors and enter the gas state (Figure 11.29 ▼). The bubbles in boiling water are pockets of gaseous water that have formed within the liquid water. The bubbles float to the surface and leave as gaseous water or steam.

The **normal boiling point** of a liquid is *the temperature at which its vapor pressure equals 1 atm*. The normal boiling point of pure water is 100 °C. However, at a lower pressure, water boils at a lower temperature. In Denver, Colorado, where the altitude is around 1600 meters (5200 feet) above sea level, for example, the average atmospheric pressure is about 83% of what it is at sea level, and water boils at approximately 94 °C. For this reason, it takes slightly longer to cook food in boiling water in Denver than in San Francisco (which is at sea level). Table 11.8 on the next page shows the boiling point of water at several locations of varied altitudes.

Once the boiling point of a liquid is reached, additional heating only causes more rapid boiling; it does not raise the temperature of the liquid above its boiling point, as

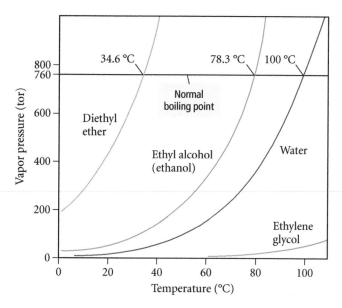

▲ **FIGURE 11.28 Vapor Pressure of Several Liquids at Different Temperatures** At higher temperatures, more molecules have enough thermal energy to escape into the gas state, so vapor pressure increases with increasing temperature.

Sometimes you see bubbles begin to form in hot water below 100 °C. These bubbles are dissolved air—not gaseous water—leaving the liquid. Dissolved air comes out of water as you heat it because the solubility of a gas in a liquid decreases with increasing temperature (as we will see in Chapter 12).

◀ **FIGURE 11.29 Boiling** A liquid boils when thermal energy is high enough to cause molecules in the interior of the liquid to become gaseous, forming bubbles that rise to the surface.

TABLE 11.8 Boiling Points of Water at Several Locations of Varied Altitudes

Location	Elevation (ft)	Approximate Pressure (atm)*	Approximate Boiling Point of Water (°C)
Mt. Everest, Tibet (highest mountain peak on Earth)	29,035	0.32	78
Mt. McKinley (Denali), Alaska (highest mountain peak in North America)	20,320	0.46	83
Mt. Whitney, California (highest mountain peak in 48 contiguous U.S. states)	14,495	0.60	87
Denver, Colorado (mile high city)	5,280	0.83	94
Boston, Massachusetts (sea level)	20	1.0	100

*The atmospheric pressure in each of these locations is subject to weather conditions and can vary significantly from the values stated here.

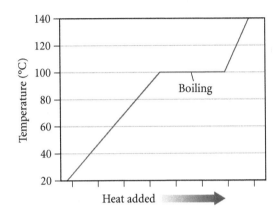

▲ **FIGURE 11.30 Temperature during Boiling** The temperature of water during boiling remains at 100 °C.

shown in the *heating curve* in Figure 11.30 ◄. Therefore, boiling water at 1 atm will always have a temperature of 100 °C. *As long as liquid water is present, its temperature cannot rise above its boiling point.* After all the water has been converted to steam, the temperature of the steam can continue to rise beyond 100 °C.

The Clausius–Clapeyron Equation Now, let's return our attention to Figure 11.28. As you can see from the graph, the vapor pressure of a liquid increases with increasing temperature. However, *the relationship is not linear*. In other words, doubling the temperature results in more than a doubling of the vapor pressure. The relationship between vapor pressure and temperature is exponential, and can be expressed as follows:

$$P_{vap} = \beta \exp\left(\frac{-\Delta H_{vap}}{RT}\right) \qquad [11.1]$$

In this expression P_{vap} is the vapor pressure, β is a constant that depends on the gas, ΔH_{vap} is the heat of vaporization, R is the gas constant (8.314 J/mol · K), and T is the temperature in kelvins. Equation 11.1 can be rearranged by taking the natural logarithm of both sides:

$$\ln P_{vap} = \ln\left[\beta \exp\left(\frac{-\Delta H_{vap}}{RT}\right)\right] \qquad [11.2]$$

Since $\ln AB = \ln A + \ln B$, we can rearrange the right side of Equation 11.2:

$$\ln P_{vap} = \ln \beta + \ln\left[\exp\left(\frac{-\Delta H_{vap}}{RT}\right)\right] \qquad [11.3]$$

Since $\ln e^x = x$ (see Appendix IB), we can simplify Equation 11.3:

$$\ln P_{vap} = \ln \beta + \frac{-\Delta H_{vap}}{RT} \qquad [11.4]$$

A slight additional rearrangement gives us the following important result:

$$\ln P_{vap} = \frac{-\Delta H_{vap}}{R}\left(\frac{1}{T}\right) + \ln \beta \qquad \text{Clausius–Clapeyron equation}$$

$$y = m\,(x) + b \qquad \text{(equation for a line)}$$

Using the Clausius–Clapeyron equation in this way ignores the relatively small temperature dependence of ΔH_{vap}.

Notice the parallel relationship between the **Clausius–Clapeyron equation** and the equation for a straight line. Just as a plot of y versus x yields a straight line with slope m and intercept b, so a plot of $\ln P_{vap}$ (equivalent to y) versus $1/T$ (equivalent to x) gives a straight line with slope $-\Delta H_{vap}/R$ (equivalent to m) and y-intercept $\ln \beta$ (equivalent to b), as shown in Figure 11.31 ►. The Clausius–Clapeyron equation gives a linear relationship—not between the vapor pressure and the temperature (which have an expo-

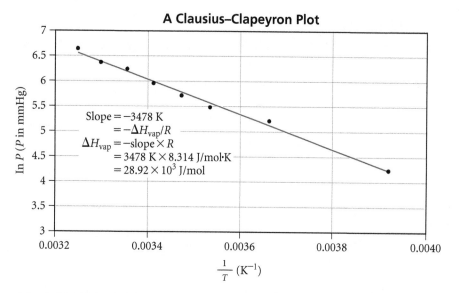

A Clausius–Clapeyron Plot

Slope $= -3478$ K
$= -\Delta H_{vap}/R$
$\Delta H_{vap} = -$slope $\times R$
$= 3478$ K $\times$ 8.314 J/mol·K
$= 28.92 \times 10^3$ J/mol

◀ **FIGURE 11.31 A Clausius–Clapeyron Plot for Diethyl Ether ($CH_3CH_2OCH_2CH_3$)** A plot of the natural log of the vapor pressure versus the inverse of the temperature in K yields a straight line with slope $-\Delta H_{vap}/R$.

nential relationship)—but between the *natural log* of the vapor pressure and the *inverse* of temperature. This is a common technique in the analysis of chemical data. If two variables are not linearly related, it is often convenient to find ways to graph *functions of those variables* that are linearly related.

The Clausius–Clapeyron equation leads to a convenient way to measure the heat of vaporization in the laboratory. We just measure the vapor pressure of a liquid as a function of temperature and create a plot of the natural log of the vapor pressure versus the inverse of the temperature. We can then determine the slope of the line to find the heat of vaporization, as shown in the following example.

EXAMPLE 11.4 Using the Clausius–Clapeyron Equation to Determine Heat of Vaporization from Experimental Measurements of Vapor Pressure

The vapor pressure of dichloromethane was measured as a function of temperature, and the following results were obtained:

Temperature (K)	Vapor Pressure (torr)
200	0.8
220	4.5
240	21
260	71
280	197
300	391

Determine the heat of vaporization of dichloromethane.

SOLUTION

To find the heat of vaporization, use an Excel spreadsheet or a graphing calculator to make a plot of the natural log of vapor pressure ($\ln P$) as a function of the inverse of the temperature in kelvins ($1/T$). Then fit the points to a line and determine the slope of the line. The slope of the best fitting line is -3773 K. Since the slope equals $-\Delta H_{vap}/R$ we find the heat of vaporization as follows:

$$\text{slope} = -\Delta H_{vap}/R$$
$$\Delta H_{vap} = -\text{slope} \times R$$
$$= -(-3773 \text{ K})(8.314 \text{ J/mol} \cdot \text{K})$$
$$= 3.14 \times 10^4 \text{ J/mol}$$
$$= 31.4 \text{ kJ/mol}$$

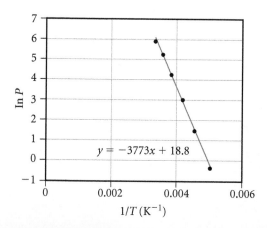

$y = -3773x + 18.8$

FOR PRACTICE 11.4

The vapor pressure of carbon tetrachloride was measured as a function of the temperature and the following results were obtained:

Temperature (K)	Vapor Pressure (torr)
255	11.3
265	21.0
275	36.8
285	61.5
295	99.0
300	123.8

Determine the heat of vaporization of carbon tetrachloride.

The Clausius–Clapeyron equation can also be expressed in a two-point form that we can use with just two measurements of vapor pressure and temperature to determine the heat of vaporization.

$$\ln \frac{P_2}{P_1} = \frac{-\Delta H_{vap}}{R}\left(\frac{1}{T_2} - \frac{1}{T_1}\right)$$ Clausius–Clapeyron equation (two-point form)

The two-point method is generally inferior to plotting multiple points because fewer data points result in greater possible error.

We can use this form of the equation to predict the vapor pressure of a liquid at any temperature if we know the enthalpy of vaporization and the normal boiling point (or the vapor pressure at some other temperature), as shown in the following example.

EXAMPLE 11.5 Using the Two-Point Form of the Clausius–Clapeyron Equation to Predict the Vapor Pressure at a Given Temperature

Methanol has a normal boiling point of 64.6 °C and a heat of vaporization (ΔH_{vap}) of 35.2 kJ/mol. What is the vapor pressure of methanol at 12.0 °C?

SORT You are given the normal boiling point of methanol (the temperature at which the vapor pressure is 760 mmHg) and the heat of vaporization. You are asked to find the vapor pressure at a specified temperature which is also given.

GIVEN: $T_1(°C) = 64.6 °C$
$\qquad P_1 = 760$ torr
$\qquad \Delta H_{vap} = 35.2$ kJ/mol
$\qquad T_2(°C) = 12.0 °C$

FIND: P_2

STRATEGIZE The conceptual plan is essentially the Clausius–Clapeyron equation, which relates the given and find quantities.

CONCEPTUAL PLAN

$$\ln \frac{P_2}{P_1} = \frac{-\Delta H_{vap}}{R}\left(\frac{1}{T_2} - \frac{1}{T_1}\right)$$

(Clausius–Clapeyron equation, two-point form)

SOLVE First, convert T_1 and T_2 from °C to K.

SOLUTION
$T_1(K) = T_1(°C) + 273.15$
$\qquad = 64.6 + 273.15$
$\qquad = 337.8$ K
$T_2(K) = T_2(°C) + 273.15$
$\qquad = 12.0 + 273.15$
$\qquad = 285.2$ K

Then, substitute the required values into the Clausius–Clapeyron equation and solve for P_2.	$\ln \dfrac{P_2}{P_1} = \dfrac{-\Delta H_{vap}}{R}\left(\dfrac{1}{T_2} - \dfrac{1}{T_1}\right)$
	$\ln \dfrac{P_2}{P_1} = \dfrac{-35.2 \times 10^3 \dfrac{J}{mol}}{8.314\dfrac{J}{mol \cdot K}}\left(\dfrac{1}{285.2\ K} - \dfrac{1}{337.8\ K}\right)$
	$= -2.31$
	$\dfrac{P_2}{P_1} = e^{-2.31}$
	$P_2 = P_1(e^{-2.31})$
	$= 760\ \text{torr}(0.0993)$
	$= 75.4\ \text{torr}$

CHECK The units of the answer are correct. The magnitude of the answer makes sense because vapor pressure should be significantly lower at the lower temperature.

FOR PRACTICE 11.5

Propane has a normal boiling point of $-42.0\ °C$ and a heat of vaporization (ΔH_{vap}) of 19.04 kJ/mol. What is the vapor pressure of propane at 25.0 °C?

The Critical Point: The Transition to an Unusual State of Matter

We have considered the vaporization of a liquid in a container open to the atmosphere with and without heating, and the vaporization of a liquid in a *sealed* container without heating. We now examine the vaporization of a liquid in a *sealed* container *during heating*. Consider liquid *n*-pentane in equilibrium with its vapor in a sealed container initially at 25 °C. At this temperature, the vapor pressure of *n*-pentane is 0.67 atm. What happens if we heat the liquid? As the temperature rises, more *n*-pentane vaporizes and the pressure within the container increases. At 100 °C, the pressure is 5.5 atm, and at 190 °C the pressure is 29 atm. As the temperature and pressure raise, more and more gaseous *n*-pentane is forced into the same amount of space, and the density of the *gas* gets higher and higher. At the same time, the increasing temperature causes the density of the *liquid* to become lower and lower. At 197 °C, the meniscus between the liquid and gaseous *n*-pentane disappears and the gas and liquid states commingle to form a *supercritical fluid* (Figure 11.32 ▼). For any substance, the *temperature* at which this transition occurs is called the **critical temperature** (T_c). The liquid cannot exist (regardless of pressure) above this temperature. The *pressure* at which this transition occurs is called the **critical pressure** (P_c).

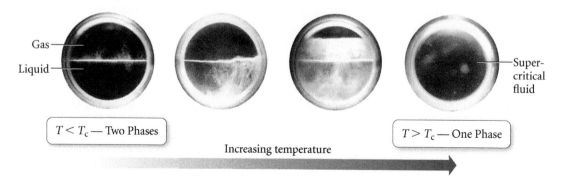

Gas —
Liquid —

Super-critical fluid

$T < T_c$ — Two Phases $T > T_c$ — One Phase

Increasing temperature

▲ **FIGURE 11.32 Critical Point Transition**   As *n*-pentane is heated in a sealed container, it undergoes a transition to a supercritical fluid. At the critical point, the meniscus separating the liquid and gas disappears, and the fluid becomes supercritical—neither a liquid nor a gas.

Researchers are interested in supercritical fluids because of their unique properties. A supercritical fluid has properties of both liquids and gases—it is in some sense intermediate between the two. Supercritical fluids can act as good solvents, selectively dissolving a number of compounds. For example, supercritical carbon dioxide is used as a solvent to extract caffeine from coffee beans. The caffeine dissolves in the supercritical carbon dioxide, but other substances—such as those responsible for the flavor of coffee—do not. Consequently, the caffeine can be removed without substantially altering the coffee's flavor. The supercritical carbon dioxide is easily removed from the mixture by simply lowering the pressure below the critical pressure, at which point the carbon dioxide evaporates away, leaving no residue.

11.6 Sublimation and Fusion

In Section 11.5, we examined a beaker of liquid water at room temperature from the molecular viewpoint. Now, let's examine a block of ice at $-10\ ^\circ C$ from the same molecular perspective, paying close attention to two common processes: sublimation and fusion.

Sublimation

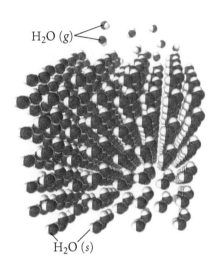

$H_2O\ (g)$

$H_2O\ (s)$

▲ **FIGURE 11.33 The Sublimation of Ice**   The water molecules at the surface of an ice cube can sublime directly into the gas state.

Even though a block of ice is solid, the water molecules have thermal energy which causes each one to vibrate about a fixed point. The motion is much less vigorous than in a liquid, but significant nonetheless. As in liquids, at any one time some molecules in the block of ice have more thermal energy than the average and some have less. The molecules with high enough thermal energy can break free from the ice surface—where, as in liquids, molecules are held less tightly than in the interior due to fewer neighbor–neighbor interactions—and go directly into the gas state (Figure 11.33 ◄). This process is **sublimation**, the transition from solid to gas. Some of the water molecules in the gas state (those at the low end of the energy distribution curve for the gaseous molecules) can collide with the surface of the ice and be captured by the intermolecular forces with other molecules. This process—the opposite of sublimation—is **deposition**, the transition from gas to solid. As is the case with liquids, the pressure of a gas in dynamic equilibrium with its solid is the vapor pressure of the solid.

Although both sublimation and deposition occur on the surface of an ice block open to the atmosphere at $-10\ ^\circ C$, sublimation usually occurs at a greater rate because most of the newly sublimed molecules escape into the surrounding atmosphere and never come back. The result is a noticeable decrease in the size of the ice block over time (even though the temperature is below the melting point).

If you live in a cold climate, you may have noticed the disappearance of ice and snow from the ground even though the temperature remains below $0\ ^\circ C$. Similarly, ice cubes left in the freezer for a long time slowly shrink, even though the freezer is always below $0\ ^\circ C$. In both cases, the ice is *subliming*, turning directly into water vapor. Ice also sublimes out of frozen foods. You may have noticed, for example, the gradual growth of ice crystals on the *inside* of airtight plastic food-storage bags in a freezer. The ice crystals are composed of water that has sublimed out of the food and redeposited on the surface of the bag or on the surface of the food. For this reason, food that remains frozen for too long becomes dried out. Such dehydration can be avoided to some degree by freezing foods to colder temperatures, a process called deep-freezing. The colder temperature lowers the vapor pressure of ice and preserves the food longer. Freezer burn on meats is another common manifestation of sublimation. When you improperly store meat (for example, in a container that is not airtight) sublimation continues unabated. The result is the dehydration of the surface of the meat, which becomes discolored and loses flavor and texture.

A substance commonly associated with sublimation is solid carbon dioxide or dry ice, which does not melt under atmospheric pressure no matter what the temperature. However, at $-78\ ^\circ C$ the CO_2 molecules have enough energy to leave the surface of the dry ice and become gaseous through sublimation.

▲ The ice crystals that form on frozen food are due to sublimation of water from the food and redeposition on its surface.

Fusion

Let's return to our ice block and examine what happens at the molecular level as we increase its temperature. The increasing thermal energy causes the water molecules to vibrate faster and faster. At the **melting point** (0 °C for water), the molecules have enough thermal energy to overcome the intermolecular forces that hold them at their stationary points, and the solid turns into a liquid. This process is **melting** or **fusion**, the transition from solid to liquid. The opposite of melting is **freezing**, the transition from liquid to solid. Once the melting point of a solid is reached, additional heating only causes more rapid melting; it does not raise the temperature of the solid above its melting point (Figure 11.34 ▼). Only after all of the ice has melted will additional heating raise the temperature of the liquid water past 0 °C. A mixture of water *and* ice will always have a temperature of 0 °C (at 1 atm pressure).

▲ Dry ice (solid CO_2) sublimes but does not melt at atmospheric pressure.

> The term fusion is used for melting because if you heat several crystals of a solid, they *fuse* into a continuous liquid upon melting.

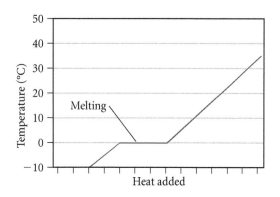

◄ **FIGURE 11.34 Temperature during Melting**   The temperature of water during melting remains at 0.0 °C as long as both solid and liquid water remain.

Energetics of Melting and Freezing

The most common way to cool a beverage quickly is to drop several ice cubes into it. As the ice melts, the drink cools because melting is endothermic—the melting ice absorbs heat from the liquid. The amount of heat required to melt 1 mol of a solid is called the **heat of fusion** (ΔH_{fus}). The heat of fusion for water is 6.02 kJ/mol:

$$H_2O(s) \longrightarrow H_2O(l) \qquad \Delta H_{fus} = 6.02 \text{ kJ/mol}$$

The heat of fusion is positive because melting is endothermic.

Freezing, the opposite of melting, is exothermic—heat is released when a liquid freezes into a solid. For example, as water in your freezer turns into ice, it releases heat, which must be removed by the refrigeration system of the freezer. If the refrigeration system did not remove the heat, the water would not completely freeze into ice. The heat released as the water began to freeze would warm the freezer, preventing further freezing. The change in enthalpy for freezing has the same magnitude as the heat of fusion but the opposite sign.

$$H_2O(l) \longrightarrow H_2O(s) \qquad \Delta H = -\Delta H_{fus} = -6.02 \text{ kJ/mol}$$

Different substances have different heats of fusion as shown in Table 11.9.

TABLE 11.9 Heats of Fusion of Several Substances

Liquid	Chemical Formula	Melting Point (°C)	ΔH_{fus} (kJ/mol)
Water	H_2O	0.00	6.02
Rubbing alcohol (isopropyl alcohol)	C_3H_8O	−89.5	5.37
Acetone	C_3H_6O	−94.8	5.69
Diethyl ether	$C_4H_{10}O$	−116.3	7.27

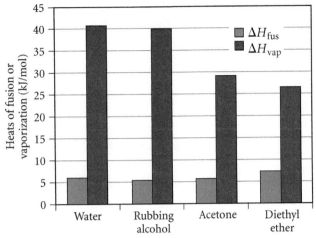

▲ **FIGURE 11.35 Heat of Fusion and Heat of Vaporization** Typical heats of fusion are significantly less than heats of vaporization.

In general, the heat of fusion is significantly less than the heat of vaporization, as shown in Figure 11.35 ◄. We have already seen that the solid and liquid states are closer to each other in many ways than they are to the gas state. It takes less energy to melt 1 mol of ice into liquid than it does to vaporize 1 mol of liquid water into gas because vaporization requires complete separation of molecules from one another, so the intermolecular forces must be completely overcome. Melting, however, requires that intermolecular forces be only partially overcome, allowing molecules to move around one another while still remaining in contact.

11.7 Heating Curve for Water

We can combine and build on the concepts from the previous two sections by examining the *heating curve* for 1.00 mol of water at 1.00 atm pressure shown in Figure 11.36 ▼. The *y*-axis of the heating curve represents the temperature of the water sample. The *x*-axis represents the amount of heat added (in kilojoules) during heating. As you can see from the diagram, the process can be divided into five segments: (1) ice warming; (2) ice melting into liquid water; (3) liquid water warming; (4) liquid water vaporizing into steam; and (5) steam warming.

In two of these segments (2 and 4) the temperature is constant as heat is added because the added heat goes into producing the transition between states, not into increasing the temperature. The two states are in equilibrium during the transition and the

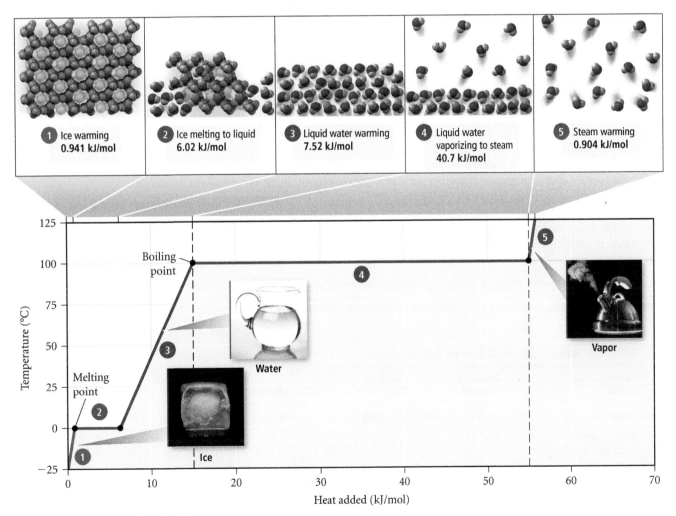

▲ **FIGURE 11.36 Heating Curve for Water**

temperature remains constant. The amount of heat required to achieve the state change is given by $q = n\,\Delta H$.

In the other three segments (1, 3, and 5), temperature increases linearly. These segments represent the heating of a single state in which the deposited heat raises the temperature in accordance with the substance's heat capacity ($q = mC_s\,\Delta T$). We examine each of these segments individually.

Segment 1 In segment 1, solid ice is warmed from $-25\,°C$ to $0\,°C$. Since no transition between states occurs here, the amount of heat required to heat the solid ice is given by $q = mC_s\,\Delta T$ (see Section 6.4), where C_s is the specific heat capacity of ice ($C_{s,\text{ice}} = 2.09\ \text{J/g}\cdot°\text{C}$). For 1.00 mol of water (18.0 g), the amount of heat is computed as follows:

$$q = mC_{s,\text{ice}}\,\Delta T$$
$$= 18.0\ \text{g}\left(2.09\frac{\text{J}}{\text{g}\cdot°\text{C}}\right)[0.0\ °\text{C} - (-25.0\ °\text{C})]$$
$$= 941\ \text{J} = 0.941\ \text{kJ}$$

So in segment 1, 0.941 kJ of heat is added to the ice, warming it from $-25°\,$C to $0\,°C$.

Segment 2 In segment 2, the added heat does not change the temperature of the ice and water mixture because the heat is absorbed by the transition from solid to liquid. The amount of heat required to convert the ice to liquid water is given by $q = n\,\Delta H_{\text{fus}}$, where n is the number of moles of water and ΔH_{fus} is the heat of fusion (see Section 11.6).

$$q = n\,\Delta H_{\text{fus}}$$
$$= 1.00\ \text{mol}\left(\frac{6.02\ \text{kJ}}{\text{mol}}\right)$$
$$= 6.02\ \text{kJ}$$

In segment 2, 6.02 kJ is added to the ice, melting it into liquid water. Notice that the temperature does not change during melting. The liquid and solid coexist at $0\,°C$ as the melting occurs.

Segment 3 In segment 3, the liquid water is warmed from $0\,°C$ to $100\,°C$. Since no transition between states occurs here, the amount of heat required to heat the liquid water is given by $q = mC_s\,\Delta T$, as in segment 1. However, now we must use the heat capacity of liquid water (not ice) for the calculation. For 1.00 mol of water (18.0 g), the amount of heat is computed as follows:

$$q = mC_{s,\text{liq}}\,\Delta T$$
$$= 18.0\ \text{g}\left(4.18\frac{\text{J}}{\text{g}\cdot°\text{C}}\right)(100.0\ °\text{C} - 0.0\ °\text{C})$$
$$= 7.52 \times 10^3\ \text{J} = 7.52\ \text{kJ}$$

So in segment 3, 7.52 kJ of heat is added to the liquid water, warming it from $0\,°C$ to $100\,°C$.

Segment 4 In segment 4, the water undergoes a second transition between states, this time from liquid to gas. The amount of heat required to convert the liquid to gas is given by $q = n\,\Delta H_{\text{vap}}$, where n is the number of moles and ΔH_{vap} is the heat of vaporization (see Section 11.5).

$$q = n\,\Delta H_{\text{vap}}$$
$$= 1.00\ \text{mol}\left(\frac{40.7\ \text{kJ}}{\text{mol}}\right)$$
$$= 40.7\ \text{kJ}$$

Thus, in segment 4, 40.7 kJ is added to the water, vaporizing it into steam. Notice that the temperature does not change during boiling. The liquid and gas coexist at $100\,°C$ as the boiling occurs.

Segment 5 In segment 5, the steam is warmed from 100 °C to 125 °C. Since no transition between states occurs here, the amount of heat required to heat the steam is given by $q = mC_s \Delta T$ (as in segments 1 and 3) except that we must use the heat capacity of steam (2.01 J/g·°C).

$$q = mC_{s, \text{steam}} \Delta T$$

$$= 18.0 \text{ g}\left(2.01\frac{\text{J}}{\text{g}\cdot{}^\circ\text{C}}\right)(125.0 \ {}^\circ\text{C} - 100.0 \ {}^\circ\text{C})$$

$$= 904 = 0.904 \text{ kJ}$$

So in segment 5, 0.904 kJ of heat is added to the steam, warming it from 100 °C to 125 °C.

 Conceptual Connection 11.3 Cooling of Water with Ice

We just saw that the heat capacity of ice is $C_{s, \text{ice}} = 2.09$ J/g·°C and that the heat of fusion of ice is 6.02 kJ/mol. When a small ice cube at −10 °C is put into a cup of water at room temperature, which of the following plays a larger role in cooling the liquid water: the warming of the ice from −10 °C to 0 °C, or the melting of the ice?

ANSWER: The warming of the ice from −10 °C to 0 °C absorbs only 20.9 J/g of ice. The melting of the ice, however, absorbs about 334 J/g of ice. (You can obtain this value by dividing the heat of fusion of water by its molar mass.) Therefore, the melting of the ice produces a larger temperature decrease in the water than does the warming of the ice.

11.8 Phase Diagrams

Throughout most of this chapter, we have examined how the state of a substance changes with temperature and pressure. We can combine both the temperature dependence and pressure dependence of the state of a particular substance in a graph called a *phase diagram*. A **phase diagram** is a map of the state or *phase* of a substance as a function of pressure (on the *y*-axis) and temperature (on the *x*-axis). We first examine the major features of a phase diagram, then turn to navigating within a phase diagram, and finally examine and compare the phase diagrams of selected substances.

The Major Features of a Phase Diagram

We can become familiar with the major features of a phase diagram by examining the phase diagram for water as an example (Figure 11.37 ▼). The *y*-axis displays the pressure

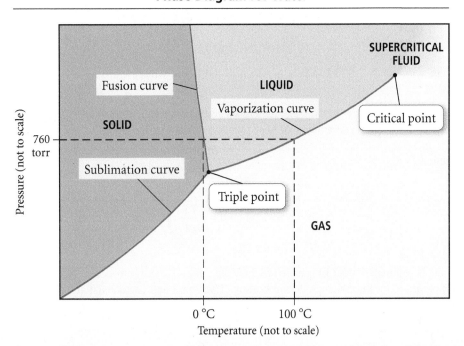

Phase Diagram for Water

▶ FIGURE 11.37 **Phase Diagram for Water**

in torr and the *x*-axis displays the temperature in degrees Celsius. We can categorize the main features of the phase diagram as regions, lines, and points.

Regions *Any of the three main regions—solid, liquid, and gas—in the phase diagram represent conditions where that particular state is stable.* For example, under any of the temperatures and pressures within the liquid region in the phase diagram of water, the liquid is the stable state. Notice that the point 25 °C and 760 torr falls within the liquid region, as we know from everyday experience. In general, low temperature and high pressure favor the solid state; high temperature and low pressure favor the gas state; and intermediate conditions favor the liquid state. A sample of matter that is not in the state indicated by its phase diagram for a given set of conditions will convert to that state when those conditions are imposed. For example, steam that is cooled to room temperature at 1 atm will condense to liquid.

Lines *Each of the lines (or curves) in the phase diagram represents a set of temperatures and pressures at which the substance is in equilibrium between the two states on either side of the line.* For example, in the phase diagram for water, consider the curved line beginning just beyond 0 °C separating the liquid from the gas. This line is the vaporization curve (also called the vapor pressure curve) for water that we examined in Section 11.5. At any of the temperatures and pressures that fall along this line, the liquid and gas states of water are equally stable and in equilibrium. For example, at 100 °C and 760 torr pressure, water and its vapor are in equilibrium—they are equally stable and will coexist. The other two major lines in a phase diagram are the sublimation curve (separating the solid and the gas) and the fusion curve (separating the solid and the liquid).

The Triple Point *The **triple point** in a phase diagram represents the unique set of conditions at which three states are equally stable and in equilibrium.* In the phase diagram for water, the triple point occurs at 0.0098 °C and 4.58 torr. Under these unique conditions (and only under these conditions), the solid, liquid, and gas states of water are equally stable and will coexist in equilibrium.

The Critical Point *The **critical point** in a phase diagram represents the temperature and pressure above which a supercritical fluid exists.* As we learned in Section 11.5, at the critical temperature and pressure, the liquid and gas states coalesce into a *supercritical fluid.*

> The triple point of a substance such as water can be reproduced anywhere to calibrate a thermometer or pressure gauge with a known temperature and pressure.

Navigation within a Phase Diagram

We can represent changes in the temperature or pressure of a sample of water as movement within the phase diagram. For example, suppose we heat a block of ice initially at 1.0 atm and −25 °C. We represent the change in temperature at constant pressure as movement along the line marked *A* in Figure 11.38 ▼. As the temperature rises, we move

Navigation within a Phase Diagram

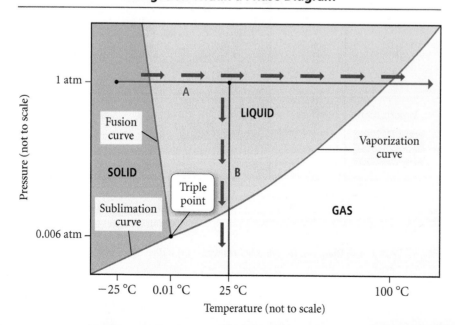

◀ **FIGURE 11.38 Navigation on the Phase Diagram for Water**

to the right along the line. At the fusion curve, the temperature stops rising and melting occurs until the solid ice is completely converted to liquid water. Crossing the fusion curve requires the complete transition from solid to liquid. Once the ice has completely melted, the temperature of the liquid water can begin to rise until the vaporization curve is reached. At this point, the temperature again stops rising and boiling occurs until all the liquid is converted to gas.

We can represent a change in pressure by a vertical line on the phase diagram. For example, suppose we lower the pressure above a sample of water initially at 1.0 atm and 25 °C. We represent the change in pressure at constant temperature as movement along the line marked *B* in Figure 11.38. As the pressure drops, we move down the line and approach the vaporization curve. At the vaporization curve, the pressure stops dropping and vaporization occurs until the liquid is completely converted to vapor. Crossing the vaporization curve requires the complete transition from liquid to gas. Only after the liquid has all vaporized can the pressure continue to drop.

The Phase Diagrams of Other Substances

Examine the phase diagrams of iodine and carbon dioxide, shown in Figure 11.39 ▼. The phase diagrams are similar to that of water in most of their general features, but some significant differences exist.

The fusion curves for both carbon dioxide and iodine have a positive slope—as the temperature increases the pressure also increases—in contrast to the fusion curve for water, which has a negative slope. The behavior of water is atypical. The fusion curve within the phase diagrams for most substances has a positive slope because increasing pressure favors the denser state, which for most substances is the solid state. For example, suppose the pressure on a sample of iodine is increased from 1 atm to 100 atm at 184 °C, as shown by line A in Figure 11.39(a). Notice that this change crosses the fusion curve, converting the liquid into a solid. In contrast, a pressure increase from 1 atm to 100 atm at −0.1 °C in water causes a state transition from solid to liquid. Unlike most substances, the liquid state of water is actually denser than the solid state.

Both water and iodine have stable solid, liquid, and gaseous states at a pressure of 1 atm. However, notice that carbon dioxide has no stable liquid state at a pressure of 1 atm. If we increase the temperature of a block of solid carbon dioxide (dry ice) at 1 atm, as indicated by line B in Figure 11.39(b), we cross the sublimation curve at −78.5 °C. At this temperature, the solid sublimes to a gas, which is one reason that dry ice is useful (it does not melt into a liquid at atmospheric pressure). Carbon dioxide will form a liquid only above pressures of 5.1 atm.

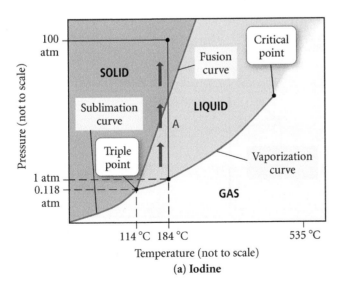

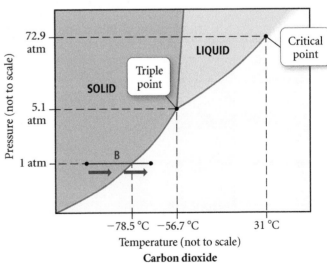

▲ **FIGURE 11.39 Phase Diagrams for Other Substances**   (a) Iodine, (b) Carbon dioxide.

Conceptual Connection 11.4 Phase Diagrams

A substance has a triple point at −24.5 °C and 225 mm Hg. What is most likely to happen to a solid sample of the substance as it is warmed from −35 °C to 0 °C at a pressure of 220 mm Hg?

(a) The solid will melt into a liquid.

(b) The solid will sublime into a gas.

(c) Nothing (the solid will remain as a solid).

ANSWER: (b) The solid will sublime into a gas. Since the pressure is below the triple point the liquid state is not stable.

11.9 Water: An Extraordinary Substance

Water is easily the most common and important liquid on Earth. It fills our oceans, lakes, and streams. In its solid form, it caps our mountains, and in its gaseous form, it humidifies our air. We drink water, we sweat water, and we excrete bodily wastes dissolved in water. Indeed, the majority of our body mass *is* water. Life is impossible without water, and in most places on Earth where liquid water exists, life exists. Recent evidence for water on Mars in the past has fueled hopes of finding life or evidence of past life there. And though it may not be obvious to us (because we take water for granted), this familiar substance turns out to have many remarkable properties.

Among liquids, water is unique. It has a low molar mass (18.02 g/mol), yet it is a liquid at room temperature. Other main-group hydrides have higher molar masses but lower boiling points, as shown in Figure 11.40 ▼. No other substance of similar molar mass (except for HF) comes close to being a liquid at room temperature. We can understand water's high boiling point (in spite of its low molar mass) by examining its molecular structure. The bent geometry of the water molecule and the highly polar nature of the O—H bonds result in a molecule with a significant dipole moment. Water's two O—H bonds (hydrogen directly bonded to oxygen) allow a water molecule to form strong hydrogen bonds with four other water molecules (Figure 11.41 ▶), resulting in a relatively high boiling point. Water's high polarity also allows it to dissolve many other polar and ionic compounds, and even a number of nonpolar gases such as oxygen and carbon dioxide (by inducing a dipole moment in their molecules). Consequently, water is the main solvent within living organisms, transporting nutrients and other important compounds throughout the body. Water is the main solvent in our environment as well, allowing

▲ The *Phoenix Mars Lander* is looking for evidence of life in frozen water that lies below the surface of Mars's north polar region.

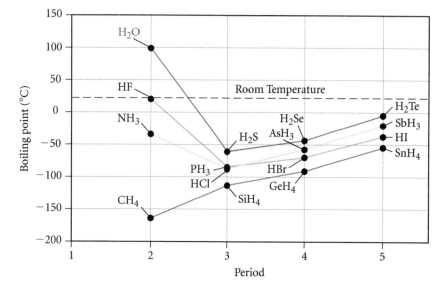

▲ **FIGURE 11.40 Boiling Points of Main Group Hydrides** Water is the only common main-group hydride that is a liquid at room temperature.

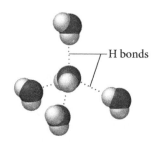

▲ **FIGURE 11.41 Hydrogen Bonding in Water** A water molecule can form four strong hydrogen bonds with four other water molecules.

aquatic animals, for example, to survive by breathing dissolved oxygen and allowing aquatic plants to survive by using dissolved carbon dioxide for photosynthesis.

We have already seen in Section 6.4 that water has an exceptionally high specific heat capacity, which has a moderating effect on the climate of coastal cities. In some cities, such as San Francisco, for example, the daily fluctuation in temperature can be less than 10 °C. This same moderating effect occurs over the entire planet, two-thirds of which is covered by water. Without water, the daily temperature fluctuations on our planet might be more like those on Mars, where temperature fluctuations of 63 °C (113 °F) have been measured between midday and early morning. Imagine awakening to below freezing temperatures, only to bake at summer desert temperatures in the afternoon! The presence of water on Earth and its uniquely high specific heat capacity are largely responsible for our planet's much smaller daily fluctuations.

As we have seen, the way water freezes is also unique. Unlike other substances, which contract upon freezing, water expands upon freezing. Consequently, ice is less dense than liquid water, and it floats. This seemingly trivial property has significant consequences. The frozen layer of ice at the surface of a winter lake insulates the water in the lake from further freezing. If this ice layer sank, it would kill bottom-dwelling aquatic life and possibly allow the lake to freeze solid, eliminating virtually all life in the lake.

The expansion of water upon freezing, however, is one reason that most organisms do not survive freezing. When the water within a cell freezes, it expands and often ruptures the cell, just as water freezing within a pipe bursts the pipe. Many foods, especially those with high water content, do not survive freezing very well either. Have you ever tried, for example, to freeze your own vegetables? If you put lettuce or spinach in the freezer, it will be limp and damaged when you defrost it. The frozen-food industry gets around this problem by *flash freezing* vegetables and other foods. In this process, foods are frozen nearly instantaneously, which prevents water molecules from settling into their preferred crystalline structure. Consequently, the water does not expand very much and the food remains largely undamaged.

▲ When lettuce freezes, the water within its cells expands, rupturing them.

CHEMISTRY IN THE ENVIRONMENT Water Pollution

Water quality is critical to human health. Many human diseases—especially in developing nations—are caused by poor water quality. Several kinds of pollutants, including biological and chemical contaminants, can enter water supplies.

◀ Uncontaminated, sanitary water supplies are critical to human health.

Biological contaminants are microorganisms that cause diseases such as hepatitis, cholera, dysentery, and typhoid. They get into drinking water primarily when human or animal waste is dumped into bodies of water. Drinking water in developed nations is usually chemically treated to kill microorganisms. Water containing biological contaminants poses an immediate danger to human health and should not be consumed. Most biological contaminants can be eliminated from untreated water by boiling.

Chemical contaminants enter drinking water supplies as a result of industrial dumping, pesticide and fertilizer use, and household dumping. These contaminants include organic compounds, such as carbon tetrachloride and dioxin, and inorganic elements and compounds, such as mercury, lead, and nitrates. Since many chemical contaminants are neither volatile nor alive (like biological contaminants), they are usually *not* eliminated through boiling.

The U.S. Environmental Protection Agency (EPA), under the Safe Drinking Water Act of 1974 and its amendments, sets standards that specify the maximum contamination level (MCL) for nearly 100 biological and chemical contaminants in water. Water providers that serve more than 25 people must periodically test the water they deliver to their consumers for these contaminants. If levels exceed the standards set by the EPA, the water provider must notify the consumer and take appropriate measures to remove the contaminant from the water. According to the EPA, if water comes from a provider that serves more than 25 people, it should be safe to consume over a lifetime. If it is not safe to drink for a short period of time, providers must notify consumers.

Question
Why does boiling not eliminate a nonvolatile contaminant such as lead?

11.10 Crystalline Solids: Determining Their Structure by X-Ray Crystallography

We have seen that crystalline solids are composed of atoms or molecules arranged in structures with long-range order (see Section 11.2). If you have ever visited the mineral section of a natural history museum and seen crystals with smooth faces and well-defined angles between them, or if you have carefully observed the hexagonal shapes of snowflakes, you have witnessed some of the effects of the underlying order in crystalline solids. The often beautiful geometric shapes that you see on the macroscopic scale are the result of specific structural patterns on the molecular and atomic scales. But how do we study these patterns? How do we look into the atomic and molecular world to determine the arrangement of the atoms and measure the distances between them? In this section, we examine **X-ray diffraction**, a powerful laboratory technique that enables us to do exactly that.

Recall from Section 7.2 that electromagnetic (or light) waves interact with each other in a characteristic way called *interference*: they can cancel each other out or reinforce each other, depending on the alignment of their crests and troughs. *Constructive interference* occurs when two waves interact with their crests and troughs in alignment. *Destructive interference* occurs when two waves interact in such a way that the crests of one align with the troughs of the other. Recall also that when light encounters two slits separated by a distance comparable to the wavelength of the light, constructive and destructive interference between the resulting beams produces a characteristic *interference pattern*, consisting of alternating bright and dark lines.

▲ The well-defined angles and smooth faces of crystalline solids reflect the underlying order of the atoms composing them.

▲ The hexagonal shape of a snowflake derives from the hexagonal arrangement of water molecules in crystalline ice.

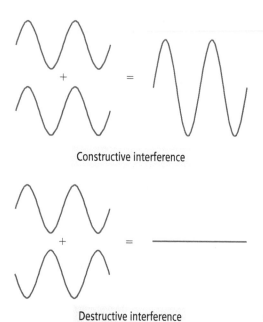

Constructive interference

Destructive interference

Atoms within crystal structures have spacings between them on the order of 10^2 pm, so light of similar wavelength (which happens to fall in the X-ray region of the electromagnetic spectrum) forms interference patterns or *diffraction patterns* when it interacts with those atoms. The exact pattern of diffraction reveals the spacings between planes of atoms. Consider two planes of atoms within a crystalline lattice separated by a distance d, as shown in Figure 11.42 ▶ on the next page. If two rays of light with wavelength λ that are initially in phase (that is, the crests of one wave are aligned with the crests of the other) diffract from the two planes, the diffracted rays may interfere with each other constructively or destructively, depending on the difference between the path lengths traveled by each ray. If the difference between the two path lengths ($2a$) is an integral number (n) of wavelengths, then the interference will be constructive.

$$n\lambda = 2a \quad \text{(criterion for constructive interference)} \quad [11.5]$$

▶ FIGURE 11.42 **Diffraction from a Crystal** When X-rays strike parallel planes of atoms in a crystal, constructive interference occurs if the difference in path length between beams reflected from adjacent planes is an integral number of wavelengths.

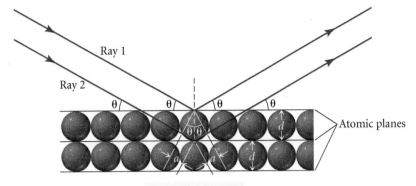

Path difference = 2*a*

Using trigonometry, we can see that the angle of reflection (θ) is related to the distance a and the separation between layers (d) by the following relation:

$$\sin \theta = \frac{a}{d} \qquad [11.6]$$

Rearranging, we get:

$$a = d \sin \theta \qquad [11.7]$$

By substituting Equation 11.7 into Equation 11.5, we arrive at the following important relationship:

$$n\lambda = 2d \sin \theta \qquad \text{Bragg's law}$$

This equation is known as *Bragg's law*. For a given wavelength of light incident on atoms arranged in layers, we can measure the angle that produces constructive interference (which appears as a bright spot on the X-ray diffraction pattern) and then compute d, the distance between the atomic layers.

$$d = \frac{n\lambda}{2 \sin \theta} \qquad [11.8]$$

In a modern X-ray diffractometer (Figure 11.43 ▼), the diffraction pattern from a crystal is collected and analyzed by a computer. By rotating the crystal and collecting the resulting diffraction patterns at different angles, the distances between various crystalline planes can be measured, eventually yielding the entire crystalline structure. This process is called X-ray crystallography. Researchers use X-ray crystallography to determine, not

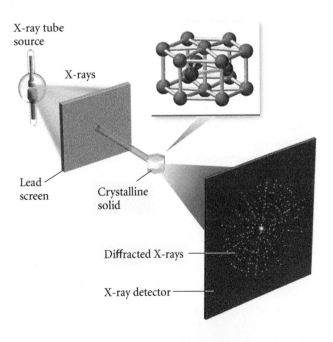

▶ FIGURE 11.43 **X-Ray Diffraction Analysis** In X-ray crystallography, an X-ray beam is passed through a sample, which is rotated to allow diffraction from different crystalline planes. The resulting patterns, representing constructive interference from various planes, are then analyzed to determine crystalline structure.

only the structures of simple atomic lattices, but also the structures of proteins, DNA, and other biologically important molecules. For example, the famous X-ray diffraction photograph shown here, obtained by Rosalind Franklin and Maurice Wilkins, helped Watson and Crick determine the double-helical structure of DNA. As we learned in Section 9.1, researchers also used X-ray diffraction to determine the structure of HIV protease, a protein critical to the reproduction of HIV and the development of AIDS. That structure was then used to design drug molecules that would inhibit the action of HIV protease, thus halting the advance of the disease.

EXAMPLE 11.6 Using Bragg's Law

When an X-ray beam of $\lambda = 154$ pm was incident on the surface of an iron crystal, it produced a maximum reflection at an angle of $\theta = 32.6°$. Assuming $n = 1$, calculate the separation between layers of iron atoms in the crystal.

SOLUTION

To solve this problem, use Bragg's law in the form given by Equation 11.8. The distance, d, is the separation between layers in the crystal.

$$d = \frac{n\lambda}{2 \sin \theta}$$
$$= \frac{154 \text{ pm}}{2 \sin(32.6°)}$$
$$= 143 \text{ pm}$$

FOR PRACTICE 11.6

The spacing between layers of molybdenum atoms is 157 pm. Compute the angle at which 154-pm X-rays would produce a maximum reflection for $n = 1$.

11.11 Crystalline Solids: Unit Cells and Basic Structures

X-Ray crystallography allows us to determine the regular arrangements of atoms within a crystalline solid. This arrangement is called the **crystalline lattice**. The crystalline lattice of any solid is nature's way of aggregating the particles to minimize their energy. We can represent the crystalline lattice with a small collection of atoms, ions, or molecules called the **unit cell**. When the unit cell is repeated over and over—like the tiles of a floor or the pattern in a wallpaper design, but in three dimensions—the entire lattice can be reproduced. For example, consider the two-dimensional crystalline lattice shown at right. The unit cell for this lattice is the dark-colored square. Each circle represents a *lattice point*, a point in space occupied by an atom, ion, or molecule. Repeating the pattern in the square throughout the two-dimensional space generates the entire lattice.

Many different unit cells exist and we often classify unit cells by their symmetry. In this book, we focus primarily on *cubic unit cells* (although we will look at one hexagonal unit cell). Cubic unit cells are characterized by equal edge lengths and 90° angles at their corners. The three cubic unit cells—simple cubic, body-centered cubic, and face-centered cubic—along with some of their basic characteristics, are presented in Figure 11.44 ► on the next page. We use two colors in this figure to help you visualize the different positions of the atoms; they *do not* represent different *kinds* of atoms. For these unit cells *each atom in any one structure is identical to the other atoms in that structure*.

The **simple cubic** unit cell (Figure 11.45 ► on the next page) consists of a cube with one atom at each corner. The atoms touch along each edge of the cube, so the edge length is twice the radius of the atoms ($l = 2r$). Even though it may seem like the unit cell contains eight atoms, it actually contains only one. Each corner atom is shared by eight other unit cells. In other words, any one unit cell actually contains only one-eighth of each of the eight atoms at its corners, for a total of only one atom per unit cell.

A characteristic feature of any unit cell is the **coordination number**, the number of atoms with which each atom is in *direct contact*. The coordination number is the number of atoms with which a particular atom can strongly interact. The simple cubic unit cell has

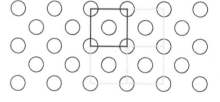

Simple cubic

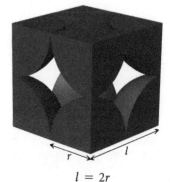

$l = 2r$

▲ In the simple cubic lattice, the atoms touch along each edge so that the edge length is 2r.

Cubic Cell Name	Atoms per Unit Cell	Structure	Coordination Number	Edge Length in terms of r	Packing Efficiency (fraction of volume occupied)
Simple Cubic	1		6	$2r$	52%
Body-centered Cubic	2		8	$\dfrac{4r}{\sqrt{3}}$	68%
Face-centered Cubic	4		12	$2\sqrt{2}r$	74%

▲ **FIGURE 11.44 The Cubic Crystalline Lattices** The different colors used for the atoms in this figure are for clarity only. All atoms within each structure are identical.

Unit cells, such as the cubic ones shown here, are customarily portrayed with "whole" atoms, even though only a part of the whole atom may actually be in the unit cell.

a coordination number of 6; any one atom touches only six others, as you can see in Figure 11.45. A quantity closely related to the coordination number is the **packing efficiency**, the percentage of the volume of the unit cell occupied by the spheres. The higher the coordination number, the greater the packing efficiency. The simple cubic unit cell has a packing efficiency of 52%—the simple cubic unit cell contains a lot of empty space.

The **body-centered cubic** unit cell (Figure 11.46 ►) consists of a cube with one atom at each corner and one atom (of the same kind) in the very center of the cube. Note that in the body-centered unit cell, the atoms *do not* touch along each edge of the cube, but instead along the diagonal line that runs from one corner, through the middle of the cube, to the opposite corner. The edge length in terms of the atomic radius is therefore

Simple Cubic Unit Cell

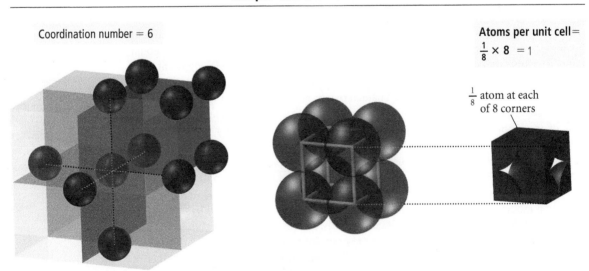

Coordination number = 6

Atoms per unit cell=
$\dfrac{1}{8} \times 8 = 1$

$\dfrac{1}{8}$ atom at each of 8 corners

▲ **FIGURE 11.45 Simple Cubic Crystal Structure**

Body-Centered Cubic Unit Cell

Coordination number = 8

Atoms per unit cell=
$$\left(\frac{1}{8} \times 8\right) + 1 = 2$$

$\frac{1}{8}$ atom at each of 8 corners

1 atom at center

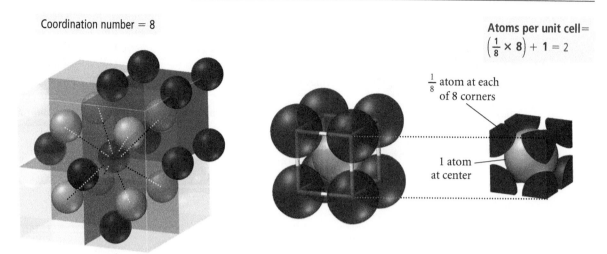

▲ **FIGURE 11.46 Body-Centered Cubic Crystal Structure** The different colors used for the atoms in this figure are for clarity only. All atoms within the structure are identical.

$l = 4r/\sqrt{3}$ as shown in the diagram at right. The body-centered unit cell contains two atoms per unit cell because the center atom is not shared with any other neighboring cells. The coordination number of the body-centered cubic unit cell is 8, which you can see by examining the atom in the very center of the cube, which touches eight atoms at the corners. The packing efficiency is 68%, significantly higher than for the simple cubic unit cell. Each atom in this structure strongly interacts with more atoms than each atom in the simple cubic unit cell.

The **face-centered cubic** unit cell (Figure 11.47 ▼) is a cube with one atom at each corner and one atom (of the same kind) in the center of each cube face. Note

Body-centered cubic

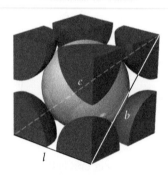

▼ In the body-centered cubic lattice, the atoms touch only along the cube diagonal. The edge length is $4r/\sqrt{3}$.

$$c^2 = b^2 + l^2 \qquad b^2 = l^2 + l^2$$
$$c = 4r \qquad b^2 = 2l^2$$
$$(4r)^2 = 2l^2 + l^2$$
$$(4r)^2 = 3l^2$$
$$l^2 = \frac{(4r)^2}{3}$$
$$l = \frac{4r}{\sqrt{3}}$$

Face-Centered Cubic Unit Cell

Face-centered cubic:
extended structure
Coordination number = 12

Face-centered cubic: unit cell
Atoms/unit $= \left(\frac{1}{8} \times 8\right) + \left(\frac{1}{2} \times 6\right) = 4$

$\frac{1}{8}$ **atom at 8 corners**

$\frac{1}{2}$ **atom at 6 faces**

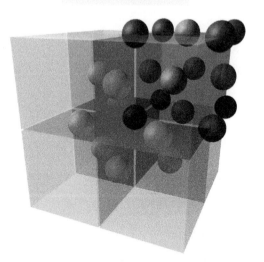
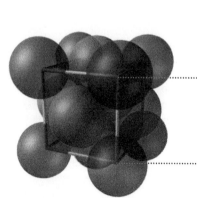
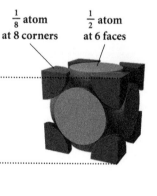

▲ **FIGURE 11.47 Face-Centered Cubic Crystal Structure** The different colors used on the atoms in this figure are for clarity only. All atoms within the structure are identical.

▼ In the face-centered cubic lattice, the atoms touch along a face diagonal. The edge length is $2\sqrt{2}r$.

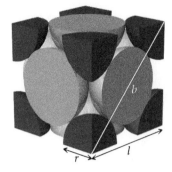

Face-centered cubic

$$b^2 = l^2 + l^2 = 2l^2$$
$$b = 4r$$
$$(4r)^2 = 2l^2$$
$$l^2 = \frac{(4r)^2}{2}$$
$$l = \frac{4r}{\sqrt{2}}$$
$$= 2\sqrt{2}r$$

that in the face-centered unit cell (like the body-centered unit cell), the atoms *do not* touch along each edge of the cube. Instead, the atoms touch *along the diagonal face*. The edge length in terms of the atomic radius is therefore $l = 2\sqrt{2}r$, as shown in the figure at left. The face-centered unit cell contains four atoms per unit cell because the center atoms on each of the six faces are shared between two unit cells. There are $^{1}/_{2} \times 6 = 3$ face-centered atoms plus $1/8 \times 8 = 1$ corner atoms, for a total of four atoms per unit cell. The coordination number of the face-centered cubic unit cell is 12 and its packing efficiency is 74%. In this structure, any one atom strongly interacts with more atoms than in either the simple cubic unit cell or the body-centered cubic unit cell.

EXAMPLE 11.7 Relating Density to Crystal Structure

Aluminum crystallizes with a face-centered cubic unit cell. The radius of an aluminum atom is 143 pm. Calculate the density of solid crystalline aluminum in g/cm^3.

SORT You are given the radius of an aluminum atom and its crystal structure. You are asked to find the density of solid aluminum.	**GIVEN:** $r = 143$ pm, face-centered cubic **FIND:** d
STRATEGIZE The conceptual plan is based on the definition of density. Since the unit cell has the physical properties of the entire crystal, you can find the mass and volume of the unit cell and use these to calculate its density.	**CONCEPTUAL PLAN** $d = m/V$ $m = $ mass of unit cell $\quad = $ number of atoms in unit cell $\times$ mass of each atom $V = $ volume of unit cell $\quad = $ (edge length)^3
SOLVE Begin by finding the mass of the unit cell. Obtain the mass of an aluminum atom from its molar mass. Since the face-centered cubic unit cell contains four atoms per unit cell, multiply the mass of aluminum by 4 to get the mass of a unit cell.	**SOLUTION** $m(\text{Al atom}) = 26.98\dfrac{g}{mol} \times \dfrac{1\ mol}{6.022 \times 10^{23}\ atoms}$ $\qquad\qquad\quad = 4.481 \times 10^{-23}$ g/atom $m(\text{unit cell}) = 4\ atoms\ (4.481 \times 10^{-23}\ \text{g/atom})$ $\qquad\qquad\quad = 1.792 \times 10^{-22}$ g
Next, compute the edge length (l) of the unit cell (in m) from the atomic radius of aluminum. For the face-centered cubic structure, $l = 2\sqrt{2}r$.	$l = 2\sqrt{2}r$ $\ = 2\sqrt{2}\ (143\ \text{pm})$ $\ = 2\sqrt{2}\ (143 \times 10^{-12}\ \text{m})$ $\ = 4.0\underline{4}5 \times 10^{-10}$ m
Compute the volume of the unit cell (in cm) by converting the edge length to cm and cubing the edge length. (We use centimeters because we want to report the density in units of g/cm^3.)	$V = l^3$ $\ = \left(4.0\underline{4}5 \times 10^{-10}\ \text{m} \times \dfrac{1\ cm}{10^{-2}\ m}\right)^3$ $\ = 6.6\underline{1}8 \times 10^{-23}\ cm^3$
Finally, compute the density by dividing the mass of the unit cell by the volume of the unit cell.	$d = \dfrac{m}{V} = \dfrac{1.792 \times 10^{-22}\ g}{6.6\underline{1}8 \times 10^{-23}\ cm^3}$ $\quad = 2.71\ g/cm^3$

CHECK The units of the answer are correct. The magnitude of the answer is reasonable because the density is greater than 1 g/cm^3 (as we would expect for metals), but still not too high (because aluminum is a low-density metal).

FOR PRACTICE 11.7
Chromium crystallizes with a body-centered cubic unit cell. The radius of a chromium atom is 125 pm. Calculate the density of solid crystalline chromium in g/cm^3.

Closest-Packed Structures

Another way to envision crystal structures, especially useful in metals where bonds are not usually directional, is to think of the atoms as stacking in layers, much as fruit is stacked at the grocery store. For example, the simple cubic structure can be envisioned as one layer of atoms arranged in a square pattern with the next layer stacking directly over the first, so that the atoms in one layer align exactly on top of the atoms in the layer beneath it, as shown here.

As we saw previously, this crystal structure has a great deal of empty space—only 52% of the volume is occupied by the spheres, and the coordination number is 6.

More space-efficient packing can be achieved by aligning neighboring rows of atoms in a pattern with one row offset from the next by one-half a sphere, as shown here.

In this way, the atoms pack more closely to each other in any one layer. We can further increase the packing efficiency by placing the next layer *not directly on top of the first*, but again offset so that any one atom actually sits in the indentation formed by three atoms in the layer beneath it, as shown here:

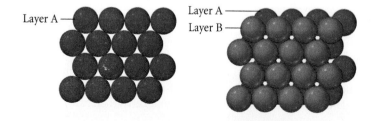

Layer A

Layer A
Layer B

This kind of packing leads to two different crystal structures called *closest-packed structures*, both of which have a packing efficiency of 74% and a coordination number of 12. In the first of these two closest-packed structures—called **hexagonal closest packing**—the third layer of atoms aligns exactly on top of the first, as shown here.

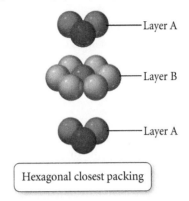

Layer A

Layer B

Layer A

Hexagonal closest packing

The pattern from one layer to the next is ABAB... with the third layer aligning exactly on top of the first. Notice that the central atom in layer B of this structure is touching 6 atoms in its own layer, 3 atoms in the layer above it, and 3 atoms in the layer below, for a coordination number of 12. The unit cell for this crystal structure is not a cubic unit cell, but a hexagonal one, as shown in Figure 11.48 ▼.

Hexagonal Closest Packing

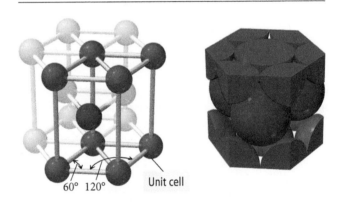

60° 120°   Unit cell

▶ FIGURE 11.48 Hexagonal Closest-Packing Crystal Structure   The unit cell is outlined in bold.

In the second of the two closest-packed structures—called **cubic closest packing**—the third layer of atoms is offset from the first, as shown here.

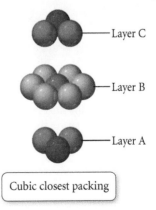

Layer C

Layer B

Layer A

Cubic closest packing

The pattern from one layer to the next is ABCABC... with every fourth layer aligning with the first. Although not simple to visualize, the unit cell for cubic closest packing is the face-centered cubic unit cell, as shown in Figure 11.49 ▶. The cubic closest-packed structure is identical to the face-centered cubic unit cell structure.

Cubic Closest Packed = Face-Centered Cubic

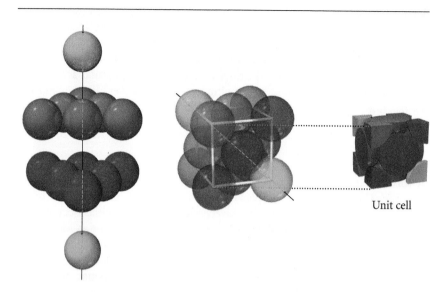

Unit cell

◀ FIGURE 11.49 **Cubic Closest-Packing Crystal Structure** The unit cell of the cubic closest-packed structure is face-centered cubic.

11.12 Crystalline Solids: The Fundamental Types

As we learned in Section 11.2, solids may be crystalline (comprising a well-ordered array of atoms or molecules) or amorphous (having no long-range order). We can classify crystalline solids into three categories—molecular, ionic, and atomic—based on the individual units that compose the solid. Atomic solids can themselves be classified into three categories—nonbonded, metallic, and network covalent—depending on the types of interactions between atoms within the solid. Figure 11.50 ▼ shows the different categories of crystalline solids.

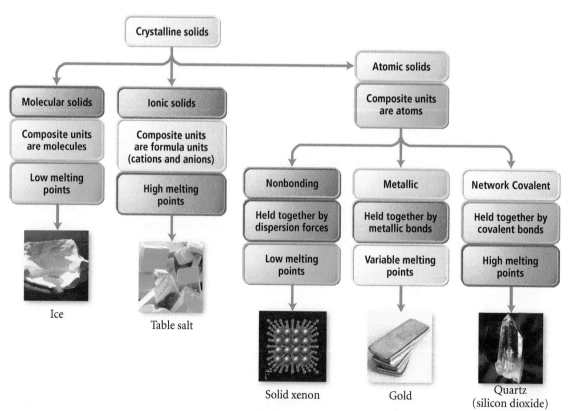

▲ FIGURE 11.50 **Types of Crystalline Solids**

Molecular Solids

Molecular solids are those solids whose composite units are *molecules*. The lattice sites in a crystalline molecular solid are therefore occupied by molecules. Ice (solid H_2O) and dry ice (solid CO_2) are examples of molecular solids. Molecular solids are held together by the kinds of intermolecular forces—dispersion forces, dipole–dipole forces, and hydrogen bonding—that we discussed earlier in this chapter. Molecular solids as a whole tend to have low to moderately low melting points. However, strong intermolecular forces (such as the hydrogen bonds in water) can increase the melting points of some molecular solids.

Ionic Solids

Ionic solids are those solids whose composite units are ions. Table salt (NaCl) and calcium fluoride (CaF_2) are good examples of ionic solids. Ionic solids are held together by the coulombic interactions that occur between the cations and anions occupying the lattice sites in the crystal. The coordination number of the unit cell for an ionic compound, therefore, represents the number of close cation–anion interactions. Since these interactions lower potential energy, the crystal structure of a particular ionic compound will be the one that maximizes the coordination number, while accommodating both charge neutrality (each unit cell must be charge neutral) and the different sizes of the cations and anions that compose the particular compound. In general, the more similar the radii of the cation and the anion, the higher the coordination number.

Cesium chloride (CsCl) is a good example of an ionic compound with cations and anions of similar size (Cs^+ radius $= 167$ pm; Cl^- radius $= 181$ pm). In the cesium chloride structure, the chloride ions occupy the lattice sites of a simple cubic cell and one cesium ion lies in the very center of the cell, as shown in Figure 11.51 ◀. (In this and subsequent figures of ionic crystal structures, the different colored spheres represent different ions.) The coordination number is 8, meaning that each cesium ion is in direct contact with eight chloride ions (and vice versa). The cesium chloride unit cell contains one chloride anion ($8 \times 1/8 = 1$) and one cesium cation for a ratio of Cs to Cl of 1:1, as the formula for the compound indicates. (Note that complete chloride ions are shown in Figure 11.51 even though only 1/8 of each ion is in the unit cell.) Calcium sulfide (CaS) has the same structure as cesium chloride.

The crystal structure of sodium chloride must accommodate the more disproportionate sizes of Na^+ (radius $= 97$ pm) and Cl^- (radius $= 181$ pm). If ion size were the only consideration, the larger chloride anion could theoretically fit many of the smaller sodium cations around it, but charge neutrality requires that each sodium cation be surrounded by an equal number of chloride anions. Therefore, the coordination number is limited by the number of chloride anions that can fit around the relatively small sodium cation. The structure that minimizes the energy is shown in Figure 11.52 ◀ and has a coordination number of 6 (each chloride anion is surrounded by six sodium cations and vice versa). You can visualize this structure, called the *rock salt* structure, as chloride anions occupying the lattice sites of a face-centered cubic structure with the smaller sodium cations occupying the holes between the anions. (Alternatively, you can visualize this structure as the *sodium cations* occupying the lattice sites of a face-centered cubic structure with the *larger chloride anions* occupying the spaces between the cations.) Each unit cell contains four chloride anions $[(8 \times 1/8) + (6 \times 1/2) = 4]$ and four sodium cations $[(12 \times 1/4) + 1 = 4]$, resulting in a ratio of 1:1, as the formula of the compound specifies. Other compounds exhibiting the sodium chloride structure include LiF, KCl, KBr, AgCl, MgO, and CaO.

An even greater disproportion between the sizes of the cations and anions in a compound makes a coordination number of even 6 physically impossible. For example, in ZnS (Zn^{2+} radius $= 74$ pm; S^{2-} radius $= 184$ pm) the crystal structure, shown in Figure 11.53 ◀, has a coordination number of only 4. You can visualize this structure, called the *zinc blende* structure, as sulfide anions occupying the lattice sites of a face-centered cubic structure with the smaller zinc cations occupying four of the eight tetrahedral holes located directly beneath each corner atom. A tetrahedral hole is the empty space that lies in the center of a tetrahedral arrangement of four atoms, as shown at right. Each unit cell contains four sulfide anions $[(8 \times 1/8) + (6 \times 1/2 = 4)]$ and four zinc cations (each of

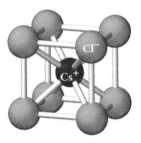

Cesium chloride (CsCl)

▲ **FIGURE 11.51 Cesium Chloride Unit Cell** The different colored spheres in this figure represent the different ions in the compound.

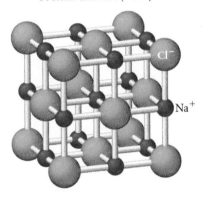

Sodium chloride (NaCl)

▲ **FIGURE 11.52 Sodium Chloride Unit Cell** The different colored spheres in this figure represent the different ions in the compound.

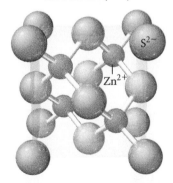

Zinc blende (ZnS)

▲ **FIGURE 11.53 Zinc Sulfide (Zinc Blende) Unit Cell** The different colored spheres in this figure represent the different ions in the compound.

the four zinc cations is completely contained within the unit cell), resulting in a ratio of 1:1, just as the formula of the compound indicates. Other compounds exhibiting the zinc blende structure include CuCl, AgI, and CdS.

When the ratio of cations to anions is not 1:1, the crystal structure must accommodate the unequal number of cations and anions. Many compounds that contain a cation to anion ratio of 1:2 adopt the *fluorite (CaF₂) structure* shown in Figure 11.54 ▶. You can visualize this structure as calcium cations occupying the lattice sites of a face-centered cubic structure with the larger fluoride anions occupying all eight of the tetrahedral holes located directly beneath each corner atom. Each unit cell contains four calcium cations $[(8 \times \frac{1}{8}) + (6 \times \frac{1}{2}) = 4]$ and eight fluoride anions (each of the eight fluoride anions is completely contained within the unit cell), resulting in a cation to anion ratio of 1:2, just as in the formula of the compound. Other compounds exhibiting the fluorite structure include PbF_2, SrF_2, and $BaCl_2$. Compounds with a cation to anion ratio of 2:1 often exhibit the *antifluorite structure*, in which the anions occupy the lattice sites of a face-centered cubic structure and the cations occupy the tetrahedral holes beneath each corner atom.

The forces holding ionic solids together are strong coulombic forces (or ionic bonds), and since these forces are much stronger than the intermolecular forces discussed previously, ionic solids tend to have much higher melting points than molecular solids. For example, sodium chloride melts at 801 °C, while carbon disulfide (CS_2)—a molecular solid with a higher molar mass—melts at −110 °C.

Atomic Solids

Solids whose composite units are individual atoms are **atomic solids**. Solid xenon (Xe), iron (Fe), and silicon dioxide (SiO_2) are examples of atomic solids. Atomic solids can themselves be classified into three categories—*nonbonding atomic solids, metallic atomic solids, and network covalent atomic solids*—each held together by a different kind of force.

Nonbonding atomic solids are held together by relatively weak dispersion forces. In order to maximize these interactions, nonbonding atomic solids form closest-packed structures, maximizing their coordination numbers and minimizing the distance between them. Nonbonding atomic solids have very low melting points that increase uniformly with molar mass. The only nonbonding atomic solids are noble gases in their solid form. Argon, for example, has a melting point of −189 °C and xenon has a melting point of −112 °C.

Metallic atomic solids, such as iron or gold, are held together by *metallic bonds*, which in the simplest model are represented by the interaction of metal cations with the sea of electrons that surround them, as described in Section 9.11 (Figure 11.55 ▶).

Since metallic bonds are not directional, metals also tend to form closest-packed crystal structures. For example, nickel crystallizes in the cubic closest-packed structure and zinc crystallizes in the hexagonal closest-packed structure (Figure 11.56 ▼). Metallic

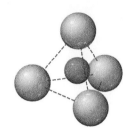

▲ A tetrahedral hole

Calcium fluoride (CaF₂)

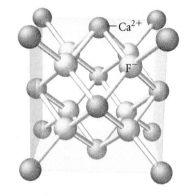

▲ **FIGURE 11.54 Calcium Fluoride Unit Cell** The different colored spheres in this figure represent the different ions in the compound.

We examine a more sophisticated model for bonding in metals in Section 11.13.

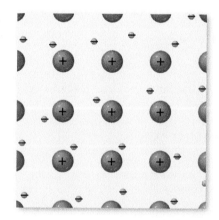

▲ **FIGURE 11.55 The Electron Sea Model** In the electron sea model for metals, the metal cations exist in a "sea" of electrons.

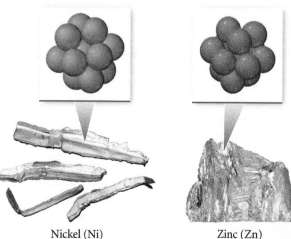

Nickel (Ni)   Zinc (Zn)

◀ **FIGURE 11.56 Closest-Packed Crystal Structures in Metals** Nickel crystallizes in the cubic closest-packed structure. Zinc crystallizes in the hexagonal closest-packed structure.

(a) Diamond   (b) Graphite

▲ **FIGURE 11.57 Network Covalent Atomic Solids** (a) In diamond, each carbon atom forms four covalent bonds to four other carbon atoms in a tetrahedral geometry. (b) In graphite, carbon atoms are arranged in sheets. Within each sheet, the atoms are covalently bonded to one another by a network of sigma and pi bonds. Neighboring sheets are held together by dispersion forces.

bonds have varying strengths. Some metals, such as mercury, have melting points below room temperature, whereas other metals, such as iron, have relatively high melting points (iron melts at 1809 °C).

Network covalent atomic solids, such as diamond, graphite, and silicon dioxide, are held together by covalent bonds. The crystal structures of these solids are more restricted by the geometrical constraints of the covalent bonds (which tend to be more directional than intermolecular forces, ionic bonds, or metallic bonds) so they *do not* tend to form closest-packed structures.

In diamond (Figure 11.57a ▲), each carbon atom forms four covalent bonds to four other carbon atoms in a tetrahedral geometry. This structure extends throughout the entire crystal, so that a diamond crystal can be thought of as a giant molecule, held together by these covalent bonds. Since covalent bonds are very strong, covalent atomic solids have high melting points. Diamond is estimated to melt at about 3800 °C. The electrons in diamond are confined to the covalent bonds and are not free to flow. Therefore diamond does not conduct electricity.

In graphite (Figure 11.57b), carbon atoms are arranged in sheets. Within each sheet, carbon atoms are covalently bonded to each other by a network of sigma and pi bonds, similar to those in benzene. Just as the electrons within the pi bonds in benzene are delocalized over the entire molecule, so the pi bonds in graphite are delocalized over the entire sheet, making graphite a good electrical conductor along the sheets. The bond length between carbon atoms *within a sheet* is 142 pm. However, the forces *between* sheets are much different. The separation between sheets is 341 pm. There are no covalent bonds between sheets, only relatively weak dispersion forces. Consequently, the sheets slide past each other relatively easily, which explains the slippery feel of graphite and its extensive use as a lubricant.

The silicates (extended arrays of silicon and oxygen) are the most common network covalent atomic solids. Geologists estimate that 90% of Earth's crust is composed of silicates; we cover these in more detail in Chapter 22. The basic silicon oxygen compound is silica (SiO_2), which in its most common crystalline form is called quartz. The structure of quartz consists of an array of SiO_4 tetrahedra with shared oxygen atoms, as shown in Figure 11.58a ▶. The strong silicon–oxygen covalent bonds that hold quartz together result in its high melting point of about 1600 °C. Common glass is also composed of SiO_2, but in its amorphous form (Figure 11.58b).

Sigma and pi bonds were discussed in Section 10.7.

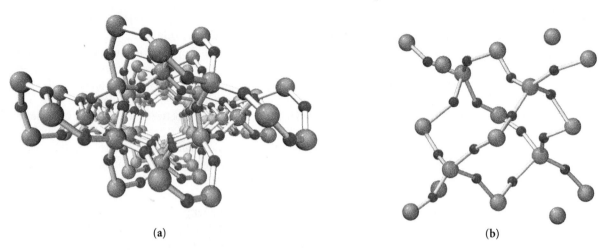

(a)   **(b)**

▲ **FIGURE 11.58 The Structure of Quartz**   **(a)** Quartz consists of an array of SiO_4 tetrahedra with shared oxygen atoms. **(b)** Glass is amorphous SiO_2.

11.13 Crystalline Solids: Band Theory

In Section 9.11, we explored a model for bonding in metals called the *electron sea model*. We now turn to a model for bonding in solids that is both more sophisticated and more broadly applicable—it applies to both metallic solids and covalent solids. The model is called **band theory** and it grows out of molecular orbital theory, first covered in Section 10.8.

Recall that in molecular orbital theory, we combine the atomic orbitals of the atoms within a molecule to form molecular orbitals. These molecular orbitals are not localized on individual atoms, but *delocalized over the entire molecule*. Similarly, in band theory, we combine the atomic orbitals of the atoms within a solid crystal to form orbitals that are not localized on individual atoms, but delocalized over the entire *crystal*. In some sense then, the crystal is like a very large molecule, and its valence electrons occupy the molecular orbitals formed from the atomic orbitals of each atom in the crystal.

Consider a series of molecules constructed from individual lithium atoms. The energy levels of the atomic orbitals and resulting molecular orbitals for Li, Li_2, Li_3, Li_4 and Li_N (where N is a large number on the order of 10^{23}) are shown in Figure 11.59 ▼. The lithium atom has a single electron in a single $2s$ atomic orbital. The Li_2 molecule contains two electrons and two molecular orbitals. The electrons occupy the lower energy bonding orbital—the higher energy, or antibonding, molecular orbital is empty. The Li_4 molecule contains four electrons and four molecular orbitals. The electrons occupy the two bonding molecular orbitals—the two antibonding orbitals are completely empty.

The Li_N molecule contains N electrons and N molecular orbitals. However, because there are so many molecular orbitals, the energy spacings between them are infinitesimally small; they are no longer discrete energy levels, but rather form a *band* of energy levels. One half of the orbitals in the band ($N/2$) are bonding molecular orbitals and (at 0 K) contain the N valence electrons. The other $N/2$ molecular orbitals are antibonding and

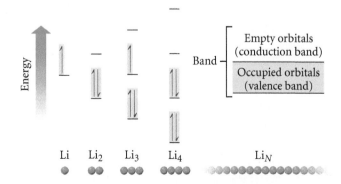

◀ **FIGURE 11.59 Energy Levels of Molecular Orbitals in Lithium Molecules** When many Li atoms are present, the energy levels of the molecular orbitals are so closely spaced that they fuse to form a band. Half of the orbitals are bonding orbitals and contain valence electrons; the other half are antibonding orbitals and are empty.

(at 0 K) are completely empty. If the atoms composing a solid have *p* orbitals available, then the same process leads to another band of orbitals at higher energies.

In band theory, electrons become mobile when they make a transition from the highest occupied molecular orbital into higher energy empty molecular orbitals. For this reason, we call the occupied molecular orbitals the *valence band* and the unoccupied orbitals the *conduction band*. In lithium metal, the highest occupied molecular orbital lies in the middle of a band of orbitals, and the energy difference between it and the next higher energy orbital is infinitesimally small. Therefore, above 0 K, electrons can easily make the transition from the valence band to the conduction band. Since electrons in the conduction band are mobile, lithium, like all metals, is a good electrical conductor. Mobile electrons in the conduction band are also responsible for the thermal conductivity of metals. When a metal is heated, electrons are excited to higher energy molecular orbitals. These electrons can then quickly transport the thermal energy throughout the crystal lattice.

In metals, the valence band and conduction band are energetically continuous—the energy difference between the top of the valence band and the bottom of the conduction band is infinitesimally small. In semiconductors and insulators, however, an energy gap, called the **band gap**, exists between the valence band and conduction band as shown in Figure 11.60 ▼. In insulators, the band gap is large, and electrons are not promoted into the conduction band at ordinary temperatures, resulting in no electrical conductivity. In semiconductors, the band gap is small, allowing some electrons to be promoted at ordinary temperatures and resulting in limited conductivity. However, the conductivity of semiconductors can be increased in a controlled way by adding minute amounts of other substances, called *dopants*, to the semiconductor.

Doping: Controlling the Conductivity of Semiconductors

Doped semiconductors contain minute amounts of impurities that result in additional electrons in the conduction band or electron "holes" in the valence band. For example, silicon is a group 4A semiconductor. Its valence electrons just fill its valence band. The band gap in silicon is large enough that only a few electrons are promoted into the conduction band at room temperature; therefore silicon is a poor electrical conductor. However, silicon can be doped with phosphorus, a group 5A element with five valence electrons, to increase its conductivity. The phosphorus atoms are incorporated into the silicon crystal structure and each phosphorus atom brings with it one additional electron. Since the valence band is completely full, the additional electrons must go into the conduction band. These electrons are then mobile and can conduct electrical current. This type of semiconductor is called an **n-type semiconductor** because the charge carriers are negatively charged electrons in the conduction band.

Silicon can also be doped with a group 3A element, such as gallium, which has only three valence electrons. When gallium is incorporated into the silicon crystal structure, it results in electron "holes," or empty molecular orbitals, in the valence band. The presence of holes also allows for the movement of electrical current because electrons in the valence band can move between holes. In this way, the holes move in the opposite direction as the electrons. This type of semiconductor is called a **p-type semiconductor** because each hole acts as a positive charge.

The heart of most modern electronic devices are silicon chips containing millions of **p–n junctions**, tiny spots that are p-type on one side and n-type on the other. These junctions can serve a number of functions including acting as **diodes** (circuit elements that allow the flow of electrical current in only one direction) or amplifiers (elements that amplify a small electrical current into a larger one).

▶ **FIGURE 11.60 Band Gap** In a conductor, there is no energy gap between the valence band and the conduction band. In semiconductors there is a small energy gap, and in insulators there is a large energy gap.

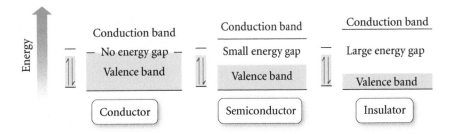

CHAPTER IN REVIEW

Key Terms

Section 11.2
crystalline (457)
amorphous (457)

Section 11.3
dispersion force (459)
dipole–dipole force (461)
permanent dipole (461)
miscibility (462)
hydrogen bonding (464)
hydrogen bond (464)
ion–dipole force (466)

Section 11.4
surface tension (468)
viscosity (469)
capillary action (470)

Section 11.5
vaporization (471)
condensation (471)

volatile (471)
nonvolatile (471)
heat of vaporization (ΔH_{vap})
   (472)
dynamic equilibrium (474)
vapor pressure (474)
boiling point (475)
normal boiling point (475)
Clausius–Clapeyron equation
   (476)
critical temperature (T_c) (479)
critical pressure (P_c) (479)

Section 11.6
sublimation (480)
deposition (480)
melting point (481)
melting (fusion) (481)
freezing (481)
heat of fusion (ΔH_{fus}) (481)

Section 11.8
phase diagram (484)
triple point (485)
critical point (485)

Section 11.10
X-ray diffraction (489)

Section 11.11
crystalline lattice (491)
unit cell (491)
simple cubic (491)
coordination number (491)
packing efficiency (492)
body-centered cubic (492)
face-centered cubic (493)
hexagonal closest packing
   (496)
cubic closest packing
   (496)

Section 11.12
molecular solids (498)
ionic solids (498)
atomic solids (499)
nonbonding atomic solids
   (499)
metallic atomic solids (499)
network covalent atomic solids
   (500)

Section 11.13
band theory (501)
band gap (502)
n-type semiconductor (502)
p-type semiconductor (502)
p–n junctions (502)
diodes (502)

Key Concepts

Solids, Liquids, and Intermolecular Forces (11.1, 11.2, 11.3)

Intermolecular forces hold molecules or atoms together in a liquid or solid. The strength of the intermolecular forces in a substance determines its state. Dispersion forces are always present because they result from the fluctuations in electron distribution within atoms and molecules. These are the weakest intermolecular forces, but they are significant in molecules with high molar masses. Dipole–dipole forces, generally stronger than dispersion forces, are present in all polar molecules. Hydrogen bonding occurs in polar molecules that contain hydrogen atoms bonded directly to fluorine, oxygen, or nitrogen. These are the strongest intermolecular forces. Ion–dipole forces occur when ionic compounds are mixed with polar compounds, and they are especially important in aqueous solutions.

Surface Tension, Viscosity, and Capillary Action (11.4)

Surface tension results from the tendency of liquids to minimize their surface area in order to maximize the interactions between their constituent particles, thus lowering their potential energy. Surface tension causes water droplets to form spheres and allows insects and paper clips to "float" on the surface of water. Viscosity is the resistance of a liquid to flow. Viscosity increases with increasing strength of intermolecular forces and decreases with increasing temperature. Capillary action is the ability of a liquid to flow against gravity up a narrow tube. It is the result of adhesive forces, the attraction between the molecules and the surface of the tube, and cohesive forces, the attraction between the molecules in the liquid.

Vaporization and Vapor Pressure (11.5, 11.7)

Vaporization, the transition from liquid to gas, occurs when thermal energy overcomes the intermolecular forces present in a liquid. The opposite process is condensation. Vaporization is endothermic and condensation is exothermic. The rate of vaporization increases with

increasing temperature, increasing surface area, and decreasing strength of intermolecular forces. The heat of vaporization (ΔH_{vap}) is the heat required to vaporize one mole of a liquid. In a sealed container, a solution and its vapor will come into dynamic equilibrium, at which point the rate of vaporization equals the rate of condensation. The pressure of a gas that is in dynamic equilibrium with its liquid is its vapor pressure. The vapor pressure of a substance increases with increasing temperature and with decreasing strength of its intermolecular forces. The boiling point of a liquid is the temperature at which its vapor pressure equals the external pressure. The Clausius–Clapeyron equation expresses the relationship between the vapor pressure of a substance and its temperature and can be used to calculate the heat of vaporization from experimental measurements. When a liquid is heated in a sealed container it eventually forms a supercritical fluid, which has properties intermediate between a liquid and a gas. This occurs at the critical temperature and critical pressure.

Fusion and Sublimation (11.6, 11.7)

Sublimation is the transition from solid to gas. The opposite process is deposition. Fusion, or melting, is the transition from solid to liquid. The opposite process is freezing. The heat of fusion (ΔH_{fus}) is the amount of heat required to melt one mole of a solid. Fusion is endothermic. The heat of fusion is generally less than the heat of vaporization because intermolecular forces do not have to be completely overcome for melting to occur.

Phase Diagrams (11.8)

A phase diagram is a map of the states of a substance as a function of its pressure (y-axis) and temperature (x-axis). The regions in a phase diagram represent conditions under which a single stable state (solid, liquid, gas) exists. The lines represent conditions under which two states are in equilibrium. The triple point represents the conditions under which all three states coexist. The critical point is the temperature and pressure above which a supercritical fluid exists.

The Uniqueness of Water (11.9)

Water is a liquid at room temperature despite its low molar mass. Water forms strong hydrogen bonds, resulting in its high boiling point. Its high polarity also enables it to dissolve many polar and ionic compounds, and even nonpolar gases. Water expands upon freezing, so that ice is less dense than liquid water. Water is critical both to the existence of life and to human health.

Crystalline Structures (11.10–11.13)

In X-ray crystallography, the diffraction pattern of X-rays is used to determine the crystal structure of solids. The crystal lattice is repre-sented by a unit cell, a structure that reproduces the entire lattice when repeated in all three dimensions. Three basic cubic unit cells are the simple cubic, the body-centered cubic, and the face-centered cubic. Some crystal lattices can also be depicted as closest-packed structures, including the hexagonal closest-packing structure (not cubic) and the cubic closest-packing structure (which has a face-centered cubic unit cell). The types of crystal solids are molecular, ionic, and atomic solids. Atomic solids can be divided into three different types: non-bonded, metallic, and covalent. Band theory is a model for bonding in solids in which the atomic orbitals of the atoms are combined and delocalized over the entire crystal solid.

Key Equations and Relationships

Clausius–Clapeyron Equation: Relationship between Vapor Pressure (P_{vap}), the Heat of Vaporization (H_{vap}), and Temperature (T) (11.5)

$$\ln P_{vap} = \frac{-\Delta H_{vap}}{RT} + \ln \beta \ (\beta \text{ is a constant})$$

$$\ln \frac{P_2}{P_1} = \frac{-\Delta H_{vap}}{R}\left[\frac{1}{T_2} - \frac{1}{T_1}\right]$$

Bragg's Law: Relationship between Light Wavelength (λ), Angle of Reflection (θ), and Distance (d) between the Atomic Layers (11.10)

$$n\lambda = 2d \sin \theta \ (n = \text{integer})$$

Key Skills

Determining Whether a Molecule Has Dipole–Dipole Forces (11.3)
 • Example 11.1 • For Practice 11.1 • Exercises 49–60

Determining Whether a Molecule Displays Hydrogen Bonding (11.3)
 • Example 11.2 • For Practice 11.2 • Exercises 49–60

Using the Heat of Vaporization in Calculations (11.5)
 • Example 11.3 • For Practice 11.3 • For More Practice 11.3 • Exercises 71–74

Using the Clausius–Clapeyron Equation (11.5)
 • Examples 11.4, 11.5 • For Practice 11.4, 11.5 • Exercises 75–78

Using Bragg's Law in X-Ray Diffraction Calculations (11.10)
 • Example 11.6 • For Practice 11.6 • Exercises 95, 96

Relating Density to Crystal Structure (11.11)
 • Example 11.7 • For Practice 11.7 • Exercises 99–102

EXERCISES

Review Questions

1. Explain why a gecko is able to walk on a polished glass surface.

2. Why are intermolecular forces important?

3. What are the main properties of liquids (in contrast to gases and solids)?

4. What are the main properties of solids (in contrast to liquids and gases)?

5. What is the fundamental difference between an amorphous solid and a crystalline solid?

6. What factors cause changes between the solid and liquid state? The liquid and gas state?

7. Describe the relationship between the state of a substance, its temperature, and the strength of its intermolecular forces.

8. From what kinds of interactions do intermolecular forces originate?

9. Why are intermolecular forces generally much weaker than bonding forces?

10. What is the dispersion force? What does the magnitude of the dispersion force depend on? How can you predict the magnitude of the dispersion force for closely related elements or compounds?

11. What is the dipole–dipole force? How can you predict the presence of dipole–dipole forces in a compound?

12. How is the miscibility of two liquids related to their polarity?

13. What is hydrogen bonding? How can you predict the presence of hydrogen bonding in a compound?

14. What is the ion–dipole force? Why is it important?

15. What is surface tension? How does surface tension result from intermolecular forces? How is it related to the strength of intermolecular forces?

16. What is viscosity? How does viscosity depend on intermolecular forces? What other factors affect viscosity?

17. What is capillary action? How does it depend on the relative strengths of adhesive and cohesive forces?

18. Explain what happens in the processes of vaporization and condensation. Why does the rate of vaporization increase with increasing temperature and surface area?

19. Why is vaporization endothermic? Why is condensation exothermic?

20. How is the volatility of a substance related to the intermolecular forces present within the substance?

21. What is the heat of vaporization for a liquid and why is it useful?

22. Explain the process of dynamic equilibrium. How is dynamic equilibrium related to vapor pressure?

23. What happens to a system in dynamic equilibrium when it is disturbed in some way?

24. How is vapor pressure related to temperature? What happens to the vapor pressure of a substance when the temperature is increased? Decreased?

25. Define the terms *boiling point* and *normal boiling point*.

26. What is the Clausius–Clapeyron equation and why is it important?

27. Explain what happens to a substance when it is heated in a closed container to its critical temperature.

28. What is sublimation? Give a common example of sublimation.

29. What is fusion? Is fusion exothermic or endothermic? Why?

30. What is the heat of fusion and why is it important?

31. Examine the heating curve for water in Section 11.7 (Figure 11.36). Explain why the curve has two segments in which heat is added to the water but the temperature does not rise.

32. Examine the heating curve for water in Section 11.7 (Figure 11.36). Explain the significance of the slopes of each of the three rising segments. Why are the slopes different?

33. What is a phase diagram? Draw a generic phase diagram and label its important features.

34. What is the significance of crossing a line in a phase diagram?

35. How do the properties of water differ from those of most other substances?

36. Explain the basic principles involved in X-ray crystallography. Include Bragg's law in your explanation.

37. What is a crystalline lattice? How is the lattice represented with the unit cell?

38. Make a drawing of each unit cell: simple cubic, body-centered cubic, and face-centered cubic.

39. For each of the cubic cells in the previous problem, give the coordination number, edge length in terms of r, and number of atoms per unit cell.

40. What is the difference between hexagonal closest packing and cubic closest packing? What are the unit cells for each of these structures?

41. What are the three basic types of solids and the composite units of each? What types of forces hold each type of solid together?

42. In an ionic compound, how are the relative sizes of the cation and anion related to the coordination number of the crystal structure?

43. Show how the cesium chloride, sodium chloride, and zinc blende unit cells each contain a cation-to-anion ratio of 1:1.

44. Show how the fluorite structure accommodates a cation-to-anion ratio of 1:2.

45. What are the three basic subtypes of atomic solids? What kinds of forces hold each of these subtypes together?

46. In band theory of bonding for solids, what is a *band*? What is the difference between the *valence band* and the *conduction band*?

47. What is a band gap? How does the band gap differ in metals, semiconductors, and insulators?

48. Explain how doping can increase the conductivity of a semiconductor. What is the difference between an n-type semiconductor and a p-type semiconductor?

Problems by Topic

Intermolecular Forces

49. Determine the kinds of intermolecular forces that are present in each element or compound:
    a. N_2 **b.** NH_3 **c.** CO   **d.** CCl_4

50. Determine the kinds of intermolecular forces that are present in each element or compound:
    a. Kr   **b.** NCl_3 **c.** SiH_4 **d.** HF

51. Determine the kinds of intermolecular forces that are present in each element or compound:
    a. HCl   **b.** H_2O **c.** Br_2 **d.** He

52. Determine the kinds of intermolecular forces that are present in each element or compound:
    a. PH_3 **b.** HBr   **c.** CH_3OH **d.** I_2

53. Arrange these compounds in order of increasing boiling point. Explain your reasoning.
    a. CH_4 **b.** CH_3CH_3
    c. CH_3CH_2Cl **d.** CH_3CH_2OH

54. Arrange these compounds in order of increasing boiling point. Explain your reasoning.
    a. H_2S **b.** H_2Se **c.** H_2O

55. For each pair of compounds, pick the one with the highest boiling point. Explain your reasoning.
    a. CH_3OH or CH_3SH **b.** CH_3OCH_3 or CH_3CH_2OH
    c. CH_4 or CH_3CH_3

56. For each pair of compounds, pick the one with the higher boiling point. Explain your reasoning.
    a. NH_3 or CH_4 **b.** CS_2 or CO_2 **c.** CO_2 or NO_2

57. For each pair of compounds, pick the one with the higher vapor pressure at a given temperature. Explain your reasoning.
a. Br_2 or I_2 **b.** H_2S or H_2O **c.** NH_3 or PH_3

58. For each pair of compounds, pick the one with the higher vapor pressure at a given temperature. Explain your reasoning.
a. CH_4 or CH_3Cl
b. $CH_3CH_2CH_2OH$ or CH_3OH
c. CH_3OH or H_2CO

59. Which pairs of substances would you expect to form homogeneous solutions when combined? For those that form homogeneous solutions, indicate the type of forces that are involved.
a. CCl_4 and H_2O **b.** KCl and H_2O
c. Br_2 and CCl_4 **d.** CH_3CH_2OH and H_2O

60. Which pairs of compounds would you expect to form homogeneous solutions when combined? For those that form homogeneous solutions, indicate the type of forces that are involved.
a. $CH_3CH_2CH_2CH_2CH_3$ and $CH_3CH_2CH_2CH_2CH_2CH_3$
b. CBr_4 and H_2O
c. $LiNO_3$ and H_2O
d. CH_3OH and $CH_3CH_2CH_2CH_2CH_3$

Surface Tension, Viscosity, and Capillary Action

61. Which compound would you expect to have greater surface tension, acetone [$(CH_3)_2CO$] or water (H_2O)? Explain.

62. Water (a) "wets" some surfaces and beads up on others. Mercury (b), in contrast, beads up on almost all surfaces. Explain this difference.

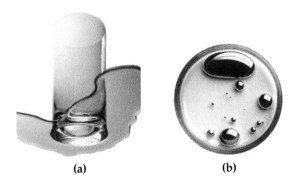

(a)   **(b)**

63. The structures of two isomers of heptane are shown here. Which of these two compounds would you expect to have the greater viscosity?

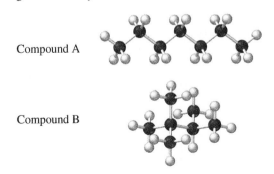

Compound A

Compound B

64. Explain why the viscosity of multigrade motor oils is less temperature dependent than that of single-grade motor oils.

65. Water in a glass tube that contains grease or oil residue displays a flat meniscus (left); whereas water in a clean glass tube displays a concave meniscus (right). Explain this difference.

66. When a thin glass tube is put into water, the water rises 1.4 cm. When the same tube is put into hexane, the hexane rises only 0.4 cm. Explain the difference.

Vaporization and Vapor Pressure

67. Which will evaporate more quickly: 55 mL of water in a beaker with a diameter of 4.5 cm, or 55 mL of water in a dish with a diameter of 12 cm? Will the vapor pressure of the water be different in the two containers? Explain.

68. Which will evaporate more quickly: 55 mL of water (H_2O) in a beaker or 55 mL of acetone [$(CH_3)_2CO$] in an identical beaker under identical conditions? Is the vapor pressure of the two substances different? Explain.

69. Spilling room-temperature water over your skin on a hot day will cool you down. Spilling room-temperature vegetable oil over your skin on a hot day will not. Explain the difference.

70. Why is the heat of vaporization of water greater at room temperature than it is at its boiling point?

71. The human body obtains 915 kJ of energy from a candy bar. If this energy were used to vaporize water at 100.0 °C, how much water (in liters) could be vaporized? (Assume the density of water is 1.00 g/mL.)

72. A 100.0-mL sample of water is heated to its boiling point. How much heat (in kJ) is required to vaporize it? (Assume a density of 1.00 g/mL.)

73. Suppose that 0.95 g of water condenses on a 75.0-g block of iron that is initially at 22 °C. If the heat released during condensation goes only to warming the iron block, what is the final temperature (in °C) of the iron block? (Assume a constant enthalpy of vaporization for water of 44.0 kJ/mol.)

74. Suppose that 1.15 g of rubbing alcohol (C_3H_8O) evaporates from a 65.0-g aluminum block. If the aluminum block is initially at 25 °C, what is the final temperature of the block after the evaporation of the alcohol? Assume that the heat required for the vaporization of the alcohol comes only from the aluminum block and that the alcohol vaporizes at 25 °C.

75. This table displays the vapor pressure of ammonia at several different temperatures. Use the data to determine the heat of vaporization and normal boiling point of ammonia.

Temperature (K)	Pressure (torr)
200	65.3
210	134.3
220	255.7
230	456.0
235	597.0

76. This table displays the vapor pressure of nitrogen at several different temperatures. Use the data to determine the heat of vaporization and normal boiling point of nitrogen.

Temperature (K)	Pressure (torr)
65	130.5
70	289.5
75	570.8
80	1028
85	1718

77. Ethanol has a heat of vaporization of 38.56 kJ/mol and a normal boiling point of 78.4 °C. What is the vapor pressure of ethanol at 15 °C?

78. Benzene has a heat of vaporization of 30.72 kJ/mol and a normal boiling point of 80.1 °C. At what temperature does benzene boil when the external pressure is 445 torr?

Sublimation and Fusion

79. How much energy is released when 65.8 g of water freezes?

80. Calculate the amount of heat required to completely sublime 50.0 g of solid dry ice (CO_2) at its sublimation temperature. The heat of sublimation for carbon dioxide is 32.3 kJ/mol.

81. An 8.5-g ice cube is placed into 255 g of water. Calculate the temperature change in the water upon the complete melting of the ice. Assume that all of the energy required to melt the ice comes from the water.

82. How much ice (in grams) would have to melt to lower the temperature of 352 mL of water from 25 °C to 5 °C? (Assume the density of water is 1.0 g/mL.)

83. How much heat (in kJ) is required to warm 10.0 g of ice, initially at −10.0 °C, to steam at 110.0 °C? The heat capacity of ice is 2.09 J/g·°C and that of steam is 2.01 J/g·°C.

84. How much heat (in kJ) is evolved in converting 1.00 mol of steam at 145.0 °C to ice at −50.0 °C? The heat capacity of steam is 2.01 J/g·°C and of ice is 2.09 J/g·°C.

Phase Diagrams

85. Consider the phase diagram shown here. Identify the states present at points *a* through *g*.

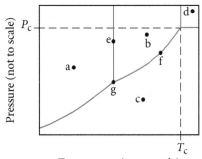

Temperature (not to scale)

86. Consider the phase diagram for iodine shown here and answer each of the following questions.
  a. What is the normal boiling point for iodine?
  b. What is the melting point for iodine at 1 atm?
  c. What state is present at room temperature and normal atmospheric pressure?
  d. What state is present at 186 °C and 1.0 atm?

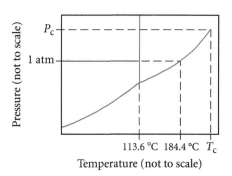

87. Nitrogen has a normal boiling point of 77.3 K and a melting point (at 1 atm) of 63.1 K. Its critical temperature is 126.2 K and critical pressure is 2.55×10^4 torr. It has a triple point at 63.1 K and 94.0 torr. Sketch the phase diagram for nitrogen. Does nitrogen have a stable liquid state at 1 atm?

88. Argon has a normal boiling point of 87.2 K and a melting point (at 1 atm) of 84.1 K. Its critical temperature is 150.8 K and critical pressure is 48.3 atm. It has a triple point at 83.7 K and 0.68 atm. Sketch the phase diagram for argon. Which has the greater density, solid argon or liquid argon?

89. The phase diagram for sulfur is shown below. The rhombic and monoclinic states are two solid states with different structures.
  a. Below what pressure will solid sulfur sublime?
  b. Which of the two solid states of sulfur is most dense?

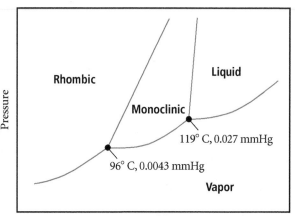

Temperature

90. The high-pressure phase diagram of ice is shown here. Notice that, under high pressure, ice can exist in several different solid forms. What three forms of ice are present at the triple point marked O? What is the density of ice II compared to ice I (the familiar form of ice). Would ice III sink or float in liquid water?

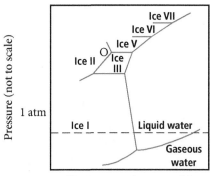

Temperature (not to scale)

The Uniqueness of Water

91. Water has a high boiling point for its relatively low molar mass. Why?

92. Water is a good solvent for many substances. What is the molecular basis for this property and why is it significant?

93. Explain the role of water in moderating Earth's climate.

94. How is the density of solid water compared to that of liquid water atypical among substances? Why is this significant?

Types of Solids and Their Structures

95. An X-ray beam with $\lambda = 154$ pm incident on the surface of a crystal produced a maximum reflection at an angle of $\theta = 28.3°$. Assuming $n = 1$, calculate the separation between layers of atoms in the crystal.

96. An X-ray beam of unknown wavelength is diffracted from a NaCl surface. If the interplanar distance in the crystal is 286 pm, and the angle of maximum reflection is found to be 7.23°, what is the wavelength of the X-ray beam? (Assume $n = 1$.)

97. Determine the number of atoms per unit cell for each metal.

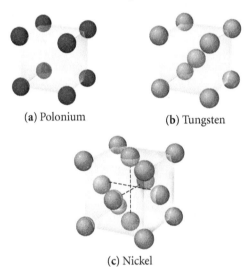

(a) Polonium   (b) Tungsten

(c) Nickel

98. Determine the coordination number for each structure.

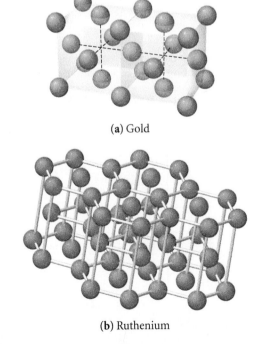

(a) Gold

(b) Ruthenium

(c) Chromium

99. Platinum crystallizes with the face-centered cubic unit cell. The radius of a platinum atom is 139 pm. Calculate the edge length of the unit cell and the density of platinum in g/cm^3.

100. Molybdenum crystallizes with the body-centered unit cell. The radius of a molybdenum atom is 136 pm. Calculate the edge length of the unit cell and the density of molybdenum.

101. Rhodium has a density of 12.41 g/cm^3 and crystallizes with the face-centered cubic unit cell. Calculate the radius of a rhodium atom.

102. Barium has a density of 3.59 g/cm^3 and crystallizes with the body-centered cubic unit cell. Calculate the radius of a barium atom.

103. Polonium crystallizes with a simple cubic structure. It has a density of 9.3 g/cm^3, a radius of 167 pm, and a molar mass of 209 g/mol. Use this data to estimate Avogadro's number (the number of atoms in one mole).

104. Palladium crystallizes with a face-centered cubic structure. It has a density of 12.0 g/cm^3, a radius of 138 pm, and a molar mass of 106.42 g/mol. Use this data to estimate Avogadro's number.

105. Identify each solid as molecular, ionic, or atomic.
    a. $Ar(s)$ b. $H_2O(s)$ c. $K_2O(s)$ d. $Fe(s)$

106. Identify each solid as molecular, ionic, or atomic.
    a. $CaCl_2(s)$ b. $CO_2(s)$ c. $Ni(s)$ d. $I_2(s)$

107. Which solid has the highest melting point? Why?

$$Ar(s), CCl_4(s), LiCl(s), CH_3OH(s)$$

108. Which solid has the highest melting point? Why?

$$C(s, \text{diamond}), Kr(s), NaCl(s), H_2O(s)$$

109. In each pair of solids, which one has the higher melting point and why?
    a. $TiO_2(s)$ or $HOOH(s)$ b. $CCl_4(s)$ or $SiCl_4(s)$
    c. $Kr(s)$ or $Xe(s)$ d. $NaCl(s)$ or $CaO(s)$

110. In each pair of solids, which one has the higher melting point and why?
    a. $Fe(s)$ or $CCl_4(s)$ b. $KCl(s)$ or $HCl(s)$
    c. $Ti(s)$ or $Ne(s)$ d. $H_2O(s)$ or $H_2S(s)$

111. An oxide of titanium crystallizes with the unit cell shown here (titanium = gray; oxygen = red). What is the formula of the oxide?

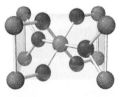

112. An oxide of rhenium crystallizes with the unit cell shown here (rhenium = gray; oxygen = red). What is the formula of the oxide?

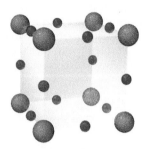

113. The unit cells for cesium chloride and barium(II) chloride are shown below. Show that the ratio of cations to anions in each unit cell corresponds to the ratio of cations to anions in the formula of each compound.

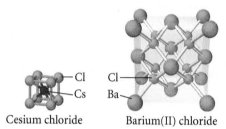

Cesium chloride   Barium(II) chloride

114. The unit cells for lithium oxide and silver iodide are shown here. Show that the ratio of cations to anions in each unit cell corresponds to the ratio of cations to anions in the formula of each compound.

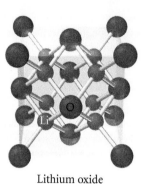 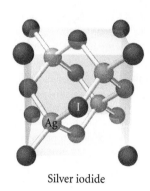

Lithium oxide   Silver iodide

Band Theory

115. Which solid would you expect to have little or no band gap?
  a. Zn(*s*)   **b.** Si(*s*)   **c.** As(*s*)

116. How many molecular orbitals are present in the valence band of a sodium crystal with a mass of 5.45 g?

117. Indicate whether each solid would form an n-type or a p-type semiconductor.
  a. germanium doped with gallium
  b. silicon doped with arsenic

118. Indicate whether each solid would form an n-type or a p-type semiconductor.
  a. silicon doped with gallium
  b. germanium doped with antimony

Cumulative Problems

119. Explain the observed trend in the melting points of the hydrogen halides.

HI	−50.8 °C
HBr	−88.5 °C
HCl	−114.8 °C
HF	−83.1 °C

120. Explain the observed trend in the boiling points of these compounds.

H_2Te	−2 °C
H_2Se	−41.5 °C
H_2S	−60.7 °C
H_2O	−100 °C

121. The vapor pressure of water at 25 °C is 23.76 torr. If 1.25 g of water is enclosed in a 1.5-L container, will any liquid be present? If so, what mass of liquid?

122. The vapor pressure of CCl_3F at 300 K is 856 torr. If 11.5 g of CCl_3F is enclosed in a 1.0-L container, will any liquid be present? If so, what mass of liquid?

123. Examine the phase diagram for iodine shown in Figure 11.39(a). What state transitions occur as you uniformly increase the pressure on a gaseous sample of iodine from 0.010 atm at 185 °C to 100 atm at 185 °C? Make a graph, analogous to the heating curve for water shown in Figure 11.36, in which you plot pressure versus time during the pressure increase.

124. Carbon tetrachloride displays a triple point at 249.0 K and a melting point (at 1 atm) of 250.3 K. Which state of carbon tetrachloride is more dense, the solid or the liquid? Explain.

125. Four ice cubes at exactly 0 °C with a total mass of 53.5 g are combined with 115 g of water at 75 °C in an insulated container. If no heat is lost to the surroundings, what will be the final temperature of the mixture?

126. A sample of steam with a mass of 0.552 g and at a temperature of 100 °C condenses into an insulated container holding 4.25 g of water at 5.0 °C. Assuming that no heat is lost to the surroundings, what will be the final temperature of the mixture?

127. Air conditioners not only cool air, but dry it as well. Suppose that a room in a home measures 6.0 m × 10.0 m × 2.2 m. If the outdoor temperature is 30 °C and the vapor pressure of water in the air is 85% of the vapor pressure of water at this temperature, what mass of water must be removed from the air each time the volume of air in the room is cycled through the air conditioner? The vapor pressure for water at 30 °C is 31.8 torr.

128. A sealed flask contains 0.55 g of water at 28 °C. The vapor pressure of water at this temperature is 28.36 mmHg. What is the minimum volume of the flask in order that no liquid water be present in the flask?

129. Silver iodide crystallizes in the zinc blende structure. The separation between nearest neighbor cations and anions is approximately 325 pm and the melting point is 558 °C. Cesium

chloride, by contrast, crystallizes in the cesium chloride structure shown in Figure 11.51. Even though the separation between nearest neighbor cations and anions is greater (348 pm), the melting point is higher (645 °C). Explain.

130. Copper iodide crystallizes in the zinc blende structure. The separation between nearest neighbor cations and anions is approximately 311 pm and the melting point is 606 °C. Potassium chloride, by contrast, crystallizes in the rock salt structure. Even though the separation between nearest neighbor cations and anions is greater (319 pm), the melting point is higher (776 °C). Explain.

131. Consider the face-centered cubic structure shown here:

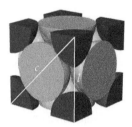

a. What is the length of the line (labeled c) that runs diagonally across one of the faces of the cube in terms of r (the atomic radius)?

b. Use the answer to part a and the Pythagorean theorem to derive the expression for the edge length (l) in terms of r.

132. Consider the body-centered cubic structure shown here:

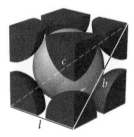

a. What is the length of the line (labeled c) that runs from one corner of the cube diagonally through the center of the cube to the other corner in terms of r (the atomic radius)?

b. Use the Pythagorean theorem to derive an expression for the length of the line (labeled b) that runs diagonally across one of the faces of the cube in terms of the edge length (l).

c. Use the answer to parts (a) and (b) along with the Pythagorean theorem to derive the expression for the edge length (l) in terms of r.

133. The unit cell in a crystal of diamond belongs to a crystal system different from any we have discussed. The volume of a unit cell of diamond is 0.0454 nm³ and the density of diamond is 3.52 g/cm³. Find the number of carbon atoms in a unit cell of diamond.

134. The density of an unknown metal is 12.3 g/cm³ and its atomic radius is 0.134 nm. It has a face-centered cubic lattice. Find the atomic mass of this metal.

135. Based on the phase diagram of CO_2 shown in Figure 11.39(b), describe the state changes that occur when the temperature of CO_2 is increased from 190 K to 350 K at a constant pressure of (a) 1 atm, (b) 5.1 atm, (c) 10 atm, (d) 100 atm.

136. Consider a planet where the pressure of the atmosphere at sea level is 2500 mmHg. Will water behave in a way that can sustain life on the planet?

137. An unknown metal is found to have a density of 7.8748 g/cm³ and to crystallize in a body-centered cubic lattice. The edge of the unit cell is found to be 0.28664 nm. Calculate the atomic mass of the metal.

138. When spheres of radius r are packed in a body-centered cubic arrangement, they occupy 68.0% of the available volume. Use the fraction of occupied volume to calculate the value of a, the length of the edge of the cube in terms of r.

Challenge Problems

139. Potassium chloride crystallizes in the rock salt structure. Estimate the density of potassium chloride using the ionic radii given in Chapter 8.

140. Butane (C_4H_{10}) has a heat of vaporization of 22.44 kJ/mol and a normal boiling point of −0.4 °C. A 250-mL sealed flask contains 0.55 g of butane at −22 °C. How much butane is present as a liquid? If the butane is warmed to 25 °C, how much is present as a liquid?

141. Liquid nitrogen can be used as a cryogenic substance to obtain low temperatures. Under atmospheric pressure, liquid nitrogen boils at 77 K, allowing low temperatures to be reached. However, if the nitrogen is placed in a sealed, insulated container connected to a vacuum pump, even lower temperatures can be reached. Why? If the vacuum pump has sufficient capacity, and is left on for an extended period of time, the liquid nitrogen will start to freeze. Explain.

142. Calculate the fraction of empty space in cubic closest packing to five significant figures.

143. A tetrahedral site in a closest-packed lattice is formed by four spheres at the corners of a regular tetrahedron. This is equivalent to placing the spheres at alternate corners of a cube. In such a closest-packed arrangement the spheres are in contact and if the spheres have a radius r, the diagonal of the face of the cube is $2r$. The tetrahedral hole is inside the middle of the cube. Find the length of the body diagonal of this cube and then find the radius of the tetrahedral hole.

144. Given that the heat of fusion of water is −6.02 kJ/mol, that the heat capacity of $H_2O(l)$ is 75.2 J/mol · K and that the heat capacity of $H_2O(s)$ is 37.7 J/mol · K, calculate the heat of fusion of water at −10 °C.

145. The heat of combustion of CH_4 is 890.4 kJ/mol and the heat capacity of H_2O is 75.2 J/mol · K. Find the volume of methane measured at 298 K and 1.00 atm required to convert 1.00 L of water at 298 K to water vapor at 373 K.

146. Two liquids, A and B, have vapor pressures at a given temperature of 24 mmHg and 36 mmHg, respectively. We prepare solu-

tions of A and B at a given temperature and measure the total pressures above the solutions. We obtain the following data:

Solution	Amt A (mol)	Amt B (mol)	P (mmHg)
1	1	1	30
2	2	1	28
3	1	2	32
4	1	3	33

Predict the total pressure above a solution of 5 mol A and 1 mol B.

147. Three 1.0-L flasks, maintained at 308 K, are connected to each other with stopcocks. Initially the stopcocks are closed. One of the flasks contains 1.0 atm of N_2, the second 2.0 g of H_2O, and the third, 0.50 g of ethanol, C_2H_6O. The vapor pressure of H_2O at 308 K is 42 mmHg and that of ethanol is 102 mmHg. The stopcocks are then opened and the contents mix freely. What is the pressure?

Conceptual Problems

148. One prediction of global warming is the melting of global ice, which may result in coastal flooding. A criticism of this prediction is that the melting of icebergs does not increase ocean levels any more than the melting of ice in a glass of water increases the level of liquid in the glass. Is this a valid criticism? Does the melting of an ice cube in a cup of water raise the level of the liquid in the cup? Why or why not? In response to this criticism, scientists have asserted that they are not worried about melting icebergs, but rather the melting of ice sheets that sit on the continent of Antarctica. Would the melting of this ice increase ocean levels? Why or why not?

149. The rate of vaporization depends on the surface area of the liquid. However, the vapor pressure of a liquid does not depend on the surface area. Explain.

150. Substance A has a smaller heat of vaporization than substance B. Which of the two substances will undergo a larger change in vapor pressure for a given change in temperature?

151. The density of a substance is greater in its solid state than in its liquid state. If the triple point in the phase diagram of the substance is below 1.0 atm, then which will necessarily be at a lower temperature, the triple point or the normal melting point?

152. A substance has a heat of vaporization of ΔH_{vap} and heat of fusion of ΔH_{fus}. Express the heat of sublimation in terms of ΔH_{vap} and ΔH_{fus}.

153. Examine the heating curve for water in Section 11.7 (Figure 11.36). If heat is added to the water at a constant rate, which of the three segments in which temperature is rising will have the least steep slope? Why?

154. A root cellar is an underground chamber used to store fruits, vegetables, and even meats. In extreme cold, farmers put large vats of water into the root cellar to prevent the fruits and vegetables from freezing. Explain why this works.

155. Suggest an explanation for the observation that the heat of fusion of a substance is always smaller than its heat of vaporization.

12

Solutions

One molecule of nonsaline substance (held in the solvent) dissolved in 100 molecules of any volatile liquid decreases the vapor pressure of this liquid by a nearly constant fraction, nearly 0.0105.

—François-Marie Raoult (1830–1901)

W E LEARNED IN CHAPTER 1 that most of the matter we encounter is in the form of mixtures. In this chapter, we focus on homogeneous mixtures, known as solutions. Solutions are mixtures in which atoms and molecules intermingle on the molecular and atomic scale. Some common examples of solutions include the ocean water we swim in, the gasoline we put into our cars, and the air we breathe. Why do solutions form? How are their properties different from the properties of the pure substances that compose them? As you read this chapter, keep in mind the great number of solutions that surround you at every moment, including those that exist within your own body.

Drinking seawater causes dehydration because seawater draws water out of body tissues.

12.1 Thirsty Solutions: Why You Should Not Drink Seawater

In a popular novel, *Life of Pi* by Yann Martel, the main character (whose name is Pi) is stranded on a lifeboat with a Bengal tiger in the middle of the Pacific Ocean for 227 days. He survives in part by rigging a solar still to distill seawater for drinking. However, in the first three days of his predicament (before he rigs the still) he becomes severely dehydrated from lack of water. He is surrounded by seawater but drinking *that* water would only have made his condition worse. Why? Seawater actually draws water *out of the body* as it passes through the stomach and intestines, resulting in diarrhea and further dehydration. We can think of seawater as a *thirsty solution*—one that draws more water to itself. Consequently, seawater should never be consumed as drinking water.

Seawater (Figure 12.1 ▶ on the next page) is a **solution**, a homogeneous mixture of two or more substances or components. The majority component is typically called the **solvent** and the minority component is called the **solute**. In seawater, water is the solvent and sodium chloride is the main solute.

In some cases, the concepts of solute and solvent are not useful. For example, a homogeneous mixture of water and ethanol can contain equal amounts of both components and neither component can then be identified as the solvent.

▶ **FIGURE 12.1 A Typical Solution** In seawater, sodium chloride is the primary solute. Water is the solvent.

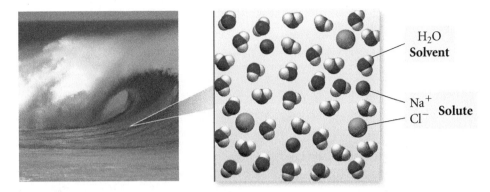

H_2O
Solvent

Na^+
Cl^- **Solute**

The reason that seawater draws water to itself is related to nature's tendency toward spontaneous mixing, which we discuss in more detail later in this chapter and in Chapter 17. For now, we simply observe that, unless it is highly unfavorable energetically, substances tend to combine into uniform mixtures, not separate into pure substances. For example, suppose we have pure water and a sodium chloride solution in separate compartments with a removable barrier between them, as shown in Figure 12.2(a) ▶. If we remove the barrier, the two liquids spontaneously mix together, eventually forming a more dilute sodium chloride solution of uniform concentration, as shown in Figure 12.2(b). The tendency toward mixing results in a uniform concentration of the final solution.

Seawater is a *thirsty* solution because of this tendency toward mixing. As seawater moves through the intestine, it flows past cells that line the digestive tract. These cells consist of largely fluid interiors surrounded by membranes. Cellular fluids themselves contain dissolved ions, including sodium and chloride, but the fluids are more dilute than seawater. Nature's tendency toward mixing (which tends to produce solutions of uniform concentration), together with the selective permeability of the cell membranes (which allow water to flow in and out, but restrict the flow of dissolved solids), causes a *flow of solvent out of the body's cells and into the seawater*. In this way, the two solutions become more similar in concentration (as though they had mixed)—the solution in the intestine becomes somewhat more dilute than it was and the solution in the cells becomes somewhat more concentrated. The accumulation of extra fluid in the intestines causes diarrhea, and the decreased fluid in the cells causes dehydration. If Pi had drunk the seawater instead of constructing the solar still, neither he nor his companion, the large Bengal tiger, would have survived their ordeal.

▶ Seawater is a more concentrated solution than the fluids in body cells. As a result, when seawater flows through the digestive tract, it draws water out of the surrounding tissues.

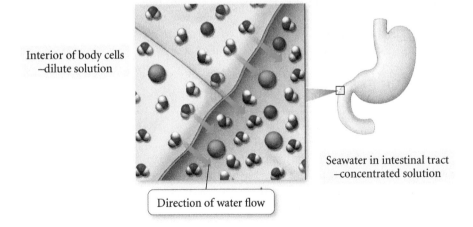

Interior of body cells
–dilute solution

Seawater in intestinal tract
–concentrated solution

Direction of water flow

CO_2 H_2O

▲ Club soda is a solution of carbon dioxide and water.

12.2 Types of Solutions and Solubility

A solution may be composed of a solid and a liquid (such as the salt and water that are the primary components of seawater), but may also be composed of a gas and a liquid, two different liquids, or other combinations (see Table 12.1). In **aqueous solutions**, water is the solvent, and a solid, liquid, or gas is the solute. For example, sugar water and salt water are both aqueous solutions. Similarly, ethyl alcohol—the alcohol in alcoholic

Spontaneous Mixing

> When the barrier is removed, spontaneous mixing occurs, producing a solution of uniform concentration.

Concentration difference

Uniform concentration

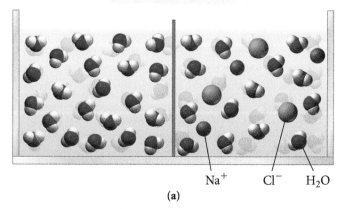

Na^+ Cl^- H_2O

(a)

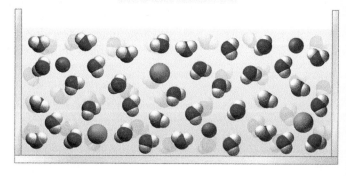

(b)

▲ **FIGURE 12.2 The Tendency to Mix** **(a)** Pure water and a sodium chloride solution are separated by a barrier. **(b)** When the barrier is removed, the two liquids spontaneously mix, producing a single solution of uniform concentration.

TABLE 12.1 Common Types of Solutions

Solution Phase	Solute Phase	Solvent Phase	Example
Gaseous solution	Gas	Gas	Air (mainly oxygen and nitrogen)
Liquid solution	Gas	Liquid	Club soda (CO_2 and water)
	Liquid	Liquid	Vodka (ethanol and water)
	Solid	Liquid	Seawater (salt and water)
Solid solution	Solid	Solid	Brass (copper and zinc) and other alloys

The general solubilities of a number of ionic compounds are described by the solubility rules in Section 4.5.

beverages—readily mixes with water to form a solution, and carbon dioxide dissolves in water to form the aqueous solution that we know as club soda.

You probably know from experience that a particular solvent, such as water, does not dissolve all possible solutes. For example, you cannot clean your greasy hands with just water because the water does not dissolve the grease. However, another solvent, such as paint thinner can easily dissolve the grease. The grease is *insoluble* in water but *soluble* in the paint thinner. The **solubility** of a substance is the amount of the substance that will dissolve in a given amount of solvent. The solubility of sodium chloride in water at 25 °C is 36 g NaCl per 100 g water, while the solubility of grease in water is nearly zero. The solubility of one substance in another depends both on nature's tendency toward mixing that we discussed in Section 12.1 and on the types of intermolecular forces that we discussed in Chapter 11.

Nature's Tendency toward Mixing: Entropy

So far in this book, we have seen that many physical systems tend toward lower *potential energy*. For example, two particles with opposite charges (such as a proton and an electron or a cation and an anion) move toward each other because their potential energy goes down as their separation decreases according to Coulomb's law. The formation of a solution, however, *does not necessarily* lower the potential energy of its constituent particles. The clearest example of this phenomenon is the formation of a homogeneous mixture (a *solution*) of two ideal gases. Suppose that we enclose neon and argon in a container with a removable barrier between them, as shown in Figure 12.3(a) ►. As soon as we remove the barrier, the neon and argon mix together to form a solution, as shown in Figure 12.3(b). *Why?*

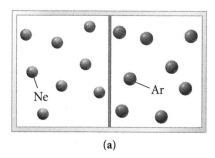

Ne   Ar

(a)

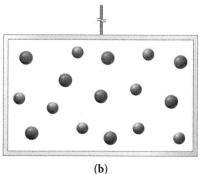

(b)

▲ **FIGURE 12.3 Spontaneous Mixing of Two Ideal Gases** **(a)** Neon and argon are separated by a barrier. **(b)** When the barrier is removed, the two gases spontaneously mix to form a uniform solution.

Recall that at low pressures and moderate temperatures both neon and argon behave as ideal gases—they do not interact with each other in any way (that is, there are no significant forces between their constituent particles). When the barrier is removed, the two gases mix, but their potential energy remains unchanged. In other words, *we cannot think of the mixing of two ideal gases as lowering their potential energy.* Rather, the tendency to mix is related to a concept called *entropy.*

Entropy is a measure of *energy randomization* or *energy dispersal* in a system. Recall that a gas at any temperature above 0 K has kinetic energy due to the motion of its atoms. When neon and argon are confined to their individual compartments, their kinetic energies are also confined to those compartments. When the barrier between the compartments is removed, each gas—along with its kinetic energy—becomes *spread out* or *dispersed* over a larger volume. Thus, the mixture of the two gases has greater energy dispersal, or greater *entropy*, than the separated components.

The pervasive tendency for energy to spread out, or disperse, whenever it is not restrained from doing so is the reason that two ideal gases mix. Another common example of the tendency toward energy dispersal is the transfer of thermal energy from hot to cold. If you heat one end of an iron rod, the thermal energy deposited at the end of the rod will spontaneously spread along the entire length of the rod. In contrast to the mixing of two ideal gases—where the kinetic energy of the particles becomes dispersed over a larger volume because the particles themselves become dispersed—the thermal energy in the rod, initially concentrated in relatively fewer particles, becomes dispersed by being distributed over a larger number of particles. The tendency for energy to disperse is why thermal energy flows from the hot end of the rod to the cold one, and not the other way around. Imagine a metal rod that became spontaneously hotter on one end and ice cold on the other—this does not happen because energy does not spontaneously concentrate itself. In Chapter 17, we will see that the dispersal of energy is actually the fundamental criterion that ultimately determines the spontaneity of any process.

The Effect of Intermolecular Forces

We have just seen that, in the absence of intermolecular forces, two substances spontaneously mix to form a homogeneous solution. We know from Chapter 11, however, that solids and liquids exhibit a number of different types of intermolecular forces including dispersion forces, dipole–dipole forces, hydrogen bonding, and ion–dipole forces (Figure 12.4 ▼). These forces may promote the formation of a solution or prevent it, depending on the nature of the forces in the particular combination of solute and solvent.

Intermolecular forces exist between: (a) the solvent and solute particles, (b) the solvent particles themselves, and (c) the solute particles themselves, as shown in Figure 12.5 ►.

Solvent–solute interactions: The interactions between a solvent particle and a solute particle.

Solvent–solvent interactions: The interactions between a solvent particle and another solvent particle.

Solute–solute interactions: The interactions between a solute particle and another solute particle.

▼ **FIGURE 12.4 Intermolecular Forces Involved in Solutions**

Intermolecular Forces

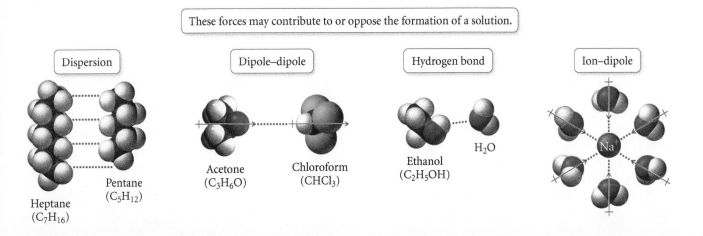

These forces may contribute to or oppose the formation of a solution.

Dispersion — Heptane (C$_7$H$_{16}$) / Pentane (C$_5$H$_{12}$)

Dipole–dipole — Acetone (C$_3$H$_6$O) / Chloroform (CHCl$_3$)

Hydrogen bond — Ethanol (C$_2$H$_5$OH) / H$_2$O

Ion–dipole — Na$^+$

TABLE 12.2 Relative Interactions and Solution Formation

Solvent–solute interactions	>	Solvent–solvent and solute–solute interactions	Solution forms
Solvent–solute interactions	=	Solvent–solvent and solute–solute interactions	Solution forms
Solvent–solute interactions	<	Solvent–solvent and solute–solute interactions	Solution may or may not form, depending on relative disparity

As shown in Table 12.2, a solution always forms if the solvent–solute interactions are comparable to, or stronger than, the solvent–solvent interactions and the solute–solute interactions. For example, consider mixing the hydrocarbons pentane (C_5H_{12}) and heptane (C_7H_{16}). The intermolecular forces present within both pentane and heptane are dispersion forces. Similarly, the intermolecular forces present *between* heptane and pentane are also dispersion forces. All three interactions are of similar magnitude so the two substances are soluble in each other in all proportions—they are said to be **miscible**. The formation of the solution is driven by the tendency toward mixing, or toward greater entropy, that we just discussed.

If solvent–solute interactions are weaker than solvent–solvent and solute–solute interactions—in other words, if solvent molecules and solute molecules each interact more strongly with molecules of their own kind than with molecules of the other kind—then a solution may still form, depending on the relative disparities between the interactions. If the disparity is small, the tendency to mix results in the formation of a solution even though the process is energetically uphill. If the disparity is large, however, a solution will not form. For example, consider mixing hexane and water. The water molecules have strong hydrogen-bonding attractions to each other but cannot form hydrogen bonds with hexane. The energy required to pull water molecules away from one another is too great, and too little energy is returned when the water molecules interact with hexane molecules. As a result, a solution does not form when hexane and water are mixed. Although the tendency to mix is strong, it cannot overcome the large energy disparity between the powerful solvent–solvent interactions and the weak solvent–solute interactions.

In general, we can use the rule of thumb that *like dissolves like* when predicting the formation of solutions. Polar solvents, such as water, tend to dissolve many polar or ionic solutes, and nonpolar solvents, such as hexane, tend to dissolve many nonpolar solutes. Similar kinds of solvents dissolve similar kinds of solutes. Table 12.3 lists some common polar and nonpolar laboratory solvents.

TABLE 12.3 Common Laboratory Solvents

Common Polar Solvents	Common Nonpolar Solvents
Water (H_2O)	Hexane (C_6H_{14})
Acetone (CH_3COCH_3)	Diethyl ether ($CH_3CH_2OCH_2CH_3$)*
Methanol (CH_3OH)	Toluene (C_7H_8)
Ethanol (CH_3CH_2OH)	Carbon tetrachloride (CCl_4)

*Diethyl ether has a small dipole moment and can be considered intermediate between polar and nonpolar.

Solution Interactions

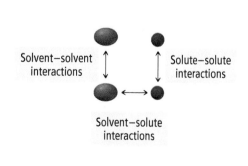

Solvent–solvent interactions

Solute–solute interactions

Solvent–solute interactions

Solution

◀ FIGURE 12.5 **Forces in a Solution** The relative strengths of these three interactions determine whether a solution will form.

EXAMPLE 12.1 Solubility

Vitamins are often categorized as either fat soluble or water soluble. Water-soluble vitamins dissolve in body fluids and are easily eliminated in the urine, so there is little danger of overconsumption. Fat-soluble vitamins, on the other hand, can accumulate in the body's fatty deposits. Overconsumption of a fat-soluble vitamin can be detrimental to health. Examine the structure of each vitamin and classify it as either fat soluble or water soluble.

(a) Vitamin C

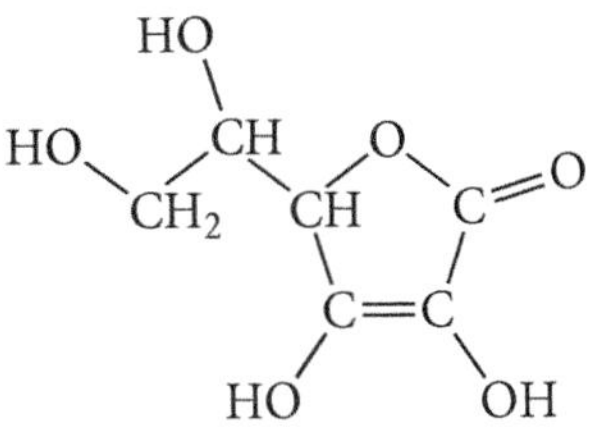

(b) Vitamin K_3

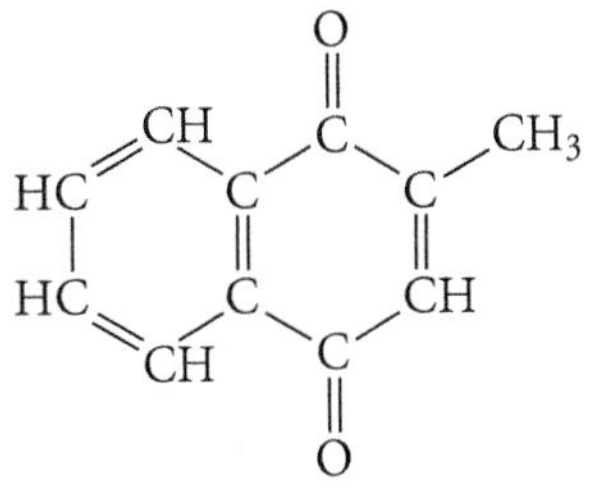

(c) Vitamin A

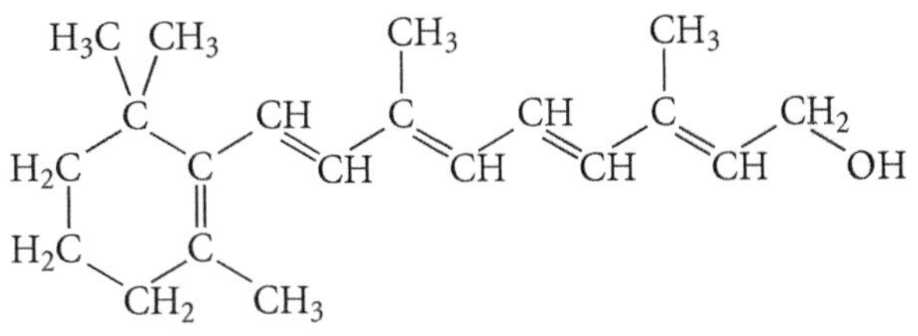

(d) Vitamin B_5

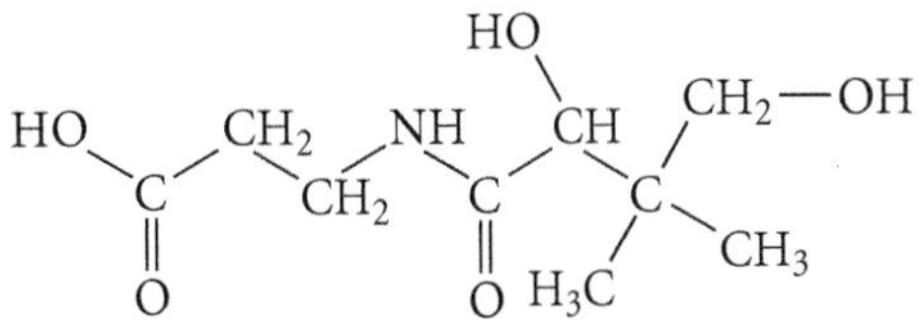

SOLUTION

(a) The four —OH bonds in vitamin C make it highly polar and allow it to hydrogen bond with water. Vitamin C is water soluble.	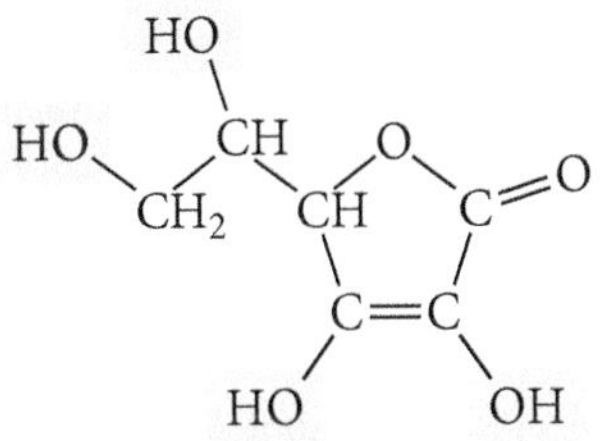
(b) The C—C bonds in vitamin K_3 are nonpolar and the C—H bonds are nearly so. The C=O bonds are polar, but the bond dipoles oppose and largely cancel each other, so the molecule is dominated by the nonpolar bonds. Vitamin K_3 is fat soluble.	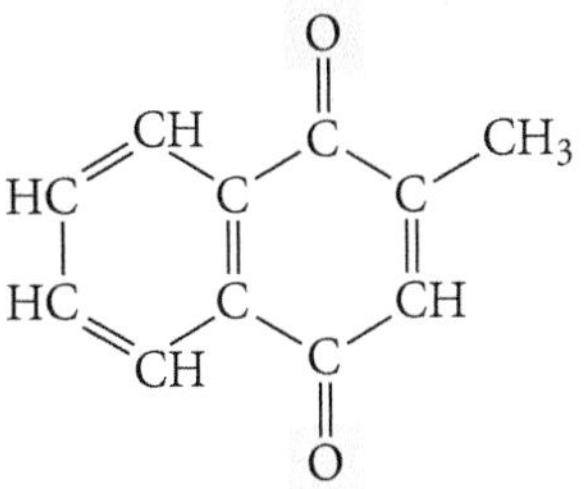
(c) The C—C bonds in vitamin A are nonpolar and the C—H bonds are nearly so. The one polar —OH bond may increase the water solubility slightly, but overall vitamin A is nonpolar and therefore fat soluble.	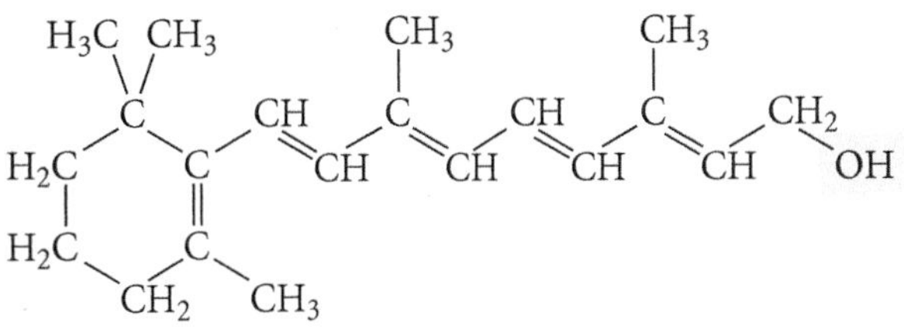
(d) The three —OH bonds and one —NH bond in vitamin B_5 make it highly polar and give it the ability to hydrogen bond with water. Vitamin B_5 is water soluble.	

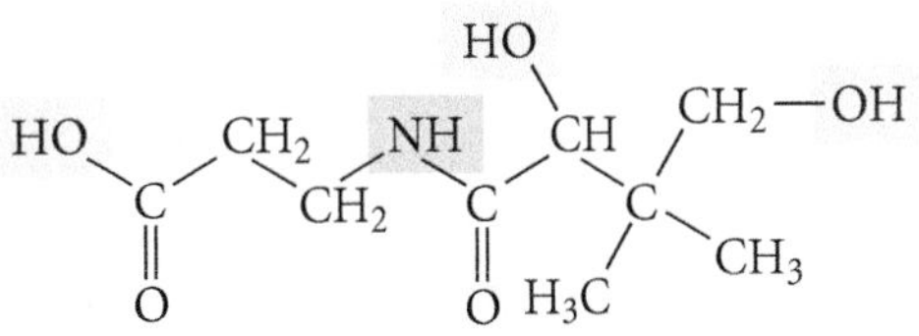

FOR PRACTICE 12.1

Determine whether each compound is soluble in hexane.

(a) water (H_2O) **(b)** propane ($CH_3CH_2CH_3$)

(c) ammonia (NH_3) **(d)** hydrogen chloride (HCl)

 Conceptual Connection 12.1 Solubility

Consider the following table showing the solubilities of several alcohols in water and in hexane. Explain the observed trend in terms of intermolecular forces.

Alcohol	Space-Filling Model	Solubility in H_2O (mol alcohol/100 g H_2O)	Solubility in Hexane (C_6H_{14}) (mol alcohol/100 g C_6H_{14})
Methanol (CH_3OH)		Miscible	0.12
Ethanol (CH_3CH_2OH)		Miscible	Miscible
Propanol ($CH_3CH_2CH_2OH$)		Miscible	Miscible
Butanol ($CH_3CH_2CH_2CH_2OH$)		0.11	Miscible
Pentanol ($CH_3CH_2CH_2CH_2CH_2OH$)		0.030	Miscible

ANSWER: The first alcohol on the list is methanol, which is highly polar and forms hydrogen bonds with water. It is miscible in water and has only limited solubility in hexane, which is nonpolar. However, as the carbon chain gets longer in the series of alcohols, the OH group becomes less important relative to the growing nonpolar carbon chain. Therefore the alcohols become progressively less soluble in water and more soluble in hexane. This table demonstrates the rule of thumb, *like dissolves like*. Methanol is like water and therefore dissolves in water. It is unlike hexane and therefore has limited solubility in hexane. As you move down the list, the alcohols become increasingly like hexane and increasingly unlike water and therefore become increasingly soluble in hexane and increasingly insoluble in water.

12.3 Energetics of Solution Formation

In Chapter 6, we examined the energy changes associated with chemical reactions. Similar energy changes can occur when a solution forms, depending on the magnitude of the interactions between the solute and solvent particles. For example, when we dissolve sodium hydroxide in water, heat is evolved—the solution process is *exothermic*. In contrast, when we dissolve ammonium nitrate (NH_4NO_3) in water, heat is absorbed—this solution process is *endothermic*. Other solutions, such as sodium chloride in water, barely absorb or evolve any heat upon formation. What causes these different behaviors?

We can understand the energy changes associated with solution formation by envisioning the process as occurring in the following three steps, each with an associated change in enthalpy:

1. Separating the solute into its constituent particles.

This step is always endothermic (positive ΔH) because energy is required to overcome the forces that hold the solute together.

2. Separating the solvent particles from each other to make room for the solute particles.

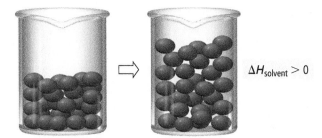

This step is also endothermic because energy is required to overcome the intermolecular forces among the solvent particles.

3. Mixing the solute particles with the solvent particles.

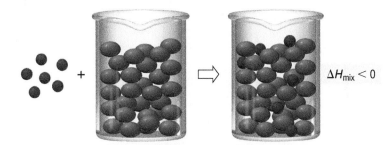

This step is exothermic, because energy is released as the solute particles interact (through intermolecular forces) with the solvent particles.

According to Hess's law, the overall enthalpy change upon solution formation, called the **enthalpy of solution** (ΔH_{soln}) is the sum of the changes in enthalpy for each step:

$$\Delta H_{soln} = \underbrace{\Delta H_{solute}}_{\text{endothermic }(+)} + \underbrace{\Delta H_{solvent}}_{\text{endothermic }(+)} + \underbrace{\Delta H_{mix}}_{\text{exothermic }(-)}$$

Since the first two terms are endothermic (positive ΔH) and the third term is exothermic (negative ΔH), the overall sign of ΔH_{soln} depends on the magnitudes of the individual terms, as shown in Figure 12.6 ▸.

1. *If the sum of the endothermic terms is about equal in magnitude to the exothermic term, then ΔH_{soln} is about zero.* The increasing entropy upon mixing drives the formation of a solution while the overall energy of the system remains nearly constant.

2. *If the sum of the endothermic terms is smaller in magnitude than the exothermic term, then ΔH_{soln} is negative and the solution process is exothermic.* In this case, both the tendency toward lower energy and the tendency toward greater entropy drive the formation of a solution.

3. *If the sum of the endothermic terms is greater in magnitude than the exothermic term, then ΔH_{soln} is positive and the solution process is endothermic.* In this case, as long as ΔH_{soln} is not too large, the tendency toward greater entropy will still drive the formation of a solution. If, on the other hand, ΔH_{soln} is too large, a solution will not form.

Energetics of Solution Formation

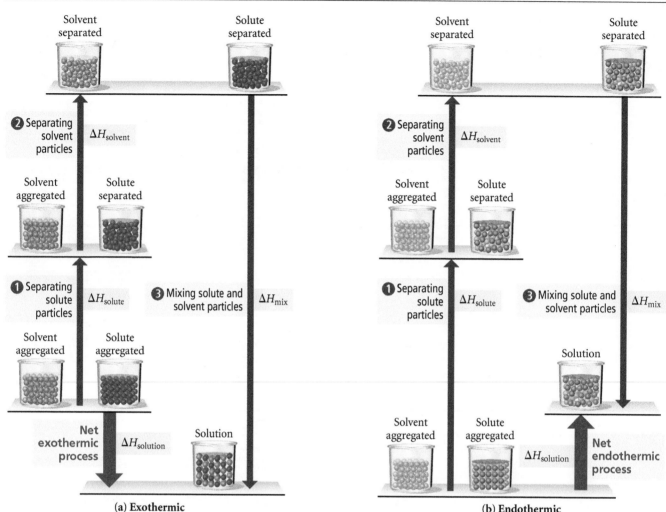

(a) Exothermic

(b) Endothermic

Aqueous Solutions and Heats of Hydration

Many common solutions, such as the seawater mentioned in the opening example of this chapter, contain an ionic compound dissolved in water. In these aqueous solutions, $\Delta H_{solvent}$ and ΔH_{mix} can be combined into a single term called the **heat of hydration** ($\Delta H_{hydration}$) Figure 12.7 ▼). The heat of hydration is the enthalpy change that occurs when 1 mol of the gaseous solute ions are dissolved in water. Because the ion–dipole interactions that occur between a dissolved ion and the surrounding water molecules

▲ **FIGURE 12.6 Energetics of the Solution Process**   **(a)** When ΔH_{mix} is greater in magnitude than the sum of ΔH_{solute} and $\Delta H_{solvent}$, the heat of solution is negative (exothermic). **(b)** When ΔH_{mix} is smaller in magnitude than the sum of ΔH_{solute} and $\Delta H_{solvent}$, the heat of solution is positive (endothermic).

Heat of Hydration

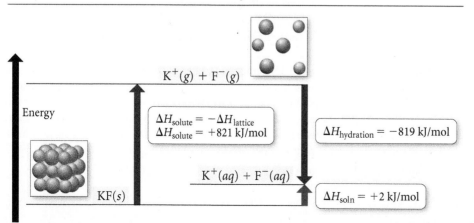

Energy

$K^+(g) + F^-(g)$

$\Delta H_{solute} = -\Delta H_{lattice}$
$\Delta H_{solute} = +821 \text{ kJ/mol}$

$\Delta H_{hydration} = -819 \text{ kJ/mol}$

$K^+(aq) + F^-(aq)$

$\Delta H_{soln} = +2 \text{ kJ/mol}$

KF(s)

◄ **FIGURE 12.7 Heat of Hydration and Heat of Solution**   The heat of hydration is the heat emitted when 1 mol of gaseous solute ions is dissolved in water. The sum of the negative of the lattice energy (which is ΔH_{solute}) and the heat of hydration is the heat of solution.

Ion–Dipole Interactions

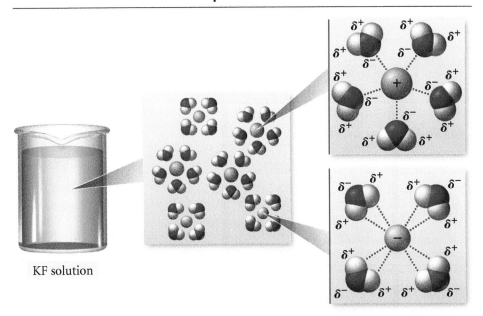

KF solution

(Figure 12.8 ▲) are much stronger than the hydrogen bonds in water, $\Delta H_{\text{hydration}}$ is always largely negative (exothermic) for ionic compounds. Using the heat of hydration, we can write the enthalpy of solution as a sum of just two terms, one endothermic and one exothermic:

$$\Delta H_{\text{soln}} = \Delta H_{\text{solute}} + \underbrace{\Delta H_{\text{solvent}} + \Delta H_{\text{mix}}}$$

$$\Delta H_{\text{soln}} = \underset{\substack{\text{endothermic} \\ \text{(positive)}}}{\Delta H_{\text{solute}}} + \underset{\substack{\text{exothermic} \\ \text{(negative)}}}{\Delta H_{\text{hydration}}}$$

For ionic compounds, ΔH_{solute}, the energy required to separate the solute into its constituent particles, is the negative of the solute's lattice energy ($\Delta H_{\text{solute}} = -\Delta H_{\text{lattice}}$), discussed in Section 9.4. For ionic aqueous solutions, then, the overall enthalpy of solution depends on the relative magnitudes of ΔH_{solute} and $\Delta H_{\text{hydration}}$, with three possible scenarios (in each case we refer to the *magnitude (absolute value)* of ΔH):

1. $|\Delta H_{\text{solute}}| < |\Delta H_{\text{hydration}}|$. The amount of energy required to separate the solute into its constituent ions is less than the energy given off when the ions are hydrated. ΔH_{soln} is therefore negative and the solution process is exothermic. Good examples of solutes with negative enthalpies of solution include lithium bromide and potassium hydroxide. When these solutes dissolve in water, the resulting solutions feel warm to the touch.

$$\text{LiBr}(s) \xrightarrow[\text{H}_2\text{O}]{} \text{Li}^+(aq) + \text{Br}^-(aq) \quad \Delta H_{\text{soln}} = -48.78 \text{ kJ/mol}$$

$$\text{KOH}(s) \xrightarrow[\text{H}_2\text{O}]{} \text{K}^+(aq) + \text{OH}^-(aq) \quad \Delta H_{\text{soln}} = -57.56 \text{ kJ/mol}$$

2. $|\Delta H_{\text{solute}}| > |\Delta H_{\text{hydration}}|$. The amount of energy required to separate the solute into its constituent ions is greater than the energy given off when the ions are hydrated. ΔH_{soln} is therefore positive and the solution process is endothermic (if a solution forms at all). Good examples of solutes that form aqueous solutions with positive enthalpies of solution include ammonium nitrate and silver nitrate. When these solutes dissolve in water, the resulting solutions feel cool to the touch.

$$\text{NH}_4\text{NO}_3(s) \xrightarrow[\text{H}_2\text{O}]{} \text{NH}_4^+(aq) + \text{NO}_3^-(aq) \quad \Delta H_{\text{soln}} = +25.67 \text{ kJ/mol}$$

$$\text{AgNO}_3(s) \xrightarrow[\text{H}_2\text{O}]{} \text{Ag}^+(aq) + \text{NO}_3^-(aq) \quad \Delta H_{\text{soln}} = +36.91 \text{ kJ/mol}$$

3. $|\Delta H_{solute}| \approx |\Delta H_{hydration}|$. The amount of energy required to separate the solute into its constituent ions is roughly equal to the energy given off when the ions are hydrated. ΔH_{soln} is therefore approximately zero and the solution process is neither appreciably exothermic nor appreciably endothermic. Good examples of solutes with enthalpies of solution near zero include sodium chloride and sodium fluoride. When these solutes dissolve in water, the resulting solutions do not undergo a noticeable change in temperature.

$$NaCl(s) \xrightarrow{H_2O} Na^+(aq) + Cl^-(aq) \quad \Delta H_{soln} = +3.88 \text{ kJ/mol}$$

$$NaF(s) \xrightarrow{H_2O} Na^+(aq) + F^-(aq) \quad \Delta H_{soln} = +0.91 \text{ kJ/mol}$$

12.4 Solution Equilibrium and Factors Affecting Solubility

The dissolution of a solute in a solvent is an equilibrium process similar to the equilibrium process associated with a phase change (discussed in Chapter 11). Imagine, from a molecular viewpoint, the dissolution of a solid solute such as sodium chloride in a liquid solvent such as water (Figure 12.9 ▼). Initially, water molecules rapidly solvate sodium cations and chloride anions, resulting in a noticeable decrease in the amount of solid

Solution Equilibrium

NaCl(s)	$NaCl(s) \longrightarrow Na^+(aq) + Cl^-(aq)$	$NaCl(s) \rightleftharpoons Na^+(aq) + Cl^-(aq)$
When sodium chloride is first added to water, sodium and chloride ions begin to dissolve into the water.	As the solution becomes more concentrated, some of the sodium and chloride ions can begin to recrystallize as solid sodium chloride.	When the rate of dissolution equals the rate of recrystallization, dynamic equilibrium has been reached.

Rate of dissolution > Rate of recrystallization

Rate of dissolution = Rate of recrystallization

(a) Initial   **(b) Dissolving**   **(c) Dynamic equilibrium**

▲ **FIGURE 12.9 Dissolution of NaCl**   **(a)** When sodium chloride is first added to water, sodium and chloride ions dissolve into the water. **(b)** As the solution becomes more concentrated, some of the sodium and chloride ions recrystallize as solid sodium chloride. **(c)** When the rate of dissolution equals the rate of recrystallization, dynamic equilibrium is reached.

► **FIGURE 12.10 Precipitation from a Supersaturated Solution** When a small piece of solid sodium acetate is added to a supersaturated sodium acetate solution, the excess solid precipitates out of the solution.

sodium chloride in the water. Over time, however, the concentration of dissolved sodium chloride in the solution increases. This dissolved sodium chloride can then begin to recrystallize as solid sodium chloride. Initially the rate of dissolution far exceeds the rate of recrystallization. But as the concentration of dissolved sodium chloride increases, the rate of recrystallization also increases. Eventually the rates of dissolution and recrystallization become equal—**dynamic equilibrium** has been reached.

$$NaCl(s) \rightleftharpoons Na^+(aq) + Cl^-(aq)$$

A solution in which the dissolved solute is in dynamic equilibrium with the solid (undissolved) solute is a **saturated solution**. *If you add additional solute to a saturated solution, it will not dissolve.* A solution containing less than the equilibrium amount of solute is an **unsaturated solution**. *If you add additional solute to an unsaturated solution, it will dissolve.*

Under certain circumstances, a **supersaturated solution**—one containing more than the equilibrium amount of solute—may form. Such solutions are unstable and the excess solute normally precipitates out of the solution. However, in some cases, if left undisturbed, a supersaturated solution can exist for an extended period of time. For example, in a common classroom demonstration a tiny piece of solid sodium acetate is added to a supersaturated solution of sodium acetate. This triggers the precipitation of the solute, which crystallizes out of solution in a dramatic and often beautiful way (Figure 12.10 ▲).

The Temperature Dependence of the Solubility of Solids

In the case of sugar dissolving in water, the higher temperature increases both *how fast* the sugar dissolves and *how much* sugar dissolves.

The solubility of solids in water can be highly dependent on temperature. Have you ever noticed how much more sugar you can dissolve in hot tea than in cold tea? Although exceptions exist, *the solubility of most solids in water increases with increasing temperature,* as shown in Figure 12.11 ▼. For example, the solubility of potassium nitrate (KNO_3) at

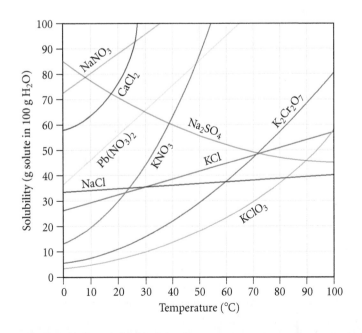

► **FIGURE 12.11 Solubility and Temperature** The solubility of most solids increases with increasing temperature.

room temperature is about 37 g KNO_3 per 100 g of water. At 50 °C, the solubility rises to 88 g KNO_3 per 100 g of water.

A common way to purify a solid is a technique called **recrystallization**. In this technique, enough solid is added to water (or some other solvent) to create a saturated solution at an elevated temperature. As the solution cools, it becomes supersaturated and the excess solid precipitates out of solution. If the solution cools slowly, the solid forms crystals as it comes out of solution. The crystalline structure tends to reject impurities, resulting in a purer solid.

You can use the temperature dependence of the solubility of solids to make rock candy. Prepare a saturated sucrose (table sugar) solution at an elevated temperature, and allow a string or stick to dangle into the solution for several days. As the solution cools and the solvent evaporates, the solution becomes supersaturated and sugar crystals grow on the string or stick. After several days, beautiful edible crystals or "rocks" of sugar cover the string.

▲ Rock candy is formed by the recrystallization of sugar.

Factors Affecting the Solubility of Gases in Water

Solutions of gases dissolved in water are common. Club soda, for example, is a solution of carbon dioxide and water, and most liquids exposed to air contain dissolved gases from air. Fish depend on the oxygen dissolved in lake or sea water for life, and our blood contains dissolved nitrogen, oxygen, and carbon dioxide. Even tap water contains dissolved gases. The solubility of a gas in a liquid is affected by both temperature and pressure.

The Effect of Temperature We can observe the effect of temperature on the solubility of a gas in water by heating ordinary tap water on a stove. Before the water reaches its boiling point, small bubbles develop in the water. These bubbles are the dissolved air (mostly nitrogen and oxygen) coming out of solution. (Once the water boils, the bubbling becomes more vigorous—these larger bubbles are composed of water vapor.) The dissolved air comes out of solution because—unlike solids, whose solubility generally increases with increasing temperature—*the solubility of gases in liquids decreases with increasing temperature.*

The inverse relationship between gas solubility and temperature is the reason that warm soda pop bubbles more than cold soda pop when you open it and warm beer goes flat faster than cold beer. More carbon dioxide comes out of solution at room temperature than at a lower temperature because the gas is less soluble at room temperature. The decreasing solubility of gases with increasing temperature is also the reason that fish don't bite much in a warm lake. The warm temperature results in a lower oxygen concentration. With lower oxygen levels, the fish become lethargic and do not strike as aggressively at the lure or bait you cast their way.

Cold soda   Warm soda
pop   pop

▲ Warm soda pop bubbles more than cold soda pop because carbon dioxide is less soluble in the warm solution.

⬭ Conceptual Connection 12.2 Solubility and Temperature

A solution is saturated in both nitrogen gas and potassium bromide at 75 °C. When the solution is cooled to room temperature, what is most likely to happen?

(a) Some nitrogen gas bubbles out of solution.

(b) Some potassium bromide precipitates out of solution.

(c) Some nitrogen gas bubbles out of solution *and* some potassium bromide precipitates out of solution.

(d) Nothing happens.

ANSWER: (b) Some potassium bromide precipitates out of solution. The solubility of most solids decreases with decreasing temperature. However, the solubility of gases increases with decreasing temperature. Therefore, the nitrogen becomes more soluble and will not bubble out of solution.

The Effect of Pressure The solubility of gases also depends on pressure. The higher the pressure of a gas above a liquid, the more soluble the gas is in the liquid. In a sealed can of soda pop, for example, the carbon dioxide is maintained in solution by a high pressure of carbon dioxide within the can. When the can is opened, this pressure is released and the solubility of carbon dioxide decreases, resulting in bubbling (Figure 12.12 ▶ on the next page).

▶ **FIGURE 12.12 Soda Fizz** The bubbling that occurs when a can of soda is opened results from the reduced pressure of carbon dioxide over the liquid. At lower pressure, the carbon dioxide is less soluble and bubbles out of solution.

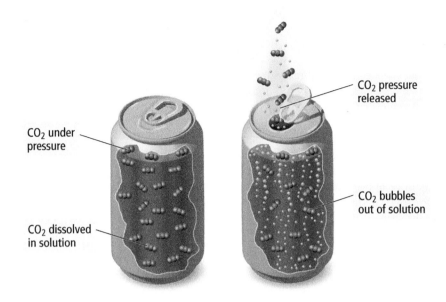

The increased solubility of a gas in a liquid can be understood by considering cylinders containing water and carbon dioxide gas.

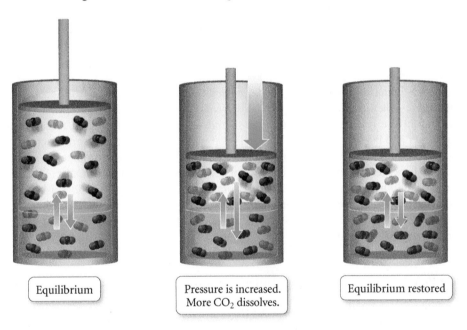

| Equilibrium | Pressure is increased. More CO_2 dissolves. | Equilibrium restored |

The first cylinder represents an equilibrium between gaseous and dissolved carbon dioxide—the rate of carbon dioxide molecules entering solution exactly equals the rate of molecules leaving the solution. Now imagine decreasing the volume, as shown in the second cylinder. The pressure of carbon dioxide now increases, causing the rate of molecules entering the solution to rise. The number of molecules in solution increases until equilibrium is established again, as shown in the third cylinder. However, the amount of carbon dioxide in solution is now greater.

We can quantify the solubility of gases with increasing pressure with **Henry's law**:

$$S_{gas} = k_H P_{gas}$$

where S_{gas} is the solubility of the gas (usually in M), k_H is a constant of proportionality (called the *Henry's law constant*) that depends on the specific solute and solvent and also on temperature, and P_{gas} is the partial pressure of the gas (usually in atm). The equation shows that the solubility of a gas in a liquid is directly proportional to the pressure of the gas above the liquid. Table 12.4 lists the Henry's law constants for several common gases.

TABLE 12.4 Henry's Law Constants for Several Gases in Water at 25 °C

Gas	k_H (M/atm)
O_2	1.3×10^{-3}
N_2	6.1×10^{-4}
CO_2	3.4×10^{-2}
NH_3	5.8×10^{1}
He	3.7×10^{-4}

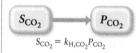

Conceptual Connection 12.3 Henry's Law

Examine the Henry's law constants in Table 12.4. Why do you suppose that the constant for ammonia is bigger than the others?

ANSWER: Ammonia is the only compound on the list that is polar, so we would expect its solubility in water to be greater than those of the other gases (which are all nonpolar).

EXAMPLE 12.2 Henry's Law

What pressure of carbon dioxide is required to keep the carbon dioxide concentration in a bottle of club soda at 0.12 M at 25 °C?

SORT You are given the desired solubility of carbon dioxide and asked to find the pressure required to achieve this solubility.	**GIVEN:** $S_{CO_2} = 0.12$ M **FIND:** P_{CO_2}
STRATEGIZE Use Henry's law to find the required pressure from the solubility. You will need the Henry's law constant for carbon dioxide.	**CONCEPTUAL PLAN** $\boxed{S_{CO_2}} \longrightarrow \boxed{P_{CO_2}}$ $S_{CO_2} = k_{H,CO_2}P_{CO_2}$ **RELATIONSHIPS USED** $S_{gas} = k_H P_{gas}$ (Henry's law) $k_{H, CO_2} = 3.4 \times 10^{-2}$ M/atm (from Table 12.4)
SOLVE Solve the Henry's law equation for P_{CO_2} and substitute the other quantities to calculate it.	**SOLUTION** $S_{CO_2} = k_{H, CO_2}P_{CO_2}$ $P_{CO_2} = \dfrac{S_{CO_2}}{k_{H,CO_2}}$ $= \dfrac{0.12 \text{ M}}{3.4 \times 10^{-2}\dfrac{\text{M}}{\text{atm}}}$ $= 3.5$ atm

CHECK The answer is in the correct units and seems reasonable. A small answer (for example, less than 1 atm) would be suspect because you know that the soda is under a pressure greater than atmospheric pressure when you open it. A very large answer (for example, over 100 atm) would be suspect because an ordinary can or bottle probably could not sustain such high pressures without bursting.

FOR PRACTICE 12.2

Determine the solubility of oxygen in water at 25 °C exposed to air at 1.0 atm. Assume a partial pressure for oxygen of 0.21 atm.

12.5 Expressing Solution Concentration

As we have seen, the amount of solute in a solution is an important property of the solution. For example, the amount of sodium chloride in a solution determines whether or not the solution will cause dehydration if consumed. A **dilute solution** is one containing small quantities of solute relative to the amount of solvent. Drinking a dilute sodium chloride solution will not cause dehydration. A **concentrated solution** is one containing large quantities of solute relative to the amount of solvent. Drinking a concentrated sodium chloride solution will cause dehydration. The common ways of reporting solution concentration include molarity, molality, parts by mass, parts by volume, mole fraction,

CHEMISTRY IN THE ENVIRONMENT Lake Nyos

Most people living near Lake Nyos in Cameroon, West Africa, began August 22, 1986, like any other day. Unfortunately, the day ended in tragedy. On that evening, a large cloud of carbon dioxide gas, burped up from the depths of Lake Nyos, killing over 1700 people and about 3000 cattle. Two years before that, a similar tragedy occurred in Lake Monoun, just 60 miles away, killing 37 people. Today, scientists are taking steps to prevent these lakes, both of which are in danger of burping again, from accumulating the carbon dioxide that caused the disaster.

◄ Lake Nyos, in Cameroon, has a deceptively peaceful appearance; in the summer of 1986, more than 1700 people died around its shores.

Lake Nyos is a water-filled volcanic crater. Some 50 miles beneath the surface of the lake, molten volcanic rock (magma) produces carbon dioxide gas that seeps into the lake through the volcano's plumbing system. The carbon dioxide forms a solution with the lake water. The high pressure at the bottom of the deep lake allows the solution to become highly concentrated in carbon dioxide. Over time—either because of the high concentration itself or because of some other natural trigger such as a landslide or small earthquake—some gaseous carbon dioxide escaped. The rising bubbles disrupted the stratified layers of lake water, causing water at the bottom of the lake to rise to a region of lower pressure. The drop in pressure decreased the solubility of the carbon dioxide, so more carbon dioxide bubbles formed. This in turn caused more churning and still more carbon dioxide release. The result was a massive cloud of carbon dioxide gas that escaped from the lake. Since carbon dioxide is heavier than air, it traveled down the sides of the volcano and into the nearby valley, displacing air and asphyxiating many of the local residents.

In an effort to keep these events from recurring, scientists are building a piping system that slowly vents carbon dioxide from the lake bottom, preventing the buildup that led to the tragedy.

◄ In efforts to prevent another tragedy, scientists have built a plumbing system to slowly vent carbon dioxide from Lake Nyos.

Question
Suppose that the water pressure at the bottom of Lake Nyos was 25 atm. What would the solubility of carbon dioxide be at that depth?

and mole percent, as summarized in Table 12.5. We have seen two of these units before: molarity in Section 4.4, and mole fraction in Section 5.6. In the following section, we review the terms we have already covered and introduce the new ones.

Molarity

The **molarity (M)** of a solution is the amount of solute (in moles) divided by the volume of solution (in liters).

$$\text{Molarity (M)} = \frac{\text{amount solute (in mol)}}{\text{volume solution (in L)}}$$

TABLE 12.5 Solution Concentration Terms

Unit	Definition	Units
Molarity (M)	$\dfrac{\text{amount solute (in mol)}}{\text{volume solution (in L)}}$	$\dfrac{\text{mol}}{\text{L}}$
Molality (m)	$\dfrac{\text{amount solute (in mol)}}{\text{mass solvent (in kg)}}$	$\dfrac{\text{mol}}{\text{kg}}$
Mole fraction (χ)	$\dfrac{\text{amount solute (in mol)}}{\text{total amount of solute and solvent (in mol)}}$	None
Mole percent (mol %)	$\dfrac{\text{amount solute (in mol)}}{\text{total amount of solute and solvent (in mol)}} \times 100\%$	%
Parts by mass	$\dfrac{\text{mass solute}}{\text{mass solution}} \times \text{multiplication factor}$	
Percent by mass (%)	Multiplication factor = 100	%
Parts per million by mass (ppm)	Multiplication factor = 10^6	ppm
Parts per billion by mass (ppb)	Multiplication factor = 10^9	ppb
Parts by volume (%, ppm, ppb)	$\dfrac{\text{volume solute}}{\text{volume solution}} \times \text{multiplication factor*}$	

*Multiplication factors for parts by volume are identical to those for parts by mass.

Note that molarity is moles of solute per liter of *solution,* not per liter of solvent. To make a solution of a specified molarity, we usually put the solute into a flask and then add water (or another solvent) to the desired volume of solution, as shown in Figure 12.13 ▼. Molarity is a convenient unit to use when making, diluting, and transferring solutions because it specifies the amount of solute per unit of solution transferred.

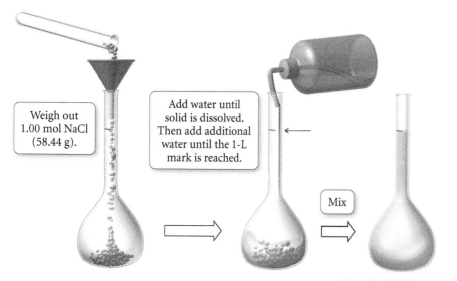

Weigh out 1.00 mol NaCl (58.44 g).

Add water until solid is dissolved. Then add additional water until the 1-L mark is reached.

Mix

A 1.00 molar NaCl solution

◀ **FIGURE 12.13 Preparing a Solution of Known Concentration**   To make a 1 M NaCl solution, add 1 mol of the solid to a flask and dilute with water to make 1 L of solution.

Molality

Molarity depends on volume, and since volume varies with temperature, molarity also varies with temperature. For example, a 1 M aqueous solution at room temperature will be slightly less than 1 M at an elevated temperature because the volume of the solution is greater at the elevated temperature. A concentration unit that is independent of temperature is **molality** (***m***), the amount of solute (in moles) divided by the mass of solvent (in kilograms).

$$\text{Molality } (m) = \dfrac{\text{amount solute (in mol)}}{\text{mass solvent (in kg)}}$$

Notice that molality is defined with respect to kilograms *solvent,* not kilograms solution. Molality is particularly useful when concentrations must be compared over a range of different temperatures.

Parts by Mass and Parts by Volume

It is often convenient to report a concentration as a ratio of masses. A **parts by mass** concentration is the ratio of the mass of the solute to the mass of the solution, all multiplied by a multiplication factor:

$$\frac{\text{Mass solute}}{\text{Mass solution}} \times \text{multiplication factor}$$

The particular unit used, which determines the size of the multiplication factor, depends on the concentration of the solution. For example, the multiplication factor for **percent by mass** is 100.

$$\text{Percent by mass} = \frac{\text{Mass solute}}{\text{Mass solution}} \times 100\%$$

Percent means *per hundred*; a solution with a concentration of 14% by mass contains 14 g of solute per 100 g of solution.

For more dilute solutions, we can use **parts per million (ppm)**, which requires a multiplication factor of 10^6, or **parts per billion (ppb)**, which requires a multiplication factor of 10^9.

$$\text{ppm} = \frac{\text{mass solute}}{\text{mass solution}} \times 10^6$$

$$\text{ppb} = \frac{\text{mass solute}}{\text{mass solution}} \times 10^9$$

A solution with a concentration of 15 ppm by mass, for example, contains 15 g of solute per 10^6 g of solution.

Sometimes concentrations are reported as a ratio of volumes, especially for solutions in which both the solute and solvent are liquids. A **parts by volume** concentration is usually the ratio of the volume of the solute to the volume of the solution, all multiplied by a multiplication factor.

$$\frac{\text{Volume solute}}{\text{Volume solution}} \times \text{multiplication factor}$$

The multiplication factors are identical to those just described for parts by mass concentrations. For example, a 22% ethanol solution by volume contains 22 mL of ethanol for every 100 mL of solution.

Using Parts by Mass (or Parts by Volume) in Calculations We can use the parts by mass (or parts by volume) concentration of a solution as a conversion factor between mass (or volume) of the solute and mass (or volume) of the solution. For example, for a solution containing 3.5% sodium chloride by mass, we would write the following conversion factor:

$$\frac{3.5 \text{ g NaCl}}{100 \text{ g solution}} \qquad \text{converts} \qquad \boxed{\text{g solution}} \longrightarrow \boxed{\text{g NaCl}}$$

This conversion factor converts from grams solution to grams NaCl. To convert the other way, we simply invert the conversion factor:

$$\frac{100 \text{ g solution}}{3.5 \text{ g NaCl}} \qquad \text{converts} \qquad \boxed{\text{g NaCl}} \longrightarrow \boxed{\text{g solution}}$$

Molality is abbreviated with a lowercase italic *m* while molarity is abbreviated with a capital M.

For dilute aqueous solutions near room temperature, the units of ppm are equivalent to milligrams solute/per liter of solution. This is because the density of a dilute aqueous solution near room temperature is 1.0 g/mL, so that 1 L has a mass of 1000 g.

EXAMPLE 12.3 Using Parts by Mass in Calculations

What volume (in mL) of a soft drink that is 10.5% sucrose ($C_{12}H_{22}O_{11}$) by mass contains 78.5 g of sucrose? (The density of the solution is 1.04 g/mL.)

SORT You are given a mass of sucrose and the concentration and density of a sucrose solution, and you are asked to find the volume of solution containing that mass.	**GIVEN:** 78.5 g $C_{12}H_{22}O_{11}$ 10.5% $C_{12}H_{22}O_{11}$ by mass density = 1.04 g/mL **FIND:** mL
STRATEGIZE Begin with the mass of sucrose in grams. Use the mass percent concentration of the solution (written as a ratio, as shown under relationships used) to find the number of grams of solution containing this quantity of sucrose. Then use the density of the solution to convert grams to milliliters of solution.	**CONCEPTUAL PLAN** 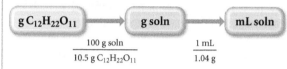 $$\frac{100 \text{ g soln}}{10.5 \text{ g } C_{12}H_{22}O_{11}} \qquad \frac{1 \text{ mL}}{1.04 \text{ g}}$$ **RELATIONSHIPS USED** $\dfrac{10.5 \text{ g } C_{12}H_{22}O_{11}}{100 \text{ g soln}}$ (percent by mass written as ratio) $\dfrac{1 \text{ mL}}{1.04 \text{ g}}$ (given density of the solution)
SOLVE Begin with 78.5 g $C_{12}H_{22}O_{11}$ and multiply by the conversion factors to arrive at the volume of solution.	**SOLUTION** $$78.5 \text{ g } \cancel{C_{12}H_{22}O_{11}} \times \frac{100 \text{ g soln}}{10.5 \text{ g } \cancel{C_{12}H_{22}O_{11}}} \times \frac{1 \text{ mL}}{1.04 \text{ g}} = 719 \text{ mL soln}$$

CHECK The units of the answer are correct. The magnitude seems correct because the solution is approximately 10% sucrose by mass. Since the density of the solution is approximately 1 g/mL, the volume containing 78.5 g sucrose should be roughly 10 times larger, as calculated ($719 \approx 10 \times 78.5$).

FOR PRACTICE 12.3

How much sucrose ($C_{12}H_{22}O_{11}$), in g, is contained in 355 mL (12 ounces) of a soft drink that is 11.5% sucrose by mass? (Assume a density of 1.04 g/mL.)

FOR MORE PRACTICE 12.3

A water sample is found to contain the pollutant chlorobenzene with a concentration of 15 ppb (by mass). What volume of this water contains 5.00×10^2 mg of chlorobenzene? (Assume a density of 1.00 g/mL.)

Mole Fraction and Mole Percent

For some applications, especially those in which the ratio of solute to solvent can vary widely, the most useful way to express concentration is the amount of solute (in moles) divided by the total amount of solute and solvent (in moles). This ratio is called the **mole fraction** (χ_{solute}):

> The mole fraction can also be defined for the solvent:
> $$\chi_{solvent} = \frac{n_{solvent}}{n_{solute} + n_{solvent}}$$

$$\chi_{solute} = \frac{\text{amount solute (in mol)}}{\text{total amount of solute and solvent (in mol)}} = \frac{n_{solute}}{n_{solute} + n_{solvent}}$$

Also in common use is the **mole percent (mol %)**, which is simply the mole fraction $\times$ 100 percent.

$$\text{mol } \% = \chi_{solute} \times 100\%$$

CHEMISTRY IN THE ENVIRONMENT The Dirty Dozen

A number of potentially harmful chemicals—such as DDT, dioxin, and polychlorinated biphenyls (PCBs)—can make their way into our water sources from industrial dumping, atmospheric emissions, agricultural use, and household dumping. Since crops, livestock, and fish also consume water, they too can accumulate these chemicals from water. Human consumption of food or water contaminated with harmful chemicals can lead to a number of diseases and adverse health effects such as increased cancer risk, liver damage, and central nervous system damage. Governments around the world have joined forces to ban the production of a number of these kinds of chemicals—called persistent organic pollutants or POPs. The original treaty targeted 12 such substances called the dirty dozen (Table 12.6).

TABLE 12.6 The Dirty Dozen

1. Aldrin—insecticide	7. Furan—industrial by-product
2. Chlordane—insecticide	8. Heptachlor—insecticide
3. DDT—insecticide	9. Hexachlorobenzene—fungicide, industrial by-product
4. Dieldrin—insecticide	10. Mirex—insecticide, fire retardant
5. Dioxin—industrial by-product	11. Polychlorinated biphenyls (PCBs)—electrical insulators
6. Eldrin—insecticide	12. Toxaphene—insecticide

One problem common to all of these chemicals is their persistence in the environment. These compounds are fairly stable and do not break down under normal environmental conditions. Once they get into the environment, they stay there for a long time. A second problem with these chemicals is their contribution to a process called *bioamplification*. Because they are nonpolar, these chemicals are stored and concentrated in the fatty tissues of the organisms that consume them. As larger organisms eat smaller ones they consume more of the stored chemicals. The result is an increase in the concentrations of these chemicals as they move up the food chain.

Under the treaty, nearly all intentional production of these chemicals has been banned. In the United States, the presence of these contaminants in water supplies is monitored under supervision of the Environmental Protection Agency (EPA). The EPA has set limits, called maximum contaminant levels (MCLs), for each of these in food and drinking water. Some MCLs for selected compounds in water supplies are listed in Table 12.7. Notice the units that the EPA uses to express the concentration of the contaminants, mg/L. This unit is a conversion factor between liters of water consumed and the mass (in mg) of the pollutant. According to the EPA, as long as the contaminant concentrations are below these levels, the water is safe to drink.

▲ Potentially harmful chemicals can make their way into water sources by many routes.

TABLE 12.7 EPA Maximum Contaminant Level (MCL) for Several "Dirty Dozen" Chemicals

Chlordane	0.002 mg/L
Dioxin	0.00000003 mg/L
Heptachlor	0.0004 mg/L
Hexachlorobenzene	0.001 mg/L

Question

Using what you know about conversion factors, calculate how much of each of the chemicals in Table 12.7 at the MCL would be present in 715 L of water, the approximate amount of water consumed by an adult in one year.

EXAMPLE 12.4 Calculating Concentrations

A solution is prepared by dissolving 17.2 g of ethylene glycol ($C_2H_6O_2$) in 0.500 kg of water. The final volume of the solution is 515 mL. For this solution, calculate:

(a) molarity   **(b)** molality   **(c)** percent by mass

(d) mole fraction   **(e)** mole percent

SOLUTION

(a) To calculate molarity, first find the amount of ethylene glycol in moles from the mass and molar mass.

$$\text{mol } C_2H_6O_2 = 17.2 \text{ g } C_2H_6O_2 \times \frac{1 \text{ mol } C_2H_6O_2}{62.07 \text{ g } C_2H_6O_2} = 0.2771 \text{ mol } C_2H_6O_2$$

Then divide the amount in moles by the volume of the solution in liters.

$$\text{Molarity (M)} = \frac{\text{amount solute (in mol)}}{\text{volume solution (in L)}}$$

$$= \frac{0.2771 \text{ mol } C_2H_6O}{0.515 \text{ L solution}}$$

$$= 0.538 \text{ M}$$

(b) To calculate molality, use the amount of ethylene glycol in moles from part a, and divide by the mass of the water in kilograms.

$$\text{Molality (m)} = \frac{\text{amount solute (in mol)}}{\text{mass solvent (in kg)}}$$

$$= \frac{0.2771 \text{ mol } C_2H_6O}{0.500 \text{ kg } H_2O}$$

$$= 0.554 \text{ m}$$

(c) To calculate percent by mass, divide the mass of the solute by the sum of the masses of the solute and solvent and multiply the ratio by 100%.

$$\text{Percent by mass} = \frac{\text{mass solute}}{\text{mass solution}} \times 100\%$$

$$= \frac{17.2 \text{ g}}{17.2 \text{ g} + 5.00 \times 10^2 \text{ g}} \times 100\%$$

$$= 3.33\%$$

(d) To calculate mole fraction, first determine the amount of water in moles from the mass of water and its molar mass.

$$\text{mol } H_2O = 5.00 \times 10^2 \text{ g } H_2O \times \frac{1 \text{ mol } H_2O}{18.02 \text{ g } H_2O} = 27.75 \text{ mol } H_2O$$

Then divide the amount of ethylene glycol in moles (from part a) by the total number of moles.

$$\chi_{\text{solute}} = \frac{n_{\text{solute}}}{n_{\text{solute}} + n_{\text{solvent}}}$$

$$= \frac{0.2771 \text{ mol}}{0.2771 \text{ mol} + 27.75 \text{ mol}}$$

$$= 9.89 \times 10^{-3}$$

(e) To calculate mole percent, simply multiply the mole fraction by 100%.

$$\text{mol \%} = \chi_{\text{solute}} \times 100\%$$

$$= 0.989\%$$

FOR PRACTICE 12.4

A solution is prepared by dissolving 50.4 g sucrose ($C_{12}H_{22}O_{11}$) in 0.332 kg of water. The final volume of the solution is 355 mL. Calculate the following for this solution:

(a) molarity   **(b)** molality   **(c)** percent by mass

(d) mole fraction   **(e)** mole percent

EXAMPLE 12.5 Converting between Concentration Units

What is the molarity of a 6.56% by mass glucose ($C_6H_{12}O_6$) solution? (The density of the solution is 1.03 g/mL.)

SORT You are given the concentration of a glucose solution in percent by mass and the density of the solution. Find the concentration of the solution in molarity.	**GIVEN:** 6.56% $C_6H_{12}O_6$ density = 1.03 g/mL **FIND:** M
STRATEGIZE Begin with the mass percent concentration of the solution written as a ratio, and separate the numerator from the denominator. Convert the numerator from g $C_6H_{12}O_6$ to mol $C_6H_{12}O_6$. Convert the denominator from g soln to mL of solution and then to L solution. Then divide the numerator (now in mol) by the denominator (now in L) to obtain molarity.	**CONCEPTUAL PLAN** 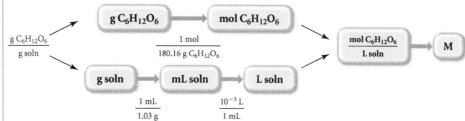 **RELATIONSHIPS USED** $\dfrac{6.56\,\text{g}\,C_6H_{12}O_6}{100\,\text{g soln}}$ (percent by mass written as ratio) $\dfrac{1\,\text{mol}}{180.16\,\text{g}\,C_6H_{12}O_6}$ (from molar mass of glucose) $\dfrac{1\,\text{mL}}{1.03\,\text{g}}$ (from given density of the solution)
SOLVE Begin with the numerator (6.56 g $C_6H_{12}O_6$) and use the molar mass to convert to mol $C_6H_{12}O_6$. Then convert the denominator (100 g solution) into mL of solution (using the density) and then to L of solution. Finally, divide mol $C_6H_{12}O_6$ by L solution to arrive at molarity.	**SOLUTION** $6.56\,\cancel{\text{g}\,C_6H_{12}O_6} \times \dfrac{1\,\text{mol}\,C_6H_{12}O_6}{180.16\,\cancel{\text{g}\,C_6H_{12}O_6}} = 0.036412\,\text{mol}\,C_6H_{12}O_6$ $100\,\cancel{\text{g soln}} \times \dfrac{1\,\cancel{\text{mL}}}{1.03\,\cancel{\text{g}}} \times \dfrac{10^{-3}\,\text{L}}{\cancel{\text{mL}}} = 0.097087\,\text{L soln}$ $\dfrac{0.036412\,\text{mol}\,C_6H_{12}O_6}{0.097087\,\text{L soln}} = 0.375\,\text{M}\,C_6H_{12}O_6$

CHECK The units of the answer are correct. The magnitude seems correct. Very high molarities (especially above 25 M) should immediately appear suspect. One liter of water contains about 55 moles of water molecules, so molarities higher than 55 M are physically impossible.

FOR PRACTICE 12.5
What is the molarity of a 10.5% by mass glucose ($C_6H_{12}O_6$) solution? (The density of the solution is 1.03 g/mL.)

FOR MORE PRACTICE 12.5
What is the molality of a 10.5% by mass glucose ($C_6H_{12}O_6$) solution? (The density of the solution is 1.03 g/mL.)

12.6 Colligative Properties: Vapor Pressure Lowering, Freezing Point Depression, Boiling Point Elevation, and Osmotic Pressure

Have you ever wondered why you add salt to ice in an ice-cream maker? Or why salt is scattered on icy roads in cold climates? Salt lowers the temperature at which a salt water solution freezes. A salt and water solution will remain liquid even below 0 °C. When salt is added to ice in the ice-cream maker, an ice/water/salt mixture forms that can reach a temperature of about −10 °C, at which point the cream freezes. On the winter road, the salt allows the ice to melt when the ambient temperature is below freezing.

▲ In winter, salt is often added to roads so that the ice will melt at lower temperatures.

The depression of the freezing point of ice by salt is an example of a **colligative property**, a property that depends on the number of particles dissolved in solution, not on the type of particle. In this section, we examine four colligative properties: vapor pressure lowering, freezing point depression, boiling point elevation, and osmotic pressure. Since these properties depend on the *number* of dissolved particles, nonelectrolytes must be treated slightly differently than electrolytes when determining colligative properties. When 1 mol of a nonelectrolyte dissolves in water, it forms 1 mol of dissolved particles.

When 1 mol of an electrolyte dissolves in water, however, it normally forms more than 1 mol of dissolved particles (as shown in Figure 12.14 ▶). For example, when 1 mol of NaCl dissolves in water, it forms 1 mol of dissolved Na^+ ions and 1 mol of dissolved Cl^- ions. Therefore the resulting solution will have 2 mol of dissolved particles. The colligative properties reflect this higher concentration of dissolved particles. In this section we examine colligative properties of nonelectrolyte solutions; we then expand the concept to include electrolyte solutions in Section 12.7.

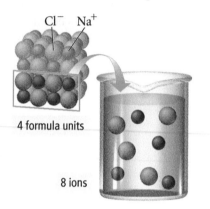

◀ **FIGURE 12.14** When sodium chloride is dissolved in water, each mole of NaCl produces 2 mol of particles: 1 mol of Na^+ cations and 1 mol of Cl^- anions.

Vapor Pressure Lowering

Recall from Section 11.5 that the vapor pressure of a liquid is the pressure of the gas above the liquid when the two are in dynamic equilibrium (that is, when the rate of vaporization equals the rate of condensation). What is the effect of a nonvolatile nonelectrolyte solute on the vapor pressure of the liquid into which it dissolves? The basic answer to this question is that *the vapor pressure of the solution will be lower than the vapor pressure of the pure solvent*. We can understand why this happens in two different ways.

The simplest explanation for why the vapor pressure of a solution is lower than that of the pure solvent is related to the concept of dynamic equilibrium itself. Consider the following representation of a liquid in dynamic equilibrium with its vapor. Here the rate of vaporization is equal to the rate of condensation.

Dynamic equilibrium

When a nonvolatile solute is added, however, the solute particles (shown in red) interfere with the ability of the solvent particles (blue) to vaporize, because they occupy some of

the surface area formerly occupied by the solvent. The rate of vaporization is thus diminished compared to that of the pure solvent.

Rate of vaporization
reduced by solute

The change in the rate of vaporization creates an imbalance in the rates; the rate of condensation is now *greater* than the rate of vaporization. The net effect is that some of the molecules that were in the gas phase condense into the liquid. As they condense, the reduced number of molecules in the gas phase causes the rate of condensation to decrease. Eventually the two rates become equal again, but only after the concentration of solvent molecules in the gas phase has decreased.

Equilibrium reestablished
but with fewer molecules
in gas phase

The result is a lower vapor pressure for the solution compared to the pure solvent.

A more fundamental explanation of why the vapor pressure of a solution is lower than that of the pure solvent is related to the tendency toward mixing (toward greater entropy) that we discussed in Sections 12.1 and 12.2. Recall from Section 12.1 that a concentrated solution is a *thirsty* solution—it has the ability to draw solvent to itself. We can observe a dramatic demonstration of this tendency by placing a concentrated solution of a nonvolatile solute and a beaker of the pure solvent in a sealed container, as shown below. Over time, the level of the pure solvent will drop and the level of the solution will rise as molecules vaporize out of the pure solvent and condense into the solution. Notice the similarity between this process and the dehydration caused by drinking seawater. In both cases, a concentrated solution has the ability to draw solvent to itself. The reason is nature's tendency to mix. If a pure solvent and concentrated solution are combined in a beaker, they naturally form a mixture in which the concentrated solution becomes less

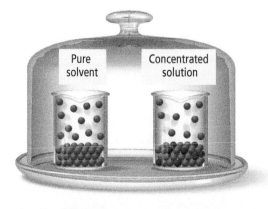

concentrated than it was initially. Similarly, if a pure solvent and concentrated solution are combined in a sealed container—even though they are in separate beakers—the two mix so that the concentrated solution becomes less concentrated.

The net transfer of solvent from the beaker containing pure solvent to the one containing the solution shows that the vapor pressure of the solution is lower than that of the pure solvent. As solvent molecules vaporize, the vapor pressure in the sealed container rises. Before dynamic equilibrium can be attained, however, the pressure exceeds the vapor pressure of the solution, causing molecules to condense into the solution (the beaker on the right). Therefore, molecules constantly vaporize from the pure solvent, but the solvent's vapor pressure is never reached because molecules are constantly leaving the beaker of pure solvent to enter the beaker of solution. The result is a continuous transfer of solvent molecules from the pure solvent to the solution.

We can quantify the vapor pressure of a solution with **Raoult's law**:

$$P_{solution} = \chi_{solvent} P^\circ_{solvent}$$

In this equation, $P_{solution}$ is the vapor pressure of the solution, $\chi_{solvent}$ is the mole fraction of the solvent, and $P^\circ_{solvent}$ is the vapor pressure of the pure solvent at the same temperature. For example, suppose a water sample at 25 °C contains 0.90 mol of water and 0.10 mol of a nonvolatile solute such as sucrose. The pure water would have a vapor pressure of 23.8 torr. We calculate the vapor pressure of the solution as follows:

$$P_{solution} = \chi_{H_2O} P^\circ_{H_2O}$$
$$= 0.90(23.8 \text{ torr})$$
$$= 21.4 \text{ torr}$$

The vapor pressure of the solution is directly proportional to the amount of the solvent in the solution. Since the solvent particles compose 90% of all of the particles in the solution, the vapor pressure of the solution is 90% of the vapor pressure of the pure solvent.

To arrive at an equation that shows how much the vapor pressure is lowered by a solute, we define the **vapor pressure lowering (ΔP)** as the difference in vapor pressure between the pure solvent and the solution:

$$\Delta P = P^\circ_{solvent} - P_{solution}$$

Then, for a two-component solution, we can substitute $\chi_{solvent} = 1 - \chi_{solute}$ into Raoult's law as follows:

$$P_{solution} = \chi_{solvent} P^\circ_{solvent}$$
$$P_{solution} = (1 - \chi_{solute}) P^\circ_{solvent}$$
$$P^\circ_{solvent} - P_{solution} = \chi_{solute} P^\circ_{solvent}$$
$$\Delta P = \chi_{solute} P^\circ_{solvent}$$

This last equation indicates that the lowering of the vapor pressure is directly proportional to the mole fraction of the solute.

EXAMPLE 12.6 Calculating the Vapor Pressure of a Solution Containing a Nonelectrolyte and Nonvolatile Solute

Calculate the vapor pressure at 25 °C of a solution containing 99.5 g sucrose ($C_{12}H_{22}O_{11}$) and 300.0 mL water. The vapor pressure of pure water at 25 °C is 23.8 torr. Assume the density of water to be 1.00 g/mL.

SORT You are given the mass of sucrose and volume of water in a solution. You are also given the vapor pressure of pure water and asked to find the vapor pressure of the solution. The density of the pure water is also provided.

GIVEN: 99.5 g $C_{12}H_{22}O_{11}$
300.0 mL H_2O
$P^{\circ}_{H_2O} = 23.8$ torr at 25 °C
$d_{H_2O} = 1.00$ g/mL

FIND: $P_{solution}$

STRATEGIZE Raoult's law relates the vapor pressure of a solution to the mole fraction of the solvent and the vapor pressure of the pure solvent. Begin by calculating the amount in moles of sucrose and water.

CONCEPTUAL PLAN

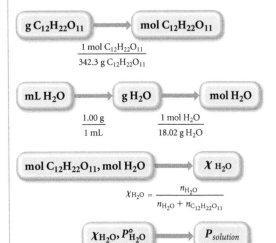

Calculate the mole fraction of the solvent from the calculated amounts of solute and solvent.

Then use Raoult's law to calculate the vapor pressure of the solution.

SOLVE Calculate the number of moles of each solution component.

SOLUTION

$$99.5 \text{ g } C_{12}H_{22}O_{11} \times \frac{1 \text{ mol } C_{12}H_{22}O_{11}}{342.30 \text{ g } C_{12}H_{22}O_{11}} = 0.2907 \text{ mol } C_{12}H_{22}O_{11}$$

$$300.0 \text{ mL } H_2O \times \frac{1.00 \text{ g}}{1 \text{ mL}} \times \frac{1 \text{ mol } H_2O}{18.02 \text{ g } H_2O} = 16.65 \text{ mol } H_2O$$

Use the number of moles of each component to compute the mole fraction of the solvent (H_2O).

$$\chi_{H_2O} = \frac{n_{H_2O}}{n_{C_{12}H_{22}O_{11}} + n_{H_2O}}$$

$$= \frac{16.65 \text{ mol}}{0.2907 \text{ mol} + 16.65 \text{ mol}}$$

$$= 0.9828$$

Use the mole fraction of water and the vapor pressure of pure water to calculate the vapor pressure of the solution.

$$P_{solution} = \chi_{H_2O} P^{\circ}_{H_2O}$$
$$= 0.9828 \,(23.8 \text{ torr})$$
$$= 23.4 \text{ torr}$$

CHECK The units of the answer are correct. The magnitude of the answer seems right because the calculated vapor pressure of the solution is just below that of the pure liquid, as expected for a solution with a large mole fraction of solvent.

FOR PRACTICE 12.6

Calculate the vapor pressure at 25 °C of a solution containing 55.3 g ethylene glycol ($HOCH_2CH_2OH$) and 285.2 g water. The vapor pressure of pure water at 25 °C is 23.8 torr.

FOR MORE PRACTICE 12.6

A solution containing ethylene glycol and water has a vapor pressure of 7.88 torr at 10 °C. Pure water has a vapor pressure of 9.21 torr at 10 °C. What is the mole fraction of ethylene glycol in the solution?

Vapor Pressures of Solutions Containing a Volatile (Nonelectrolyte) Solute

Some solutions contain, not only a volatile solvent, but also a volatile *solute*. In this case, *both* the solvent and the solute contribute to the overall vapor pressure of the solution. A solution like this may be an **ideal solution** (in which case it follows Raoult's law at all concentrations for both the solvent and the solute) or it may be nonideal (in which case it does not follow Raoult's law). An ideal solution is similar in concept to an ideal gas. Just as an ideal gas follows the ideal gas law exactly, so an ideal solution follows Raoult's law exactly. In an ideal solution, the solute–solvent interactions are similar in magnitude to the solute–solute and solvent–solvent interactions. In this type of solution, the solute simply dilutes the solvent and ideal behavior is observed. The vapor pressure of each of the solution components is given by Raoult's law throughout the entire composition range of the solution. For a two-component solution containing liquids A and B, we can write:

$$P_A = \chi_A P_A^\circ$$
$$P_B = \chi_B P_B^\circ$$

The total pressure above such a solution is the sum of the partial pressures of the components:

$$P_{tot} = P_A + P_B$$

Figure 12.15(a) ▼ shows a plot of vapor pressure versus solution composition for an ideal two-component solution.

In a nonideal solution, the solute–solvent interactions are either stronger or weaker than the solvent–solvent interactions. If the solute–solvent interactions are stronger, then the solute tends to prevent the solvent from vaporizing as readily as it would otherwise. If the solution is sufficiently dilute, then the effect will be small and Raoult's law works as an approximation. However, if the solution is not dilute, the effect will be significant and the vapor pressure of the solution will be *less than* that predicted by Raoult's law, as shown in Figure 12.15(b).

Over a complete range of composition of a solution, it no longer makes sense to designate a solvent and solute, so we simply label the two components A and B.

Deviations from Raoult's Law

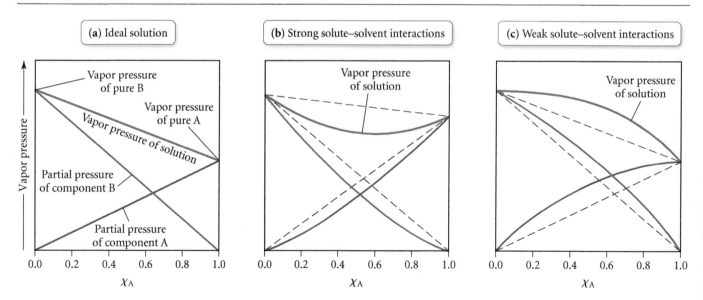

▲ **FIGURE 12.15 Behavior of Nonideal Solutions**   (a) An ideal solution follows Raoult's law for both components. (b) A solution with particularly strong solute–solvent interactions displays negative deviations from Raoult's law. (c) A solution with particularly weak solute–solvent interactions displays positive deviations from Raoult's law. (The dashed lines in parts b and c represent ideal behavior.)

If, on the other hand, the solute–solvent interactions are weaker than solvent–solvent interactions, then the solute tends to allow more vaporization than would occur with just the solvent. If the solution is not dilute, the effect will be significant and the vapor pressure of the solution will be *greater than* predicted by Raoult's law, as shown in Figure 12.15(c).

EXAMPLE 12.7 Calculating the Vapor Pressure of a Two-Component Solution

A solution contains 3.95 g of carbon disulfide (CS_2) and 2.43 g of acetone (CH_3COCH_3). The vapor pressures at 35 °C of pure carbon disulfide and pure acetone are 515 torr and 332 torr, respectively. Assuming ideal behavior, calculate the vapor pressures of each of the components and the total vapor pressure above the solution. The experimentally measured total vapor pressure of the solution at 35 °C is 645 torr. Is the solution ideal? If not, what can you say about the relative strength of carbon disulfide–acetone interactions compared to the acetone–acetone and carbon disulfide–carbon disulfide interactions?

SORT You are given the masses and vapor pressures of carbon disulfide and acetone and are asked to find the vapor pressures of each component in the mixture and the total pressure assuming ideal behavior.	**GIVEN:** 3.95 g CS_2 2.43 g CH_3COCH_3 $P°_{CS_2} = 515$ torr (at 35 °C) $P°_{CH_3COCH_3} = 332$ torr (at 35 °C) $P_{tot}(exp) = 645$ torr (at 35 °C) **FIND:** P_{CS_2}, $P_{CH_3COCH_3}$, $P_{tot}(ideal)$
STRATEGIZE This problem requires the use of Raoult's law to calculate the partial pressures of each component. In order to use Raoult's law, you must first compute the mole fractions of the two components. Convert the masses of each component to moles and then use the definition of mole fraction to calculate the mole fraction of carbon disulfide. The mole fraction of acetone can easily be found because the mole fractions of the two components add up to 1.	**CONCEPTUAL PLAN** $3.95 \text{ g } CS_2 \longrightarrow \text{mol } CS_2$ $$\frac{1 \text{ mol } CS_2}{76.15 \text{ g } CS_2}$$ $2.43 \text{ g } CH_3COCH_3 \longrightarrow \text{mol } CH_3COCH_3$ $$\frac{1 \text{ mol } CH_3COCH_3}{58.08 \text{ g } CH_3COCH_3}$$ $\text{mol } CS_2, \text{mol } CH_3OCH_3 \longrightarrow \chi_{CS_2}, \chi_{CH_3COCH_3}$ $$\chi_{CS_2} = \frac{n_{CS_2}}{n_{CS_2} + n_{CH_3COCH_3}}$$
Use the mole fraction of each component along with Raoult's law to compute the partial pressure of each component. The total pressure is the sum of the partial pressures.	$P_{CS_2} = \chi_{CS_2}P°_{CS_2}$ $P_{CH_3COCH_3} = \chi_{CH_3COCH_3}P°_{CH_3COCH_3}$ $P_{tot} = P_{CS_2} + P_{CH_3COCH_3}$ **RELATIONSHIPS USED** $\chi_A = \dfrac{n_A}{n_A + n_B}$ (mole fraction definition) $P_A = \chi_A P°_A$ (Raoult's law)

SOLVE Begin by converting the masses of each component to the amounts in moles.	**SOLUTION** $$3.95 \text{ g } CS_2 \times \frac{1 \text{ mol } CS_2}{76.15 \text{ g } CS_2} = 0.05187 \text{ mol } CS_2$$ $$2.43 \text{ g } CH_3COCH_3 \times \frac{1 \text{ mol } CH_3COCH_3}{58.0 \text{ g } CH_3COCH_3} = 0.04184 \text{ mol } CH_3COCH_3$$
Then calculate the mole fraction of carbon disulfide.	$$\chi_{CS_2} = \frac{n_{CS_2}}{n_{CS_2} + n_{CH_3COCH_3}}$$ $$= \frac{0.05187 \text{ mol}}{0.05187 \text{ mol} + 0.04184 \text{ mol}}$$ $$= 0.5535$$
Calculate the mole fraction of acetone by subtracting the mole fraction of carbon disulfide from one.	$$\chi_{CH_3COCH_3} = 1 - 0.5535$$ $$= 0.4465$$
Calculate the partial pressures of carbon disulfide and acetone by using Raoult's law and the given values of the vapor pressures of the pure substances.	$$P_{CS_2} = \chi_{CS_2} P^\circ_{CS_2}$$ $$= 0.5535(515 \text{ torr})$$ $$= 285 \text{ torr}$$ $$P_{CH_3COCH_3} = \chi_{CH_3COCH_3} P^\circ_{CH_3COCH_3}$$ $$= 0.4465(332 \text{ torr})$$ $$= 148 \text{ torr}$$
Calculate the total pressure by summing the partial pressures.	$$P_{tot}(\text{ideal}) = 285 \text{ torr} + 148 \text{ torr}$$ $$= 433 \text{ torr}$$
Lastly, compare the calculated total pressure for the ideal case to the experimentally measured total pressure. Since the experimentally measured pressure is greater than the calculated pressure, we can conclude that the interactions between the two components must be weaker than the interactions between the components themselves.	$$P_{tot}(\text{exp}) = 645 \text{ torr}$$ $$P_{tot}(\text{exp}) > P_{tot}(\text{ideal})$$ The solution is not ideal and shows positive deviations from Raoult's law. Therefore, carbon disulfide–acetone interactions must be weaker than acetone–acetone and carbon disulfide–carbon disulfide interactions.

CHECK The units of the answer (torr) are correct. The magnitude seems reasonable given the partial pressures of the pure substances.

FOR PRACTICE 12.7

A solution of benzene (C_6H_6) and toluene (C_7H_8) is 25.0% benzene by mass. The vapor pressures of pure benzene and pure toluene at 25 °C are 94.2 torr and 28.4 torr, respectively. Assuming ideal behavior, calculate each of the following:

(a) The vapor pressure of each of the solution components in the mixture.

(b) The total pressure above the solution.

(c) The composition of the vapor in mass percent.

Why is the composition of the vapor different from the composition of the solution?

Conceptual Connection 12.4 Raoult's Law

A solution contains equal amounts (in moles) of liquid components A and B. The vapor pressure of pure A is 100 mmHg and that of pure B is 200 mmHg. The experimentally measured vapor pressure of the solution is 120 mmHg. What can you say about the relative strengths of the solute–solute, solute–solvent, and solvent–solvent interactions in this solution?

ANSWER: The solute–solvent interactions must be stronger than the solute–solute and solvent–solvent interactions. The stronger interactions lower the vapor pressure from the expected ideal value of 150 mmHg.

Freezing Point Depression and Boiling Point Elevation

Vapor pressure lowering occurs at all temperatures. We can see the effect of vapor pressure lowering over a range of temperatures by comparing the phase diagrams for a pure solvent and for a solution containing a nonvolatile solute:

▶ A nonvolatile solute lowers the vapor pressure of a solution, resulting in a lower freezing point and an elevated boiling point.

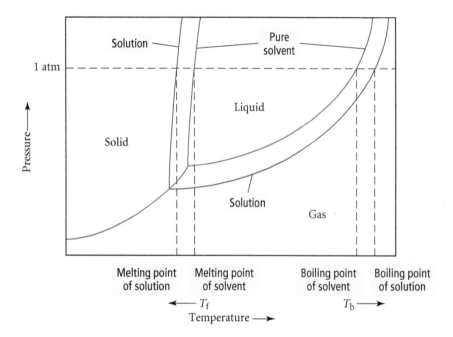

Notice that the vapor pressure for the solution is shifted downward compared to that of the pure solvent. Consequently, the vapor pressure curve intersects the solid–gas curve at a lower temperature. The net effect is that the solution has a *lower melting point* and a *higher boiling point* than the pure solvent. These effects are called **freezing point depression** and **boiling point elevation**, both of which are colligative properties (like vapor pressure lowering).

The freezing point of a solution containing a nonvolatile solute is lower than the freezing point of the pure solvent. For example, antifreeze, used to prevent the freezing of engine blocks in cold climates, is an aqueous solution of ethylene glycol ($C_2H_6O_2$). The more concentrated the solution, the lower the freezing point becomes.

The amount that the freezing point is lowered is given by the equation:

$$\Delta T_f = m \times K_f$$

where

▲ Antifreeze is an aqueous solution of ethylene glycol. The solution has a lower freezing point and higher boiling point than pure water.

- ΔT_f is the change in temperature of the freezing point in Celsius degrees (relative to the freezing point of the pure solvent), usually reported as a positive number;
- m is the molality of the solution in moles solute per kilogram solvent;
- K_f is the freezing point depression constant for the solvent.

TABLE 12.8 Freezing Point Depression and Boiling Point Elevation Constants for Several Liquid Solvents

Solvent	Normal Freezing Point (°C)	K_f (°C/m)	Normal Boiling Point (°C)	K_b (°C/m)
Benzene (C_6H_6)	5.5	5.12	80.1	2.53
Carbon tetrachloride (CCl_4)	−22.9	29.9	76.7	5.03
Chloroform ($CHCl_3$)	−63.5	4.70	61.2	3.63
Ethanol (C_2H_5OH)	−114.1	1.99	78.3	1.22
Diethyl ether ($C_4H_{10}O$)	−116.3	1.79	34.6	2.02
Water (H_2O)	0.00	1.86	100.0	0.512

For water,

$$K_f = 1.86 \text{ °C/m}$$

When an aqueous solution containing a dissolved solid solute freezes slowly, the ice that forms does not normally contain much of the solute. For example, when ice forms in ocean water, the ice is not salt water, but freshwater. As the ice forms, the crystal structure of the ice tends to exclude the solute particles. You can verify this yourself by partially freezing a salt water solution in the freezer. Take out the newly formed ice, rinse it several times, and taste it. Compare its taste to the taste of the original solution. The ice is much less salty.

Freezing point depression and boiling point elevation constants for several liquids are listed in Table 12.8. Calculating the freezing point of a solution involves substituting into the above equation, as the following example demonstrates.

EXAMPLE 12.8 Freezing Point Depression

Calculate the freezing point of a 1.7 m aqueous ethylene glycol solution.

SORT You are given the molality of a solution and asked to find its freezing point.	**GIVEN:** 1.7 m solution **FIND:** freezing point (from ΔT_f)
STRATEGIZE To solve this problem, use the freezing point depression equation.	**CONCEPTUAL PLAN** m → ΔT_f $\Delta T_f = m \times K_f$
SOLVE Substitute into the equation to calculate ΔT_f. The actual freezing point is the freezing point of pure water (0.00 °C) − ΔT_f.	**SOLUTION** $\Delta T_f = m \times K_f$ $= 1.7\,\cancel{m} \times 1.86$ °C/$\cancel{m}$ $= 3.2$ °C Freezing point = 0.00 °C − 3.2 °C $= -3.2$ °C

CHECK The units of the answer are correct. The magnitude seems about right. The expected range for freezing points of an aqueous solution is anywhere from −10 °C to just below 0 °C. Any answers out of this range would be suspect.

FOR PRACTICE 12.8

Calculate the freezing point of a 2.6 m aqueous sucrose solution.

The boiling point of a solution containing a nonvolatile solute is higher than the boiling point of the pure solvent. In automobiles, antifreeze not only prevents the freezing of water within engine blocks in cold climates, it also prevents the boiling of water within

engine blocks in hot climates. The amount that the boiling point rises in solutions is given by the equation

$$\Delta T_b = m \times K_b$$

where

- ΔT_b is the change in temperature of the boiling point in Celsius degrees (relative to the boiling point of the pure solvent);
- m is the molality of the solution in moles solute per kilogram solvent;
- K_b is the boiling point elevation constant for the solvent.

For water,

$$K_b = 0.512\ °C/m$$

The boiling point of a solution is calculated by substituting into the above equation, as the following example demonstrates.

EXAMPLE 12.9 Boiling Point Elevation

What mass of ethylene glycol ($C_2H_6O_2$), in grams, must be added to 1.0 kg of water to produce a solution that boils at 105.0 °C?

SORT You are given the desired boiling point of an ethylene glycol solution containing 1.0 kg of water and asked to find the mass of ethylene glycol required to achieve the boiling point.	**GIVEN:** $\Delta T_b = 5.0\,°C$, 1.0 kg H_2O **FIND:** g $C_2H_6O_2$
STRATEGIZE To solve this problem, use the boiling-point elevation equation to calculate the desired molality of the solution from ΔT_b. Then use the molality you just found to determine how many moles of ethylene glycol are needed per kilogram of water. Finally, calculate the molar mass of ethylene glycol and use it to convert from moles of ethylene glycol to mass of ethylene glycol.	**CONCEPTUAL PLAN** 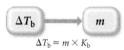 $\Delta T_b = m \times K_b$ 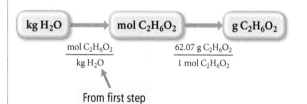 **RELATIONSHIPS USED** $C_2H_6O_2$ molar mass $= 62.07\ g/mol$ $\Delta T_b = m \times K_b$ (boiling point elevation)
SOLVE Begin by solving the boiling point elevation equation for molality and substituting the required quantities to calculate m.	**SOLUTION** $\Delta T_b = m \times K_b$ $m = \dfrac{\Delta T_b}{K_b} = \dfrac{5.0\,°C}{0.512\,\dfrac{°C}{m}} = 9.77m$ $1.0\ \cancel{kg\ H_2O} \times \dfrac{9.77\ \cancel{mol\ C_2H_6O_2}}{\cancel{kg\ H_2O}} \times \dfrac{62.07\ g\ C_2H_6O_2}{1\ \cancel{mol\ C_2H_6O_2}} = 6.1 \times 10^2\ g\ C_2H_6O_2$

CHECK The units of the answer are correct. The magnitude might seem a little high initially, but the boiling point elevation constant is so small that a lot of solute is required to raise the boiling point by a small amount.

FOR PRACTICE 12.9

Calculate the boiling point of a 3.60 m aqueous sucrose solution.

CHEMISTRY IN YOUR DAY   Antifreeze in Frogs

Wood frogs (*Rana sylvatica*) look like most other frogs. They are a few inches long and have characteristic greenish-brown skin. However, wood frogs survive cold winters in a remarkable way—they partially freeze. In its partially frozen state, the frog has no heartbeat, no blood circulation, no breathing, and no brain activity. Within 1–2 hours of thawing, however, these vital functions return and the frog hops off to find food. How does the wood frog do this?

Most cold-blooded animals cannot survive freezing temperatures because the water within their cells freezes. As we learned in Section 11.9, when water freezes, it expands, irreversibly damaging cells. When the wood frog hibernates for the winter, however, it produces large amounts of glucose that is secreted into its bloodstream and fills the interior of its cells. When the temperature drops below freezing, extracellular body fluids, such as those in the abdominal cavity, freeze solid. Fluids within cells, however, remain liquid because the high glucose concentration lowers their freezing point. In other words, the concentrated glucose solution within the frog's cells acts as antifreeze, preventing the water within the cells from freezing and allowing the frog to survive.

▲ The wood frog survives winter by partially freezing. It protects its cells by flooding them with glucose, which acts as an antifreeze.

Question

The wood frog can survive at body temperatures as low as −8.0 °C. Calculate the molality of a glucose solution ($C_6H_{12}O_6$) required to lower the freezing point of water to −8.0 °C.

Osmotic Pressure

The process by which seawater causes dehydration (discussed in the opening section of this chapter) is called *osmosis*. **Osmosis** is the flow of solvent from a solution of lower solute concentration to one of higher solute concentration. Concentrated solutions draw solvent from more dilute solutions because of nature's tendency to mix.

Figure 12.16 ▼ shows an osmosis cell. The left side of the cell contains a concentrated saltwater solution and the right side of the cell contains pure water. A **semipermeable**

Osmosis and Osmotic Pressure

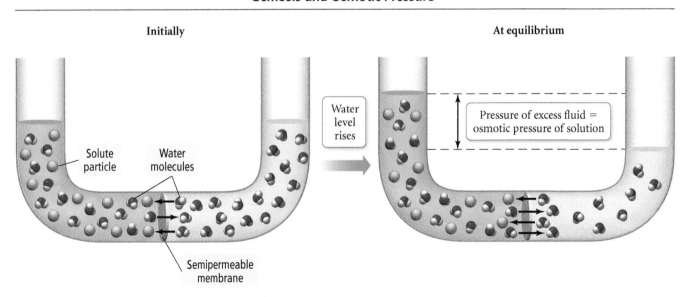

Initially

At equilibrium

Water level rises

Pressure of excess fluid = osmotic pressure of solution

Solute particle

Water molecules

Semipermeable membrane

▲ **FIGURE 12.16 An Osmosis Cell**   In an osmosis cell, water flows from the pure-water side of the cell through the semipermeable membrane to the salt water side.

membrane—a membrane that selectively allows some substances to pass through but not others—separates the two halves of the cell. Water flows by osmosis from the pure-water side of the cell through the semipermeable membrane and into the saltwater side. Over time, the water level on the left side of the cell rises, while the water level on the right side of the cell falls. If external pressure is applied to the water in the left cell, this process can be opposed and even stopped. The pressure required to stop the osmotic flow, called the **osmotic pressure**, is given by the following equation:

$$\Pi = MRT$$

where M is the molarity of the solution, T is the temperature (in kelvins), and R is the ideal gas constant (0.08206 L · atm/mol · K).

EXAMPLE 12.10 Osmotic Pressure

The osmotic pressure of a solution containing 5.87 mg of an unknown protein per 10.0 mL of solution is 2.45 torr at 25 °C. Find the molar mass of the unknown protein.

SORT You are given that a solution of an unknown protein contains 5.87 mg of the protein per 10.0 mL of solution. You are also given the osmotic pressure of the solution at a particular temperature and asked to find the molar mass of the unknown protein.	**GIVEN:** 5.87 mg protein 10.0 mL solution Π = 2.45 torr T = 25 °C **FIND:** molar mass of protein (g/mol)
STRATEGIZE Step 1: Use the given osmotic pressure and temperature to find the molarity of the protein solution.	**CONCEPTUAL PLAN** 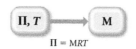 $\Pi = MRT$
Step 2: Use the molarity calculated in step 1 to find the number of moles of protein in 10 mL of solution.	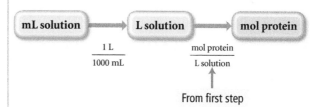 From first step
Step 3: Finally, use the number of moles of the protein calculated in step 2 and the given mass of the protein in 10.0 mL of solution to find the molar mass.	$\text{Molar mass} = \dfrac{\text{mass protein}}{\text{moles protein}}$ **RELATIONSHIPS USED** $\Pi = MRT$ (osmotic pressure equation)
SOLVE Step 1: Begin by solving the osmotic pressure equation for molarity and substituting in the required quantities in the correct units to calculate M.	**SOLUTION** $\Pi = MRT$ $M = \dfrac{\Pi}{RT} = \dfrac{2.45 \ \text{torr} \times \dfrac{1 \ \text{atm}}{760 \ \text{torr}}}{0.08206 \ \dfrac{\text{L} \cdot \text{atm}}{\text{mol} \cdot \text{K}} (298 \ \text{K})}$ $= 1.3\underline{1}8 \times 10^{-4} \ \text{M}$
Step 2: Begin with the given volume, convert to liters, then use the molarity to find the number of moles of protein.	$10.0 \ \text{mL} \times \dfrac{1 \ \text{L}}{1000 \ \text{mL}} \times \dfrac{1.3\underline{1}8 \times 10^{-4} \ \text{mol}}{\text{L}}$ $\qquad\qquad\qquad = 1.3\underline{1}8 \times 10^{-6} \ \text{mol}$
Step 3: Use the given mass and the number of moles from step 2 to calculate the molar mass of the protein.	$\text{Molar mass} = \dfrac{\text{mass protein}}{\text{moles protein}}$ $= \dfrac{5.87 \times 10^{-3} \ \text{g}}{1.3\underline{1}8 \times 10^{-6} \ \text{mol}} = 4.45 \times 10^{3} \ \text{g/mol}$

CHECK The units of the answer are correct. The magnitude might seem a little high initially, but proteins are large molecules and therefore have high molar masses.

FOR PRACTICE 12.10

Calculate the osmotic pressure (in atm) of a solution containing 1.50 g ethylene glycol ($C_2H_6O_2$) in 50.0 mL of solution at 25 °C.

12.7 Colligative Properties of Strong Electrolyte Solutions

At the beginning of Section 12.6, we saw that colligative properties depend on the number of dissolved particles, and that electrolytes must therefore be treated slightly differently than nonelectrolytes when determining colligative properties. For example, the freezing point depression of a 0.10 m sucrose solution is $\Delta T_f = 0.186$ °C. However, the freezing point depression of a 0.10 m sodium chloride solution is nearly twice this large. Why? Because 1 mol of sodium chloride dissociates into nearly 2 mol of ions in solution. The ratio of moles of particles in solution to moles of formula units dissolved is called the **van't Hoff factor (i)**:

$$i = \frac{\text{moles of particles in solution}}{\text{moles of formula units dissolved}}$$

TABLE 12.9 Van't Hoff Factors at 0.05 m Concentration in Aqueous Solution		
Solute	i Expected	i Measured
Nonelectrolyte	1	1
NaCl	2	1.9
MgSO$_4$	2	1.3
MgCl$_2$	3	2.7
K$_2$SO$_4$	3	2.6
FeCl$_3$	4	3.4

Since 1 mol of NaCl produces 2 mol of particles in solution, we expect the van't Hoff factor for NaCl to be exactly 2. In reality, this expected factor only occurs in very dilute solutions. For example, the van't Hoff factor for a 0.10 m NaCl solution is 1.87 and that for a 0.010 m NaCl solution is 1.94. The van't Hoff factor approaches the expected value at infinite dilution (as the concentration approaches zero). Table 12.9 lists the actual and expected van't Hoff factors for a number of solutes.

The reason that the van't Hoff factors do not exactly equal the expected values is that some ions effectively pair in solution. Ideally we expect the dissociation of an ionic compound to be complete in solution. In reality, however, the dissociation is not complete—at any moment, some cations pair with anions (Figure 12.17 ▶), slightly reducing the number of particles in solution.

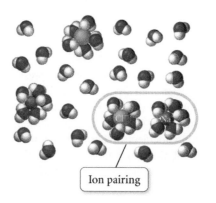

Ion pairing

◀ FIGURE 12.17 Ion Pairing
Hydrated anions and cations may get close enough together to effectively pair, lowering the concentration of particles below what would be expected ideally.

To calculate freezing point depression, boiling point elevation, and osmotic pressure of ionic solutions use the van't Hoff factor in each equation as follows:

$$\Delta T_f = im \times K_f \text{ (freezing point depression)}$$

$$\Delta T_b = im \times K_b \text{ (boiling point elevation)}$$

$$\Pi = iMRT \text{ (osmotic pressure)}$$

Conceptual Connection 12.5 Colligative Properties

Which solution will have the highest boiling point?

(a) 0.50 M $C_{12}H_{22}O_{11}$ **(b)** 0.50 M NaCl **(c)** 0.50 M MgCl$_2$

ANSWER: (c) The 0.50 M MgCl$_2$ solution will have the highest boiling point because it has the highest concentration of particles. We expect 1 mol of MgCl$_2$ to form 3 mol of particles in solution (although it effectively forms slightly fewer).

EXAMPLE 12.11 Van't Hoff Factor and Freezing Point Depression

The freezing point of an aqueous 0.050 m $CaCl_2$ solution is -0.27 °C. What is the van't Hoff factor (i) for $CaCl_2$ at this concentration? How does it compare to the expected value of i?

SORT You are given the molality of a solution and its freezing point. You are asked to find the value of i, the van't Hoff factor, and compare it to the expected value.	**GIVEN:** 0.050 m $CaCl_2$ solution, $\Delta T_f = 0.27$ °C **FIND:** i
STRATEGIZE To solve this problem, use the freezing point depression equation including the van't Hoff factor.	**CONCEPTUAL PLAN** $\Delta T_f = im \times K_f$
SOLVE Solve the freezing point depression equation for i and substitute in the given quantities to calculate its value. The expected value of i for $CaCl_2$ is 3 because calcium chloride forms 3 mol of ions for each mole of calcium chloride that dissolves. The experimental value is slightly less than 3, probably because of ion pairing.	**SOLUTION** $\Delta T_f = im \times K_f$ $i = \dfrac{\Delta T_f}{m \times K_f}$ $= \dfrac{0.27\ °C}{0.050\ m \times \dfrac{1.86\ °C}{m}}$ $= 2.9$

CHECK The answer has no units, as expected since i is a ratio. The magnitude is about right since it is close to the value you would expect upon complete dissociation of $CaCl_2$.

FOR PRACTICE 12.11

Calculate the freezing point of an aqueous 0.10 m $FeCl_3$ solution using a van't Hoff factor of 3.2.

Strong Electrolytes and Vapor Pressure

Just as the freezing point depression of a solution containing an electrolyte solute is greater than that of a solution containing the same concentration of a nonelectrolyte solute, so the vapor pressure lowering is greater (for the same reasons). The vapor pressure for a sodium chloride solution, for example, is lowered about twice as much as it is for a nonelectrolyte solution of the same concentration. To calculate the vapor pressure of a solution containing an ionic solute, we must account for the dissociation of the solute when we calculate the mole fraction of the solvent, as shown in the following example.

EXAMPLE 12.12 Calculating the Vapor Pressure of a Solution Containing an Ionic Solute

A solution contains 0.102 mol $Ca(NO_3)_2$ and 0.927 mol H_2O. Calculate the vapor pressure of the solution at 55 °C. The vapor pressure of pure water at 55 °C is 118.1 torr. (Assume that the solute completely dissociates.)

SORT You are given the number of moles of each component of a solution and asked to find the vapor pressure of the solution. You are also given the vapor pressure of pure water at the appropriate temperature.	**GIVEN:** 0.102 mol $Ca(NO_3)_2$ 0.927 mol H_2O $P^\circ_{H_2O} = 118.1$ torr (at 55 °C) **FIND:** $P_{solution}$
STRATEGIZE To solve this problem, use Raoult's law as in Example 12.6. Calculate $\chi_{solvent}$ from the given amounts of solute and solvent.	**CONCEPTUAL PLAN** $\boxed{\chi_{H_2O},\ P^\circ_{H_2O}} \longrightarrow \boxed{P_{solution}}$ $P_{solution} = \chi_{H_2O} P^\circ_{H_2O}$

SOLVE The key to this problem is to understand the dissociation of calcium nitrate. Write an equation showing the dissociation.	**SOLUTION** $Ca(NO_3)_2(s) \longrightarrow Ca^{2+}(aq) + 2\,NO_3^-(aq)$
Since 1 mol of calcium nitrate dissociates into 3 mol of dissolved particles, the number of moles of calcium nitrate must be multiplied by 3 when computing the mole fraction.	$\chi_{H_2O} = \dfrac{n_{H_2O}}{3 \times n_{Ca(NO_3)_2} + n_{H_2O}}$ $= \dfrac{0.927 \text{ mol}}{3(0.102) \text{ mol} + 0.927 \text{ mol}}$ $= 0.75\underline{1}8$
Use the mole fraction of water and the vapor pressure of pure water to calculate the vapor pressure of the solution.	$P_{solution} = \chi_{H_2O} P^\circ_{H_2O}$ $= 0.75\underline{1}8(118.1 \text{ torr})$ $= 88.8 \text{ torr}$

CHECK The units of the answer are correct. The magnitude also seems right because the computed vapor pressure of the solution is significantly less than that of the pure solvent, as expected for a solution with a significant amount of solute.

FOR PRACTICE 12.12

A solution contains 0.115 mol H_2O and an unknown number of moles of sodium chloride. The vapor pressure of the solution at 30 °C is 25.7 torr. The vapor pressure of pure water at 30 °C is 31.8 torr. Calculate the number of moles of sodium chloride in the solution.

Colligative Properties and Medical Solutions

Doctors and others healthcare workers often administer solutions to patients. The osmotic pressure of these solutions is controlled for the desired effect on the patient. Solutions having osmotic pressures greater than those of body fluids are called *hyperosmotic*. These solutions take water out of cells and tissues. When a human cell is placed in a hyperosmotic solution, it tends to shrivel as it loses water to the surrounding solution (Figure 12.18b ▼). Solutions having osmotic pressures less than those of body fluids are called *hyposmotic*. These solutions pump water into cells. When a human cell is placed in a hyposmotic solution—such as pure water, for example—water enters the cell, sometimes causing it to burst (Figure 12.18c).

Isosmotic solution

Hyperosmotic solution

Hyposmotic solution

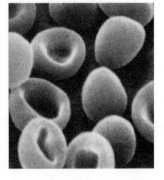

(a) Normal red blood cells

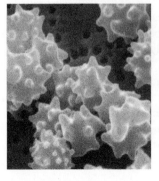

(b) Shriveled red blood cells

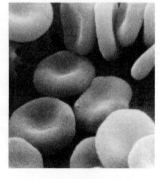

(c) Swollen red blood cells

◀ **FIGURE 12.18 Red Blood Cells and Osmosis** (a) In an isosmotic solution, red blood cells have the normal shape shown here. In a hyperosmotic solution (b), they lose water and shrivel. In a hyposmotic solution (c), they swell up and may burst as water flows into the cell.

Intravenous solutions—those that are administered directly into a patient's veins—must have osmotic pressures equal to those of body fluids. These solutions are called *isosmotic* (or *isotonic*). When a patient is given an IV in a hospital, the majority of the fluid is usually an isosmotic saline solution—a solution containing 0.9 g NaCl per 100 mL of solution. In medicine and in other health-related fields, solution concentrations are often reported in units that indicate the mass of the solute per given volume of solution. Also common is *percent mass to volume*—which is simply the mass of the solute in grams divided by the volume of the solution in milliliters times 100%. In these units, the concentration of an isotonic saline solution is 0.9%mass/volume.

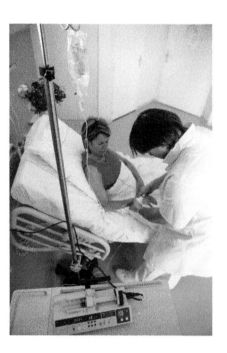
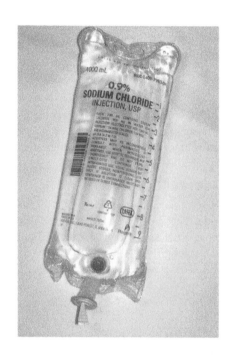

▶ Fluids used for intravenous transfusion must be isosmotic with bodily fluids—that is, they must have the same osmotic pressure.

▲ **FIGURE 12.19 A Colloid** Soapy water is an example of a colloidal dispersion. The haze is due to the scattering of light by the colloidal particles.

12.8 Colloids

When you mix water and soap together, the resulting mixture has a distinctive haze (Figure 12.19 ◄). Soapy water is hazy because soap and water form a *colloidal dispersion,* rather than a true solution. A **colloidal dispersion**, or more simply a **colloid**, is a mixture in which a dispersed substance (which is solute-like) is finely divided in a dispersing medium (which is solvent-like). Examples of colloids include fog, smoke, whipped cream, and milk, as shown in Table 12.10.

Whether or not a mixture is a colloid is determined by the size of the particles it contains. If the particles are small (for example, individual small molecules), then the mixture is a solution. If the particles have a diameter greater than 1 μm (for example, grains of sand), then the mixture is a heterogeneous mixture. Sand stirred into water will slowly settle out of the water. *If the particles are between 1 nm and 1000 nm in size, the mixture is a colloid.* Colloidal particles are small enough that they stay dispersed throughout the dispersing medium by collisions with other molecules or atoms. When you view a colloidal particle dispersed in a liquid under a microscope, you can witness its jittery motion, which proceeds along a random path, as shown in Figure 12.20 ▶. This motion, called Brownian motion, is caused by collisions with molecules in the liquid. In the beginning of the twentieth century, Brownian motion was a decisive factor in confirming the molecular and atomic nature of matter.

Soap has a unique structure, shown in Figure 12.21 ▶. One end of the molecule is ionic and therefore interacts strongly with water molecules via ion–dipole interactions. However, the other end of the soap molecule is a long, nonpolar, hydrocarbon tail. When

TABLE 12.10 Types of Colloidal Dispersions

Classification	Dispersing Substance (Solute-like)	Dispersing Medium (Solvent-like)		Example
Aerosol	Liquid	Gas		Fog (water droplets in air)
Solid aerosol	Solid	Gas		Smoke (ash in air)
Foam	Gas	Liquid		Whipped cream (air bubbles in butterfat)
Emulsion	Liquid	Liquid		Milk (milk fat globules in water)
Solid emulsion	Liquid	Solid		Opal (water in silica glass)

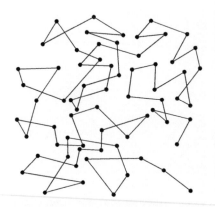

▲ **FIGURE 12.20 Brownian Motion**
A colloidal particle exhibits Brownian motion, moving in a jerky, haphazard path as it undergoes collisions with other molecules.

enough soap is added to water, the soap molecules aggregate in structures called *micelles* (Figure 12.22 ▼). In a micelle, the nonpolar hydrocarbon tails crowd into the center of a sphere to maximize their interactions with one another. The ionic heads orient toward the surface of the sphere where they can interact with water molecules. The micelle structures are responsible for the haze seen in soapy water—they are too small to be seen by the naked eye, but they still scatter light. This scattering of light by a colloidal

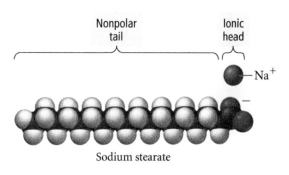

▲ **FIGURE 12.21 Structure of a Soap** A soap molecule has a charged ionic head and a long nonpolar hydrocarbon tail.

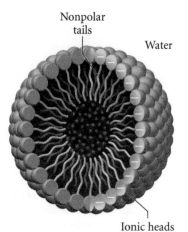

◀ **FIGURE 12.22 Micelle Structure**
In a micelle, the nonpolar tails of soap molecules are oriented inward (where they can interact with one another) and the ionic heads are oriented outward (where they can interact with the polar water molecules).

▲ **FIGURE 12.23 The Tyndall Effect** When a light beam passes through a colloidal suspension (left), it is visible because the colloid particles scatter some of the light. The beam is not visible in pure water (right), nor would it be visible in a non-colloidal solution.

▲ Light beams are invisible when they are not scattered by colloidally dispersed particles such as dust or mist in the air.

dispersion is known as the **Tyndall effect** (Figure 12.23 ▲). You can observe the Tyndall effect in other colloids such as fog (water droplets dispersed in air) or dusty air. In fact, you can use the Tyndall effect as a test to determine whether a mixture is a solution or a colloid, since solutions contain completely dissolved solute molecules that are too small to scatter light.

The particles in a colloid need not be clusters of molecules. Some colloids, such as many protein solutions, contain dispersed macromolecules. For example, blood contains dispersed hemoglobin. The hemoglobin molecules are so large that they scatter light; thus, blood is considered a colloid.

Colloidal suspensions are kept stable by electrostatic repulsions that occur at their surfaces. For example, in a micelle, the ionic heads of many soap molecules compose the surface of the spherical particle (Figure 12.24 ▼). These ionic heads interact strongly with water molecules, but repel other colloid particles. Heating a colloid can destroy it because, in a heated colloid, collisions occur with enough force to overcome the electrostatic repulsions and allow the colloid particles to coalesce. Similarly, adding an electrolyte to a colloidal suspension can also disrupt the electrostatic repulsions that occur between colloid particles and thus destroy the colloid. For this reason, soap does not work well in a salt water solution.

▲ **FIGURE 12.24 Micelle Repulsions** Micelles do not coalesce because the charged surface of one micelle repels the charged surface of another.

CHAPTER IN REVIEW

Key Terms

Section 12.1
solution (513)
solvent (513)
solute (513)

Section 12.2
aqueous solution (514)
solubility (515)
entropy (516)
miscible (517)

Section 12.3
enthalpy of solution
   (ΔH_{soln}) (520)
heat of hydration
   ($\Delta H_{hydration}$) (521)

Section 12.4
dynamic equilibrium (524)
saturated solution (524)
unsaturated solution (524)
supersaturated solution (524)
recrystallization (525)
Henry's law (526)

Section 12.5
dilute solution (527)
concentrated solution (527)
molarity (M) (528)
molality (m) (529)
parts by mass (530)
percent by mass (530)
parts per million (ppm) (530)

parts per billion (ppb) (530)
parts by volume (530)
mole fraction (χ_{solute}) (531)
mole percent (mol %) (531)

Section 12.6
colligative property (535)
Raoult's law (537)
vapor pressure lowering (ΔP)
   (537)
ideal solution (539)
freezing point depression (542)
boiling point elevation (542)
osmosis (545)
semipermeable membrane (545)
osmotic pressure (546)

Section 12.7
van't Hoff factor (i) (547)

Section 12.8
colloidal dispersion (colloid)
   (550)
Tyndall effect (552)

Key Concepts

Solutions (12.1, 12.2)

A solution is a homogeneous mixture of two or more substances. In a solution, the majority component is the solvent and the minority component is the solute. The tendency toward greater entropy (or greater energy dispersal) is the driving force for solution formation. Aqueous solutions contain water as a solvent and a solid, liquid, or gas as the solute.

Solubility and Energetics of Solution Formation (12.2, 12.3)

The solubility of a substance is the amount of the substance that will dissolve in a given amount of solvent. The solubility of one substance in another depends on the types of intermolecular forces that exist *between* the substances as well as *within* each substance. The overall enthalpy change upon solution formation can be determined by adding the enthalpy changes for the three steps of solution formation: (1) separation of the solute particles, (2) separation of the solvent particles, and (3) mixing of the solute and solvent particles. The first two steps are both endothermic, while the last is exothermic. In aqueous solutions of an ionic compound, the change in enthalpy for steps 2 and 3 can be combined as the heat of hydration ($\Delta H_{hydration}$), which is always negative.

Solution Equilibrium (12.4)

Dynamic equilibrium in a solution occurs when the rates of dissolution and recrystallization in a solution are equal. A solution in this state is said to be saturated. Solutions containing less than or more than the equilibrium amount of solute are unsaturated or supersaturated, respectively. The solubility of most solids in water increases with increasing temperature. The solubility of gases in liquids generally decreases with increasing temperature, but increases with increasing pressure.

Concentration Units (12.5)

Common units used to express solution concentration include molarity (M), molality (m), mole fraction (χ), mole percent (mol %), percent (%) by mass or volume, parts per million (ppm) by mass or volume, and parts per billion (ppb) by mass or volume. These units are summarized in Table 12.5.

Vapor Pressure Lowering, Freezing Point Depression, Boiling Point Elevation, and Osmosis (12.6, 12.7)

The presence of a nonvolatile solute in a liquid results in a lower vapor pressure of the solution relative to the vapor pressure of the pure liquid. This lower vapor pressure is predicted by Raoult's law for an ideal solution. If the solute–solvent interactions are particularly strong, the actual vapor pressure is lower than that predicted by Raoult's law. If the solute–solvent interactions are particularly weak, the actual vapor pressure is higher than that predicted by Raoult's law. The addition of a nonvolatile solute to a liquid will result in a solution with a lower freezing point and a higher boiling point than those of the pure solvent. The flow of solvent from a solution of lower concentration to a solution of higher concentration is called osmosis. These phenomena are colligative properties and depend only on the number of solute particles added, not the type of solute particles. Electrolyte solutes have a greater effect on these properties than the corresponding amount of a nonelectrolyte solute as specified by the van't Hoff factor.

Colloids (12.8)

A colloid is a mixture in which a substance is finely divided in a dispersing medium. Colloidal mixtures occur when the dispersed substance ranges in size from 1 nm to 1000 nm. One way to identify colloidal mixtures is by their tendency to scatter light, known as the Tyndall effect.

Key Equations and Relationships

Henry's Law: Solubility of Gases with Increasing Pressure (12.4)

$$S_{gas} = k_H P_{gas} \quad (k_H \text{ is Henry's law constant})$$

Molarity (M) of a Solution (12.5)

$$M = \frac{\text{amount solute (in mol)}}{\text{volume solution (in L)}}$$

Molality (m) of a Solution (12.5)

$$m = \frac{\text{amount solute (in mol)}}{\text{mass solvent (in kg)}}$$

Concentration of a Solution in Parts by Mass and Parts by Volume (12.5)

$$\text{Percent by mass} = \frac{\text{mass solute} \times 100\%}{\text{mass solution}}$$

$$\text{Parts per million (ppm)} = \frac{\text{mass solute} \times 10^6}{\text{mass solution}}$$

$$\text{Parts per billion (ppb)} = \frac{\text{mass solute} \times 10^9}{\text{mass solution}}$$

$$\text{Parts by volume} = \frac{\text{volume solute} \times \text{multiplication factor}}{\text{volume solution}}$$

Concentration of a Solution in Mole Fraction (χ) and Mole Percent (12.5)

$$\chi_{solute} = \frac{n_{solute}}{n_{solute} + n_{solvent}}$$

$$\text{Mol \%} = \chi \times 100\%$$

Raoult's Law: Relationship between the Vapor Pressure of a Solution ($P_{solution}$), the Mole Fraction of the Solvent ($\chi_{solvent}$), and the Vapor Pressure of the Pure Solvent ($P^\circ_{solvent}$) (12.6)

$$P_{solution} = \chi_{solvent} P^\circ_{solvent}$$

The Vapor Pressure of a Solution Containing Two Volatile Components (12.6)

$$P_A = \chi_A P^\circ_A$$

$$P_B = \chi_B P^\circ_B$$

$$P_{tot} = P_A + P_B$$

Relationship between Freezing Point Depression (ΔT_f), molality (m), and Freezing Point Depression Constant (K_f) (12.6)

$$\Delta T_f = m \times K_f$$

Relationship between Boiling Point Elevation (ΔT_b), Molality (m), and Boiling Point Elevation Constant (K_b) (12.6)

$$\Delta T_b = m \times K_b$$

Relationship between Osmotic Pressure (Π), Molarity (M), the Ideal Gas Constant (R), and Temperature (T, in K) (12.6)

$$\Pi = MRT \quad (R = 0.08206 \text{ L} \cdot \text{atm/mol} \cdot \text{K})$$

van't Hoff Factor (i): Ratio of Moles of Particles in Solution to Moles of Formula Units Dissolved (12.7)

$$i = \frac{\text{moles of particles in solution}}{\text{moles of formula units dissolved}}$$

Key Skills

Determining Whether a Solute Is Soluble in a Solvent (12.2)
- Example 12.1 • For Practice 12.1 • Exercises 31–34

Using Henry's Law to Predict the Solubility of Gases with Increasing Pressure (12.4)
- Example 12.2 • For Practice 12.2 • Exercises 49, 50

Calculating Concentrations of Solutions (12.5)
- Examples 12.3, 12.4 • For Practice 12.3, 12.4 • For More Practice 12.3 • Exercises 51–56, 63, 64

Converting between Concentration Units (12.5)
- Example 12.5 • For Practice 12.5 • Exercises 65–68

Determining the Vapor Pressure of a Solution Containing a Nonelectrolyte and Nonvolatile Solute (12.6)
- Example 12.6 • For Practice 12.6 • For More Practice 12.6 • Exercises 71, 72

Determining the Vapor Pressure of a Two-Component Solution (12.6)
- Example 12.7 • For Practice 12.7 • Exercises 73–76

Calculating Freezing Point Depression (12.6)
- Example 12.8 • For Practice 12.8 • Exercises 77–80, 85, 86

Calculating Boiling Point Elevation (12.6)
- Example 12.9 • For Practice 12.9 • Exercises 77, 78, 85, 86

Determining the Osmotic Pressure (12.6)
- Example 12.10 • For Practice 12.10 • Exercises 81–84

Determining and Using the van't Hoff Factor (12.7)
- Example 12.11 • For Practice 12.11 • Exercises 87–90

Determining the Vapor Pressure of a Solution Containing an Ionic Solute (12.7)
- Example 12.12 • For Practice 12.12 • Exercises 91, 92

EXERCISES

Review Questions

1. Explain why drinking seawater results in dehydration.

2. What is a solution? What are the solute and solvent?

3. What does it mean to say that a substance is soluble in another substance? What kinds of units are used in reporting solubility?

4. Why do two ideal gases thoroughly mix when combined? What drives the mixing?

5. What is entropy? Why is entropy important in discussing the formation of solutions?

6. What kinds of intermolecular forces are involved in solution formation?

7. Explain how the relative strengths of solute–solute interactions, solvent–solvent interactions, and solvent–solute interactions affect solution formation.

8. What does the statement, *like dissolves like*, mean with respect to solution formation?

9. What are three steps involved in evaluating the enthalpy changes associated with solution formation?

10. What is the heat of hydration ($\Delta H_{hydration}$)? How does the enthalpy of solution depend on the relative magnitudes of ΔH_{solute} and $\Delta H_{hydration}$?

11. Explain dynamic equilibrium with respect to solution formation. What is a saturated solution? An unsaturated solution? A supersaturated solution?

12. How does the solubility of a solid in a liquid depend on temperature? How is this temperature dependence exploited to purify solids through recrystallization?

13. How does the solubility of a gas in a liquid depend on temperature? How does this temperature dependence affect the amount of oxygen available for fish and other aquatic animals?

14. How does the solubility of a gas in a liquid depend on pressure? How does this pressure dependence account for the bubbling that occurs upon opening a can of soda?

15. What is Henry's law? For what kinds of calculations is Henry's law useful?

16. What are the common units for expressing solution concentration?

17. How are parts by mass and parts by volume used in calculations?

18. What is the effect of a nonvolatile solute on the vapor pressure of a liquid? Why is the vapor pressure of a solution different from the vapor pressure of the pure liquid solvent?

19. What is Raoult's law? For what kind of calculations is Raoult's law useful?

20. Explain the difference between an ideal and a nonideal solution.

21. What is the effect on vapor pressure of a solution with particularly *strong* solute–solvent interactions? With particularly *weak* solute–solvent interactions?

22. Explain why the lower vapor pressure for a solution containing a nonvolatile solute results in a higher boiling point and lower melting point compared to the pure solvent.

23. What are colligative properties?

24. What is osmosis? What is osmotic pressure?

25. Explain the role and meaning of the van't Hoff factor in determining the colligative properties of solutions containing ionic solutes.

26. Describe a colloidal dispersion. What is the difference between a colloidal dispersion and a true solution?

27. What is the Tyndall effect and how can it be used to help identify colloidal dispersions?

28. What keeps the particles in a colloidal dispersion from coalescing?

Problems by Topic

Solubility

29. Pick an appropriate solvent from Table 12.3 to dissolve each substance. State the kind of intermolecular forces that would occur between the solute and solvent in each case.
    a. motor oil (nonpolar)
    b. ethanol (polar, contains an OH group)
    c. lard (nonpolar)
    d. potassium chloride (ionic)

30. Pick an appropriate solvent from Table 12.3 to dissolve each substance.
    a. isopropyl alcohol (polar, contains an OH group)
    b. sodium chloride (ionic)
    c. vegetable oil (nonpolar)
    d. sodium nitrate (ionic)

31. Which molecule would you expect to be more soluble in water, $CH_3CH_2CH_2OH$ or $HOCH_2CH_2CH_2OH$?

32. Which molecule would you expect to be more soluble in water, CCl_4 or CH_2Cl_2?

33. For each compound, would you expect greater solubility in water or in hexane? Indicate the kinds of intermolecular forces that occur between the solute and the solvent in which the molecule is most soluble.

    a. glucose

    b. naphthalene

    c. dimethyl ether

    d. alanine
       (an amino acid)

34. For each compound, would you expect greater solubility in water or in hexane? Indicate the kinds of intermolecular forces that would occur between the solute and the solvent in which the molecule is most soluble.

    a. toluene

    b. sucrose
       (table sugar)

    c. isobutene

    d. ethylene glycol

Energetics of Solution Formation

35. When ammonium chloride (NH_4Cl) is dissolved in water, the solution becomes colder.
    a. Is the dissolution of ammonium chloride endothermic or exothermic?
    b. What can you say about the relative magnitudes of the lattice energy of ammonium chloride and its heat of hydration?
    c. Sketch a qualitative energy diagram similar to Figure 12.7 for the dissolution of NH_4Cl.
    d. Why does the solution form? What drives the process?

36. When lithium iodide (LiI) is dissolved in water, the solution becomes hotter.
    a. Is the dissolution of lithium iodide endothermic or exothermic?
    b. What can you say about the relative magnitudes of the lattice energy of lithium iodide and its heat of hydration?
    c. Sketch a qualitative energy diagram similar to Figure 12.7 for the dissolution of LiI.
    d. Why does the solution form? What drives the process?

37. Silver nitrate has a lattice energy of -820 kJ/mol and a heat of solution of $+22.6$ kJ/mol. Calculate the heat of hydration for silver nitrate.

38. Use the data to calculate the heats of hydration of lithium chloride and sodium chloride. Which of the two cations, lithium or sodium, has stronger ion–dipole interactions with water? Why?

Compound	Lattice Energy (kJ/mol)	ΔH_{soln} (kJ/mol)
LiCl	-834	-37.0
NaCl	-769	$+3.88$

39. Lithium iodide has a lattice energy of -7.3×10^2 (kJ/mol) and a heat of hydration of -793 kJ/mol. Find the heat of solution for lithium iodide and determine how much heat is evolved or absorbed when 15.0 g of lithium iodide completely dissolves in water.

40. Potassium nitrate has a lattice energy of -163.8 kcal/mol and a heat of hydration of -155.5 kcal/mol. How much potassium nitrate has to dissolve in water to absorb 1.00×10^2 kJ of heat?

Solution Equilibrium and Factors Affecting Solubility

41. A solution contains 25 g of NaCl per 100.0 g of water at 25 °C. Is the solution unsaturated, saturated, or supersaturated? (Use Figure 12.11.)

42. A solution contains 32 g of KNO_3 per 100.0 g of water at 25 °C. Is the solution unsaturated, saturated, or supersaturated? (Use Figure 12.11.)

43. A KNO_3 solution containing 45 g of KNO_3 per 100.0 g of water is cooled from 40 °C to 0 °C. What happens during cooling? (Use Figure 12.11.)

44. A KCl solution containing 42 g of KCl per 100.0 g of water is cooled from 60 °C to 0 °C. What happens during cooling? (Use Figure 12.11.)

45. Some laboratory procedures involving oxygen-sensitive reactants or products call for using preboiled (and then cooled) water. Explain.

46. A person preparing a fish tank uses preboiled (and then cooled) water to fill it. When the person puts the fish into the tank, it dies. Explain.

47. Scuba divers breathing air at increased pressure can suffer from nitrogen narcosis—a condition resembling drunkenness—when the partial pressure of nitrogen exceeds about 4 atm. What property of gas/water solutions causes this to happen? How could the diver reverse this effect?

48. Scuba divers breathing air at increased pressure can suffer from oxygen toxicity—too much oxygen in their bloodstream—when the partial pressure of oxygen exceeds about 1.4 atm. What happens to the amount of oxygen in a diver's bloodstream when he or she breathes oxygen at elevated pressures? How can this be reversed?

49. Calculate the mass of nitrogen dissolved at room temperature in an 80.0-L home aquarium. Assume a total pressure of 1.0 atm and a mole fraction for nitrogen of 0.78.

50. Use Henry's law to determine the molar solubility of helium at a pressure of 1.0 atm and 25 °C.

Concentrations of Solutions

51. An aqueous NaCl solution is made using 112 g of NaCl diluted to a total solution volume of 1.00 L. Calculate the molarity, molality, and mass percent of the solution. (Assume a density of 1.08 g/mL for the solution.)

52. An aqueous KNO_3 solution is made using 72.5 g of KNO_3 diluted to a total solution volume of 2.00 L. Calculate the molarity, molality, and mass percent of the solution. (Assume a density of 1.05 g/mL for the solution.)

53. To what volume should you dilute 50.0 mL of a 5.00 M KI solution so that 25.0 mL of the diluted solution contains 3.05 g of KI?

54. To what volume should you dilute 125 mL of an 8.00 M $CuCl_2$ solution so that 50.0 mL of the diluted solution contains 4.67 g $CuCl_2$?

55. Silver nitrate solutions are often used to plate silver onto other metals. What is the maximum amount of silver (in grams) that can be plated out of 4.8 L of an $AgNO_3$ solution containing 3.4% Ag by mass? Assume that the density of the solution is 1.01 g/mL.

56. A dioxin-contaminated water source contains 0.085% dioxin by mass. How much dioxin is present in 2.5 L of this water? Assume a density of 1.00 g/mL.

57. A hard water sample contains 0.0085% Ca by mass (in the form of Ca^{2+} ions). How much water (in grams) contains 1.2 g of Ca? (1.2 g of Ca is the recommended daily allowance of calcium for those between 19 and 24 years old.)

58. Lead is a toxic metal that affects the central nervous system. A Pb-contaminated water sample contains 0.0011% Pb by mass. How much of the water (in mL) contains 150 mg of Pb? (Assume a density of 1.0 g/mL.)

59. You can purchase nitric acid in a concentrated form that is 70.3% HNO_3 by mass and has a density of 1.41 g/mL. Describe exactly how you would prepare 1.15 L of 0.100 M HNO_3 from the concentrated solution.

60. You can purchase hydrochloric acid in a concentrated form that is 37.0% HCl by mass and has a density of 1.20 g/mL. Describe exactly how you would prepare 2.85 L of 0.500 M HCl from the concentrated solution.

61. Describe how you would prepare each solution from the dry solute and the solvent.
  a. 1.00×10^2 mL of 0.500 M KCl
  b. 1.00×10^2 g of 0.500 m KCl
  c. 1.00×10^2 g of 5.0% KCl solution by mass

62. Describe how you would prepare each solution from the dry solute and the solvent.
  a. 125 mL of 0.100 M $NaNO_3$
  b. 125 g of 0.100 m $NaNO_3$
  c. 125 g of 1.0% $NaNO_3$ solution by mass

63. A solution is prepared by dissolving 28.4 g of glucose ($C_6H_{12}O_6$) in 355 g of water. The final volume of the solution is 378 mL. For this solution, calculate the concentration in each unit:
  a. molarity   **b.** molality
  c. percent by mass   **d.** mole fraction
  e. mole percent

64. A solution is prepared by dissolving 20.2 mL of methanol (CH_3OH) in 100.0 mL of water at 25 °C. The final volume of the solution is 118 mL. The densities of methanol and water at this temperature are 0.782 g/mL and 1.00 g/mL, respectively. For this solution, calculate the concentration in each unit:
  a. molarity   **b.** molality
  c. percent by mass   **d.** mole fraction
  e. mole percent

65. Household hydrogen peroxide is an aqueous solution containing 3.0% hydrogen peroxide by mass. What is the molarity of this solution? (Assume a density of 1.01 g/mL.)

66. One brand of laundry bleach is an aqueous solution containing 4.55% sodium hypochlorite (NaOCl) by mass. What is the molarity of this solution? (Assume a density of 1.02 g/mL.)

67. An aqueous solution contains 36% HCl by mass. Calculate the molality and mole fraction of the solution.

68. An aqueous solution contains 5.0% NaCl by mass. Calculate the molality and mole fraction of the solution.

Vapor Pressure of Solutions

69. A beaker contains 100.0 mL of pure water. A second beaker contains 100.0 mL of seawater. The two beakers are left side by side on a lab bench for one week. At the end of the week, the

liquid level in both beakers has decreased. However, the level has decreased more in one of the beakers than in the other. Which one and why?

70. Which solution has the highest vapor pressure?
  a. 20.0 g of glucose ($C_6H_{12}O_6$) in 100.0 mL of water
  b. 20.0 g of sucrose ($C_{12}H_{22}O_{11}$) in 100.0 mL of water
  c. 10.0 g of potassium acetate $KC_2H_3O_2$ in 100.0 mL of water

71. Calculate the vapor pressure of a solution containing 24.5 g of glycerin ($C_3H_8O_3$) in 135 mL of water at 30.0 °C. The vapor pressure of pure water at this temperature is 31.8 torr. Assume that glycerin is not volatile and dissolves molecularly (i.e., it is not ionic) and use a density of 1.00 g/mL for the water.

72. A solution contains naphthalene ($C_{10}H_8$) dissolved in hexane (C_6H_{14}) at a concentration of 12.35% naphthalene by mass. Calculate the vapor pressure at 25 °C of hexane above the solution. The vapor pressure of pure hexane at 25 °C is 151 torr.

73. A solution contains 50.0 g of heptane (C_7H_{16}) and 50.0 g of octane (C_8H_{18}) at 25 °C. The vapor pressures of pure heptane and pure octane at 25 °C are 45.8 torr and 10.9 torr, respectively. Assuming ideal behavior, calculate:
  a. the vapor pressure of each of the solution components in the mixture
  b. the total pressure above the solution
  c. the composition of the vapor in mass percent
  d. Why is the composition of the vapor different from the composition of the solution?

74. A solution contains a mixture of pentane and hexane at room temperature. The solution has a vapor pressure of 258 torr. Pure pentane and hexane have vapor pressures of 425 torr and 151 torr, respectively, at room temperature. What is the mole fraction composition of the mixture? (Assume ideal behavior.)

75. A solution contains 4.08 g of chloroform ($CHCl_3$) and 9.29 g of acetone (CH_3COCH_3). The vapor pressures at 35 °C of pure chloroform and pure acetone are 295 torr and 332 torr, respectively. Assuming ideal behavior, calculate the vapor pressures of each of the components and the total vapor pressure above the solution. The experimentally measured total vapor pressure of the solution at 35 °C was 312 torr. Is the solution ideal? If not, what can you say about the relative strength of chloroform–acetone interactions compared to the acetone–acetone and chloroform–chloroform interactions?

76. A solution of methanol and water has a mole fraction of water of 0.312 and a total vapor pressure of 211 torr at 39.9 °C. The vapor pressures of pure methanol and pure water at this temperature are 256 torr and 55.3 torr, respectively. Is the solution ideal? If not, what can you say about the relative strengths of the solute–solvent interactions compared to the solute–solute and solvent–solvent interactions?

Freezing Point Depression, Boiling Point Elevation, and Osmosis

77. A glucose solution contains 55.8 g of glucose ($C_6H_{12}O_6$) in 455 g of water. Determine the freezing point and boiling point of the solution.

78. An ethylene glycol solution contains 21.2 g of ethylene glycol ($C_2H_6O_2$) in 85.4 mL of water. Determine the freezing point and boiling point of the solution. (Assume a density of 1.00 g/mL for water.)

79. An aqueous solution containing 17.5 g of an unknown molecular (nonelectrolyte) compound in 100.0 g of water was found to have a freezing point of −1.8 °C. Calculate the molar mass of the unknown compound.

80. An aqueous solution containing 35.9 g of an unknown molecular (nonelectrolyte) compound in 150.0 g of water was found to have a freezing point of −1.3 °C. Calculate the molar mass of the unknown compound.

81. Calculate the osmotic pressure of a solution containing 24.6 g of glycerin ($C_3H_8O_3$) in 250.0 mL of solution at 298 K.

82. What mass of sucrose ($C_{12}H_{22}O_{11}$) would you combine with 5.00×10^2 g of water to make a solution with an osmotic pressure of 8.55 atm at 298 K? (Assume a density of 1.0 g/mL for the solution.)

83. A solution containing 27.55 mg of an unknown protein per 25.0 mL solution was found to have an osmotic pressure of 3.22 torr at 25 °C. What is the molar mass of the protein?

84. Calculate the osmotic pressure of a solution containing 18.75 mg of hemoglobin in 15.0 mL of solution at 25 °C. The molar mass of hemoglobin is 6.5×10^4 g/mol.

85. Calculate the freezing point and boiling point of each aqueous solution, assuming complete dissociation of the solute.
  a. 0.100 *m* K_2S
  b. 21.5 g of $CuCl_2$ in 4.50×10^2 g water
  c. 5.5% $NaNO_3$ by mass (in water)

86. Calculate the freezing point and boiling point in each solution, assuming complete dissociation of the solute.
  a. 10.5 g $FeCl_3$ in 1.50×10^2 g water
  b. 3.5% KCl by mass (in water)
  c. 0.150 *m* MgF_2

87. Use the van't Hoff factors in Table 12.9 to compute each colligative property:
  a. the melting point of a 0.100 *m* iron(III) chloride solution
  b. the osmotic pressure of a 0.085 M potassium sulfate solution at 298 K
  c. the boiling point of a 1.22% by mass magnesium chloride solution

88. Assuming the van't Hoff factors in Table 12.9, calculate the mass of solute required to make each aqueous solution:
  a. a sodium chloride solution containing 1.50×10^2 g of water that has a melting point of −1.0 °C.
  b. 2.50×10^2 mL of a magnesium sulfate solution that has an osmotic pressure of 3.82 atm at 298 K
  c. an iron(III) chloride solution containing 2.50×10^2 g of water that has a boiling point of 102 °C

89. A 0.100 M ionic solution has an osmotic pressure of 8.3 atm at 25 °C. Calculate the van't Hoff factor (*i*) for this solution.

90. A solution contains 8.92 g of KBr in 500.0 mL of solution and has an osmotic pressure of 6.97 atm at 25 °C. Calculate the van't Hoff factor (*i*) for KBr at this concentration.

91. Calculate the vapor pressure at 25 °C of an aqueous solution that is 5.50% NaCl by mass. (Assume complete dissociation of the solute.)

92. An aqueous $CaCl_2$ solution has a vapor pressure of 81.6 mmHg at 50 °C. The vapor pressure of pure water at this temperature is 92.6 mmHg. What is the concentration of $CaCl_2$ in mass percent? (Assume complete dissociation of the solute.)

Cumulative Problems

93. The solubility of carbon tetrachloride (CCl_4) in water at 25 °C is 1.2 g/L. The solubility of chloroform ($CHCl_3$) at the same temperature is 10.1 g/L. Why is chloroform almost 10 times more soluble in water than is carbon tetrachloride?

94. The solubility of phenol in water at 25 °C is 8.7 g/L. The solubility of naphthol at the same temperature is only 0.074 g/L. Examine the structures of phenol and napthol and explain why phenol is so much more soluble than naphthol.

Phenol   Naphthol

95. Potassium perchlorate ($KClO_4$) has a lattice energy of −599 kJ/mol and a heat of hydration of −548 kJ/mol. Find the heat of solution for potassium perchlorate and determine the temperature change that occurs when 10.0 g of potassium perchlorate is dissolved with enough water to make 100.0 mL of solution. (Assume a heat capacity of 4.05 J/g · °C for the solution and a density of 1.05 g/mL.)

96. Sodium hydroxide (NaOH) has a lattice energy of −887 kJ/mol and a heat of hydration of −932 kJ/mol. How much solution could be heated to boiling by the heat evolved by the dissolution of 25.0 g of NaOH? (For the solution, assume a heat capacity of 4.0 J/g · °C, an initial temperature of 25.0 °C, a boiling point of 100.0 °C, and a density of 1.05 g/mL.)

97. A saturated solution forms when 0.0537 L of argon, at a pressure of 1.0 atm and temperature of 25 °C, is dissolved in 1.0 L of water. Calculate the Henry's law constant for argon.

98. A gas has a Henry's law constant of 0.112 M/atm. What total volume of solution is needed to completely dissolve 1.65 L of the gas at a pressure of 725 torr and a temperature of 25 °C?

99. The Safe Drinking Water Act (SDWA) sets a limit for mercury—a toxin to the central nervous system—at 0.0020 ppm by mass. Water suppliers must periodically test their water to ensure that mercury levels do not exceed this limit. Suppose water becomes contaminated with mercury at twice the legal limit (0.0040 ppm). How much of this water would have to be consumed for someone to ingest 50.0 mg of mercury?

100. Water softeners often replace calcium ions in hard water with sodium ions. Since sodium compounds are soluble, the presence of sodium ions in water does not cause the white, scaly residues caused by calcium ions. However, calcium is more beneficial to human health than sodium because calcium is a necessary part of the human diet, while high levels of sodium intake are linked to increases in blood pressure. The U.S. Food and Drug Administration (FDA) recommends that adults ingest less than 2.4 g of sodium per day. How many liters of softened water, containing a sodium concentration of 0.050% sodium by mass, have to be consumed to exceed the FDA recommendation? (Assume a water density of 1.0 g/mL.)

101. An aqueous solution contains 12.5% NaCl by mass. What mass of water (in grams) is contained in 2.5 L of the vapor above this solution at 55 °C? The vapor pressure of pure water at 55 °C is 118 torr. (Assume complete dissociation of NaCl.)

102. The vapor above an aqueous solution contains 19.5 mg water per liter at 25 °C. Assuming ideal behavior, what is the concentration of the solute within the solution in mole percent?

103. What is the freezing point of an aqueous solution that boils at 106.5 °C?

104. What is the boiling point of an aqueous solution that has a vapor pressure of 20.5 torr at 25 °C? (Assume a nonvolatile solute.)

105. An isotonic solution contains 0.90% NaCl mass to volume. Calculate the percent mass to volume for isotonic solutions containing each solute at 25 °C. Assume a van't Hoff factor of 1.9 for all *ionic* solutes.
    a. KCl   **b.** NaBr   **c.** Glucose ($C_6H_{12}O_6$)

106. Magnesium citrate, $Mg_3(C_6H_5O_7)_2$ belongs to a class of laxatives called *hyperosmotics*, which cause rapid emptying of the bowel. When a concentrated solution of magnesium citrate is consumed, it passes through the intestines, drawing water and promoting diarrhea, usually within 6 hours. Calculate the osmotic pressure of a magnesium citrate laxative solution containing 28.5 g of magnesium citrate in 235 mL of solution at 37 °C (approximate body temperature). Assume complete dissociation of the ionic compound.

107. A solution is prepared from 4.5701 g of magnesium chloride and 43.238 g of water. The vapor pressure of water above this solution is found to be 0.3624 atm at 348.0 K. The vapor pressure of pure water at this temperature is 0.3804 atm. Find the value of the van't Hoff factor *i* for magnesium chloride in this solution.

108. When HNO_2 is dissolved in water it partially dissociates according to the equation $HNO_2 \rightleftharpoons H^+ + NO_2^-$. A solution is prepared that contains 7.050 g of HNO_2 in 1.000 kg of water. Its freezing point is found to be −0.2929 °C. Calculate the fraction of HNO_2 that has dissociated.

109. A solution of a nonvolatile solute in water has a boiling point of 375.3 K. Calculate the vapor pressure of water above this solution at 338 K. The vapor pressure of pure water at this temperature is 0.2467 atm.

110. The density of a 0.438 M solution of potassium chromate (K_2CrO_4) at 298 K is 1.063 g/mL. Calculate the vapor pressure of water above the solution. The vapor pressure of pure water at this temperature is 0.0313 atm. Assume complete dissociation of the solute.

111. The vapor pressure of carbon tetrachloride, CCl_4, is 0.354 atm and the vapor pressure of chloroform, $CHCl_3$, is 0.526 atm at 316 K. A solution is prepared from equal masses of these two compounds at this temperature. Calculate the mole fraction of the chloroform in the vapor above the solution. If the vapor above the original solution is condensed and isolated into a separate flask, what would the vapor pressure of chloroform be above this new solution?

112. Distillation is a method of purification based on successive separations and recondensations of vapor above a solution. Use the result of the previous problem to calculate the mole fraction of chloroform in the vapor above a solution obtained by three successive separations and condensations of the vapors above the original solution of carbon tetrachloride and chloroform. Show how this result explains the use of distillation as a separation method.

113. A solution of 49.0% H_2SO_4 by mass has a density of 1.39 g/cm^3 at 293 K. A 25.0-cm^3 sample of this solution is mixed with enough water to increase the volume of the solution to 99.8 cm^3. Find the molarity of sulfuric acid in this solution.

114. Find the mass of urea (CH_4N_2O) needed to prepare 50.0 g of a solution in water in which the mole fraction of urea is 0.0770.

115. A solution contains 10.05 g of unknown compound dissolved in 50.0 mL of water. (Assume a density of 1.00 g/mL for water.) The freezing point of the solution is −3.16 °C. The mass percent composition of the compound is 60.97% C, 11.94% H, and the rest is O. What is the molecular formula of the compound?

116. The osmotic pressure of a solution containing 2.10 g of an unknown compound dissolved in 175.0 mL of solution at 25 °C is 1.93 atm. The combustion of 24.02 g of the unknown compound produced 28.16 g CO_2 and 8.64 g H_2O. What is the molecular formula of the compound (which contains only carbon, hydrogen, and oxygen)?

117. A 100.0-mL aqueous sodium chloride solution is 13.5% NaCl by mass and has a density of 1.12 g/mL. What would you add (solute or solvent) and what mass of it to make the boiling point of the solution 104.4 °C? (Use $i = 1.8$ for NaCl)

118. A 50.0-mL solution is initially 1.55% $MgCl_2$ by mass and has a density of 1.05 g/mL. What is the freezing point of the solution after you add an additional 1.35 g $MgCl_2$? (Use $i = 2.5$ for $MgCl_2$.)

Challenge Problems

119. The small bubbles that form on the bottom of a water pot that is being heated (before boiling) are due to dissolved air coming out of solution. Use Henry's law and the solubilities given below to calculate the total volume of nitrogen and oxygen gas that should bubble out of 1.5 L of water upon warming from 25 °C to 50 °C. Assume that the water is initially saturated with nitrogen and oxygen gas at 25 °C and a total pressure of 1.0 atm. Assume that the gas bubbles out at a temperature of 50 °C. The solubility of oxygen gas at 50 °C is 27.8 mg/L at an oxygen pressure of 1.00 atm. The solubility of nitrogen gas at 50 °C is 14.6 mg/L at a nitrogen pressure of 1.00 atm. Assume that the air above the water contains an oxygen partial pressure of 0.21 atm and a nitrogen partial pressure of 0.78 atm.

120. The vapor above a mixture of pentane and hexane at room temperature contains 35.5% pentane by mass. What is the mass percent composition of the solution? Pure pentane and hexane have vapor pressures of 425 torr and 151 torr, respectively, at room temperature.

121. A 1.10-g sample contains only glucose ($C_6H_{12}O_6$) and sucrose ($C_{12}H_{22}O_{11}$). When the sample is dissolved in water to a total solution volume of 25.0 mL, the osmotic pressure of the solution is 3.78 atm at 298 K. What is the mass percent composition of glucose and sucrose in the sample?

122. A solution is prepared by mixing 631 mL of methanol with 501 mL of water. The molarity of methanol in the resulting solution is 14.29 M. The density of methanol at this temperature is 0.792 g/mL. Calculate the difference in volume between this solution and the total volume of water and methanol that were mixed to prepare the solution.

123. Two alcohols, isopropyl alcohol and propyl alcohol, have the same molecular formula, C_3H_8O. A solution of the two that is two-thirds by mass isopropyl alcohol has a vapor pressure of 0.110 atm at 313 K. A solution that is one-third by mass isopropyl alcohol has a vapor pressure of 0.089 atm at 313 K. Calculate the vapor pressure of each pure alcohol at this temperature. Explain the difference given that the formula of propyl alcohol is $CH_3CH_2CH_2OH$ and that of isopropyl alcohol is $(CH_3)_2CHOH$.

124. A metal, M, of atomic mass 96 amu reacts with fluorine to form a salt that can be represented as MF_x. In order to determine x and therefore the formula of the salt, a boiling point elevation experiment is performed. A 9.18-g sample of the salt is dissolved in 100.0 g of water and the boiling point of the solution is found to be 374.38 K. Find the formula of the salt. Assume complete dissociation of the salt in solution.

125. Sulfuric acid in water dissociates completely into H^+ and HSO_4^- ions. The HSO_4^- ion dissociates to a limited extent into H^+ and SO_4^{2-}. The freezing point of a 0.1000 m solution of sulfuric acid in water is 272.76 K. Calculate the molality of SO_4^{2-} in the solution, assuming ideal solution behavior.

126. A solution of 75.0 g of benzene (C_6H_6) and 75.0 g of toluene (C_7H_8) has a total vapor pressure of 80.9 mmHg at 303 K. Another solution of 100.0 g benzene and 50.0 g toluene has a total vapor pressure of 93.9 mmHg at this temperature. Find the vapor pressure of pure benzene and pure toluene at 303 K.

127. A solution is prepared by dissolving 11.60 g of a mixture of sodium carbonate and sodium bicarbonate in 1.00 L of water. A 300.0-cm^3 sample of the solution is then treated with excess HNO_3 and boiled to remove all the dissolved gas. A total of 0.940 L of dry CO_2 is collected at 298 K and 0.972 atm. Find the molarity of the carbonate and bicarbonate in the solution.

Conceptual Problems

128. Substance A is a nonpolar liquid and has only dispersion forces among its constituent particles. Substance B is also a nonpolar liquid and has about the same magnitude of dispersion forces among its constituent particles. When substance A and B are combined, they spontaneously mix.
  a. Why do the two substances mix?
  b. Predict the sign and magnitude of ΔH_{soln}.
  c. Give the signs and relative magnitudes of ΔH_{solute}, $\Delta H_{solvent}$, and ΔH_{mix}.

129. A power plant built on a river uses river water as a coolant. The water is warmed as it is used in heat exchangers within the plant. Should the warm water be immediately cycled back into the river? Why or why not?

130. The vapor pressure of a 1 M ionic solution is different from the vapor pressure of a 1 M nonelectrolyte solution. In both cases, the solute is nonvolatile. Which set of diagrams best represents the differences between the two solutions and their vapors?

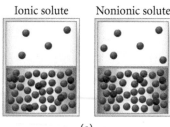

Solvent particles
Solute particles

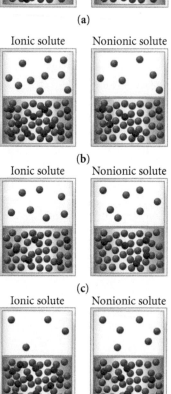

(a)

(b)

(c)

(d)

131. If each substance costs the same amount per kilogram, which would be most cost-effective as a way to lower the freezing point of water? (Assume complete dissociation for all ionic compounds.) Explain.
  a. $HOCH_2CH_2OH$ **b.** $NaCl$
  c. KCl **d.** $MgCl_2$
  e. $SrCl_2$

132. A helium balloon inflated on one day will fall to the ground by the next day. The volume of the balloon decreases somewhat overnight, but not by enough to explain why it no longer floats. (If you inflate a new balloon with helium to the same size as the balloon that fell to the ground, the newly inflated balloon floats.) Explain.

Appendix I:

Common Mathematical Operations in Chemistry

A. Scientific Notation

A number written in scientific notation consists of a **decimal part**, a number that is usually between 1 and 10, and an **exponential part**, 10 raised to an **exponent**, n.

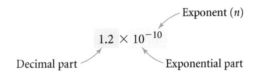

Each of the following numbers is written in both scientific and decimal notation.

$$1.0 \times 10^5 = 100,000 \qquad 1.0 \times 10^{-5} = 0.000001$$
$$6.7 \times 10^3 = 6700 \qquad 6.7 \times 10^{-3} = 0.0067$$

A positive exponent means 1 multiplied by 10 n times.

$$10^0 = 1$$
$$10^1 = 1 \times 10$$
$$10^2 = 1 \times 10 \times 10 = 100$$
$$10^3 = 1 \times 10 \times 10 \times 10 = 1000$$

A negative exponent $(-n)$ means 1 divided by 10 n times.

$$10^{-1} = \frac{1}{10} = 0.1$$

$$10^{-2} = \frac{1}{10 \times 10} = 0.01$$

$$10^{-3} = \frac{1}{10 \times 10 \times 10} = 0.001$$

To convert a number to scientific notation, we move the decimal point to obtain a number between 1 and 10 and then multiply by 10 raised to the appropriate power. For example, to write 5983 in scientific notation, we move the decimal point to the left three places to get 5.983 (a number between 1 and 10) and then multiply by 1000 to make up for moving the decimal point.

$$5983 = 5.983 \times 1000$$

Since 1000 is 10^3, we write

$$5983 = 5.983 \times 10^3$$

We can do this in one step by counting how many places we move the decimal point to obtain a number between 1 and 10 and then writing the decimal part multiplied by 10 raised to the number of places we moved the decimal point.

$$5983 = 5.983 \times 10^3$$

If the decimal point is moved to the left, as in the previous example, the exponent is positive. If the decimal is moved to the right, the exponent is negative.

$$0.00034 = 3.4 \times 10^{-4}$$

To express a number in scientific notation:

1. **Move the decimal point to obtain a number between 1 and 10.**
2. **Write the result from step 1 multiplied by 10 raised to the number of places you moved the decimal point.**
   - *The exponent is positive if you moved the decimal point to the left.*
   - *The exponent is negative if you moved the decimal point to the right.*

Consider the following additional examples:

$$290{,}809{,}000 \quad\quad = 2.90809 \times 10^8$$
$$0.000000000070 \text{ m} = 7.0 \times 10^{-11} \text{ m}$$

Multiplication and Division

To multiply numbers expressed in scientific notation, multiply the decimal parts and add the exponents.

$$(A \times 10^m)(B \times 10^n) = (A \times B) \times 10^{m+n}$$

To divide numbers expressed in scientific notation, divide the decimal parts and subtract the exponent in the denominator from the exponent in the numerator.

$$\frac{(A \times 10^m)}{(B \times 10^n)} = \left(\frac{A}{B}\right) \times 10^{m-n}$$

Consider the following example involving multiplication:

$$(3.5 \times 10^4)(1.8 \times 10^6) = (3.5 \times 1.8) \times 10^{4+6}$$
$$= 6.3 \times 10^{10}$$

Consider the following example involving division:

$$\frac{(5.6 \times 10^7)}{(1.4 \times 10^3)} = \left(\frac{5.6}{1.4}\right) \times 10^{7-3}$$
$$= 4.0 \times 10^4$$

Addition and Subtraction

To add or subtract numbers expressed in scientific notation, rewrite all the numbers so that they have the same exponent, then add or subtract the decimal parts of the numbers. The exponents remained unchanged.

$$
\begin{array}{r}
A \times 10^n \\
\pm B \times 10^n \\
\hline
(A \pm B) \times 10^n
\end{array}
$$

Notice that the numbers *must have* the same exponent. Consider the following example involving addition:

$$
\begin{array}{r}
4.82 \times 10^7 \\
+3.4 \times 10^6 \\
\hline
\end{array}
$$

First, express both numbers with the same exponent. In this case, we rewrite the lower number and perform the addition as follows:

$$
\begin{array}{r}
4.82 \times 10^7 \\
+0.34 \times 10^7 \\
\hline
5.16 \times 10^7
\end{array}
$$

Consider the following example involving subtraction.

$$
\begin{array}{r}
7.33 \times 10^5 \\
-1.9 \times 10^4 \\
\hline
\end{array}
$$

First, express both numbers with the same exponent. In this case, we rewrite the lower number and perform the subtraction as follows:

$$
\begin{array}{r}
7.33 \times 10^5 \\
-0.19 \times 10^5 \\
\hline
7.14 \times 10^5
\end{array}
$$

Powers and Roots

To raise a number written in scientific notation to a power, raise the decimal part to the power and multiply the exponent by the power:

$$
\begin{aligned}
(4.0 \times 10^6)^2 &= 4.0^2 \times 10^{6 \times 2} \\
&= 16 \times 10^{12} \\
&= 16 \times 10^{13}
\end{aligned}
$$

To take the nth root of a number written in scientific notation, take the nth root of the decimal part and divide the exponent by the root:

$$
\begin{aligned}
(4.0 \times 10^6)^{1/3} &= 4.0^{1/3} \times 10^{6/3} \\
&= 1.6 \times 10^2
\end{aligned}
$$

B. Logarithms

Common (or Base 10) Logarithms

The common or base 10 logarithm (abbreviated log) of a number is the exponent to which 10 must be raised to obtain that number. For example, the log of 100 is 2 because 10 must be raised to the second power to get 100. Similarly, the log of 1000 is 3 because 10 must be raised to the third power to get 1000. The logs of several multiples of 10 are shown below.

$$
\begin{aligned}
\log 10 &= 1 \\
\log 100 &= 2 \\
\log 1000 &= 3 \\
\log 10{,}000 &= 4
\end{aligned}
$$

Because $10^0 = 1$ by definition, $\log 1 = 0$.

The log of a number smaller than one is negative because 10 must be raised to a negative exponent to get a number smaller than one. For example, the log of 0.01 is -2 because 10 must be raised to -2 to get 0.01. Similarly, the log of 0.001 is -3 because 10 must be raised to -3 to get 0.001. The logs of several fractional numbers are shown below.

$$
\begin{aligned}
\log 0.1 &= -1 \\
\log 0.01 &= -2 \\
\log 0.001 &= -3 \\
\log 0.0001 &= -4
\end{aligned}
$$

The logs of numbers that are not multiples of 10 can be computed on your calculator. See your calculator manual for specific instructions.

Inverse Logarithms

The inverse logarithm or invlog function is exactly the opposite of the log function. For example, the log of 100 is 2 and the inverse log of 2 is 100. The log function and the invlog function undo one another.

$$
\begin{aligned}
\log 100 &= 2 \\
\text{invlog } 2 &= 100 \\
\text{invlog}(\log 100) &= 100
\end{aligned}
$$

The inverse log of a number is simply 10 rasied to that number.

$$\text{invlog } x = 10^x$$
$$\text{invlog } 3 = 10^3 = 1000$$

The inverse logs of numbers can be computed on your calculator. See your calculator manual for specific instructions.

Natural (or Base *e*) Logarithms

The natural (or base *e*) logarithm (abbreviated ln) of a number is the exponent to which *e* (which has the value of 2.71828...) must be raised to obtain that number. For example, the ln of 100 is 4.605 because *e* must be raised to 4.605 to get 100. Similarly, the ln of 10.0 is 2.303 because *e* must be raised to 2.303 to get 10.0.

    The inverse natural logarithm or invln function is exactly the opposite of the ln function. For example, the ln of 100 is 4.605 and the inverse ln of 4.605 is 100. The inverse ln of a number is simply *e* raised to that number.

$$\text{invln } x = e^x$$
$$\text{invln } 3 = e^3 = 20.1$$

The invln of a number can be computed on your calculator. See your calculator manual for specific instructions.

Mathematical Operations Using Logarithms

Because logarithms are exponents, mathematical operations involving logarithms are similar to those involving exponents as follows:

$$\log(a \times b) = \log a + \log b \qquad \ln(a \times b) = \ln a + \ln b$$

$$\log\frac{a}{b} = \log a - \log b \qquad \ln\frac{a}{b} = \ln a - \ln b$$

$$\log a^n = n \log a \qquad \ln a^n = n \ln a$$

C. Quadratic Equations

A quadratic equation contains at least one term in which the variable x is raised to the second power (and no terms in which x is raised to a higher power). A quadratic equation has the following general form:

$$ax^2 + bx + c = 0$$

A quadratic equation can be solved for x using the quadratic formula:

$$x = \frac{-b \pm \sqrt{b^2 - 4ac}}{2a}$$

Quadratic equations are often encountered when solving equilibrium problems. Below we show how to use the quadratic formula to solve a quadratic equation for x.

$$3x^2 - 5x + 1 = 0 \quad (quadratic\ equation)$$

$$x = \frac{-b \pm \sqrt{b^2 - 4ac}}{2a}$$

$$= \frac{-(-5) \pm \sqrt{(-5)^2 - 4(3)(1)}}{2(3)}$$

$$= \frac{5 \pm 3.6}{6}$$

$$x = 1.43 \quad \text{or} \quad x = 0.233$$

As you can see, the solution to a quadratic equation usually has two values. In any real chemical system, one of the values can be eliminated because it has no physical significance. (For example, it may correspond to a negative concentration, which does not exist.)

D. Graphs

Graphs are often used to visually show the relationship between two variables. For example, in Chapter 5 we show the following relationship between the volume of a gas and its pressure:

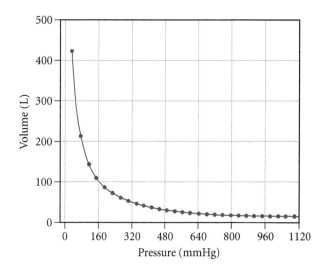

Volume versus Pressure   A plot of the volume of a gas sample—as measured in a J-tube—versus pressure. The plot shows that volume and pressure are inversely related.

The horizontal axis is the x-axis and is normally used to show the independent variable. The vertical axis is the y-axis and is normally used to show how the other variable (called the dependent variable) varies with a change in the independent variable. In this case, the graph shows that as the pressure of a gas sample increases, its volume decreases.

Many relationships in chemistry are *linear*, which means that if you change one variable by a factor of n the other variable will also change by a factor of n. For example, the volume of a gas is linearly related to the number of moles of gas. When two quantities are linearly related, a graph of one versus the other produces a straight line. For example, the graph below shows how the volume of an ideal gas sample depends on the number of moles of gas in the sample:

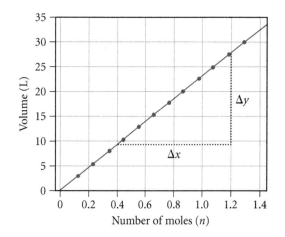

Volume versus Number of Moles
The volume of a gas sample increases linearly with the number of moles of gas in the sample.

A linear relationship between any two variables x and y can be expressed by the following equation:

$$y = mx + b$$

where m is the slope of the line and b is the y-intercept. The slope is the change in y divided by the change in x.

$$m = \frac{\Delta y}{\Delta x}$$

For the graph above, we can estimate the slope by simply estimating the changes in y and x for a given interval. For example, between $x = 0.4\,\text{mol}$ and $1.2\,\text{mol}$, $\Delta x = 0.80\,\text{mol}$ and we can estimate that $\Delta y = 18\,\text{L}$. Therefore the slope is

$$m = \frac{\Delta y}{\Delta x} = \frac{18\,\text{L}}{0.80\,\text{mol}} = 23\,\text{mol/L}$$

In several places in this book, logarithmic relationships between variables can be plotted in order to obtain a linear relationship. For example, the variables $[A]_t$ and t in the following equation are not linearly related, but the natural logarithm of $[A]_t$ and t are linearly related.

$$\ln[A]_t = -kt + \ln[A]_0$$
$$y = mx + b$$

A plot of $\ln[A]_t$ versus t will therefore produce a straight line with slope $= -k$ and y-intercept $= \ln[A]_0$.

Appendix II:
Useful Data

A. Atomic Colors

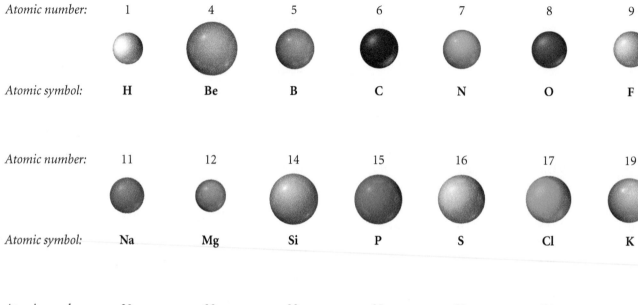

Atomic number:	1	4	5	6	7	8	9
Atomic symbol:	H	Be	B	C	N	O	F

Atomic number:	11	12	14	15	16	17	19
Atomic symbol:	Na	Mg	Si	P	S	Cl	K

Atomic number:	20	29	30	35	53	54
Atomic symbol:	Ca	Cu	Zn	Br	I	Xe

B. Standard Thermodynamic Quantities for Selected Substances at 25 °C

Substance	ΔH_f° (kJ/mol)	ΔG_f° (kJ/mol)	S° (J/mol · K)	Substance	ΔH_f° (kJ/mol)	ΔG_f° (kJ/mol)	S° (J/mol · K)
Aluminum				**Beryllium**			
Al(s)	0	0	28.32	Be(s)	0	0	9.5
Al(g)	330.0	289.4	164.6	BeO(s)	−609.4	−580.1	13.8
Al³⁺(aq)	−538.4	−483	−325	Be(OH)₂(s)	−902.5	−815.0	45.5
AlCl₃(s)	−704.2	−628.8	109.3	**Bismuth**			
Al₂O₃(s)	−1675.7	−1582.3	50.9	Bi(s)	0	0	56.7
Barium				BiCl₃(s)	−379.1	−315.0	177.0
Ba(s)	0	0	62.5	Bi₂O₃(s)	−573.9	−493.7	151.5
Ba(g)	180.0	146.0	170.2	Bi₂S₃(s)	−143.1	−140.6	200.4
Ba²⁺(aq)	−537.6	−560.8	9.6	**Boron**			
BaCO₃(s)	−1213.0	−1134.4	112.1	B(s)	0	0	5.9
BaCl₂(s)	−855.0	−806.7	123.7	B(g)	565.0	521.0	153.4
BaO(s)	−548.0	−520.3	72.1	BCl₃(g)	−403.8	−388.7	290.1
Ba(OH)₂(s)	−944.7			BF₃(g)	−1136.0	−1119.4	254.4
BaSO₄(s)	−1473.2	−1362.2	132.2				

(continued on the next page)

Substance	ΔH_f° (kJ/mol)	ΔG_f° (kJ/mol)	S° (J/mol · K)
$B_2H_6(g)$	36.4	87.6	232.1
$B_2O_3(s)$	−1273.5	−1194.3	54.0
$H_3BO_3(s)$	−1094.3	−968.9	90.0
Bromine			
$Br(g)$	111.9	82.4	175.0
$Br_2(l)$	0	0	152.2
$Br_2(g)$	30.9	3.1	245.5
$Br^-(aq)$	−121.4	−102.8	80.71
$HBr(g)$	−36.3	−53.4	198.7
Cadmium			
$Cd(s)$	0	0	51.8
$Cd(g)$	111.8	77.3	167.7
$Cd^{2+}(aq)$	−75.9	−77.6	−73.2
$CdCl_2(s)$	−391.5	−343.9	115.3
$CdO(s)$	−258.4	−228.7	54.8
$CdS(s)$	−161.9	−156.5	64.9
$CdSO_4(s)$	−933.3	−822.7	123.0
Calcium			
$Ca(s)$	0	0	41.6
$Ca(g)$	177.8	144.0	154.9
$Ca^{2+}(aq)$	−542.8	−553.6	−53.1
$CaC_2(s)$	−59.8	−64.9	70.0
$CaCO_3(s)$	−1207.6	−1129.1	91.7
$CaCl_2(s)$	−795.4	−748.8	108.4
$CaF_2(s)$	−1228.0	−1175.6	68.5
$CaH_2(s)$	−181.5	−142.5	41.4
$Ca(NO_3)_2(s)$	−938.2	−742.8	193.2
$CaO(s)$	−634.9	−603.3	38.1
$Ca(OH)_2(s)$	−985.2	−897.5	83.4
$CaSO_4(s)$	−1434.5	−1322.0	106.5
$Ca_3(PO_4)_2(s)$	−4120.8	−3884.7	236.0
Carbon			
$C(s, graphite)$	0	0	5.7
$C(s, diamond)$	1.88	2.9	2.4
$C(g)$	716.7	671.3	158.1
$CH_4(g)$	−74.6	−50.5	186.3
$CH_3Cl(g)$	−81.9	−60.2	234.6
$CH_2Cl_2(g)$	−95.4		270.2
$CH_2Cl_2(l)$	−124.2	−63.2	177.8
$CHCl_3(l)$	−134.1	−73.7	201.7
$CCl_4(g)$	−95.7	−62.3	309.7
$CCl_4(l)$	−128.2	−66.4	216.4
$CH_2O(g)$	−108.6	−102.5	218.8
CH_2O_2 (l, formic acid)	−425.0	−361.4	129.0
CH_3NH_2 (g, methylamine)	−22.5	32.7	242.9
$CH_3OH(l)$	−238.6	−166.6	126.8
$CH_3OH(g)$	−201.0	−162.3	239.9
$C_2H_2(g)$	227.4	209.9	200.9
$C_2H_4(g)$	52.4	68.4	219.3
$C_2H_6(g)$	−84.68	−32.0	229.2

Substance	ΔH_f° (kJ/mol)	ΔG_f° (kJ/mol)	S° (J/mol · K)
$C_2H_5OH(l)$	−277.6	−174.8	160.7
$C_2H_5OH(g)$	−234.8	−167.9	281.6
C_2H_3Cl (g, vinyl chloride)	37.2	53.6	264.0
$C_2H_4Cl_2$ (l, dichloroethane)	−166.8	−79.6	208.5
C_2H_4O (g, acetaldehyde	−166.2	−133.0	263.8
$C_2H_4O_2$ (l, acetic acid)	−484.3	−389.9	159.8
$C_3H_8(g)$	−103.85	−23.4	270.3
C_3H_6O (l, acetone)	−248.4	−155.6	199.8
C_3H_7OH (l, isopropanol)	−318.1		181.1
$C_4H_{10}(l)$	−147.3	−15.0	231.0
$C_4H_{10}(g)$	−125.7	−15.71	310.0
$C_6H_6(l)$	49.1	124.5	173.4
$C_6H_5NH_2$ (l, aniline)	31.6	149.2	191.9
C_6H_5OH (s, phenol)	−165.1	−50.4	144.0
$C_6H_{12}O_6$ (s, glucose)	−1273.3	−910.4	212.1
$C_{10}H_8$ (s, naphthalene)	78.5	201.6	167.4
$C_{12}H_{22}O_{11}$ (s, sucrose)	−2226.1	−1544.3	360.24
$CO(g)$	−110.5	−137.2	197.7
$CO_2(g)$	−393.5	−394.4	213.8
$CO_2(aq)$	−413.8	−386.0	117.6
$CO_3^{2-}(aq)$	−677.1	−527.8	−56.9
$HCO_3^-(aq)$	−692.0	−586.8	91.2
$H_2CO_3(aq)$	−699.7	−623.2	187.4
$CN^-(aq)$	151	166	118
$HCN(l)$	108.9	125.0	112.8
$HCN(g)$	135.1	124.7	201.8
$CS_2(l)$	89.0	64.6	151.3
$CS_2(g)$	116.7	67.1	237.8
$COCl_2(g)$	−219.1	−204.9	283.5
$C_{60}(s)$	2327.0	2302.0	426.0
Cesium			
$Cs(s)$	0	0	85.2
$Cs(g)$	76.5	49.6	175.6
$Cs^+(aq)$	−258.0	−292.0	132.1
$CsBr(s)$	−400	−387	117
$CsCl(s)$	−438	−414	101.2
$CsF(s)$	−553.5	−525.5	92.8
$CsI(s)$	−342	−337	127
Chlorine			
$Cl(g)$	121.3	105.3	165.2
$Cl_2(g)$	0	0	223.1
$Cl^-(aq)$	−167.1	−131.2	56.6
$HCl(g)$	−92.3	−95.3	186.9
$HCl(aq)$	−167.2	−131.2	56.5

Substance	ΔH_f° (kJ/mol)	ΔG_f° (kJ/mol)	S° (J/mol · K)
$ClO_2(g)$	102.5	120.5	256.8
$Cl_2O(g)$	80.3	97.9	266.2
Chromium			
$Cr(s)$	0	0	23.8
$Cr(g)$	396.6	351.8	174.5
$Cr^{3+}(aq)$	−1971		
$CrO_4^{2-}(aq)$	−872.2	−717.1	44
$Cr_2O_3(s)$	−1139.7	−1058.1	81.2
$Cr_2O_7^{2-}(aq)$	−1476	−1279	238
Cobalt			
$Co(s)$	0	0	30.0
$Co(g)$	424.7	380.3	179.5
$CoO(s)$	−237.9	−214.2	53.0
$Co(OH)_2(s)$	−539.7	−454.3	79.0
Copper			
$Cu(s)$	0	0	33.2
$Cu(g)$	337.4	297.7	166.4
$Cu^+(aq)$	51.9	50.2	−26
$Cu^{2+}(aq)$	64.9	65.5	−98
$CuCl(s)$	−137.2	−119.9	86.2
$CuCl_2(s)$	−220.1	−175.7	108.1
$CuO(s)$	−157.3	−129.7	42.6
$CuS(s)$	−53.1	−53.6	66.5
$CuSO_4(s)$	−771.4	−662.2	109.2
$Cu_2O(s)$	−168.6	−146.0	93.1
$Cu_2S(s)$	−79.5	−86.2	120.9
Fluorine			
$F(g)$	79.38	62.3	158.75
$F_2(g)$	0	0	202.79
$F^-(aq)$	−335.35	−278.8	−13.8
$HF(g)$	−273.3	−275.4	173.8
Gold			
$Au(s)$	0	0	47.4
$Au(g)$	366.1	326.3	180.5
Helium			
$He(g)$	0	0	126.2
Hydrogen			
$H(g)$	218.0	203.3	114.7
$H^+(aq)$	0	0	0
$H^+(g)$	1536.3	1517.1	108.9
$H_2(g)$	0	0	130.7
Iodine			
$I(g)$	106.76	70.2	180.79
$I_2(s)$	0	0	116.14
$I_2(g)$	62.42	19.3	260.69
$I^-(aq)$	−56.78	−51.57	106.45
$HI(g)$	26.5	1.7	206.6
Iron			
$Fe(s)$	0	0	27.3
$Fe(g)$	416.3	370.7	180.5

Substance	ΔH_f° (kJ/mol)	ΔG_f° (kJ/mol)	S° (J/mol · K)
$Fe^{2+}(aq)$	−87.9	−84.94	113.4
$Fe^{3+}(aq)$	−47.69	−10.54	293.3
$FeCO_3(s)$	−740.6	−666.7	92.9
$FeCl_2(s)$	−341.8	−302.3	118.0
$FeCl_3(s)$	−399.5	−334.0	142.3
$FeO(s)$	−272.0	−255.2	60.75
$Fe(OH)_3(s)$	−823.0	−696.5	106.7
$FeS_2(s)$	−178.2	−166.9	52.9
$Fe_2O_3(s)$	−824.2	−742.2	87.4
$Fe_3O_4(s)$	−1118.4	−1015.4	146.4
Lead			
$Pb(s)$	0	0	64.8
$Pb(g)$	195.2	162.2	175.4
$Pb^{2+}(aq)$	0.92	−24.4	18.5
$PbBr_2(s)$	−278.7	−261.9	161.5
$PbCO_3(s)$	−699.1	−625.5	131.0
$PbCl_2(s)$	−359.4	−314.1	136.0
$PbI_2(s)$	−175.5	−173.6	174.9
$Pb(NO_3)_2(s)$	−451.9		
$PbO(s)$	−217.3	−187.9	68.7
$PbO_2(s)$	−277.4	−217.3	68.6
$PbS(s)$	−100.4	−98.7	91.2
$PbSO_4(s)$	−920.0	−813.0	148.5
Lithium			
$Li(s)$	0	0	29.1
$Li(g)$	159.3	126.6	138.8
$Li^+(aq)$	−278.47	−293.3	12.24
$LiBr(s)$	−351.2	−342.0	74.3
$LiCl(s)$	−408.6	−384.4	59.3
$LiF(s)$	−616.0	−587.7	35.7
$LiI(s)$	−270.4	−270.3	86.8
$LiNO_3(s)$	−483.1	−381.1	90.0
$LiOH(s)$	−487.5	−441.5	42.8
$Li_2O(s)$	−597.9	−561.2	37.6
Magnesium			
$Mg(s)$	0	0	32.7
$Mg(g)$	147.1	112.5	148.6
$Mg^{2+}(aq)$	−467.0	−455.4	−137
$MgCl_2(s)$	−641.3	−591.8	89.6
$MgCO_3(s)$	−1095.8	−1012.1	65.7
$MgF_2(s)$	−1124.2	−1071.1	57.2
$MgO(s)$	−601.6	−569.3	27.0
$Mg(OH)_2(s)$	−924.5	−833.5	63.2
$MgSO_4(s)$	−1284.9	−1170.6	91.6
$Mg_3N_2(s)$	−461	−401	88
Manganese			
$Mn(s)$	0	0	32.0
$Mn(g)$	280.7	238.5	173.7
$Mn^{2+}(aq)$	−219.4	−225.6	−78.8
$MnO(s)$	−385.2	−362.9	59.7

(continued on the next page)

Substance	ΔH_f° (kJ/mol)	ΔG_f° (kJ/mol)	S° (J/mol · K)	Substance	ΔH_f° (kJ/mol)	ΔG_f° (kJ/mol)	S° (J/mol · K)
$MnO_2(s)$	−520.0	−465.1	53.1	$H_2O(l)$	−285.8	−237.1	70.0
$MnO_4^-(aq)$	−529.9	−436.2	190.6	$H_2O(g)$	−241.8	−228.6	188.8
				$H_2O_2(l)$	−187.8	−120.4	109.6
Mercury				$H_2O_2(g)$	−136.3	−105.6	232.7
$Hg(l)$	0	0	75.9				
$Hg(g)$	61.4	31.8	175.0	**Phosphorus**			
$Hg^{2+}(aq)$	170.21	164.4	−36.19	$P(s, \text{white})$	0	0	41.1
$Hg_2^{2+}(aq)$	166.87	153.5	65.74	$P(s, \text{red})$	−17.6	−12.1	22.8
$HgCl_2(s)$	−224.3	−178.6	146.0	$P(g)$	316.5	280.1	163.2
$HgO(s)$	−90.8	−58.5	70.3	$P_2(g)$	144.0	103.5	218.1
$HgS(s)$	−58.2	−50.6	82.4	$P_4(g)$	58.9	24.4	280.0
$Hg_2Cl_2(s)$	−265.4	−210.7	191.6	$PCl_3(l)$	−319.7	−272.3	217.1
				$PCl_3(g)$	−287.0	−267.8	311.8
Nickel				$PCl_5(s)$	−443.5		
$Ni(s)$	0	0	29.9	$PCl_5(g)$	−374.9	−305.0	364.6
$Ni(g)$	429.7	384.5	182.2	$PF_5(g)$	−1594.4	−1520.7	300.8
$NiCl_2(s)$	−305.3	−259.0	97.7	$PH_3(g)$	5.4	13.5	210.2
$NiO(s)$	−239.7	−211.7	37.99	$POCl_3(l)$	−597.1	−520.8	222.5
$NiS(s)$	−82.0	−79.5	53.0	$POCl_3(g)$	−558.5	−512.9	325.5
				$PO_4^{3-}(aq)$	−1277.4	−1018.7	−220.5
Nitrogen				$HPO_4^{2-}(aq)$	−1292.1	−1089.2	−33.5
$N(g)$	472.7	455.5	153.3	$H_2PO_4^-(aq)$	−1296.3	−1130.2	90.4
$N_2(g)$	0	0	191.6	$H_3PO_4(s)$	−1284.4	−1124.3	110.5
$NF_3(g)$	−132.1	−90.6	260.8	$H_3PO_4(aq)$	−1288.3	−1142.6	158.2
$NH_3(g)$	−45.9	−16.4	192.8	$P_4O_6(s)$	−1640.1		
$NH_3(aq)$	−80.29	−26.50	111.3	$P_4O_{10}(s)$	−2984	−2698	228.9
$NH_4^+(aq)$	−133.26	−79.31	111.17				
$NH_4Br(s)$	−270.8	−175.2	113.0	**Platinum**			
$NH_4Cl(s)$	−314.4	−202.9	94.6	$Pt(s)$	0	0	41.6
$NH_4CN(s)$	0.4			$Pt(g)$	565.3	520.5	192.4
$NH_4F(s)$	−464.0	−348.7	72.0				
$NH_4HCO_3(s)$	−849.4	−665.9	120.9	**Potassium**			
$NH_4I(s)$	−201.4	−112.5	117.0	$K(s)$	0	0	64.7
$NH_4NO_3(s)$	−365.6	−183.9	151.1	$K(g)$	89.0	60.5	160.3
$NH_4NO_3(aq)$	−339.9	−190.6	259.8	$K^+(aq)$	−252.14	−283.3	101.2
$HNO_3(g)$	−133.9	−73.5	266.9	$KBr(s)$	−393.8	−380.7	95.9
$HNO_3(aq)$	−207	−110.9	146	$KCN(s)$	−113.0	−101.9	128.5
$NO(g)$	91.3	87.6	210.8	$KCl(s)$	−436.5	−408.5	82.6
$NO_2(g)$	33.2	51.3	240.1	$KClO_3(s)$	−397.7	−296.3	143.1
$NO_3^-(aq)$	−206.85	−110.2	146.70	$KClO_4(s)$	−432.8	−303.1	151.0
$NOBr(g)$	82.2	82.4	273.7	$KF(s)$	−567.3	−537.8	66.6
$NOCl(g)$	51.7	66.1	261.7	$KI(s)$	−327.9	−324.9	106.3
$N_2H_4(l)$	50.6	149.3	121.2	$KNO_3(s)$	−494.6	−394.9	133.1
$N_2H_4(g)$	95.4	159.4	238.5	$KOH(s)$	−424.6	−379.4	81.2
$N_2O(g)$	81.6	103.7	220.0	$KOH(aq)$	−482.4	−440.5	91.6
$N_2O_4(l)$	−19.5	97.5	209.2	$KO_2(s)$	−284.9	−239.4	116.7
$N_2O_4(g)$	9.16	99.8	304.4	$K_2CO_3(s)$	−1151.0	−1063.5	155.5
$N_2O_5(s)$	−43.1	113.9	178.2	$K_2O(s)$	−361.5	−322.1	94.14
$N_2O_5(g)$	13.3	117.1	355.7	$K_2O_2(s)$	−494.1	−425.1	102.1
				$K_2SO_4(s)$	−1437.8	−1321.4	175.6
Oxygen							
$O(g)$	249.2	231.7	161.1	**Rubidium**			
$O_2(g)$	0	0	205.2	$Rb(s)$	0	0	76.8
$O_3(g)$	142.7	163.2	238.9	$Rb(g)$	80.9	53.1	170.1
$OH^-(aq)$	−230.02	−157.3	−10.90	$Rb^+(aq)$	−251.12	−283.1	121.75

Substance	ΔH_f° (kJ/mol)	ΔG_f° (kJ/mol)	S° (J/mol · K)
RbBr(s)	−394.6	−381.8	110.0
RbCl(s)	−435.4	−407.8	95.9
RbClO$_3$(s)	−392.4	−292.0	152
RbF(s)	−557.7		
RbI(s)	−333.8	−328.9	118.4
Scandium			
Sc(s)	0	0	34.6
Sc(g)	377.8	336.0	174.8
Selenium			
Se(s, gray)	0	0	42.4
Se(g)	227.1	187.0	176.7
H$_2$Se(g)	29.7	15.9	219.0
Silicon			
Si(s)	0	0	18.8
Si(g)	450.0	405.5	168.0
SiCl$_4$(l)	−687.0	−619.8	239.7
SiF$_4$(g)	−1615.0	−1572.8	282.8
SiH$_4$(g)	34.3	56.9	204.6
SiO$_2$(s, quartz)	−910.7	−856.3	41.5
Si$_2$H$_6$(g)	80.3	127.3	272.7
Silver			
Ag(s)	0	0	42.6
Ag(g)	284.9	246.0	173.0
Ag$^+$(aq)	105.79	77.11	73.45
AgBr(s)	−100.4	−96.9	107.1
AgCl(s)	−127.0	−109.8	96.3
AgF(s)	−204.6	−185	84
AgI(s)	−61.8	−66.2	115.5
AgNO$_3$(s)	−124.4	−33.4	140.9
Ag$_2$O(s)	−31.1	−11.2	121.3
Ag$_2$S(s)	−32.6	−40.7	144.0
Ag$_2$SO$_4$(s)	−715.9	−618.4	200.4
Sodium			
Na(s)	0	0	51.3
Na(g)	107.5	77.0	153.7
Na$^+$(aq)	−240.34	−261.9	58.45
NaBr(s)	−361.1	−349.0	86.8
NaCl(s)	−411.2	−384.1	72.1
NaCl(aq)	−407.2	−393.1	115.5
NaClO$_3$(s)	−365.8	−262.3	123.4
NaF(s)	−576.6	−546.3	51.1
NaHCO$_3$(s)	−950.8	−851.0	101.7
NaHSO$_4$(s)	−1125.5	−992.8	113.0
NaI(s)	−287.8	−286.1	98.5
NaNO$_3$(s)	−467.9	−367.0	116.5
NaNO$_3$(aq)	−447.5	−373.2	205.4
NaOH(s)	−425.8	−379.7	64.4
NaOH(aq)	−470.1	−419.2	48.2
NaO$_2$(s)	−260.2	−218.4	115.9
Na$_2$CO$_3$(s)	−1130.7	−1044.4	135.0

Substance	ΔH_f° (kJ/mol)	ΔG_f° (kJ/mol)	S° (J/mol · K)
Na$_2$O(s)	−414.2	−375.5	75.1
Na$_2$O$_2$(s)	−510.9	−447.7	95.0
Na$_2$SO$_4$(s)	−1387.1	−1270.2	149.6
Na$_3$PO$_4$(s)	−1917	−1789	173.8
Strontium			
Sr(s)	0	0	55.0
Sr(g)	164.4	130.9	164.6
Sr^{2+}(aq)	−545.51	−557.3	−39
SrCl$_2$(s)	−828.9	−781.1	114.9
SrCO$_3$(s)	−1220.1	−1140.1	97.1
SrO(s)	−592.0	−561.9	54.4
SrSO$_4$(s)	−1453.1	−1340.9	117.0
Sulfur			
S(s, rhombic)	0	0	32.1
S(s, monoclinic)	0.3	0.096	32.6
S(g)	277.2	236.7	167.8
S$_2$(g)	128.6	79.7	228.2
S$_8$(g)	102.3	49.7	430.9
S^{2-}(aq)	41.8	83.7	22
SF$_6$(g)	−1220.5	−1116.5	291.5
HS$^-$(aq)	−17.7	12.4	62.0
H$_2$S(g)	−20.6	−33.4	205.8
H$_2$S(aq)	−39.4	−27.7	122
SOCl$_2$(l)	−245.6		
SO$_2$(g)	−296.8	−300.1	248.2
SO$_3$(g)	−395.7	−371.1	256.8
SO$_4^{2-}$(aq)	−909.3	−744.6	18.5
HSO$_4^-$(aq)	−886.5	−754.4	129.5
H$_2$SO$_4$(l)	−814.0	−690.0	156.9
H$_2$SO$_4$(aq)	−909.3	−744.6	18.5
S$_2$O$_3^{2-}$(aq)	−648.5	−522.5	67
Tin			
Sn(s, white)	0	0	51.2
Sn(s, gray)	−2.1	0.1	44.1
Sn(g)	301.2	266.2	168.5
SnCl$_4$(l)	−511.3	−440.1	258.6
SnCl$_4$(g)	−471.5	−432.2	365.8
SnO(s)	−280.7	−251.9	57.2
SnO$_2$(s)	−577.6	−515.8	49.0
Titanium			
Ti(s)	0	0	30.7
Ti(g)	473.0	428.4	180.3
TiCl$_4$(l)	−804.2	−737.2	252.3
TiCl$_4$(g)	−763.2	−726.3	353.2
TiO$_2$(s)	−944.0	−888.8	50.6
Tungsten			
W(s)	0	0	32.6
W(g)	849.4	807.1	174.0
WO$_3$(s)	−842.9	−764.0	75.9

(continued on the next page)

Substance	ΔH_f° (kJ/mol)	ΔG_f° (kJ/mol)	S° (J/mol · K)	Substance	ΔH_f° (kJ/mol)	ΔG_f° (kJ/mol)	S° (J/mol · K)
Uranium				**Zinc**			
U(s)	0	0	50.2	Zn(s)	0	0	41.6
U(g)	533.0	488.4	199.8	Zn(g)	130.4	94.8	161.0
UF₆(s)	−2197.0	−2068.5	227.6	Zn²⁺(aq)	−153.39	−147.1	−109.8
UF₆(g)	−2147.4	−2063.7	377.9	ZnCl₂(s)	−415.1	−369.4	111.5
UO₂(s)	−1085.0	−1031.8	77.0	ZnO(s)	−350.5	−320.5	43.7
Vanadium				ZnS			
V(s)	0	0	28.9	(s, zinc blende)	−206.0	−201.3	57.7
V(g)	514.2	754.4	182.3	ZnSO₄(s)	−982.8	−871.5	110.5

C. Aqueous Equilibrium Constants

1. Dissociation Constants for Acids at 25 °C

Name	Formula	K_{a_1}	K_{a_2}	K_{a_3}	Name	Formula	K_{a_1}	K_{a_2}	K_{a_3}
Acetic	HC₂H₃O₂	1.8×10^{-5}			Hypobromous	HBrO	2.8×10^{-9}		
Acetylsalicylic	HC₉H₇O₄	3.3×10^{-4}			Hypochlorous	HClO	2.9×10^{-8}		
Adipic	H₂C₆H₈O₄	3.9×10^{-5}	3.9×10^{-6}		Hypoiodous	HIO	2.3×10^{-11}		
Arsenic	H₃AsO₄	5.5×10^{-3}	1.7×10^{-7}	5.1×10^{-12}	Iodic	HIO₃	1.7×10^{-1}		
Arsenous	H₃AsO₃	5.1×10^{-10}			Lactic	HC₃H₅O₃	1.4×10^{-4}		
Ascorbic	H₂C₆H₆O₆	8.0×10^{-5}	1.6×10^{-12}		Maleic	H₂C₄H₂O₄	1.2×10^{-2}	5.9×10^{-7}	
Benzoic	HC₇H₅O₂	6.5×10^{-5}			Malonic	H₂C₃H₂O₄	1.5×10^{-3}	2.0×10^{-6}	
Boric	H₃BO₃	5.4×10^{-10}			Nitrous	HNO₂	4.6×10^{-4}		
Butanoic	HC₄H₇O₂	1.5×10^{-5}			Oxalic	H₂C₂O₄	6.0×10^{-2}	6.1×10^{-5}	
Carbonic	H₂CO₃	4.3×10^{-7}	5.6×10^{-11}		Paraperiodic	H₅IO₆	2.8×10^{-2}	5.3×10^{-9}	
Chloroacetic	HC₂H₂O₂Cl	1.4×10^{-3}			Phenol	HC₆H₅O	1.3×10^{-10}		
Chlorous	HClO₂	1.1×10^{-2}			Phosphoric	H₃PO₄	7.5×10^{-3}	6.2×10^{-8}	4.2×10^{-13}
Citric	H₃C₆H₅O₇	7.4×10^{-4}	1.7×10^{-5}	4.0×10^{-7}	Phosphorous	H₃PO₃	5×10^{-2}	2.0×10^{-7}	
Cyanic	HCNO	2×10^{-4}			Propanoic	HC₃H₅O₂	1.3×10^{-5}		
Formic	HCHO₂	1.8×10^{-4}			Pyruvic	HC₃H₃O₃	4.1×10^{-3}		
Hydrazoic	HN₃	2.5×10^{-5}			Pyrophosphoric	H₄P₂O₇	1.2×10^{-1}	7.9×10^{-3}	2.0×10^{-7}
Hydrocyanic	HCN	4.9×10^{-10}			Selenous	H₂SeO₃	2.4×10^{-3}	4.8×10^{-9}	
Hydrofluoric	HF	3.5×10^{-4}			Succinic	H₂C₄H₄O₄	6.2×10^{-5}	2.3×10^{-6}	
Hydrogen chromate ion	HCrO₄⁻	3.0×10^{-7}			Sulfuric	H₂SO₄	Strong acid	1.2×10^{-2}	
Hydrogen peroxide	H₂O₂	2.4×10^{-12}			Sulfurous	H₂SO₃	1.6×10^{-2}	6.4×10^{-8}	
					Tartaric	H₂C₄H₄O₆	1.0×10^{-3}	4.6×10^{-5}	
Hydrogen selenate ion	HSeO₄⁻	2.2×10^{-2}			Trichloroacetic	HC₂Cl₃O₂	2.2×10^{-1}		
Hydrosulfuric	H₂S	8.9×10^{-8}	1×10^{-19}		Trifluoroacetic acid	HC₂F₃O₂	3.0×10^{-1}		
Hydrotelluric	H₂Te	2.3×10^{-3}	1.6×10^{-11}						

2. Dissociation Constants for Hydrated Metal Ions at 25 °C

Cation	Hydrated Ion	K_a	Cation	Hydrated Ion	K_a
Al³⁺	Al(H₂O)₆³⁺	1.4×10^{-5}	Fe³⁺	Fe(H₂O)₆³⁺	6.3×10^{-3}
Be²⁺	Be(H₂O)₆²⁺	3×10^{-7}	Ni²⁺	Ni(H₂O)₆²⁺	2.5×10^{-11}
Co²⁺	Co(H₂O)₆²⁺	1.3×10^{-9}	Pb²⁺	Pb(H₂O)₆²⁺	3×10^{-8}
Cr³⁺	Cr(H₂O)₆³⁺	1.6×10^{-4}	Sn²⁺	Sn(H₂O)₆²⁺	4×10^{-4}
Cu²⁺	Cu(H₂O)₆²⁺	3×10^{-8}	Zn²⁺	Zn(H₂O)₆²⁺	2.5×10^{-10}
Fe²⁺	Fe(H₂O)₆²⁺	3.2×10^{-10}			

3. Dissociation Constants for Bases at 25 °C

Name	Formula	K_b	Name	Formula	K_b
Ammonia	NH_3	1.76×10^{-5}	Ketamine	$C_{13}H_{16}ClNO$	3×10^{-7}
Aniline	$C_6H_5NH_2$	3.9×10^{-10}	Methylamine	CH_3NH_2	4.4×10^{-4}
Bicarbonate ion	HCO_3^-	2.3×10^{-8}	Morphine	$C_{17}H_{19}NO_3$	1.6×10^{-6}
Carbonate ion	CO_3^{2-}	1.8×10^{-4}	Nicotine	$C_{10}H_{14}N_2$	1.0×10^{-6}
Codeine	$C_{18}H_{21}NO_3$	1.6×10^{-6}	Piperidine	$C_5H_{10}NH$	1.33×10^{-3}
Diethylamine	$(C_2H_5)_2NH$	6.9×10^{-4}	Propylamine	$C_3H_7NH_2$	3.5×10^{-4}
Dimethylamine	$(CH_3)_2NH$	5.4×10^{-4}	Pyridine	C_5H_5N	1.7×10^{-9}
Ethylamine	$C_2H_5NH_2$	5.6×10^{-4}	Strychnine	$C_{21}H_{22}N_2O_2$	1.8×10^{-6}
Ethylenediamine	$C_2H_8N_2$	8.3×10^{-5}	Triethylamine	$(C_2H_5)_3N$	5.6×10^{-4}
Hydrazine	H_2NNH_2	1.3×10^{-6}	Trimethylamine	$(CH_3)_3N$	6.4×10^{-5}
Hydroxylamine	$HONH_2$	1.1×10^{-8}			

4. Solubility Product Constants for Compounds at 25 °C

Compound	Formula	K_{sp}	Compound	Formula	K_{sp}
Aluminum hydroxide	$Al(OH)_3$	1.3×10^{-33}	Iron(III) hydroxide	$Fe(OH)_3$	2.79×10^{-39}
Aluminum phosphate	$AlPO_4$	9.84×10^{-21}	Lanthanum fluoride	LaF_3	2×10^{-19}
Barium carbonate	$BaCO_3$	2.58×10^{-9}	Lanthanum iodate	$La(IO_3)_3$	7.50×10^{-12}
Barium chromate	$BaCrO_4$	1.17×10^{-10}	Lead(II) bromide	$PbBr_2$	4.67×10^{-6}
Barium fluoride	BaF_2	2.45×10^{-5}	Lead(II) carbonate	$PbCO_3$	7.40×10^{-14}
Barium hydroxide	$Ba(OH)_2$	5.0×10^{-3}	Lead(II) chloride	$PbCl_2$	1.17×10^{-5}
Barium oxalate	BaC_2O_4	1.6×10^{-6}	Lead(II) chromate	$PbCrO_4$	2.8×10^{-13}
Barium phosphate	$Ba_3(PO_4)_2$	6×10^{-39}	Lead(II) fluoride	PbF_2	3.3×10^{-8}
Barium sulfate	$BaSO_4$	1.07×10^{-10}	Lead(II) hydroxide	$Pb(OH)_2$	1.43×10^{-20}
Cadmium carbonate	$CdCO_3$	1.0×10^{-12}	Lead(II) iodide	PbI_2	9.8×10^{-9}
Cadmium hydroxide	$Cd(OH)_2$	7.2×10^{-15}	Lead(II) phosphate	$Pb_3(PO_4)_2$	1×10^{-54}
Cadmium sulfide	CdS	8×10^{-28}	Lead(II) sulfate	$PbSO_4$	1.82×10^{-8}
Calcium carbonate	$CaCO_3$	4.96×10^{-9}	Lead(II) sulfide	PbS	9.04×10^{-29}
Calcium chromate	$CaCrO_4$	7.1×10^{-4}	Magnesium carbonate	$MgCO_3$	6.82×10^{-6}
Calcium fluoride	CaF_2	1.46×10^{-10}	Magnesium fluoride	MgF_2	5.16×10^{-11}
Calcium hydroxide	$Ca(OH)_2$	4.68×10^{-6}	Magnesium hydroxide	$Mg(OH)_2$	2.06×10^{-13}
Calcium hydrogen phosphate	$CaHPO_4$	1×10^{-7}	Magnesium oxalate	MgC_2O_4	4.83×10^{-6}
Calcium oxalate	CaC_2O_4	2.32×10^{-9}	Manganese(II) carbonate	$MnCO_3$	2.24×10^{-11}
Calcium phosphate	$Ca_3(PO_4)_2$	2.07×10^{-33}	Manganese(II) hydroxide	$Mn(OH)_2$	1.6×10^{-13}
Calcium sulfate	$CaSO_4$	7.10×10^{-5}	Manganese(II) sulfide	MnS	2.3×10^{-13}
Chromium(III) hydroxide	$Cr(OH)_3$	6.3×10^{-31}	Mercury(I) bromide	Hg_2Br_2	6.40×10^{-23}
Cobalt(II) carbonate	$CoCO_3$	1.0×10^{-10}	Mercury(I) carbonate	Hg_2CO_3	3.6×10^{-17}
Cobalt(II) hydroxide	$Co(OH)_2$	5.92×10^{-15}	Mercury(I) chloride	Hg_2Cl_2	1.43×10^{-18}
Cobalt(II) sulfide	CoS	5×10^{-22}	Mercury(I) chromate	Hg_2CrO_4	2×10^{-9}
Copper(I) bromide	$CuBr$	6.27×10^{-9}	Mercury(I) cyanide	$Hg_2(CN)_2$	5×10^{-40}
Copper(I) chloride	$CuCl$	1.72×10^{-7}	Mercury(I) iodide	Hg_2I_2	5.2×10^{-29}
Copper(I) cyanide	$CuCN$	3.47×10^{-20}	Mercury(II) hydroxide	$Hg(OH)_2$	3.1×10^{-26}
Copper(II) carbonate	$CuCO_3$	2.4×10^{-10}	Mercury(II) sulfide	HgS	1.6×10^{-54}
Copper(II) hydroxide	$Cu(OH)_2$	2.2×10^{-20}	Nickel(II) carbonate	$NiCO_3$	1.42×10^{-7}
Copper(II) phosphate	$Cu_3(PO_4)_2$	1.40×10^{-37}	Nickel(II) hydroxide	$Ni(OH)_2$	5.48×10^{-16}
Copper(II) sulfide	CuS	1.27×10^{-36}	Nickel(II) sulfide	NiS	3×10^{-20}
Iron(II) carbonate	$FeCO_3$	3.07×10^{-11}	Silver bromate	$AgBrO_3$	5.38×10^{-5}
Iron(II) hydroxide	$Fe(OH)_2$	4.87×10^{-17}	Silver bromide	$AgBr$	5.35×10^{-13}
Iron(II) sulfide	FeS	3.72×10^{-19}	Silver carbonate	Ag_2CO_3	8.46×10^{-12}

(*continued on the next page*)

Compound	Formula	K_{sp}	Compound	Formula	K_{sp}
Silver chloride	$AgCl$	1.77×10^{-10}	Strontium phosphate	$Sr_3(PO_4)_2$	1×10^{-31}
Silver chromate	Ag_2CrO_4	1.12×10^{-12}	Strontium sulfate	$SrSO_4$	3.44×10^{-7}
Silver cyanide	$AgCN$	5.97×10^{-17}	Tin(II) hydroxide	$Sn(OH)_2$	5.45×10^{-27}
Silver iodide	AgI	8.51×10^{-17}	Tin(II) sulfide	SnS	1×10^{-26}
Silver phosphate	Ag_3PO_4	8.89×10^{-17}	Zinc carbonate	$ZnCO_3$	1.46×10^{-10}
Silver sulfate	Ag_2SO_4	1.20×10^{-5}	Zinc hydroxide	$Zn(OH)_2$	3×10^{-17}
Silver sulfide	Ag_2S	6×10^{-51}	Zinc oxalate	ZnC_2O_4	2.7×10^{-8}
Strontium carbonate	$SrCO_3$	5.60×10^{-10}	Zinc sulfide	ZnS	2×10^{-25}
Strontium chromate	$SrCrO_4$	3.6×10^{-5}			

5. Complex Ion Formation Constants in Water at 25 °C

Complex Ion	K_f	Complex Ion	K_f
$[Ag(CN)_2]^-$	1×10^{21}	$[Fe(CN)_6]^{3-}$	2×10^{43}
$[Ag(EDTA)]^{3-}$	2.1×10^7	$[Fe(EDTA)]^{2-}$	2.1×10^{14}
$[Ag(en)_2]^+$	5.0×10^7	$[Fe(EDTA)]^-$	1.7×10^{24}
$[Ag(NH_3)_2]^+$	1.7×10^7	$[Fe(en)_3]^{2+}$	5.0×10^9
$[Ag(SCN)_4]^{3-}$	1.2×10^{10}	$[Fe(ox)_3]^{4-}$	1.7×10^5
$[Ag(S_2O_3)_2]^-$	2.8×10^{13}	$[Fe(ox)_3]^{3-}$	2×10^{20}
$[Al(EDTA)]^-$	1.3×10^{16}	$[Fe(SCN)]^{2+}$	8.9×10^2
$[AlF_6]^{3-}$	7×10^{19}	$[Hg(CN)_4]^{2-}$	1.8×10^{41}
$[Al(OH)_4]^-$	3×10^{33}	$[HgCl_4]^{2-}$	1.1×10^{16}
$[Al(ox)_3]^{3-}$	2×10^{16}	$[Hg(EDTA)]^{2-}$	6.3×10^{21}
$[CdBr_4]^{2-}$	5.5×10^3	$[Hg(en)_2]^{2+}$	2×10^{23}
$[Cd(CN)_4]^{2-}$	3×10^{18}	$[HgI_4]^{2-}$	2×10^{30}
$[CdCl_4]^{2-}$	6.3×10^2	$[Hg(ox)_2]^{2-}$	9.5×10^6
$[Cd(en)_3]^{2+}$	1.2×10^{12}	$[Ni(CN)_4]^{2-}$	2×10^{31}
$[CdI_4]^{2-}$	2×10^6	$[Ni(EDTA)]^{2-}$	3.6×10^{18}
$[Co(EDTA)]^{2-}$	2.0×10^{16}	$[Ni(en)_3]^{2+}$	2.1×10^{18}
$[Co(EDTA)]^-$	1×10^{36}	$[Ni(NH_3)_6]^{2+}$	2.0×10^8
$[Co(en)_3]^{2+}$	8.7×10^{13}	$[Ni(ox)_3]^{4-}$	3×10^8
$[Co(en)_3]^{3+}$	4.9×10^{48}	$[PbCl_3]^-$	2.4×10^1
$[Co(NH_3)_6]^{2+}$	1.3×10^5	$[Pb(EDTA)]^{2-}$	2×10^{18}
$[Co(NH_3)_6]^{3+}$	2.3×10^{33}	$[PbI_4]^{2-}$	3.0×10^4
$[Co(OH)_4]^{2-}$	5×10^9	$[Pb(OH)_3]^-$	8×10^{13}
$[Co(ox)_3]^{4-}$	5×10^9	$[Pb(ox)_2]^{2-}$	3.5×10^6
$[Co(ox)_3]^{3-}$	1×10^{20}	$[Pb(S_2O_3)_3]^{4-}$	2.2×10^6
$[Co(SCN)_4]^{2-}$	1×10^3	$[PtCl_4]^{2-}$	1×10^{16}
$[Cr(EDTA)]^-$	1×10^{23}	$[Pt(NH_3)_6]^{2+}$	2×10^{35}
$[Cr(OH)_4]^-$	8.0×10^{29}	$[Sn(OH)_3]^-$	3×10^{25}
$[CuCl_3]^{2-}$	5×10^5	$[Zn(CN)_4]^{2-}$	2.1×10^{19}
$[Cu(CN)_4]^{2-}$	1.0×10^{25}	$[Zn(EDTA)]^{2-}$	3×10^{16}
$[Cu(EDTA)]^{2-}$	5×10^{18}	$[Zn(en)_3]^{2+}$	1.3×10^{14}
$[Cu(en)_2]^{2+}$	1×10^{20}	$[Zn(NH_3)_4]^{2+}$	2.8×10^9
$[Cu(NH_3)_4]^{2+}$	1.7×10^{13}	$[Zn(OH)_4]^{2-}$	2×10^{15}
$[Cu(ox)_2]^{2-}$	3×10^8	$[Zn(ox)_3]^{4-}$	1.4×10^8
$[Fe(CN)_6]^{4-}$	1.5×10^{35}		

D. Standard Electrode Potentials at 25 °C

Half-Reaction	$E°$ (V)	Half-Reaction	$E°$ (V)
$F_2(g) + 2\,e^- \longrightarrow 2\,F^-(aq)$	2.87	$BiO^+(aq) + 2\,H^+(aq) + 3\,e^- \longrightarrow Bi(s) + H_2O(l)$	0.32
$O_3(g) + 2\,H^+(aq) + 2\,e^- \longrightarrow O_2(g) + H_2O(l)$	2.08	$Hg_2Cl_2(s) + 2\,e^- \longrightarrow 2\,Hg(l) + 2\,Cl^-(aq)$	0.27
$Ag^{2+}(aq) + e^- \longrightarrow Ag^+(aq)$	1.98	$AgCl(s) + e^- \longrightarrow Ag(s) + Cl^-(aq)$	0.22
$Co^{3+}(aq) + e^- \longrightarrow Co^{2+}(aq)$	1.82	$SO_4^{2-}(aq) + 4\,H^+(aq) + 2\,e^- \longrightarrow H_2SO_3(aq) + H_2O(l)$	0.20
$H_2O_2(aq) + 2\,H^+(aq) + 2\,e^- \longrightarrow 2\,H_2O(l)$	1.78	$Cu^{2+}(aq) + e^- \longrightarrow Cu^+(aq)$	0.16
$PbO_2(s) + 4\,H^+(aq) + SO_4^{2-}(aq) + 2\,e^- \longrightarrow$ $\qquad PbSO_4(s) + 2\,H_2O(l)$	1.69	$Sn^{4+}(aq) + 2\,e^- \longrightarrow Sn^{2+}(aq)$	0.15
$MnO_4^-(aq) + 4\,H^+(aq) + 3\,e^- \longrightarrow MnO_2(s) + 2\,H_2O(l)$	1.68	$S(s) + 2\,H^+(aq) + 2\,e^- \longrightarrow H_2S(g)$	0.14
$2\,HClO(aq) + 2\,H^+(aq) + 2\,e^- \longrightarrow Cl_2(g) + 2\,H_2O(l)$	1.61	$AgBr(s) + e^- \longrightarrow Ag(s) + Br^-(aq)$	0.071
$MnO_4^-(aq) + 8\,H^+(aq) + 5\,e^- \longrightarrow Mn^{2+}(aq) + 4\,H_2O(l)$	1.51	$2\,H^+(aq) + 2\,e^- \longrightarrow H_2(g)$	0.00
$Au^{3+}(aq) + 3\,e^- \longrightarrow Au(s)$	1.50	$Fe^{3+}(aq) + 3\,e^- \longrightarrow Fe(s)$	−0.036
$2\,BrO_3^-(aq) + 12\,H^+(aq) + 10\,e^- \longrightarrow Br_2(l) + 6\,H_2O(l)$	1.48	$Pb^{2+}(aq) + 2\,e^- \longrightarrow Pb(s)$	−0.13
$PbO_2(s) + 4\,H^+(aq) + 2\,e^- \longrightarrow Pb^{2+}(aq) + 2\,H_2O(l)$	1.46	$Sn^{2+}(aq) + 2\,e^- \longrightarrow Sn(s)$	−0.14
$Cl_2(g) + 2\,e^- \longrightarrow 2\,Cl^-(aq)$	1.36	$AgI(s) + e^- \longrightarrow Ag(s) + I^-(aq)$	−0.15
$Cr_2O_7^{2-}(aq) + 14\,H^+(aq) + 6\,e^- \longrightarrow 2\,Cr^{3+}(aq) + 7\,H_2O(l)$	1.33	$N_2(g) + 5\,H^+(aq) + 4\,e^- \longrightarrow N_2H_5^+(aq)$	−0.23
$O_2(g) + 4\,H^+(aq) + 4\,e^- \longrightarrow 2\,H_2O(l)$	1.23	$Ni^{2+}(aq) + 2\,e^- \longrightarrow Ni(s)$	−0.23
$MnO_2(s) + 4\,H^+(aq) + 2\,e^- \longrightarrow Mn^{2+}(aq) + 2\,H_2O(l)$	1.21	$Co^{2+}(aq) + 2\,e^- \longrightarrow Co(s)$	−0.28
$IO_3^-(aq) + 6\,H^+(aq) + 5\,e^- \longrightarrow \frac{1}{2}I_2(aq) + 3\,H_2O(l)$	1.20	$PbSO_4(s) + 2\,e^- \longrightarrow Pb(s) + SO_4^{2-}(aq)$	−0.36
$Br_2(l) + 2\,e^- \longrightarrow 2\,Br^-(aq)$	1.09	$Cd^{2+}(aq) + 2\,e^- \longrightarrow Cd(s)$	−0.40
$AuCl_4^-(aq) + 3\,e^- \longrightarrow Au(s) + 4\,Cl^-(aq)$	1.00	$Fe^{2+}(aq) + 2\,e^- \longrightarrow Fe(s)$	−0.45
$VO_2^+(aq) + 2\,H^+(aq) + e^- \longrightarrow VO^{2+}(aq) + H_2O(l)$	1.00	$2\,CO_2(g) + 2\,H^+(aq) + 2\,e^- \longrightarrow H_2C_2O_4(aq)$	−0.49
$HNO_2(aq) + H^+(aq) + e^- \longrightarrow NO(g) + 2\,H_2O(l)$	0.98	$Cr^{3+}(aq) + e^- \longrightarrow Cr^{2+}(aq)$	−0.50
$NO_3^-(aq) + 4\,H^+(aq) + 3\,e^- \longrightarrow NO(g) + 2\,H_2O(l)$	0.96	$Cr^{3+}(aq) + 3\,e^- \longrightarrow Cr(s)$	−0.73
$ClO_2(g) + e^- \longrightarrow ClO_2^-(aq)$	0.95	$Zn^{2+}(aq) + 2\,e^- \longrightarrow Zn(s)$	−0.76
$2\,Hg^{2+}(aq) + 2\,e^- \longrightarrow 2\,Hg_2^{2+}(aq)$	0.92	$2\,H_2O(l) + 2\,e^- \longrightarrow H_2(g) + 2\,OH^-(aq)$	−0.83
$Ag^+(aq) + e^- \longrightarrow Ag(s)$	0.80	$Mn^{2+}(aq) + 2\,e^- \longrightarrow Mn(s)$	−1.18
$Hg_2^{2+}(aq) + 2\,e^- \longrightarrow 2\,Hg(l)$	0.80	$Al^{3+}(aq) + 3\,e^- \longrightarrow Al(s)$	−1.66
$Fe^{3+}(aq) + e^- \longrightarrow Fe^{2+}(aq)$	0.77	$H_2(g) + 2\,e^- \longrightarrow 2\,H^-(aq)$	−2.23
$PtCl_4^{2-}(aq) + 2\,e^- \longrightarrow Pt(s) + 4\,Cl^-(aq)$	0.76	$Mg^{2+}(aq) + 2\,e^- \longrightarrow Mg(s)$	−2.37
$O_2(g) + 2\,H^+(aq) + 2\,e^- \longrightarrow H_2O_2(aq)$	0.70	$La^{3+}(aq) + 3\,e^- \longrightarrow La(s)$	−2.38
$MnO_4^-(aq) + e^- \longrightarrow MnO_4^{2-}(aq)$	0.56	$Na^+(aq) + e^- \longrightarrow Na(s)$	−2.71
$I_2(s) + 2\,e^- \longrightarrow 2\,I^-(aq)$	0.54	$Ca^{2+}(aq) + 2\,e^- \longrightarrow Ca(s)$	−2.76
$Cu^+(aq) + e^- \longrightarrow Cu(s)$	0.52	$Ba^{2+}(aq) + 2\,e^- \longrightarrow Ba(s)$	−2.90
$O_2(g) + 2\,H_2O(l) + 4\,e^- \longrightarrow 4\,OH^-(aq)$	0.40	$K^+(aq) + e^- \longrightarrow K(s)$	−2.92
$Cu^{2+}(aq) + 2\,e^- \longrightarrow Cu(s)$	0.34	$Li^+(aq) + e^- \longrightarrow Li(s)$	−3.04

E. Vapor Pressure of Water at Various Temperatures

T (°C)	P (torr)	T (°C)	P (torr)	T (°C)	P (torr)	T (°C)	P (torr)
0	4.58	21	18.65	35	42.2	92	567.0
5	6.54	22	19.83	40	55.3	94	610.9
10	9.21	23	21.07	45	71.9	96	657.6
12	10.52	24	22.38	50	92.5	98	707.3
14	11.99	25	23.76	55	118.0	100	760.0
16	13.63	26	25.21	60	149.4	102	815.9
17	14.53	27	26.74	65	187.5	104	875.1
18	15.48	28	28.35	70	233.7	106	937.9
19	16.48	29	30.04	80	355.1	108	1004.4
20	17.54	30	31.82	90	525.8	110	1074.6

Appendix III:
Answers to Selected Exercises

Chapter 1

33. a. theory   **b.** observation
   c. law   **d.** observation
35. Several answers possible.
37. a. mixture, homogeneous
   b. pure substance, compound
   c. pure substance, element
   d. mixture, heterogeneous

39.

Substance	Pure or Mixture	Type
Aluminum	Pure	Element
Apple juice	Mixture	Homogeneous
Hydrogen peroxide	Pure	Compound
Chicken soup	Mixture	Heterogeneous

41. a. pure substance, compound
   b. mixture, heterogeneous
   c. mixture, homogeneous
   d. pure substance, element
43. physical, chemical, physical, physical, physical
45. a. chemical   **b.** physical
   c. physical   **d.** chemical
47. a. chemical   **b.** physical
   c. chemical   **d.** chemical
49. a. physical   **b.** chemical
   c. physical
51. a. 0 °C   **b.** -321 °F
   c. -78.3 °F   **d.** 310.2 K
53. -62.2 °C, 210.9 K
55. a. 1.2 nm   **b.** 22 fs
   c. 1.5 Gg   **d.** 3.5 ML
57. a. 4.5×10^{-9} s   **b.** 1.8×10^{-14} s
   c. 1.28×10^{-10} m   **d.** 3.5×10^{-5} m

59.

1245 kg	1.245×10^{6} g	1.245×10^{9} mg
515 km	5.15×10^{6} dm	5.15×10^{7} cm
122.355 s	1.22355×10^{5} ms	0.122355 ks
3.345 kJ	3.345×10^{3} J	3.345×10^{6} mJ

61. a. 254.998 km   **b.** 2.54998×10^{-1} Mm
   c. 254998×10^{3} mm   **d.** 254998×10^{2} cm
63. 10,000 1-cm squares
65. no
67. 1.26 g/cm^3
69. a. 463 g   **b.** 3.7 L
71. $201. \times 10^{3}$ g
73. a. 73.0 mL   **b.** 88.2 °C   **c.** 645 mL
75. a. 1,050,5̲0̲1̲   **b.** 0.0̲0̲20
   c. 0.000000000000002 **d.** 0.001̲090
77. a. 3   **b.** ambiguous, without more informa-
      tion assume 3 significant figures
   c. 3   **d.** 5

e. ambiguous, without more information assume 1
   significant figure
79. a. not exact   **b.** exact
   c. not exact   **d.** exact
81. a. 156.9   **b.** 156.8
   c. 156.8   **d.** 156.9
83. a. 1.84   **b.** 0.033
   c. 0.500   **d.** 34
85. a. 41.4   **b.** 133.5
   c. 73.0   **d.** 0.42
87. a. 391.3   **b.** 1.1×10^{4}
   c. 5.96   **d.** 5.93×10^{4}
89. a. 60.6 in   **b.** 3.14×10^{3} g
   c. 3.7 qt   **d.** 4.29 in
91. 5.0×10^{1} min
93. 4.0×10^{1} mi/gal
95. a. 1.95×10^{-4} km^2 **b.** 1.95×10^{4} dm^2
   c. 1.95×10^{6} cm^2
97. 0.680 mi^2
99. 0.95 mL
101. 3.1557×10^{7} s/solar year
103. a. extensive   **b.** intensive
   c. intensive   **d.** intensive
   e. extensive
105. $-34°$
107. $F = \text{kg}(\text{m/s}^2) = \text{N}$ (for newton), kN, pN
109. a. 2.2×10^{-6} **b.** 0.0159
   c. 6.9×10^{4}
111. a. mass of can of gold $= 1.9 \times 10^{4}$ g
      mass of can of sand $= 3.0 \times 10^{3}$ g
   b. Yes, the thief sets off the trap because the can of sand
      is lighter than the gold cylinder.
113. 22 in^3
115. 7.6 g/cm^3
117. 3.11×10^{5} lb
119. 3.3×10^{2} km
121. 6.8×10^{-15}
123. 2.4×10^{19} km
125. 488 grams
127. 0.492
129. 18.2 atm
131. $1 \text{ J} = 1 \text{ kg m}^2/\text{s}^2$
   $m = \text{kg}, v^2 = (\text{m/s})^2 \; mv = \text{kg m}^2/\text{s}^2$
   $P = \text{N/m}^2 = \text{kg m s}^2/\text{m}^2 = \text{kg/m s}^2$
   $V = \text{m}^3 \; PV = \text{kg m}^3/\text{m s}^2 = \text{kg m}^2/\text{s}^2$
133. 9.0×10^{1} mg CO
135. 13% increase
137. No. Since the container is sealed the atoms and molecules can move around, but they can not leave. If no
   atoms or molecules can leave, the mass must be constant.

139. 343 1-cm cubes
141. a. The dark block   **b.** The light-colored block
c. Cannot tell

Chapter 2

29. 13.5 g
31. These results are not consistent with the law of definite proportions because sample 1 is composed of 11.5 parts Cl to 1 part C and sample 2 is composed of 9.05 parts Cl to 1 part C. The law of definite proportions states that a given compound always contains exactly the same proportion of elements by mass.
33. 23.8 g
35. For the law of multiple proportions to hold, the ratio of the masses of O combining with 1 g of O's in the compound should be a small whole number. $0.3369/0.168 = 2.00$
37. Sample 1: 1.00 g $O_2/1.00$ g S;
sample 2: 1.50 g $O_2/1.00$ g S
Sample 2/sample 1 $= 1.50/1.00 = 1.50$
3 O atoms/2 O atoms $= 1.5$
39. a. not consistent
b. consistent: Dalton's atomic theory states that the atoms of a given element are identical.
c. consistent: Dalton's atomic theory states that atoms combine in simple whole-number ratios to form compounds.
d. not consistent
41. a. consistent: Rutherford's nuclear model states that the atom is largely empty space.
b. consistent: Rutherford's nuclear model states that most of the atom's mass is concentrated in a tiny region called the nucleus.
c. not consistent   **d.** not consistent
43. -2.3×10^{-19} C
45. 9.4×10^{13} excess electrons, 8.5×10^{-17} kg
47. a, b, c
49. 1.83×10^3 e$^-$
51. a. $^{63}_{29}$Cu   **b.** $^{65}_{29}$Cu
c. $^{40}_{19}$K   **d.** $^{40}_{18}$Ar
53. a. 7 $^1_1$p and 7 $^0_1$n   **b.** 11 $^1_1$p and 12 $^0_1$n
c. 86 $^1_1$p and 136 $^0_1$n   **d.** 82 $^1_1$p and 126 $^0_1$n
55. 6 $^1_1$p and 8 $^0_0$n, $^{14}_6$C
57. a. 28 $^1_1$p and 26 e$^-$ **b.** 16 $^1_1$p and 18 e$^-$
c. 35 $^1_1$p and 36 e$^-$ **d.** 24 $^1_1$p and 21 e$^-$
59. a. 2$-$ **b.** 1$+$ **c.** 3$+$ **d.** 1$+$

61.

Symbol	Ion Formed	Number of Electrons in Ion	Number of Protons in Ion
Ca	Ca^{2+}	18	20
Be	Be^{2+}	2	4
Se	Se^{2-}	36	34
In	In^{3+}	46	49

63. a. potassium, metal   **b.** barium, metal
c. iodine, nonmetal   **d.** oxygen, nonmetal
e. antimony, metalloid

65. a, b
67. a. alkali metal   **b.** halogen
c. alkaline earth metal   **d.** alkaline earth metal
e. noble gas
69. Cl and F because they are in the same group or family. Elements in the same group or family have similar chemical properties.
71. The atomic mass of gallium is 69.723 amu.
73. The fluorine-19 isotope must have a large percent abundance, which would make fluorine produce a large peak at this mass. Chlorine has two isotopes (Cl-35 and Cl-37). The atomic mass is simply the weighted average of these two, which means that there is no chlorine isotope with a mass of 35.45 amu.
75. 121.8 amu, Sb
77. Br-79 78.92 amu 50.96%
79. 2.3×10^{24} atoms
81. a. 0.295 mol Ar   **b.** 0.0543 mol Zn
c. 0.144 mol Ta   **d.** 0.0304 mol Li
83. 2.11×10^{22} atoms
85. a. 1.01×10^{23} atoms   **b.** 6.78×10^{21} atoms
c. 5.39×10^{21} atoms   **d.** 5.6×10^{20} atoms
87. a. 36 grams   **b.** 0.187 grams
c. 62 grams   **d.** 3.1 grams
89. 2.6×10^{21} atoms
91. 3.239×10^{-22} g
93. 1.50 g
95. C_2O_3
97. 4.82241×10^7 C/kg
99. ^{237}Pa, ^{238}U, ^{239}Np, ^{240}Pu, ^{235}Ac, ^{234}Ra, etc.

101.

Symbol	Z	A	#p	#e$^-$	#n	Charge
O	8	16	8	10	8	2$-$
Ca^{2+}	20	40	20	18	20	2$+$
Mg^{2+}	12	25	12	10	13	2$+$
N^{3-}	7	14	7	10	7	3$-$

103. $V_n = 8.2 \times 10^{-8}$ pm^3, $V_a = 1.4 \times 10^6$ pm^3, $5.9 \times 10^{-12}\%$
105. 6.022×10^{21} dollars total, 9.3×10^{11} dollars per person, billionaires
107. 15.985 amu
109. 4.76×10^{24} atoms
111. Li $- 6 = 7.494\%$, Li $- 7 = 92.506\%$
113. 75.0% gold
115. 106.91 amu
117. 1.66×10^{22} gold atoms
119. 1×10^{78} atoms/universe
121. 0.423
123. 63.67 g/mol
125. 25.06 g/mol
127. If the amu and mole were not based on the same isotope, the numerical values obtained for an atom of material and a mole of material would not be the same. If, for example, the mole was based on the number of particles in C-12 but the amu was changed to a fraction of the mass of an atom of Ne-20, the number of particles and the number of amu that make up one mole of material would no longer be the same. We would no longer have the

relationship where the mass of an atom in amu is numerically equal to the mass of a mole of those atoms in grams.

129. The different isotopes of the same element have the same number of protons and electrons, so the attractive forces between the nucleus and the electrons is constant and there is no difference in the radii of the isotopes. Ions, on the other hand, have a different number of electrons than the parent atom from which they are derived. Cations have fewer electrons than the parent atom. The attractive forces are greater because there is a larger positive charge in the nucleus than the negative charge in the electron cloud. So, cations are smaller than the atom they are derived from. Anions have more electrons than the parent. The electron cloud has a greater negative charge than the nucleus, so the anions have larger radii than the parent.

Chapter 3

23. **a.** 3 Mg, 2 P, 8 O   **b.** 1 Ba, 2 Cl
   c. 1 Fe, 2 N, 4 O   **d.** 1 Ca, 2 O, 2 H

25. **a.** NH_3 **b.** C_2H_6 **c.** SO_3

27. **a.** atomic   **b.** molecular
   c. atomic   **d.** molecular

29. **a.** molecular   **b.** ionic
   c. ionic   **d.** molecular

31. **a.** molecular element   **b.** molecular compound
   c. atomic element

33. **a.** CaO   **b.** ZnS
   c. RbBr   **d.** Al_2O_3

35. **a.** $Ca(OH)_2$ **b.** $CaCrO_4$
   c. $Ca_3(PO_4)_2$ **d.** $Ca(CN)_2$

37. **a.** magnesium nitride   **b.** potassium fluoride
   c. sodium oxide   **d.** lithium sulfide
   e. cesium fluoride   **f.** potassium iodide
   g. strontium chloride   **h.** barium chloride

39. **a.** tin(II) oxide   **b.** chromium(III) sulfide
   c. rubidium iodide   **d.** barium bromide

41. **a.** copper(I) nitrite   **b.** magnesium acetate
   c. barium nitrate   **d.** lead(II) acetate
   e. potassium chlorate   **f.** lead(II) sulfate

43. **a.** $NaHSO_3$ **b.** $LiMnO_4$
   c. $AgNO_3$ **d.** K_2SO_4
   e. $RbHSO_4$ **f.** $KHCO_3$

45. **a.** cobalt(II) sulfate heptahydrate
   b. $IrBr_3 \cdot 4 H_2O$
   c. Magnesium bromate hexahydrate
   d. $K_2CO_3 \cdot 2 H_2O$

47. **a.** carbon monoxide   **b.** nitrogen triiodide
   c. silicon tetrachloride   **d.** tetranitrogen tetraselenide
   e. diiodine pentaoxide

49. **a.** PCl_3 **b.** ClO   **c.** S_2F_4
   d. PF_5 **e.** P_2S_5

51. **a.** hydroiodic acid   **b.** nitric acid
   c. carbonic acid   **d.** acetic acid

53. **a.** HF   **b.** HBr   **c.** H_2SO_3

55. **a.** 46.01 amu   **b.** 58.12 amu
   c. 180.16 amu   **d.** 238.03 amu

57. **a.** 0.554 mol   **b.** 28.4 mol
   c. 0.378 mol   **d.** 1093 mol

59. **a.** 2.2×10^{23} molecules
   b. 7.06×10^{23} molecules
   c. 4.16×10^{23} molecules
   d. 1.09×10^{23} molecules

61. **a.** 0.0790 g   **b.** 0.84 g   **c.** 2.992×10^{-22} g

63. 0.10 mg

65. **a.** 74.87% C   **b.** 79.88% C
   c. 92.24% C   **d.** 37.23% C

67. NH_3: 82.27% N
   $CO(NH_2)_2$: 46.65% N
   NH_4NO_3: 35.00% N
   $(NH_4)_2SO_4$: 21.20% N
   NH_3 has the highest N content

69. 20.8 g F

71. 196 μg KI

73. **a.** 2 : 1   **b.** 4 : 1   **c.** 6 : 2 : 1

75. **a.** 0.885 mol H   **b.** 5.2 mol H
   c. 29 mol H   **d.** 33.7 mol H

77. **a.** 3.3 g Na   **b.** 3.6 g Na
   c. 1.4 g Na   **d.** 1.7 g Na

79. **a.** Ag_2O **b.** $Co_3As_2O_8$ **c.** $SeBr_4$

81. **a.** C_5H_7N **b.** $C_4H_5N_2O$

83. $C_{13}H_{18}O_2$

85. NCl_3

87. **a.** $C_{12}H_{14}N_2$ **b.** $C_6H_3Cl_3$ **c.** $C_{10}H_{20}N_2S_4$

89. CH_2

91. C_2H_4O

93. $2 SO_2(g) + O_2(g) + 2 H_2O(l) \longrightarrow 2 H_2SO_4(aq)$

95. $2 Na(s) + 2 H_2O(l) \longrightarrow H_2(g) + 2 NaOH(aq)$

97. $C_{12}H_{22}O_{11}(s) + H_2O(l) \longrightarrow 4 C_2H_5OH(aq) + 4 CO_2(g)$

99. **a.** $PbS(s) + 2 HBr(aq) \longrightarrow PbBr_2(s) + H_2S(g)$
   b. $CO(g) + 3 H_2(g) \longrightarrow CH_4(g) + H_2O(l)$
   c. $4 HCl(aq) + MnO_2(s) \longrightarrow$
   $\qquad\qquad MnCl_2(aq) + 2 H_2O(l) + Cl_2(g)$
   d. $C_5H_{12}(l) + 8 O_2(g) \longrightarrow 5 CO_2(g) + 6 H_2O(g)$

101. **a.** $2 CO_2(g) + CaSiO_3(s) + H_2O(l) \longrightarrow$
   $\qquad\qquad SiO_2(s) + Ca(HCO_3)_2(aq)$
   b. $2 Co(NO_3)_3(aq) + 3 (NH_4)_2S(aq) \longrightarrow$
   $\qquad\qquad Co_2S_3(s) + 6 NH_4NO_3(aq)$
   c. $Cu_2O(s) + C(s) \longrightarrow 2 Cu(s) + CO(g)$
   d. $H_2(g) + Cl_2(g) \longrightarrow 2 HCl(g)$

103. **a.** inorganic   **b.** organic
   c. organic   **d.** inorganic

105. **a.** alkene   **b.** alkane
   c. alkyne   **d.** alkane

107. **a.** $CH_3CH_2CH_3$ **b.** propane
   c. $CH_3CH_2CH_2CH_2CH_2CH_2CH_2CH_3$
   d. pentane

109. **a.** functionalized hydrocarbon, alcohol
   b. hydrocarbon
   c. functionalized hydrocarbon, ketone
   d. functionalized hydrocarbon, amine

111. 1.50×10^{24} molecules EtOH

113. **a.** K_2CrO_4, 40.27% K, 26.78% Cr, 32.95% O
   b. $Pb_3(PO_4)_2$, 76.60% Pb, 7.63% P, 15.77% O

c. H_2SO_3, 2.46% H, 39.07% S, 58.47% O

d. $CoBr_2$, 26.94% Co, 73.06% Br

115. 1.80×10^2 g Cl/yr

117. M = Fe

119. estradiol = $C_{18}H_{24}O_2$

121. $C_{18}H_{20}O_2$

123. $7 H_2O$

125. C_6H_9BrO

127. 1.87×10^{21} atoms

129. 92.93 amu

131. $x = 1, y = 2$

133. 41.7 mg

135. 0.224 g

137. 22.0% by mass

139. 1.6×10^7 kg Cl

141. 7.8×10^3 kg rock

143. $C_5H_{10}SI$

145. X_2Y_3

147. The sphere in the molecular models represents the electron cloud of the atom. On this scale, the nucleus would be too small to see.

149. The statement is incorrect because a chemical formula is based on the ratio of atoms combined not the ratio of grams combined. The statement should read: "The chemical formula for ammonia (NH_3) indicates that ammonia contains three hydrogen atoms to each nitrogen atom."

151. O, S, H

Chapter 4

25. $2 C_6H_{14}(g) + 19 O_2(g) \longrightarrow$
$$12 CO_2(g) + 14 H_2O(g), 68 \text{ mol } O_2$$

27. a. 5.0 mol NO_2 **b.** 14. mol NO_2

c. 0.281 mol NO_2 **d.** 53.1 mol NO_2

29.

mol SiO_2	mol C	mol SiC	mol CO
3	9	3	6
2	6	2	4
5	15	5	10
2.8	8.4	2.8	5.6
0.517	1.55	0.517	1.03

31. a. 9.3 g HBr, 0.12 g H_2

33. a. 5.56 g $BaCl_2$ **b.** 6.55 g $CaCO_3$

c. 6.09 g MgO   **d.** 6.93 g Al_2O_3

35. a. 4.42 g HCl   **b.** 8.25 g HNO_3

c. 4.24 g H_2SO_4

37. a. Na   **b.** Na   **c.** Br_2 **d.** Na

39. 3 molecules Cl_2

41. a. 2 mol   **b.** 7 mol   **c.** 9.40 mol

43. 0.5 mol O_2

45. a. 2.5 g   **b.** 31.1 g   **c.** 1.16 g

47. 2.91 grams CO remaining

49. limiting reactant: Pb^{2+}, theoretical yield: 34.5 g $PbCl_2$, percent yield: 85.3%

51. limiting reactant: NH_3, theoretical yield: 240.5 kg CH_4N_2O, percent yield: 70.01%

53. a. 1.17 M LiCl   **b.** 0.123 M $C_6H_{12}O_6$

c. 0.00453 M NaCl

55. a. 1.3 mol   **b.** 1.5 mol   **c.** 0.211 mol

57. 37 g

59. 0.27 M

61. 6.0 L

63. 37.1 mL

65. 2.1 L

67. a. yes   **b.** no   **c.** yes   **d.** no

69. a. soluble Ag^+, NO_3^- **b.** soluble Pb^{2+}, $C_2H_3O_2^-$

c. soluble K^+, NO_3^- **d.** soluble NH_4^+, S^{2-}

71. a. NO REACTION   **b.** NO REACTION

c. $CrBr_2(aq) + Na_2CO_3(aq) \longrightarrow CrCO_3(s) + 2 NaBr(aq)$

d. $3 NaOH(aq) + FeCl_3(aq) \longrightarrow Fe(OH)_3(s) + 3 NaCl(aq)$

73. a. $K_2CO_3(aq) + Pb(NO_3)_2(aq) \longrightarrow$
$$PbCO_3(s) + 2 KNO_3(aq)$$

b. $Li_2SO_4(aq) + Pb(C_2H_3O_2)_2(aq) \longrightarrow$
$$PbSO_4(s) + 2 LiC_2H_3O_2(aq)$$

c. $Cu(NO_3)_2(aq) + MgS(aq) \longrightarrow$
$$CuS(s) + Mg(NO_3)_2(aq)$$

d. NO REACTION

75. a. Complete:
$$H^+(aq) + Cl^-(aq) + Li^+(aq) + OH^-(aq) \longrightarrow$$
$$H_2O(l) + Li^+(aq) + Cl^-(aq)$$
Net: $H^+(aq) + OH^-(aq) \longrightarrow H_2O(l)$

b. Complete:
$$Mg^{2+}(aq) + S^{2-}(aq) + Cu^{2+}(aq) + 2 Cl^-(aq) \longrightarrow$$
$$CuS(s) + Mg^{2+}(aq) + 2 Cl^-(aq)$$
Net: $Cu^{2+}(aq) + S^{2-}(aq) \longrightarrow CuS(s)$

c. Complete:
$$Na^+(aq) + OH^-(aq) + H^+(aq) + NO_3^-(aq) \longrightarrow$$
$$H_2O(l) + Na^+(aq) + NO_3^-(aq)$$
Net: $H^+(aq) + OH^-(aq) \longrightarrow H_2O(l)$

d. Complete:
$$6 Na^+(aq) + 2 PO_4^{3-}(aq) + 3 Ni^{2+}(aq) + 6 Cl^-(aq) \longrightarrow$$
$$Ni_3(PO_4)_2(s) + 6 Na^+(aq) + 6 Cl^-(aq)$$
Net: $3 Ni^{2+}(aq) + 2 PO_4^{3-}(aq) \longrightarrow Ni_3(PO_4)_2(s)$

77. Complete:
$$Hg_2^{2+}(aq) + 2 NO_3^-(aq) + 2 Na^+(aq) + 2 Cl^-(aq) \longrightarrow$$
$$Hg_2Cl_2(s) + 2 Na^+(aq) + 2 NO_3^-(aq)$$
Net: $Hg_2^{2+}(aq) + 2 Cl^-(aq) \longrightarrow Hg_2Cl_2(s)$

79. Molecular: $HBr(aq) + KOH(aq) \longrightarrow H_2O(l) + KBr(aq)$
Net ionic: $H^+(aq) + OH^-(aq) \longrightarrow H_2O(l)$

81. a. $H_2SO_4(aq) + Ca(OH)_2(aq) \longrightarrow 2 H_2O(l) + CaSO_4(s)$

b. $HClO_4(aq) + KOH(aq) \longrightarrow H_2O(l) + KClO_4(aq)$

c. $H_2SO_4(aq) + 2 NaOH(aq) \longrightarrow$
$$2 H_2O(l) + Na_2SO_4(aq)$$

83. 0.1810 M $HClO_4$

85. a. $2 HBr(aq) + NiS(s) \longrightarrow H_2S(g) + NiBr_2(aq)$

b. $NH_4I(aq) + NaOH(aq) \longrightarrow$
$$H_2O(l) + NH_3(g) + NaI(aq)$$

c. $2 HBr(aq) + Na_2S(aq) \longrightarrow H_2S(g) + 2 NaBr(aq)$

d. $2 HClO_4(aq) + Li_2CO_3(aq) \longrightarrow$
$$H_2O(l) + CO_2(g) + 2 LiClO_4(aq)$$

87. a. Ag: 0   **b.** Ag: +1   **c.** Ca: +2, F: −1

d. H: +1, S: −2   **e.** C: +4, O: −2   **f.** Cr: +6, O: −2

89. a. +2   **b.** +6   **c.** +3

91. a. redox reaction, oxidizing agent: O_2, reducing agent: Li
  b. redox reaction, oxidizing agent: Fe^{2+}, reducing agent: Mg
  c. not a redox reaction   **d.** not a redox reaction
93. a. $S(s) + O_2(g) \longrightarrow SO_2(g)$
  b. $2\,C_3H_6(g) + 9\,O_2(g) \longrightarrow 6\,CO_2(g) + 6\,H_2O(g)$
  c. $2\,Ca(s) + O_2(g) \longrightarrow 2\,CaO(g)$
  d. $C_5H_{12}S(l) + 9\,O_2(g) \longrightarrow$
  $\qquad\qquad\qquad 5\,CO_2(g) + SO_2(g) + 6\,H_2O(g)$
95. 3.32 M
97. 1.1 g
99. 3.1 kg
101. limiting reactant: $C_7H_6O_3$, theoretical yield: 1.63 g $C_9H_8O_4$, percent yield: 74.8%
103. b
105. a. $2\,HCl(aq) + Hg_2(NO_3)_2(aq) \longrightarrow$
  $\qquad\qquad\qquad Hg_2Cl_2(s) + 2\,HNO_3(aq)$
  b. $KHSO_3(aq) + HNO_3(aq) \longrightarrow$
  $\qquad\qquad\qquad H_2O(l) + SO_2(g) + KNO_3(aq)$
  c. $2\,NH_4Cl(aq) + Pb(NO_3)_2(aq) \longrightarrow$
  $\qquad\qquad\qquad PbCl_2(s) + 2\,NH_4NO_3(aq)$
  d. $2\,NH_4Cl(aq) + Ca(OH)_2(aq) \longrightarrow$
  $\qquad\qquad 2\,NH_3(g) + 2\,H_2O(g) + CaCl_2(aq)$
107. 22 g
109. 6.9 g
111. $NaNO_3$ is more economical
113. Br is the oxidizing agent, Au is the reducing agent, 38.8 g $KAuF_4$
115. Ca^{2+} and Cu^{2+} present in the original solution
  Net ionic for first precipitate:
  $Ca^{2+}(aq) + SO_4^{2-}(aq) \longrightarrow CaSO_4(s)$
  Net ionic for second precipitate:
  $Cu^{2+}(aq) + CO_3^{2-}(aq) \longrightarrow CuCO_3(s)$
117. 0.333 g PH_3
119. 30.8 kg CO_2
121. 1.6 g C_2H_2
123. 11.8 g AgI
125. 5.5% by mass
127. 14 g KO_2, In designing the unit you would need to consider the theoretical yield and % yield of the reaction, how changing the limiting reactant would affect the reaction, the stoichiometry between KO_2 and O_2 to determine the mass of KO_2 required to produce enough O_2 for 10 minutes. You might also consider the speed of the reaction and whether or not the reaction produced heat. Additionally, because your body does not use 100% of the oxygen taken in with each breath, the apparatus would only need to replenish the oxygen used. The percentage of oxygen in air is about 20% and the percentage in exhaled air is about 16%, so we will assume that 4% of the air would need to be replenished with oxygen.
129. 37.9 g B_5H_9
131. a. Since the mol ratio of H_2 to NO is 5:2, the 10 mol of H_2 will require 4 mole NO and H_2 is the limiting reactant. This eliminates answers b and c. Since there is excess NO, this eliminates d, leaving answer a.
133. a

Chapter 5

29. a. 0.832 atm   **b.** 632 mmHg
  c. 12.2 psi   **d.** 8.43×10^4 Pa
31. a. 809.0 mmHg   **b.** 1.064 atm
  c. 809.0 torr   **d.** 107.9 kPa
33. a. 832 mmHg   **b.** 718 mmHg
35. 4.4×10^2 mmHg
37. 58.9 mL
39. 4.22 L
41. 3.0 L The volume would not be different if the gas was argon.
43. 1.16 atm
45. 2.1 mol
47. Yes, the final gauge pressure is 43.5 psi which exceeds the maximum rating.
49. 16.2 L
51. 286 atm, 17.5 bottles purged
53. b
55. 4.76 atm
57. 37.3 L
59. 9.43 g/L
61. 44.0 g/mol
63. 4.00 g/mol
65. $P_{tot} = 434$ torr, $mass_{N_2} = 0.437$ g, $mass_{O_2} = 0.237$ g, $mass_{He} = 0.0340$ g
67. 1.84 atm
69. $\chi_{N_2} = 0.627$, $\chi_{O_2} = 0.373$, $P_{N_2} = 0.687$ atm, $P_{O_2} = 0.409$ atm
71. $P_{H_2} = 0.921$ atm, $mass_{H_2} = 0.0539$ g
73. 7.47×10^{-2} g
75. 38 L
77. $V_{H_2} = 48.2$ L, $V_{CO} = 24.1$ L
79. 22.8 g NaN_3
81. 60.4%
83. a. yes   **b.** no
  c. No. Even though the argon atoms are more massive than the helium atoms, both have the same kinetic energy at a given temperature. The argon atoms therefore move more slowly, and so exert the same pressure as the helium atoms.
  d. He
85. F_2: $u_{rms} = 442$ m/s, $KE_{avg} = 3.72 \times 10^3$ J;
  Cl_2: $u_{rms} = 324$ m/s, $KE_{avg} = 3.72 \times 10^3$ J;
  Br_2: $u_{rms} = 216$ m/s, $KE_{avg} = 3.72 \times 10^3$ J;
  rankings: u_{rms}: $Br_2 < Cl_2 < F_2$, KE_{avg}: $Br_2 = Cl_2 = F_2$, rate of effusion: $Br_2 < Cl_2 < F_2$
87. rate $^{238}UF_6$/rate $^{235}UF_6 = 0.99574$
89. krypton
91. A has the higher molar mass, B has the higher rate of effusion.
93. That the volume of gas particles is small compared to the space between them breaks down under conditions of high pressure. At high pressure the particles themselves occupy a significant portion of the total gas volume.
95. 0.05826 L (ideal); 0.0708 L (V.D.W.); Difference because of high pressure, at which Ne no longer acts ideally.
97. 97.8%

99. 27.8 g/mol

101. C_4H_{10}

103. 4.70 L

105. $2\ HCl(aq) + K_2S(s) \longrightarrow$
$$H_2S(g) + 2\ KCl(aq), 0.191\ g\ K_2S(s)$$

107. 11.7 L

109. $mass_{air}$ = 8.56 g, $mass_{He}$ = 1.20 g, mass difference = 7.36 g

111. 4.76 L/s

113. total force = 6.15×10^3 pounds; no, the can cannot withstand this force

115. 5.8×10^3 balloons

117. 4.0 cm

119. 77.7%

121. 0.32 grams

123. 311 K

125. 5.0 g

127. C_3H_8

129. 0.39 g Ar

131. 74.0 mmHg

133. 25% N_2H_4

135. 25%

137. $P_{CH_4} = 7.30 \times 10^{-2}$ atm, $P_{O_2} = 4.20 \times 10^{-1}$ atm, $P_{NO} = 2.79 \times 10^{-3}$ atm, $P_{CO_2} = 5.03 \times 10^{-3}$ atm, $P_{H_2O} = 5.03 \times 10^{-3}$ atm, $P_{NO_2} = 2.51 \times 10^{-2}$ atm, $P_{OH} = 1.01 \times 10^{-2}$ atm, $P_{tot} = 0.542$ atm

139. 0.42

141. Because helium is less dense than air, the balloon moves in a direction opposite the direction the air inside the car is moving due to the acceleration and deceleration of the car.

143. −29%

145. a. false   **b.** false   **c.** false   **d.** true

Chapter 6

33. a. 1.92×10^9 J   **b.** 5.14×10^4 cal
c. 2.37×10^6 J   **d.** 0.681 Cal

35. a. 9.987×10^6 J   **b.** 9.987×10^3 kJ
c. 2.78 kWh

37. d

39. a. heat, +   **b.** work, −   **c.** heat, +

41. -7.27×10^2 kJ

43. 311 J

45. The drinks that went into cooler B had more thermal energy than the refrigerated drinks that went into cooler A. The temperature difference between the drinks in cooler B and the ice was greater than the difference between the drinks and the ice in cooler A. More thermal energy was exchanged between the drinks and the ice in cooler B, which resulted in more melting.

47. 4.7×10^5 J

49. a. $7.6 \times 10^2\ °C$ **b.** $4.3 \times 10^2\ °C$
c. $1.3 \times 10^2\ °C$ **d.** 49 °C

51. -2.8×10^2 J

53. 489 J

55. $\Delta E = -3463$ J, $\Delta H = -3452$ kJ

57. a. exothermic, −   **b.** endothermic, +
c. exothermic, −

59. -4.30×10^3 kJ

61. 9.5×10^2 g CO_2

63. mass of silver 77.1 grams

65. Final temperature 28.4 °C

67. Specific heat capacity of substance A 1.10 J/g · °C

69. Measurement B corresponds to conditions of constant pressure. Measurement A corresponds to conditions of constant volume. When a fuel is burned under constant pressure some of the energy released does work on the atmosphere by expanding against it. Less energy is manifest as heat due to this work. When a fuel is burned under constant volume, all of the energy released by the combustion reaction is evolved as heat.

71. -6.3×10^3 kJ/mol

73. -1.6×10^5 J

75. a. $-\Delta H_1$ **b.** $2\ \Delta H_1$ **c.** $-\frac{1}{2}\Delta H_1$

77. −23.9 kJ

79. 87.8 kJ

81. a. $N_2(g) + 3\ H_2(g) \longrightarrow$
$$2\ NH_3(g),\ \Delta H_f^\circ = -45.9\ kJ/mol$$
b. $C(s,\ graphite) + O_2(g) \longrightarrow$
$$CO_2(g),\ \Delta H_f^\circ = -393.5\ kJ/mol$$
c. $2\ Fe(s) + 3/2\ O_2(g) \longrightarrow$
$$Fe_2O_3(s),\ \Delta H_f^\circ = -824.2\ kJ/mol$$
d. $C(s,\ graphite) + 2\ H_2(g) \longrightarrow$
$$CH_4(g),\ \Delta H_f^\circ = -74.6\ kJ/mol$$

83. −382.1 kJ/mol

85. a. −137.1 kJ   **b.** −41.2 kJ
c. −137 kJ   **d.** 290.7 kJ

87. $6\ CO_2(g) + 6\ H_2O(l) \longrightarrow$
$$C_6H_{12}O_6(s) + 6\ O_2(g),\ \Delta H_{rxn}^\circ = 2803\ kJ$$

89. −113.0 kJ/mol

91. a. 5.49 g CO_2 **b.** 5.96 g CO_2
c. 6.94 g CO_2
Natural gas, $CH_4(g)$, contributes the least to global warming by producing the least $CO_2(g)$ per kJ of heat produced.

93. 2×10^{13} kg CO_2 produced per year, 150 years

95. $\Delta E = -1.7$ J, $q = -0.5$ J, $w = -1.2$ J

97. 78 g

99. $\Delta H = 6.0$ kJ/mol, 1.1×10^2 g

101. 26.1 °C

103. palmitic acid: 9.9378 Cal/g, sucrose: 3.938 Cal/g, fat contains more Cal/g than sugar

105. $\Delta H = \Delta E + nR\ \Delta T$

107. 5.7 Cal/g

109. $\Delta E = 0$, $\Delta H = 0$, $q = -w = 3.0 \times 10^3$ J

111. −294 kJ/mol

113. 94.0 kJ

115. 23.9 °C

117. 7.3×10^3 g H_2SO_4

119. 7.2×10^2 g

121. 78.2 °C

123. $C_v = \frac{3}{2}R$, $C_p = \frac{5}{2}R$

125. $q = 1030$ kJ, $\Delta H = 1030$ kJ, $\Delta E = 952$ kJ, $w = -78$ kJ

127. -1292 kJ

129. d

131. a. At constant pressure, heat can be added and work can be done on the system. $\Delta E = q + w$, therefore $q = \Delta E - w$.

133. The aluminum is cooler because it has a lower heat capacity (specific heat).

135. $q = -2418$ J, $w = -5$ kJ, $\Delta H = -2418$ J/mol, $\Delta E = -2423$ J/mol

137. b. $\Delta H > \Delta E$

Chapter 7

37. 499 s

39. (i) d, c, b, a
(ii) a, b, c, d

41. a. 4.74×10^{14} Hz   **b.** 5.96×10^{14} Hz
c. 5.8×10^{18} Hz

43. a. 3.14×10^{-19} J   **b.** 3.95×10^{-19} J
c. 3.8×10^{-15} J

45. 1.03×10^{16} photons

47. a. 79.8 kJ/mol   **b.** 239 kJ/mol
c. 798 kJ/mol

49.

51. 3.6×10^6 m/s

53. 5.39 nm

55. 1.1×10^{-34} m. The wavelength of a baseball is negligible with respect to its size.

57. $\Delta v = 1.04 \times 10^5$ m/s

59. $2s$

61. a. $l = 0$ **b.** $l = 0, 1$
c. $l = 0, 1, 2$ **d.** $l = 0, 1, 2, 3$

63. c

65. See Figures 7.25 and 7.26. The $2s$ and $3p$ orbitals would, on average, be farther from the nucleus and have more nodes than the $1s$ and $2p$ orbitals.

67. $n = 1$

69. $2p \longrightarrow 1s$

71. a. 122 nm, UV   **b.** 103 nm, UV
c. 486 nm, visible   **d.** 434 nm, visible

73. $n = 2$

75. 344 nm

77. 6.4×10^{17} photons/s

79. 0.0547 nm

81. 91.2 nm

83. a. 4   **b.** 9   **c.** 16

85. $n = 4 \longrightarrow n = 3$, $n = 5 \longrightarrow n = 3$, $n = 6 \longrightarrow n = 3$, respectively

87. 4.84×10^{14} s^{-1}

89. 11 m

91. 6.78×10^{-3} J

93. 632 nm

95. a. $E_1 = 2.51 \times 10^{-18}$ J, $E_2 = 1.00 \times 10^{-17}$ J, $E_3 = 2.26 \times 10^{-17}$ J
b. 26.5 nm, UV; 15.8 nm, UV

97.

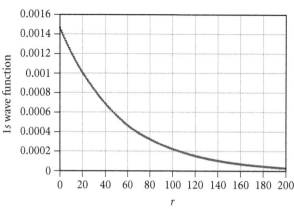

The plot for the $2s$ wave function extends below the x-axis. The x-intercept represents the radial node of the orbital.

99. 7.39×10^5 m/s

101. $\Delta E = 1.1 \times 10^{-20}$ J, 7.0×10^2 nm

103. 11 m

105. In the Bohr model, electrons exist in specific orbits encircling the atom. In the quantum mechanical model, electrons exist in orbitals that are really probability density maps of where the electron is likely to be found. The Bohr model is inconsistent with Heisenberg's uncertainty principle.

107. a. yes   **b.** no   **c.** yes   **d.** no

Chapter 8

43. a. $1s^2 2s^2 2p^6 3s^2 3p^2$
b. $1s^2 2s^2 2p^4$
c. $1s^2 2s^2 2p^6 3s^2 3p^6 4s^1$
d. $1s^2 2s^2 2p^6$

45. a.

↑↓	↑↓	↑	↑	↑
$1s$	$2s$		$2p$	

b.

↑↓	↑↓	↑↓	↑↓	↑
$1s$	$2s$		$2p$	

c.

↑↓	↑↓	↑↓	↑↓	↑↓	↑↓
$1s$	$2s$		$2p$		$3s$

d.

↑↓	↑↓	↑↓	↑↓	↑↓	↑↓	↑	
$1s$	$2s$		$2p$		$3s$		$3p$

47. a. [Ne] $3s^23p^3$ **b.** [Ar] $4s^23d^{10}4p^2$
   c. [Kr] $5s^24d^2$ **d.** [Kr] $5s^24d^{10}5p^5$
49. a. 1   **b.** 10   **c.** 5   **d.** 2
51. a. V, As   **b.** Se   **c.** V   **d.** Kr
53. a. 2   **b.** 1   **c.** 10   **d.** 6
55. reactive metal: **a**, reactive nonmetal: **c**
57. The valence electrons of nitrogen will experience a greater effective nuclear charge. The valence electrons of both atoms are screened by two core electrons but N has a greater number of protons and therefore a greater net nuclear charge.
59. a. 1+   **b.** 2+   **c.** 6+   **d.** 4+
61. a. In   **b.** Si   **c.** Pb   **d.** C
63. F, S, Si, Ge, Ca, Rb
65. a. [Ne]   **b.** [Kr]   **c.** [Kr]
   d. [Ar] $3d^6$ **e.** [Ar] $3d^9$
67. a. [Ar] Diamagnetic

   b. [Ar] ↑ ↑ ↑ _ _   Paramagnetic
$3d$

   c. [Ar] ↑↓ ↑↓ ↑↓ ↑ ↑   Paramagnetic
$3d$

   d. [Ar] ↑ ↑ ↑ ↑ ↑   Paramagnetic
$3d$

69. a. Li   **b.** I⁻   **c.** Cr   **d.** O^{2-}
71. O^{2-}, F⁻, Ne, Na⁺, Mg^{2+}
73. a. Br   **b.** Na
   c. cannot tell based on periodic trends
   d. P
75. In, Si, N, F
77. a. second and third   **b.** fifth and sixth
   c. sixth and seventh   **d.** first and second
79. a. Na   **b.** S   **c.** C   **d.** F
81. a. Sr
   b. Bi
   c. cannot tell based on periodic trends
   d. As
83. S, Se, Sb, In, Ba, Fr
85. $Sr(s) + I_2(g) \longrightarrow SrI_2(s)$
87. $2 Li(s) + 2 H_2O(l) \longrightarrow 2 Li^+(aq) + 2 OH^-(aq) + H_2(g)$
89. $H_2(g) + Br_2(g) \longrightarrow 2 HBr(g)$
91. Br: $1s^22s^22p^63s^23p^64s^23d^{10}4p^5$
   Kr: $1s^22s^22p^63s^23p^64s^23d^{10}4p^6$
   Krypton's outer electron shell is filled, giving it chemical stability. Bromine is missing an electron from its outer shell and subsequently has a high electron affinity. Bromine tends to be easily reduced by gaining an electron, giving the bromide ion stability due to the filled p subshell which corresponds to krypton's chemically stable electron configuration.
93. V: [Ar] $4s^23d^3$
   V^{3+}:[Ar] $3d^2$

Both V and V^{3+} contain unpaired electrons in their $3d$ orbitals.
95. A substitute for K⁺ would need to exhibit a 1+ electric charge and have similar mass and atomic radius. Na⁺ and Rb⁺ would not be good substitutes because their radii are significantly smaller and larger, respectively. Based on mass, Ca⁺ and Ar⁺ are the closest to K⁺. Because the first ionization energy of Ca⁺ is closest to that of K⁺, Ca⁺ is the best choice for a substitute. The difficulty lies in Ca's low second ionization energy, making it easily oxidized.
97. Si, Ge
99. a. N: [He] $2s^22p^3$, Mg: [Ne] $3s^2$, O: [He] $2s^22p^4$, F: [He] $2s^22p^5$, Al: [Ne] $3s^23p^1$
   b. Mg, Al, O, F, N
   c. Al, Mg, O, N, F
   d. Aluminum's first ionization energy is lower than Mg because its $3p$ electron is shielded by the $3s$ orbital. Oxygen's first ionization energy is lower than that of N because its fourth $2p$ electron experiences electron–electron repulsion by the other electron in its orbital.
101. For main-group elements, atomic radii decrease across a period because the addition of a proton in the nucleus and an electron in the outermost energy level increases Z_{eff}. This does not happen in the transition metals because the electrons are added to the $n_{highest-1}$ orbital and the Z_{eff} stays roughly the same.
103. Noble gases are exceptionally unreactive due to the stability of their completely filled outer quantum levels and their high ionization energies. The ionization energies of Kr, Xe, and Rn are low enough to form some compounds.
105. 6A: ns^2np^4, 7A: ns^2np^5, group 7A elements require only one electron to achieve a noble gas configuration. Since group 6A elements require two electrons, their affinity for one electron is less negative, because one electron will merely give them an np^5 configuration.
107. 85
109. a. One If By Land (O, Ne, I, F, B, Y, La, Nd)
   b. Atoms are Fun (N, U, Fe, Ra, S, Mo, Ta backwards)
111. 1.390×10^3 kJ/mol, 86.14 nm
113. a. $d_{Ar} \approx 2$ g/L, $d_{Xe} \approx 6.5$ g/L
   b. $d_{118} \approx 13$ g/L
   c. mass = 3.35×10^{-23} g/Ne atom, density of Ne atom = 2.3×10^4 g/L. The separation of Ne atoms relative to their size is immense.
   d. Kr: 2.69×10^{22} atoms/L, Ne: 2.69×10^{22} atoms/L. It seems Ar will also have 2.69×10^{22} atoms/L. $d_{Ar} = 1.78$ g/L. This corresponds to accepted values.
115. Density increases to the right, because, though electrons are added successively across the period, they are added to the $3d$ subshell which is not a part of the outermost principal energy level. As a result, the atomic radius does not increase significantly across the period while mass does.

117. Longest λ :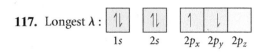

       1s   2s $2p_x$ $2p_y$ $2p_z$

Next longest λ : ⬚⬚⬚

       1s   2s $2p_x$ $2p_y$ $2p_z$

Next longest λ : ⬚⬚⬚

       1s   2s $2p_x$ $2p_y$ $2p_z$

119. 168, noble gas

121. A relatively high effective nuclear charge is found in gallium with its completed 3*d* subshell and in thallium with its completed 4*f* subshell, accounting for the relatively high first ionization energies of these elements.

123. The second electron affinity requires the addition of an electron to something that is already negatively charged. The monoanions of both of these elements have relatively high electron density in a relatively small volume. As we shall see in Chapter 9 the dianions of these elements do exist in many compounds because they are stabilized by chemical bonding.

125. 120, 170

127. Fr, [Rn] $7s^1$, > 265, < 376, > 1.879, < 29
    a. $Fr^+(aq)$, $OH^-(aq)$, $H_2(g)$ **b.** $Fr_2O(s)$ **c.** $FrCl(s)$

129. **a.** any group 6A element   **b.** any group 5A element
    c. any group 1A element

131. **a.** true   **b.** true   **c.** false   **d.** true

133. Since Ca has valence electrons of $4s^2$, it has a relatively low ionization energy to lose 2 electrons. Whereas, F has a highly exothermic electron affinity when gaining 1 electron, but not a second electron because of its $2s^2 2p^5$ valence electrons. Therefore, calcium and fluoride combine in a 2 : 1 ratio.

Chapter 9

35. $1s^2 2s^2 2p^3$ ·N̈:

37. **a.** ·Äl·   **b.** Na^+

    c. :C̈l: **d.** $\left[:\ddot{C}l:\right]^-$

39. **a.** $Na^+\left[:\ddot{F}:\right]^-$ **b.** $Ca^{2+}\left[:\ddot{O}:\right]^{2-}$

    c. $Sr^{2+} 2\left[:\ddot{B}r:\right]^-$ **d.** $2\ K^+\left[:\ddot{O}:\right]^{2-}$

41. **a.** SrSe   **b.** $BaCl_2$
    c. Na_2S **d.** Al_2O_3

43. As the size of the alkaline earth metal ions increases, so does the distance between the metal cations and oxygen anions. Therefore, the magnitude of the lattice energy decreases accordingly because the potential energy decreases as the distance increases.

45. One factor of lattice energy is the product of the charges of the two ions. The product of the ion charges for CsF is −1 while that for BaO is −4. Because this product is four times greater, the lattice energy is also four times greater.

47. −708 kJ/mol

49. **a.** H:H, filled duets, 0 formal charge on both atoms
    b. :C̈l:C̈l:, filled octets, 0 formal charge on both atoms
    c. Ö=Ö, filled octets, 0 formal charge on both atoms
    d. :N≡N:, filled octets, 0 formal charge on both atoms

51. **a.** H—P̈—H   **b.** :S̈—C̈l:
        | |
        H   :C̈l:

    c. H—Ï: **d.** H—C—H with H above and below

53. **a.** :F̈—S̈—F̈:   **b.** H—Si—H with H below

    c. :Ö=C—Ö: with H below   **d.** H—C—S̈—H with H above and below

55. **a.** pure covalent   **b.** polar covalent
    c. pure covalent   **d.** ionic bond

57. :C=Ö:, 25%

59. **a.** :Ï—C—Ï: with :Ï: above and below   **b.** :N≡N—Ö:

    c. H—Si—H with H above and below   **d.** :C̈l—C—C̈l: with :O: above (double bond)

61. **a.** H—N̈=N̈—H   **b.** H—N̈—N̈—H with H H below

    c. H—C≡C—H   **d.** H—C=C—H with H H below

63. **a.** :Ö—S̈e=Ö: ⟷ :Ö=S̈e—Ö:
       −1   +1   0   0 +1 −1

    b. $\left[\begin{array}{c}:O:^0 \\ C^0 \\ {}^{-1}:\ddot{O}\quad\ddot{O}:^{-1}\end{array}\right]^{2-}$ ⟷ $\left[\begin{array}{c}:\ddot{O}:^{-1} \\ C^0 \\ {}^{-1}:\ddot{O}\quad\ddot{O}:^{0}\end{array}\right]^{2-}$ ⟷

          $\left[\begin{array}{c}:\ddot{O}:^{-1} \\ C^0 \\ {}^{0}:\ddot{O}\quad\ddot{O}:^{-1}\end{array}\right]^{2-}$

    c. $\left[:\ddot{C}l—\ddot{O}:\right]^-$ with 0 −1

    d. $\left[:\ddot{O}=\ddot{N}—\ddot{O}:\right]^-$ ⟷ $\left[:\ddot{O}—\ddot{N}=\ddot{O}:\right]^-$
         0   0 −1   −1 0   0

65. 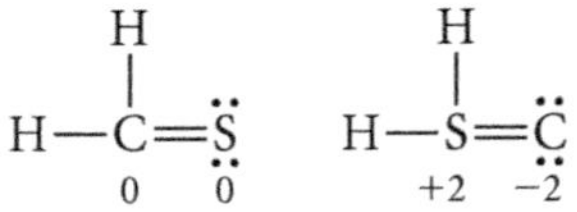 $H-C=\ddot{S}$ (0, 0) $H-\ddot{S}=\ddot{C}$ (+2, −2) H_2CS is the better structure

67. $:O\equiv C-\ddot{O}:$ does not provide a significant contribution to the resonance hybrid as it has a +1 formal charge on a very electronegative atom (oxygen).

69. a. 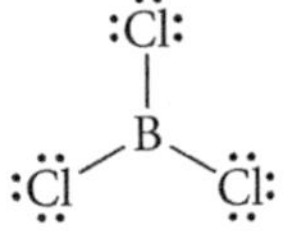 $:\ddot{C}l:$ with B bonded to three $:\ddot{C}l:$

b. $\ddot{O}=\dot{N}-\ddot{O}: \longleftrightarrow :\ddot{O}-\dot{N}=\ddot{O}$

c. H with B bonded to three H (BH$_3$)

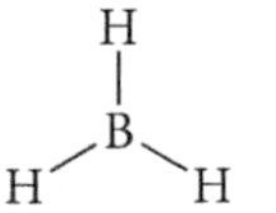

71. a. 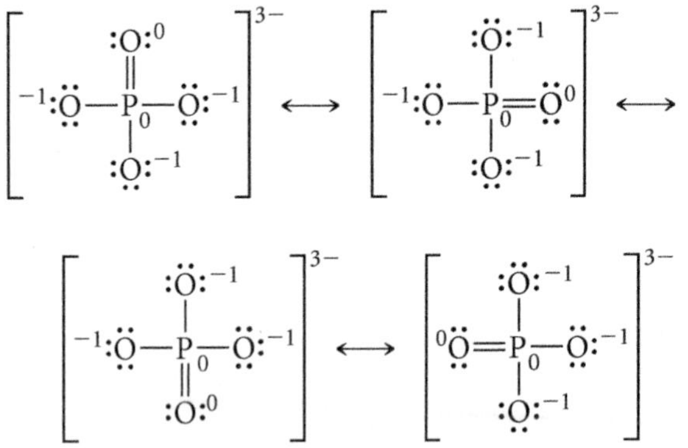 $\left[\ ^{-1}:\ddot{O}-P-\ddot{O}:^{-1}\ \right]^{3-}$ with $:O:^{0}$ double bonded top and $:\ddot{O}:^{-1}$ below, P formal charge 0 $\longleftrightarrow$ (three further resonance structures shown)

b. $\left[:C\equiv N:\right]^{-}$ (−1, 0)

c. $\left[:\ddot{O}-S-\ddot{O}:\right]^{2-}$ with $:O:^{0}$ (−1, 0, −1) $\longleftrightarrow$ (resonance structures shown)

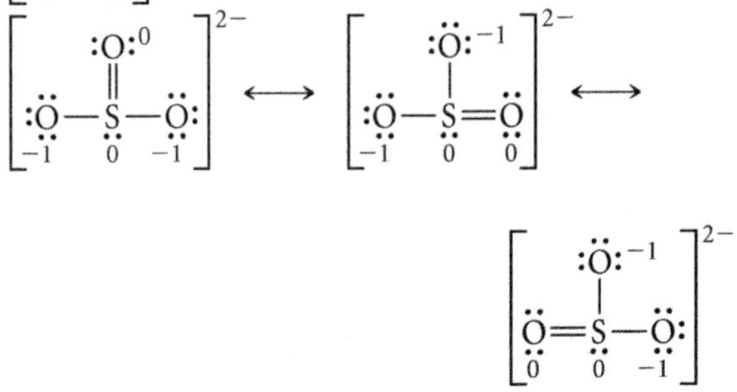

d. 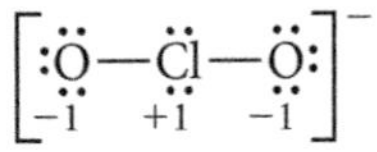 $\left[:\ddot{O}-\ddot{C}l-\ddot{O}:\right]^{-}$ (−1, +1, −1)

73. a. 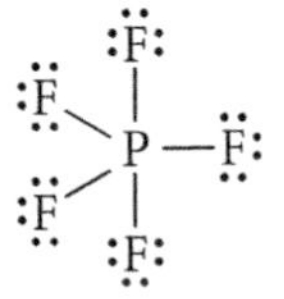 PF_5 structure with P bonded to five $:\ddot{F}:$

b. 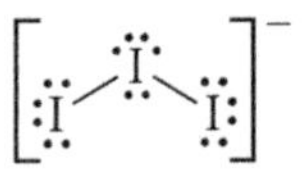 $\left[:\ddot{I}-\ddot{I}-\ddot{I}:\right]^{-}$

c. 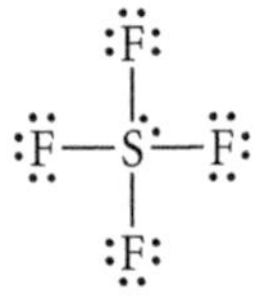 $:\ddot{F}-\dot{S}-\ddot{F}:$ with F above and below (SF$_4$)

d. 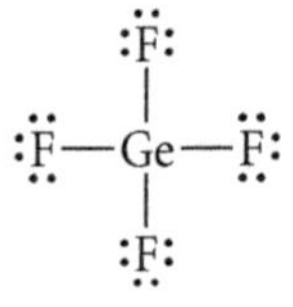 $:\ddot{F}-Ge-\ddot{F}:$ with F above and below (GeF$_4$)

75. H_3CCH_3, H_2CCH_2, HCCH

77. −128 kJ

79. −614 kJ

81. a. 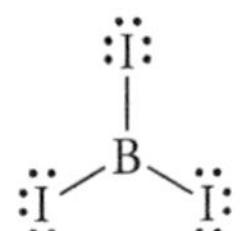 $:\ddot{I}$ with B bonded to three $:\ddot{I}:$ (BI$_3$)

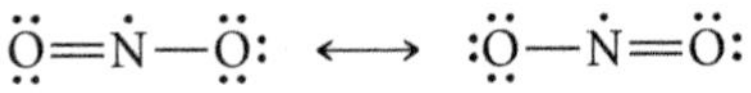

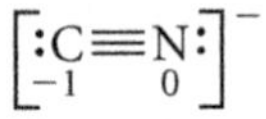

b. $2\,K^{+}\left[:\ddot{S}:\right]^{2-}$

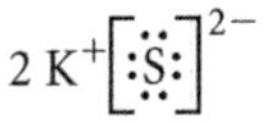

c. 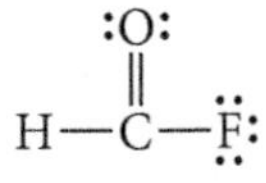 $H-C-\ddot{F}:$ with $:O:$ double bonded above

d. 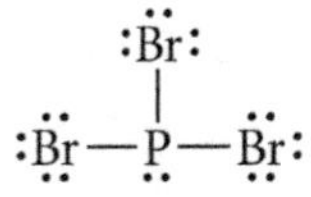 $:\ddot{Br}-P-\ddot{Br}:$ with $:\ddot{Br}:$ above

83. a. 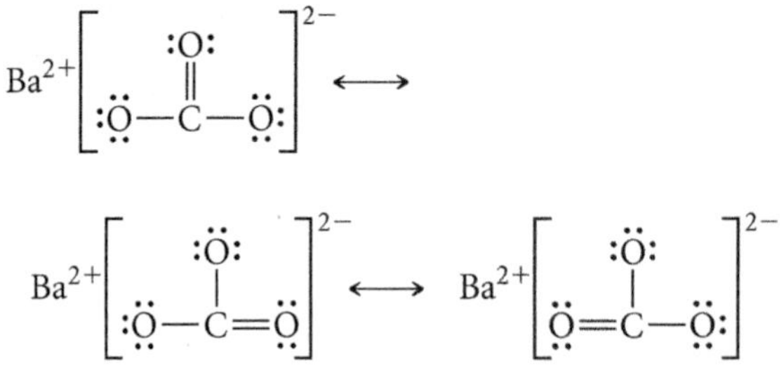 $Ba^{2+}\left[\ :\ddot{O}-C-\ddot{O}:\ \right]^{2-}$ with $:O:$ double bonded above $\longleftrightarrow$

$Ba^{2+}\left[:\ddot{O}-C=\ddot{O}\ \right]^{2-}$ with $:O:$ above $\longleftrightarrow$ $Ba^{2+}\left[\ddot{O}=C-\ddot{O}:\right]^{2-}$ with $:O:$ above

b. $Ca^{2+}\ 2\left[:\ddot{O}-H\right]^{-}$

c. $K^{+}\left[:\ddot{O}-N-\ddot{O}:\right]^{-}$ with $:O:$ double bonded above $\longleftrightarrow$ $K^{+}\left[:\ddot{O}-N=\ddot{O}\right]^{-}$ with $:O:$ above $\longleftrightarrow$ $K^{+}\left[\ddot{O}=N-\ddot{O}:\right]^{-}$ with $:O:$ above

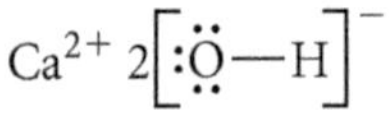

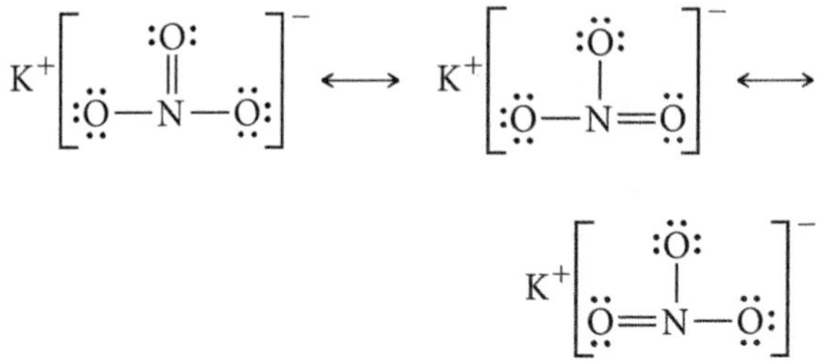

d. 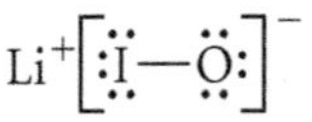 $Li^{+}\left[:\ddot{I}-\ddot{O}:\right]^{-}$

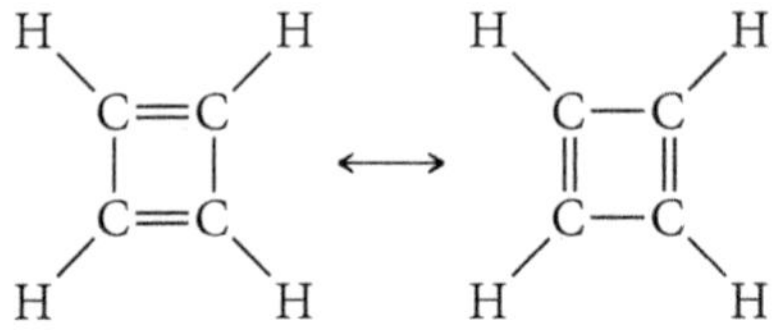

85. a. 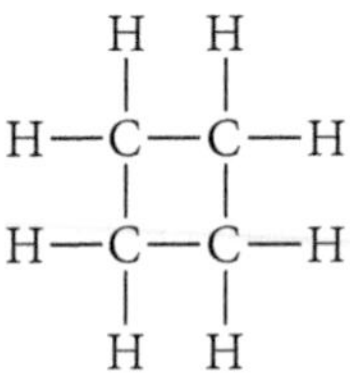 cyclobutane structure

$H-C-C-H$ (with H, H top and H, H bottom on each carbon, four-membered ring)

b. cyclobutadiene resonance structures

c. cyclohexane structure

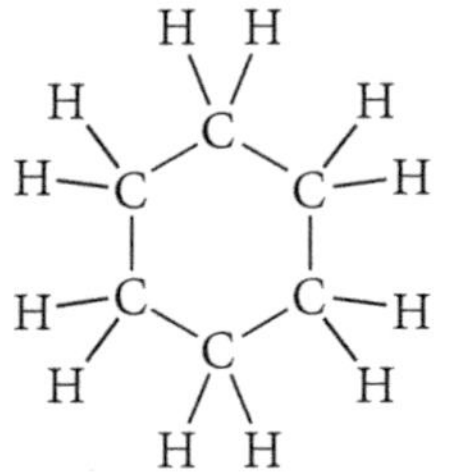

d. 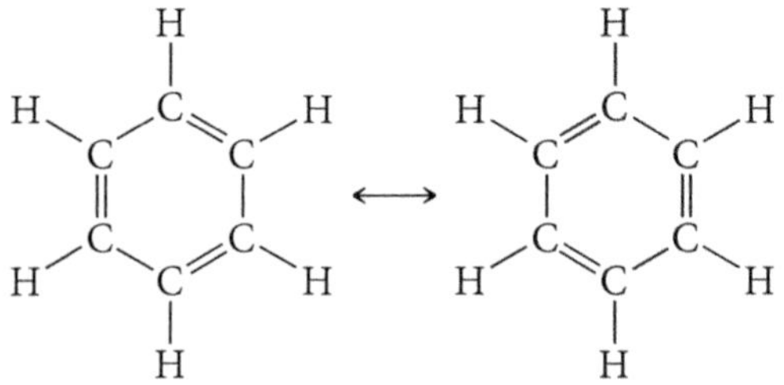 benzene resonance structures

87. CH_2O_2, $H-C-\ddot{O}-H$ with $:O:$ double bonded above

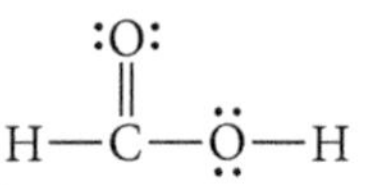

89. The reaction is exothermic due to the energy released when the Al_2O_3 lattice forms.

91.

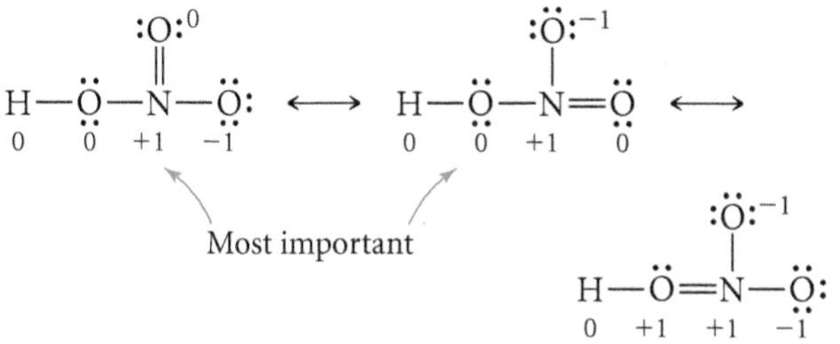

Most important

93.

The fulminate ion is less stable because nitrogen is more electronegative than carbon and should therefore be terminal to accomodate the negative formal charge.

95.

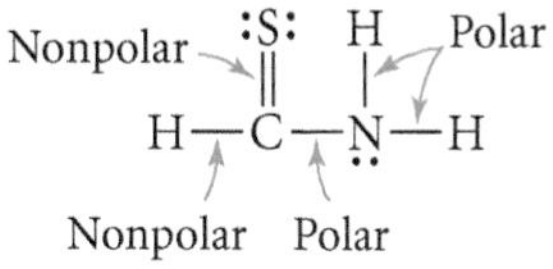

97. a. 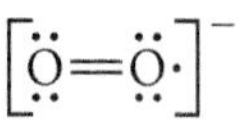 $\left[\ddot{O}=\ddot{O}\cdot\right]^{-}$ **b.** 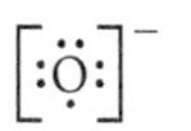 $\left[:\ddot{O}:\right]^{-}$

c. 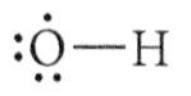 $:\dot{O}-H$ **d.**

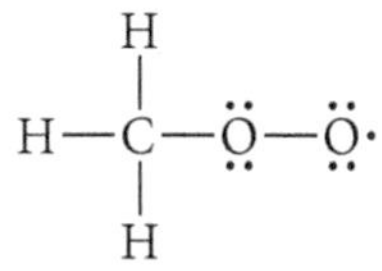

99. $\Delta H_{rxn(H_2)} = -243$ kJ/mol $= -121$ kJ/g
$\Delta H_{rxn(CH_4)} = -802$ kJ/mol $= -50.0$ kJ/g
CH_4 yields more energy per mole while H_2 yields more energy per gram.

101. a.

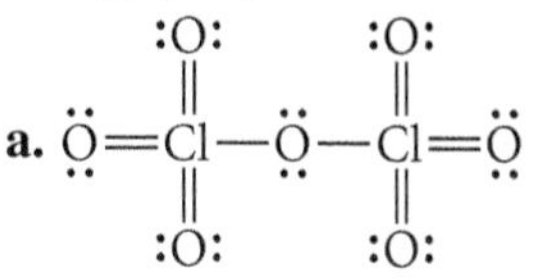

b.

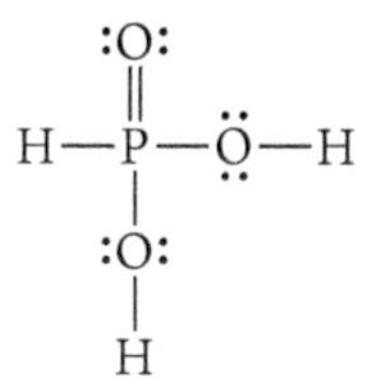

c.

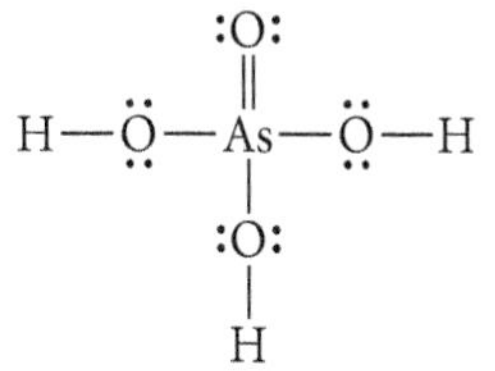

103. Na^+F^-, Na^+O^{2-}, $Mg^{2+}F^-$, $Mg^{2+}O^{2-}$, $Al^{3+}O^{2-}$
105. 333 kJ/mol
107. $H-C\equiv C-H$

109.

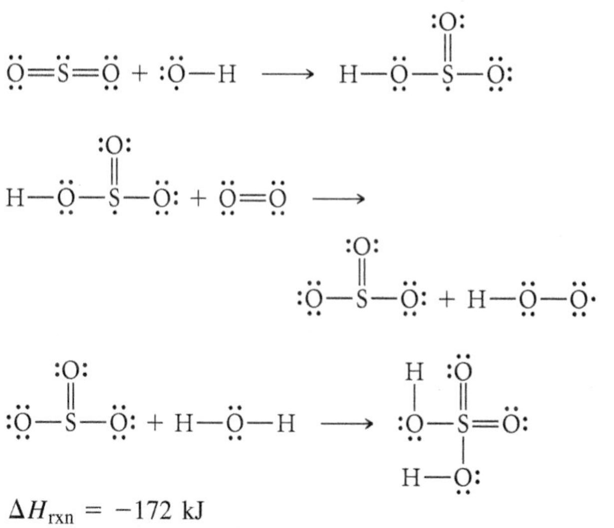

$\Delta H_{rxn} = -172$ kJ

111. $r_{HCl} = 113$ pm
$r_{HF} = 84$ pm
These values are close to the accepted values.

113.

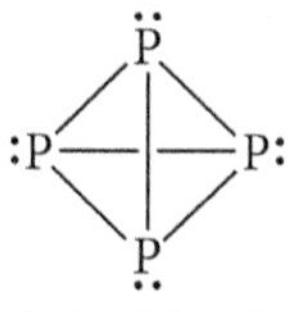

115. 126 kJ/mol
117. The oxidation number of the S atoms bonded directly to hydrogen atoms is -1. The oxidation number of interior S atoms is 0.
119. 536 kJ
121. The compounds are energy rich because a great deal of energy is released when these compounds undergo a reaction that breaks weak bonds and forms strong ones.
123. The theory is successful because it allows us to predict and account for many chemical observations. The theory is limited because electrons cannot be treated as localized "dots."

Chapter 10

31. 4
33. a. 4 e⁻ groups, 4 bonding groups, 0 lone pairs
b. 5 e⁻ groups, 3 bonding groups, 2 lone pairs
c. 6 e⁻ groups, 5 bonding groups, 1 lone pair
35. a. e⁻ geometry: tetrahedral
molecular geometry: trigonal pyramidal
idealized bond angle: 109.5°, deviation
b. e⁻ geometry: tetrahedral
molecular geometry: bent
idealized bond angle: 109.5°, deviation
c. e⁻ geometry: tetrahedral
molecular geometry: tetrahedral
idealized bond angle: 109.5°, deviation (due to large size of Cl compared to H)
d. e⁻ geometry: linear
molecular geometry: linear
idealized bond angle: 180°
37. H_2O has a smaller bond angle due to lone pair–lone pair repulsions, the strongest electron group repulsion.

39. a. seesaw,

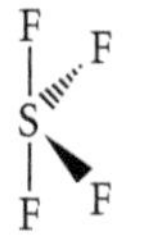

b. T-shape,

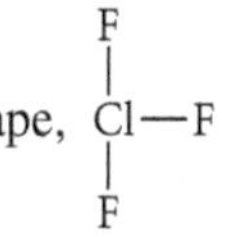

c. linear, $F-I-F$ **d.** square planar,

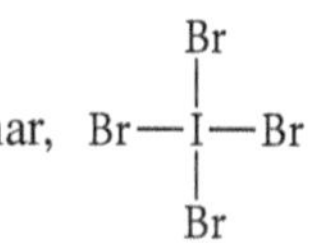

41. a. linear, $H-C\equiv C-H$

b. Trigonal planar,

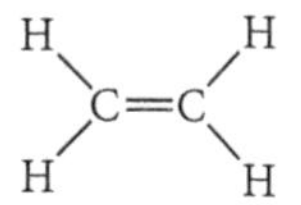

c. tetrahedral,

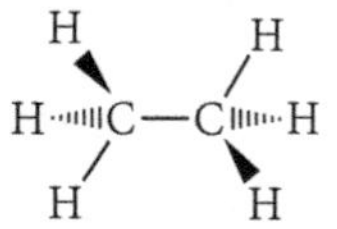

43. a. The lone pair will cause lone pair–bonding pair repulsions, pushing the three bonding pairs out of the same plane. The correct molecular geometry is trigonal pyramidal.
  b. The lone pair should take an equatorial position to minimize 90° bonding pair interactions. The correct molecular geometry is seesaw.
  c. The lone pairs should take positions on opposite sides of the central atom to reduce lone pair–lone pair interactions. The correct molecular geometry is square planar.

45. a. C: tetrahedral   O: bent

  b. C's: tetrahedral
     O: bent
  c. O's: bent

47. The vectors of the polar bonds in both CO_2 and CCl_4 oppose each other with equal magnitude and sum to 0.

49. PF_3, polar
   SBr_2, nonpolar
   $CHCl_3$, polar
   CS_2, nonpolar

51. a. polar   **b.** polar
   c. polar   **d.** nonpolar

53. a. 0   **b.** 3   **c.** 1

55. P:

  H$_1$:   Expected bond angle = 90°

  Valence bond theory is compatible with experimentally determined bond angle of 93.3° without hybrid orbitals.

  H$_2$:

  H$_3$:

57.

   (2s   2p   →Hybridization→   sp³)

59. sp^2

61. a. sp^3

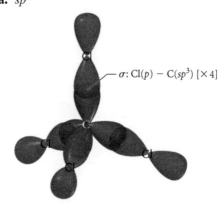

σ: Cl(p) − C(sp^3) [×4]

  b. sp^3

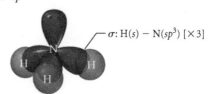

σ: H(s) − N(sp^3) [×3]

  c. sp^3

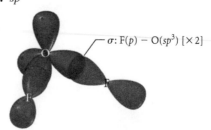

σ: F(p) − O(sp^3) [×2]

  d. sp

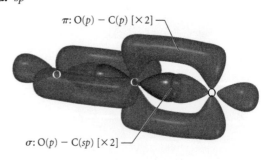

π: O(p) − C(p) [×2]

σ: O(p) − C(sp) [×2]

63. a. sp^2

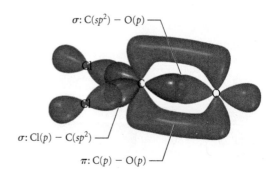

σ: C(sp^2) − O(p)

σ: Cl(p) − C(sp^2)

π: C(p) − O(p)

b. sp^3d^2

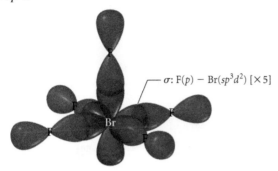

σ: F(p) − Br(sp^3d^2) [×5]

c. sp^3d

σ: F(p) − Xe(sp^3d) [×2]

d. sp^3d

σ: I(p) − I(sp^3d) [×2]

65. a. N's: sp^2

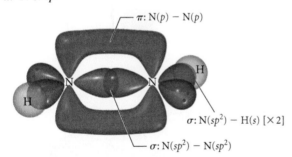

π: N(p) − N(p)

σ: N(sp^2) − H(s) [×2]

σ: N(sp^2) − N(sp^2)

b. N's: sp^3

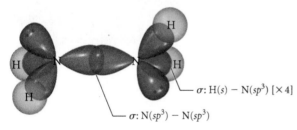

σ: H(s) − N(sp^3) [×4]

σ: N(sp^3) − N(sp^3)

c. C: sp^3
 N: sp^3

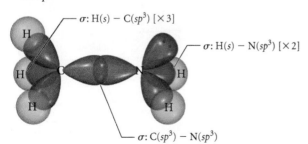

σ: H(s) − C(sp^3) [×3]

σ: H(s) − N(sp^3) [×2]

σ: C(sp^3) − N(sp^3)

67.

sp^3

sp^3 sp^2

69.

Constructive interference

71. Be$_2{}^+$ $\underline{1}$ σ_{2s}^* Be$_2{}^-$

$\underline{1\!\!\downarrow}$ σ_{2s} $\underline{1}$ σ_{2p}

$\underline{1\!\!\downarrow}$ σ_{2s}^*

$\underline{1\!\!\downarrow}$ σ_{2s}

bond order Be$_2{}^+$ = 1/2
bond order Be$_2{}^-$ = 1/2
Both will exist in gas phase.

Bonding

73.

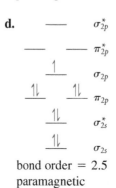

Antibonding

75. a.

—	σ_{2p}^*
— —	π_{2p}^*
—	σ_{2p}
— —	π_{2p}
$\underline{1\!\!\downarrow}$	σ_{2s}^*
$\underline{1\!\!\downarrow}$	σ_{2s}

bond order = 0
diamagnetic

b.

—	σ_{2p}^*
— —	π_{2p}^*
—	σ_{2p}
$\underline{1}$ $\underline{1}$	π_{2p}
$\underline{1\!\!\downarrow}$	σ_{2s}^*
$\underline{1\!\!\downarrow}$	σ_{2s}

bond order = 1
paramagnetic

c.

—	σ_{2p}^*
— —	π_{2p}^*
—	σ_{2p}
$\underline{1\!\!\downarrow}$ $\underline{1\!\!\downarrow}$	π_{2p}
$\underline{1\!\!\downarrow}$	σ_{2s}^*
$\underline{1\!\!\downarrow}$	σ_{2s}

bond order = 2
diamagnetic

d.

—	σ_{2p}^*
— —	π_{2p}^*
$\underline{1}$	σ_{2p}
$\underline{1\!\!\downarrow}$ $\underline{1\!\!\downarrow}$	π_{2p}
$\underline{1\!\!\downarrow}$	σ_{2s}^*
$\underline{1\!\!\downarrow}$	σ_{2s}

bond order = 2.5
paramagnetic

77. a. not stable   **b.** not stable
    c. stable   **d.** not stable

79. C_2^- has the highest bond order, the highest bond energy, and the shortest bond length.

81.

$$\underline{\quad\quad} \quad \sigma^*_{2p}$$

$$\underline{\quad\quad} \;\; \underline{\quad\quad} \quad \pi^*_{2p}$$

$$\underline{\uparrow\downarrow} \;\; \underline{\uparrow\downarrow} \quad \pi_{2p}$$

$$\underline{\uparrow\downarrow} \quad \sigma_{2p}$$

$$\underline{\uparrow\downarrow} \quad \sigma^*_{2s}$$

$$\underline{\uparrow\downarrow} \quad \sigma_{2s}$$

bond order $= 3$

83. a.
:F—C—F:
with :O: double-bonded on top
trigonal planar
polar
C: sp^2

b. :Cl—S—S—Cl:
bent polar
S's: sp^3

c.
:F—S—F:
with :F: on top and :F: on bottom
seesaw polar
S: sp^3d

85. a.

sp^3, Bent sp^3, Tetrahedral

H H H :O:
| | | ‖
:O—C—C—C—Ö—H
    | :N—H
    H |
         H

sp^3, Tetrahedral

sp^3, bent

sp^2, Trigonal planar

sp^3, Trigonal pyramidal

(structure with OH, O, H_2N, OH)

85. b.

sp^3, Tetrahedral sp^3, Tetrahedral

sp^2, Trigonal planar H_2N

H :O: H H :O:
| ‖ | | ‖
:N—C—C—C—C—Ö—H
| | :N—H
H   H |
          H

sp^3, Bent

sp^2, Trigonal planar

sp^3, Trigonal pyramidal

sp^3, Trigonal pyramidal

(structure with H_2N, O, H, O, OH)

85. c.

sp^3, Bent sp^3, Tetrahedral

H H H :O: sp^3, Bent
| | | ‖
:S—C—C—C—Ö—H
| | :N—H
H   H |
          H

sp^3, Tetrahedral

sp^2, Trigonal planar

sp^3, Trigonal pyramidal

(structure with SH, O, H, N, H, OH)

87. σ bonds: 25
π bonds: 4
lone pairs: on O's and N (without methyl group):
         sp^2 orbitals
         on N's (with methyl group): sp^3 orbitals

89. a. water soluble   **b.** fat soluble
    c. water soluble   **d.** fat soluble

91.

$$\underline{\quad\quad} \quad \sigma^*_p$$

$$\underline{\uparrow\downarrow} \;\; \underline{\uparrow\downarrow} \quad \pi^*_p$$

$$\underline{\uparrow\downarrow} \;\; \underline{\uparrow\downarrow} \quad \pi_p$$

$$\underline{\uparrow\downarrow} \quad \sigma_p$$

$$\underline{\uparrow\downarrow} \quad \sigma^*_s$$

$$\underline{\uparrow\downarrow} \quad \sigma_s$$

bond order $= 1$

93. BrF, unhybridized, linear

:Br—F:

BrF_2^- has two bonds and three lone pairs on the central atom. The hybridization is sp^3d. The electron geometry is trigonal bipyramidal with the three lone pairs equatorial. The molecular geometry is linear.

$$\left[:F—Br—F: \right]^-$$

BrF_3 has three bonds and two lone pairs on the central atom. The hybridization is sp^3d. The electron geometry is trigonal bipyramidal with the two lone pairs equatorial. The molecular geometry is T-shaped.

$$\left[:F—Br—F: \atop :F: \right]^-$$

BrF_4^- has four bonds and two lone pairs on the central atom. The hybridization is sp^3d^2. The electron geometry is octahedral with the two lone pairs on the same axis. The molecular geometry is square planar.

$$\left[:F—Br—F: \text{ with } :F: \text{ top and bottom} \right]^-$$

BrF_5 has five bonds and one lone pair on the central atom. The hybridization is sp^3d^2. The electron geometry is octahedral. The molecular geometry is square pyramidal.

:F—Br—F: with :F: on top and :F: :F: on bottom

95. The moments of the two Cl's cancel.

$$
\begin{array}{c}
\text{Cl} \\
| \\
H_3C-C\!\!=\!\!C-CH_3 \\
| \\
\text{Cl}
\end{array}
$$

97. a. 10 **b.** 14 **c.** 2

99. According to valence bond theory, CH_4, NH_3, and H_2O are all sp^3 hybridized. This hybridization results in a tetrahedral electron group configuration with a 109.5° bond angle. NH_3 and H_2O deviate from this idealized bond angle because their lone electron pairs exist in their own sp^3 orbitals. The presence of lone pairs lowers the tendency for the central atom's orbitals to hybridize. As a result, as lone pairs are added, the bond angle moves further from the 109.5° hybrid angle and closer to the 90° unhybridized angle.

101. NH_3 is stable due to its bond order of 3.

103. In $NO_2{}^+$, the central N has two electron groups, so the hybridization is sp and the ONO angle is 180°. In $NO_2{}^-$ the central N has three electron groups, two bonds and one lone pair. The ideal hybridization is sp^2 but the ONO bond angle should close down a bit because of the lone pair. A bond angle around 115° is a good guess. In NO_2 there are three electron groups, but one group is a single electron. Again the ideal hybridization would be sp^2, but since one unpaired electron must be much smaller than a lone pair or even a bonding pair, we predict that the ONO bond angle will spread and be greater than 120°. As a guess the angle is probably significantly greater than 120°.

$$
\left[\ddot{\text{O}}\!\!=\!\!\text{N}\!\!=\!\!\ddot{\text{O}} \right]^+
$$

$$
\left[:\ddot{\text{O}}\!\!=\!\!\ddot{\text{N}}\!\!-\!\!\ddot{\ddot{\text{O}}}: \right]^-
$$

$$
\ddot{\text{O}}\!\!=\!\!\ddot{\text{N}}\!\!-\!\!\ddot{\ddot{\text{O}}}:
$$

105. In addition to the $2s$ and the three $2p$ orbitals one more orbital is required to make 5 hybrid orbitals. The closest in energy is the $3s$ orbital. So the hybridization is s^2p^3. VSEPR predicts trigonal bipyramidal geometry for five identical substituents.

107. a. This is the best.

b. This statement is similar to **a.** but leaves out non-bonding lone-pair electron groups.

c. Molecular geometries are not determined by overlapping orbitals, but rather by the number and type of electron groups around each central atom.

109. Lewis theory defines a single bond, double bond, and triple bond as a sharing of two electrons, four electrons, and six electrons respectively between two atoms. Valence bond theory defines a single bond as a sigma overlap of two orbitals, a double bond as a single sigma bond combined with a pi bond, and a triple bond as a double bond with an additional pi bond. Molecular orbital theory defines a single bond, double bond, and triple bond as a bond order of 1, 2, or 3 respectively between two atoms.

Chapter 11

49. a. dispersion
  b. dispersion, dipole–dipole, hydrogen bonding
  c. dispersion, dipole–dipole
  d. dispersion
51. a. dispersion, dipole–dipole
  b. dispersion, dipole–dipole, hydrogen bonding
  c. dispersion
  d. dispersion
53. a, b, c, d, Boiling point increases with increasing intermolecular forces. The molecules increase in their intermolecular forces as follows: **a,** dispersion forces; **b,** stronger dispersion forces (broader electron cloud); **c,** dispersion forces and dipole–dipole interactions; **d,** dispersion forces, dipole–dipole interactions, and hydrogen bonding.
55. a. CH_3OH, hydrogen bonding
  b. CH_3CH_2OH, hydrogen bonding
  c. CH_3CH_3, greater mass, broader electron cloud causes greater dispersion forces
57. a. Br_2, smaller mass results in weaker dispersion forces
  b. H_2S, lacks hydrogen bonding
  c. PH_3, lacks hydrogen bonding
59. a. not homogeneous
  b. homogeneous, dispersion, dipole–dipole, hydrogen bonding, ion–dipole
  c. homogeneous, dispersion
  d. homogeneous, dispersion, dipole–dipole, hydrogen bonding
61. Water. Surface tension increases with increasing intermolecular forces, and water can hydrogen bond while acetone cannot.
63. compound A
65. When the tube is clean, water experiences adhesive forces with glass that are stronger than its cohesive forces, causing it to climb the surface of a glass tube. Water does not experience strong intermolecular forces with oil, so if the tube is coated in oil, the water's cohesive forces will be greater and it will not be attracted to the surface of the tube.
67. The water in the 12-cm dish will evaporate more quickly. The vapor pressure does not change but the surface area

does. The water in the dish evaporates more quickly because the greater surface area allows for more molecules to obtain enough energy at the surface and break free.

69. Water is more volatile than vegetable oil. When the water evaporates, the endothermic process results in cooling.

71. 0.405 L

73. 91 °C

75. ΔH_{vap} = 24.7 kJ/mol, bp = 239 K

77. 41 torr

79. 22.0 kJ

81. 2.7 °C

83. 30.5 kJ

85. a. solid   **b.** liquid
    c. gas   **d.** supercritical fluid
    e. solid/liquid   **f.** liquid/gas
    g. solid/liquid/gas

87. N_2 has a stable liquid phase at 1 atm.

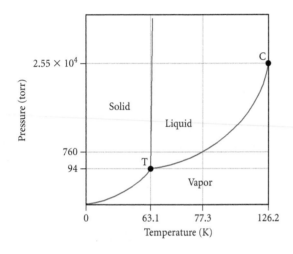

89. a. 0.027 mmHg   **b.** rhombic

91. Water has strong intermolecular forces. It is polar and experiences hydrogen bonding.

93. Water's exceptionally high specific heat capacity has a moderating effect on Earth's climate. Also, its high ΔH_{vap} causes water evaporation and condensation to have a strong effect on temperature.

95. 162 pm

97. a. 1   **b.** 2   **c.** 4

99. l = 393 pm, d = 21.3 g/cm^3

101. 134.5 pm

103. 6.0×10^{23} atoms/mol

105. a. atomic   **b.** molecular
    c. ionic   **d.** atomic

107. LiCl(s). The other three solids are held together by intermolecular forces while LiCl is held together by stronger coulombic interactions between the cations and anions of the crystal lattice.

109. a. $TiO_2(s)$, ionic solid
    b. $SiCl_4(s)$, larger, stronger dispersion forces
    c. Xe(s), larger, stronger dispersion forces
    d. CaO, ions have greater charge, and therefore stronger coulombic forces

111. TiO_2

113. Cs: 1(1) = 1
    Cl: 8(1/8) = 1
    1 : 1
    CsCl
    Ba: 8(1/8) + 6(1/2) = 4
    Cl: 8(1) = 8
    4 : 8 = 1 : 2
    $BaCl_2$

115. a

117. a. p-type   **b.** n-type

119. The general trend is that melting point increases with increasing mass. This is due to the fact that the electrons of the larger molecules are held more loosely and a stronger dipole moment can be induced more easily. HF is the exception to the rule. It has a relatively high melting point due to hydrogen bonding.

121. yes, 1.22 g

123. gas ⟶ liquid ⟶ solid

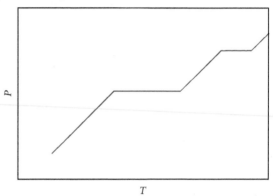

125. 26 °C

127. 3.4×10^3 g H_2O

129. CsCl has a higher melting point than AgI because of its higher coordination number. In CsCl, one anion bonds to eight cations (and vice versa) while in AgI, one anion bonds only to four cations.

131. a. 4r
    b. $c^2 = a^2 + b^2$ $c = 4r$, $a = l$, $b = l$
    $(4r)^2 = l^2 + l^2$
    $16r^2 = 2l^2$
    $8r^2 = l^2$
    $l = \sqrt[3]{8r^2}$
    $l = 2\sqrt{2}r$

133. 8 atoms/unit

135. a. $CO_2(s)$ ⟶ $CO_2(g)$ at 195 K
    b. $CO_2(s)$ ⟶ triple point at 216 K ⟶ $CO_2(g)$ just above 216 K
    c. $CO_2(s)$ ⟶ $CO_2(l)$ at somewhat above 216 K ⟶ $CO_2(g)$ at around 250 K
    d. $CO_2(s)$ ⟶ $CO_2(g)$ ⟶ supercritical fluid

137. 55.843 g/mol

139. 2.00 g/cm^3

141. Decreasing the pressure will decrease the temperature of liquid nitrogen. Because the nitrogen is boiling, its temperature must be constant at a given pressure. As the

pressure decreases, the boiling point decreases, and therefore so does the temperature. If the pressure drops below the pressure of the triple point, the phase change will shift from vaporization to sublimation and the liquid nitrogen will become solid.

143. body diagonal $= \sqrt{6}r$, radius $= (\sqrt{3} - \sqrt{2})r/\sqrt{2} = 0.2247r$

145. 70.7 L

147. 0.48 atm

149. The water within a container with a larger surface area will evaporate more quickly because there is more surface area for the molecules to evaporate from. Vapor pressure is the pressure of the gas when it is in dynamic equilibrium with the liquid. The vapor pressure is dependent only on the substance and the temperature. The larger the surface area, the more quickly it will reach the dynamic state.

151. The triple point will be at a lower temperature since the fusion equilibrium line has a positive slope. This means that we will be increasing both temperature and pressure as we travel from the triple point to the normal melting point.

153. The liquid segment will have the least steep slope because it takes the most kJ/mol to raise the temperature of the phase.

155. There are substantial intermolecular attractions in the liquid, but virtually none in the gas.

Chapter 12

29. a. hexane, toluene, or CCl_4; dispersion forces
b. water, methanol; dispersion, dipole–dipole, hydrogen bonding
c. hexane, toluene, or CCl_4; dispersion forces
d. water, acetone, methanol, ethanol; dispersion, ion–dipole

31. $HOCH_2CH_2CH_2OH$

33. a. water; dispersion, dipole–dipole, hydrogen bonding
b. hexane; dispersion
c. water; dispersion, dipole–dipole
d. water; dispersion, dipole–dipole, hydrogen bonding

35. a. endothermic
b. The lattice energy is greater in magnitude than the heat of hydration.
c.

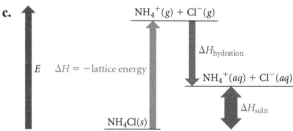

d. The solution forms because chemical systems tend toward greater entropy.

37. -797 kJ/mol

39. $\Delta H_{soln} = -6 \times 10^1$ kJ/mol, -7 kJ of energy evolved

41. unsaturated

43. About 31 g will precipitate.

45. Boiling water releases any O_2 dissolved in it. The solubility of gases decreases with increasing temperature.

47. As pressure increases, nitrogen will more easily dissolve in blood. To reverse this process, divers should ascend to lower pressures.

49. 1.1 g

51. 1.92 M, 2.0 m, 10.4%

53. 0.340 L

55. 1.6×10^2 g Ag

57. 1.4×10^4 g

59. Add water to 7.31 mL of concentrated solution until a total volume of 1.15 L is acquired.

61. a. Add water to 3.73 g KCl to a volume of 100 mL.
b. Add 3.59 g KCl to 96.41 g H_2O.
c. Add 5.0 g KCl to 95 g H_2O.

63. a. 0.417 M
b. 0.444 m
c. 7.41% by mass
d. 0.00794
e. 0.794% by mole

65. 0.89 M

67. 15 m, 0.22

69. The level has decreased more in the beaker filled with pure water. The dissolved salt in the seawater decreases the vapor pressure and subsequently lowers the rate of vaporization.

71. 30.7 torr

73. a. $P_{hep} = 24.4$ torr, $P_{oct} = 5.09$ torr
b. 29.5 torr
c. 80.8% heptane by mass, 19.2% octane by mass
d. The vapor is richer in the more volatile component.

75. $P_{chl} = 51.9$ torr, $P_{ace} = 274$ torr, $P_{tot} = 326$ torr. The solution is not ideal. The chloroform–acetone interactions are stronger than the chloroform–chloroform and acetone–acetone interactions.

77. freezing point (fp) $= -1.27$ °C, bp $= 100.349$ °C

79. 1.8×10^2 g/mol

81. 26.1 atm

83. 6.36×10^3 g/mol

85. a. fp $= -0.558$ °C, bp $= 100.154$ °C
b. fp $= -1.98$ °C, bp $= 100.546$ °C
c. fp $= -2.5$ °C, bp $= 100.70$ °C

87. a. -0.632 °C **b.** 5.4 atm **c.** 100.18 °C

89. 3.4

91. 23.0 torr

93. Chloroform is polar and has stronger solute–solvent interactions than nonpolar carbon tetrachloride.

95. $\Delta H_{soln} = 51$ kJ/mol, -8.7 °C

97. 2.2×10^{-3} M/atm

99. 1.3×10^4 L

101. 0.24 g

103. -24 °C

105. a. 1.1% by mass/V **b.** 1.6% by mass/V
c. 5.3% by mass/V

107. 2.484

109. 0.229 atm

111. χ_{CHCl_3}(original) $= 0.657$, P_{CHCl_3}(condensed) $= 0.346$ atm

113. 1.74 M

115. $C_6H_{14}O_2$

117. 12 grams

119. 6.4×10^{-3} L

121. 22.4% glucose by mass, 77.6% sucrose by mass

123. $P_{iso} = 0.131$ atm, $P_{pro} = 0.068$ atm. The major intermolecular attractions are between the OH groups. The OH group at the end of the chain in propyl alcohol is more accessible than the one in the middle of the chain in isopropyl alcohol. In addition, the molecular shape of propyl alcohol is a straight chain of carbon atoms, while that of isopropyl alcohol is a branched chain and is more like a ball. The contact area between two ball-like objects is smaller than that of two chain-like objects. The smaller contact area in isopropyl alcohol means the molecules don't attract each other as strongly as do those of propyl alcohol. As a result of both of these factors, the vapor pressure of isopropyl alcohol is higher.

125. 0.0097 m

127. Na_2CO_3 0.050 M, $NaHCO_3$ 0.075 M

129. The water should not be immediately cycled back into the river. As the water was warmed, dissolved oxygen would have been released, since the amount of a gas able to be dissolved into a liquid decreases as the temperature of the liquid increases. As such, the water returned to the river would lack dissolved oxygen if it was still hot. To preserve the dissolved oxygen necessary for the survival of fish and other aquatic life, the water must first be cooled.

131. b. NaCl

Chapter 13

25. a. Rate $= -\dfrac{1}{2}\dfrac{\Delta[HBr]}{\Delta t} = \dfrac{\Delta[H_2]}{\Delta t} = \dfrac{\Delta[Br_2]}{\Delta t}$

b. 1.8×10^{-3} M/s

c. 0.040 mol Br_2

27. a. Rate $= -\dfrac{1}{2}\dfrac{\Delta[A]}{\Delta t} = -\dfrac{\Delta[B]}{\Delta t} = \dfrac{1}{3}\dfrac{\Delta[C]}{\Delta t}$

b. $\dfrac{\Delta[B]}{\Delta t} = -0.0500$ M/s, $\dfrac{\Delta[C]}{\Delta t} = 0.150$ M/s

29.

$\Delta[Cl_2]/\Delta t$	$\Delta[F_2]/\Delta t$	$\Delta[ClF_3]/\Delta t$	Rate
-0.012 M/s	-0.036 M/s	0.024 M/s	0.012 M/s

31. a. $0 \longrightarrow 10$ s: Rate $= 8.7 \times 10^{-3}$ M/s

$40 \longrightarrow 50$ s: Rate $= 6.0 \times 10^{-3}$ M/s

b. 1.4×10^{-2} M/s

33. a. (i) 1.0×10^{-2} M/s

(ii) 8.5×10^{-3} M/s

(iii) 0.013 M/s

b.

35. a. first order

b.

c. Rate $= k[A]^1$, $k = 0.010$ s^{-1}

37. a. s^{-1} **b.** M^{-1}s^{-1} **c.** M$\cdot$s^{-1}

39. a. Rate $= k[A][B]^2$ **b.** third order

c. 2   **d.** 4

e. 1   **f.** 8

41. second order, Rate $= 5.25$ M^{-1} s^{-1}[A]^2

43. Rate $= k[NO_2][F_2]$, $k = 2.57$ M^{-1} s^{-1}, second order

45. a. zero order   **b.** first order   **c.** second order

47. second order, $k = 2.25 \times 10^{-2}$ M^{-1}s^{-1}, [AB] at 25 s $= 0.619$ M

49. first order, $k = 1.12 \times 10^{-2}$ s^{-1}, Rate $= 2.8 \times 10^{-3}$ M/s

51. a. 4.5×10^{-3} s^{-1} **b.** Rate $= 4.5 \times 10^{-3}$ s^{-1}[A]

c. 1.5×10^2 s   **d.** [A] $= 0.0908$ M

53. a. 4.88×10^3 s   **b.** 9.8×10^3 s

c. 1.7×10^3 s   **d.** 0.146 M at 200 s, 0.140 M at 500 s

55. 6.8×10^8 yrs; 1.8×10^{17} atoms

57.

59. 17 s^{-1}

61. 61.90 kJ/mol

63. $E_a = 251$ kJ/mol, $A = 7.93 \times 10^{11}$ s^{-1}

65. $E_a = 23.0$ kJ/mol, $A = 8.05 \times 10^{10}$ s^{-1}

67. a. 122 kJ/mol   **b.** 0.101 s^{-1}

69. 47.85 kJ/mol

71. a

73. The mechanism is valid.

75. a. $Cl_2(g) + CHCl_3(g) \longrightarrow HCl(g) + CCl_4(g)$

 b. $Cl(g), CCl_3(g)$

 c. Rate $= k[Cl_2]^{1/2}[CHCl_3]$

77. Heterogeneous catalysts require a large surface area because catalysis can only happen at the surface. A greater surface area means greater opportunity for the substrate to react, which results in a faster reaction.

79. 10^{12}

81. a. first order, $k = 0.0462$ hr^{-1} **b.** 15 hr

 c. 5.0×10^1 hr

83. 0.0531 M/s

85. rate $= 4.5 \times 10^{-4}$ [CH$_3$CHO]^2, $k = 4.5 \times 10^{-4}$, 0.37 atm

87. 219 torr

89. 1×10^{-7} s

91. 1.6×10^2 seconds

93. a. 2

 b.

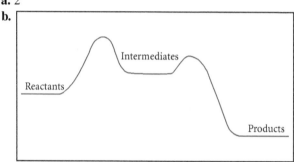

 c. first step   **d.** exothermic

95. a. 5.41 s   **b.** 2.2 s for 25%, 5.4 s for 50%

 c. 0.28 at 10 s, 0.077 at 20 s

97. a. $E_a = 89.5$ kJ/mol, $A = 4.22 \times 10^{11}$ s^{-1}

 b. 2.5×10^{-5} M^{-1} s^{-1}

 c. 6.0×10^{-4} M/s

99. a. No

 b. No bond is broken and the two radicals attract each other.

 c. Formation of diatomic gases from atomic gases.

101. 1.35×10^4 years

103. a. Both are valid. For both, all steps sum to overall reaction and the predicted rate law is consistent with experimental data.

 b. Buildup of I(g)

105. rate $= k_2[(k_1/k_{-1})[Br_2]]^{1/2}[H_2]$

 The rate law is 3/2 order overall.

107. a. 0%   **b.** 25%   **c.** 33%

109. 174 kJ

111. a. second order

 b. $CH_3NC + CH_3NC \underset{k_2}{\overset{k_1}{\rightleftharpoons}} CH_3NC^* + CH_3NC$ (fast)

 $CH_3NC^* \overset{k_3}{\longrightarrow} CH_3CN$ (slow)

Rate $= k_3[CH_3NC^*]$

$k_1[CH_3NC]^2 = k_2[CH_3NC^*][CH_3NC]$

$[CH_3NC^*] = \dfrac{k_1}{k_2}[CH_3NC]$

Rate $= k_3 \times \dfrac{k_1}{k_2}[CH_3NC]$

Rate $= k[CH_3NC]$

113. Rate $= k[A]^2$

$$Rate = -\frac{d[A]}{dt}$$

$$\frac{d[A]}{dt} = -k[A]^2$$

$$-\frac{d[A]}{[A]^2} = k\,dt$$

$$\int_{[A]_0}^{[A]} -\frac{1}{[A]^2}d[A] = \int_0^t k\,dt$$

$$\left[\frac{1}{[A]}\right]_{[A]_0}^{[A]} = k\,[t]_0^t$$

$$\frac{1}{[A]} - \frac{1}{[A]_0} = kt$$

$$\frac{1}{[A]} = kt + \frac{1}{[A]_0}$$

115. Rate $= k[CO][Cl_2]^{\frac{3}{2}}$

117. $[Cl_2] = 0.0084$ mol/L, [NO] $= 0.017$ mol/L

119. B is first order and A is second order.

 B will be linear if you plot ln[B] vs. time, A will be linear if you plot 1/[A] vs. time.

Chapter 14

21. a. $K = \dfrac{[SbCl_3][Cl_2]}{[SbCl_5]}$ **b.** $K = \dfrac{[NO]^2[Br_2]}{[BrNO]^2}$

 c. $K = \dfrac{[CS_2][H_2]^4}{[CH_4][H_2S]^2}$ **d.** $K = \dfrac{[CO_2]^2}{[CO]^2[O_2]}$

23. The concentration of the reactants will be greater. No, this is not dependent on initial concentrations; it is dependent on the value of K_c.

25. a. figure v

 b. The change in the decrease of reactants and increase of products would be faster.

 c. No, catalysts affect kinetics, not equilibrium.

27. a. 4.42×10^{-5}, reactants favored

 b. 1.50×10^2, products favored

 c. 1.96×10^{-9}, reactants favored

29. 1.3×10^{-29}

31. a. 2.56×10^{-23} **b.** 1.3×10^{22} **c.** 81.9

33. a. $K_c = \dfrac{[HCO_3^-][OH^-]}{[CO_3^{2-}]}$ **b.** $K_c = [O_2]^3$

 c. $K_c = \dfrac{[H_3O^+][F^-]}{[HF]}$ **d.** $K_c = \dfrac{[NH_4^+][OH^-]}{[NH_3]}$

35. 136

37.

$T(K)$	$[N_2]$	$[H_2]$	$[NH_3]$	K_c
500	0.115	0.105	0.439	1.45×10^{-3}
575	0.110	0.249	0.128	9.6
775	0.120	0.140	4.39×10^{-3}	0.0584

39. 234 torr

41. 3.3×10^2

43. 764

45. More solid will form.

47. Additional solid will not dissolve.

49. a. [A] = 0.20 M, [B] = 0.80 M
b. [A] = 0.33 M, [B] = 0.67 M
c. [A] = 0.38 M, [B] = 1.2 M

51. $[N_2O_4]$ = 0.0115 M, $[NO_2]$ = 0.0770 M

53. 0.199 M

55. 1.9×10^{-3} M

57. 7.84 torr

59. a. [A] = 0.38 M, [B] = 0.62 M, [C] = 0.62 M
b. [A] = 0.90 M, [B] = 0.095 M, [C] = 0.095 M
c. [A] = 1.0 M, [B] = 3.2×10^{-3} M,
[C] = 3.2×10^{-3} M

61. a. shift left **b.** shift right
c. shift right

63. a. shift right **b.** no effect
c. no effect **d.** shift left

65. a. shift right **b.** shift left
c. no effect

67. Increase temperature $\longrightarrow$ shift right, decrease temperature $\longrightarrow$ shift left. Increasing the temperature will increase the equilibrium constant.

69. b, d

71. a. 1.7×10^2

b. $\dfrac{[\text{Hb}-\text{CO}]}{[\text{Hb}-\text{O}_2]}$ = 0.85 or 17/20

CO is highly toxic, as it blocks O_2 uptake by hemoglobin. CO at a level of 0.1% will replace nearly half of the O_2 in blood.

73. a. 1.68 atm **b.** 1.41 atm

75. 0.406 g

77. b, c, d

79. 0.0144 atm

81. 3.1×10^2 g, 20% yield

83. 0.12 atm

85. 0.72 atm

87. 0.017 g

89. 0.226

91. a. 29.3 **b.** 86.3 torr

93. $P_{\text{NO}} = P_{\text{Cl}_2}$ = 429 torr

95. 1.27×10^{-2}

97. $K_P = 5.1 \times 10^{-2}$

99. Yes, because the volume affects Q.

101. a = 1, b = 2

Chapter 15

33. a. acid, $HNO_3(aq) \longrightarrow H^+(aq) + NO_3^-(aq)$
b. acid, $NH_4^+(aq) \rightleftharpoons H^+(aq) + NH_3(aq)$

c. base, $KOH(aq) \longrightarrow K^+(aq) + OH^-(aq)$
d. acid, $HC_2H_3O_2(aq) \rightleftharpoons H^+(aq) + C_2H_3O_2^-(aq)$

35. a. $\underset{\text{acid}}{H_2CO_3(aq)} + \underset{\text{base}}{H_2O(l)} \rightleftharpoons \underset{\text{conj. acid}}{H_3O^+(aq)} + \underset{\text{conj. base}}{HCO_3^-(aq)}$

b. $\underset{\text{base}}{NH_3(aq)} + \underset{\text{acid}}{H_2O(l)} \rightleftharpoons \underset{\text{conj. acid}}{NH_4^+(aq)} + \underset{\text{conj. base}}{OH^-(aq)}$

c. $\underset{\text{acid}}{HNO_3(aq)} + \underset{\text{base}}{H_2O(l)} \longrightarrow \underset{\text{conj. acid}}{H_3O^+(aq)} + \underset{\text{conj. base}}{NO_3^-(aq)}$

d. $\underset{\text{base}}{C_5H_5N(aq)} + \underset{\text{acid}}{H_2O(l)} \rightleftharpoons \underset{\text{conj. acid}}{C_5H_5NH^+(aq)} + \underset{\text{conj. base}}{OH^-(aq)}$

37. a. Cl^- **b.** HSO_3^- **c.** CHO_2^- **d.** F^-

39. $H_2PO_4^-(aq) + H_2O(l) \rightleftharpoons HPO_4^{2-}(aq) + H_3O^+(aq)$
$H_2PO_4^-(aq) + H_2O(l) \rightleftharpoons H_3PO_4(aq) + OH^-(aq)$

41. a. strong **b.** strong
c. strong **d.** weak, $K_a = \dfrac{[H_3O^+][HSO_3^-]}{[H_2SO_3]}$

43. a, b, c

45. a. F^- **b.** NO_2^- **c.** ClO^-

47. a. 8.3×10^{-7}, basic **b.** 1.2×10^{-10}, acidic
c. 2.9×10^{-13}, acidic

49. a. pH = 7.77, pOH = 6.23
b. pH = 7.00, pOH = 7.00
c. pH = 5.66, pOH = 8.34

51.

$[H_3O^+]$	$[OH^-]$	pH	*Acidic or Basic*
7.1×10^{-4}	1.4×10^{-11}	3.15	Acidic
3.7×10^{-9}	2.7×10^{-6}	8.43	Basic
7.9×10^{-12}	1.3×10^{-3}	11.1	Basic
6.3×10^{-4}	1.6×10^{-11}	3.20	Acidic

53. $[H_3O^+]$ = 1.5×10^{-7} M, pH = 6.81

55. a. $[H_3O^+]$ = 0.25 M, $[OH^-]$ = 4.0×10^{-14} M, pH = 0.60
b. $[H_3O^+]$ = 0.015 M, $[OH^-]$ = 6.7×10^{-13} M, pH = 1.82
c. $[H_3O^+]$ = 0.072 M, $[OH^-]$ = 1.4×10^{-13} M, pH = 1.14
d. $[H_3O^+]$ = 0.105 M, $[OH^-]$ = 9.5×10^{-14} M, pH = 0.979

57. a. 1.8 g **b.** 0.57 g **c.** 0.045 g

59. 2.21

61. $[H_3O^+]$ = 2.5×10^{-3} M, pH = 2.59

63. a. 1.82 (approximation valid)
b. 2.18 (approximation breaks down)
c. 2.72 (approximation breaks down)

65. 2.75

67. 6.8×10^{-6}

69. 0.0063%

71. a. 0.42% **b.** 0.60% **c.** 1.3% **d.** 1.9%

73. 3.61×10^{-5}

75. a. pH = 2.03, percent ionization = 3.7%
b. pH = 2.24, percent ionization = 5.7%
c. pH = 2.40, percent ionization = 8.0%

77. a. 0.939 **b.** 1.07 **c.** 2.19 **d.** 3.02

79. a. $[OH^-]$ = 0.15 M, $[H_3O^+]$ = 6.7×10^{-14} M, pH = 13.17, pOH = 0.83
b. $[OH^+]$ = 0.003 M, $[H_3O^+]$ = 3.3×10^{-12} M, pH = 11.48, pOH = 2.52
c. $[OH^-]$ = 9.6×10^{-4} M, $[H_3O^+]$ = 1.0×10^{-11} M, pH = 10.98, pOH = 3.02
d. $[OH^-]$ = 8.7×10^{-5} M, $[H_3O^+]$ = 1.1×10^{-10} M, pH = 9.93, pOH = 4.07

81. 13.842

83. 0.104 L

85. a. $NH_3(aq) + H_2O(l) \rightleftharpoons NH_4^+(aq) + OH^-(aq)$,
$$K_b = \frac{[NH_4^+][OH^-]}{[NH_3]}$$

b. $HCO_3^-(aq) + H_2O(l) \rightleftharpoons$
$$H_2CO_3(aq) + OH^-(aq), \quad K_b = \frac{[H_2CO_3][OH^-]}{[HCO_3^-]}$$

c. $CH_3NH_2(aq) + H_2O(l) \rightleftharpoons$
$$CH_3NH_3^+(aq) + OH^-(aq), \quad K_b = \frac{[CH_3NH_3^+][OH^-]}{[CH_3NH_2]}$$

87. $[OH^-] = 1.6 \times 10^{-3}$ M, pOH = 2.79, pH = 11.21

89. 7.48

91. 6.7×10^{-7}

93. a. neutral
b. basic,
$$ClO^-(aq) + H_2O(l) \rightleftharpoons HClO(aq) + OH^-(aq)$$
c. basic,
$$CN^-(aq) + H_2O(l) \rightleftharpoons HCN(aq) + OH^-(aq)$$
d. neutral

95. $[OH^-] = 2.0 \times 10^{-6}$ M, pH = 8.30

97. a. acidic,
$$NH_4^+(aq) + H_2O(l) \rightleftharpoons NH_3(aq) + H_3O^+(aq)$$
b. neutral
c. acidic, $Co(H_2O)_6^{3+}(aq) + H_2O(l) \rightleftharpoons$
$$Co(H_2O)_5(OH)^{2+}(aq) + H_3O^+(aq)$$
d. acidic, $CH_2NH_3^+(aq) + H_2O(l) \rightleftharpoons$
$$CH_2NH_2(aq) + H_3O^+(aq)$$

99. a. acidic   **b.** basic   **c.** neutral
d. acidic   **e.** acidic

101. NaOH, NaHCO_3, NaCl, NH_4ClO_2, NH_4Cl

103. a. 5.13   **b.** 8.87   **c.** 7.0

105. $[K^+] = 0.15$ M, $[F^-] = 0.15$ M, $[HF] = 2.1 \times 10^{-6}$ M,
$[OH^-] = 2.1 \times 10^{-6}$ M; $[H_3O^+] = 4.8 \times 10^{-9}$ M

107. $H_3PO_4(aq) + H_2O(l) \rightleftharpoons H_2PO_4^-(aq) + H_3O^+(aq)$,
$$K_{a_i} = \frac{[H_3O^+][H_2PO_4^-]}{[H_3PO_4]}$$
$H_2PO_4^-(aq) + H_2O(l) \rightleftharpoons HPO_4^{2-}(aq) + H_3O^+(aq)$,
$$K_{a_2} = \frac{[H_3O^+][HPO_4^{2-}]}{[H_2PO_4^-]}$$
$HPO_4^{2-}(aq) + H_2O(l) \rightleftharpoons PO_4^{3-}(aq) + H_3O^+(aq)$,
$$K_{a_3} = \frac{[H_3O^+][PO_4^{3-}]}{[HPO_4^{2-}]}$$

109. a. $[H_3O^+] = 0.048$ M, pH = 1.32
b. $[H_3O^+] = 0.12$ M, pH = 0.92

111. $[H_2SO_3] = 0.418$ M
$[HSO_3^-] = 0.082$ M
$[SO_3^{2-}] = 6.4 \times 10^{-8}$ M
$[H_3O^+] = 0.082$ M

113. a. $[H_3O^+] = 0.50$ M, pH = 0.30
b. $[H_3O^+] = 0.11$ M, pH = 0.96 (*x is small* approximation breaks down)
c. $[H_3O^+] = 0.059$ M, pH = 1.23

115. a. HCl, weaker bond   **b.** HF, bond polarity
c. H_2Se, weaker bond

117. a. H_2SO_4, more oxygen atoms bonded to S
b. $HClO_2$, more oxygen atoms bonded to Cl
c. HClO, Cl has higher electronegativity
d. CCl_3COOH, Cl has higher electronegativity

119. S^{2-}, its conjugate acid (H_2S), is a weaker acid than H_2S

121. a. Lewis acid   **b.** Lewis acid
c. Lewis base   **d.** Lewis base

123. a. acid: Fe^{3+}, base: H_2O **b.** acid: Zn^{2+}, base: NH_3
c. acid: BF_3, base: $(CH_3)_3N$

125. a. weak   **b.** strong   **c.** weak   **d.** strong

127. If blood became acidic, the H^+ concentration would increase. According to Le Châtelier's principle, equilibrium would be shifted to the left and the concentration of oxygenated Hb would decrease.

129. All acid will be neutralized.

131. $[H_3O^+]$(Great Lakes) $= 3 \times 10^{-5}$ M,
$[H_3O^+]$(West Coast) $= 4 \times 10^{-6}$ M. The rain over the Great Lakes is about 8 times more concentrated.

133. 2.7

135. a. 2.000   **b.** 1.52   **c.** 12.95
d. 11.12   **e.** 5.03

137. a. 1.260   **b.** 8.22   **c.** 0.824
d. 8.57   **e.** 1.171

139. a. $CN^-(aq) + H^+(aq) \rightleftharpoons HCN(aq)$
b. $NH_4^+(aq) + OH^-(aq) \rightleftharpoons NH_3(aq) + H_2O(l)$
c. $CN^-(aq) + NH_4^+(aq) \rightleftharpoons HCN(aq) + NH_3(aq)$
d. $HSO_4^-(aq) + C_2H_3O_2^-(aq) \rightleftharpoons$
$$SO_4^{2-}(aq) + HC_2H_3O_2(aq)$$
e. no reaction between the major species

141. 0.794

143. $K_a = 8.3 \times 10^{-4}$

145. 6.79

147. 2.14

149. $[A^-] = 4.5 \times 10^{-5}$ M
$[H^+] = 2.2 \times 10^{-4}$ M
$[HA_2^-] = 1.8 \times 10^{-4}$ M

151. 9.28

153. 50.1 g NaHCO_3

155. b

157. $CH_3COOH < CH_2ClCOOH < CHCl_2COOH < CCl_3COOH$

Chapter 16

27. d

29. a. 3.62   **b.** 9.11

31. pure water: 2.1%, in $NaC_7H_5O_2$: 0.065%. The percent ionization in the sodium benzoate solution is much smaller because the presence of the benzoate ion shifts the equilibrium to the left.

33. a. 2.14   **b.** 8.32   **c.** 3.46

35. $HCl + NaC_2H_3O_2 \longrightarrow HC_2H_3O_2 + NaCl$
$NaOH + HC_2H_3O_2 \longrightarrow NaC_2H_3O_2 + H_2O$

37. a. 3.62   **b.** 9.11

39. a. 7.60   **b.** 11.18   **c.** 4.61

41. a. 3.86   **b.** 8.95

43. 3.5

45. 3.7 g

47. a. 4.74   **b.** 4.68   **c.** 4.81

49. a. initial 7.00   **b.** initial 4.71   **c.** initial 10.78
     after 1.70   after 4.56   after 10.66

51. 1.2 g; 2.7 g

53. a. yes   **b.** no   **c.** yes
     d. no   **e.** no

55. a. 7.4   **b.** 0.3 g   **c.** 0.14 g

57. $KClO/HClO = 0.79$

59. a. does not exceed capacity
     b. does not exceed capacity
     c. does not exceed capacity
     d. does not exceed capacity

61. i. (a) pH = 8, (b) pH = 7
     ii. (a) weak acid, (b) strong acid

63. a. 40.0 mL HI for both
     b. KOH: neutral, CH_3NH_2: acidic
     c. CH_3NH_2
     d. Titration of KOH with HI:

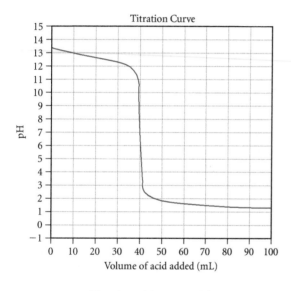

Titration of CH_3NH_2 with HI:

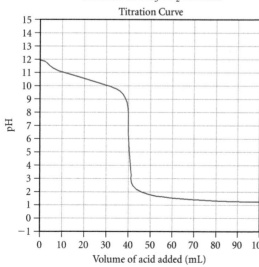

65. a. pH = 9, added base = 30 mL
     b. 0 mL   **c.** 15 mL
     d. 30 mL   **e.** 30 mL

67. a. 0.757   **b.** 30.6 mL   **c.** 1.038
     d. 7   **e.** 12.15

69. a. 13.06   **b.** 28.8 mL   **c.** 12.90
     d. 7   **e.** 2.07

71. a. 2.86   **b.** 16.8 mL   **c.** 4.37
     d. 4.74   **e.** 8.75   **f.** 12.17

73. a. 11.94   **b.** 29.2 mL   **c.** 11.33
     d. 10.64   **e.** 5.87   **f.** 1.90

75. i. (a)   **ii.** (b)

77. $pK_a = 3$, 82 g/mol

79. First equivalence: 22.7 mL
     Second equivalence: 45.4 mL

81. The indicator will appear red. The pH range is 4 to 6.

83. a. phenol red, *m*-nitrophenol
     b. alizarin, bromothymol blue, phenol red
     c. alizarin yellow R

85. a. $BaSO_4(s) \rightleftharpoons Ba^{2+}(aq) + SO_4^{2-}(aq)$,
$$K_{sp} = [Ba^{2+}][SO_4^{2-}]$$
     b. $PbBr_2(s) \rightleftharpoons Pb^{2+}(aq) + 2\ Br^-(aq)$,
$$K_{sp} = [Pb^{2+}][Br^-]^2$$
     c. $Ag_2CrO_4(s) \rightleftharpoons 2\ Ag^+(aq) + CrO_4^{2-}(aq)$,
$$K_{sp} = [Ag^+]^2[CrO_4^{2-}]$$

87. a. 7.31×10^{-7} M   **b.** 3.72×10^{-5} M
     c. 3.32×10^{-4} M

89. a. 1.07×10^{-21} **b.** 7.14×10^{-7}
     c. 7.44×10^{-11}

91. AX_2

93. 2.07×10^{-5} g/100 mL

95. a. 0.0183 M   **b.** 0.00755 M
     c. 0.00109 M

97. a. 5×10^{14} M   **b.** 5×10^8 M
     c. 5×10^4 M

99. a. more soluble, CO_3^{2-} is basic
     b. more soluble, S^{2-} is basic
     c. not, neutral
     d. not, neutral

101. precipitate will form, CaF_2

103. precipitate will form, $Mg(OH)_2$

105. a. 0.018 M   **b.** 1.4×10^{-7} M
     c. 1.1×10^{-5} M

107. a. $BaSO_4$, 1.1×10^{-8} M
     b. 3.0×10^{-8} M

109. 8.7×10^{-10} M

111. 5.6×10^{16}

113. 4.03

115. 3.57

117. HCl, 4.7 g

119. a. $NaOH(aq) + KHC_8H_4O_4(aq) \longrightarrow Na^+(aq) +$
$$K^+(aq) + C_8H_4O_4^{2-}(aq) + H_2O(l)$$
     b. 0.1046 M

121. 4.73

123. 176 g/mol; 1.0×10^{-4}

125. 14.2 L

127. 1.6×10^{-7} M

129. 8.0×10^{-8} M

131. 6.29

133. 0.172 M

135. The ratio by mass of dimethyl ammonium chloride to dimethyl amine needed is 3.6.

137. 0.18 M benzoic acid, 0.41 M sodium benzoate

139. 51.6 g

141. 1.8×10^{-11} (based on this data)

143. a. 5.5×10^{-25} M   **b.** 5.5×10^{-4} M

145. 1.38 L

147. 12.97

149. a. $pH < pK_a$ **b.** $pH > pK_a$
   c. $pH = pK_a$ **d.** $pH > pK_a$

151. b

153. a. no difference   **b.** less soluble
   c. more soluble

Chapter 17

27. a, c

29. System B has the greatest entropy. There is only one energetically equivalent arrangement for System A. However, the particles of System B may exchange positions for a second energetically equivalent arrangement.

31. a. $\Delta S > 0$ **b.** $\Delta S < 0$
   c. $\Delta S < 0$ **d.** $\Delta S < 0$

33. a. $\Delta S_{sys} > 0$, $\Delta S_{surr} > 0$, spontaneous at all temperatures
   b. $\Delta S_{sys} < 0$, $\Delta S_{surr} < 0$, nonspontaneous at all temperatures
   c. $\Delta S_{sys} < 0$, $\Delta S_{surr} < 0$, nonspontaneous at all temperatures
   d. $\Delta S_{sys} > 0$, $\Delta S_{surr} > 0$, spontaneous at all temperatures

35. a. 1.29×10^3 J/K   **b.** 5.00×10^3 J/K
   c. -3.83×10^2 J/K   **d.** -1.48×10^3 J/K

37. a. -649 J/K >, nonspontaneous
   b. 649 J/K, spontaneous
   c. 123 J/K, spontaneous
   d. -76 J/K, nonspontaneous

39. a. 1.93×10^5 J, nonspontaneous
   b. -1.93×10^5 J, spontaneous
   c. -3.7×10^4 J, spontaneous
   d. 4.7×10^4 J, nonspontaneous

41. -2.247×10^6 J, spontaneous

43.

ΔH	ΔS	ΔG	Low Temperature	High Temperature
$-$	$+$	$-$	Spontaneous	Spontaneous
$-$	$-$	Temperature dependent	Spontaneous	Nonspontaneous
$+$	$+$	Temperature dependent	Nonspontaneous	Spontaneous
$+$	$-$	$+$	Nonspontaneous	Nonspontaneous

45. It increases.

47. a. $CO_2(g)$, greater molar mass and complexity
   b. $CH_3OH(g)$, gas phase
   c. $CO_2(g)$, greater molar mass and complexity
   d. $SiH_4(g)$, greater molar mass
   e. $CH_3CH_2CH_3(g)$, greater molar mass and complexity
   f. $NaBr(aq)$, aqueous

49. a. He, Ne, SO_2, NH_3, CH_3CH_2OH. From He to Ne there is an increase in molar mass, beyond that, the molecules increase in complexity.
   b. $H_2O(s)$, $H_2O(l)$, $H_2O(g)$; increase in entropy in going from solid to liquid to gas phase.
   c. CH_4, CF_4, CCl_4; increasing entropy with increasing molar mass.

51. a. -120.8 J/K, decrease in moles of gas
   b. 133.9 J/K, increase in moles of gas
   c. -42.0 J/K, small change because moles of gas stay constant
   d. -390.8 J/K, decrease in moles of gas

53. -89.3 J/K, decrease in moles of gas

55. $\Delta H^\circ_{rxn} = -1277$ kJ, $\Delta S^\circ_{rxn} = 313.6$ J/K, $\Delta G^\circ_{rxn} = -1.370 \times 10^3$ kJ; yes

57. a. $\Delta H^\circ_{rxn} = 57.2$ kJ, $\Delta S^\circ_{rxn} = 175.8$ J/K, $\Delta G^\circ_{rxn} = 4.8 \times 10^3$ J/mol; nonspontaneous, becomes spontaneous at high temperatures
   b. $\Delta H^\circ_{rxn} = 176.2$ kJ, $\Delta S^\circ_{rxn} = 285.1$ J/K, $\Delta G^\circ_{rxn} = 91.2$ kJ; nonspontaneous, becomes spontaneous at high temperatures
   c. $\Delta H^\circ_{rxn} = 98.8$ kJ, $\Delta S^\circ_{rxn} = 141.5$ J/K, $\Delta G^\circ_{rxn} = 56.6$ kJ; nonspontaneous, becomes spontaneous at high temperatures
   d. $\Delta H^\circ_{rxn} = -91.8$ kJ, $\Delta S^\circ_{rxn} = -198.1$ J/K, $\Delta G^\circ_{rxn} = -32.8$ kJ; spontaneous

59. a. 2.8 kJ   **b.** 91.2 kJ
   c. 56.4 kJ   **d.** -32.8 kJ
   Values are comparable. The method using ΔH° and ΔS° can be used to determine how ΔG° changes with temperature.

61. a. -72.5 kJ, spontaneous
   b -11.4 kJ, spontaneous
   c. 9.1 kJ, nonspontaneous

63. -29.4 kJ

65. a. 19.3 kJ   **b.** (i) 2.9 kJ
                        (ii) -2.9 kJ
   c. The partial pressure of iodine is very low.

67. 11.9 kJ

69. a. 1.48×10^{90} **b.** 2.09×10^{-26}

71. a. -24.8 kJ   **b.** 0   **c.** 9.4 kJ

73. a. 1.90×10^{47} **b.** 1.51×10^{-13}

75. $\Delta H^\circ = 50.6$ kJ
   $\Delta S^\circ = 226$ J·K

77. 4.8

79. a. $+$ **b.** $-$ **c.** $-$

81. a. $\Delta G^\circ = 175.2$ kJ, $K = 1.95 \times 10^{-31}$, nonspontaneous
   b. 133 kJ, yes

83. Cl_2: $\Delta H_{rxn}^{\circ} = -182.1$ kJ, $\Delta S_{rxn}^{\circ} = -134.4$ J/K,

$\Delta G_{rxn}^{\circ} = -142.0$ kJ $K = 7.94 \times 10^{24}$

Br_2: $\Delta H_{rxn}^{\circ} = -121.6$ kJ, $\Delta S_{rxn}^{\circ} = -134.2$ J/K,

$\Delta G_{rxn}^{\circ} = -81.6$ kJ $K = 2.02 \times 10^{14}$

I_2: $\Delta H_{rxn}^{\circ} = -48.3$ kJ, $\Delta S_{rxn}^{\circ} = -132.2$ J/K,

$\Delta G_{rxn}^{\circ} = -8.9$ kJ $K = 37$

Cl_2 is the most spontaneous, I_2 is the least. Spontaneity is determined by the standard enthalpy of formation of the dihalogenated ethane. Higher temperatures make the reactions less spontaneous.

85. a. 107.8 kJ   **b.** 5.0×10^{-7} atm

c. spontaneous at higher temperatures, $T = 923.4$ K

87. a. 2.22×10^5 **b.** 94.4 mol

89. a. $\Delta G^{\circ} = -689.6$ kJ, ΔG° becomes less negative

b. $\Delta G^{\circ} = -665.2$ kJ, ΔG° becomes less negative

c. $\Delta G^{\circ} = -632.4$ kJ, ΔG° becomes less negative

d. $\Delta G^{\circ} = -549.3$ kJ, ΔG° becomes less negative

91. With one exception, the formation of any oxide of nitrogen at 298 K requires more moles of gas as reactants than are formed as products. For example, 1 mol of N_2O requires 0.5 mol of O_2 and 1 mol of N_2, 1 mol of N_2O_3 requires 1 mol of N_2 and 1.5 mol of O_2, and so on. The exception is NO, where 1 mol of NO requires 0.5 mol of O_2 and 0.5 mol of N_2:

$$\frac{1}{2}N_2(g) + \frac{1}{2}O_2(g) \longrightarrow NO(g)$$

This reaction has a positive ΔS because what is essentially mixing of the N and O has taken place in the product.

93. 15.0 kJ

95. a. Positive, the process is spontaneous. It is slow unless a spark is applied.

b. Positive, although the change in the system is not spontaneous; the overall change, which includes such processes as combustion or water flow to generate electricity, is spontaneous.

c. Positive, the acorn oak/tree system is becoming more ordered, so the processes associated with growth are not spontaneous. But they are driven by spontaneous processes such as the generation of heat by the sun and the reactions that produce energy in the cell.

97. At 18.3 mmHg $\Delta G = 0$, At 760 mmHg $\Delta G^{\circ} = 55.4$ kJ

99. a. 3.24×10^{-3}

b.

$NH_3 + ATP + H_2O \longrightarrow NH_3 - P_i + ADP$

$NH_3 - P_i + C_5H_8O_4N^- \longrightarrow C_5H_9O_3N_2 + P_i + H_2O$

$\overline{NH_3 + C_5H_8O_4N^- + ATP \longrightarrow C_5H_9O_3N_2 + ADP + P_i}$

$\Delta G^{\circ} = -16.3$ kJ, $K = 7.20 \times 10^2$

101. a. -95.3 kJ/mol. Since the number of moles of reactants and products are the same, the decrease in volume affects the entropy of both equally, so there is no change in ΔG.

b. 102.8 kJ/mol. The entropy of the reactants (1.5 mol) is decreased more than the entropy of the product (1 mol). Since the product is relatively more favored at lower volume, ΔG is less positive.

c. 204.2 kJ/mol. The entropy of the product (1 mol) is decreased more than the entropy of the reactant (0.5 mol). Since the product is relatively less favored, ΔG is more positive.

103. $\Delta H^{\circ} = -93$ kJ, $\Delta S^{\circ} = -2.0 \times 10^2$ J/K

105. ΔS_{vap} diethyl ether $= 86.1$ J/mol K, ΔS_{vap} acetone $= 88.4$ J/mol K, ΔS_{vap} benzene $= 87.3$ J/mol K, ΔS_{vap} chloroform $= 88.0$ J/mol K Because water and ethanol hydrogen bond they are more ordered in the liquid and we expect ΔS_{vap} to be more positive. ethanol $38600/351.0 = 110$ J/mol K, $H_2O = 40700/373.2 = 109$ J/mol K

107. c

109. b

111. c

Chapter 18

37. a. $3 K(s) + Cr^{3+}(aq) \longrightarrow Cr(s) + 3 K^+(aq)$

b. $2 Al(s) + 3 Fe^{2+}(aq) \longrightarrow 2 Al^{3+}(aq) + 3 Fe(s)$

c. $2 BrO_3^-(aq) + 3 N_2H_4(g) \longrightarrow$
$\qquad 2 Br^-(aq) + 3 N_2(g) + 6 H_2O(l)$

39. a. $PbO_2(s) + 2 I^-(aq) + 4 H^+(aq) \longrightarrow$
$\qquad Pb^{2+}(aq) + I_2(s) + 2 H_2O(l)$

b. $5 SO_3^{2-}(aq) + 2 MnO_4^-(aq) + 6 H^+(aq) \longrightarrow$
$\qquad 5 SO_4^{2-}(aq) + 2 Mn^{2+}(aq) + 3 H_2O(l)$

c. $S_2O_3^{2-}(aq) + 4 Cl_2(g) + 5 H_2O(l) \longrightarrow$
$\qquad 2 SO_4^{2-}(aq) + 8 Cl^-(aq) + 10 H^+(aq)$

41. a. $H_2O_2(aq) + 2 ClO_2(aq) + 2 OH^-(aq) \longrightarrow$
$\qquad O_2(g) + 2 ClO_2^-(aq) + 2 H_2O(l)$

b. $Al(s) + MnO_4^-(aq) + 2 H_2O(l) \longrightarrow$
$\qquad Al(OH)_4^-(aq) + MnO_2(s)$

c. $Cl_2(g) + 2 OH^-(aq) \longrightarrow$
$\qquad Cl^-(aq) + ClO^-(aq) + H_2O(l)$

43. a.

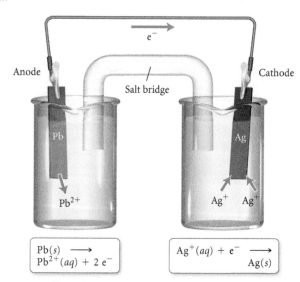

Anode e^- Cathode

Salt bridge

Pb   Ag

Pb^{2+} Ag^+ Ag^+

$Pb(s) \longrightarrow$
$Pb^{2+}(aq) + 2 e^-$

$Ag^+(aq) + e^- \longrightarrow$
$Ag(s)$

b.

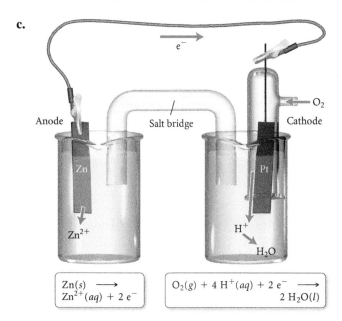

2 $I^-(aq) \longrightarrow I_2(s) + 2\ e^-$

$ClO_2(g) + e^- \longrightarrow ClO_2^-(aq)$

c.

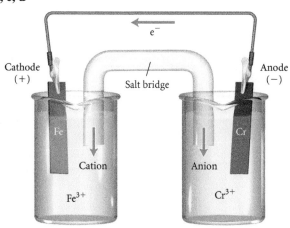

$Zn(s) \longrightarrow Zn^{2+}(aq) + 2\ e^-$

$O_2(g) + 4\ H^+(aq) + 2\ e^- \longrightarrow 2\ H_2O(l)$

45. a. 0.93 V   **b.** 0.41 V   **c.** 1.99 V

47. a, c, d

b. $Cr(s) + Fe^{3+}(aq) \longrightarrow Cr^{3+}(aq) + Fe(s)$, $E^\circ_{cell} = 0.69$ V

49. a. $Pb(s)|Pb^{2+}(aq) \parallel Ag^+(aq)|Ag(s)$
 b. $Pt(s),\ I_2(s)|I^-(aq) \parallel ClO_2^-(aq)|ClO_2(g)|Pt(s)$
 c. $Zn(s)|Zn^{2+}(aq) \parallel H_2O(l)|H^+(aq)|O_2(g)|Pt(s)$

51.

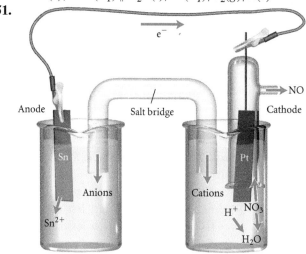

$3\ Sn(s) + 2\ NO_3^-(aq) + 8\ H^+(aq) \longrightarrow$
    $3\ Sn^{2+}(aq) + 2\ NO(g) + 4\ H_2O(l),\ E^\circ_{cell} = 1.10$ V

53. b, c

55. aluminum

57. a. yes, $2\ Al(s) + 6\ H^+(aq) \longrightarrow 2\ Al^{3+}(aq) + 3\ H_2(g)$
 b. no
 c. yes, $Pb(s) + 2\ H^+(aq) \longrightarrow Pb^{2+}(aq) + H_2(g)$

59. a. yes, $3\ Cu(s) + 2\ NO_3^-(aq) + 8\ H^+(aq) \longrightarrow$
            $3\ Cu^{2+}(aq) + 2\ NO(g) + 4\ H_2O(l)$
 b. no

61. a. -1.70 V, nonspontaneous   **b.** 1.97 V, spontaneous
 c. -1.51, nonspontaneous

63. a

65. a. -432 kJ   **b.** 52 kJ   **c.** -1.7×10^2 kJ

67. a. 5.31×10^{75} **b.** 7.7×10^{-10} **c.** 6.3×10^{29}

69. 5.6×10^5

71. $\Delta G^\circ = -7.97$ kJ, $E^\circ_{cell} = 0.041$ V

73. a. 1.04 V   **b.** 0.97 V   **c.** 1.11 V

75. 1.87 V

77. a. 0.56 V   **b.** 0.52 V
 c. $[Ni^{2+}] = 0.003$ M, $[Zn^{2+}] = 1.60$ M

79.

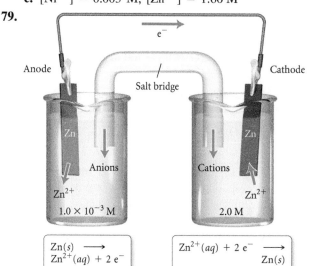

$Zn(s) \longrightarrow Zn^{2+}(aq) + 2\ e^-$

$Zn^{2+}(aq) + 2\ e^- \longrightarrow Zn(s)$

81. $\dfrac{[Sn^{2+}](ox)}{[Sn^{2+}](red)} = 4.2 \times 10^{-4}$

83. 0.3762

85. 1.038 V

87. **a, c**

89.

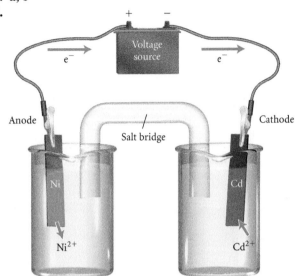

minimum voltage = 0.17 V

91. oxidation: $2\ Br^-(l) \longrightarrow Br_2(g) + 2\ e^-$
reduction: $K^+(l) + e^- \longrightarrow K(l)$

93. oxidation: $2\ Br^-(l) \longrightarrow Br_2(g) + 2\ e^-$
reduction: $K^+(l) + e^- \longrightarrow K(l)$

95. a. anode: $2\ Br^- \longrightarrow Br_2(l) + 2\ e^-$
cathode: $2\ H_2O(l) + 2\ e^- \longrightarrow H_2(g) + 2\ OH^-(aq)$
  b. anode: $2\ I^-(aq) \longrightarrow I_2(s) + 2\ e^-$
cathode: $Pb^{2+}(aq) + 2\ e^- \longrightarrow Pb(s)$
  c. anode: $2\ H_2O(l) \longrightarrow O_2(g) + 4\ H^+(aq) + 4\ e^-$
cathode: $2\ H_2O(l) + 2\ e^- \longrightarrow H_2(g) + 2\ OH^-(aq)$

97.

99. 1.8×10^2 s

101. 1.2×10^3 A

103. $2\ MnO_4^-(aq) + 5\ Zn(s) + 16\ H^+(aq) \longrightarrow$
$2\ Mn^{2+}(aq) + 5\ Zn^{2+}(aq) + 8\ H_2O(l)$
34.9 mL

105. The drawing should show that several Al atoms dissolve into solution as Al^{3+} ions and that several Cu^{2+} ions are deposited on the Al surface as solid Cu.

107. a. 68.3 mL   **b.** cannot be dissolved
  c. cannot be dissolved

109. 0.25

111. There are no paired reactions that produce more than about 5 or 6 V.

113. a. 2.83 V   **b.** 2.71 V   **c.** 16 hr

115. 176 hr

117. 0.71 V

119. a. $\Delta G° = 461$ kJ, $K = 1.4 \times 10^{-81}$
  b. $\Delta G° = 2.7 \times 10^2$ kJ, $K = 2.0 \times 10^{-48}$

121. MCl_4

123. 51.3%

125. pH = 0.85

127. 0.83 M

129. 4.1×10^5 L

131. 435 s

133. 8.39% U

135. The overall cell reaction for both cells is $2\ Cu^+(aq) \longrightarrow Cu^{2+}(aq) + Cu(s)$. The difference in $E°$ is because n = 1 for the first cell and n = 2 for the second cell. For both cells, $\Delta G° = -35.1$ kJ.

137. a

Chapter 19

31. a. $^{234}_{92}U \longrightarrow ^{4}_{2}He + ^{230}_{90}Th$
  b. $^{230}_{90}Th \longrightarrow ^{4}_{2}He + ^{226}_{88}Ra$
  c. $^{214}_{82}Pb \longrightarrow ^{0}_{-1}e + ^{214}_{83}Bi$
  d. $^{13}_{7}N \longrightarrow ^{0}_{+1}e + ^{13}_{6}C$
  e. $^{51}_{24}Cr + ^{0}_{-1}e \longrightarrow ^{51}_{23}V$

33. $^{232}_{90}Th \longrightarrow ^{4}_{2}He + ^{228}_{88}Ra$
$^{228}_{88}Ra \longrightarrow ^{0}_{-1}e + ^{228}_{89}Ac$
$^{228}_{89}Ac \longrightarrow ^{0}_{-1}e + ^{228}_{90}Th$
$^{228}_{90}Th \longrightarrow ^{4}_{2}He + ^{224}_{88}Ra$

35. a. $^{221}_{87}Fr$ **b.** $^{0}_{-1}e$ **c.** $^{0}_{+1}e$ **d.** $^{0}_{-1}e$

37. a. stable, N/Z ratio is close to 1, acceptable for low Z atoms
  b. not stable, N/Z ratio much too high for low Z atom
  c. not stable, N/Z ratio is less than 1, much too low
  d. stable, N/Z ratio is acceptable for this Z

39. Sc, V, and Mn, each have odd numbers of protons. Atoms with an odd number of protons typically have less stable isotopes than those with an even number of protons.

41. a. beta decay   **b.** positron emission
  c. positron emission   **d.** positron emission

43. a. Cs-125   **b.** Fe-62

45. 2.34×10^9 years

47. 0.57 g

49. 10.8 hrs

51. 2.66×10^3 yr

53. 2.4×10^4 yr

55. 2.7×10^9 yr

57. $^{235}_{92}U + ^1_0n \longrightarrow ^{144}_{54}Xe + ^{90}_{38}Sr + 2\,^1_0n$

59. $^2_1H + ^2_1H \longrightarrow ^3_2He + ^1_0n$

61. $^{238}_{92}U + ^1_0n \longrightarrow ^{239}_{92}U$

$^{239}_{92}U \longrightarrow ^{239}_{93}Np + ^0_{-1}e$

$^{239}_{93}Np \longrightarrow ^{239}_{94}Pu + ^0_{-1}e$

63. $^{249}_{98}Cf + ^{12}_6C \longrightarrow ^{257}_{104}Rf + 4\,^1_0n$

65. 9.0×10^{13} J

67. a. mass defect = 0.13701 amu
binding energy = 7.976 MeV/nucleon
b. mass defect = 0.54369 amu
binding energy = 8.732 MeV/nucleon
c. mass defect = 1.16754 amu
binding energy = 8.431 MeV/nucleon

69. 7.228×10^{10} J/g U-235

71. 7.84×10^{10} J/g H-2

73. radiation: 25 J, fall: 370 J

75. 68 mi

77. a. $^1_1p + ^9_4Be \longrightarrow ^6_3Li + ^4_2He$
1.03×10^{11} J/mol
b. $^{209}_{83}Bi + ^{64}_{28}Ni \longrightarrow ^{272}_{111}Rg + ^1_0n$
1.141×10^{13} J/mol
c. $^{179}_{74}W + ^0_{-1}e \longrightarrow ^{179}_{73}Ta$
7.59×10^{10} J/mol

79. a. $^{114}_{44}Ru \longrightarrow ^0_{-1}e + ^{114}_{45}Rh$
b. $^{216}_{88}Ra \longrightarrow ^0_{+1}e + ^{216}_{87}Fr$
c. $^{58}_{30}Zn \longrightarrow ^0_{+1}e + ^{58}_{29}Cu$
d. $^{31}_{10}Ne \longrightarrow ^0_{-1}e + ^{31}_{11}Na$

81. 2.9×10^{21} beta emissions, 3700 Ci

83. 1.6×10^{-5} L

85. 4.94×10^7 kJ/mol

87. 7.72 MeV

89. ^{14}N

91. 0.15%

93. 1.24×10^{21} atoms

95. 2.42×10^{-12} m

97. −0.7 MeV, there is no coulombic barrier for collision with a neutron.

99. a. 1.164×10^{10} kJ   **b.** 0.1299 g

101. U-235 forms Pb-207 in seven α-decays and four β-decays and Th-232 forms Pb-208 in six α-decays and four β-decays.

103. 3.0×10^2 K

105. $^{21}_9F \longrightarrow ^{21}_{10}Ne + ^0_{-1}e$

107. Nuclide A is more dangerous because the half-life is shorter (18.5 days) and so it decays faster.

109. Iodine is used by the thyroid gland to make hormones. Normally we ingest iodine in foods, especially iodized salt. The thyroid gland cannot tell the difference between stable and radioactive iodine and will absorb both. KI tablets work by blocking radioactive iodine from entering the thyroid. When a person takes KI, the stable iodine in the tablet gets absorbed by the thyroid. Because KI contains so much stable iodine, the thyroid gland becomes "full" and cannot absorb any more iodine—either stable or radioactive—for the next 24 hours.

Chapter 20

35. a. alkane   **b.** alkene   **c.** alkyne   **d.** alkene

37. $CH_3-CH_2-CH_2-CH_2-CH_2-CH_2-CH_3$

$CH_3-CH-CH_2-CH_2-CH_2-CH_3$
$\qquad\;\; |$
$\qquad\; CH_3$

$CH_3-CH_2-CH-CH_2-CH_2-CH_3$
$\qquad\qquad\;\; |$
$\qquad\qquad\; CH_3$

$\qquad\qquad CH_3$
$\qquad\qquad\;\; |$
$CH_3-CH-CH-CH_2-CH_3$
$\qquad\; |$
$\qquad CH_3$

$\qquad\qquad\;\; CH_3$
$\qquad\qquad\quad |$
$CH_3-CH_2-C-CH_2-CH_3$
$\qquad\qquad\quad |$
$\qquad\qquad\;\; CH_3$

$\qquad\quad CH_3$
$\qquad\quad\;\; |$
$H_3C-C-CH_2-CH_2-CH_3$
$\qquad\quad\;\; |$
$\qquad\quad CH_3$

$H_3C-CH-CH_2-CH-CH_3$
$\qquad\quad |\qquad\qquad |$
$\qquad\; CH_3\qquad\; CH_3$

$\qquad\qquad CH_3$
$\qquad\qquad\;\; |$
$H_3C-C-CH-CH_3$
$\qquad\quad |\quad\;\; |$
$\qquad\; CH_3\; CH_3$

$H_3C-CH_2-CH-CH_2-CH_3$
$\qquad\qquad\quad |$
$\qquad\qquad\;\; CH_2$
$\qquad\qquad\quad |$
$\qquad\qquad\;\; CH_3$

39. a. no   **b.** yes   **c.** yes   **d.** no

41. a. enantiomers   **b.** same   **c.** enantiomers

43. a. pentane   **b.** 2-methylbutane
c. 4-isopropyl-2-methylheptane
d. 4-ethyl-2-methylhexane

45. a. $CH_3-CH_2-CH-CH_2-CH_2-CH_3$
$\qquad\qquad\qquad |$
$\qquad\qquad\quad CH_2-CH_3$

$\qquad\qquad\qquad\; CH_3$
$\qquad\qquad\qquad\;\; |$
b. $CH_3-CH_2-C-CH_2-CH_3$
$\qquad\qquad\qquad\;\; |$
$\qquad\qquad\quad CH_2-CH_3$

c. $CH_3-CH-CH-CH_3$
$\qquad\qquad\; |\quad\;\; |$
$\qquad\quad CH_3\; CH_3$

$\qquad\qquad CH_3\qquad\qquad\qquad\qquad CH_2-CH_3$
$\qquad\qquad\;\; |\qquad\qquad\qquad\qquad\qquad\; |$
d. $CH_3-C-CH_2-CH-CH_2-CH_2-CH-CH_2-CH_3$
$\qquad\qquad\;\; |\qquad\qquad\; |$
$\qquad\qquad CH_3\qquad\; CH_2-CH_3$

47. a. $CH_3CH_2CH_3 + 5\,O_2 \longrightarrow 3\,CO_2 + 4\,H_2O$
b. $CH_3CH_2CH{=}CH_2 + 6\,O_2 \longrightarrow 4\,CO_2 + 4\,H_2O$
c. $2\,CH{\equiv}CH + 5\,O_2 \longrightarrow 4\,CO_2 + 2\,H_2O$
49. a. CH_3CH_2Br **b.** $CH_3CH_2CH_2Cl,\ CH_3CHClCH_3$
c. $CHCl_2Br$ **d.**

51. $CH_2{=}CH{-}CH_2{-}CH_2{-}CH_2{-}CH_3$
$CH_3{-}CH{=}CH{-}CH_2{-}CH_2{-}CH_3$
$CH_3{-}CH_2{-}CH{=}CH{-}CH_2{-}CH_3$
53. a. 1-butene   **b.** 3,4-dimethyl-2-pentene
c. 3-isopropyl-1-hexene   **d.** 2,4-dimethyl-3-hexene
55. a. 2-butyne   **b.** 4,4-dimethyl-2-hexyne
c. 3-isopropyl-1-hexyne   **d.** 3,6-dimethyl-4-nonyne
57. a. $CH_3{-}CH_2{-}CH{-}C{\equiv}C{-}CH_2{-}CH_2{-}CH_3$
b., **c.**, **d.**

59. a.–d.

61. a. $CH_2{=}CH{-}CH_3 + H_2 \longrightarrow CH_3{-}CH_2{-}CH_3$
b., **c.**

63. a. methylbenzene or toluene
b. bromobenzene
c. chlorobenzene
65. a. 3,5-dimethyl-7-phenylnonane
b. 2-phenyl-3-octene
c. 4,5-dimethyl-6-phenyl-2-octyne
67. a. 1,4-dibromobenzene or *p*-dibromobenzene
b. 1,3-diethylbenzene or *m*-diethylbenzene
c. 1-chloro-2-fluorobenzene or *o*-chlorofluorobenzene
69. a.–c., **71. a.–b.**

73. a. 1-propanol   **b.** 4-methyl-2-hexanol
c. 2,6-dimethyl-4-heptanol   **d.** 3-methyl-3-pentanol
75. a. $CH_3CH_2CH_2Br + H_2O$ **b.**, **c.** $CH_3CH_2ONa + \frac{1}{2}H_2$ **d.**

77. a. butanone   **b.** pentanal
c. 3,5,5-trimethylhexanal   **d.** 4-methyl-2-hexanone
79.

81. a. methylbutanoate   **b.** propanoic acid
c. 5-methylhexanoic acid   **d.** ethylpentanoate
83. a.–b.

85. a. ethyl propyl ether   **b.** ethyl pentyl ether
c. dipropyl ether   **d.** butyl ethyl ether
87. a. diethylamine   **b.** methylpropylamine
c. butylmethylpropylamine
89. a. acid–base, $(CH_3)_2NH_2{}^+(aq) + Cl^-(aq)$
b. condensation, $CH_3CH_2CONHCH_2CH_3(aq) + H_2O$
c. acid–base, $CH_3NH_3{}^+(aq) + HSO_4{}^-(aq)$
91., **93.**

95. a. ester, methyl 3-methylbutanoate
b. ether, ethyl 2-methylbutyl ether
c. aromatic, 1-ethyl-3-methylbenzene or
m-ethylmethylbenzene
d. alkyne, 5-ethyl-4-methyl-2-heptyne
e. aldehyde, butanal
f. alcohol, 2-methyl-1-propanol
97. a. 5-isobutyl-3-methylnonane
b. 5-methyl-3-hexanone
c. 3-methyl-2-butanol
d. 4-ethyl-3,5-dimethyl-1-hexyne
99. a. isomers   **b.** isomers   **c.** same
101. 558 g
103. a. combustion   **b.** alkane substitution
c. alcohol elimination   **d.** aromatic substitution

105. a. 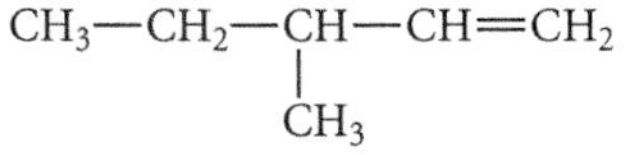 $CH_3-CH_2-CH-CH=CH_2$
     CH_3
Can exist as a stereoisomer

b. 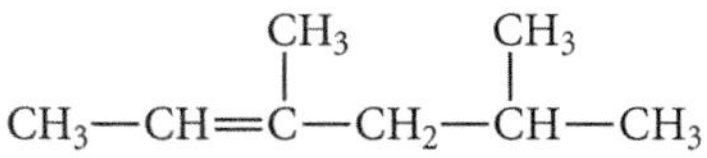 $CH_3-CH=C-CH_2-CH-CH_3$
     CH_3 CH_3
Can exist as a stereoisomer

c. 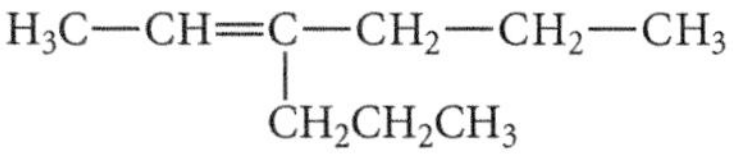 $H_3C-CH=C-CH_2-CH_2-CH_3$
     $CH_2CH_2CH_3$
Can exist as a stereoisomer

107. **1.** 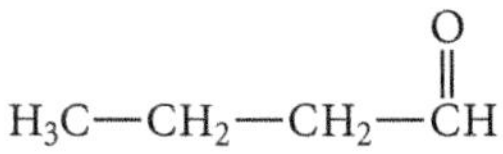 $H_3C-CH_2-CH_2-CH$
          O
Aldehyde

2. 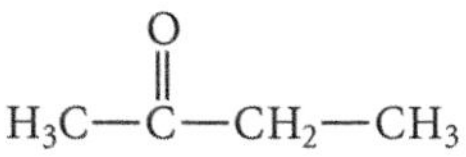 $H_3C-C-CH_2-CH_3$
     O
Ketone

3. $H_3C-CH=CH-O-CH_3$
Alkene, ether

4. $H_2C=CH-O-CH_2-CH_3$
Alkene, ether

5. $H_2C=CH-CH_2-O-CH_3$
Alkene, ether

6. $H_3C-CH=CH-CH_2-OH$
Alkene, alcohol

7. 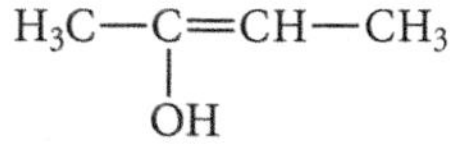 $H_3C-C=CH-CH_3$
     OH
Alkene, alcohol

8. 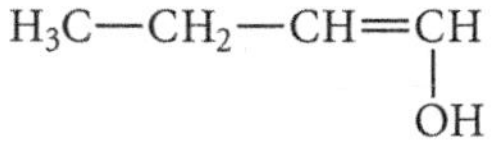 $H_3C-CH_2-CH=CH$
         OH
Alkene, alcohol

9. 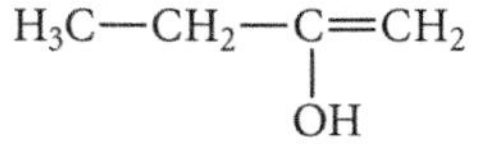 $H_3C-CH_2-C=CH_2$
       OH
Alkene, alcohol

10. 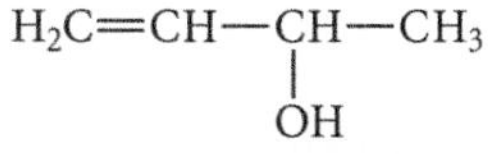 $H_2C=CH-CH-CH_3$
       OH
Alkene, alcohol

11. $H_2C=CH-CH_2-CH_2-OH$
Alkene, alcohol

109. In the acid form of the carboxylic acid, electron withdrawal by the C=O enhances acidity. The conjugate base, the carboxylate anion, is stabilized by resonance so the two O atoms are equivalent and bear the negative charge equally.

111. a.

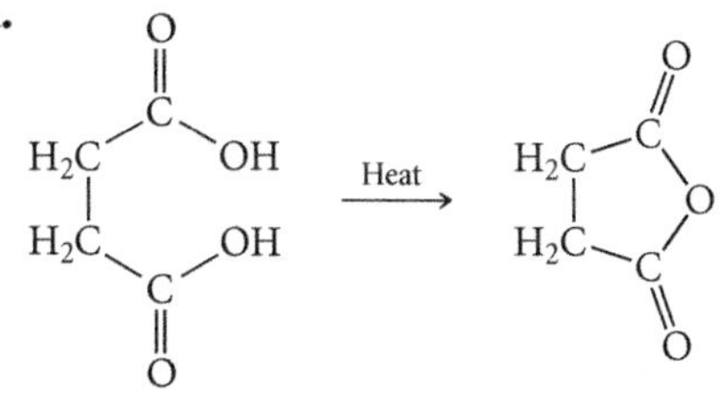

b.

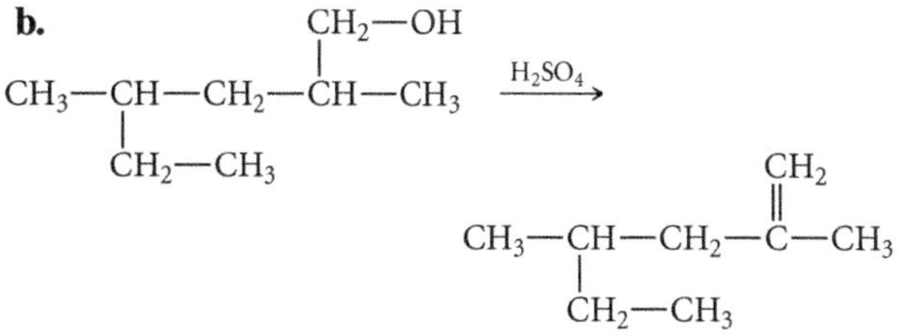

c.

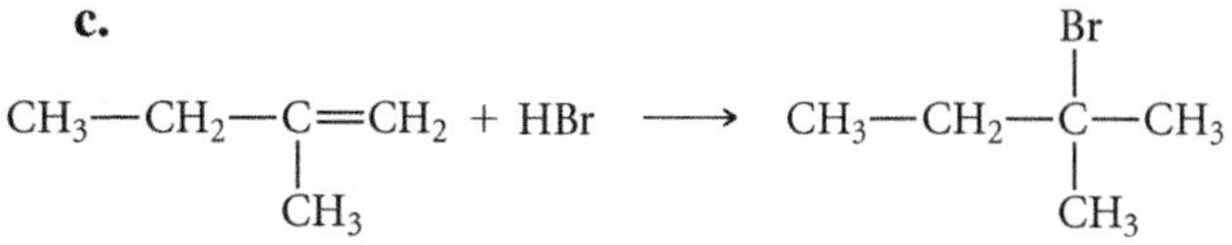

113. a. 3 : 1
b. 2° hydrogen atoms are more reactive. The reactivity of 2° hydrogens to 1° hydrogens is 11 : 3.

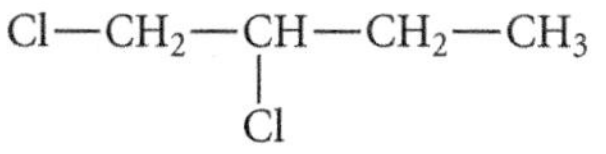

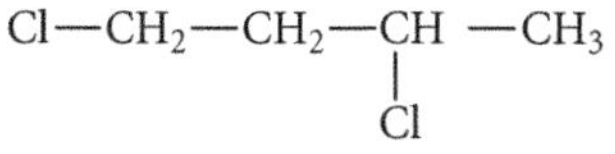

115.

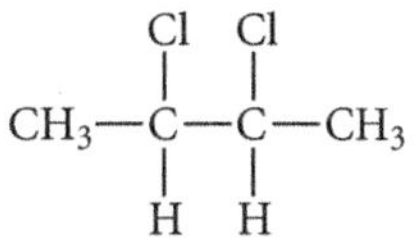

117. The first propagation step for F is very rapid and exothermic because of the strength of the H—F bond which forms. For I the first propagation step is endothermic and slow because the H—I bond that forms is relatively weak.

119.

$Cl-C\equiv C-Cl$ trans
No dipole moment

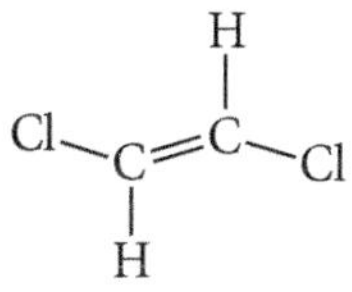

$ClCH_2-CH_2Cl$

cis

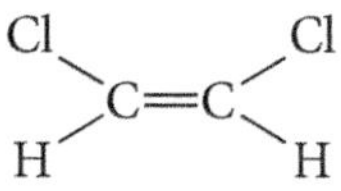

Cl_2CHCH_3 Dipole moment

121. 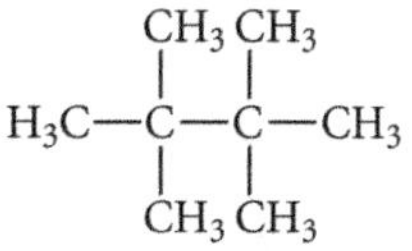 $H_3C-C-C-CH_3$
2,2,3,3-tetramethylbutane

Chapter 21

31. **c.** saturated fatty acid; **d.** steroid

33. **a.** saturated fatty acid   **b.** not a fatty acid

  c. not a fatty acid   **d.** monounsaturated fatty acid

35.

$$\begin{array}{l} \text{OH} \\ \text{H}_2\text{C} \\ \text{HO—CH} \\ \text{H}_2\text{C} \\ \text{OH} \end{array} + 3\,\text{H}_3\text{C} \begin{array}{l} (\text{CH}_2)_4\text{—(CH=CHCH}_2)_2 \quad \text{O} \\ \quad (\text{CH}_2)_6\text{—C—OH} \end{array} \longrightarrow$$

$$\begin{array}{l} \text{H}_2\text{C—O—C—(CH}_2)_6\text{—(CH}_2\text{CH=CH)}_2\text{—(CH}_2)_4\text{—CH}_3 \\ \\ \text{H—C—O—C—(CH}_2)_6\text{—(CH}_2\text{CH=CH)}_2\text{—(CH}_2)_4\text{—CH}_3 \\ \\ \text{H}_2\text{C—O—C—(CH}_2)_6\text{—(CH}_2\text{CH=CH)}_2\text{—(CH}_2)_4\text{—CH}_3 \end{array}$$

Triglyceride is expected to be an oil.

37. **a.** monosaccharide; **c.** disaccharide

39. **a.** aldose, hexose   **b.** aldose, pentose

  c. ketose, tetrose   **d.** aldose, tetrose

41. **a.** 5   **b.** 3   **c.** 1   **d.** 3

43.

$$\begin{array}{l} \text{O} \\ \text{CH} \\ \text{H—C—OH} \\ \text{HO—C—H} \\ \text{H—C—OH} \\ \text{H—C—OH} \\ \text{H}_2\text{C—OH} \end{array}$$

45.

47.

Glucose   Fructose

49. **a.**

$$\begin{array}{l} \text{O} \\ \text{H}_3\text{N}^+\text{—CH—C—O}^- \\ \text{HO—CH} \\ \text{CH}_3 \end{array}$$

b.

$$\begin{array}{l} \text{O} \\ \text{H}_3\text{N}^+\text{—CH—C—O}^- \\ \text{CH}_3 \end{array}$$

c.

$$\begin{array}{l} \text{O} \\ \text{H}_3\text{N}^+\text{—CH—C—O}^- \\ \text{CH}_2 \\ \text{H}_3\text{C—CH} \\ \text{CH}_3 \end{array}$$

d.

$$\begin{array}{l} \text{O} \\ \text{H}_3\text{N}^+\text{—CH—C—O}^- \\ \text{CH}_2 \\ \text{CH}_2 \\ \text{CH}_2 \\ \text{CH}_2 \\ \text{NH}_2 \end{array}$$

51.

$$\begin{array}{l} \text{H}_2\text{N} \quad \text{H} \quad \text{O} \\ \quad \text{C—C—OH} \\ \text{H}_3\text{C} \end{array} \qquad \begin{array}{l} \text{H}_3\text{C} \quad \text{H} \quad \text{O} \\ \quad \text{C—C—OH} \\ \text{H}_2\text{N} \end{array}$$

53. 6, SerGlyCys, SerCysGly, GlySerCys, GlyCysSer, CysSerGly, CysGlySer

55.

$$\begin{array}{l} \text{H} \quad \text{O} \\ \text{H}_2\text{N—C—C—OH} \\ \text{CH}_2 \\ \text{OH} \end{array} + \begin{array}{l} \text{H} \quad \text{O} \\ \text{H}_2\text{N—C—C—OH} \\ \text{CH}_2 \\ \quad \bigcirc \\ \text{OH} \end{array} \longrightarrow$$

$$\begin{array}{l} \text{H} \quad \text{O} \quad \text{H} \quad \text{O} \\ \text{H}_2\text{N—C—C—NH—C—C—OH} \\ \text{CH}_2 \quad\quad \text{CH}_2 \\ \text{OH} \quad\quad\quad \bigcirc \\ \quad\quad\quad\quad\quad \text{OH} \end{array}$$

$$+\, \text{H}_2\text{O}$$

57. **a.**

$$\begin{array}{l} \text{H} \quad \text{O} \quad \text{H} \quad \text{O} \quad \text{H} \quad \text{O} \\ \text{H}_2\text{N—C—C—NH—C—C—NH—C—C—OH} \\ \text{CH}_2 \quad\quad \text{CH}_2 \quad\quad \text{CH}_2 \\ \text{CH}_2 \quad\quad \text{CH}_2 \quad\quad \text{SH} \\ \text{C=O} \quad\quad \text{S} \\ \text{NH}_2 \quad\quad \text{CH}_3 \end{array}$$

b.

c.

59. tertiary

61. primary

63. **a.** A;   **c.** T

65.

67. A C A T G C G

69. 154 codons, 462 nucleotides

71. **a.** protein   **b.** carbohydrate   **c.** lipid

73. A codon is composed of three nucleotides. A codon codes for a specific amino acid while a gene codes for an entire protein.

75.

77. valine, leucine, isoleucine, phenylalanine

79. Gly-Arg-Ala-Leu-Phe-Gly-Asn-Lys-Trp-Glu-Cys

81.

a.

b.

83. As the temperature increases the favorable entropy for uncoiling a chain becomes dominant. On cooling the favorable enthalpy of forming hydrogen bonds between paired bases is dominant.

85. When the fake thymine nucleotide is added to the replicating DNA, the chain cannot continue to form because the $-N{=}N^+{=}NH$ group on the sugar prevents future phosphate linkages.

87. $V_{max} = 47.6$, $K_t = 1.68$

89. $H_3N^+CH_2COO^- + H^+ \rightleftharpoons$
$\qquad\qquad (H_3N^+CH_2COOH \text{ [HA]/[A}^-] = 2,$
$H_3N^+CH_2COO^- \rightleftharpoons$
$\qquad H_2NCH_2COO^- + H^+ \text{ [HA]/[A}^-] = 0.4, pH = 6.0$

91. A three-base codon codes for a single amino acid. If there are only three bases, there could be 27 different three-base codon arrangements. Therefore, you could theoretically code for the 20 different amino acids needed.

Chapter 22

17. **a.** +4   **b.** +4   **c.** +4

19. $Ca_3Al_2(SiO_4)_3$

21. 4

23. tetrahedrons stand alone, orthosilicates

25. amphibole or double-chain structure;
Ca^{2+}, Mg^{2+}, Fe^{2+}, Al^{3+}

27. 950 g

29. NCl_3 has a lone pair that BCl_3 lacks, giving it a trigonal pyramidal shape, as opposed to BCl_3's trigonal planar shape.

31. **a.** 6 vertices, 8 faces   **b.** 12 vertices, 20 faces

33. *closo*-Boranes have the formula $B_nH_n^{2-}$ and form fully closed polyhedra, *nido*-boranes have the formula B_nH_{n+4} and consist of a cage missing a corner, and *arachno*-boranes have the formula B_nH_{n+6} and consist of a cage missing two or three corners.

35. Graphite consists of covalently bonded sheets that are held to each other by weak interactions, allowing them to slip past each other. Diamond is not a good lubricant because it is an extremely strong network covalent solid, where all of the carbon atoms are covalently bonded.

37. Activated charcoal consists of fine particles, rather than a lump of charcoal, and subsequently has a much higher surface area.

39. Ionic carbides are composed of carbon, generally in the form of the carbide ion, C_2^{2-}, and low-electronegativity metals, such as the alkali and alkaline earth metals. Covalent carbides are composed of carbon and low-electronegativity nonmetals or metalloids, such as silicon.

41. **a.** solid $\longrightarrow$ gas
b. gas $\longrightarrow$ liquid $\longrightarrow$ solid
c. solid $\longrightarrow$ gas

43. **a.** $CO(g) + CuO(s) \longrightarrow CO_2(g) + Cu(s)$
b. $SiO_2(s) + 3\,C(s) \longrightarrow SiC(s) + 2\,CO(g)$
c. $S(s) + CO(g) \longrightarrow COS(g)$

45. **a.** +2   **b.** +4   **c.** +4/3

47. Fixing nitrogen refers to converting N_2 to a nitrogen-containing compound.

49. White phosphorus consists of P_4 molecules in a tetrahedral shape with the atoms at the corners of the tetrahedron. This allotrope is unstable because of the strain from the bond angles. Red phosphorus is much more sta-

ble because one bond of the tetrahedron is broken, allowing the phosphorus atoms to make chains with bond angles that are less strained.

51. saltpeter: 13.86% N by mass
Chile saltpeter: 16.48% N by mass

53. HN_3 has a positive ΔG_f°, meaning that it spontaneously decomposes into H_2 and N_2 at room temperature. There are no temperatures at which HN_3 will be stable. ΔH_f is positive and ΔS_f is negative, so ΔG_f will always be negative.

55. a. $NH_4NO_3(aq) + heat \longrightarrow N_2O(g) + 2\ H_2O(l)$
b. $3\ NO_2(g) + H_2O(l) \longrightarrow 2\ HNO_3(l) + NO(g)$
c. $2\ PCl_3(l) + O_2(g) \longrightarrow 2\ POCl_3(l)$

57. NO_3^-, NO_2^-, N_3^-, $N_2H_5^+$, NH_4^+

59.

Trigonal pyramidal   Trigonal bipyramidal

61. $CO(NH_2)_2 + 2\ H_2O \longrightarrow (NH_4)_2CO_3$
14 g

63. P_4O_6 forms if there is only a limited amount of oxygen available, while P_4O_{10} will form with greater amounts of oxygen.

65. The major source of oxygen is the fractionation of air by which air is cooled and liquefied and oxygen is separated from the other components.

67. a. superoxide **b.** oxide   **c.** peroxide

69. Initially, liquid sulfur becomes less viscous when heated because the S_8 rings have greater thermal energy which overcomes intermolecular forces. Above $150\ ^\circ C$ the rings break and the broken rings entangle one another, causing greater viscosity.

71. a. 4×10^{-22} g **b.** 4.0×10^{-19} g

73. $2\ FeS_2(s) \xrightarrow{heat} 2\ FeS(s) + S_2(g)$
510 L

75. a. +2, linear **b.** +6, octahedral
c. +6, square pyramidal

77. $Cl_2(g) + 2\ Br^-(aq) \longrightarrow 2\ Cl^-(aq) + Br_2(l)$
Oxidizing agent: Cl_2
Reducing agent: Br^-

79. No, there is not enough HF to dissolve all of the SiO_2. HF is the limiting reagent. 1.6 g SiO_2.

81. 8 kg from lignite, 40 kg from bituminous

83. Chlorine is much more electronegative than iodine, allowing it to withdraw an electron and ionize in solution much more easily.

85. a. $rate_{HCl}/rate_{Cl_2} = 1.395$
b. $rate_{HCl}/rate_{HF} = 0.7407$
c. $rate_{HCl}/rate_{HI} = 1.873$

87. $4\ Na_2O_2 + 3\ Fe \longrightarrow 4\ Na_2O + Fe_3O_4$

89. The bond length of the O_2 species increases as electrons are added because they are added to the π^* antibonding orbital. O_2^{2-} is diamagnetic.

91. 2.0 mol of C–C bonds, 715 kJ/mol, 6.9×10^2 kJ/mol, This value calculated from the bond energy is too low because it doesn't include van der Waals attractions between C atoms not directly bonded to each other.

93. −50 kJ/mol

95. a. −13.6 kJ/mol **b.** −11.0 kJ/mol **c.** −24.8 kJ/mol
Fe_2O_3 is the most exothermic because it has the highest oxidation state and is therefore able to oxidize the most CO per mol Fe.

97. a. $\ddot{O}{=}C{=}C{=}C{=}\ddot{O}$ **b.** sp
c. −92 kJ/mol

99. a. 7.6×10^{-22} **b.** 1.2×10^{-8}
c. $[N_2H_4] = 0.009$ M, $[N_2H_5^+] = 0.0025$ M,
$[N_2H_6^{2+}] = 7.0 \times 10^{-13}$ M

101. The acid is HO—$\overset{..}{N}$=N—OH and the base is

The acid is weaker than nitrous acid because of electron donation by resonance in contributing structures such as

The base is weaker than ammonia because of electron withdrawal by the electronegative nitro group.

103. The triple bond in nitrogen is much stronger than the double bond in oxygen, so it is much harder to break. This makes it less likely that the bond in nitrogen will be broken.

105. Sodium dinitrogen phosphate (NaH_2PO_4) can act as a weak base or a weak acid. A buffer can be made by mixing it with either Na_2HPO_4 or with Na_3PO_4, depending on the desired pH of the buffer solution.

107. F is extremely small and so there is a huge driving force to fill the octet by adding an electron, giving a −1 oxidation state. Other halogens have access to d orbitals, which allows for more hybridization and oxidation state options.

109. SO_3 cannot be a reducing agent, because the oxidation state of S is +6, the highest possible oxidation state for S. Reducing agents need to be able to be oxidized. SO_2 can be a reducing agent or an oxidizing agent, because the oxidation state of S is +4.

Chapter 23

15. Metals are typically opaque, are good conductors of heat and electricity, and are ductile and malleable, meaning they can be drawn into wires and flattened into sheets.

17. aluminum, iron, calcium, magnesium, sodium, potassium

19. Fe: hematite (Fe_2O_3), magnetite (Fe_3O_4)
Hg: cinnabar (HgS)
V: vanadite [$Pb_5(VO_4)Cl$], carnotite
[$K_2(UO_2)_2(VO_4)_2 \cdot 3\ H_2O$]
Nb: columbite [$Fe(NbO_3)_2$]

21. $MgCO_3(s) + heat \longrightarrow MgO(s) + CO_2(g)$
$Mg(OH)_2(s) + heat \longrightarrow MgO(s) + H_2O(g)$

23. The flux is a material that will react with the gangue to form a substance with a low melting point. MgO is the flux.

25. Hydrometallurgy is used to separate metals from ores by selectively dissolving the metal in a solution, filtering out impurities, and then reducing the metal to its elemental form.

27. The Bayer process is a hydrometallurgical process by which Al_2O_3 is selectively dissolved, leaving other oxides as solids. The soluble form of aluminum is $Al(OH)_4^-$.

29. Sponge powdered iron contains many small holes in the iron particles due to the escaping of the oxygen when the iron is reduced. Water atomized powdered iron has much more smooth and dense particles as the powder is formed from molten iron.

31. a. 50% Cr, 50% V by moles; 50.5% Cr, 49.5% V by mass
   b. 25% Fe, 75% V by moles; 26.8% Fe, 73.2% V by mass
   c. 25% Cr, 25% Fe, 50% V by moles; 24.8% Cr, 26.6% Fe, 48.6% V by mass

33. Cr and Fe are very close to each other in mass, so their respective atomic radii are probably close enough to form an alloy. Also, they both form body-centered cubic structures.

35. A: solid, 20% Cr, 80% Fe
   B: liquid, 50% Cr, 50% Fe

37. A: solid (20% Co and 80% Cu overall. Two phases; one is the Cu structure with 4% Co, and the other is the Co structure with 7% Cu. There will be more of the Cu structure).
   B: solid (Co structure), 90% Co, 10% Cu

39. C would fill interstitial holes; Mn and Si would substitute for Fe.

41. a. Mo_2N **b.** CrH_2

43. a. zinc   **b.** copper   **c.** manganese

45. −19.4 kJ/mol

47. When Cr is added to steel it reacts with oxygen in steel to prevent it from rusting. A Cr steel alloy would be used in any situation where the steel might be easily oxidized, such as when it comes in contact with water.

49. rutile: 33.3% Ti by moles, 59.9% Ti by mass
   ilmenite: 20.0% Ti by moles, 31.6% Ti by mass

51. Titanium must be arc-melted in an inert atmosphere because the high temperature and flow of electrons would cause the metal to oxidize in a normal atmosphere.

53. TiO_2 is the most important industrial product of titanium and it is often used as a pigment in white paint.

55. The Bayer process is a hydrometallurgical process used to separate Al_2O_3 from other oxides. The Al_2O_3 is selectively dissolved by hot, concentrated NaOH. The other oxides are removed as solids and the Al_2O_3 precipitates out of solution when the solution is neutralized.

57. cobalt and tungsten

59. 3.3 kg Fe, 2.0 kg Ti

61. Four atoms surround a tetrahedral hole and six atoms surround an octahedral hole. The octahedral hole is larger because it is surrounded by a greater number of atoms.

63. Mn has one more electron orbital available for bonding than does chromium.

65. Ferromagnetic atoms, like paramagnetic ones, have unpaired electrons. However, in ferromagnetic atoms, these electrons align with their spin oriented in the same direction, resulting in a permanent magnetic field.

67. The nuclear charge of the last three is relatively high because of the lanthanide series in which the $4f$ subshell falls between them and the other six metals of the group.

69. a. 16.0 cm   **b.** 4.95 cm   **c.** 14%

71. 92%

73. 5.4×10^7

75. First, roast to form the oxide.
$$4\,CoAsS(s) + 9\,O_2(g) \longrightarrow$$
$$4\,CoO(s) + 4\,SO_{2(g)} + As_4O_6(s)$$
Then reduce the oxide with coke.
$$CoO(s) + C(s) \longrightarrow Co(s) + CO(g)$$
The oxides of arsenic are relatively volatile and can be separated, but they are poisonous.

77. Au and Ag are found in elemental form because of their low reactivity. Na and Ca are group 1 and group 2 metals, respectively, and are highly reactive as they readily lose their valence electrons to obtain octets.

Chapter 24

17. a. $[Ar]\,4s^2 3d^8,\ [Ar]\,3d^8$
   b. $[Ar]\,4s^2 3d^5,\ [Ar]\,3d^3$
   c. $[Kr]\,5s^2 4d^1,\ [Kr]\,5s^1 4d^1$
   d. $[Xe]\,6s^2 4f^{14} 5d^3,\ [Xe]\,4f^{14} 5d^3$

19. a. +5   **b.** +7   **c.** +4

21. a. +3, 6   **b.** +2, 6
   c. +2, 4   **d.** +1, 2

23. a. hexaaquachromium(III)
   b. tetracyanocuprate(II)
   c. pentaaminebromoiron(III) sulfate
   d. aminetetraaquahydroxycobalt(III) chloride

25. a. $[Cr(NH_3)_6]^{3+}$ **b.** $K_3[Fe(CN)_6]$
   c. $[Cu(en)(SCN)_2]$ **d.** $[Pt(H_2O)_4][PtCl_6]$

27. a. $[Co(NH_3)_3(CN)_3]$, triaminetricyanocobalt(III)
   b. $[Cr(en)_3]^{3+}$, tris(ethylenediamine)chromium(III)

29.

31. $[Fe(H_2O)_5Cl]Cl \cdot H_2O$, pentaaquachloroiron(II) chloride monohydrate
   $[Fe(H_2O)_4Cl_2] \cdot 2\,H_2O$, tetraaquadichloroiron(II) dihydrate

33. b, c, e

35. a. 3   **b.** No geometric isomers.

37. a.
Fac   Mer

b.

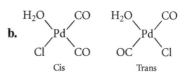

Cis   Trans

39. *cis* isomer is optically active

41. a.

$$\underline{\uparrow\downarrow}\ \underline{\uparrow\downarrow}$$
$$\underline{\uparrow\downarrow}\ \underline{\uparrow\downarrow}\ \underline{\uparrow\downarrow}$$

b.

$$\underline{\uparrow}\ \underline{\uparrow}\qquad\underline{\ \ }\ \underline{\ \ }$$
$$\underline{\uparrow}\ \underline{\uparrow}\ \underline{\uparrow}\quad\underline{\uparrow\downarrow}\ \underline{\uparrow\downarrow}\ \underline{\uparrow}$$

c.

$$\underline{\ \ }\ \underline{\ \ }\ \underline{\ \ }$$
$$\underline{\uparrow}\ \underline{\uparrow}$$

d.

$$\underline{\uparrow}\ \underline{\uparrow}$$
$$\underline{\uparrow\downarrow}\ \underline{\uparrow\downarrow}\ \underline{\uparrow}$$

43. 163 kJ/mol

45. $[Co(CN)_6]^{3-}\ \longrightarrow\ 290$ nm, colorless
$[Co(NH_3)_6]^{3+}\ \longrightarrow\ 440$ nm, yellow
$[CoF_6]^{3-}\ \longrightarrow\ 770$ nm, green

47. weak

49. a. 4   **b.** 3   **c.** 5

51. 3

53. porphyrin

55. Water is a weak field ligand that forms a high-spin complex with hemoglobin. Because deoxyhemoglobin is weak field it absorbs large wavelength light and appears blue. Oxyhemoglobin is a low-spin complex and absorbs small wavelength light, so O_2 must be a strong field ligand.

57. a. [Ar] $4s^1 3d^5$, [Ar] $3d^5$, [Ar] $3d^4$, [Ar] $3d^3$
b. [Ar] $4s^1 3d^{10}$, [Ar] $3d^{10}$, [Ar] $3d^9$

59. a. H—N̈—H   **b.** $\left[\ddot{S}=C=\ddot{N}\right]$ **c.** (H₂O structure)
with H below N

61. $[MA_2B_2C_2]$ all cis; A trans and B and C cis; B trans and A and C cis; C trans and A and B cis; all trans.
$[MA_2B_3C]$ will have fac–mer isomers.
$[MAB_2C_3]$ will have fac–mer isomers.
$[MAB_3C_2]$ will have fac–mer isomers.
$[MA_3B_2C]$ will have fac–mer isomers.
$[MA_2BC_3]$ will have fac–mer isomers.
$[MA_3BC_2]$ will have fac–mer isomers.
$[MABC_2]$ will have AB cis–trans isomers.
$[MAB_4C]$ will have AC cis–trans isomers.
$[MA_4BC]$ will have BC cis–trans isomers.
$[MABC_4]$ will have AB cis–trans isomers.

63.

, optical isomers

65.

$$\underline{\ \ }\ \underline{\ \ }\ \underline{\ \ }$$
$$\underline{\uparrow\downarrow}\ \underline{\uparrow}\ \underline{\uparrow}$$

, paramagnetic

67.

1., 2., 3., 4., 5. Ru complexes

Only structure 3. is chiral. This is its mirror image.

69.

cis-dichlorobis (trimethyl phosphine) platinum(II)

trans-dichlorobis (trimethyl phosphine) platinum(II)

71.

$$\underline{\ \ }\quad d_{z^2}$$
$$\underline{\ \ }\ \underline{\ \ }\quad d_{x^2-y^2}\text{ and }d_{xy}$$
$$\underline{\ \ }\ \underline{\ \ }\quad d_{xz}\text{ and }d_{yz}$$

73. a. 2×10^{-8} M
b. 6.6×10^{-3} M
c. NiS will dissolve more easily in the ammonia solution because the formation of the complex ion is favorable, removing Ni^{2+} ions from the solution allowing more NiS to dissolve.

75. Prepare a solution that contains both $[MCl_6]^{3-}$ and $[MBr_6]^{3-}$ and see if any complex ions that contain both Cl and Br form. If they do it would demonstrate that these complexes are labile.

77. pH = 10.1

79. Au

Appendix IV:
Answers to In-Chapter Practice Problems

Chapter 1

1.1. **a.** The composition of the copper is not changing, thus, being hammered flat is a physical change that signifies a physical property.

   b. The dissolution and color change of the nickel indicate that it is undergoing a chemical change and exhibiting a chemical property.

   c. Sublimation is a physical change indicative of a physical property.

   d. When a match ignites, a chemical change begins as the match reacts with oxygen to form carbon dioxide and water. Flammability is a chemical property.

1.2. **a.** 29.8 °C

   b. 302.9 K

1.3. 21.4 g/cm^3 This matches the density of platinum.

1.3. **For More Practice**

   4.50 g/cm^3 The metal is titanium.

1.4. The thermometer shown has markings every 1 °F; thus, the first digit of uncertainty is 0.1. The answer is 103.4 °F.

1.5. **a.** Each figure in this number is significant by rule 1: three significant figures.

   b. This is a defined quantity that has an unlimited number of significant figures.

   c. Both 1's are significant (rule 1) and the interior zero is significant as well (rule 2): three significant figures.

   d. Only the two 9's are significant, the leading zeroes are not (rule 3): two significant figures.

   e. There are five significant figures because the 1, 4, and 5 are nonzero (rule 1) and the trailing zeroes are after a decimal point so they are significant as well (rule 4).

   f. The number of significant figures is ambiguous because the trailing zeroes occur before an implied decimal point (rule 4). Assume two significant figures.

1.6. **a.** 0.381

   b. 121.0

   c. 1.174

   d. 8

1.7. 3.15 yd

1.8. 2.446 gal

1.9. 1.61×10^6 cm^3

1.9. **For More Practice**

   3.23×10^3 kg

1.10. 1.03 kg

1.10. **For More Practice**

   2.9×10^{-2} cm^3

1.11. 0.855 cm

1.12. 2.70 g/cm^3

Chapter 2

2.1. For the first sample:

$$\frac{\text{mass of oxygen}}{\text{mass of carbon}} = \frac{17.2 \text{ g O}}{12.9 \text{ g C}} = 1.33 \text{ or } 1.33 : 1$$

For the second sample:

$$\frac{\text{mass of oxygen}}{\text{mass of carbon}} = \frac{10.5 \text{ g O}}{7.88 \text{ g C}} = 1.33 \text{ or } 1.33 : 1$$

The ratios of oxygen to carbon are the same in the two samples of carbon monoxide, so these results are consistent with the law of definite proportions.

2.2. $\dfrac{\text{mass of hydrogen to 1 g of oxygen in hydrogen peroxide}}{\text{mass of hydrogen to 1 g of oxygen in water}} = \dfrac{0.250}{0.125} = 2.00$

The ratio of the mass of hydrogen from one compound to the mass of hydrogen in the other is equal to 2. This is a simple whole number and therefore consistent with the law of multiple proportions.

2.3. a. $Z = 6$, $A = 13$, $^{13}_{6}\text{C}$

   b. 19 protons, 20 neutrons

2.4. a. N^{3-}

   b. Rb^{+}

2.5. 24.31 amu

2.5. For More Practice

   70.92 amu

2.6. 4.65×10^{-2} mol Ag

2.7. 0.563 mol Cu

2.7. For More Practice

   22.6 g Ti

2.8. 1.3×10^{22} C atoms

2.8. For More Practice

   6.87 g W

2.9. $l = 1.72$ cm

2.9. For More Practice

   2.90×10^{24} Cu atoms

Chapter 3

3.1. a. C_5H_{12}

   b. HgCl

   c. CH_2O

3.2. a. molecular element

   b. molecular compound

   c. atomic element

   d. ionic compound

   e. ionic compound

3.3. K_2S

3.4. AlN

3.5. silver nitride

3.5. For More Practice
Rb_2S

3.6. iron(II) sulfide

3.6. For More Practice
RuO_2

3.7. tin(II) chlorate

3.7. For More Practice
$Co_3(PO_4)_2$

3.8. dinitrogen pentoxide

3.8. For More Practice
PBr_3

3.9. hydrofluoric acid

3.10. nitrous acid

3.10. For More Practice
$HClO_4$

3.11. 164.10 amu

3.12. 5.839×10^{20} $C_{13}H_{18}O_2$ molecules

3.12. For More Practice
1.06 g H_2O

3.13. 53.29%

3.13. For More Practice
74.19% Na

3.14. 83.9 g Fe_2O_3

3.14. For More Practice
8.6 g Na

3.15. 4.0 g O

3.15. For More Practice
3.60 g C

3.16. CH_2O

3.17. $C_{13}H_{18}O_2$

3.18. C_6H_6

3.18. For More Practice
$C_2H_8N_2$

3.19. C_2H_5

3.20. C_2H_4O

3.21. $SiO_2(s) + 3\,C(s) \longrightarrow SiC(s) + 2\,CO(g)$

3.22. $2\,C_2H_6(g) + 7\,O_2(g) \longrightarrow 4\,CO_2(g) + 6\,H_2O(g)$

Chapter 4

4.1. 4.08 g HCl

4.2. 22 kg HNO_3

4.3. H_2 is the limiting reagent, since it produces the least amount of NH_3. Therefore, 29.4 kg NH_3 is the theoretical yield.

4.4. CO is the limiting reagent, since it only produces 114 g Fe. Therefore, 114 g Fe is the theoretical yield: percentage yield = 63.4% yield

4.5. 0.214 M $NaNO_3$

4.5. For More Practice
44.6 g KBr

4.6. 402 g $C_{12}H_{22}O_{11}$

4.6. For More Practice
221 mL of KCl solution

4.7. 667 mL

4.7. For More Practice
0.105 L

4.8. 51.4 mL HNO_3 solution

4.8. For More Practice
0.170 g CO_2

4.9. a. Insoluble.
b. Insoluble.
c. Soluble.
d. Soluble.

4.10. $NH_4Cl(aq) + Fe(NO_3)_3(aq) \longrightarrow$ NO REACTION

4.11. $2\,NaOH(aq) + CuBr_2(aq) \longrightarrow Cu(OH)_2(s) + 2\,NaBr(aq)$

4.12. $2\,H^+(aq) + 2\,I^-(aq) + Ba^{2+}(aq) + 2\,OH^-(aq) \longrightarrow$
$$2\,H_2O(l) + Ba^{2+}(aq) + 2\,I^-(aq)$$

$H^+(aq) + OH^-(aq) \longrightarrow H_2O(l)$

4.12. For More Practice
$2\,Ag^+(aq) + 2\,NO_3^-(aq) + Mg^{2+}(aq) + 2\,Cl^-(aq) \longrightarrow$
$$2\,AgCl(s) + Mg^{2+}(aq) + 2\,NO_3^-(aq)$$

$Ag^+(aq) + Cl^-(aq) \longrightarrow AgCl(s)$

4.13. $H_2SO_4(aq) + 2\,LiOH(aq) \longrightarrow 2\,H_2O(l) + Li_2SO_4(aq)$
$H^+(aq) + OH^-(aq) \longrightarrow H_2O(aq)$

4.14. 9.03×10^{-2} M H_2SO_4

4.14. For More Practice
24.5 mL NaOH solution

4.15. $2\,HBr(aq) + K_2SO_3(aq) \longrightarrow H_2O(l) + SO_2(g) + 2\,KBr(aq)$

4.15. For More Practice
$2\,H^+(aq) + S^{2-}(aq) \longrightarrow H_2S(g)$

4.16. a. $Cr = 0$.
b. $Cr^{3+} = +3$.
c. $Cl^- = -1, C = +4$.
d. $Br = -1, Sr = +2$.
e. $O = -2, S = +6$.
f. $O = -2, N = +5$.

4.17. Sn is oxidized and N is reduced.

4.17. For More Practice
b. Reaction b is the only redeox reaction. Al is oxidized and O is reduced.

4.18. a. This is a redox reaction in which Li is the reducing agent (it is oxidized) and Cl_2 is the oxidizing reagent (it is reduced).
b. This is a redox reaction in which Al is the reducing agent and Sn^{2+} is the oxidizing agent.
c. This is not a redox reaction because no oxidation states change.
d. This is a redox reaction in which C is the reducing agent and O_2 is the oxidizing agent.

4.19. $2\,C_2H_5SH(l) + 9\,O_2(g) \longrightarrow 4\,CO_2(g) + 2\,SO_2(g) + 6\,H_2O(g)$

Chapter 5

5.1. 15.0 psi

5.1. For More Practice

80.6 kPa

5.2. 2.1 atm at a depth of approximately 11 m.

5.3. 123 mL

5.4. 11.3 L

5.5. 1.63 atm, 23.9 psi

5.6. 16.1 L

5.6. For More Practice

976 mmHg

5.7. $d = 4.91$ g/L

5.7. For More Practice

44.0 g/mol

5.8. 70.7 g/mol

5.9. 0.0610 mol H_2

5.10. 4.2 atm

5.11. 12.0 mg H_2

5.12. 82.3 g Ag_2O

5.12. For More Practice

7.10 g Ag_2O

5.13. 6.53 L O_2

5.14. $u_{rms} = 238$ m/s

5.15. $\dfrac{\text{rate}_{H_2}}{\text{rate}_{Kr}} = 6.44$

Chapter 6

6.1. $\Delta E = 71$ J

6.2. $C_s = 0.38\dfrac{\text{J}}{\text{g} \cdot {}^\circ\text{C}}$

The specific heat capacity of gold is 0.128 J/g · °C; therefore the rock cannot be pure gold.

6.2. For More Practice

$T_f = 42.1\ {}^\circ\text{C}$

6.3. 37.8 grams Cu

6.4. -122 J

6.4. For More Practice

$\Delta E = -998$ J

6.5. $\Delta E_{\text{reaction}} = -3.91 \times 10^3$ kJ/mol C_6H_{14}

6.5. For More Practice

$C_{\text{cal}} = 4.55\dfrac{\text{kJ}}{{}^\circ\text{C}}$

6.6. **a.** endothermic, positive ΔH.
b. endothermic, positive ΔH.
c. exothermic, negative ΔH.

6.7. -2.06×10^3 kJ

6.7. For More Practice

33 g C_4H_{10}

99 g CO_2

6.8. $\Delta H_{rxn} = -68$ kJ

6.9. $N_2O(g) + NO_2(g) \longrightarrow 3\,NO(g)$, $\Delta H_{rxn} = +157.6$ kJ

6.9. For More Practice

$3\,H_2(g) + O_3(g) \longrightarrow 3\,H_2O(g)$, $\Delta H = -868.1$ kJ

6.10. a. $Na(s) + \dfrac{1}{2}Cl_2(g) \longrightarrow NaCl(s)$, $\Delta H_f^\circ = -411.2$ kJ/mol

b. $Pb(s) + N_2(g) + 3\,O_2(g) \longrightarrow Pb(NO_3)_2(s)$, $\Delta H_f^\circ = -451.9$ kJ/mol

6.11. $\Delta H_{rxn}^\circ = -851.5$ kJ

6.12. $\Delta H_{rxn}^\circ = -1648.4$ kJ

111 kJ emitted (-111 kJ)

6.13. 1.2×10^2 kg CO_2

Chapter 7

7.1. 5.83×10^{14} s^{-1}

7.2. 2.64×10^{20} photons

7.2. For More Practice

435 nm

7.3. a. blue<green<red.

b. red<green<blue.

c. red<green<blue.

7.4. 6.1×10^6 m/s

7.5. For the 5d orbitals:

$n = 5$

$l = 2$

$m_l = -2, -1, 0, 1, 2$

The 5 integer values for m_l signify that there are five 5d orbitals.

7.6. a. l cannot equal 3 if $n = 3$. $l = 2$

b. m_l cannot equal -2 if $l = -1$. Possible values for $m_l = -1, 0,$ or 1

c. 1 cannot be 1 if $n = 1$. $l = 0$

7.7. 397 nm

7.7. For More Practice

$n = 1$

Chapter 8

8.1. a. Cl $1s^2 2s^2 2p^6 3s^2 3p^5$ or [Ne] $3s^2 3p^5$

b. Si $1s^2 2s^2 2p^6 3s^2 3p^2$ or [Ne] $3s^2 3p^2$

c. Sr $1s^2 2s^2 2p^6 3s^2 3p^6 4s^2 3d^{10} 4p^6 5s^2$ or [Kr] $5s^2$

d. O $1s^2 2s^2 2p^4$ or [He] $2s^2 p^4$

8.2. There are no unpaired electrons.

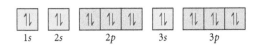

8.3. $1s^2 2s^2 2p^6 3s^2 3p^3$ or [Ne] $3s^2 3p^3$. The five electrons in the $3s^2 3p^3$ orbitals are the valence electrons, while the 10 electrons in the $1s^2 2s^2 2p^6$ orbitals belong to the core.

8.4. Bi [Xe] $6s^2 4f^{14} 5d^{10} 6p^3$

8.4. For More Practice

I [Kr] $5s^2 4d^{10} 5p^5$

8.5. a. Sn
b. cannot predict
c. W
d. Se

8.5. For More Practice

Rb > Ca > Si > S > F

8.6. a. [Ar] $4s^0 3d^7$. Co^{2+} is paramagnetic.

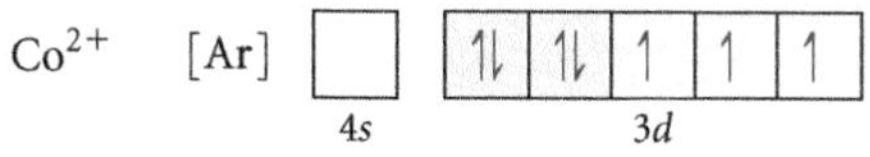

Co^{2+} [Ar] — 4s — 3d

b. [He] $2s^2 2p^6$. N^{3-} is diamagnetic.

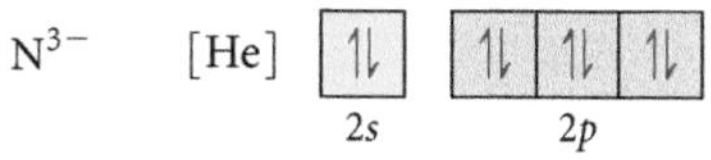

N^{3-} [He] — 2s — 2p

c. [Ne] $3s^2 3p^6$. Ca^{2+} is diamagnetic.

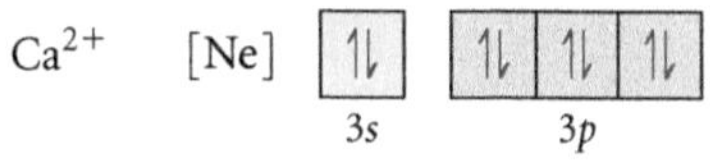

Ca^{2+} [Ne] — 3s — 3p

8.7. a. K
b. F^-
c. Cl^-

8.7. For More Practice

$Cl^- > Ar > Ca^{2+}$

8.8. a. I
b. Ca
c. cannot predict
d. F

8.8. For More Practice

F > S > Si > Ca > Rb

8.9. a. Sn
b. cannot predict based on simple trends (Po is larger)
c. Bi
d. B

8.9. For More Practice

Cl < Si < Na < Rb

8.10. a. $2 Al(s) + 3 Cl_2(g) \longrightarrow 2 AlCl_3(s)$
b. $2 Li(s) + 2 H_2O(l) \longrightarrow 2 Li^+(aq) + 2 OH^-(aq) + H_2(g)$
c. $H_2(g) + Br_2(l) \longrightarrow 2 HBr(g)$

Chapter 9

9.1. Mg_3N_2

9.2. KI < LiBr < CaO

9.2. For More Practice

$MgCl_2$

9.3. a. pure covalent
b. ionic
c. polar covalent

9.4. $:C{\equiv}O:$

9.5.

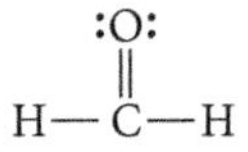

$$
\begin{array}{c}
:\!O\!: \\
\parallel \\
H\!-\!C\!-\!H
\end{array}
$$

9.6. $\left[:\!\ddot{C}l\!:\!\ddot{O}\!:\right]^{-}$

9.7. $\left[:\!\ddot{O}{=}\ddot{N}{-}\ddot{O}\!:\right]^{-} \longleftrightarrow \left[:\!\ddot{O}{-}\ddot{N}{=}\ddot{O}\!:\right]^{-}$

9.8.

Structure	A			B			C		
	$:\!\ddot{N}{=}N{=}\ddot{O}\!:$			$:N{\equiv}N{-}\ddot{O}\!:$			$:\!\ddot{N}{-}N{\equiv}O\!:$		
number of valence e⁻	5	5	6	5	5	6	5	5	6
number of nonbonding e⁻	−4	−0	−4	−2	−0	−6	−6	−0	−2
1/2 (number of bonding e⁻)	−2	−4	−2	−3	−4	−1	−1	−4	−3
Formal charge	**−1**	**+1**	**0**	**0**	**+1**	**−1**	**−2**	**+1**	**+1**

Structure B contributes the most to the correct overall structure of N_2O.

9.8. For More Practice

The nitrogen is +1, the singly bonded oxygen atoms are −1, and the double-bonded oxygen atom has no formal charge.

9.9.

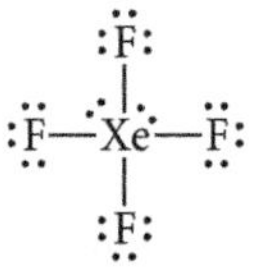

$$
\begin{array}{c}
:\!\ddot{F}\!: \\
| \\
:\!\ddot{F}\!-\!\overset{\cdot}{X}\!\overset{\cdot}{e}\!-\!\ddot{F}\!: \\
| \\
:\!\ddot{F}\!:
\end{array}
$$

9.9. For More Practice

$$
\begin{array}{c}
H \\
| \\
:\!O\!: \\
| \\
H\!-\!\ddot{O}\!-\!P^{0}\!-\!\ddot{O}\!-\!H \\
\parallel \\
:\!O\!:^{0}
\end{array}
$$

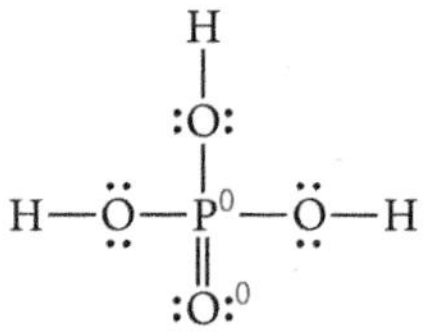

9.10. $CH_3OH(g) + \dfrac{3}{2}O_2(g) \longrightarrow CO_2(g) + 2\,H_2O(g)$

$\Delta H_{rxn} = -641\ \text{kJ}$

9.10. For More Practice

$\Delta H_{rxn} = -8.0 \times 10^{1}\ \text{kJ}$

Chapter 10

10.1. tetrahedral

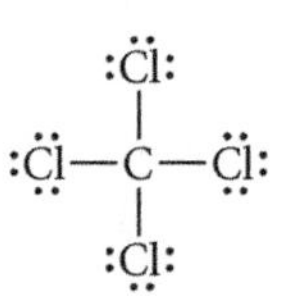

$$
\begin{array}{c}
:\!\ddot{C}l\!: \\
| \\
:\!\ddot{C}l\!-\!C\!-\!\ddot{C}l\!: \\
| \\
:\!\ddot{C}l\!:
\end{array}
$$

10.2. bent

10.3. linear

10.4.

Atom	Number of Electron Groups	Number of Lone Pairs	Molecular Geometry
Carbon (left)	4	0	Tetrahedral
Carbon (right)	3	0	Trigonal planar
Oxygen	4	2	Bent

10.5. The molecule is nonpolar.

10.6. The xenon atom has six electron groups and therefore has an octahedral electron geometry. An octahedral electron geometry corresponds to sp^3d^2 hybridization (refer to Table 10.3).

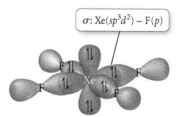

10.7. Since there are only two electron groups around the central atom (C), the electron geometry is linear. According to Table 10.3, the corresponding hybridization on the carbon atom is sp.

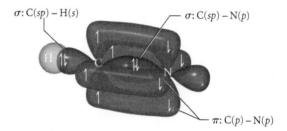

10.8. Since there are only two electron groups about the central atom (C) the electron geometry is linear. The hybridization on C is sp (refer to Table 10.3).

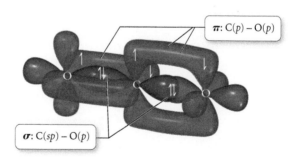

10.8. For More Practice

There are five electron groups about the central atom (I); therefore the electron geometry is trigonal bipyramidal and the corresponding hybridization of I is sp^3d (refer to Table 10.3).

10.9. H_2^+ bond order $= +\dfrac{1}{2}$

Since the bond order is positive, the H_2^+ ion should be stable; however, the bond order of H_2^+ is lower than the bond order of H_2 (bond order $= 1$). Therefore, the bond in H_2^+ is weaker than in H_2.

10.10. The bond order of N_2^+ is 2.5, which is lower than that of the N_2 molecule (bond order $= 3$), therefore the bond is weaker. The MO diagram shows that the N_2^+ ion has one unpaired electron and is therefore paramagnetic.

$$\sigma_{2p}^* \; \boxed{}$$

$$\pi_{2p}^* \; \boxed{}\;\boxed{}$$

$$\sigma_{2p} \; \boxed{\uparrow}$$

$$\pi_{2p} \; \boxed{\uparrow\downarrow}\;\boxed{\uparrow\downarrow}$$

$$\sigma_{2s}^* \; \boxed{\uparrow\downarrow}$$

$$\sigma_{2s} \; \boxed{\uparrow\downarrow}$$

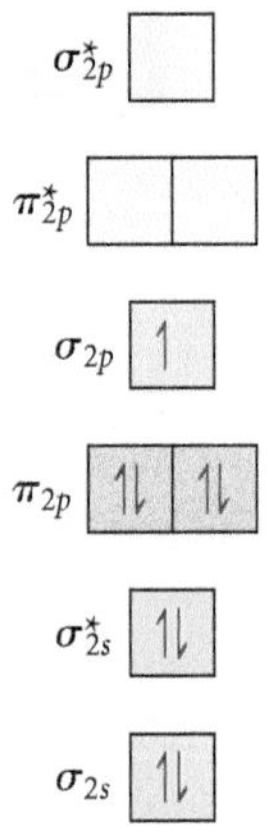

10.10. For More Practice

The bond order of Ne_2 is 0, which indicates that dineon does not exist.

10.11. The bond order of NO is $+2.5$. The MO diagram shows that the NO ion has one unpaired electron and is therefore paramagnetic.

Chapter 11

11.1. b, c

11.2. HF has a higher boiling point than HCl because, unlike HCl, HF is able to form hydrogen bonds. The hydrogen bond is the strongest of the intermolecular forces and requires more energy to break.

11.3. 5.83×10^3 kJ

11.3. For More Practice

49 °C

11.4. 33.8 kJ/mol

11.5. 7.04×10^3 torr

11.6. 29.4°

11.7. $7.18 \dfrac{\text{g}}{\text{cm}^3}$

Chapter 12

12.1. **a.** not soluble
b. soluble
c. not soluble
d. not soluble

12.2. 2.7×10^{-4} M

12.3. 42.5 g $C_{12}H_{22}O_{11}$

12.3. For More Practice

3.3×10^4 L

12.4. **a.** $M = 0.415$ M
b. $m = 0.443$ m
c. % by mass $= 13.2\%$
d. $\chi_{C_{12}H_{22}O_{11}} = 0.00793$
e. mole percent $= 0.793\%$

12.5. 0.600 M

12.5. For More Practice

0.651 m

12.6. 22.5 torr

12.6. For More Practice

0.144

12.7. a. $P_{\text{benzene}} = 26.6$ torr

$P_{\text{toluene}} = 20.4$ torr

b. 47.0 torr

c. 52.5% benzene; 47.5% toluene

The vapor will be richer in the more volatile component, which in this case is benzene.

12.8. $T_f = -4.8\,°C$

12.9. 101.84 °C

12.10. 11.8 atm

12.11. −0.60 °C

12.12. 0.014 mol NaCl

Chapter 13

13.1. $\dfrac{\Delta[H_2O_2]}{\Delta t} = -4.40 \times 10^{-3}$ M/s

$\dfrac{\Delta[I_3^-]}{\Delta t} = 4.40 \times 10^{-3}$ M/s

13.2. a. Rate $= k[CHCl_3][Cl_2]^{1/2}$. (Fractional-order reactions are not common but are occasionally observed.)

b. $3.5\ \text{M}^{-1/2} \cdot \text{s}^{-1}$

13.3. 5.78×10^{-2} M

13.4. 0.0277 M

13.5. 1.64×10^{-3} M

13.6. 79.2 s

13.7. $2.07 \times 10^{-5} \dfrac{\text{L}}{\text{mol} \cdot \text{s}}$

13.8. $6.13 \times 10^{-4} \dfrac{\text{L}}{\text{mol} \cdot \text{s}}$

13.9. $2\,A + B \longrightarrow A_2B$

Rate $= k[A]^2$

Chapter 14

14.1. $K = \dfrac{[CO_2]^3[H_2O]^4}{[C_3H_8][O_2]^5}$

14.2. 2.1×10^{-13}

14.2. For More Practice

1.4×10^2

14.3. 6.2×10^2

14.4. $K_c = \dfrac{[Cl_2]^2}{[HCl]^4[O_2]}$

14.5. 9.4

14.6. 1.1×10^{-6}

14.7. $Q_c = 0.0196$

Reaction proceeds to the left.

14.8. 0.033 M

14.9. $[N_2] = 4.45 \times 10^{-3}$ M

$[O_2] = 4.45 \times 10^{-3}$ M

$[NO] = 1.1 \times 10^{-3}$ M

14.10. $[N_2O_4] = 0.005$ M

$[NO_2] = 0.041$ M

14.11. $P_{I_2} = 0.027$ atm

$P_{Cl_2} = 0.027$ atm

$P_{ICl} = 0.246$ atm

14.12. 1.67×10^{-7} M

14.13. 6.78×10^{-6} M

14.14. Adding Br_2 increases the concentration of Br_2, causing a shift to the left (away from the Br_2). Adding BrNO increases the concentration of BrNO, causing a shift to the right.

14.15. Decreasing the volume causes the reaction to shift right. Increasing the volume causes the reaction to shift left.

14.16. If we increase the temperature, the reaction shifts to the left. If we decrease the temperature, the reaction shifts to the right.

Chapter 15

15.1. **a.** H_2O donates a proton to C_5H_5N, making it the acid. The conjugate base is therefore OH^-. Since C_5H_5N accepts the proton, it is the base and becomes the conjugate acid $C_5H_5NH^+$.

b. Since HNO_3 donates a proton to H_2O, it is the acid, making NO_3^- the conjugate base. Since H_2O is the proton acceptor, it is the base and becomes the conjugate acid, H_3O^+.

15.2. **a.** $[H_3O^+] = 6.7 \times 10^{-13}$ M

Since $[H_3O^+] < [OH^-]$, the solution is basic.

b. $[H_3O^+] = 1.0 \times 10^{-7}$ M

Neutral solution.

c. $[H_3O^+] = 1.2 \times 10^{-5}$ M

Since $[H_3O^+] > [OH^-]$, the solution is acidic.

15.3. **a.** 8.02 (basic)

b. 11.85 (basic)

15.4. 4.3×10^{-9} M

15.5. 9.4×10^{-3} M

15.6. 3.28

15.7. 2.72

15.8. 1.8×10^{-6}

15.9. 0.85%

15.10. 4.0×10^{-7} M

15.11. $[OH^-] = 0.020$ M

pH = 12.30

15.12. $[OH^-] = 1.2 \times 10^{-2}$ M

pH = 12.08

15.13. a. weak base
   b. pH-neutral
15.14. 9.07
15.15. a. pH-neutral
   b. weak acid
   c. weak acid
15.16. a. basic
   b. acidic
   c. pH-neutral
   d. acidic
15.17. 3.83
15.18. $[SO_4^{2-}] = 0.00386$ M
   pH $= 1.945$
15.19. 5.6×10^{-11} M

Chapter 16

16.1. 4.44

16.1. For More Practice
   3.44

16.2. 9.14

16.3. 4.87

16.3. For More Practice
   4.65

16.4. 9.68

16.4. For More Practice

   9.56

16.5. hypochlorous acid (HClO); 2.4 g NaClO

16.6. 1.74

16.7. 18.08

16.8. 2.30×10^{-6} M

16.9. 5.3×10^{-13}

16.10. 1.21×10^{-5} M

16.11. $FeCO_3$ will be more soluble in an acidic solution than $PbBr_2$ because the CO_3^{2-} ion is a basic anion, whereas Br^- is the conjugate base of a strong acid (HBr) and is therefore pH-neutral.

16.12. $Q > K_{sp}$; therefore, a precipitate forms.

16.13. 2.9×10^{-6} M

16.14. a. AgCl precipitates first; $[NaCl] = 7.1 \times 10^{-9}$ M
   b. $[Ag^+]$ is 1.5×10^{-8} M when $PbCl_2$ begins to precipitate, and $[Pb^{2+}]$ is 0.085 M.
16.15. 9.6×10^{-6} M

Chapter 17

17.1. a. positive
   b. negative
   c. positive

17.2. **a.** -548 J/K

  b. ΔS_{sys} is negative.

  c. ΔS_{univ} is negative, and the reaction is not spontaneous.

17.2. **For More Practice**

  375 K

17.3. $\Delta G = -101.6 \times 10^3$ J

  Therefore the reaction is spontaneous. Since both ΔH and ΔS are negative, as the temperature increases ΔG will become more positive.

17.4. -153.2 J/K

17.5. $\Delta G^\circ_{rxn} = -36.3$ kJ

  Since ΔG°_{rxn} is negative, the reaction is spontaneous at this temperature.

17.6. $\Delta G^\circ_{rxn} = -42.1$ kJ

  Since the value of ΔG°_{rxn} at the lowered temperature is more negative (or less positive) (which is -36.3 kJ), the reaction is more spontaneous.

17.7. $\Delta G^\circ_{rxn} = -689.6$ kJ

  Since ΔG°_{rxn} is negative, the reaction is spontaneous at this temperature.

17.7. **For More Practice**

  $\Delta G^\circ_{rxn} = -689.7$ kJ (at 25°)

  The value calculated for ΔG°_{rxn} from the tabulated values (-689.6 kJ) is the same, to within 1 in the least significant digit, as the value calculated using the equation for ΔG°_{rxn}.

  $\Delta G^\circ_{rxn} = -649.7$ kJ (at 500.0 K)

  You could not calculate ΔG°_{rxn} at 500.0 K using tabulated ΔG°_f values because the tabulated values of free energy are calculated at a standard temperature of 298 K, much lower than 500 K.

17.8. $+107.1$ kJ

17.9. $\Delta G_{rxn} = -129$ kJ

  The reaction is more spontaneous under these conditions than under standard conditions because ΔG_{rxn} is more negative than ΔG°_{rxn}.

17.10. -10.9 kJ

Chapter 18

18.1. $2 \text{ Cr}(s) + 4 \text{ H}^+(aq) \longrightarrow 2 \text{ Cr}^{2+}(aq) + 2 \text{ H}_2(g)$

18.2. $\text{Cu}(s) + 4 \text{ H}^+(aq) + 2 \text{ NO}_3^-(aq) \longrightarrow \text{Cu}^{2+}(aq) + 2 \text{ NO}_2(g) + 2 \text{ H}_2\text{O}(l)$

18.3. $3 \text{ ClO}^-(aq) + 2 \text{ Cr(OH)}_4^-(aq) + 2 \text{ OH}^-(aq) \longrightarrow$
$$3 \text{ Cl}^-(aq) + 2 \text{ CrO}_4^{2-}(aq) + 5 \text{ H}_2\text{O}(l)$$

18.4. $+0.60$ V

18.5. **a.** The reaction *will* be spontaneous as written.

  b. The reaction *will not* be spontaneous as written.

18.6. $\Delta G^\circ = -3.63 \times 10^5$ J

  Since ΔG° is negative, the reaction is spontaneous.

18.7. 4.5×10^3

18.8. 1.08 V

18.9. *Anode:* $2 \text{ H}_2\text{O}(l) \longrightarrow \text{O}_2(g) + 4 \text{ H}^+(aq) + 4 \text{ e}^-$

  Cathode: $2 \text{ H}_2\text{O}(l) + 2 \text{ e}^- \longrightarrow \text{H}_2(g) + 2 \text{ OH}^-(aq)$

18.10. 6.0×10^1 min

Chapter 19

19.1. $^{216}_{84}Po \longrightarrow {}^{212}_{82}Pb + {}^{4}_{2}He$

19.2. a. $^{235}_{92}U \longrightarrow {}^{231}_{90}Th + {}^{4}_{2}He$

$^{231}_{90}Th \longrightarrow {}^{231}_{91}Pa + {}^{0}_{-1}e$

$^{231}_{91}Pa \longrightarrow {}^{227}_{89}Ac + {}^{4}_{2}He$

b. $^{22}_{11}Na \longrightarrow {}^{22}_{10}Ne + {}^{0}_{+1}e$

c. $^{76}_{36}Kr + {}^{0}_{-1}e \longrightarrow {}^{76}_{35}Br$

19.2. For More Practice

Positron emission $\left({}^{40}_{19}K \longrightarrow {}^{40}_{18}Ar + {}^{0}_{+1}e \right)$ or electron capture

$\left({}^{40}_{19}K + {}^{0}_{+1}e \longrightarrow {}^{40}_{18}Ar \right)$

19.3. a. positron emission

b. beta decay

c. positron emission

19.4. 10.7 yr

19.5. $t = 964$ yr

No, the C-14 content suggests that the scroll is from about A.D. 1000, not 500 B.C.

19.6. 1.0×10^{9} yr

19.7. Mass defect $= 1.934$ amu

Nuclear binding energy $= 7.569$ MeV/nucleon

Chapter 20

20.1.

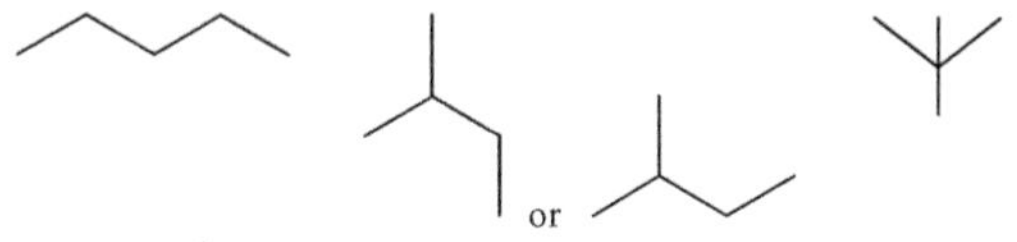

20.2. 3-methylhexane

20.3. 3,5-dimethylheptane

20.4. 2,3,5-trimethylhexane

20.5. a. 4,4-dimethyl-2-pentyne

b. 3-ethyl-4,6-dimethyl-1-heptene

20.6. a. 2-methylbutane

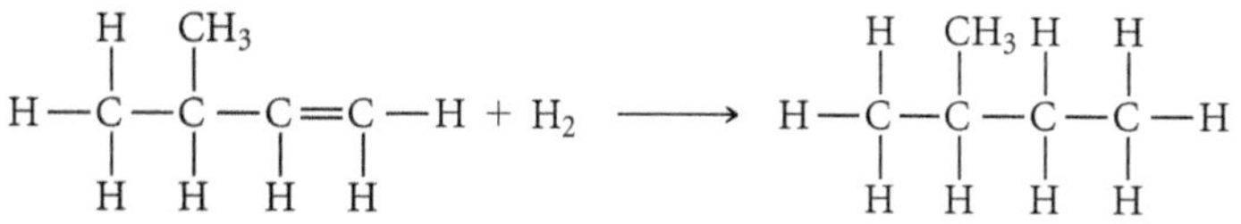

b. 2-chloro-3-methylbutane

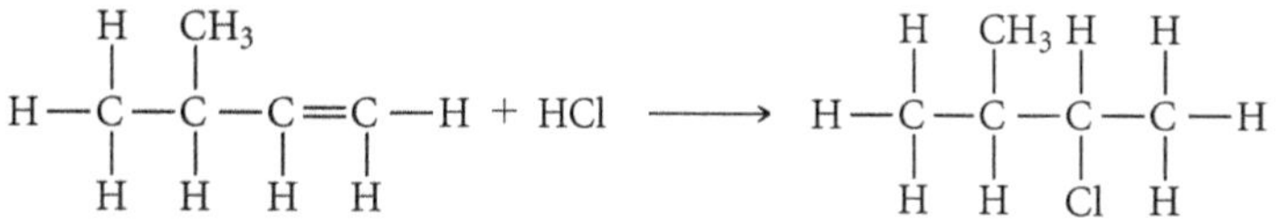

20.7. a. Alcohol reacting with an active metal.

$$CH_3CH_2OH + Na \longrightarrow CH_3CH_2ONa + \frac{1}{2}H_2$$

b. dehydration reaction

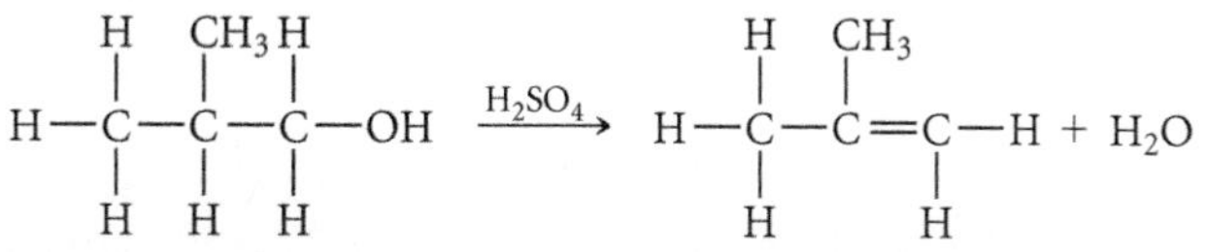

Chapter 21

21.1. Fructose exhibits optical isomerism. It contains three chiral carbons.

21.2.

Chapter 22

22.1. $KAlSi_3O_8$

22.2. $x = 2$

22.3. Orthosilicate (or neosilicate): Each of the two Be ions has a charge of $2+$ for a total of $4+$, and the SiO_4 unit has a charge of $4-$.

22.4. Inosilicate (or pyroxene): Ca and Mg each have a charge of $2+$ for a total of $4+$, and the Si_2O_6 unit has a charge of $4-$ (two SiO_3^{2-} units).

22.5. $2\,H_2S(g) + 3\,O_2(g) \longrightarrow 2\,H_2O(g) + SO_2(g)$

S changes from the -2 to $+4$ oxidation state.

22.6. The oxidation state for Cl is $+7$ in ClO_4^- and -1 in Cl^-.

22.7. $I_2(s) + 5\,F_2(g) \longrightarrow 2\,IF_5(g)$

22.8. The electron geometry is tetrahedral and the shape is bent for ICl_2^+.

22.9. The electron geometry is octahedral for BrF_5, and the molecular geometry is square pyramidal.

22.10. The oxidation number changes from -1 to 0 for the oxidation of the Cl in HCl to Cl_2 and from $+5$ to $+4$ for the reduction of the Cl in $NaClO_3$ to ClO_2. The oxidizing agent is $NaClO_3$, and the reducing agent is HCl.

Chapter 23

23.1. At 50 mol % Ni and 1000 °C this is a solid phase with half of the atoms each Ni and Cu.

23.2. At 50 mol % Ni and 1400 °C this is a liquid phase with half of the atoms each Ni and Cu.

23.3. At 900 °C and 60 mol % Cr this is a two-phase region with more Ni-rich face-centered cubic crystals than Cr-rich body-centered cubic crystals. The Ni-rich phase is about 42 mol % Cr and 58 mol % Ni. The Cr-rich phase is about 94 mol % Cr and 6 mol % Ni.

23.4. At 900 °C and 98 mol % Cr this is a single-phase region with 100 mol % of the Cr-rich body-centered cubic crystals which contains 2% Ni.

Chapter 24

24.1. [Xe] $6s^2 4f^{14} 5d^6$

24.2. [Kr] $5s^0 4d^3$ or [Kr] $4d^3$

24.3. pentaamminecarbonylmanganese(II) sulfate

24.4. sodium tetrachloroplatinate(II)

24.5. The complex ion $[Cr(H_2O)_3Cl_3]^+$ fits the general formula MA_3B_3, which results in fac and mer isomers.

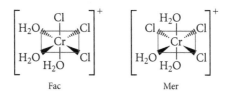

24.6. The oxalate ligand is a small bidentate ligand so it will have to occupy two adjacent (cis) positions of the octahedron. There are three ways to arrange the two NH_3 and two Cl^- ligands in the four remaining positions. One has both NH_3 and both Cl^- in cis positions (cis isomer). Another has the NH_3 ligands in a trans arrangement with both Cl^- in cis positions (*trans*-ammine isomer). The third has both NH_3 ligands cis and the Cl^- ligands trans (*trans*-chloro isomer).

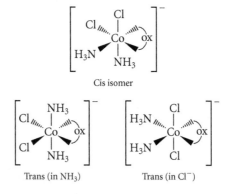

24.7. Both the fac and mer isomers are superimposable (by rotating 180°) on their mirror images, so neither one is optically active.

24.8. 288 kJ/mol

24.9. 5 unpaired electrons

24.10. 1 unpaired electron

Appendix V:
Chapters 1-12
from *Selected Solutions Manual*
by Kathleen Thrush Shaginaw and Mary Beth Kramer
to accompany *Chemistry: A Molecular Approach*

1 Matter, Measurement, and Problem Solving

Review Questions

1.1 "The properties of the substances around us depend on the atoms, ions, or molecules that compose them" means that the specific types of atoms and molecules that compose something tell us a great deal about which properties to expect from a substance. A material composed of only sodium and chloride ions will have the properties of table salt. A material composed of molecules with one carbon atom and two oxygen atoms will have the properties of the gas carbon dioxide. If the atoms and molecules change, so do the properties that we expect the material to have.

1.3 The scientific approach to knowledge is based on observation and experiment. Scientists observe and perform experiments on the physical world to learn about it. Observations often lead scientists to formulate a hypothesis, a tentative interpretation or explanation of their observations. Hypotheses are tested by experiments, highly controlled procedures designed to generate such observations. The results of an experiment may support a hypothesis or prove it wrong—in which case the hypothesis must be modified or discarded. A series of similar observations can lead to the development of scientific law, a brief statement that summarizes past observations and predicts future ones. One or more well-established hypotheses may form the basis for a scientific theory. A scientific theory is a model for the way nature is and tries to explain not merely what nature does, but why.

The Greek philosopher Plato (427 – 347 B.C.) took an opposite approach. He thought that the best way to learn about reality was not through the senses, but through reason. He believed that the physical world was an imperfect representation of a perfect and transcendent world (a world beyond space and time). For him, true knowledge came, not through observing the real physical world, but through reasoning and thinking about the ideal one.

1.5 Antoine Lavoisier studied combustion and made careful measurements of the mass of objects before and after burning them in closed containers. He noticed that there was no change in the total mass of material within the container during combustion. Lavoisier summarized his observations on combustion with the law of conservation of mass, which states that, "In a chemical reaction, matter is neither created nor destroyed."

1.7 The statement "that is just a theory" is generally taken to mean that there is no scientific proof behind the statement. This statement is the opposite of the meaning in the context of the scientific theory, where theories are tested again and again.

1.9 In solid matter, atoms or molecules pack close to each other in fixed locations. Although the atoms and molecules in a solid vibrate, they do not move around or past each other. Consequently, a solid has a fixed volume and rigid shape.

In liquid matter, atoms or molecules pack about as closely as they do in solid matter, but they are free to move relative to each other, giving liquids a fixed volume but not a fixed shape. Liquids assume the shape of their container.

In gaseous matter, atoms or molecules have a lot of space between them and are free to move relative to one another, making gases compressible. Gases always assume the shape and volume of their container.

1.11   A pure substance is composed of only one type of atom or molecule. In contrast, a mixture is a substance composed of two or more different types of atoms or molecules that can be combined in variable proportions.

1.13   A homogeneous mixture has the same composition throughout, while a heterogeneous mixture has different compositions in different regions.

1.15   Mixtures of miscible liquids (substances that easily mix) can usually be separated by distillation, a process in which the mixture is heated to boil off the more volatile (easily vaporizable) liquid. The volatile liquid is then recondensed in a condenser and collected in a separate flask.

1.17   Changes that alter only state or appearance, but not composition, are called physical changes. The atoms or molecules that compose a substance *do not change* their identity during a physical change. For example, when water boils, it changes its state from a liquid to a gas, but the gas remains composed of water molecules, so this a physical change. When sugar dissolves in water, the sugar molecules are separated from each other, but the molecules of sugar and water remain intact.

In contrast, changes that alter the composition of matter are called chemical changes. During a chemical change, atoms rearrange, transforming the original substances into different substances. For example, the rusting of iron, the combustion of natural gas to form carbon dioxide and water, and the denaturing of proteins when an egg is cooked are examples of chemical changes.

1.19   Chemical energy is potential energy. It is the energy that is contained in the bonds that hold the molecules together. This energy arises primarily from electrostatic forces between the electrically charged particles (protons and electrons) that compose atoms and molecules. Some of these arrangements—such as the one within the molecules that compose gasoline—have a much higher potential energy than others. When gasoline undergoes combustion the arrangement of these particles changes, creating molecules with much lower potential energy and transferring a great deal of energy (mostly in the form of heat) to the surroundings. A raised weight has a certain amount of potential energy (dependent on the height the weight is raised) that can be converted to kinetic energy when the weight is released.

1.21   The three different temperature scales are Kelvin (K), Celsius (°C), and Fahrenheit (°F). The size of the degree is the same in the Kelvin and the Celsius scales, and they are 1.8 times larger than the degree size for the Fahrenheit scale.

1.23   A derived unit is a combination of other units. Examples of derived units include: speed in meters per second (m/s), volume in meters cubed (m^3), and density in grams per cubic centimeter (g/cm^3).

1.25   An intensive property is a property that is independent of the amount of the substance. An extensive property is a property that depends on the amount of the substance.

1.27   In multiplication or division, the result carries the same number of significant figures as the factor with the fewest significant figures.

1.29   When rounding to the correct number of significant figures, round down if the last (or left-most) digit dropped is four or less; and round up if the last (or left-most) digit dropped is five or more.

1.31   Random error is error that has equal probability of being too high or too low. Almost all measurements have some degree of random error. Random error can, with enough trials, average itself out. Systematic error is error that tends towards being either too high or too low. Systematic error does not average out with repeated trials.

The Scientific Approach to Knowledge

1.33   (a)   This statement is a theory because it attempts to explain why. It is not possible to observe individual atoms.

(b)   This statement is an observation.

(c)   This statement is a law because it summarizes many observations and can explain future behavior.

(d)   This statement is an observation.

1.35   (a)   If we divide the mass of the oxygen by the mass of the carbon the result is always 4/3.

       (b)   If we divide the mass of the oxygen by the mass of the hydrogen the result is always 16.

       (c)   These observations suggest that the masses of elements in molecules are ratios of whole numbers (4 and 3; and 16 and 1, respectively).

       (d)   Atoms combine in small whole number ratios and not as random weight ratios.

The Classification and Properties of Matter

1.37   (a)   Sweat is a homogeneous mixture of water, sodium chloride, and other components.

       (b)   Carbon dioxide is a pure substance that is a compound (two or more elements bonded together).

       (c)   Aluminum is a pure substance that is an element (element 13 in the periodic table).

       (d)   Vegetable soup is a heterogeneous mixture of broth, chunks of vegetables, and extracts from the vegetables.

1.39

substance	pure or mixture	Type (element or compound)
aluminum	pure	element
apple juice	mixture	neither – mixture
hydrogen peroxide	pure	compound
chicken soup	mixture	neither – mixture

1.41   (a)   pure substance that is a compound (one type of molecule that contains two different elements)

       (b)   heterogeneous mixture (two different molecules that are segregated into regions)

       (c)   homogeneous mixture (two different molecules that are randomly mixed)

       (d)   pure substance that is an element (individual atoms of one type)

1.43   (a)   physical property (color can be observed without making or breaking chemical bonds)

       (b)   chemical property (must observe by making or breaking chemical bonds)

       (c)   physical property (the phase can be observed without making or breaking chemical bonds)

       (d)   physical property (density can be observed without making or breaking chemical bonds)

       (e)   physical property (mixing does not involve making or breaking chemical bonds, so this can be observed without making or breaking chemical bonds)

1.45   (a)   chemical property (burning involves breaking and making bonds, so bonds must be broken and made to observe this property)

       (b)   physical property (shininess is a physical property and so can be observed without making or breaking chemical bonds)

       (c)   physical property (odor can be observed without making or breaking chemical bonds)

       (d)   chemical property (burning involves breaking and making bonds, so bonds must be broken and made to observe this property)

1.47   (a)   chemical change (new compounds are formed as methane and oxygen react to form carbon dioxide and water)

       (b)   physical change (vaporization is a phase change and does not involve the making or breaking of chemical bonds)

(c)   chemical change (new compounds are formed as propane and oxygen react to form carbon dioxide and water)

(d)   chemical change (new compounds are formed as the metal in the frame is converted to oxides)

1.49   (a)   physical change (vaporization is a phase change and does not involve the making or breaking of chemical bonds)

(b)   chemical change (new compounds are formed)

(c)   physical change (vaporization is a phase change and does not involve the making or breaking of chemical bonds)

Units in Measurement

1.51   (a)   To convert from °F to °C, first find the equation that relates these two quantities. $°C = \dfrac{°F - 32}{1.8}$ Now substitute °F into the equation and compute the answer. Note: The number of digits reported in this answer follow significant figure conventions, covered in Section 1.6. $°C = \dfrac{°F - 32}{1.8} = \dfrac{0.}{1.8} = 0. °C$

(b)   To convert from K to °F, first find the equations that relate these two quantities.

$K = °C + 273.15$ and $°C = \dfrac{°F - 32}{1.8}$

Since these equations do not directly express K in terms of °F, you must combine the equations and then solve the equation for °F. Substituting for °C:

$K = \dfrac{°F - 32}{1.8} + 273.15$ rearrange $K - 273.15 = \dfrac{°F - 32}{1.8}$

rearrange $1.8 (K - 273.15) = (°F - 32)$ finally $°F = 1.8 (K - 273.15) + 32$ Now substitute K into the equation and compute the answer.

$°F = 1.8 (77 - 273.15) + 32 = 1.8 (-196) + 32 = -353 + 32 = -321 °F$

(c)   To convert from °F to °C, first find the equation that relates these two quantities. $°C = \dfrac{°F - 32}{1.8}$ Now substitute °F into the equation and compute the answer.

$°C = \dfrac{-109 °F - 32 °F}{1.8} = \dfrac{-141}{1.8} = -78.3 °C$

(d)   To convert from °F to K, first find the equations that relate these two quantities.

$K = °C + 273.15$ and $°C = \dfrac{°F - 32}{1.8}$

Since these equations do not directly express K in terms of °F, you must combine the equations and then solve the equation for K. Substituting for °C: $K = \dfrac{°F - 32}{1.8} + 273.15$

Now substitute °F into the equation and compute the answer.

$K = \dfrac{(98.6 - 32)}{1.8} + 273.15 = \dfrac{66.6}{1.8} + 273.15 = 37.0 + 273.15 = 310.2 \text{ K}$

1.53   To convert from °F to °C, first find the equation that relates these two quantities. $°C = \dfrac{°F - 32}{1.8}$ Now substitute °F into the equation and compute the answer. Note: The number of digits reported in this answer follow significant figure conventions, covered in Section 1.6. $°C = \dfrac{-80. °F - 32 °F}{1.8} = \dfrac{-112}{1.8} = -62.2 °C$

Begin by finding the equation that relates the quantity that is given (°C) and the quantity you are trying to find (K). $K = °C + 273.15$. Since this equation gives the temperature in K directly, simply substitute in the correct value for the temperature in °C and compute the answer. $K = -62.2 °C + 273.15 = 210.9 \text{ K}$.

1.55   Use Table 1.2 to determine the appropriate prefix multiplier and substitute the meaning into the expressions.

(a) 10^{-9} is equivalent to "nano" so 1.2×10^{-9} m = 1.2 nanometers = 1.2 nm

(b) 10^{-15} is equivalent to "femto" so 22×10^{-15} s = 22 femtoseconds = 22 fs

(c) 10^9 is equivalent to "giga" so 1.5×10^9 g = 1.5 gigagrams = 1.5 Gg

(d) 10^6 is equivalent to "mega" so 3.5×10^6 L = 3.5 megaliters = 3.5 ML

1.57   Use Table 1.2 to determine the appropriate prefix multiplier and substitute the meaning into the expressions.

(a) 10^{-9} is equivalent to "nano" so 4.5 ns = 4.5 nanoseconds = 4.5×10^{-9} s

(b) 10^{-15} is equivalent to "femto" so 18 fs = 18 femtoseconds = 18×10^{-15} s = 1.8×10^{-14} s
       Remember that in scientific notation the first number should be smaller than 10.

(c) 10^{-12} is equivalent to "pico" so 128 pm = 128×10^{-12} m = 1.28×10^{-10} m
       Remember that in scientific notation the first number should be smaller than 10.

(d) 10^{-6} is equivalent to "micro" so 35 μm = 35 micrograms = 35×10^{-6} g = 3.5×10^{-5} m
       Remember that in scientific notation the first number should be smaller than 10.

1.59   (b)   **Given:** 515 km **Find:** dm
              Conceptual Plan: km $\rightarrow$ m $\rightarrow$ dm
              $$\frac{1000\ m}{1 km} \quad \frac{10\ dm}{1 m}$$
              Solution: 515 km x $\dfrac{1000\ m}{1 km}$ x $\dfrac{10\ dm}{1 m}$ = 5.15×10^6 dm
              Check: The units (dm) are correct. The magnitude of the answer (10^6) makes physical sense because a decimeter is a much smaller unit than a kilometer.
              Given: 515 km **Find:** cm
              Conceptual Plan: km $\rightarrow$ m $\rightarrow$ cm
              $$\frac{1000\ m}{1 km} \quad \frac{100\ cm}{1 m}$$
              Solution: 515 km x $\dfrac{1000\ m}{1 km}$ x $\dfrac{100\ cm}{1 m}$ = 5.15×10^7 cm
              Check: The units (cm) are correct. The magnitude of the answer (10^7) makes physical sense because a centimeter is a much smaller unit than either a kilometer or a decimeter.

       (c)   **Given:** 122.355 s **Find:** ms
              Conceptual Plan: s $\rightarrow$ ms
              $$\frac{1000\ ms}{1 s}$$
              Solution: 122.355 s x $\dfrac{1000\ ms}{1 s}$ = 1.22355×10^5 ms
              Check: The units (ms) are correct. The magnitude of the answer (10^5) makes physical sense because a millisecond is a much smaller unit than a second.
              Given: 122.355 s **Find:** ks
              Conceptual Plan: s $\rightarrow$ ks
              $$\frac{1\ ks}{1000\ s}$$
              Solution: 122.355 s x $\dfrac{1\ ks}{1000\ s}$ = 1.22355×10^{-1} ks = 0.122355 ks
              Check: The units (ks) are correct. The magnitude of the answer (10^{-1}) makes physical sense because a kilosecond is a much larger unit than a second.

       (d)   **Given:** 3.345 kJ **Find:** J
              Conceptual Plan: kJ $\rightarrow$ J
              $$\frac{1000\ J}{1 kJ}$$
              Solution: 3.345 kJ x $\dfrac{1000\ J}{1 kJ}$ = 3.345×10^3 J
              Check: The units (J) are correct. The magnitude of the answer (10^3) makes physical sense because a joule is a much smaller unit than a kilojoule.
              Given: 3.345×10^3 J (from above) **Find:** mJ
              Conceptual Plan: J $\rightarrow$ mJ
              $$\frac{1000\ mJ}{1 J}$$

Solution: $3.345 \times 10^3 \text{ J} \times \dfrac{1000 \text{ mJ}}{1 \text{ J}} = 3.345 \times 10^6 \text{ mJ}$

Check: The units (mJ) are correct. The magnitude of the answer (10^6) makes physical sense because a millijoule is a much smaller unit than a joule.

1.61   (a)   **Given:** 254,998 m **Find:** km

Conceptual Plan: m $\rightarrow$ km
$$\dfrac{1 \text{ km}}{1000 \text{ m}}$$

Solution: $254,998 \text{ m} \times \dfrac{1 \text{ km}}{1000 \text{ m}} = 2.54998 \times 10^2 \text{ km} = 254.998 \text{ km}$

Check: The units (km) are correct. The magnitude of the answer (10^2) makes physical sense because a kilometer is a much larger unit than a meter.

     (b)   **Given:** 254,998 m **Find:** Mm

Conceptual Plan: m $\rightarrow$ Mm
$$\dfrac{1 \text{ Mm}}{10^6 \text{ m}}$$

Solution: $254,998 \text{ m} \times \dfrac{1 \text{ Mm}}{10^6 \text{ m}} = = 2.54998 \times 10^{-1} \text{ Mm} = 0.254998 \text{ Mm}$

Check: The units (Mm) are correct. The magnitude of the answer (10^{-1}) makes physical sense because a megameter is a much larger unit than a meter or kilometer.

     (c)   **Given:** 254,998 m **Find:** mm

Conceptual Plan: m $\rightarrow$ mm
$$\dfrac{1000 \text{ mm}}{1 \text{ m}}$$

Solution: $254,998 \text{ m} \times \dfrac{1000 \text{ mm}}{1 \text{ m}} = 2.54998 \times 10^8 \text{ mm}$

Check: The units (mm) are correct. The magnitude of the answer (10^8) makes physical sense because a millimeter is a much smaller unit than a meter.

     (d)   **Given:** 254,998 m **Find:** cm

Conceptual Plan: m $\rightarrow$ cm
$$\dfrac{100 \text{ cm}}{1 \text{ m}}$$

Solution: $254,998 \text{ m} \times \dfrac{100 \text{ cm}}{1 \text{ m}} = 2.54998 \times 10^7 \text{ cm}$

Check: The units (cm) are correct. The magnitude of the answer (10^7) makes physical sense because a centimeter is a much smaller unit than a meter, but larger than a millimeter.

1.63   **Given:** 1 m square 1 m^2 **Find:** cm^2

Conceptual Plan: 1 m^2 $\rightarrow$ cm^2
$$\dfrac{100 \text{ cm}}{1 \text{ m}}$$

Notice that for squared units, the conversion factors must be squared.

Solution: $1 \text{ m}^2 \times \dfrac{(100 \text{ cm})^2}{(1 \text{ m})^2} = 1 \times 10^4 \text{ cm}^2$

Check: The units of the answer are correct and the magnitude makes sense. The unit centimeter is smaller than a meter, so the value in square centimeters should be larger than in square meters.

Density

1.65   **Given:** $m = 2.49$ g, $V = 0.349$ cm^3 **Find:** d in g/cm^3 and compare to pure copper.

Conceptual Plan: $m, V \rightarrow d$
$$d = m/V$$

Compare to the published value. d (pure copper) = 8.96 g/cm^3 (This value is in Table 1.4.)

Solution: $d = \dfrac{2.49 \text{ g}}{0.349 \text{ cm}^3} = 7.13 \dfrac{\text{g}}{\text{cm}^3}$

The density of the penny is much smaller than the density of pure copper (7.13 g/cm^3; 8.96 g/cm^3) so the penny is not pure copper.

Check: The units (g/cm^3) are correct. The magnitude of the answer seems correct. Many coins are layers of metals, so it is not surprising that the penny is not pure copper.

1.67   **Given:** $m = 4.10 \times 10^3$ g, $V = 3.25$ L **Find:** d in g/cm^3
Conceptual Plan: $m, V \rightarrow d$ **then L** $\rightarrow$ **cm^3**
$$d = m/V \qquad \frac{1000 \text{ cm}^3}{1 \text{ L}}$$
Solution: $d = \dfrac{4.10 \times 10^3 \text{ g}}{3.25 \text{ L}} \times \dfrac{1 \text{ L}}{1000 \text{ cm}^3} = 1.26 \dfrac{\text{g}}{\text{cm}^3}$
Check: The units (g/cm^3) are correct. The magnitude of the answer seems correct.

1.69   (a)   **Given:** $d = 1.11$ g/cm^3, $V = 417$ mL **Find:** m
Conceptual Plan: $d, V \rightarrow m$ **then cm^3** $\rightarrow$ **mL**
$$d = m/V \qquad \frac{1 \text{ mL}}{1 \text{ cm}^3}$$
Solution: $d = m/V$ Rearrange by multiplying both sides of equation by V. $m = d \times V$
$$m = 1.11 \frac{\text{g}}{\text{cm}^3} \times \frac{1 \text{ cm}^3}{1 \text{ mL}} \times 417 \text{ mL} = 4.63 \times 10^2 \text{ g}$$
Check: The units (g) are correct. The magnitude of the answer seems correct considering the value of the density is about 1 g/cm^3.

(b)   **Given:** $d = 1.11$ g/cm^3, $m = 4.1$ kg **Find:** V in L
Conceptual Plan: $d, V \rightarrow m$ **then kg** $\rightarrow$ **g and cm^3** $\rightarrow$ **L**
$$d = m/V \qquad \frac{1000 \text{ g}}{1 \text{ kg}} \qquad \frac{1 \text{ L}}{1000 \text{ cm}^3}$$
Solution: $d = m/V$ Rearrange by multiplying both sides of equation by V and dividing both sides of the equation by d.
$$V = \frac{m}{d} = \frac{4.1 \text{ kg}}{1.11 \dfrac{\text{g}}{\text{cm}^3}} \times \frac{1000 \text{ g}}{1 \text{ kg}} = 3.7 \times 10^3 \text{ cm}^3 \times \frac{1 \text{ L}}{1000 \text{ cm}^3} = 3.7 \text{ L}$$
Check: The units (L) are correct. The magnitude of the answer seems correct considering the value of the density is about 1 g/cm^3.

1.71   **Given:** $V = 245$ L $d = 0.821$ g/mL, **Find:** m
Conceptual Plan: **g/mL** $\rightarrow$ **g/L then** $d, V \rightarrow m$
$$\frac{1000 \text{ mL}}{1 \text{ L}} \qquad d = m/V$$
Solution: $d = m/V$ Rearrange by multiplying both sides of equation by V. $m = d \times V$
$$m = 245 \text{ L} \times \frac{1000 \text{ mL}}{1 \text{ L}} \times \left(0.821 \frac{\text{g}}{\text{mL}}\right) = 2.01 \times 10^5 \text{ g}$$
Check: The units (g) are correct. The magnitude of the answer seems correct considering the value of the density is less than 1 g/mL and the volume is very large.

The Reliability of a Measurement and Significant Figures

1.73   In order to obtain the readings, look to see where the bottom of the meniscus lies. Estimate the distance between two markings on the device.

(a)   73.0 mL – the meniscus appears to be sitting on the 73 mL mark.

(b)   88.2 °C – the mercury is between the 84 °C mark and the 85 °C mark, but it is closer to the lower number.

(c)   645 mL – the meniscus appears to be just above the 640 mL mark.

1.75   Remember that

1.   interior zeroes (zeroes between two numbers) are significant.

2.   leading zeroes (zeroes to the left of the first non-zero number) are not significant. They only serve to locate the decimal point.

3. trailing zeroes (zeroes at the end of a number) are categorized as follows:

- Trailing zeroes after a decimal point are always significant.

- Trailing zeroes before an implied decimal point are ambiguous and should be avoided by using scientific notation or by inserting a decimal point at the end of the number.

    (a)   1,050,501 km

    (b)   0.0020 m

    (c)   0.000000000000002 s

    (d)   0.001090 cm

1.77   Remember all of the rules from Section 1.7.

    (a)   Three significant figures. The 3, 1, and the 2 are significant (rule 1). The leading zeroes only mark the decimal place and are therefore not significant (rule 3).

    (b)   Ambiguous. The 3, 1, and the 2 are significant (rule 1). The trailing zeroes occur before an implied decimal point and are therefore ambiguous (rule 4). Without more information, we would assume 3 significant figures. It is better to write this as 3.12×10^5 to indicate three significant figures or as 3.12000×10^5 to indicate six (rule 4).

    (c)   Three significant figures. The 3, 1, and the 2 are significant (rule 1).

    (d)   Five significant figures. The 1s, 3, 2, and 7 are significant (rule 1).

    (e)   Ambiguous. The 2 is significant (rule 1). The trailing zeroes occur before an implied decimal point and are therefore ambiguous (rule 4). Without more information, we would assume one significant figure. It is better to write this as 2×10^3 to indicate one significant figure or as 2.000×10^3 to indicate four (rule 4).

1.79   (a)   This is not exact because π is an irrational number. The number 3.14 only shows three of the infinite number of significant figures that π has.

    (b)   This is an exact conversion because it comes from a definition of the units, and so has an unlimited number of significant figures.

    (c)   This is a measured number and so it is not an exact number. There are two significant figures.

    (d)   This is an exact conversion because it comes from a definition of the units, and so has an unlimited number of significant figures.

1.81   (a)   156.9 – The 8 is rounded up since the next digit is a 5.

    (b)   156.8 – The last two digits are dropped since 4 is less than 5.

    (c)   156.8 – The last two digits are dropped since 4 is less than 5.

    (d)   156.9 – The 8 is rounded up since the next digit is a 9, which is greater than 5.

Significant Figures in Calculations

1.83   (a) $9.15 \div 4.970 = 1.84$ – Three significant figures are allowed to reflect the three significant figures in the least precisely known quantity (9.15).

    (b) $1.54 \times 0.03060 \times 0.69 = 0.033$ – Two significant figures are allowed to reflect the two significant figures in the least precisely known quantity (0.69). The intermediate answer (0.03251556) is rounded up since the first non-significant digit is a 5.

    (c) $27.5 \times 1.82 \div 100.04 = 0.500$ – Three significant figures are allowed to reflect the three significant figures in the least precisely known quantity (27.5 and 1.82). The intermediate answer (0.50029988) is truncated since the first non-significant digit is a 2, which is less than 5.

    (d) $(2.290 \times 10^6) \div (6.7 \times 10^4) = 34$ – Two significant figures are allowed to reflect the two significant figures in the least precisely known quantity (6.7×10^4). The intermediate answer (34.17910448) is truncated since the first non-significant digit is a 1, which is less than 5.

1.85   (a)   43.7
    $\underline{-\ 2.341}$
    41.359 = 41.4

Round the intermediate answer to one decimal place to reflect the quantity with the fewest decimal places (43.7). Round the last digit up since the first non-significant digit is 5.

    (b)   17.6
    + 2.838
    + 2.3
    $\underline{+\ 110.77}$
    133.508 = 133.5

Round the intermediate answer to one decimal place to reflect the quantity with the fewest decimal places (2.3). Truncate non-significant digits since the first non-significant digit is 0.

    (c)   19.6
    + 58.33
    $\underline{-\ 4.974}$
    72.956 = 73.0

Round the intermediate answer to one decimal place to reflect the quantity with the fewest decimal places (19.6). Round the last digit up since the first non-significant digit is 5.

    (d)   5.99
    $\underline{-\ 5.572}$
    0.418 = 0.42

Round the intermediate answer to two decimal places to reflect the quantity with the fewest decimal places (5.99). Round the last digit up since the first non-significant digit is 8.

1.87   Perform operations in parentheses first. Keep track of significant figures in each step, by noting which is the last significant digit in an intermediate result.

    (a) $(24.6681 \times 2.38) + 332.58 = 58.\underline{7}10078$
    $\underline{+\ 332.58}$
    391.290078 = 391.3

The first intermediate answer has one significant digit to the right of the decimal, because it is allowed three significant figures (reflecting the quantity with the fewest significant figures (2.38)). Underline the most significant digit in this answer. Round the next intermediate answer to one decimal place to reflect the quantity with the fewest decimal places (58.7). Round the last digit up since the first non-significant digit is 9.

    (b) $\dfrac{(85.3\ -\ 21.489)}{0.0059} = \dfrac{63.\underline{8}11}{0.0059} = 1.\underline{0}81542 \times 10^4 = 1.1 \times 10^4$

The first intermediate answer has one significant digit to the right of the decimal, to reflect the quantity with the fewest decimal places (85.3). Underline the most significant digit in this answer. Round the next intermediate answer to two significant figures to reflect the quantity with the fewest significant figures (0.0059). Round the last digit up since the first non-significant digit is 8.

(c) $(512 \div 986.7) + 5.44 = 0.51\underline{8}9014$
$$+ \underline{5.44}$$
$$5.9589014 = 5.96$$

The first intermediate answer has three significant figures and three significant digits to the right of the decimal, reflecting the quantity with the fewest significant figures (512). Underline the most significant digit in this answer. Round the next intermediate answer to two decimal places to reflect the quantity with the fewest decimal places (5.44). Round the last digit up since the first non-significant digit is 8.

(d) $[(28.7 \times 10^5) \div 48.533] + 144.99 = 591\underline{3}5.01$
$$+ \underline{144.99}$$
$$59280.01 = 59300 = 5.93 \times 10^4$$

The first intermediate answer has three significant figures, reflecting the quantity with the fewest significant figures (28.7×10^5). Underline the most significant digit in this answer. Since the number is so large this means that when the addition is performed, the most significant digit is the 100's place. Round the next intermediate answer to the 100's places and put in scientific notation to remove any ambiguity. Note that the last digit is rounded up since the first non-significant digit is 8.

Unit Conversions

1.89   (a)   **Given:** 154 cm   **Find:** in
Conceptual Plan: cm → in
$$\frac{1 \text{ in}}{2.54 \text{ cm}}$$
Solution: $154 \cancel{cm} \times \dfrac{1 \text{ in}}{2.54 \cancel{cm}} = 60.\underline{6}2992 \text{ in} = 60.6 \text{ in}$
Check: The units (in) are correct. The magnitude of the answer (60.6) makes physical sense because an inch is a larger unit than a cm. Three significant figures are allowed because 154 cm has three significant figures.

(b)   **Given:** 3.14 kg   **Find:** g
Conceptual Plan: kg → g
$$\frac{1000 \text{ g}}{1 \text{ kg}}$$
Solution: $3.14 \cancel{kg} \times \dfrac{1000 \text{ g}}{1 \cancel{kg}} = 3.14 \times 10^3 \text{ g}$
Check: The units (g) are correct. The magnitude of the answer (10^3) makes physical sense because a kg is a much larger unit than a gram. Three significant figures are allowed because 3.14 kg has three significant figures.

(c)   **Given:** 3.5 L   **Find:** qt
Conceptual Plan: L → qt
$$\frac{1.057 \text{ qt}}{1 \text{ L}}$$
Solution: $3.5 \cancel{L} \times \dfrac{1.057 \text{ qt}}{1 \cancel{L}} = 3.6995 \text{ qt} = 3.7 \text{ qt}$
Check: The units (qt) are correct. The magnitude of the answer (3.7) makes physical sense because a L is a smaller unit than a qt. Two significant figures are allowed because 3.5 L has two significant figures.

Round the last digit up because the first non-significant digit is a 9.

(d)   **Given:** 109 mm   **Find:** in
Conceptual Plan: mm → m → in
$$\frac{1 \text{ m}}{1000 \text{ mm}} \qquad \frac{39.37 \text{ in}}{1 \text{ m}}$$
Solution: $109 \cancel{mm} \times \dfrac{1 \cancel{m}}{1000 \cancel{mm}} \times \dfrac{39.37 \text{ in}}{1 \cancel{m}} = 4.2\underline{9}133 \text{ in} = 4.29 \text{ in}$
Check: The units (in) are correct. The magnitude of the answer (4) makes physical sense because a mm is a much smaller unit than an inch. Three significant figures are allowed because 109 mm has three significant figures.

1.91 $\qquad$ 10.0 km **Find:** minutes **Other:** running pace = 7.5 miles per hour

Conceptual Plan: km $\rightarrow$ **mi** $\rightarrow$ **hr** $\rightarrow$ **min**

$$\frac{0.6214 \text{ mi}}{1 \text{ km}} \quad \frac{1 \text{hr}}{7.5 \text{ mi}} \quad \frac{60 \text{ min}}{1 \text{ hr}}$$

Solution: $10.0 \text{ km} \times \dfrac{0.6214 \text{ mi}}{1 \text{ km}} \times \dfrac{1 \text{hr}}{7.5 \text{ mi}} \times \dfrac{60 \text{ min}}{1 \text{hr}} = 49.712 \text{ min} = 50. \text{ min} = 5.0 \times 10^1 \text{ min}$

Check: The units (min) are correct. The magnitude of the answer (50) makes physical sense because she is running almost 7.5 miles (which would take her 60 min = 1 hr). Two significant figures are allowed because of the limitation of 7.5 mi/hr (two significant figures). Round the last digit up because the first non-significant digit is a 7.

1.93 $\qquad$ **Given:** 17 km/L **Find:** miles per gallon

Conceptual Plan: $\underline{\text{km}} \rightarrow \underline{\text{mi}} \rightarrow \underline{\text{mi}}$

$\qquad\qquad\qquad$ L $\qquad$ L $\qquad$ gal

$$\frac{0.6214 \text{ mi}}{1 \text{ km}} \quad \frac{3.785 \text{ L}}{1 \text{ gallon}}$$

Solution: $\dfrac{17 \text{ km}}{1 \text{ L}} \times \dfrac{0.6214 \text{ mi}}{1 \text{ km}} \times \dfrac{3.785 \text{ L}}{1 \text{ gallon}} = 39.98398 \dfrac{\text{miles}}{\text{gallon}} = 40. \dfrac{\text{miles}}{\text{gallon}}$

Check: The units (mi/gal) are correct. The magnitude of the answer (40) makes physical sense because the dominating factor is that a L is much smaller than a gallon, so the answer should go up. Two significant figures are allowed because of the limitation of 17 km/L (two significant figures). Round the last digit up because the first non-significant digit is a 9.

1.95 (a) **Given:** 195 m^2 **Find:** km^2

Conceptual Plan: m^2 $\rightarrow$ **km^2**

$$\frac{(1 \text{ km})^2}{(1000 \text{ m})^2}$$

Notice that for squared units, the conversion factors must be squared.

Solution: $195 \text{ m}^2 \times \dfrac{(1 \text{ km})^2}{(1000 \text{ m})^2} = 1.95 \times 10^{-4} \text{ km}^2$

Check: The units (km^2) are correct. The magnitude of the answer (10^{-4}) makes physical sense because a kilometer is a much larger unit than a meter.

(b) **Given:** 195 m^2 **Find:** dm^2

Conceptual Plan: m^2 $\rightarrow$ **dm**

$$\frac{(10 \text{ dm})^2}{(1 \text{ m})^2}$$

Notice that for squared units, the conversion factors must be squared.

Solution: $195 \text{ m}^2 \times \dfrac{(10 \text{ dm})^2}{(1 \text{ m})^2} = 1.95 \times 10^4 \text{ dm}^2$

Check: The units (dm^2) are correct. The magnitude of the answer (10^4) makes physical sense because a decimeter is a much smaller unit than a meter.

(c) **Given:** 195 m^2 **Find:** cm^2

Conceptual Plan: m^2 $\rightarrow$ **cm^2**

$$\frac{(100 \text{ cm})^2}{(1 \text{ m})^2}$$

Notice that for squared units, the conversion factors must be squared.

Solution: $195 \text{ m}^2 \times \dfrac{(100 \text{ cm})^2}{(1 \text{ m})^2} = \quad = 1.95 \times 10^6 \text{ cm}^2$

Check: The units (cm^2) are correct. The magnitude of the answer (10^6) makes physical sense because a centimeter is a much smaller unit than a meter.

1.97 $\qquad$ **Given:** 435 acres **Find:** square miles **Other:** 1 acre = 43,560 ft^2, 1 mile = 5280 ft

Conceptual Plan: acres $\rightarrow$ **ft^2** $\rightarrow$ **mi^2**

$$\frac{43560 \text{ ft}^2}{1 \text{ acre}} \quad \frac{(1 \text{ mi})^2}{(5280 \text{ ft})^2}$$

Notice that for squared units, the conversion factors must be squared.

Solution: $435 \text{ acres} \times \dfrac{43560 \text{ ft}^2}{1 \text{ acre}} \times \dfrac{(1 \text{ mi})^2}{(5280 \text{ ft})^2} = 0.6796875 \text{ mi}^2 = 0.680 \text{ mi}^2$

Check: The units (mi^2) are correct. The magnitude of the answer (0.7) makes physical sense because an acre is much smaller than a mi^2, so the answer should go down several orders of magnitude. Three significant

because the first non-significant digit is a 7.

1.99   **Given:** 14 lbs   **Find:** mL **Other:** 80 mg/0.80 mL and 15 mg/kg body
Conceptual Plan: lb $\rightarrow$ kg body $\rightarrow$ mg $\rightarrow$ mL
$$\dfrac{1 \text{ kg body}}{2.205 \text{ lb}} \qquad \dfrac{15 \text{ mg}}{1 \text{ kg body}} \quad \dfrac{0.80 \text{ mL}}{80 \text{ mg}}$$
Solution: $14 \text{ lb} \times \dfrac{1 \text{ kg body}}{2.205 \text{ lb}} \times \dfrac{15 \text{ mg}}{1 \text{ kg body}} \times \dfrac{0.80 \text{ mL}}{80 \text{ mg}} = 0.9523809524 \text{ mL} = 0.95 \text{ mL}$

Check: The units (cm^3) are correct. The magnitude of the answer (1 mL) makes physical sense because it is reasonable amount of liquid to give to a baby. Two significant figures are allowed because of the statement in the problem. Truncate the last digit because the first non-significant digit is a 2.

Cumulative Problems

1.101   **Given:** solar year   **Find:** seconds
Other: 60 seconds/minute; 60 minutes/ hour; 24 hours/solar day; and 365.24 solar days/solar year
Conceptual Plan: yr $\rightarrow$ day $\rightarrow$ hr $\rightarrow$ min $\rightarrow$ sec
$$\dfrac{365.24 \text{ day}}{1 \text{ solar yr}} \quad \dfrac{24 \text{ hr}}{1 \text{ day}} \quad \dfrac{60 \text{ min}}{1 \text{ hr}} \quad \dfrac{60 \text{ sec}}{1 \text{ min}}$$
Solution: $1 \text{ solar yr} \times \dfrac{365.24 \text{ day}}{1 \text{ solar yr}} \times \dfrac{24 \text{ hr}}{1 \text{ day}} \times \dfrac{60 \text{ min}}{1 \text{ hr}} \times \dfrac{60 \text{ sec}}{1 \text{ min}} = 3.1556736 \times 10^7 \text{ sec} = 3.1557 \times 10^7 \text{ sec}$

Check: The units (seconds) are correct. The magnitude of the answer (10^7) makes physical sense because each conversion factor increases the value of the answer—a second is many orders of magnitude smaller than a year. Five significant figures are allowed because all conversion factors are assumed to be exact, except for the 365.24 days/ solar year (five significant figures). Round up the last digit because the first non-significant digit is a 7.

1.103   (a)   Extensive – The volume of a material depends on how much there is present.

   (b)   Intensive – The boiling point of a material is independent of how much material you have, so these values can be published in reference tables.

   (c)   Intensive – The temperature of a material depends on how much there is present.

   (d)   Intensive – The electrical conductivity of a material is independent of how much material you have, so these values can be published in reference tables.

   (e)   Extensive – The energy contained in material depends on how much there is present. Many times energy is expressed in terms of Joules/mole, which then turns this quantity into an intensive property.

1.105   **Given:** 130 °X = 212 °F and 10 °X = 32 °F   **Find:** temperature where °X = °F.
Conceptual Plan: Use data to derive an equation relating °X and °F. Then set °F = °X = z and solve for z.
Solution: Assume a linear relationship between the two temperatures (y = mx + b).
Let y = °F and let x = °X.
The slope of the line (m) is the relative change in the two temperature scales:
$$m = \dfrac{\Delta \text{ °F}}{\Delta \text{ °X}} = \dfrac{212 \text{ °F} - 32 \text{ °F}}{130 \text{ °X} - 10 \text{ °X}} = \dfrac{180 \text{ °F}}{120 \text{ °X}} = 1.5$$
Solve for intercept (b) by plugging one set of temperatures into the equation:
y = 1.5 x + b $\rightarrow$ 32 = (1.5)(10) + b $\rightarrow$ 32 = 15 + b $\rightarrow$ b = 17 $\rightarrow$ °F = (1.5) °X + 17
Set °F = °X = z and solve for z.
z = 1.5 z + 17 $\rightarrow$ −17 = 1.5 z − z $\rightarrow$ −17 = 0.5 z $\rightarrow$ z = − 34 $\rightarrow$ − 34°F = − 34 °X

Check: The units (°F and °X) are correct. Plugging the result back into the equation confirms that the calculations were done correctly. The magnitude of the answer seems correct, since it is known that the result is not between 32°F and 212 °F. The numbers are getting closer together as the temperature is dropped.

1.107   1G. F = ma = kg(m/s^2). Let's call it N for Newton. Ten tons = 20,000 lb = (1 kg/2.2 lb) x 20,000 lb = 4.4 x 10 x 10^4 kg, deceleration = 55 mi x .6 km/mi x 10^3 m/km x $1/3.6 \times 10^3 \, s^2$. Exponents = $10^4 \times 10^3 \times 10^{-3} = 10^4$. So the kN is convenient.

For one molecule, the mass is 10^{-20} kg and deceleration is $3 \times 10^8 \, m/s^2$. So Exponents = $10^{-20} \times 10^8 = 10^{-12}$. So the pN is convenient.

1.109   (a) $1.76 \times 10-3/8.0 \times 102 = 2.2 \times 10^{-6}$ Two significant figures are allowed to reflect the quantity with the fewest significant figures (8.0×10^2).

(b)   Write all figures so that the decimal points can be aligned:

    0.0187
 + 0.0002 All quantities are known to four places to the right of the decimal place,
 − 0.0030 so the answer should be reported to four places to the right of the
    0.0159 decimal place or three significant figures.

(c) $[(136000)(0.000322)/0.082](129.2) = 6.899910244 \times 10^4 = 6.9 \times 10^4$ Round the intermediate answer to two significant figures to reflect the quantity with the fewest significant figures (0.082). Round up the last digit since the first non-significant digit is 9.

1.111   (a)   **Given:** cylinder dimensions: length = 22 cm, radius = 3.8 cm, d(gold) = 19.3 g/cm^3 and d(sand) = 3.00 g/cm^3 **Find:** m(gold) and m(sand)
Conceptual Plan: $l, r \rightarrow V$ then $\rightarrow$
$$V = l \pi r^2 \qquad d = m/V$$
V(gold) = V(sand) = (22 cm)(π)(3.8 cm)^2 _8.0212 cm^3 $d = m/V$
Rearrange by multiplying both sides of equation by V. $\rightarrow m = d \times V$
$$m\text{(gold)} = \left(19.3 \frac{g}{cm^3}\right) \times (998.0212 \, cm^3) = 1.926181 \times 10^4 \, g = 1.9 \times 10^4 \, g$$
Check: The units (g) are correct. The magnitude of the answer seems correct considering the value of the density is ~20 g/cm^3. Two significant figures are allowed to reflect the significant figures in 22 cm and 3.8 cm. Truncate the non-significant digits because the first non-significant digit is a 2.
$$m\text{(sand)} = \left(3.00 \frac{g}{cm^3}\right) \times (998.0212 \, cm^3) = 2.99206 \times 10^3 \, g = 3.0 \times 10^3 \, g$$
Check: The units (g) are correct. The magnitude of the answer seems correct considering the value of the density is 3 g/cm^3. This number is much lower than the gold mass. Two significant figures are allowed to reflect the significant figures in 22 cm and 3.8 cm. Round the last digit up because the first non-significant digit is a 9.

(b)   Comparing the two values 1.9×10^4 g versus 3.0×10^3 g shows a difference in weight of almost a factor of 10. This difference should be enough to trip the alarm and alert the authorities to the presence of the thief.

1.113   **Given:** 3.5 lb of titanium   **Find:** volume in in^3 **Other:** density of titanium is 4.51 g/cm^3
Conceptual Plan: lb $\rightarrow$ g then $m, d \rightarrow V$ then $cm^3 \rightarrow in^3$
$$\frac{453.6 \, g}{1 \, lb} \qquad d = m/V \qquad \frac{(1 \, in)^3}{(2.54 \, cm)^3}$$
Solution: $3.5 \, lb \times \dfrac{453.6 \, g}{1 \, lb} = 1.5876 \times 10^3 \, g$

$d = m/V$ Rearrange by multiplying both sides of the equation by V and dividing both sides of the equation by d.
$$V = \frac{m}{d} = \frac{1.5876 \times 10^3 \, g}{4.51 \, \dfrac{g}{cm^3}} = 3.520 \times 10^2 \, cm^3 = 3.5 \times 10^2 \, cm^3 \times \frac{(1 \, in)^3}{(2.54 \, cm)^3} = 21 \, in^3$$

Check: The units (in^3) are correct. The magnitude of the answer seems correct considering many grams we have. Two significant figures are allowed to reflect the significant figures in 3.5 lb. Truncate the non-significant digits because the first non-significant digit is a 2.

1.115   **Given:** cylinder dimensions: length = 2.16 in, radius = 0.22 in, m= 41 g   **Find:** density (g /cm^3)
Conceptual Plan: in $\rightarrow$ **cm then** $l, r \rightarrow V$ **then** $m, V \rightarrow d$

$$\frac{2.54\ cm}{1\ in} \qquad V = l\pi\ r^2 \qquad d = m/V$$

Solution: $2.16\ \cancel{in}\ x\ \dfrac{2.54\ cm}{1\ \cancel{in}} = 5.4\underline{8}64\ cm = l \qquad 0.22\ \cancel{in}\ x\ \dfrac{2.54\ cm}{1\ \cancel{in}} = 0.5\underline{5}88\ cm = r$

$V = l\ \pi\ r^2 = (5.4\underline{8}64\ cm)(\ \pi)(\ 0.5\underline{5}88\ cm)^2 = 5.3\underline{8}20798\ cm^3$

$d = \dfrac{m}{V} = \dfrac{41\ g}{5.3820798\ cm^3} = 7.6178729\dfrac{g}{cm^3} = 7.6\dfrac{g}{cm^3}$

Check: The units (g/cm^3) are correct. The magnitude of the answer seems correct considering the value of the density of iron (a major component in steel) is 7.86 g/cm^3. Two significant figures are allowed to reflect the significant figures in 0.22 in and 41 g. Truncate the non-significant digits because the first non-significant digit is a 2.

1.117   **Given:** 185 cubic yards (yd^3) of H_2O **Find:** mass of the H_2O (pounds)
Other: $d(H_2O) = 1.00\ g/cm^3$ at 0°C
Conceptual Plan: $yd^3 \rightarrow m^3 \rightarrow cm^3 \rightarrow g \rightarrow lb$

$$\frac{(1\ m)^3}{(1.094\ yd)^3} \quad \frac{(100\ cm)^3}{(1m)^3} \quad \frac{1.00\ g}{1.00\ cm^3} \quad \frac{1\ lb}{453.59\ g}$$

Solution: $185\ \cancel{yd^3}\ x\ \dfrac{(1\cancel{m})^3}{(1.094\ \cancel{yd})^3}\ x\ \dfrac{(100\ \cancel{cm})^3}{(1\cancel{m})^3}\ x\ \dfrac{1.00\ \cancel{g}}{1.00\ \cancel{cm^3}}\ x\ \dfrac{1\ lb}{453.59\ \cancel{g}} = 3.114987377\ x\ 10^5\ lbs = 3.11\ x\ 10^5\ lbs$

Check: The units (lb) are correct. The magnitude of the answer (10^5) makes physical sense because a pool is not a small object. Three significant figures are allowed because the conversion factor with the least precision is the density (1.00 g/cm^3 – 3 significant figures) and the initial size has three significant figures. Truncate after the last digit because the first non-significant digit is a 4.

1.119   **Given:** 15 liters of gasoline   **Find:** kilometers   **Other:** 52 mi/gal in the city
Conceptual Plan: L $\rightarrow$ **gal** $\rightarrow$ **mi** $\rightarrow$ **km**

$$\frac{1\ gallon}{3.785\ L} \quad \frac{52\ mi}{1.0\ gallon} \quad \frac{1\ km}{0.6214\ mi}$$

Solution: $15\ \cancel{L}\ x\ \dfrac{1\ \cancel{gallon}}{3.785\ \cancel{L}}\ x\ \dfrac{52\ \cancel{mi}}{1.0\ \cancel{gallon}}\ x\ \dfrac{1\ km}{0.6214\ \cancel{mi}} = 3.316327941\ x\ 10^2\ km = 3.3\ x\ 10^2\ km$

Check: The units (km) are correct. The magnitude of the answer (10^2) makes physical sense because the dominating conversion factor is the mileage, which increases the answer. Two significant figures are allowed because the conversion factor with the least precision is 52 mi/gallon (2 significant figures) and the initial volume (15 L) has 2 significant figures. Truncate the last digit because the first non-significant digit is a 1. It is best to put the answer in scientific notation so that it is unambiguous how many significant figures are expressed.

1.121   **Given:** radius of nucleus of the hydrogen atom = $1.0\ x\ 10^{-13}$ cm; radius of the hydrogen atom = 52.9 pm.
Find: percent of volume occupied by nucleus (%)
Conceptual Plan: cm $\rightarrow$ **m then pm** $\rightarrow$ **m then** $r \rightarrow V$ **then** $V_{atom}, V_{nucleus} \rightarrow \%\ V_{nucleus}$

$$\frac{1\ m}{100\ cm} \qquad \frac{1\ m}{10^{12}\ pm} \qquad V = (4/3)\pi r^3 \qquad \%\ V_{nucleus} = \frac{V_{nucleus}}{V_{atom}}\ x\ 100\%$$

Solution: $1.0\ x\ 10^{-13}\ \cancel{cm}\ x\ \dfrac{1\ m}{100\ \cancel{cm}} = 1.0\ x\ 10^{-15}\ m$ and $52.9\ \cancel{pm}\ x\ \dfrac{1\ m}{10^{12}\ \cancel{pm}} = 5.29\ x\ 10^{-11}\ m$

$V = (4/3)\pi r^3$ Substitute into %V equation.

$\%\ V_{nucleus} = \dfrac{V_{nucleus}}{V_{atom}}\ x\ 100\% \quad \rightarrow \%\ V_{nucleus} = \dfrac{(4/3)\ \pi r^3_{nucleus}}{(4/3)\ \pi r^3_{atom}}\ x\ 100\%$ Simplify equation.

$\%\ V_{nucleus} = \dfrac{r^3_{nucleus}}{r^3_{atom}}\ x\ 100\%$ Substitute numbers and calculate result.

$$\% \, V_{nucleus} = \frac{(1.0 \times 10^{-15} \text{ m})^3}{(5.29 \times 10^{-11} \text{ m})^3} \times 100\% = (1.\underline{8}90359168 \times 10^{-5})^3 \times 100\% = 6.\underline{7}55118685 \times 10^{-13} = 6.8 \times 10^{-13}$$

Check: The units (none) are correct. The magnitude of the answer seems correct (10^{-15}), since a proton is so small. Two significant figures are allowed to reflect the significant figures in 1.0×10^{-13} cm. Round up the last digits because the first non-significant digit is a 5.

1.123   **Given:** radius of hydrogen = 212 pm; radius of ping pong ball = 4.0 cm, 6.02×10^{23} atoms and balls in a row
Find: row length (km)
Conceptual Plan: atoms → pm → m → km and ball → cm → m → km

$$\frac{212 \text{ pm}}{1 \text{ atom}} \quad \frac{1 \text{ m}}{10^{12} \text{ pm}} \quad \frac{1 \text{ km}}{1000 \text{ m}} \qquad \frac{4.0 \text{ cm}}{1 \text{ ball}} \quad \frac{100 \text{ cm}}{1 \text{ m}} \quad \frac{1 \text{ km}}{1000 \text{ m}}$$

Solution: $6.02 \times 10^{23} \text{ atoms} \times \dfrac{212 \text{ pm}}{1 \text{ atom}} \times \dfrac{1 \text{ m}}{10^{12} \text{ pm}} \times \dfrac{1 \text{ km}}{1000 \text{ m}} = 1.28 \times 10^{11} \text{ km}$

$6.02 \times 10^{23} \text{ balls} \times \dfrac{4.0 \text{ cm}}{1 \text{ ball}} \times \dfrac{1 \text{ m}}{100 \text{ cm}} \times \dfrac{1 \text{ km}}{1000 \text{ m}} = 2.4 \times 10^{19} \text{ km}$

Check: The units (km) are correct. The magnitude of the answers seem correct (10^{11} and 10^{19}). The answers are driven by the large number of atoms or balls. The ping pong ball row is 10^8 times longer. Three significant figures are allowed to reflect the significant figures in 212 pm. Two significant figures are allowed to reflect the significant figures in 4.0 cm.

1.125   **Given:** 39.33 g sodium/100 g salt; 1.25 g salt/100 g snack mix; FDA maximum 2.40 g sodium/day
Find: g snack mix
Conceptual Plan: g sodium → g salt → g snack mix

$$\frac{100 \text{ g salt}}{39.33 \text{ g sodium}} \quad \frac{100 \text{ g snack mix}}{1.25 \text{ g salt}}$$

Solution: $\dfrac{2.40 \text{ g sodium}}{1 \text{ day}} \times \dfrac{100 \text{ g salt}}{39.33 \text{ g sodium}} \times \dfrac{100 \text{ g snack mix}}{1.25 \text{ g salt}} = 488.1770 \text{ g snack mix/day}$

= 488 g snack mix/day

Check: The units (g) are correct. The magnitude of the answer seems correct (500) since salt is less than half sodium and there is a little over a gram of salt per 100 grams of snack mix. Three significant figures are allowed to reflect the significant figures in the FDA maximum and in the amount of salt in the snack mix.

1.127   **Given:** d(liquid nitrogen) = 0.808 g/mL; d(gaseous nitrogen) = 1.15 g/L; 175 L liquid nitrogen; 10.00 m x 10.00 m x 2.50 m room   **Find:** fraction of room displaced by nitrogen gas
Conceptual Plan: L → mL then V_{liquid}, d_{liquid} → m_{liquid} then set $m_{liquid} = m_{gas}$ then m_{gas}, d_{gas} → V_{gas} then

$$\frac{1000 \text{ mL}}{1 \text{ L}} \qquad\qquad d = m/V \qquad\qquad\qquad\qquad d = m/V$$

Calculate the V_{room} → cm^3 → **L then calculate the fraction displaced**

$$V = l \times w \times h \quad \frac{(100 \text{ cm})^3}{(1 \text{ m})^3} \quad \frac{1 \text{ L}}{1000 \text{ cm}^3} \qquad\qquad \frac{V_{gas}}{V_{room}}$$

Solution: $175 \text{ L} \times \dfrac{1000 \text{ mL}}{1 \text{ L}} = 1.75 \times 10^5 \text{ mL}$. Solve for m by multiplying both sides of the equation by V.

$m = V \times d = 1.75 \times 10^5 \text{ mL} \times \dfrac{0.808 \text{ g}}{1 \text{ mL}} = 1.\underline{4}14 \times 10^5 \text{ g nitrogen liquid} = 1.\underline{4}14 \times 10^5 \text{ g nitrogen gas}$

$d = m/V$. Rearrange by multiplying both sides of the equation by V and dividing both sides of the equation by d.

$$V = \frac{m}{d} = \frac{1.\underline{4}14 \times 10^5 \text{ g}}{1.15 \dfrac{\text{g}}{\text{L}}} = 1.\underline{2}29565 \times 10^5 \text{ L nitrogen gas}$$

$$V_{room} = l \times w \times h = 10.00 \text{ m} \times 10.00 \text{ m} \times 2.50 \text{ m} \times \frac{(100 \text{ cm})^3}{(1 \text{ m})^3} \times \frac{1 \text{ L}}{1000 \text{ cm}^3} = 2.50 \times 10^5 \text{ L}$$

$$\frac{V_{gas}}{V_{room}} = \frac{1.\underline{2}2 \times 10^5 \text{ L}}{2.50 \times 10^5 \text{ L}} = 0.49\underline{1}8272 = 0.492$$

Check: The units (none) are correct. The magnitude of the answer seems correct (0.5) since there is a large volume of liquid and the density of the gas is about a factor of 1000 less than the density of the liquid. Three significant figures are allowed to reflect the significant figures in the densities and the volume of the liquid given.

Challenge Problems

$F = ma$ and Pressure = force / area. So if a force of 2.31 x 10^4 N is applied on an area of 125 cm², the

$$\text{Pressure} = \frac{2.31 \times 10^4 \, \text{N}}{125 \, \cancel{cm^2} \times \dfrac{(1 \, \text{m})^2}{(100 \, \cancel{cm})^2}} = 1.\underline{8}46 \times 10^6 \frac{\text{N}}{\text{m}^2}.$$

Referring to Chapter 5, 1 N/m² = 1 Pa and

$$1 \, \text{atm} = 101{,}325 \, \text{Pa, so } 1.\underline{8}46 \times 10^6 \frac{\text{N}}{\text{m}^2} = 1.\underline{8}46 \times 10^6 \, \cancel{\text{Pa}} \times \frac{1 \, \text{atm}}{101{,}325 \, \cancel{\text{Pa}}} = 18.2 \, \text{atm}$$

1.131   Referring to the definition of energy in Chapter 6, 1 Joule = 1J = kg·m²/s². For kinetic energy, if the units of mass are the kilogram (kg) and the units of the velocity are meters/second (m/s) then

$$\text{kinetic energy units} = mv^2 = \text{kg} \left(\frac{\text{m}}{\text{s}}\right)^2 = \frac{\text{kg} \cdot \text{m}^2}{\text{s}^2} = \text{J. Since a Newton (N) is a unit of force and has units}$$

of kg·m/s² Pressure = force / area and has units of N/m², and Force = (mass) x (acceleration) or $F = ma$, then

$$3/2 \, PV \text{ units} = \frac{\text{N}}{\cancel{\text{m}^2}} \cdot \cancel{\text{m}^3} = \frac{\text{kg} \cdot \text{m}}{\text{s}^2} \cdot \text{m} = \frac{\text{kg} \cdot \text{m}^2}{\text{s}^2} = \text{J.}$$

1.133   **Given:** 15.0 ppm CO; eight hour period   **Find:** milligrams of carbon monoxide
Other: 0.50 L of air per breath; 20 breaths per minute; carbon monoxide has a density of 1.2 g/L; and 15.0 ppm CO means 15.0 L CO per 10^6 L air
Conceptual plan: hr → min → breaths → L_{air} → L_{CO} → g_{CO} → mg_{CO}

$$\frac{60 \, \text{min}}{1 \, \text{hr}} \quad \frac{20 \, \text{breath}}{1 \, \text{min}} \quad \frac{0.50 \, L_{air}}{1 \, \text{breath}} \quad \frac{15.0 \, L_{CO}}{1 \times 10^6 \, L_{air}} \quad \frac{1.2 \, g_{CO}}{1 \, L_{CO}} \quad \frac{1000 \, mg_{CO}}{1 \, g_{CO}}$$

Solution:

$$8 \, \cancel{hr} \times \frac{60 \, \cancel{\text{min}}}{1 \, \cancel{hr}} \times \frac{20 \, \cancel{\text{breath}}}{1 \, \cancel{\text{min}}} \times \frac{0.50 \, \cancel{L_{air}}}{1 \, \cancel{\text{breath}}} \times \frac{15.0 \, \cancel{L_{CO}}}{1 \times 10^6 \, \cancel{L_{air}}} \times \frac{1.2 \, \cancel{g_{CO}}}{1 \, \cancel{L_{CO}}} \times \frac{1000 \, mg_{CO}}{1 \, \cancel{g_{CO}}} = 86.4 \, mg_{CO} = 9 \times 10^1 \, mg_{CO}$$

Check: The units (mg) are correct. The magnitude of the answer (10^2) makes physical sense because there are more than 6 powers of 10 visible in these conversion factors in the numerator and one factor of 10^6 in the denominator. This means that most of the conversions cancel each other out, but there is still some left in the numerator. One significant figure is allowed because the conversion factor with the least precision is 20 breaths/minute (1 significant figure) and the starting time (8 hours) also has one significant figure. Round up the last digit because the first non-significant digit is a 6.

1.135   Since the person weighs 155 lbs and has a density of 1.0 g/cm³, the volume of the person can be

calculated as $155 \, \cancel{lbs} \times \dfrac{453.59 \, \cancel{g}}{1 \, \cancel{lb}} \times \dfrac{1 \, \text{cm}^3}{1.0 \, \cancel{g}} = 7.0\underline{3}0645 \times 10^4 \text{cm}^3.$

Approximating the volume of a person as a cylinder 4.0 feet tall, $V = l \, \pi \, r^2$. Rearranging the equation, solving for r.

$$r = \left(\frac{V}{l\pi}\right)^{\frac{1}{2}} = \sqrt{\frac{7.0\underline{3}0645 \times 10^4 \text{cm}^3}{4.0 \, \cancel{ft} \times \dfrac{30.48 \, \text{cm}}{1 \, \cancel{ft}} \times \pi}} = 13.\underline{5}4831 \, \text{cm.}$$

The circumference is $2 \, \pi \, r = 2\pi(13.54831 \, \text{cm}) = 85.\underline{1}2655 \, \text{cm}$. When the person gains 40.0 lbs of fat the

volume increase is $40.0 \, \cancel{lbs} \times \dfrac{453.59 \, \cancel{g}}{1 \, \cancel{lb}} \times \dfrac{1 \, \text{cm}^3}{0.918 \, \cancel{g}} = \underline{6}43 \times 10^4 \text{cm}^3.$

Thus the new volume is $7.0\underline{3}0645 \times 10^4 \text{cm}^3 + 1.9\underline{7}643 \times 10^4 \text{cm}^3 = 9.00\underline{7}07 \times 10^4 \, \text{cm}^3.$ So the new radius is

$$r \quad \left(\frac{V}{l}\right)^{\frac{1}{2}} = \sqrt{\frac{9.00707 \times 10^4 \text{cm}^3}{4.0\,\text{ft} \times \dfrac{30.48\,\text{cm}}{1\,\text{ft}} \times \pi}} = 15.33485 \text{ cm and the new circumference is}$$

$2 \pi r = 2 \pi (15.33485 \text{ cm}) = 96.35167 \text{ cm}.$

The percent increase in circumference $\dfrac{96.35167 \text{ cm} - 85.12655 \text{ cm}}{85.12655 \text{ cm}} \times 100\,\% = 13.1864\,\% = 13\,\%.$

Conceptual Problems

1.137   No. Since the container is sealed the atoms and molecules can move around, but they cannot leave. If no atoms or molecules can leave, the mass must be constant.

1.139   This problem is similar to Problem 64, only the dimension is changed to 7 cm on each edge.
Given: 7 cm on each edge cube   **Find:** cm^3
Conceptual plan: Read the information given carefully. The cube is 7 cm on each side.
l, w, h → *V*
    V = l w h
  in a cube l = w = h
Solution: 7 cm x 7 cm x 7 cm = (7 cm)^3 = = 343 cm^3 or 343 cubes

1.141   Remember that density = mass/volume.

(a)   The darker colored box has a heavier mass, but a smaller volume, so it is denser than the lighter-colored box.

(b)   The lighter colored box is heavier than the darker colored box and both boxes have the same volume, so the lighter colored box is denser.

(c)   The larger box is the heavier box, so it cannot be determined with this information which box is denser.

2 Atoms and Elements

Review Questions

2.1   Scanning tunneling microscopy is a technique that can image, and even move, individual atoms and molecules. A scanning tunneling microscope works by moving an extremely sharp electrode over a surface and measuring the resulting tunneling current, the electrical current that flows between the tip of the electrode, and the surface even though the two are not in physical contact.

2.3   The law of conservation of mass states the following: In a chemical reaction, matter is neither created nor destroyed. In other words, when you carry out any chemical reaction, the total mass of the substances involved in the reaction does not change.

2.5   The law of multiple proportions states the following: When two elements (call them A and B) form two different compounds, the masses of element B that combine with 1 g of element A can be expressed as a ratio of small whole numbers. This means that when two atoms (A and B) combine to form more than one compound, the ratio of B in one compound to B in the second compound will be a small whole number.

2.7   In the late 1800s, an English physicist named J.J. Thomson performed experiments to probe the properties of cathode rays. Thomson found that these rays were actually streams of particles with the following properties: They traveled in straight lines; they were independent of the composition of the material from which they originated; and they carried a negative electrical charge. He measured the charge to mass ratio of the particles and found that the cathode ray particle was about 2000 times lighter than hydrogen.

2.9   The plum-pudding model of the atom, proposed by J.J. Thomson hypothesized that the negatively charged electrons were small particles electrostatically held within a positively charged sphere.

2.11   Rutherford's nuclear model of the atom has three basic parts: 1) Most of the atom's mass and all of its positive charge are contained in a small core called the **nucleus.** 2) Most of the volume of the atom is empty space, throughout which tiny negatively charged electrons are dispersed. 3) There are as many negatively-charged electrons outside the nucleus as there are positively-charged particles within the nucleus, so that the atom is electrically neutral. The revolutionary part of this theory is the idea that matter, at its core, is much less uniform than it appears.

2.13   The three subatomic particles that compose atoms are as follows:

Protons, which have a mass of 1.67262×10^{-27} kg or 1.00727 amu and a relative charge of $+1$

Neutrons, which have a mass of 1.67493×10^{-27} kg or 1.00866 amu and a relative charge of 0

Electrons, which have a mass of 0.00091×10^{-27} kg or 0.00055 amu and a relative charge of -1

2.15   The atomic number, Z, is the number of protons in an atom's nucleus. The atomic mass number (A) is the

2.17   Isotopes are atoms with the same number of protons but different numbers of neutrons. The percent natural abundance is the relative amount of each different isotope in a naturally occurring sample of a given element.

2.19   An ion is a charged particle. Positively charged ions are called cations. Negatively charged ions are called anions.

2.21   Metals are found on the left side and the middle of the periodic table. They are good conductors of heat and electricity; they can be pounded into flat sheets (malleable), they can be drawn into wires (ductile), they are often shiny, and they tend to lose electrons when they undergo chemical changes.

            Nonmetals are found on the upper-right side of the periodic table. Their properties are more varied: Some are solids at room temperature, while others are liquids or gases. As a whole they tend to be poor conductors of heat and electricity and they all tend to gain electrons when they undergo chemical changes.

            Metalloids lie along the zigzag diagonal line that divides metals and nonmetals. They show mixed properties. Several metalloids are also classified as semiconductors because of their intermediate and temperature-dependent electrical conductivity.

2.23   Main group metals tend to lose electrons, forming cations with the same number of electrons as the nearest noble gas. Main group nonmetals tend to gain electrons, forming anions with the same number of electrons as the nearest following noble gas.

2.25   In a mass spectrometer, the sample is injected into the instrument and vaporized. The vaporized atoms are then ionized by an electron beam. The electrons in the beam collide with the vaporized atoms, removing electrons from the atoms and creating positively charged ions. Charged plates with slits in them accelerate the positively charged ions into a magnetic field, which deflects them. The amount of deflection depends on the mass of the ions—lighter ions are deflected more than heavier ones. Finally, the ions strike a detector and produce an electrical signal that is recorded.

2.27   A mole is an amount of material. It is defined as the amount of material containing 6.0221421×10^{23} particles (Avogadro's number). The numerical value of the mole is defined as being equal to the number of atoms in exactly 12 grams of pure carbon-12. It is useful for converting number of atoms to moles of atoms and moles of atoms to number of atoms.

Problems by Topic

The Laws of Conservation of Mass, Definite Proportions, and Multiple Proportions

2.29   **Given:** 1.50 g hydrogen; 12.0 g oxygen   **Find:** grams water vapor
            Conceptual Plan: total mass reactants = total mass products
            Solution: Mass of reactants = 1.50 g hydrogen + 12.0 g oxygen = 13.5 grams
                        Mass of products = mass of reactants = 13.5 grams water vapor.
            Check: According to the law of conservation of mass, matter is not created or destroyed in a chemical reaction, so, since water vapor is the only product, the masses of hydrogen and oxygen must combine to form the mass of water vapor.

2.31   **Given:** sample 1: 38.9 g carbon, 448 g chlorine; sample 2: 14.8 g carbon, 134 g chlorine
            Find: consistent with definite proportions
            Conceptual Plan: determine mass ratio of sample 1 and 2 and compare
                                    $\dfrac{\text{mass of chlorine}}{\text{mass of carbon}}$
            Solution: Sample 1: $\dfrac{448 \text{ g chorine}}{38.9 \text{ g carbon}} = 11.5$ Sample 2: $\dfrac{134 \text{ g chlorine}}{14.8 \text{ g carbon}} = 9.05$

                Results are not consistent with the law of definite proportions because the ratio of chlorine to carbon is not the same.

Check: According to the law of definite proportions, the mass ratio of one element to another is the same for all samples of the compound.

2.33   **Given:** mass ratio sodium to fluorine = 1.21:1; sample = 28.8 g sodium **Find:** g fluorine
Conceptual Plan: g sodium → g fluorine

$$\frac{\text{mass of fluorine}}{\text{mass of sodium}}$$

Solution: $28.8 \, \overline{\text{g sodium}} \times \dfrac{1 \, \text{g fluorine}}{1.21 \, \overline{\text{g sodium}}} = 23.8 \, \text{g fluorine}$

Check: The units of the answer (g fluorine) are correct. The magnitude of the answer is reasonable since it is less than the grams of sodium.

2.35   **Given:** 1 gram osmium: sample 1 = 0.168 g oxygen; sample 2 = 0.3369 g oxygen
Find: consistent with multiple proportions
Conceptual Plan: determine mass ratio of oxygen

$$\frac{\text{mass of oxygen sample 2}}{\text{mass of oxygen sample 1}}$$

Solution: $\dfrac{0.3369 \, \text{g oxygen}}{0.168 \, \text{g oxygen}} = 2.00$ Ratio is a small whole number. Results are consistent with multiple proportions

Check: According to the law of multiple proportions, when two elements form two different compounds, the masses of element B that combine with 1 g of element A can be expressed as a ratio of small whole numbers.

2.37   **Given:** sulfur dioxide = 3.49 g oxygen and 3.50 g sulfur; sulfur trioxide = 6.75 g oxygen and 4.50 g sulfur
Find: mass oxygen per g S for each compound and then determine the mass ratio of oxygen

$$\frac{\text{mass of oxygen in sulfur dioxide}}{\text{mass of sulfur in sulfur dioxide}} \quad \frac{\text{mass of oxygen in sulfur trioxide}}{\text{mass of sulfur in sulfur trioxide}} \quad \frac{\text{mass of oxyen in sulfur trioxide}}{\text{mass of oxyen in sulfur dioxide}}$$

Solution: $\text{sulfur dioxide} = \dfrac{3.49 \, \text{g oxygen}}{3.50 \, \text{g sulfur}} = \dfrac{0.997 \, \text{g oxygen}}{1 \, \text{g sulfur}}$ $\text{sulfur trioxide} = \dfrac{6.75 \, \text{g oxygen}}{4.50 \, \text{g sulfur}} = \dfrac{1.50 \, \text{g oxygen}}{1 \, \text{g sulfur}}$

$\dfrac{1.50 \, \text{g oxygen in sulfur trioxide}}{0.997 \, \text{g oxygen in sulfur dioxide}} = \dfrac{1.50}{1} = \dfrac{3}{2}$

Ratio is in small whole numbers and is consistent with multiple proportions.

Check: According to the law of multiple proportions, when two elements form two different compounds, the masses of element B that combine with 1 g of element A can be expressed as a ratio of small whole numbers.

Atomic Theory, Nuclear Theory, and Subatomic Particles

2.39   (a)   Sulfur and oxygen atoms have the same mass. INCONSISTENT with Dalton's atomic theory because only atoms of the same element have the same mass.

(b)   All cobalt atoms are identical. CONSISTENT with Dalton's atomic theory because all atoms of a given element have the same mass and other properties that distinguish them from atoms of other elements.

(c)   Potassium and chlorine atoms combine in a 1:1 ratio to form potassium chloride. CONSISTENT with Dalton's atomic theory because atoms combine in simple, whole-number ratios to form compounds.

(d)   Lead atoms can be converted into gold. INCONSISTENT with Dalton's atomic theory because atoms of one element cannot change into atoms of another element.

2.41   (a)   The volume of an atom is mostly empty space. CONSISTENT with Rutherford's nuclear theory because most of the volume of the atom is empty space, throughout which tiny, negatively-charged electrons are dispersed.

(b)   The nucleus of an atom is small compared to the size of the atom. CONSISTENT with Rutherford's nuclear theory because most of the atom's mass and all of its positive charge are contained in a small core called the nucleus.

    (c)   Neutral lithium atoms contain more neutrons than protons. INCONSISTENT with Rutherford's nuclear theory because it did not distinguish where the mass of the nucleus came from other than from the protons.

    (d)   Neutral lithium atoms contain more protons than electrons. INCONSISTENT with Rutherford's nuclear theory because there are as many negatively charged particles outside the nucleus as there are positively charged particles within the nucleus.

2.43   **Given:** drop A $= -6.9 \times 10^{-19}$ C; drop B $= -9.2 \times 10$ C; drop C $= -11.5 \times 10^{-19}$ C; drop D $= -4.6 \times 10^{-19}$ C
    Find: The charge on a single electron
    Conceptual Plan: determine the ratio of charge for each set of drops

$$\frac{\text{charge on drop 1}}{\text{charge on drop 2}}$$

    Solution: $\dfrac{-6.9 \times 10^{-19}\text{C drop A}}{4.6 \times 10^{-19}\text{ C drop D}} = 1.5$ $\dfrac{-9.2 \times 10^{-19}\text{C drop B}}{-4.6 \times 10^{-19}\text{ C drop D}} = 2$ $\dfrac{-11.5 \times 10^{-19}\text{C drop C}}{-4.6 \times 10^{-19}\text{ C drop D}} = 2.5$

    The ratios obtained are not whole numbers, but can be converted to whole numbers by multiplying by 2.

    Therefore, the charge on the electron has to be $1/2$ the smallest value experimentally obtained. The charge on the electron $= -2.3 \times 10^{-19}$ C.

    Check: The units of the answer (Coulombs) are correct. The magnitude of the answer is reasonable since all the values experimentally obtained are integer multiples of -2.3×10^{-19}.

2.45   **Given:** charge on body $= -15$ μC   **Find:** number of electrons, mass of the electrons
    Conceptual Plan: μC $\rightarrow$ C $\rightarrow$ number of electrons $\rightarrow$ mass of electrons

$$\frac{1\,\text{C}}{10^6\,\mu\text{C}} \quad \frac{1\,\text{electron}}{-1.60 \times 10^{-19}\text{C}} \qquad \frac{9.10 \times 10^{-28}\,\text{g}}{1\,\text{electron}}$$

    Solution: $-15\,\mu\text{C} \times \dfrac{1\,\text{C}}{10^6\,\mu\text{C}} \times \dfrac{1\,\text{electron}}{-1.60 \times 10^{-19}\,\text{C}} = 9.375 \times 10^{13}\text{ electrons} = 9.4 \times 10^{13}\text{ electrons}$

$$9.375 \times 10^{13}\text{ electrons} \times \frac{9.10 \times 10^{-28}\,\text{g}}{1\,\text{electron}} = 8.5 \times 10^{-14}\,\text{g}$$

    Check: The units of the answers (number of electrons and grams) are correct. The magnitude of the answers is reasonable since the charge on an electron and the mass of an electron are very small.

2.47   (a)   True: Protons and electrons have equal and opposite charges.

    (b)   True: Protons and electrons have opposite charge so they will attract each other.

    (c)   True: The mass of the electron is much less than the mass of the neutron.

    (d)   False: The mass of the proton and the mass of the neutron are about the same.

2.49   **Given:** mass of proton   **Find:** number of electron in equal mass
    Conceptual Plan: mass of protons $\rightarrow$ number of electrons

$$\frac{1.67262 \times 10^{-27}\,\text{kg}}{1\,\text{proton}} \qquad \frac{1\,\text{electron}}{9.10938 \times 10^{-31}\,\text{kg}}$$

    Solution: $1.67262 \times 10^{-27}\text{ kg} \times \dfrac{1\,\text{electron}}{9.10938 \times 10^{-31}\text{ kg}} = 1.83615 \times 10^3\text{ electrons}$

    Check: The units of the answer (electrons) are correct. The magnitude of the answer is reasonable since the mass of the electron is much less than the mass of the proton.

Isotope and Ions

2.51   For each of the isotopes determine Z (the number of protons) from the periodic table and determine A (protons + neutrons). Then, write the symbol in the form $^A_Z X$.

    (a)   The copper isotope with 34 neutrons: Z = 29; A = 29 + 34 = 63; $^{63}_{29}\text{Cu}$

    (b)   The copper isotope with 36 neutrons: Z = 29; A = 29 + 36 = 65; $^{65}_{29}$Cu

    (c)   The potassium isotope with 21 neutrons: Z = 19; A = 19 + 21 = 40; $^{40}_{19}$K

    (d)   The argon isotope with 22 neutrons: Z = 18; A = 18 + 22 = 40; $^{40}_{18}$Ar

2.53   (a) $^{14}_{7}$N: Z = 7 ; A = 14; protons = Z = 7; neutrons = A − Z = 14 − 7 = 7

    (b) $^{23}_{11}$Na: Z = 11; A = 23; protons = Z = 11; neutrons = A − Z = 23 − 11 = 12

    (c) $^{222}_{86}$Rn: Z = 86; A = 222; protons = Z = 86; neutrons = A − Z = 222 − 86 = 136

    (d) $^{208}_{82}$Pb: Z = 82; A = 208; protons = Z = 82; neutrons = A − Z = 208 − 82 = 126

2.55   Carbon − 14: A = 14, Z = 6: $^{14}_{6}$C   # protons = Z = 6   # neutrons = A − Z = 14 − 6 = 8

2.57   In a neutral atom the number of protons = the number of electrons = Z. For an ion, electrons are lost (cations) or gained (anions)

    (a) Ni^{2+}: Z = 28 = protons; Z − 2 = 26 = electrons

    (b) S^{2-}: Z = 16 = protons; Z + 2 = 18 = electrons

    (c) Br^{-}: Z = 35 = protons; Z + 1 = 36 = electrons

    (d) Cr^{3+}: Z = 24 = protons; Z − 3 = 21 = electrons

2.59   Main group metal atoms will lose electrons to form a cation with the same number of electrons as the nearest, previous noble gas.

    Nonmetal atoms will gain electrons to form an anion with the same number of electrons as the nearest noble gas.

    (a) O^{2-} O is a nonmetal and has 8 electrons. It will gain electrons to form an anion. The nearest noble gas is neon with 10 electrons, so O will gain 2 electrons.

    (b) K^{+} K is a main group metal and has 19 electrons. It will lose electrons to form a cation. The nearest noble gas is argon with 18 electrons, so K will lose 1 electron.

    (c) Al^{3+} Al is a main group metal and has 13 electrons. It will lose electrons to form a cation. The nearest noble gas is neon with 10 electrons, so Al will lose 3 electrons.

    (d) Rb^{+} Rb is a main group metal and has 37 electrons. It will lose electrons to form a cation. The nearest noble gas is krypton with 36 electrons, so Rb will lose 1 electron.

2.61   Main group metal atoms will lose electrons to form a cation with the same number of electrons as the nearest, previous noble gas. Atoms in period 4 and higher lose electrons to form the same ion as the element at the top of the group.

    Nonmetal atoms will gain electrons to form an anion with the same number of electrons as the nearest noble gas.

Symbol	Ion Formed	Number of Electrons in Ion	Number of Protons in Ion
Ca	Ca^{2+}	18	20
Be	Be^{2+}	2	4
Se	Se^{2-}	36	34
In	In^{3+}	46	49

The Periodic Table and Atomic Mass

2.63   (a)   K   Potassium is a metal

    (b)   Ba   Barium is a metal

(c)   I   Iodine is a nonmetal

(d)   O   Oxygen is a nonmetal

(e)   Sb   Antimony is a metalloid

2.65   (a)   tellurium   Te is in group 6A and is a main group element

       (b)   potassium   K is in group 1A and is a main group element

       (c)   vanadium   V is in group 5B and is a transition element

       (d)   manganese   Mn is in group 7B and is a transition element

2.67   (a)   sodium   Na is in group 1A and is an alkali metal

       (b)   iodine   I is in group 7A and is a halogen

       (c)   calcium   Ca is in group 2A and is an alkaline earth metal

       (d)   barium   Ba is in group 2A and is an alkaline earth metal

       (e)   krypton   Kr is in group 8A and is a noble gas

2.69   (a)   N and Ni would not be similar. Nitrogen is a nonmetal, nickel is a metal.

       (b)   Mo and Sn would not be most similar. Although both are metals, molybdenum is a transition metal and tin is a main group metal.

       (c)   Na and Mg would not be similar. Although both are main group metals, sodium is in group 1A and magnesium is in group 2A.

       (d)   Cl and F would be most similar. Chlorine and fluorine are both in group 7A. Elements in the same group have similar chemical properties.

       (e)   Si and P would not be most similar. Silicon is a metalloid and phosphorus is a nonmetal.

2.71   **Given:** Ga-69; mass = 68.92558 amu; 60.108%: Ga-71; mass = 70.92470 amu; 39.892 % **Find:** atomic mass Ga
       Conceptual Plan: % abundance → fraction and then find atomic mass

$$\frac{\%\,\text{abundance}}{100} \qquad \text{Atomic mass} = \sum_{n}(\text{fraction of isotope n}) \times (\text{mass of isotope n})$$

Solution: Fraction Ga-69 $= \dfrac{60.108}{100} = 0.60108 \qquad$ Fraction Ga-71 $= \dfrac{39.892}{100} = 0.39892$

$$\text{Atomic mass} = \sum_{n}(\text{fraction of isotope n}) \times (\text{mass of isotope n})$$

$$= 0.60108(68.92588\ \text{amu}) + 0.39892(70.92470\ \text{amu}) = 69.723\ \text{amu}$$

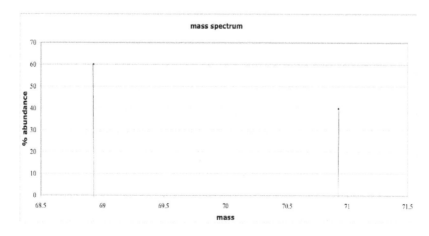

Check: Units of the answer (amu) are correct. The magnitude of the answer is reasonable because it lies between 68.92588 amu and 70.92470 amu and is closer to 68.92588, which has the higher % abundance. The mass spectrum is reasonable because it has two mass lines corresponding to the two isotopes and the line at 68.92588 is about 1.5 times larger than the line at 70.92470.

2.73   Fluorine has an isotope F-19 with a very large abundance so that the mass of fluorine is very close to the mass of the isotope and the line in the mass spectrum reflects the abundance of F-19. Chlorine has two isotopes Cl-35 and Cl-37 and the mass of 35.45 amu is the weighted average of these two isotopes, so there is no line at 35.45 amu.

2.75   **Given:** Isotope – 1 mass = 120.9038 amu, 57.4%. Isotope – 2 mass = 122.9042 amu.
Find: atomic mass of the element and identify the element
Conceptual Plan:
% abundance Isotope 2 → and then % abundance → fraction and then find atomic mass

$$100\% - \%\text{ abundance Isotope 1} \qquad \frac{\%\text{ abundance}}{100} \qquad \text{Atomic mass} = \sum_n (\text{fraction of isotope n}) \times (\text{mass of isotope n})$$

Solution: 100.0% – 57.4 % Isotope 1 = 42.6 % Isotope 2

$$\text{Fraction Isotope 1} = \frac{57.4}{100} = 0.574 \qquad \text{Fraction Isotope 2} = \frac{42.6}{100} = 0.426$$

$$\text{Atomic mass} = \sum_n (\text{fraction of isotope n}) \times (\text{mass of isotope n})$$

$$= 0.574(120.9038\text{ amu}) + 0.426(122.9042\text{ amu}) = 121.8\text{ amu}$$

From the periodic table Sb has a mass of 121.757 amu, so it is the closest mass and the element is antimony.
Check: The units of the answer (amu) are correct. The magnitude of the answer is reasonable because it lies between 120.9038 and 122.9042 and is slightly less than halfway between the two values because the lower value has a slightly greater abundance.

2.77   **Given:** Br-81; mass = 80.9163 amu; 49.31 %: atomic mass Br = 79.904 amu **Find:** mass and abundance
Conceptual Plan: % abundance Br-79 → then % abundance → fraction → mass Br-79

$$100\% - \%\text{ Br-81} \qquad \frac{\%\text{ abundance}}{100} \qquad \text{Atomic mass} = \sum_n (\text{fraction of isotope n}) \times (\text{mass of isotope n})$$

Solution: 100.00% – 49.31 % = 50.69%

$$\text{Fraction Br-79} = \frac{50.69}{100} = 0.5069 \qquad \text{Fraction Br-81} = \frac{49.31}{100} = 0.4931$$

Let X be the mass of Br-79

$$\text{Atomic mass} = \sum_n (\text{fraction of isotope n}) \times (\text{mass of isotope n})$$

$$79.904\text{ amu} = 0.5069(X\text{ amu}) + 0.4931(80.9163\text{ amu})$$

$$X = 78.92\text{ amu} = \text{mass Br-79}$$

Check: The units of the answer (amu) are correct. The magnitude of the answer is reasonable because it is less than the mass of the atom and the second isotope (Br-81) has a mass greater than the mass of the atom.

The Mole Concept

2.79   **Given:** 3.8 mol sulfur **Find:** atoms of sulfur
Conceptual Plan: mol S → atoms S

$$\frac{6.022 \times 10^{23}\text{ atoms}}{\text{mol}}$$

Solution: $3.8 \text{ mol S} \times \dfrac{6.022 \times 10^{23}\text{ atoms S}}{\text{mol S}} = 2.3 \times 10^{24}\text{ atoms S}$

Check: The units of the answer (atoms S) are correct. The magnitude of the answer is reasonable since there is more than 1 mole of material present.

2.81   (a)   **Given:** 11.8 g Ar **Find:** mol Ar
               Conceptual Plan: g Ar → mol Ar

$$\frac{1\,mol\,Ar}{39.95\,g\,Ar}$$

Solution: $11.8 \ \cancel{g\,Ar} \times \dfrac{1\ mol\ Ar}{39.95\ \cancel{g\,Ar}} = 0.295$ mol Ar

Check: The units of the answer (mol Ar) are correct. The magnitude of the answer is reasonable since there is less than the mass of 1 mol present.

        (b)   **Given:** 3.55 g Zn **Find:** mol Zn
               Conceptual Plan: g Zn → mol Zn

$$\frac{1\,mol\,Zn}{65.41\,g\,Zn}$$

Solution: $3.55 \ \cancel{g\,Zn} \times \dfrac{1\ mol\ Zn}{65.41\ \cancel{g\,Zn}} = 0.0543$ mol Zn

Check: The units of the answer (mol Zn) are correct. The magnitude of the answer is reasonable since there is less than the mass of 1 mol present.

        (c)   **Given:** 26.1 g Ta **Find:** mol Ta
               Conceptual Plan: g Ta → mol Ta

$$\frac{1\,mol\,Ta}{180.95\,g\,Ta}$$

Solution: $26.1 \ \cancel{g\,Ta} \times \dfrac{1\ mol\ Ta}{180.95\ \cancel{g\,Ta}} = 0.144$ mol Ta

Check: The units of the answer (mol Ta) are correct. The magnitude of the answer is reasonable since there is less than the mass of 1 mol present.

        (d)   **Given:** 0.211 g Li **Find:** mol Li
               Conceptual Plan: g Li → mol Li

$$\frac{1\,mol\,Li}{6.941\,g\,Li}$$

Solution: $0.211 \ \cancel{g\,Li} \times \dfrac{1\ mol\ Li}{6.941\ \cancel{g\,Li}} = 0.0304$ mol Li

Check: The units of the answer (mol Li) are correct. The magnitude of the answer is reasonable since there is less than the mass of 1 mol present.

2.83   **Given:** 3.78 g silver **Find:** atoms Ag
        Conceptual Plan: g Ag → mol Ag → atoms Ag

$$\frac{1\,mol\,Ag}{107.87\,g\,Ag} \qquad \frac{6.022 \times 10^{23}\,atoms}{mol}$$

Solution: $3.78 \ \cancel{g\,Ag} \times \dfrac{1\ \cancel{mol\,Ag}}{107.87\ \cancel{g\,Ag}} \times \dfrac{6.022 \times 10^{23}\ atoms\ Ag}{1\ \cancel{mol\,Ag}} = 2.11 \times 10^{22}$ atoms Ag

Check: The units of the answer (atoms Ag) are correct. The magnitude of the answer is reasonable since there is less than the mass of 1 mol of Ag present.

2.85   (a)   **Given:** 5.18 g P **Find:** atoms P
               Conceptual Plan: g P → mol P → atoms P

$$\frac{1\,mol\,P}{30.97\,g\,P} \qquad \frac{6.022 \times 10^{23}\,atoms}{mol}$$

Solution: $5.18 \ \cancel{g\,P} \times \dfrac{1\ \cancel{mol\,P}}{30.97\ \cancel{g\,P}} \times \dfrac{6.022 \times 10^{23}\ atoms\ P}{1\ \cancel{mol\,P}} = 1.01 \times 10^{23}$ atoms P

Check: The units of the answer (atoms P) are correct. The magnitude of the answer is reasonable since there is less than the mass of 1 mol of P present.

        (b)   **Given:** 2.26 g Hg **Find:** atoms Hg
               Conceptual Plan: g Hg → mol Hg → atoms Hg

$$\frac{1\,mol\,Hg}{200.59\,g\,Hg} \qquad \frac{6.022 \times 10^{23}\,atoms}{mol}$$

Solution: $2.26 \ \cancel{g \ Hg} \times \dfrac{1 \ \cancel{mol \ Hg}}{200.59 \ \cancel{g \ Hg}} \times \dfrac{6.022 \times 10^{23} \ \text{atoms Hg}}{1 \ \cancel{mol \ Hg}} = 6.78 \times 10^{21} \ \text{atoms Hg}$

Check: The units of the answer (atoms Hg) are correct. The magnitude of the answer is reasonable since there is much less than the mass of 1 mol of Hg present.

(c)   **Given:** 1.87 g Bi   **Find:** atoms Bi
Conceptual Plan: g Bi → mol Bi → atoms Bi

$$\dfrac{1 \ mol \ Bi}{208.98 \ g \ Bi} \quad \dfrac{6.022 \times 10^{23} \ atoms}{mol}$$

Solution: $1.87 \ \cancel{g \ Bi} \times \dfrac{1 \ \cancel{mol \ Bi}}{208.98 \ \cancel{g \ Bi}} \times \dfrac{6.022 \times 10^{23} \ \text{atoms Bi}}{1 \ \cancel{mol \ Bi}} = 5.39 \times 10^{21} \ \text{atoms Bi}$

Check: The units of the answer (atoms Bi) are correct. The magnitude of the answer is reasonable since there is less than the mass of 1 mol of Bi present.

(d)   **Given:** 0.082 g Sr   **Find:** atoms Sr
Conceptual Plan: g Sr → mol Sr → atoms Sr

$$\dfrac{1 \ mol \ Sr}{87.62 \ g \ Sr} \quad \dfrac{6.022 \times 10^{23} \ atoms}{mol}$$

Solution: $0.082 \ \cancel{g \ Sr} \times \dfrac{1 \ \cancel{mol \ Sr}}{87.62 \ \cancel{g \ Sr}} \times \dfrac{6.022 \times 10^{23} \ \text{atoms Sr}}{1 \ \cancel{mol \ Sr}} = 5.6 \times 10^{20} \ \text{atoms Sr}$

Check: The units of the answer (atoms Sr) are correct. The magnitude of the answer is reasonable since there is less than the mass of 1 mol of Sr present.

2.87   (a)   **Given:** 1.1×10^{23} gold atoms   **Find:** grams Au
Conceptual Plan: atoms Au → mol Au → g Au

$$\dfrac{1 \ mol}{6.022 \times 10^{23} \ atoms} \quad \dfrac{196.97 \ g \ Au}{1 \ mol \ Au}$$

Solution: $1.1 \times 10^{23} \ \cancel{\text{atoms Au}} \times \dfrac{1 \ \cancel{mol \ Au}}{6.022 \times 10^{23} \ \cancel{\text{atoms Au}}} \times \dfrac{196.97 \ g \ Au}{1 \ \cancel{mol \ Au}} = 36 \ g \ Au$

Check: The units of the answer (g Au) are correct. The magnitude of the answer is reasonable since there are fewer than Avogadro's number of atoms in the sample.

(b)   **Given:** 2.82×10^{22} helium atoms   **Find:** grams He
Conceptual Plan: atoms He → mol He → g He

$$\dfrac{1 \ mol}{6.022 \times 10^{23} \ atoms} \quad \dfrac{4.002 \ g \ He}{1 \ mol \ He}$$

Solution: $2.82 \times 10^{22} \ \cancel{\text{atoms He}} \times \dfrac{1 \ \cancel{mol \ He}}{6.022 \times 10^{23} \ \cancel{\text{atoms He}}} \times \dfrac{4.002 \ g \ He}{1 \ \cancel{mol \ He}} = 0.187 \ g \ He$

Check: The units of the answer (g He) are correct. The magnitude of the answer is reasonable since there are fewer than Avogadro's number of atoms in the sample.

(c)   **Given:** 1.8×10^{23} lead atoms   **Find:** grams Pb
Conceptual Plan: atoms Pb → mol Pb → g Pb

$$\dfrac{1 \ mol}{6.022 \times 10^{23} \ atoms} \quad \dfrac{207.2 \ g \ Pb}{1 \ mol \ Pb}$$

Solution: $1.8 \times 10^{23} \ \cancel{\text{atoms Pb}} \times \dfrac{1 \ \cancel{mol \ Pb}}{6.022 \times 10^{23} \ \cancel{\text{atoms Pb}}} \times \dfrac{207.2 \ g \ Pb}{1 \ \cancel{mol \ Pb}} = 62 \ g \ Pb$

Check: The units of the answer (g Pb) are correct. The magnitude of the answer is reasonable since there are fewer than Avogadro's number of atoms in the sample.

(d)   **Given:** 7.9×10^{21} uranium atoms   **Find:** grams U
Conceptual Plan: atoms U → mol U → g U

$$\dfrac{1 \ mol}{6.022 \times 10^{23} \ atoms} \quad \dfrac{238.029 \ g \ U}{1 \ mol \ U}$$

Solution: $7.9 \times 10^{21} \ \cancel{\text{atoms U}} \times \dfrac{1 \ \cancel{mol \ U}}{6.022 \times 10^{23} \ \cancel{\text{atoms U}}} \times \dfrac{238.029 \ g \ U}{1 \ \cancel{mol \ U}} = 3.1 \ g \ U$

Check: The units of the answer (g U) are correct. The magnitude of the answer is reasonable since there are fewer than Avogadro's number of atoms in the sample.

2.89   **Given:** 52 mg diamond (carbon) **Find:** atoms C
        Conceptual Plan: mg C $\rightarrow$ g C $\rightarrow$ mol C $\rightarrow$ atoms C

$$\frac{1\,\text{g C}}{1000\,\text{mg C}} \quad \frac{1\,\text{mol C}}{12.011\,\text{g C}} \quad \frac{6.022 \times 10^{23}\,\text{atoms}}{\text{mol}}$$

        Solution: $52\ \cancel{\text{mg C}} \times \dfrac{1\ \cancel{\text{g C}}}{1000\ \cancel{\text{mg C}}} \times \dfrac{1\ \cancel{\text{mol C}}}{12.011\ \cancel{\text{g C}}} \times \dfrac{6.022 \times 10^{23}\ \text{atoms C}}{1\ \cancel{\text{mol C}}} = 2.6 \times 10^{21}\ \text{atoms C}$

        Check: The units of the answer (atoms C) are correct. The magnitude of the answer is reasonable since there is less than the mass of 1 mol of C present.

2.91   **Given:** 1 atom platinum **Find:** g Pt
        Conceptual Plan: atoms Pt $\rightarrow$ mol Pt $\rightarrow$ g Pt

$$\frac{1\,\text{mol}}{6.022 \times 10^{23}\,\text{atoms}} \quad \frac{195.08\,\text{g Pt}}{1\,\text{mol Pt}}$$

        Solution: $1\ \cancel{\text{atom Pt}} \times \dfrac{1\ \cancel{\text{mol Pt}}}{6.022 \times 10^{23}\ \cancel{\text{atoms Pt}}} \times \dfrac{195.08\ \text{g Pt}}{1\ \cancel{\text{mol Pt}}} = 3.239 \times 10^{-22}\ \text{g Pt}$

        Check: The units of the answer (g Pt) are correct. The magnitude of the answer is reasonable since there is only 1 atom in the sample.

Cumulative Problems

2.93   **Given:** 7.83 g HCN sample 1: 0.290 g H; 4.06 g N. 3.37 g HCN sample 2 **Find:** g C in sample 2
        Conceptual Plan: g HCN sample 1 $\rightarrow$ g C in HCN sample 1 $\rightarrow$ ratio g C to g HCN $\rightarrow$ g C in HCN sample 2

$$\text{g HCN} - \text{g H} - \text{g N} \qquad \frac{\text{g C}}{\text{g HCN}} \qquad \text{g HCN} \times \frac{\text{g C}}{\text{g HCN}}$$

        Solution: $7.83\ \text{g HCN} - 0.290\ \text{g H} - 4.06\ \text{g N} = 3.48\ \text{g C}$

$$3.37\ \cancel{\text{g HCN}} \times \frac{3.48\ \text{g C}}{7.83\ \cancel{\text{g HCN}}} = 1.50\ \text{g C}$$

        Check: The units of the answer (g C) are correct. The magnitude of the answer is reasonable since the sample size is about half the original sample size, the g C are about half the original g C.

2.95   **Given:** In CO mass ratio O:C = 1.33:1; in compound X, mass ratio O:C = 2:1. **Find:** formula of X
        Conceptual Plan: determine the mass ratio of O:O in the two compounds
        Solution: For 1 gram of C $\dfrac{2\ \text{g O in compound X}}{1.33\ \text{g O in CO}} = 1.5$

          So, the ratio of O to C in compound X has to be 1.5:1 and the formula is C_2O_3.
        Check: The answer is reasonable since it fulfills the criteria of multiple proportions and the mass ratio of O:C is 2:1.

2.97   **Given:** $^4\text{He}^{2+}$ = 4.00151 amu **Find:** charge to mass ratio C/kg
        Conceptual Plan: determine total charge on $^4\text{He}^{2+}$ and then amu $^4\text{He}^{2+} \rightarrow$ g $^4\text{He}^{2+} \rightarrow$ kg $^4\text{He}^{2+}$

$$\frac{+\ 1.60218 \times 10^{-19}\,\text{C}}{\text{proton}} \qquad \frac{1\,\text{g}}{1.66054 \times 10^{-24}\,\text{amu}} \quad \frac{1\,\text{kg}}{1000\,\text{g}}$$

        Solution: $\dfrac{2\ \cancel{\text{protons}}}{1\ \text{atom}\ ^4\text{He}^{2+}} \times \dfrac{+\ 1.60218 \times 10^{-19}\ \text{C}}{\cancel{\text{proton}}} = \dfrac{3.20436 \times 10^{-19}\ \text{C}}{\text{atom}\ ^4\text{He}^{2+}}$

$$\frac{4.00151\ \cancel{\text{amu}}}{1\ \text{atom}\ ^4\text{He}^{2+}} \times \frac{1.66054 \times 10^{-24}\ \cancel{\text{g}}}{1\ \cancel{\text{amu}}} \times \frac{1\ \text{kg}}{1000\ \cancel{\text{g}}} = \frac{6.64466742 \times 10^{-27}\ \text{kg}}{1\ \text{atom}\ ^4\text{He}^{2+}}$$

$$\frac{3.20436 \times 10^{-19}\ \text{C}}{\cancel{\text{atom}\ ^4\text{He}^{2+}}} \times \frac{1\ \cancel{\text{atom}\ ^4\text{He}^{2+}}}{6.64466742 \times 10^{-27}\ \text{kg}} = 4.82245 \times 10^7\ \text{C/kg}$$

        Check: The units of the answer (C/kg) are correct. The magnitude of the answer is reasonable when compared to the charge to mass ratio of the electron.

2.99 $^{236}_{90}\text{Th}$ A − Z = number of neutrons. 236 − 90 = 146 neutrons. So, any nucleus with 146 neutrons is an isotone of $^{236}_{90}\text{Th}$.

        Some would be $^{238}_{92}\text{U}$; $^{239}_{93}\text{Np}$; $^{241}_{95}\text{Am}$; $^{237}_{91}\text{Pa}$; $^{235}_{89}\text{Ac}$; $^{244}_{98}\text{Cf}$ etc.

2.101

Symbol	Z	A	Number protons	Number electrons	Number neutrons	Charge
O^{2-}	8	16	8	10	8	2 –
Ca^{2+}	20	40	20	18	20	2+
Mg^{2++}	12	25	12	10	13	2+
N^{3-}	7	14	7	10	7	3 –

2.103 **Given:** r(nucleus) = 2.7 fm; r(atom) = 70 pm (assume two significant figures)
Find: vol(nucleus); vol(atom); % vol(nucleus)
Conceptual Plan:

r(nucleus)(fm) → r(nucleus)(pm) → vol(nucleus) and then r(atom) → vol(atom) and then % vol

$$\frac{10^{-15}\text{m}}{1\,\text{fm}} \quad \frac{1\,\text{pm}}{10^{-12}\text{m}} \qquad V = \frac{4}{3}\pi r^3 \qquad\qquad V = \frac{4}{3}\pi r^3 \qquad \frac{\text{vol(nucleus)}}{\text{vol(atom)}} \times 100$$

Solution:

$$2.7\,\cancel{\text{fm}} \times \frac{10^{-15}\,\cancel{\text{m}}}{\cancel{\text{fm}}} \times \frac{1\,\text{pm}}{10^{-12}\,\cancel{\text{m}}} = 2.7 \times 10^{-3}\text{pm} \qquad V_{\text{nucleus}} = \frac{4}{3}\pi (2.7 \times 10^{-3}\text{pm})^3 = 8.2 \times 10^{-8}\,\text{pm}^3$$

$$V_{\text{atom}} = \frac{4}{3}\pi (70\,\text{pm})^3 = 1.4 \times 10^6\,\text{pm}^3 \qquad \frac{8.2 \times 10^{-8}\,\cancel{\text{pm}^3}}{1.4 \times 10^6\,\cancel{\text{pm}^3}} \times 100\% = 5.9 \times 10^{-12}\%$$

Check: The units of the answer (% vol) are correct. The magnitude of the answer is reasonable because the nucleus only occupies a very small % of the vol of the atom.

2.105 **Given:** 6.022×10^{23} pennies **Find:** the amount in dollars; the dollars/person
Conceptual Plan: pennies → dollars → dollars/person

$$\frac{1\,\text{dollar}}{100\,\text{pennies}} \qquad 6.5\ \text{billion people}$$

Solution:

$$6.022 \times 10^{23}\,\cancel{\text{pennies}} \times \frac{1\,\text{dollar}}{100\,\cancel{\text{pennies}}} = 6.022 \times 10^{21}\text{dollars} \qquad \frac{6.022 \times 10^{21}\ \text{dollars}}{6.5 \times 10^9\ \text{people}} = 9.3 \times 10^{11}\text{dollars/person}$$

They are billionaires.

2.107 **Given:** O = 16.00 amu when C = 12.01 amu **Find:** mass O when C = 12.000 amu
Conceptual Plan: determine ratio O:C for ^{12}C system then use the same ratio when C = 12.00

$$\frac{\text{mass O}}{\text{mass C}}$$

Solution: Based on ^{12}C = 12.00, O = 15.9994 and C = 12.011 so, $\dfrac{\text{mass O}}{\text{mass C}} = \dfrac{16.00\,\text{amu}}{12.01\,\text{amu}} = \dfrac{1.33\underline{2}2\,\text{amu O}}{1\,\text{amu C}}$

Based on C = 12.00, the ratio has to be the same,

$$12.000\,\cancel{\text{amu C}} \times \frac{1.33\underline{2}2\ \text{amu O}}{1\ \cancel{\text{amu C}}} = 15.98\underline{6}\ \text{amu O} = 15.99\ \text{amu O}$$

Check: The units of the answer (amu O) are correct. The magnitude of the answer is reasonable because the value for the new mass basis is smaller then the original mass basis, therefore, the mass of O should be less.

2.109 **Given:** Cu sphere: r = 0.935 in; d = 8.96 g/cm³ **Find:** number of Cu atoms
Conceptual Plan: r in inch → r in cm → vol sphere → g Cu → mol Cu → atoms Cu

$$\frac{2.54\,\text{cm}}{1\,\text{inch}} \qquad V = \frac{4}{3}\pi r^3 \qquad \frac{8.96\,\text{g}}{\text{cm}^3} \qquad \frac{1\,\text{mol Cu}}{63.546\,\text{g}} \qquad \frac{6.022 \times 10^{23}\,\text{atoms}}{\text{mol}}$$

Solution: $\quad 0.935\,\cancel{\text{in}} \times \dfrac{2.54\,\text{cm}}{\cancel{\text{in}}} = 2.374\underline{9}\,\text{cm}$

$$\frac{4}{3}\pi (2.374\underline{9}\,\cancel{\text{cm}})^3 \times \frac{8.96\,\cancel{\text{g}}}{\cancel{\text{cm}^3}} \times \frac{1\,\cancel{\text{mol Cu}}}{63.546\,\cancel{\text{g}}} \times \frac{6.022 \times 10^{23}\ \text{atoms Cu}}{1\,\cancel{\text{mol Cu}}} = 4.76 \times 10^{24}\ \text{atoms Cu}$$

Check: The units of the answer (atoms Cu) are correct. The magnitude of the answer is reasonable because there are about 8 mol Cu present.

2.111   **Given:** Li-6 = 6.01512 amu; Li-7 = 7.01601 amu; B = 6.941 amu
           Find: % abundance Li-6 and Li-7
           Conceptual Plan: Let x = fraction Li-6 then 1 − x = fraction Li-7 → abundances

$$\text{Atomic mass} = \sum_n (\text{fraction of isotope n}) \times (\text{mass of isotope n})$$

           Solution: Atomic mass $= \sum_n (\text{fraction of isotope n}) \times (\text{mass of isotope n})$

$$6.941 = (x)(6.01512 \text{ amu}) + (1 - x)(7.01601 \text{ amu})$$
$$0.07501 = 1.00089\, x$$
$$x = 0.07494 \qquad 1 - x = 0.92506$$
$$\text{Li-6} = 0.07494 \times 100 = 7.494 \,\% \text{ and Li-7} = 0.92506 \times 100 = 92.506 \,\%$$

           Check: The units of the answer (%, which gives the relative abundance of each isotope) are correct. The relative abundances are reasonable because Li has an atomic mass closer to the mass of Li-7 than to Li-6.

2.113   **Given:** Alloy of Au and Pd = 67.2 g; 2.49×10^{23} atoms **Find:** % composition by mass
           Conceptual Plan: atoms Au and Pd → mol Au and Pd → g Au and Pd → g Au

$$\frac{1 \text{ mol}}{6.022 \times 10^{23} \text{atoms}} \qquad \frac{196.97 \text{g Au}}{1 \text{ mol Au}} , \frac{106.42 \text{ g Pd}}{1 \text{ mol Pd}}$$

           Solution: Let X = atoms Au and Y = atoms Pd, develop expressions that will permit atoms to be related to moles and then to grams.

$$(X \text{ atoms Au})\left(\frac{1 \text{ mol Au}}{6.022 \times 10^{23} \text{atoms Au}}\right) = \frac{X}{6.022 \times 10^{23}} \text{mol Au}$$
$$(Y \text{ atoms Pd})\left(\frac{1 \text{ mol Pd}}{6.022 \times 10^{23} \text{atoms Pd}}\right) = \frac{Y}{6.022 \times 10^{23}} \text{mol Pd}$$
$$X + Y = 2.49 \times 10^{23} \text{ atoms}; \quad Y = 2.49 \times 10^{23} - X$$
$$\left(\frac{X}{6.022 \times 10^{23}} \text{mol Au}\right)\left(\frac{196.97 \text{ g Au}}{\text{mol Au}}\right) = \frac{196.97X}{6.022 \times 10^{23}} \text{ g Au}$$
$$\left(\frac{2.49 \times 10^{23} - X}{6.022 \times 10^{23}} \text{mol Pd}\right)\left(\frac{106.42 \text{ g Pd}}{\text{mol Pd}}\right) = \frac{106.42(2.49 \times 10^{23} - X)}{6.022 \times 10^{23}} \text{ g Pd}$$

g Au + g Pd = 67.2 g total

$$\frac{196.97X}{6.022 \times 10^{23}} \text{g Au} + \frac{106.42(2.49 \times 10^{23} - X)}{6.022 \times 10^{23}} \text{g Pd} = 67.2 \text{ g}$$
$$X = 1.5\underline{4}26 \times 10^{23} \text{ atoms Au}$$
$$(1.54 \times 10^{23} \text{atoms Au})\left(\frac{1 \text{mol Au}}{6.022 \times 10^{23} \text{atoms Au}}\right)\left(\frac{196.97 \text{ g Au}}{\text{mol Au}}\right) = 50.\underline{3}7 \text{ g Au}$$
$$\left(\frac{50.\underline{3}7 \text{ g Au}}{67.2 \text{ g sample}}\right) \times 100 = 74.\underline{9}5\% \text{ Au} = 75.0\% \text{ Au}$$

% Pd = 100.0% − 75.0% Au = 25.0% Pd

           Check: Units of the answer (% composition) is correct.

2.115   **Given:** Ag-107, 51.839%, Ag-109, $\dfrac{\text{mass Ag-109}}{\text{mass Ag-107}} = 1.0187$ **Find:** mass Ag-107

           Conceptual Plan: % abundance Ag-107 → % abundance Ag-109 → fraction → mass Ag-107

$$100\% - (\% \text{Ag-107}) \qquad \frac{\% \text{abundance}}{100}$$
$$\text{Atomic mass} = \sum_n (\text{fraction of isotope n}) \times (\text{mass of isotope n})$$

           Solution: 100.00% − 51.839 % = 48.161% Ag − 109

$$\text{Fraction Ag-107} = \frac{51.839}{100.00} = 0.51839 \qquad \text{Fraction Ag-109} = \frac{48.161}{100.00} = 0.48161$$

           Let X be the mass of Ag-107 then mass Ag-109 = 1.0187X

$$\text{Atomic mass} = \sum_n (\text{fraction of isotope n}) \times (\text{mass of isotope n})$$
$$107.87 \text{ amu} = 0.51839(X \text{ amu}) + 0.48161(1.0187X \text{ amu})$$
$$X = 106.9\underline{0}7 \text{ amu} = 106.91 \text{ amu mass Ag-107}$$

Check: The units of the answer (amu) are correct. The answer is reasonable since it is close to the atomic mass number of Ag-107.

2.117   **Given:** 0.255 ounce 18K Au   **Find:** atoms Au

        Conceptual Plan: Ounces 18K Au → ounces pure Au → g Au → mol Au → atoms Au

$$\frac{75\ oz\ Au}{100\ oz\ 18K\ Au} \qquad \frac{453.59\ g\ Au}{16\ oz\ Au} \qquad \frac{1\ mol\ Au}{196.97\ g\ Au} \qquad \frac{6.022 \times 10^{23}\ atoms\ Au}{1\ mol\ Au}$$

        Solution: $0.255\ \overline{oz\ 18K\ Au} \times \left(\dfrac{75\overline{oz\ pure\ Au}}{100\ \overline{oz\ 18K\ Au}}\right) \times \left(\dfrac{453.59\ g}{16\ \overline{oz}}\right) \times \left(\dfrac{1\ \overline{mol\ Au}}{196.97\ \overline{g\ Au}}\right) \times \left(\dfrac{6.022 \times 10^{23}\ atoms\ Au}{1\ \overline{mol\ Au}}\right)$

$$= 1.\underline{6}57 \times 10^{22} \text{atoms Au} = 1.7 \times 10^{22} \text{atoms Au}$$

        Check: The units of the answer (atoms Au) are correct. The magnitude of the answer is reasonable since there is less than 1 mol of Au in the sample.

Challenge Problems

2.119   **Given:** sun: d = 1.4 g/cm^3, r = 7 × 10^8 m; 100 billion stars/galaxy; 10 billion galaxies/universe

        Find: number of atoms in the universe

        Conceptual Plan: r (star) in m → r (star) in cm → vol (star) → g H/star → mol H star → atoms H/star

$$\frac{100\ cm}{m} \qquad V = \frac{4}{3}\pi r^3 \qquad \frac{1.4\ g\ H}{cm^3} \qquad \frac{1\ mol\ H}{1.008\ g} \qquad \frac{6.022 \times 10^{23}\ atoms}{mol}$$

        → atoms H/galaxy → atoms H/universe

$$\frac{100 \times 10^9\ stars}{galaxy} \qquad \frac{10 \times 10^9\ galaxies}{universe}$$

        Solution: $7 \times 10^8\ \overline{m} \times \dfrac{100\ cm}{\overline{m}} = 7 \times 10^{10}\ cm$

$$\frac{4}{3}\pi \frac{(7 \times 10^{10}\ \overline{cm})^3}{\overline{star}} \times \frac{1.4\ \overline{g\ H}}{\overline{cm^3}} \times \frac{1\ \overline{mol\ H}}{1.008\ \overline{g\ H}} \times \frac{6.022 \times 10^{23}\ \overline{atoms\ H}}{\overline{mol\ H}} \times \frac{100 \times 10^9\ \overline{stars}}{\overline{galaxy}} \times \frac{10 \times 10^9\ \overline{galaxies}}{universe}$$

$$= 1 \times 10^{78}\ atoms/universe$$

        Check: The units of the answer (atoms/universe) are correct.

2.121   **Given:** $\dfrac{mass\ 2\ O}{mass\ 1\ N} = \dfrac{2.29}{1.00}$; $\dfrac{mass\ 3\ F}{mass\ 1\ N} = \dfrac{4.07}{1.00}$ **Find:** $\dfrac{mass\ O}{mass\ 2\ F}$

        Conceptual Plan: Mass O/N and mass F/N → mass O/F → mass O/2F

$$\frac{mass\ 2\ O}{mass\ 1\ N} \qquad \frac{mass\ 3\ F}{mass\ 1\ N} \qquad \frac{mass\ 2\ O}{mass\ 3\ F}$$

        Solution: $\dfrac{mass\ 2\ O}{mass\ 1\ N} = \dfrac{2.29}{1.00}$; $\dfrac{mass\ 3\ F}{mass\ 1\ N} = \dfrac{4.07}{1.00}$ $\left(\dfrac{2.29\ mass\ 2\ \overline{O}}{4.07\ mass\ 3\ \overline{F}}\right)\left(\dfrac{1\overline{O}}{2\overline{O}}\right)\left(\dfrac{3\overline{F}}{2\ F}\right) = \dfrac{0.422\ mass\ O}{mass\ 2\ F}$

        Check: Mass ratio of O to F is reasonable since the mass of O is slightly less than the mass of fluorine.

2.123   **Given:** 7.36 g Cu, 0.51 g Zn   **Find:** atomic mass of sample

        Conceptual Plan: fraction Cu and Zn → atomic mass

$$\text{Atomic mass} = \sum_n (\text{fraction of atom n}) \times (\text{mass of atom n})$$

        Solution: 7.36 g Cu + 0.51 g Zn = 7.87 g sample

$$\left(\frac{7.36\ g\ Cu}{7.87\ g\ sample}\right)\left(\frac{63.55\ g\ Cu}{mol\ Cu}\right) + \left(\frac{0.51\ g\ Zn}{7.87\ g\ sample}\right)\left(\frac{65.41\ g\ Zn}{mol\ Zn}\right) = 63.67\ g/mol$$

        Check: Units of the answer (g/mol) are correct. The magnitude of the answer is reasonable since it is between the mass of Cu (63.55g/mol) and Zn (65.41 g/mol) and is closer to the mass of Cu.

2.125   **Given:** Mg = 24.312 amu, ^{24}Mg = 23.98504, 78.99%, ^{26}Mg = 25.98259 amu, $\dfrac{\text{abundance } ^{25}\text{Mg}}{\text{abundance } ^{26}\text{Mg}} = \dfrac{0.9083}{1}$

               Find: mass ^{25}Mg

               Conceptual Plan: Abundance of ^{24}Mg and ratio ^{25}Mg $/^{26}$Mg $\longrightarrow$ abundance ^{25}Mg and ^{26}Mg $\rightarrow$ mass ^{25}Mg

$$\text{Atomic mass} = \sum_n (\text{fraction of isotope } n) \times (\text{mass of isotope } n)$$

               Solution: 100.00% − % abundance ^{24} = % abundance ^{25}Mg and ^{26}Mg

                        100.00% − 78 99% = 21.01% ^{25}Mg and ^{26}Mg

                        fraction ^{25}Mg and ^{26}Mg $= \dfrac{21.01}{100.0} = 0.2101$

                        $\dfrac{\text{abundance } ^{25}\text{Mg}}{\text{abundance } ^{26}\text{Mg}} = \dfrac{0.9083}{1}$

                        Let X = fraction ^{26}Mg, 0.9083X = fraction ^{25}Mg

                        fraction ^{25}Mg and ^{26}Mg = X + 0.9083X = 0.2101

                        X = ^{26}Mg = 0.1101, 0.9083X = ^{25}Mg = 0.1000

$$\text{Atomic mass} = \sum_n (\text{fraction of isotope } n) \times (\text{mass of isotope } n)$$

                        24.312 = (0.7899)(23.98504 amu) + (0.1000)(mass ^{25}Mg) + (0.1101)(25.98259 amu)

                        mass ^{25}Mg = 25.0$\underline{5}$6 amu = 25.06 amu

Check: The units of the answer (amu) are correct. The magnitude of the answer is reasonable since it is between the masses of ^{24}Mg and ^{26}Mg.

Conceptual Problems

2.127   If the amu and mole were not based on the same isotope, the numerical values obtained for an atom of material and a mole of material would not be the same. If, for example, the mole was based on the number of particles in C − 12 but the amu was changed to a fraction of the mass of an atom of Ne − 20 the number of particles and the number of amu that make up one mole of material would no longer be the same. We would no longer have the relationship where the mass of an atom in amu is numerically equal to the mass of a mole of those atoms in grams.

2.129   The different isotopes of the same element have the same number of protons and electrons, so the attractive forces between the nucleus and the electrons is constant and there is no difference in the radii of the isotopes. Ions, on the other hand, have a different number of electrons than the parent atom from which they are derived. Cations have fewer electrons than the parent atom. The attractive forces are greater because there is a larger positive charge in the nucleus than the negative charge in the electron cloud. So, cations are smaller than the parent atom from which they are derived. Anions have more electrons than the parent. The electron cloud has a greater negative charge than the nucleus, so the anions have larger radii than the parent.

3 Molecules, Compounds, and Chemical Equations

Review Questions

3.1   The properties of compounds are generally very different from the properties of the elements that compose them. When two elements combine to form a compound, an entirely new substance results.

3.3   Chemical compounds can be represented by chemical formulas and molecular models. The type of formula or model you use depends on how much information you have about the compound and how much you want to communicate. An empirical formula gives the relative number of atoms of each element in the compound. It contains the smallest whole number ratio of the elements in the compound. A molecular formula gives the actual number of atoms of each element in the compound. A structural formula shows how the atoms are connected. A ball and stick model shows the geometry of the compound. A space-filling model shows the relative sizes of the atoms and how they merge together.

3.5   Atomic elements are those that exist in nature with single atoms as their base units. Neon (Ne), gold (Au), and potassium (K) are a few examples of atomic elements.

        Molecular elements do not normally exist in nature with single atoms as their base unit, rather they exist as molecules, two or more atoms of the same element bonded together. Most exist as diatomic molecules, for example hydrogen (H_2), nitrogen (N_2), and oxygen (O_2). Some exist as polyatomic molecules: phosphorus (P_4) and sulfur (S_8).

        Ionic compounds are generally composed of a one or more metal cations (usually one type of metal) and one or more nonmetal anions bound together by ionic bonds. Sodium chloride (NaCl), potassium sulfate (Na_2SO_4) would be examples of ionic compounds.

        Molecular compounds are composed of two or more covalently bonded nonmetals. Examples would be water (H_2O), sulfur dioxide (SO_2), and nitrogen dioxide (NO_2

3.7   Binary ionic compounds are named by using the name of the cation (metal) and the base name of the anion (nonmetal) + the suffix -ide. Ionic compounds that contain a polyatomic anion are named by using the name of the cation (metal) and the name of the polyatomic anion.

3.9   To name a binary molecular inorganic compound list the name of the first element with a prefix to indicate the number of atoms in the compound if there is more than one, followed by the base name of the second element with a prefix to indicate the number of atoms in the compound if there is more than one, followed by the suffix -ide.

3.11   Binary acids are composed of hydrogen and a nonmetal. The names for binary acids have the form: hydro plus the base name of the nonmetal + ic acid. Oxyacids contain hydrogen and an oxyanion. The names of oxyacids depend on the ending of the oxyanion and have the following forms: oxyanions ending with -ate: base name of the oxyanion + ic acid; oxyanions ending with -ite: base name of the oxyanion + ous acid.

3.13   The chemical formula indicates the elements present in the compound and the relative number of atoms of each type. The chemical formula gives the conversion factor between the kind of element and the formula; it also allows the determination of mass percent composition.

3.15   Chemical formulas contain within them inherent relationships between atoms (or moles of atoms) and molecules (or moles of molecules). For example, the formula CCl_2F_2 tells us that one mole of CCl_2F_2 contains one mole of C atoms, two moles of Cl atoms, and two moles of F atoms.

3.17   The molecular formula is a whole-number multiple of the empirical formula. To find the molecular formula the molar mass of the compound must be known. The molecular molar mass divided by the empirical molar mass gives the whole number multiple used to convert the empirical formula to the molecular formula.

3.19   Organic compounds are composed of carbon, hydrogen and a few other elements including nitrogen, oxygen, and sulfur.

3.21   Functionalized hydrocarbons are hydrocarbons in which a functional group—a characteristic atom or group of atoms—has been incorporated into the hydrocarbon. The family or organic compounds known as alcohols have an –OH functional group.

Problems by Topic

Chemical Formulas and Molecular View of the Elements

3.23   The chemical formula gives you the kind of atom and the number of each atom in the compound.

   (a) $Mg_3(PO_4)_2$ contains: 3 magnesium atoms, 2 phosphorus atoms, and 8 oxygen atoms

   (b) $BaCl_2$ contains: 1 barium atom and 2 chlorine atoms

   (c) $Fe(NO_2)_2$ contains: 1 iron atom, 2 nitrogen atoms, and 4 oxygen atoms

   (d) $Ca(OH)_2$ contains: 1 calcium atom, 2 oxygen atoms, and 2 hydrogen atoms

3.25   (a)   1 blue = nitrogen, 3 white = hydrogen: NH_3

   (b)   2 black = carbon, 6 white = hydrogen: C_2H_6

   (c)   1 yellow – green = sulfur, 3 red = oxygen: SO_3

3.27   (a)   Neon is an element and it is not one of the elements that exist as diatomic molecules, therefore it is an atomic element.

   (b)   Fluorine is one of the elements that exist as diatomic molecules, therefore it is a molecular element.

   (c)   Potassium is not one of the elements that exist as diatomic molecules, therefore it is an atomic element.

   (d)   Nitrogen is one of the elements that exist as diatomic molecules, therefore it is a molecular element.

3.29   (a) CO_2 is a compound composed of a nonmetal and a nonmetal, therefore it is a molecular compound.

   (b) $NiCl_2$ is a compound composed of a metal and a nonmetal, therefore it is an ionic compound.

   (c)   NaI is a compound composed of a metal and a nonmetal, therefore it is an ionic compound.

   (d) PCl_3 is a compound composed of a nonmetal and a nonmetal, therefore it is a molecular compound.

3.31   (a)   white – hydrogen: a molecule composed of two of the same element, therefore it is a molecular element.

   (b)   blue – nitrogen, white – hydrogen: a molecule composed of a nonmetal and a nonmetal, therefore it is a molecular compound.

   (c)   purple – sodium: a substance composed of all the same atoms, therefore it is an atomic element.

Formulas and Names for Ionic Compounds

3.33   To write the formula for an ionic compound do the following: 1) Write the symbol for the metal cation and its charge and the symbol for the nonmetal anion and its charge. 2) Adjust the subscript on each cation and anion to balance the overall charge. 3) Check that the sum of the charges of the cations equals the sum of the charges of the anions.

(a)   calcium and oxygen: Ca^{2-} O^{2-} CaO   cations 2+, anions 2–

(b)   zinc and sulfur: Zn^{2+} S^{2-} ZnS   cations 2+, anions 2–

(c)   rubidium and bromine: Rb^+ Br^- RbBr   cation +, anions –

(d)   aluminum and oxygen: Al^{3+} O^{2-} Al_2O_3 cation 2(3+) = 6+, anions 3(2–) = 6–

3.35   To write the formula for an ionic compound do the following: 1) Write the symbol for the metal cation and its charge and the symbol for the polyatomic anion and its charge. 2) Adjust the subscript on each cation and anion to balance the overall charge. 3) Check that the sum of the charges of the cations equals the sum of the charges of the anions.

Cation = calcium: Ca^{2+}

(a)   hydroxide: OH^- $Ca(OH)_2$ cation 2+, anion 2(1–) = 2–

(b)   chromate: CrO_4^{2-} $CaCrO_4$ cation 2+, anion 2–

(c)   phosphate: PO_4^{3-} $Ca_3(PO_4)_2$ cation 3(2+) = 6+, anion 2(3–) = 6–

(d)   cyanide: CN^- $Ca(CN)_2$ cation 2+, anion 2(1–) = 2–

3.37   To name a binary ionic compound name the metal cation followed by the base name of the anion + -ide.

(a) Mg_3N_2:   The cation is magnesium; the anion is from nitrogen, which becomes nitride: magnesium nitride.

(b)   KF: The cation is potassium; the anion is from fluorine, which becomes fluoride: potassium fluoride.

(c) Na_2O: The cation is sodium; the anion is from oxygen, which becomes oxide: sodium oxide.

(d) Li_2S: The cation is lithium; the anion is from sulfur, which becomes sulfide: lithium sulfide.

(e)   CsF: The cation is cesium; the anion is fluorine, which becomes fluoride: cesium fluoride.

(f)   KI: The cation is potassium; the anion is iodine, which becomes iodide: potassium iodide.

(g) $SrCl_2$:   The cation is strontium; the anion is chlorine, which becomes chloride: strontium chloride.

(h) $BaCl_2$:   The cation is barium; the anion is chlorine, which becomes chloride: barium chloride.

3.39   To name these compounds you must first decide if the metal cation is invariant or can have more than one ide.

(a)   SnO: Sn can have more than one charge. The charge on Sn must be 2+ for the compound to be charge neutral: The cation is tin(II); the anion is from oxygen, which becomes oxide: tin(II) oxide.

(b) Cr_2S_3:   Cr can have more than one charge. The charge on Cr must be 3+ for the compound to be charge neutral: The cation is chromium(III); the anion is from sulfur, which becomes sulfide: chromium(III) sulfide.

(c)   RbI: Rb is invariant: The cation is rubidium; the anion is from iodine, which becomes iodide: rubidium iodide.

(d) $BaBr_2$:   Ba is invariant: The cation is barium; the anion is from bromine, which becomes bromide: barium bromide.

3.41   To name these compounds you must first decide if the metal cation is invariant or can have more than one charge. Then, name the metal cation followed by the name of the polyatomic anion.

(a) $CuNO_2$:   Cu can have more than one charge. The charge on Cu must be 1+ for the compound to be charge neutral: The cation is copper(I); the anion is nitrite: copper(I) nitrite.

(b) $Mg(C_2H_3O_2)_2$:   Mg is invariant: The cation is magnesium; the anion is acetate: magnesium acetate.

(c) $Ba(NO_3)_2$:   Ba is invariant: The cation is barium; the anion is nitrate: barium nitrate.

(d) $Pb(C_2H_3O_2)_2$: Pb can have more than one charge. The charge on Pb must be 2+ for the compound to be charge neutral: The cation is lead(II); the anion is acetate: lead(II) acetate.

(e) $KClO_3$:   K is invariant: The cation is potassium; the anion is chlorate: potassium chlorate.

(f) $PbSO_4$:   Pb can have more than one charge. The charge on Pb must be 2+ for the compound to be charge neutral: The cation is lead(II); the anion is sulfate: lead(II) sulfate.

3.43   To write the formula for an ionic compound do the following: 1) Write the symbol for the metal cation and its charge and the symbol for the nonmetal anion or polyatomic anion and its charge. 2) Adjust the subscript on each cation and anion to balance the overall charge. 3) Check that the sum of the charges of the cations equals the sum of the charges of the anions.

(a)   sodium hydrogen sulfite: Na^+ HSO_3^- $NaHSO_3$ cation 1+, anion 1–

(b)   lithium permanganate: Li^+ MnO_4^- $LiMnO_4$ cation 1+, anion 1–

(c)   silver nitrate: Ag^+ NO_3^- $AgNO_3$ cation 1+, anion 1–

(d)   potassium sulfate: K^+ SO_4^{2-} K_2SO_4 cation 2(1+) = 2+, anion 2–

(e)   rubidium hydrogen sulfate: Rb^+ HSO_4^- $RbHSO_4$ cation 1+, anion 1–

(f)   potassium hydrogen carbonate: K^+ HCO_3^- $KHCO_3$ cation 1+, anion 1–

3.45   Hydrates are named the same way as other ionic compounds with the addition of the term *prefix*hydrate, where the prefix is the number of water molecules associated with each formula unit.

(a) $CoSO_4 \cdot 7H_2O$ cobalt(II) sulfate heptahydrate

(b)   iridium(III) bromide tetrahydrate $IrBr_3 \cdot 4H_2O$

(c) $Mg(BrO_3)_2 \cdot 6H_2O$ magnesium bromate hexahydrate

(d)   potassium carbonate dihydrate $K_2CO_3 \cdot 2H_2O$

Formulas and Names for Molecular Compounds and Acids

3.47   (a)   CO   The name of the compound is the name of the first element, *carbon*, followed by the base name of the second element, *ox*, prefixed by *mono-* to indicate one and given the suffix *-ide*: carbon monoxide.

(b) NI_3 The name of the compound is the name of the first element, *nitrogen*, followed by the base name of the second element, *iod*, prefixed by *tri-* to indicate three and given the suffix *-ide*: nitrogen triiodide.

(c) $SiCl_4$ The name of the compound is the name of the first element, *silicon*, followed by the base name of the second element, *chlor*, prefixed by *tetra-* to indicate four and given the suffix *-ide*: silicon tetrachloride.

(d) N_4Se_4 The name of the compound is the name of the first element, *nitrogen*, prefixed by *tetra-* to indicate four followed by the base name of the second element, *selen*, prefixed by *tetra-* to indicate four and given the suffix *-ide*: tetranitrogen tetraselenide.

$\quad\quad$ (e) $\quad$ I$_2$O$_5$ $\quad\quad$ The name of the compound is the name of the first element, *iodine*, prefixed by *di-* to indicate two followed by the base name of the second element, *ox*, prefixed by *penta-* to indicate five and given the suffix -*ide*: diiodine pentaoxide.

3.49 $\quad$ (a) $\quad$ phosphorus trichloride: $\quad\quad$ PCl$_3$

$\quad\quad$ (b) $\quad$ chlorine monoxide: $\quad\quad\quad$ ClO

$\quad\quad$ (c) $\quad$ disulfur tetrafluoride: $\quad\quad$ S$_2$F$_4$

$\quad\quad$ (d) $\quad$ phosphorus pentafluoride: $\quad$ PF$_5$

$\quad\quad$ (e) $\quad$ diphosphorus pentasulfide: $\quad$ P$_2$S$_5$

3.51 $\quad$ (a) $\quad$ HI: $\quad\quad\quad$ The base name of I is *iod* so the name is hydroiodic acid.

$\quad\quad$ (b) $\quad$ HNO$_3$: $\quad\quad$ The oxyanion is *nitrate*, which ends in -*ate*; therefore, the name of the acid is nitric acid.

$\quad\quad$ (c) $\quad$ H$_2$CO$_3$: $\quad\quad$ The oxyanion is *carbonate*, which ends in -*ate*; therefore, the name of the acid is carbonic acid.

$\quad\quad$ (d) $\quad$ HC$_2$H$_3$O$_2$: $\quad$ The oxyanion is *acetate*, which ends in -*ate*; therefore, the name of the acid is acetic acid.

3.53 $\quad$ (a) $\quad$ hydrofluoric acid: $\quad\quad$ HF

$\quad\quad$ (b) $\quad$ hydrobromic acid: $\quad\quad$ HBr

$\quad\quad$ (c) $\quad$ sulfurous acid: $\quad\quad\quad$ H$_2$SO$_3$

Formula Mass and the Mole Concept for Compounds

3.55 $\quad$ To find the formula mass, we sum the atomic masses of each atom in the chemical formula.

$\quad\quad$ (a) $\quad$ NO$_2$ $\quad\quad$ formula mass $\quad$ = 1 x (atomic mass N) + 2 x (atomic mass O)
$\quad\quad\quad\quad\quad\quad\quad\quad\quad\quad\quad\quad\quad\quad$ = 1 x (14.01 amu) + 2 x (16.00 amu)
$\quad\quad\quad\quad\quad\quad\quad\quad\quad\quad\quad\quad\quad\quad$ = 46.01 amu

$\quad\quad$ (b) $\quad$ C$_4$H$_{10}$ $\quad\quad$ formula mass $\quad$ = 4 x (atomic mass C) + 10 x (atomic mass H)
$\quad\quad\quad\quad\quad\quad\quad\quad\quad\quad\quad\quad\quad\quad$ = 4 x (12.01 amu) + 10 x (1.008 amu)
$\quad\quad\quad\quad\quad\quad\quad\quad\quad\quad\quad\quad\quad\quad$ = 58.12 amu

$\quad\quad$ (c) $\quad$ C$_6$H$_{12}$O$_6$ $\quad$ formula mass $\quad$ = 6 x (atomic mass C) + 12 x (atomic mass H) + 6 x (atomic mass O)
$\quad\quad\quad\quad\quad\quad\quad\quad\quad\quad\quad\quad\quad\quad$ = 6 x (12.01 amu) + 12 x (1.008 amu) + 6 x (16.00 amu)
$\quad\quad\quad\quad\quad\quad\quad\quad\quad\quad\quad\quad\quad\quad$ = 180.16 amu

$\quad\quad$ (d) $\quad$ Cr(NO$_3$)$_3$ $\quad$ formula mass $\quad$ = 1 x (atomic mass Cr) + 3 x (atomic mass N) + 9 x (atomic mass O)
$\quad\quad\quad\quad\quad\quad\quad\quad\quad\quad\quad\quad\quad\quad$ = 1 x (52.00 amu) + 3 x (14.01 amu) + 9 x (16.00 amu)
$\quad\quad\quad\quad\quad\quad\quad\quad\quad\quad\quad\quad\quad\quad$ = 238.03 amu

3.57 $\quad$ (a) $\quad$ **Given:** 25.5 g NO$_2$ **Find:** number of moles
$\quad\quad\quad$ **Conceptual Plan: g NO$_2$** $\rightarrow$ **mole NO$_2$**
$$\frac{1 \text{ mol}}{46.01 \text{ g NO}_2}$$
$\quad\quad\quad$ **Solution:** $25.5 \text{ g NO}_2 \times \dfrac{1 \text{ mol NO}_2}{46.01 \text{ g NO}_2} = 0.554 \text{ mol NO}_2$

$\quad\quad\quad$ **Check:** The units of the answer (mole NO$_2$) are correct. The magnitude is appropriate because it is less than 1 mole of NO$_2$.

(b)   **Given:** 1.25 kg CO_2 **Find:** number of moles
     Conceptual Plan: kg CO2 $\rightarrow$ g CO2 $\rightarrow$ mole CO2

$$\frac{1000 \text{ g } CO_2}{\text{kg } CO_2} \qquad \frac{1 \text{ mol}}{44.01 \text{ g } NO_2}$$

     Solution: $1.25 \text{ kg } CO_2 \times \dfrac{1000 \text{ g } CO_2}{\text{kg } CO_2} \times \dfrac{1 \text{ mol } CO_2}{44.01 \text{ g } CO_2} = 28.4 \text{ mol } CO_2$

     Check: The units of the answer (mole CO_2) are correct. The magnitude is appropriate because there is over a kg of CO_2 present.

(c)   **Given:** 38.2 g KNO_3 **Find:** number of moles
     Conceptual Plan: g KNO_3 $\rightarrow$ mole KNO_3

$$\frac{1 \text{ mol}}{101.11 \text{ g } KNO_3}$$

     Solution: $38.2 \text{ g } KNO_3 \times \dfrac{1 \text{ mol } KNO_3}{101.11 \text{ g } KNO_3} = 0.378 \text{ mol } KNO_3$

     Check: The units of the answer (mole KNO_3) are correct. The magnitude is appropriate because there is less than 1 mole of KNO_3.

(d)   **Given:** 155.2 kg Na_2SO_4 **Find:** number of moles
     Conceptual Plan: kg Na_2SO_4 $\rightarrow$ g Na_2SO_4 $\rightarrow$ mole Na_2SO_4

$$\frac{1000 \text{ g } Na_2SO_4}{\text{kg } Na_2SO_4} \qquad \frac{1 \text{ mol}}{2SO_4}$$

     Solution: $155.2 \text{ kg } Na_2SO_4 \times \dfrac{1000 \text{ g } Na_2SO_4}{\text{kg } Na_2SO_4} \times \dfrac{1 \text{ mol } Na_2SO_4}{142.05 \text{ g } Na_2SO_4} = 1092 \text{ mol } Na_2SO_4$

     Check: The units of the answer (mole Na_2SO_4) are correct. The magnitude is appropriate because there is over 100 kg of Na_2SO_4 present.

3.59   (a)   6.5 g H_2O **Find:** number of molecules
     Conceptual Plan: g H_2O $\rightarrow$ mole H_2O $\rightarrow$ number H_2O molecules

$$\frac{1 \text{ mol}}{18.02 \text{ g } H_2O} \qquad \frac{6.022 \times 10^{23} \ H_2O \text{ molecules}}{\text{mol } H_2O}$$

     Solution: $6.5 \text{ g } H_2O \times \dfrac{1 \text{ mol } H_2O}{18.02 \text{ g } H_2O} \times \dfrac{6.022 \times 10^{23} \ H_2O \text{ molecules}}{\text{mol } H_2O} = 2.2 \times 10^{23} \ H_2O$ molecules

     Check: The units of the answer (H_2O molecules) are correct. The magnitude is appropriate: it is smaller than Avogadro's number, as expected, since we have less than 1 mole of H_2O.

(b)   **Given:** 389 g CBr_4 **Find:** number of molecules
     Conceptual Plan: g CBr_4 $\rightarrow$ mole CBr_4 $\rightarrow$ number CBr_4 molecules

$$\frac{1 \text{ mol}}{331.6 \text{ g } CBr_4} \qquad \frac{6.022 \times 10^{23} \ CBr_4 \text{ molecules}}{\text{mol } CBr_4}$$

     Solution: $389 \text{ g } CBr_4 \times \dfrac{1 \text{ mol } CBr_4}{331.6 \text{ g } CBr_4} \times \dfrac{6.022 \times 10^{23} \ CBr_4 \text{ molecules}}{\text{mol } CBr_4} = 7.06 \times 10^{23} \ CBr_4$ molecules

     Check: The units of the answer (CBr_4 molecules) are correct. The magnitude is appropriate: it is larger than Avogadro's number, as expected, since we have more than 1 mole of CBr_4.

(c)   **Given:** 22.1 g O_2 **Find:** number of molecules
     Conceptual Plan: g O_2 $\rightarrow$ mole O_2 $\rightarrow$ number O_2 molecules

$$\frac{1 \text{ mol}}{32.00 \text{ g } O_2} \qquad \frac{6.022 \times 10^{23} \ O_2 \text{ molecules}}{\text{mol } O_2}$$

     Solution: $22.1 \text{ g } O_2 \times \dfrac{1 \text{ mol } O_2}{32.00 \text{ g } O_2} \times \dfrac{6.022 \times 10^{23} \ O_2 \text{ molecules}}{\text{mol } O_2} = 4.16 \times 10^{23} \ O_2$ molecules

     Check: The units of the answer (O_2 molecules) are correct. The magnitude is appropriate: it is smaller than Avogadro's number, as expected, since we have less than 1 mole of O_2.

(d)   **Given:** 19.3 g C_8H_{10} **Find:** number of molecules
     Conceptual Plan: g C_8H_{10} $\rightarrow$ mole C_8H_{10} $\rightarrow$ number C_8H_{10} molecules

$$\frac{1 \text{ mol}}{106.16 \text{ g } C_8H_{10}} \qquad \frac{6.022 \times 10^{23} \ C_8H_{10} \text{ molecules}}{\text{mol } C_8H_{10}}$$

Solution:

$$19.3 \; \bcancel{\text{g } C_8H_{10}} \times \frac{1 \; \bcancel{\text{mol } C_8H_{10}}}{106.16 \; \bcancel{\text{g } C_8H_{10}}} \times \frac{6.022 \times 10^{23} \; \bcancel{C_8H_{10} \text{ molecules}}}{\bcancel{\text{mol } C_8H_{10}}} = 1.09 \times 10^{23} \; C_8H_{10} \text{ molecules}$$

Check: The units of the answer (C_8H_{10} molecules) are correct. The magnitude is appropriate: it is smaller than Avogadro's number, as expected, since we have less than 1 mole of C_8H_{10}.

3.61   (a)   **Given:** 5.94×10^{20} SO_3 molecules **Find:** mass in g

Conceptual Plan: number SO_3 molecules $\rightarrow$ mole SO_3 $\rightarrow$ g SO_3

$$\frac{1 \text{ mol } SO_3}{6.022 \times 10^{23} \; SO_3 \text{ molecules}} \qquad \frac{80.07 \text{ g } SO_3}{1 \text{ mol } SO_3}$$

Solution: $5.94 \times 10^{20} \; \bcancel{SO_3 \text{ molecules}} \times \dfrac{1 \; \bcancel{\text{mol } SO_3}}{6.022 \times 10^{23} \; \bcancel{SO_3 \text{ molecules}}} \times \dfrac{80.07 \text{ g } SO_3}{1 \; \bcancel{\text{mol } SO_3}} = 0.0790 \text{ g } SO_3$

Check: The units of the answer (grams SO_3) are correct. The magnitude is appropriate: there is less than Avogadro's number of molecules so we have less than 1 mole of SO_3.

(b)   **Given:** 2.8×10^{22} H_2O molecules **Find:** mass in g

Conceptual Plan: number H_2O molecules $\rightarrow$ mole H_2O $\rightarrow$ g H_2O

$$\frac{1 \text{ mol } H_2O}{6.022 \times 10^{23} \; H_2O \text{ molecules}} \qquad \frac{18.02 \text{ g } H_2O}{1 \text{ mol } H_2O}$$

Solution: $2.8 \times 10^{22} \; \bcancel{H_2O \text{ molecules}} \times \dfrac{1 \; \bcancel{\text{mol } H_2O}}{6.022 \times 10^{23} \; \bcancel{H_2O \text{ molecules}}} \times \dfrac{18.02 \text{ g } H_2O}{1 \; \bcancel{\text{mol } H_2O}} = 0.84 \text{ g } H_2O$

Check: The units of the answer (grams H_2O) are correct. The magnitude is appropriate: there is less than Avogadro's number of molecules so we have less than 1 mole of H_2O.

(c)   **Given:** 1 $C_6H_{12}O_6$ molecule **Find:** mass in g

Conceptual Plan: number $C_6H_{12}O_6$ molecules $\rightarrow$ mole $C_6H_{12}O_6$ $\rightarrow$ g $C_6H_{12}O_6$

$$\frac{1 \text{ mol } C_6H_{12}O_6}{6.022 \times 10^{23} \; C_6H_{12}O_6 \text{ molecules}} \qquad \frac{180.16 \text{ g } C_6H_{12}O_6}{1 \text{ mol } C_6H_{12}O_6}$$

Solution:

$$1 \; \bcancel{C_6H_{12}O_6 \text{ molecule}} \times \frac{1 \; \bcancel{\text{mol } C_6H_{12}O_6}}{6.022 \times 10^{23} \; \bcancel{C_6H_{12}O_6 \text{ molecules}}} \times \frac{180.16 \text{ g } C_6H_{12}O_6}{1 \; \bcancel{\text{mol } C_6H_{12}O_6}} = 2.992 \times 10^{-22} \text{ g } C_6H_{12}O_6$$

Check: The units of the answer (grams $C_6H_{12}O_6$) are correct. The magnitude is appropriate: there is much less than Avogadro's number of molecules so we have much less than 1 mole of $C_6H_{12}O_6$.

3.63   **Given:** 1.8×10^{17} $C_{12}H_{22}O_{11}$ molecule **Find:** mass in mg

Conceptual Plan: number $C_{12}H_{22}O_{11}$ molecules $\rightarrow$ mole $C_{12}H_{22}O_{11}$ $\rightarrow$ g $C_{12}H_{22}O_{11}$ $\rightarrow$ mg $C_{12}H_{22}O_{11}$

$$\frac{1 \text{ mol } C_{12}H_{22}O_{11}}{6.022 \times 10^{23} \; C_{12}H_{22}O_{11} \text{ molecules}} \qquad \frac{342.3 \text{ g } C_{12}H_{22}O_{11}}{1 \text{ mol } C_{12}H_{22}O_{11}} \qquad \frac{1 \times 10^3 \text{ mg } C_{12}H_{22}O_{11}}{1 \text{ g } C_{12}H_{22}O_{11}}$$

Solution:

$$1.8 \times 10^{17} \; \bcancel{C_{12}H_{22}O_{11} \text{ molecules}} \times \frac{1 \; \bcancel{\text{mol } C_{12}H_{22}O_{11}}}{6.022 \times 10^{23} \; \bcancel{C_{12}H_{22}O_{11} \text{ molecules}}} \times \frac{342.3 \; \bcancel{\text{g } C_{12}H_{22}O_{11}}}{1 \; \bcancel{\text{mol } C_{12}H_{22}O_{11}}} \times \frac{1 \times 10^3 \text{ mg } \bcancel{C_{12}H_{22}O_{11}}}{1 \; \bcancel{\text{g } C_{12}H_{22}O_{11}}}$$

$$= 0.10 \text{ mg } C_{12}H_{22}O_{11}$$

Check: The units of the answer (milligrams $C_{12}H_{22}O_{11}$) are correct. The magnitude is appropriate: there is much less than Avogadro's number of molecules so we have much less than 1 mole of C $H_{22}O_{11}$.

Composition of Compounds

3.65   (a)   **Given:** CH_4 **Find:** mass percent C

Conceptual Plan: mass $\% C = \dfrac{1 \times \text{molar mass C}}{\text{molar mass } CH_4} \times 100$

Solution:

$$1 \times \text{molar mass C} = 1(12.01\,\text{g/mol}) = 12.01\,\text{g C}$$
$$\text{molar mass CH}_4 = 1(12.01\,\text{g/mol}) + 4(1.008\,\text{g/mol}) = 16.04\,\text{g/mol}$$
$$\text{mass \% C} = \frac{1 \times \text{molar mass C}}{\text{molar mass CH}_4} \times 100\%$$
$$= \frac{12.01\,\cancel{\text{g/mol}}}{16.04\,\cancel{\text{g/mol}}} \times 100\%$$
$$= 74.87\,\%$$

Check: The units of the answer (%) are correct. The magnitude is reasonable because it is between 0 and 100% and carbon is the heaviest element.

(b)   **Given:** C_2H_6 **Find:** mass percent C

        Conceptual Plan: mass %C $= \dfrac{2 \times \text{molar mass C}}{\text{molar mass C}_2\text{H}_6} \times 100$

Solution:

$$2 \times \text{molar mass C} = 2(12.01\,\text{g/mol}) = 24.02\,\text{g C}$$
$$\text{molar mass C}_2\text{H}_6 = 2(12.01\,\text{g/mol}) + 6(1.008\,\text{g/mol}) = 30.07\,\text{g/mol}$$
$$\text{mass \% C} = \frac{2 \times \text{molar mass C}}{\text{molar mass C}_2\text{H}_6} \times 100\%$$
$$= \frac{24.02\,\cancel{\text{g/mol}}}{30.07\,\cancel{\text{g/mol}}} \times 100\%$$
$$= 79.89\,\%$$

Check: The units of the answer (%) are correct. The magnitude is reasonable because it is between 0 and 100% and carbon is the heaviest element.

(c)   **Given:** C_2H_2 **Find:** mass percent C

        Conceptual Plan: mass %C $= \dfrac{2 \times \text{molar mass C}}{\text{molar mass C}_2\text{H}_2} \times 100$

Solution:

$$2 \times \text{molar mass C} = 2(12.01\,\text{g/mol}) =$$
$$\text{molar mass C}_2\text{H}_2 = 2(12.01\,\text{g/mol}) + 2(1.008\,\text{g/mol}) = 26.04\,\text{g/mol}$$
$$\text{mass \% C} = \frac{2 \times \text{molar mass C}}{\text{molar mass C}_2\text{H}_2} \times 100\%$$
$$= \frac{24.02\,\cancel{\text{g/mol}}}{26.04\,\cancel{\text{g/mol}}} \times 100\%$$
$$= 92.26\,\%$$

Check: The units of the answer (%) are correct. The magnitude is reasonable because it is between 0 and 100% and carbon is the heaviest element.

(d)   **Given:** C_2H_5Cl **Find:** mass percent C

        Conceptual Plan: mass %C $= \dfrac{2 \times \text{molar mass C}}{\text{molar mass C}_2\text{H}_5\text{Cl}} \times 100$

Solution:

$$2 \times \text{molar mass C} = 2(12.01\,\text{g/mol}) = 24.02\,\text{g C}$$
$$\text{molar mass C}_2\text{H}_5\text{Cl} = 2(12.01\,\text{g/mol}) + 5(1.008\,\text{g/mol}) + 1(35.45\,\text{g/mol}) = 64.51\,\text{g/mol}$$
$$\text{mass \% C} = \frac{2 \times \text{molar mass C}}{\text{molar mass C}_2\text{H}_5\text{Cl}} \times 100\%$$
$$= \frac{24.02\,\cancel{\text{g/mol}}}{64.51\,\cancel{\text{g/mol}}} \times 100\%$$
$$= 37.23\,\%$$

Check: The units of the answer (%) are correct. The magnitude is reasonable because it is between 0 and 100% and chlorine is heavier than carbon.

3.67   **Given:** NH_3 **Find:** mass percent N

         Conceptual Plan: mass % N $= \dfrac{1 \times \text{molar mass N}}{\text{molar mass } NH_3} \times 100$

         Solution:

$$1 \times \text{molar mass N} = 1(14.01 \text{g/mol}) = 14.01 \text{ g N}$$
$$\text{molar mass } NH_3 = 3(1.008 \text{ g/mol}) + (14.01 \text{ g/mol}) = 17.03 \text{ g/mol}$$

$$\text{mass \% N} \quad \dfrac{1 \times \text{molar mass N}}{\text{molar mass } NH_3} \times 100\%$$

$$= \dfrac{14.01 \, \cancel{\text{g/mol}}}{17.03 \, \cancel{\text{g/mol}}} \times 100\%$$

$$= 82.27 \%$$

Check: The units of the answer (%) are correct. The magnitude is reasonable because it is between 0 and 100% and nitrogen is the heaviest atom present.

         Given: $CO(NH_2)_2$ **Find:** mass percent N

         Conceptual Plan: mass % N $= \dfrac{2 \times \text{molar mass N}}{\text{molar mass } CO(NH_2)_2} \times 100$

         Solution:

$$2 \times \text{molar mass N} = 1(14.01 \text{g/mol}) = 28.02 \text{ g N}$$
$$\text{molar mass } CO(NH_2)_2 = (12.01 \text{ g/mol}) + (16.00 \text{ g/mol}) + 2(14.01 \text{ g/mol}) + 4(1.008 \text{ g/mol}) = 60.06 \text{ g/mol}$$

$$\text{mass \% N} = \dfrac{2 \times \text{molar mass N}}{\text{molar mass } CO(NH_2)_2} \times 100\%$$

$$= \dfrac{28.02 \, \cancel{\text{g/mol}}}{60.06 \, \cancel{\text{g/mol}}} \times 100\%$$

$$= 46.65 \%$$

Check: The units of the answer (%) are correct. The magnitude is reasonable. It is between 0 and 100% and there are two nitrogens and only one carbon and one oxygen per molecule.

         Given: NH_4NO_3 **Find:** mass percent N

         Conceptual Plan: mass % N $= \dfrac{2 \times \text{molar mass N}}{\text{molar mass } NH_4NO_3} \times 100$

         Solution:

$$2 \times \text{molar mass N} = 2(14.01 \text{g/mol}) = 28.02 \text{ g N}$$
$$\text{molar mass } NH_4NO_3 = 2(14.01 \text{ g/mol}) + 4(1.008 \text{ g/mol}) + 3(16.00 \text{ g/mol}) = 80.05 \text{ g/mol}$$

$$\text{mass \% N} = \dfrac{2 \times \text{molar mass N}}{\text{molar mass } NH_4NO_3} \times 100\%$$

$$= \dfrac{28.02 \, \cancel{\text{g/mol}}}{80.05 \, \cancel{\text{g/mol}}} \times 100\%$$

$$= 35.00 \%$$

Check: The units of the answer (%) are correct. The magnitude is reasonable because it is between 0 and 100%. The mass of nitrogen is less than the mass of oxygen and there are two nitrogens and three oxygens per molecule.

         Given: $(NH_4)_2SO_4$ **Find:** mass percent N

         Conceptual Plan: mass % N $= \dfrac{2 \times \text{molar mass N}}{\text{molar mass } (NH_4)_2SO_4} \times 100$

         Solution:

$$2 \times \text{molar mass N} = 2(14.01 \text{g/mol}) = 28.02 \text{ g N}$$
$$\text{molar mass } (NH_4)_2SO_4 = 2(14.01 \text{ g/mol}) + 8(1.008 \text{ g/mol}) + (32.07 \text{ g/mol}) + 4(16.00 \text{ g/mol}) = 132.15 \text{ g/mol}$$

$$\text{mass \% N} = \dfrac{2 \times \text{molar mass N}}{\text{molar mass } (NH_4)_2SO_4} \times 100\%$$

$$= \dfrac{28.02 \, \cancel{\text{g/mol}}}{132.15 \, \cancel{\text{g/mol}}} \times 100\%$$

$$= 21.20 \%$$

Check: The units of the answer (%) are correct. The magnitude is reasonable because it is between 0 and 100% and the mass of nitrogen is less than the mass of oxygen and sulfur.

The fertilizer with the highest nitrogen content is NH_3 with a N content of 82.27% N.

3.69   **Given:** 55.5 g CuF_2; 37.42 % F **Find:** g F in CuF_2
        Conceptual Plan: **g CuF_2** → **g F**

$$\frac{37.42 \text{ g F}}{100.0 \text{ g } CuF_2}$$

        Solution: $55.5 \text{ g } CuF_2 \times \dfrac{37.42 \text{ g F}}{100.0 \text{ g } CuF_2} = 20.77 = 20.8$ g F

        Check: The units of the answer (g F) are correct. The magnitude is reasonable because it is less than the original mass.

3.71   **Given:** 150 μg I; 76.45% I in KI **Find:** μg KI
        Conceptual Plan: μg I → g I → g KI → μg KI

$$\frac{1 \text{ g I}}{1 \times 10^6 \, \mu\text{g I}} \quad \frac{100.0 \text{ g KI}}{76.45 \text{ g I}} \quad \frac{1 \times 10^6 \, \mu\text{g KI}}{1 \text{ g KI}}$$

        Solution: $150 \, \mu\text{g I} \times \dfrac{1 \text{ g I}}{1 \times 10^6 \, \mu\text{g I}} \times \dfrac{100.0 \text{ g KI}}{76.45 \text{ g I}} \times \dfrac{1 \times 10^6 \, \mu\text{g KI}}{1 \text{ g KI}} = 196 \, \mu$g KI

        Check: The units of the answer (μg KI) are correct. The magnitude is reasonable because it is greater than the original mass.

3.73   (a)   red – oxygen, white – hydrogen: 2H:O H_2O

        (b)   black – carbon, white – hydrogen: 4H:C CH_4

        (c)   black – carbon, white – hydrogen, red – oxygen: 2C:O:6H CH_3CH_2OH or C_2H_6O

3.75   (a)   **Given:** 0.0885 mol C_4H_{10} **Find:** mol H atoms
               Conceptual Plan: mol C_4H_{10} → mole H atom

$$\frac{10 \text{ mol H}}{1 \text{ mol } C_4H_{10}}$$

               Solution: $0.0885 \text{ mol } C_4H_{10} \times \dfrac{10 \text{ mol H}}{1 \text{ mol } C_4H_{10}} = 0.885$ mol H atoms

               Check: The units of the answer (mol H atoms) are correct. The magnitude is reasonable because it is greater than the original mol C_4H_{10}.

        (b)   **Given:** 1.3 mol CH_4 **Find:** mol H atoms
               Conceptual Plan: mol CH_4 → mole H atom

$$\frac{4 \text{ mol H}}{1 \text{ mol } CH_4}$$

               Solution: $1.3 \text{ mol } CH_4 \times \dfrac{4 \text{ mol H}}{1 \text{ mol } CH_4} = 5.2$ mol H atoms

               Check: The units of the answer (mol H atoms) are correct. The magnitude is reasonable because it is greater than the original mol CH_4.

        (c)   **Given:** 2.4 mol C_6H_{12} **Find:** mol H atoms
               Conceptual Plan: mol C_6H_{12} → mole H atom

$$\frac{12 \text{ mol H}}{1 \text{ mol } C_6H_{12}}$$

               Solution: $2.4 \text{ mol } C_6H_{12} \times \dfrac{12 \text{ mol H}}{1 \text{ mol } C_6H_{12}} = 29$ mol H atoms

               Check: The units of the answer (mol H atoms) are correct. The magnitude is reasonable because it is greater than the original mol C_6H_{12}.

        (d)   **Given:** 1.87 mol C_8H_{18} **Find:** mol H atoms
               Conceptual Plan: mol C_8H_{18} → mole H atom

$$\frac{18 \text{ mol H}}{1 \text{ mol } C_8H_{18}}$$

Solution: $1.87 \ \overline{\text{mol } C_8H_{18}} \times \dfrac{18 \text{ mol H}}{1 \ \overline{\text{mol } C_8H_{18}}} = 33.7 \text{ mol H atoms}$

Check: The units of the answer (mol H atoms) are correct. The magnitude is reasonable because it is greater than the original mol C_8H_{18}.

3.77   (a)   **Given:** 8.5 g NaCl   **Find:** g Na

       Conceptual Plan: g NaCl → **mole NaCl** → **mol Na** → **g Na**

$$\dfrac{1 \text{ mol NaCl}}{58.44 \text{ g NaCl}} \qquad \dfrac{1 \text{ mol Na}}{1 \text{ mol NaCl}} \qquad \dfrac{22.99 \text{ g Na}}{1 \text{ mol Na}}$$

       Solution: $8.5 \ \overline{\text{g NaCl}} \times \dfrac{1 \ \overline{\text{mol NaCl}}}{58.44 \ \overline{\text{g NaCl}}} \times \dfrac{1 \ \overline{\text{mol Na}}}{1 \ \overline{\text{mol NaCl}}} \times \dfrac{22.99 \text{ g Na}}{1 \ \overline{\text{mol Na}}} = 3.3 \text{ g Na}$

       Check: The units of the answer (g Na) are correct. The magnitude is reasonable because it is less than the original g NaCl.

   (b)   **Given:** 8.5 g Na_3PO_4 **Find:** g Na

       Conceptual Plan: g Na_3PO_4 → **mole Na_3PO_4** → **mol Na** → **g Na**

$$\dfrac{1 \text{ mol } Na_3PO_4}{163.94 \text{ g } Na_3PO_4} \qquad \dfrac{3 \text{ mol Na}}{1 \text{ mol } Na_3PO_4} \qquad \dfrac{22.99 \text{ g Na}}{1 \text{ mol Na}}$$

       Solution: $8.5 \ \overline{\text{g } Na_3PO_4} \times \dfrac{1 \ \overline{\text{mol } Na_3PO_4}}{163.94 \ \overline{\text{g } Na_3PO_4}} \times \dfrac{3 \ \overline{\text{mol Na}}}{1 \ \overline{\text{mol } Na_3PO_4}} \times \dfrac{22.99 \text{ g Na}}{1 \ \overline{\text{mol Na}}} = 3.6 \text{ g Na}$

       Check: The units of the answer (g Na) are correct. The magnitude is reasonable because it is less than the original g Na_3PO_4.

   (c)   **Given:** 8.5 g $NaC_7H_5O_2$ **Find:** g Na

       Conceptual Plan: g $NaC_7H_5O_2$ → **mole $NaC_7H_5O_2$** → **mol Na** → **g Na**

$$\dfrac{1 \text{ mol } NaC_7H_5O_2}{144.10 \text{ g } NaC_7H_5O_2} \qquad \dfrac{1 \text{ mol Na}}{1 \text{ mol } NaC_7H_5O_2} \qquad \dfrac{22.99 \text{ g Na}}{1 \text{ mol Na}}$$

       Solution: $8.5 \ \overline{\text{g } NaC_7H_5O_2} \times \dfrac{1 \ \overline{\text{mol } NaC_7H_5O_2}}{144.10 \ \overline{\text{g } NaC_7H_5O_2}} \times \dfrac{1 \ \overline{\text{mol Na}}}{1 \ \overline{\text{mol } NaC_7H_5O_2}} \times \dfrac{22.99 \text{ g Na}}{1 \ \overline{\text{mol Na}}} = 1.4 \text{ g Na}$

       Check: The units of the answer (g Na) are correct. The magnitude is reasonable because it is less than the original g $NaC_7H_5O_2$.

   (d)   **Given:** 8.5 g $Na_2C_6H_6O_7$ **Find:** g Na

       Conceptual Plan: g Na C H_6O_7 → **mole $Na_2C_6H_6O_7$** → **mol Na** → **g Na**

$$\dfrac{1 \text{ mol } Na_2C_6H_6O_7}{236.1 \text{ g } Na_2C_6H_6O_7} \qquad \dfrac{2 \text{ mol Na}}{1 \text{ mol } Na_2C_6H_6O_7} \qquad \dfrac{22.99 \text{ g Na}}{1 \text{ mol Na}}$$

       Solution:

$8.5 \ \overline{\text{g } Na_2C_6H_6O_7} \times \dfrac{1 \ \overline{\text{mol } Na_2C_6H_6O_7}}{236.1 \ \overline{\text{g } Na_2C_6H_6O_7}} \times \dfrac{2 \ \overline{\text{mol Na}}}{1 \ \overline{\text{mol } Na_2C_6H_6O_7}} \times \dfrac{22.99 \text{ g Na}}{1 \ \overline{\text{mol Na}}} = 1.7 \text{ g Na}$

       Check: The units of the answer (g Na) are correct. The magnitude is reasonable because it is less than the original g $Na_2C_6H_6O_7$.

Chemical Formulas from Experimental Data

3.79   (a)   **Given:** 1.651 g Ag; 0.1224 g O   **Find:** empirical formula

       Conceptual Plan:

       convert mass to mol of each element → **write pseudoformula** → **write empirical formula**

$$\dfrac{1 \text{ mol Ag}}{107.9 \text{ g Ag}} \qquad \dfrac{1 \text{ mol O}}{16.00 \text{ g O}} \qquad \text{divide by smallest number}$$

       Solution: $1.651 \ \overline{\text{g Ag}} \times \dfrac{1 \text{ mol Ag}}{107.9 \ \overline{\text{g Ag}}} = 0.01530 \text{ mol Ag}$

$0.1224 \text{ g O} \times \dfrac{1 \text{ mol O}}{16.00 \ \overline{\text{g O}}} = 0.007650 \text{ mol O}$

$Ag_{0.01530} O_{0.007650}$

$Ag_{\frac{0.01530}{0.007650}} O_{\frac{0.007650}{0.007650}} \rightarrow Ag_2O$

       The correct empirical formula is Ag_2O.

(b)   **Given:** 0.672 g Co; 0.569 g As; 0.486 g O **Find:** empirical formula
Conceptual Plan:
convert mass to mol of each element → **write pseudoformula** → **write empirical formula**

$$\frac{1\ mol\ Co}{58.93\ g\ Co} \quad \frac{1\ mol\ As}{74.92\ g\ As} \quad \frac{1\ mol\ O}{16.00\ g\ O} \qquad \text{divide by smallest number}$$

Solution: $0.672\ \cancel{g\ Co} \times \dfrac{1\ mol\ Co}{58.93\ \cancel{g\ Co}} = 0.0114\ mol\ Co$

$0.569\ \cancel{g\ As} \times \dfrac{1\ mol\ As}{74.92\ \cancel{g\ As}} = 0.00759\ mol\ O$

$0.486\ \cancel{g\ O} \times \dfrac{1\ mol\ O}{16.00\ \cancel{g\ O}} = 0.0304\ mol\ O$

$Co_{0.0114}\ As_{0.00759}\ O_{0.0304}$

$Co_{\frac{0.0114}{0.00759}}\ As_{\frac{0.00759}{0.00759}}\ O_{\frac{0.0304}{0.00759}} \rightarrow Co_{1.5}As_1O_4$

$Co_{1.5}As_1O_4 \times 2 \rightarrow Co_3As_2O_8$

The correct empirical formula is $Co_3As_2O_8$.

(c)   **Given:** 1.443 g Se; 5.841 g Br **Find:** empirical formula
Conceptual Plan:
convert mass to mol of each element → **write pseudoformula** → **write empirical formula**

$$\frac{1\ mol\ Se}{78.96\ g\ Se} \quad \frac{1\ mol\ Br}{79.90\ g\ Br} \qquad \text{divide by smallest number}$$

Solution: $1.443\ \cancel{g\ Se} \times \dfrac{1\ mol\ Se}{78.96\ \cancel{g\ Se}} = 0.01828\ mol\ Se$

$5.841\ \cancel{g\ Br} \times \dfrac{1\ mol\ Br}{79.90\ \cancel{g\ Br}} = 0.07310\ mol\ Br$

$Se_{0.01828}Br_{0.07310}$

$Se_{\frac{0.01828}{0.01828}}Br_{\frac{0.07310}{0.01828}} \rightarrow SeBr_4$

The correct empirical formula is $SeBr_4$.

3.81   (a)   **Given:** In a 100 g sample: 74.03 g C, 8.70 g H, 17.27 g N **Find:** empirical formula
Conceptual Plan:
convert mass to mol of each element → **write pseudoformula** → **write empirical formula**

$$\frac{1\ mol\ C}{12.01\ g\ C} \quad \frac{1\ mol\ H}{1.008\ g\ H} \quad \frac{1\ mol\ N}{14.01\ g\ N} \qquad \text{divide by smallest number}$$

Solution: $74.03\ \cancel{g\ C} \times \dfrac{1\ mol\ C}{12.01\ \cancel{g\ C}} = 6.164\ mol\ C$

$8.70\ \cancel{g\ H} \times \dfrac{1\ mol\ H}{1.008\ \cancel{g\ H}} = 8.63\ mol\ H$

$17.27\ \cancel{g\ N} \times \dfrac{1\ mol\ N}{14.01\ \cancel{g\ N}} = 1.233\ mol\ N$

$C_{6.164}H_{8.63}N_{1.233}$

$C_{\frac{6.164}{1.233}}H_{\frac{8.63}{1.233}}N_{\frac{1.233}{1.233}} \rightarrow C_5H_7N$

The correct empirical formula is C_5H_7N.

(b)   **Given:** In a 100 g sample: 49.48 g C, 5.19 g H, 28.85 g N, 16.48 g O **Find:** empirical formula
Conceptual Plan:
convert mass to mol of each element → **write pseudoformula** → **write empirical formula**

$$\frac{1\ mol\ C}{12.01\ g\ C} \quad \frac{1\ mol\ H}{1.008\ g\ H} \quad \frac{1\ mol\ N}{14.01\ g\ N} \quad \frac{1\ mol\ O}{16.00\ g\ O} \qquad \text{divide by smallest number}$$

Solution: $49.48\ \cancel{g\ C} \times \dfrac{1\ mol\ C}{12.01\ \cancel{g\ C}} = 4.120\ mol\ C$

$5.19\ \cancel{g\ H} \times \dfrac{1\ mol\ H}{1.008\ \cancel{g\ H}} = 5.15\ mol\ H$

$28.85\ \cancel{g\ N} \times \dfrac{1\ mol\ N}{14.01\ \cancel{g\ N}} = 2.059\ mol\ N$

$16.48\ \cancel{g\ O} \times \dfrac{1\ mol\ O}{16.00\ \cancel{g\ O}} = 1.030\ mol\ O$

$$C_{4.120} H_{5.15} N_{2.059} O_{1.030}$$

$$C_{\frac{4.120}{1.030}} H_{\frac{5.15}{1.030}} N_{\frac{2.059}{1.030}} O_{\frac{1.030}{1.030}} \rightarrow C_4H_5N_2O$$

The correct empirical formula is $C_4H_5N_2O$.

3.83   **Given:** In a 100 g sample: 75.69 g C, 8.80 g H, 15.51 g O **Find:** empirical formula

Conceptual Plan:

convert mass to mol of each element → write pseudoformula → write empirical formula

$$\frac{1\ mol\ C}{12.01\ g\ C} \quad \frac{1\ mol\ H}{1.008\ g\ H} \quad \frac{1\ mol\ O}{16.00\ g\ O} \qquad \text{divide by smallest number}$$

Solution: $75.69\ \cancel{g\ C} \times \dfrac{1\ mol\ C}{12.01\ \cancel{g\ C}} = 6.302\ mol\ C$

$8.80\ \cancel{g\ H} \times \dfrac{1\ mol\ H}{1.008\ \cancel{g\ H}} = 8.73\ mol\ H$

$15.51\ \cancel{g\ O} \times \dfrac{1\ mol\ O}{16.00\ \cancel{g\ O}} = 0.9694\ mol\ O$

$$C_{6.302}H_{8.73}O_{0.9694}$$

$$C_{\frac{6.302}{0.9694}} H_{\frac{8.73}{0.9694}} O_{\frac{0.9694}{0.9694}} \rightarrow C_{6.50}H_{9.01}O$$

$$C_{6.50}H_{9.01}O \times 2 = C_{13}H_{18}O_2$$

The correct empirical formula is $C_{13}H_{18}O_2$.

3.85   **Given:** 0.77 mg N, 6.61 mg N_xCl_y **Find:** empirical formula

Conceptual Plan:

Find mg Cl → convert mg to g for each element → convert mass to mol of each element →

$$mg\ N_xCl_y - mg\ N \qquad \frac{1\ g}{1000\ mg} \qquad \frac{1\ mol\ N}{14.01\ g\ N} \qquad \frac{1\ mol\ Cl}{35.45\ g\ Cl}$$

write pseudoformula → write empirical formula

divide by smallest number

Solution: $6.61\ mg\ N_xCl - 0.77\ mg\ N = 5.84\ mg\ Cl$

$0.77\ \cancel{mg\ N} \times \dfrac{1\ \cancel{g\ N}}{1000\ \cancel{mg\ N}} \times \dfrac{1\ mol\ N}{14.01\ \cancel{g\ N}} = 5.5 \times 10^{-5}\ mol\ N$

$5.84\ \cancel{mg\ Cl} \times \dfrac{1\ \cancel{g\ Cl}}{1000\ \cancel{mg\ Cl}} \times \dfrac{1\ mol\ Cl}{35.45\ \cancel{g\ Cl}} = 1.6 \times 10^{-4}\ mol\ Cl$

$$N_{5.5 \times 10^{-5}} Cl_{1.6 \times 10^{-4}}$$

$$N_{\frac{5.5 \times 10^{-5}}{5.5 \times 10^{-5}}} Cl_{\frac{1.6 \times 10^{-4}}{5.5 \times 10^{-5}}} \rightarrow NCl_3$$

The correct empirical formula is NCl_3.

3.87 (a) **Given:** empirical formula = C_6H_7N, molar mass = 186.24 g/mol **Find:** molecular formula

Conceptual Plan: molecular formula = empirical formula x n $n = \dfrac{molar\ mass}{empirical\ formula\ mass}$

Solution: empirical formula mass = 6(12.01 g/mol) + 7(1.008 g/mol) + 1(14.01 g/mol) = 93.13 g/mol

$n = \dfrac{molar\ mass}{formula\ molar\ mass} = \dfrac{186.24\ g/mol}{93.13\ g/mol} = 1.998 = 2$

molecular formula $= C_6H_7N \times 2$

$= C_{12}H_{14}N_2$

(b) **Given:** empirical formula = C_2HCl, molar mass = 181.44 g/mol **Find:** molecular formula

Conceptual Plan: molecular formula = empirical formula x n $n = \dfrac{molar\ mass}{empirical\ formula\ mass}$

Solution: empirical formula mass = 2(12.01 g/mol) + 1(1.008 g/mol) + 1(35.45 g/mol) = 60.48 g/mol

$n = \dfrac{molar\ mass}{formula\ molar\ mass} = \dfrac{181.44\ g/mol}{60.48\ g/mol} = 3$

molecular formula $= C_2HCl \times 3$

$= C_6H_3Cl_3$

(c)   **Given:** empirical formula = $C_5H_{10}NS_2$, molar mass = 296.54 g/mol **Find:** molecular formula

Conceptual Plan: molecular formula = empirical formula x n $n = \dfrac{\text{molar mass}}{\text{empirical formula mass}}$

Solution: empirical formula mass = 5(12.01 g/mol) + 10(1.008 g/mol)
+ 1(14.01 g/mol) + 2(32.07) =   148.28 g/mol

$$n = \frac{\text{molar mass}}{\text{formula molar mass}} = \frac{296.54 \text{ g/mol}}{148.28 \text{ g/mol}} = 2$$

$$\text{molecular formula} = C_5H_{10}NS_2 \times 2$$
$$= C_{10}H_{20}N_2S_4$$

3.89   **Given:** 33.01 g CO_2, 13.51 g H_2O **Find:** empirical formula
Conceptual Plan:

$$\text{mass } CO_2, H_2O \rightarrow \text{mol } CO_2, H_2O \rightarrow \text{mol C, mol H} \rightarrow \text{pseudoformula} \rightarrow \text{empirical formula}$$

$\dfrac{1 \text{ mol } CO_2}{44.01 \text{ g } CO_2}$ $\dfrac{1 \text{ mol } H_2O}{18.02 \text{ g } H_2O}$ $\dfrac{1 \text{ mol C}}{1 \text{ mol } CO_2}$ $\dfrac{2 \text{ mol H}}{1 \text{ mol } H_2O}$ divide by smallest number

Solution:

$$33.01 \text{ g } CO_2 \times \frac{1 \text{ mol } CO_2}{44.01 \text{ g } CO_2} = 0.7500 \text{ mol } CO_2$$

$$13.51 \text{ g } H_2O \times \frac{1 \text{ mol } H_2O}{18.02 \text{ g } H_2O} = 0.7497 \text{ mol } H_2O$$

$$0.7500 \text{ mol } CO_2 \times \frac{1 \text{ mol C}}{1 \text{ mol } CO_2} = 0.7500 \text{ mol C}$$

$$0.7497 \text{ mol } H_2O \times \frac{2 \text{ mol H}}{1 \text{ mol } H_2O} = 1.499 \text{ mol H}$$

$$C_{0.7500} H_{1.499}$$
$$C_{\frac{0.7500}{0.7500}} H_{\frac{1.499}{0.7500}} \rightarrow CH_2$$

The correct empirical formula is CH_2.

3.91   **Given:** 4.30 g sample, 8.59 g CO_2, 3.52 g H_2O **Find:** empirical formula
Conceptual Plan:

$$\text{mass } CO_2, H_2O \rightarrow \text{mol } CO_2, H_2O \rightarrow \text{mol C, mol H} \rightarrow \text{mass C, mass H, mass O} \rightarrow \text{mol O} \rightarrow$$

$\dfrac{1 \text{ mol } CO_2}{44.01 \text{ g } CO_2}$ $\dfrac{1 \text{ mol } H_2O}{18.02 \text{ g } H_2O}$ $\dfrac{1 \text{ mol C}}{1 \text{ mol } CO_2}$ $\dfrac{2 \text{ mol H}}{1 \text{ mol } H_2O}$ $\dfrac{12.01 \text{ g C}}{1 \text{ mol C}}$ $\dfrac{1.008 \text{ g H}}{1 \text{ mol H}}$ g sample – gC – g H $\dfrac{1 \text{ mol O}}{16.00 \text{ g O}}$

pseudoformula $\rightarrow$ empirical formula

divide by smallest number

Solution:

$$8.59 \text{ g } CO_2 \times \frac{1 \text{ mol } CO_2}{44.01 \text{ g } CO_2} = 0.195 \text{ mol } CO_2$$

$$3.52 \text{ g } H_2O \times \frac{1 \text{ mol } H_2O}{18.02 \text{ g } H_2O} = 0.195 \text{ mol } H_2O$$

$$0.195 \text{ mol } CO_2 \times \frac{1 \text{ mol C}}{1 \text{ mol } CO_2} = 0.195 \text{ mol C}$$

$$0.195 \text{ mol } H_2O \times \frac{2 \text{ mol H}}{1 \text{ mol } H_2O} = 0.390 \text{ mol H}$$

$$0.195 \text{ mol C} \times \frac{12.01 \text{ mol C}}{} = 2.34 \text{ g C}$$

$$0.390 \text{ mol } H_2O \times \frac{1.008 \text{ g H}}{1 \text{ mol H}} = 0.393 \text{ g H}$$

$$4.30 \text{ g} - 2.34 \text{ g} - 0.393 \text{ g} = 1.57 \text{ g O}$$

$$1.57 \text{ g O} \times \frac{1 \text{ mol O}}{16.00 \text{ g O}} = 0.0979 \text{ mol O}$$

$$C_{0.195} H_{0.390} O_{0.0979}$$
$$C_{\frac{0.195}{0.0979}} H_{\frac{0.390}{0.0979}} O_{\frac{0.0979}{0.0979}} \rightarrow C_2H_4O$$

The correct empirical formula is C_2H_4O.

Writing and Balancing Chemical Equations

3.93   **Conceptual Plan: write a skeletal reaction → balance atoms in more complex compounds → balance elements that occur as free elements → clear fractions**

   Solution: Skeletal reaction: $SO_2(g) + O_2(g) + H_2O(l) \rightarrow H_2SO_4(aq)$

   Balance O: $SO_2(g) + 1/2O_2(g) + H_2O(l) \rightarrow H_2SO_4(aq)$

   Clear fraction: $2SO_2(g) + O_2(g) + 2H_2O(l) \rightarrow 2H_2SO_4(aq)$

   Check:

left side	right side
2 S atoms	2 S atoms
8 O atoms	8 O atoms
4 H atoms	4 H atoms

3.95   **Conceptual Plan: write a skeletal reaction → balance atoms in more complex compounds → balance elements that occur as free elements → clear fractions**

   Solution: Skeletal reaction: $Na(s) + H_2O(l) \rightarrow H_2(g) + NaOH(aq)$

   Balance H: $Na(s) + H_2O(l) \rightarrow 1/2H_2(g) + NaOH(aq)$

   Clear fraction: $2Na(s) + 2H_2O(l) \rightarrow H_2(g) + 2NaOH(aq)$

   Check:

left side	right side
2 Na atoms	2 Na atoms
4 H atoms	4 H atoms
2 O atoms	2 O atoms

3.97   **Conceptual Plan: write a skeletal reaction → balance atoms in more complex compounds → balance elements that occur as free elements → clear fractions**

   Solution: Skeletal reaction: $C_{12}H_{22}O_{11}(aq) + H_2O(l) \rightarrow C_2H_5OH(aq) + CO_2(g)$

   Balance H: $C_{12}H_{22}O_{11}(aq) + H_2O(l) \rightarrow 4C_2H_5OH(aq) + CO_2(g)$

   Balance C: $C_{12}H_{22}O_{11}(aq) + H_2O(l) \rightarrow 4C_2H_5OH(aq) + 4CO_2(g)$

   Check:

left side	right side
12 C atoms	12 C atoms
24 H atoms	24 H atoms
12 O atoms	12 O atoms

3.99   (a)   **Conceptual Plan: write a skeletal reaction → balance atoms in more complex compounds → balance elements that occur as free elements → clear fractions**

   Solution: Skeletal reaction: $PbS(s) + HBr(aq) \rightarrow PbBr_2(s) + H_2S(g)$

   Balance Br: $PbS(s) + 2HBr(aq) \rightarrow PbBr_2(s) + H_2S(g)$

   Check:

left side	right side
1 Pb atom	1 Pb atom
1 S atom	1 S atom
2 H atoms	2 H atoms
2 Br atoms	2 Br atoms

   (b)   **Conceptual Plan: write a skeletal reaction → balance atoms in more complex compounds → balance elements that occur as free elements → clear fractions**

   Solution: Skeletal reaction: $CO(g) + H_2(g) \rightarrow CH_4(g) + H_2O(l)$

   Balance H: $CO(g) + 3H_2(g) \rightarrow CH_4(g) + H_2O(l)$

   Check:

left side	right side
1 C atom	1 C atom
1 O atom	1 O atom
6 H atoms	6 H atoms

(c)   **Conceptual Plan: write a skeletal reaction → balance atoms in more complex compounds → balance elements that occur as free elements → clear fractions**

    Solution: Skeletal reaction: $HCl(aq) + MnO_2(s) \rightarrow MnCl_2(aq) + H_2O(l) + Cl_2(g)$

                        Balance Cl: $4HCl(aq) + MnO_2(s) \rightarrow MnCl_2(aq) + H_2O(l) + Cl_2(g)$

                        Balance O: $4HCl(aq) + MnO_2(s) \rightarrow MnCl_2(aq) + 2H_2O(l) + Cl_2(g)$

    Check:

	left side	right side
	4 H atoms	4 H atoms
	4 Cl atoms	4 Cl atoms
	1 Mn atom	1 Mn atom
	2 O atoms	2 O atoms

(d)   **Conceptual Plan: write a skeletal reaction → balance atoms in more complex compounds → balance elements that occur as free elements → clear fractions**

    Solution: Skeletal reaction: $C_5H_{12}(l) + O_2(g) \rightarrow CO_2(g) + H_2O(l)$

                        Balance C: $C_5H_{12}(l) + O_2(g) \rightarrow 5CO_2(g) + H_2O(l)$

                        Balance H: $C_5H_{12}(l) + O_2(g) \rightarrow 5CO_2(g) + 6H_2O(l)$

                        Balance O: $C_5H_{12}(l) + 8O_2(g) \rightarrow 5CO_2(g) + 6H_2O(l)$

    Check:

	left side	right side
	5 C atoms	5 C atoms
	12 H atoms	12 H atoms
	16 O atoms	16 O atoms

3.101   (a)   **Conceptual Plan: balance atoms in more complex compounds → balance elements that occur as free elements → clear fractions**

    Solution: Skeletal reaction: $CO_2(g) + CaSiO_3(s) + H_2O(l) \rightarrow SiO_2(s) + Ca(HCO_3)_2(aq)$

                        Balance C: $2CO_2(g) + CaSiO_3(s) + H_2O(l) \rightarrow SiO_2(s) + Ca(HCO_3)_2(aq)$

    Check:

	left side	right side
	2 C atoms	2 C atoms
	8 O atoms	8 O atoms
	1 Ca atom	1 Ca atom
	1 Si atom	1 Si atom
	2 H atoms	2 H atoms

(b)   **Conceptual Plan: balance atoms in more complex compounds → balance elements that occur as free elements → clear fractions**

    Solution: Skeletal reaction: $Co(NO_3)_3(aq) + (NH_4)_2S(aq) \rightarrow Co_2S_3(s) + NH_4NO_3(aq)$

                        Balance S: $Co(NO_3)_3(aq) + 3(NH_4)_2S(aq) \rightarrow Co_2S_3(s) + NH_4NO_3(aq)$

                        Balance Co: $2Co(NO_3)_3(aq) + 3(NH_4)_2S(aq) \rightarrow Co_2S_3(s) + NH_4NO_3(aq)$

                        Balance N: $2Co(NO_3)_3(aq) + 3(NH_4)_2S(aq) \rightarrow Co_2S_3(s) + 6NH_4NO_3(aq)$

    Check:

	left side	right side
	2 Co atoms	2 Co atoms
	12 N atoms	12 N atoms
	18 O atoms	18 O atoms
	24 H atoms	24 H atoms
	3 S atoms	3 S atoms

(c)   **Conceptual Plan: balance atoms in more complex compounds → balance elements that occur as free elements → clear fractions**

    Solution: Skeletal reaction: $Cu_2O(s) + C(s) \rightarrow Cu(s) + CO(g)$

                        Balance Cu: $Cu_2O(s) + C(s) \rightarrow 2Cu(s) + CO(g)$

    Check:

	left side	right side
	2 Cu atoms	2 Cu atoms
	1 O atom	1 O atom
	1 C atom	1 C atom

    (d)   **Conceptual Plan: balance atoms in more complex compounds → balance elements that occur as free elements → clear fractions**

Solution:	Skeletal reaction:	$H_2(g) + Cl_2(g) \rightarrow HCl(g)$
	Balance Cl:	$H_2(g) + Cl_2(g) \rightarrow 2HCl(g)$
Check:		left side right side
		2 H atoms 2 H atoms
		2 Cl atoms 2 Cl atoms

Organic Compounds

3.103   (a)   composed of metal cation and polyatomic anion – inorganic compound

        (b)   composed of carbon and hydrogen – organic compound

        (c)   composed of carbon, hydrogen, and oxygen – organic compound

        (d)   composed of metal cation and nonmetal anion – inorganic compound

3.105   (a)   contains a double bond – alkene

        (b)   contains only single bonds – alkane

        (c)   contains triple bond – alkyne

        (d)   contains only single bonds – alkane

3.107   (a)   prop = 3 C, ane = single bonds: $CH_3CH_2CH_3$

        (b)   3 C = prop, single bonds = ane: propane

        (c)   oct = 8 C, ane = single bonds: $CH_3CH_2CH_2CH_2CH_2CH_2CH_2CH_3$

        (d)   5 C = pent, single bonds = ane: pentane

3.109   (a)   contains O: functionalized hydrocarbon: alcohol

        (b)   contains only C and H: hydrocarbon

        (c)   contains O: functionalized hydrocarbon: ketone

        (d)   contains N: functionalized hydrocarbon: amine

Cumulative Problems

3.111   **Given:** 145 mL C_2H_5OH, d = 0.789g/cm^3 **Find:** number of molecules

    Conceptual Plan: cm^3 → mL: mL C_2H_5OH → g C_2H_5OH → mol C_2 $_5$ → $_2H_5OH$

$$\frac{1 \text{ cm}^3}{1 \text{ mL}} \qquad \frac{1 \text{ mL } C_2H_5OH}{0.789 \text{ g } C_2H_5OH} \qquad \frac{1 \text{ mol } C_2H_5OH}{46.07 \text{ g } C_2H_5OH} \qquad \frac{6.022 \times 10^{23} \text{ molecules } C_2H_5OH}{1 \text{ mol } C_2H_5OH}$$

    Solution:

$$145 \text{ mL } C_2H_5OH \times \frac{0.789 \text{ g } C_2H_5OH}{\text{cm}^3} \times \frac{1 \text{ cm}^3}{1 \text{ mL}} \times \frac{1 \text{ mol } C_2H_5OH}{46.07 \text{ g } C_2H_5OH} \times \frac{6.022 \times 10^{23} \text{ molecules } C_2H_5OH}{1 \text{ mol } C_2H_5OH}$$

$$= 1.50 \times 10^{24} \text{ molecules } C_2H_5OH$$

    Check: The units of the answer (molecules C_2H_5OH) are correct. The magnitude is reasonable because we had more than 2 moles of C_2H_5OH and we have more than 2 times Avogadro's number of molecules.

3.113   (a)   To write the formula for an ionic compound do the following: 1) Write the symbol for the metal cation and its charge and the symbol for the nonmetal anion or polyatomic anion and its charge. 2) Adjust the subscript on each cation and anion to balance the overall charge. 3) Check that the sum of the charges of the cations equals the sum of the charges of the anions.
           potassium chromate: K^+ $CrO_4{}^{2-}$; K_2CrO_4 cation 2(1+) = 2+; anion 2–

Given: K_2CrO_4 **Find:** mass percent of each element

Conceptual Plan: %K, then %Cr, then %O

$$\text{mass \%K} = \frac{2 \times \text{molar mass K}}{\text{molar mass } K_2CrO_4} \times 100 \quad \text{mass \%Cr} = \frac{1 \times \text{molar mass Cr}}{\text{molar mass } K_2CrO_4} \times 100 \quad \text{mass \%O} = \frac{4 \times \text{molar mass O}}{\text{molar mass } K_2CrO_4} \times 100$$

molar mass of K = 39.10 g/mol, molar mass Cr = 52.00 g/mol, molar mass O = 16.00 g/mol

Solution: molar mass K_2CrO_4 = 2(39.10 g/mol) + 1(52.00 g/mol) + 4(16.00 g/mol) = 194.20 g/mol

$2 \times$ molar mass K = 2(39.10 g/mol) = 78.20 g K $\qquad$ $1 \times$ molar mass Cr = 1(52.00 g/mol) = 52.00 g Cr

$$\text{mass \% K} = \frac{2 \times \text{molar mass K}}{\text{molar mass } K_2CrO_4} \times 100\% \qquad\qquad \text{mass \% Cr} = \frac{1 \times \text{molar mass Cr}}{\text{molar mass } K_2CrO_4} \times 100\%$$

$$= \frac{78.20 \text{ g/mol}}{194.20 \text{ g/mol}} \times 100\% \qquad\qquad\qquad\qquad = \frac{52.00 \text{ g/mol}}{194.20 \text{ g/mol}} \times 100\%$$

$$= 40.27\% \qquad\qquad\qquad\qquad\qquad\qquad\qquad = 26.78\%$$

$4 \times$ molar mass O = 4(16.00 g/mol) = 64.00 g O

$$\text{mass \% O} = \frac{4 \times \text{molar mass O}}{\text{molar mass } K_2CrO_4} \times 100\%$$

$$= \frac{64.00 \text{ g/mol}}{194.20 \text{ g/mol}} \times 100\%$$

$$= 32.96\%$$

Check: The units of the answer (%) are correct. The magnitude is reasonable because each is between 0 and 100% and the total is 100%.

(b) To write the formula for an ionic compound do the following: 1) Write the symbol for the metal cation and its charge and the symbol for the nonmetal anion or polyatomic anion and its charge. 2) Adjust the subscript on each cation and anion to balance the overall charge. 3) Check that the sum of the charges of the cations equals the sum of the charges of the anions.

Lead(II)phosphate: Pb^{2+} PO_4^{3-}; $Pb_3(PO_4)_2$ $\qquad$ cation 3(2+) = 6+; anion 2(3−) = 6−

Given: $Pb_3(PO_4)_2$ **Find:** mass percent of each element

Conceptual Plan: %Pb, then % P, then %O

$$\text{mass \%PB} = \frac{3 \times \text{molar mass Pb}}{\text{molar mass } Pb_3(PO_4)_2} \times 100 \quad \text{mass \%P} = \frac{2 \times \text{molar mass P}}{\text{molar mass } Pb_3(PO_4)_2} \times 100 \quad \text{mass \%O} = \frac{8 \times \text{molar mass O}}{\text{molar mass } Pb_3(PO_4)_2} \times 100$$

Solution: molar mass $Pb_3(PO_4)_2$ = 3(207.2 g/mol) + 2(30.97 g/mol) + 8(16.00 g/mol) = 811.5 g/mol

$3 \times$ molar mass Pb = 3(207.2 g/mol) = 621.6 g Pb $\qquad$ $2 \times$ molar mass P = 2(30.97 g/mol) = 61.94 g P

$$\text{mass \% Pb} \quad \frac{3 \times \text{molar mass Pb}}{\text{molar mass } Pb_3(PO_4)_2} \times 100\% \qquad\qquad \text{mass \% P} = \frac{2 \times \text{molar mass P}}{\text{molar mass } Pb_3(PO_4)_2} \times 100\%$$

$$= \frac{621.6 \text{ g/mol}}{811.5 \text{ g/mol}} \times 100\% \qquad\qquad\qquad\qquad = \frac{61.94 \text{ g/mol}}{811.5 \text{ g/mol}} \times 100\%$$

$$= 76.60\% \qquad\qquad\qquad\qquad\qquad\qquad\qquad = 7.632\%$$

$4 \times$ molar mass O = 8(16.00 g/mol) = 128.0 g O

$$\text{mass \% O} = \frac{8 \times \text{molar mass O}}{\text{molar mass } Pb_3(PO_4)_2} \times 100\%$$

$$= \frac{128.0 \text{ g/mol}}{811.5 \text{ g/mol}} \times 100\%$$

$$= 15.77\%$$

Check: The units of the answer (%) are correct. The magnitude is reasonable because each is between 0 and 100% and the total is 100%.

(c) sulfurous acid: H_2SO_3

Given: H_2SO_3 **Find:** mass percent of each element

Conceptual Plan: %H, then %S, then %O

$$\text{mass \%H} = \frac{2 \times \text{molar mass H}}{\text{molar mass } H_2SO_3} \times 100 \quad \text{mass \%S} = \frac{1 \times \text{molar mass S}}{\text{molar mass } H_2SO_3} \times 100 \quad \text{mass \%O} = \frac{3 \times \text{molar mass O}}{\text{molar mass } H_2SO_3} \times 100$$

Solution: molar mass H_2SO_3 = 2(1.008 g/mol) + 1(32.07 g/mol) + 3(16.00 g/mol) = 82.0$\underline{8}$6 g/mol

2 x molar mass H = 1(1.008 g/mol) = 2.016 g H   1 x molar mass S = 1(32.07 g/mol) = 32.07 g S

$$\text{mass \%H} = \frac{2 \times \text{molar mass H}}{\text{molar mass } H_2SO_3} \times 100\%$$
$$= \frac{2.016 \text{ g/mol}}{82.086 \text{ g/mol}} \times 100\%$$
$$= 2.456\%$$

$$\text{mass \% S} = \frac{1 \times \text{molar mass S}}{\text{molar mass } H_2SO_3} \times 100\%$$
$$= \frac{32.07 \text{ g/mol}}{82.086 \text{ g/mol}} \times 100\%$$
$$= 39.07\%$$

3 x molar mass O = 3(16.00 g/mol) = 48.00 g O

$$\text{mass \% O} = \frac{3 \times \text{molar mass O}}{\text{molar mass } H_2SO_3} \times 100\%$$
$$= \frac{48.00 \text{ g/mol}}{82.086 \text{ g/mol}} \times 100\%$$
$$= 58.48\%$$

Check: The units of the answer (%) are correct. The magnitude is reasonable because each is between 0 and 100% and the total is 100%.

(d)   To write the formula for an ionic compound do the following: 1) Write the symbol for the metal cation and its charge and the symbol for the nonmetal anion or polyatomic anion and its charge. 2) Adjust the subscript on each cation and anion to balance the overall charge. 3) Check that the sum of the charges of the cations equals the sum of the charges of the anions.
cobalt(II)bromide: Co^{2+} Br^-; $CoBr_2$ cation 2+ = 2+; anion 2(1–) = 2–

Given: $CoBr_2$ **Find:** mass percent of each element

Conceptual Plan: %Co, then %Br

$$\text{mass \%Co} = \frac{1 \times \text{molar mass Co}}{\text{molar mass } CoBr_2} \times 100 \quad \text{mass \%Br} = \frac{2 \times \text{molar mass Br}}{\text{molar mass } CoBr_2} \times 100$$

Solution: molar mass $CoBr_2$ = (58.93 g/mol) + 2(79.90 g/mol) = 218.73 g/mol

2 x molar mass Co = 1(58.93 g/mol) = 58.93 g Co 1 x molar mass Br = 2(79.90 g/mol) = 159.80 g Br

$$\text{mass \% Co} = \frac{1 \times \text{molar mass Co}}{\text{molar mass } CoBr_2} \times 100\%$$
$$= \frac{58.93 \text{ g/mol}}{218.73 \text{ g/mol}} \times 100\%$$
$$= 26.94\%$$

$$\text{mass \% Br} = \frac{2 \times \text{molar mass Br}}{\text{molar mass } CoBr_2} \times 100\%$$
$$= \frac{159.80 \text{ g/mol}}{218.73 \text{ g/mol}} \times 100\%$$
$$= 73.058\%$$

Check: The units of the answer (%) are correct. The magnitude is reasonable because each is between 0 and 100% and the total is 100%.

3.115   **Given:** 25 g CF_2Cl_2/mo. **Find:** g Cl /yr.

Conceptual Plan: g CF_2Cl_2/mo $\rightarrow$ g Cl/mo $\rightarrow$ g Cl/yr.

$$\frac{70.90 \text{ g Cl}}{120.91 \text{ g } CF_2Cl_2} \qquad \frac{12 \text{ mo.}}{1 \text{ yr.}}$$

Solution: $\dfrac{25 \text{ g } CF_2Cl_2}{\text{mo.}} \times \dfrac{70.90 \text{ g Cl}}{120.91 \text{ g } CF_2Cl_2} \times \dfrac{12 \text{ mo.}}{1 \text{ yr.}} = 1.8 \times 10^2$ g Cl/yr.

Check: The units of the answer (g Cl) is correct. Magnitude is reasonable because it is less than the total CF_2Cl_2 /yr.

3.117   **Given:** MCl_3, 65.57% Cl **Find:** identify M

Conceptual Plan: g Cl $\rightarrow$ mol Cl $\rightarrow$ mol M $\rightarrow$ atomic mass M

$$\frac{1 \text{ mol Cl}}{35.45 \text{ g Cl}} \qquad \frac{1 \text{ mol M}}{3 \text{ mol Cl}} \qquad \frac{g \text{ M}}{\text{mol M}}$$

Solution: in 100 g sample: 65.57 g Cl, 34.43 g M

$$65.57 \text{ g Cl} \times \frac{1 \text{ mol Cl}}{35.45 \text{ g Cl}} \times \frac{1 \text{ mol M}}{3 \text{ mol Cl}} = 0.6165 \text{ mol M} \qquad \frac{34.43 \text{ g M}}{0.6165 \text{ mol M}} = 55.84 \text{ g/mol M}$$

molar mass of 55.84 = Fe
The identity of M = Fe.

3.119   **Given:** In a 100 g sample: 79.37 g C, 8.88 g H, 11.75 g O, molar mass = 272.37g/mol
Find: molecular formula
Conceptual Plan:
convert mass to mol of each element → pseudoformula → empirical formula → molecular formula

$$\frac{1 \text{ mol C}}{12.01 \text{ g C}} \qquad \frac{1 \text{ mol H}}{1.008 \text{ g H}} \qquad \frac{1 \text{ mol O}}{16.00 \text{ g O}}$$

divide by smallest number   empirical formula x n

Solution: $79.37 \text{ g C} \times \dfrac{1 \text{ mol C}}{12.01 \text{ g C}} = 6.609 \text{ mol C}$

$8.88 \text{ g H} \times \dfrac{1 \text{ mol H}}{1.008 \text{ g H}} = 8.81 \text{ mol H}$

$11.75 \text{ g O} \times \dfrac{1 \text{ mol O}}{16.00 \text{ g O}} = 0.7344 \text{ mol O}$

$C_{6.609}H_{8.81}O_{0.7344}$

$C_{\frac{6.609}{0.7344}} H_{\frac{8.81}{0.7344}} O_{\frac{0.7344}{0.7344}} \rightarrow C_9H_{12}O$

The correct empirical formula is $C_9H_{12}O$.

empirical formula mass = 9(12.01 g/mol) + 12(1.008 g/mol) + 1(16.00 g/mol) = 136.19 g/mol

$$n = \frac{\text{molar mass}}{\text{formula molar mass}} = \frac{272.37 \text{ g/mol}}{136.19 \text{ g/mol}} = 2$$

molecular formula $= C_9H_{12}O \times 2 = C_{18}H_{24}O_2$

3.121   **Given:** 13.42 g sample, 39.61 g CO_2, 9.01 g H_2O, molar mass = 268.34 g/mol
Find: molecular formula
Conceptual Plan:
mass CO_2, H_2O → mol CO_2, H_2O → mol C, mol H → mass C, mass H, mass O → mol O →

$$\frac{1 \text{ mol CO}_2}{44.01 \text{ g CO}_2} \quad \frac{1 \text{ mol H}_2O}{18.02 \text{ g H}_2O} \quad \frac{1 \text{ mol C}}{1 \text{ mol CO}_2} \quad \frac{2 \text{ mol H}}{1 \text{ mol H}_2O} \quad \frac{12.01 \text{ g C}}{1 \text{ mol C}} \quad \frac{1.008 \text{ g H}}{1 \text{ mol H}} \quad \text{g sample} - \text{gC} - \text{g H} \quad \frac{1 \text{ mol O}}{16.00 \text{ g O}}$$

pseudoformula → empirical formula → molecular formula

divide by smallest number   empirical formula x n

$39.61 \text{ g CO}_2 \times \dfrac{1 \text{ mol CO}_2}{44.01 \text{ g CO}_2} = 0.9000 \text{ mol CO}_2$

$9.01 \text{ g H}_2O \times \dfrac{1 \text{ mol H}_2O}{18.02 \text{ g H}_2O} = 0.5000 \text{ mol H}_2O$

$0.9000 \text{ mol CO}_2 \times \dfrac{1 \text{ mol C}}{1 \text{ mol CO}_2} = 0.9000 \text{ mol C}$

$0.5000 \text{ mol H}_2O \times \dfrac{2 \text{ mol H}}{1 \text{ mol H}_2O} = 1.000 \text{ mol H}$

$0.9000 \text{ mol C} \times \dfrac{12.01 \text{ g C}}{1 \text{ mol C}} = 10.81 \text{ g C}$

$1.000 \text{ mol H}_2O \times \dfrac{1.008 \text{ g H}}{1 \text{ mol H}} = 1.008 \text{ g H}$

$13.42 \text{ g} - 10.81 \text{ g} - 1.008 \text{ g} = 1.60 \text{ g O}$

$1.60 \text{ g O} \times \dfrac{1 \text{ mol O}}{16.00 \text{ g O}} = 0.100 \text{ mol O}$

$C_{0.9000}H_{1.000}O_{0.100}$

$C_{\frac{0.9000}{0.100}} H_{\frac{1.000}{0.100}} O_{\frac{0.100}{0.100}} \rightarrow C_9H_{10}O$

The correct empirical formula is $C_9H_{10}O$.

empirical formula mass = 9(12.01 g/mol) + 10(1.008 g/mol) + 1(16.00 g/mol) = 134.2 g/mol

$$n = \frac{\text{molar mass}}{\text{formula molar mass}} = \frac{268.34 \text{ g/mol}}{134.2 \text{ g/mol}} = 2$$

molecular formula $= C_9H_{10}O \times 2 = C_{18}H_{20}O_2$

3.123 **Given:** 4.93 g $MgSO_4 \cdot xH_2O$, 2.41 g $MgSO_4$ **Find:** value of x
Conceptual Plan: g $MgSO_4$ → mol $MgSO_4$ g H_2O → mol H_2O Determine mole ratio

$$\frac{1 \text{ mol } MgSO_4}{120.38 \text{ g } MgSO} \qquad \frac{1 \text{ mol } H_2O}{18.02 \text{ g } H_2O} \qquad \frac{\text{mol } HO_2}{\text{mol } MgSO_4}$$

Solution:

$$2.41 \ \overline{\text{g } MgSO_4} \times \frac{1 \text{ mol } MgSO_4}{120.38 \ \overline{\text{g } MgSO_4}} = 0.0200 \text{ mol } MgSO_4$$

Determine g H_2O: 4.93 g $MgSO_4 \cdot xH_2O$ – 2.41 g $MgSO_4$ = 2.52 g H_2O

$$2.52 \ \overline{\text{g } H_2O} \times \frac{1 \text{ mol } H_2O}{18.02 \ \overline{\text{g } H_2O}} = 0.140 \text{ mol } H_2O$$

$$\frac{0.140 \text{ mol } H_2O}{0.0200 \text{ mol } MgSO_4} = 7$$

x = 7

3.125 **Given:** molar mass = 177 g/mol, g C = 8(g H) **Find:** molecular formula
Conceptual Plan: C_xH_yBrO
Solution: in 1 mol compound, let x = mol C and y = mol H, assume mol Br = 1, assume mol O = 1

177 g/mol = x(12.01 g/mol) + y(1.008 g/mol) + 1(79.90 g/mol) + 1(16.00 g/mol)

x(12.01 g/mol) = 8 {y(1.008 g/mol)}

177 g/mol = 8y(1.008 g/mol) + y(1.008 g/mol) + 79.90 g/mol + 16.00 g/mol

81 = 9y(1.008)

y = 9 = mol H

x(12.01) = 8 x 9(1.008)

x = 6 = mol C

molecular formula = C_6H_9BrO

Check: molar mass = 6(12.01 g/mol) + 9(1.008 g/mol) + 1(79.90 g/mol) + 1(16.00 g/mol) = 177.0 g/mol

3.127 **Given:** 23.5 mg $C_{17}H_{22}ClNO_4$ **Find:** total number of atoms
Conceptual Plan: mg compound → g compound → mol compound → mol atoms → number of atoms

$$\frac{1 \text{ g}}{1000 \text{ mg}} \qquad \frac{1 \text{ mol}}{339.8 \text{ g}} \qquad \frac{45 \text{ mol atoms}}{1 \text{ mol compound}} \qquad \frac{6.022 \times 10^{23} \text{ atoms}}{1 \text{ mol atoms}}$$

Solution: $23.5 \ \overline{\text{mg}} \times \dfrac{1 \ \overline{\text{g}}}{1000 \ \overline{\text{mg}}} \times \dfrac{1 \ \overline{\text{mol cpd}}}{339.8 \ \overline{\text{g}}} \times \dfrac{45 \ \overline{\text{mol atoms}}}{1 \ \overline{\text{mol cpd}}} \times \dfrac{6.022 \times 10^{23} \text{ atoms}}{\overline{\text{mol}}} = 1.87 \times 10^{21}$ atoms

Check: The units of the answer (number of atoms) is correct. The magnitude of the answer is reasonable since the molecule is so complex.

3.129 **Given:** MCl_3, 2.395 g sample, 3.606×10^{-2} mol Cl **Find:** atomic mass M
Conceptual Plan: mol Cl → g Cl → g X

$$\frac{35.45 \text{ g Cl}}{1 \text{ mol Cl}} \quad \text{g sample} - \text{g Cl} = \text{g M}$$

mol Cl → mol M → atomic mass M

$$\frac{1 \text{ mol M}}{3 \text{ mol Cl}} \qquad \frac{\text{g M}}{\text{mol M}}$$

Solution:

$$3.606 \times 10^{-2} \ \overline{\text{mol Cl}} \times \frac{35.45 \text{ g}}{1 \ \overline{\text{mol Cl}}} = 1.278 \text{ g Cl}$$

$$2.395 \text{ g} \ - \ 1.278 \text{ g} = 1.117 \text{ g M}$$

$$3.606 \times 10^{-2} \ \overline{\text{mol Cl}} \times \frac{1 \text{ mol M}}{3 \ \overline{\text{mol Cl}}} = 1.202 \times 10^{-2} \text{ mol M}$$

$$\frac{1.117 \text{ g M}}{0.01202 \text{ mol M}} = 92.93 \text{ g/mol M}$$

molar mass of M = 92.93 g/mol

3.131   **Given:** $Fe_xCr_yO_4$; 28.59% O   **Find:** x and y
         Conceptual Plan: %O → molar mass $Fe_xCr_yO_4$ → mass Fe + Cr

$$\frac{\text{mass O}}{\text{molar mass compound}} \times 100 = \%O \qquad \text{mass cpd – mass O = mass Fe+Cr}$$

Solution: $\dfrac{28.59 \text{ g O}}{100.0} = \dfrac{64.00 \text{ g O}}{\text{molar mass cpd}}$ molar mass = 223.8 g/mol

Mass Fe + Cr = molar mass – (4x molar mass O) = 223.8 – 64.00 = 159.8 g
Molar mass Fe = 55.85, molar mass Cr = 52.00
Since the mass of the two metals is close, the average mass can be used to determine the total moles of
Fe and Cr present in the compound. Average mass of Fe and Cr = 53.5. $\dfrac{159.8\text{g}}{53.5\text{g/mol}} = 2.96 = 3$ mol metal.

Let x = mol Fe and y = mol Cr
x mol Fe + y mol Cr = 3 mol total
x mol Fe(55.85 g Fe/mol) + y mol Cr(52.00 g/ mol) = 159.8
y mol Cr = 3 – x mol Fe
x(55.85) + (3-x)(52.00) = 159.8
So x = 1 and y = 2.

Check: Formula = $FeCr_2O_4$ would have a molar mass of Fe + 2Cr + 4O = 55.85 + 2(52.00) + 4(16.00) = 223.85 and the molar mass of the compound is 223.8.

3.133   **Given:** 0.0552% $NaNO_2$; 8.00 oz bag   **Find:** mass Na in bag
         Conceptual Plan: oz. bag → g bag → g NaNO2 → g Na

$$\frac{453.6 \text{ g}}{16.00 \text{ oz}} \quad \frac{0.0552 \text{ g NaNO}_2}{100.0 \text{ g bag}} \quad \frac{22.99 \text{ g Na}}{69.00 \text{ g NaNO}_2}$$

Solution: $8 \, \overline{\text{oz bag}} \times \dfrac{453.6 \, \overline{\text{g bag}}}{16.00 \, \overline{\text{oz bag}}} \times \dfrac{0.0552 \, \overline{\text{g NaNO}_2}}{100.0 \, \overline{\text{g bag}}} \times \dfrac{22.99 \, \overline{\text{g Na}}}{69.00 \, \overline{\text{g NaNO}_2}} \times \dfrac{1000 \text{ mg Na}}{\overline{\text{g Na}}} = 41.7 \text{ mg Na}$

Check: The units of the answer (mg Na) are correct. The magnitude of the answer is reasonable because only a small % of the total mass is Na.

Challenge Problems

3.135   **Given:** g NaCl + g NaBr = 2.00 g, g Na = 0.75 g   **Find:** g NaBr
         Conceptual Plan:
         Let x = mol NaCl, y = mol NaBr, then x(molar mass NaCl) = g NaCl, y(molar mass NaBr) = g NaBr
         Solution: x(58.4) + y(102.9) = 2.00
                          x(23.0) + y(23.0) = 0.75   y = 0.0326 –x
                          58.4x + 102.9(0.0326-x) = 2.00
                          58.4x + 3.354 – 102.9x = 2.00
                          44.5x   = 1.354
                              x   = 0.03043 mol NaCl
                              y   = 0.0326 – 0.03043 = 0.00217 mol NaBr
                          g NaBr = (0.00217)(102.9g/mol) = 0.223 g NaBr

Check: The units of the answer (g NaBr) are correct. The magnitude is reasonable since it is less than the total mass.

3.137   **Given:** Sample of $CaCO_3$ and $(NH_4)_2CO_3$ is 61.9% CO_3^{2-} **Find:** % $CaCO_3$
         Conceptual Plan: Let x = $CaCO_3$, y = $(NH_4)_2CO_3$, then x(molar mass $CaCO_3$) = g $CaCO_3$,
                 y(molar mass $(NH_4)_2CO_3$) = g $(NH_4)_2CO_3$
                 then, a 100.0 g sample contains: x(100.0) g $CaCO_3$; y(96.1) g $(NH_4)_2CO_3$; and 61.9 g CO_3^{2-}

Solution: $x(100.0) + y(96.1) = 100.0$

$x(60.0) + y(60.0) = 61.9$ $\qquad$ $y = 1.03\underline{1}67 - x$

$100.0x + 96.1(1.032-x) = 100$

$100.0x + 99.14 - 96.1x = 100$

$3.9x \qquad = 0.96$

$x \quad = 0.22 \text{ mol } CaCO_3$

$y \quad = 1.032 - 0.22 = 0.81 \text{ mol } (NH_4)_2CO_3$

$g \ CaCO_3 = (0.22 \text{ mol})(100.0 g/mol) = 22.0 \text{ g } CaCO_3$ in a 100 g sample:

mass % $CaCO_3 = 22.0\%$

Check: The units of the answer (mass % $CaCO_3$) are correct. The magnitude is reasonable since it is between 0 and 100%.

3.139 $\quad$ **Given:** 1.1 kg CF_2Cl_2/automobile, 25% leak/year, 100×10^6 automobiles **Find:** kg Cl/yr

$\quad$ **Conceptual Plan:** $\quad$ kg CF_2Cl_2 /auto $\rightarrow$ kg CF_2Cl_2 leaked/yr $\rightarrow$ kg Cl/yr/auto $\rightarrow$ kg Cl

$$\frac{25 \text{ kg } CF_2Cl_2}{100 \text{ kg } CF_2Cl_2} \qquad \frac{70.9 \text{ g Cl}}{120.91 \text{ g } CF_2Cl_2} \qquad 100 \times 10^6 \text{ auto}$$

$\quad$ **Solution:** $\dfrac{\cancel{Cl_2}}{\cancel{auto}} \times \dfrac{25 \text{ kg } \cancel{CF_2Cl_2}}{100 \text{ kg } \cancel{CF_2Cl_2}} \times \dfrac{70.9 \text{ kg Cl}}{120.91 \text{ kg } \cancel{CF_2Cl_2}} \times 100 \times 10^6 \cancel{auto} = 1.6 \times 10^7 \text{ kg Cl/yr}$

$\quad$ **Check:** The units of the answer (kg Cl) are correct. The magnitude is reasonable because it is less than the kg CF_2Cl_2 leaked per year.

3.141 $\quad$ **Given:** rock contains: 38.0% PbS, 25.0% $PbCO_3$, 17.4% $PbSO_4$ **Find:** kg rock needed for 5.0 metric ton Pb

$\quad$ **Conceptual Plan: determine kg Pb/ 100 kg rock then ton Pb $\rightarrow$ kg Pb $\rightarrow$ kg rock**

$$\frac{1000 \text{ kg}}{\text{metric ton}} \quad \frac{100 \text{ kg rock}}{64.2 \text{ kg rock}}$$

$\quad$ **Solution:** in 100 kg rock:

$(38.0 \text{ kg } \cancel{PbS} \times \dfrac{207.2 \text{ kg Pb}}{239.3 \text{ kg } \cancel{PbS}}) + (25.0 \text{ kg } \cancel{PbCO_3} \times \dfrac{207.2 \text{ kg Pb}}{267.2 \text{ kg } \cancel{PbCO_3}}) + (17.4 \text{ kg } \cancel{PbSO_4} \times \dfrac{207.2 \text{ kg Pb}}{303.1 \text{ kg } \cancel{PbSO_4}})$

$= 64.2 \text{ kg Pb}$

$5.0 \cancel{\text{metric ton Pb}} \times \dfrac{1000 \text{ kg } \cancel{Pb}}{\cancel{\text{metric ton Pb}}} \times \dfrac{100 \text{ kg rock}}{64.2 \text{ kg } \cancel{Pb}} = 7.8 \times 10^3 \text{ kg rock}$

$\quad$ **Check:** The units of the answer (kg rock) are correct. Magnitude is reasonable since it is greater than the amount of Pb needed.

3.143 $\quad$ **Given:** molar mass = 229 g/mol, 6 times mass C as H, **Find:** molecular formula

$\quad$ **Conceptual Plan: Let x = mass of C, then 6x = mass of C**

$\quad$ **Solution:** in 1 mol of the compound: $g \ C + g \ H + g \ S + g \ I = 229 \ g$

$\qquad$ Since the molar mass of I = 127, there can not be more than 1 mol of I in the compound, so

$\qquad$ $x + 6x + g \ S + 127 = 229$

$\qquad$ $x + 6x + g \ S = 102$

$\qquad$ If the compound contains 1 mol S, then $7x = 102 - 32 = 70$ and x = 10 g H and 6x = 60 g C

$\qquad$ $10 \ \cancel{g \ H} \times \dfrac{1 \text{ mol H}}{1.0 \ \cancel{g \ H}} = 10 \text{ mol H}$

$\qquad$ $60 \ \cancel{g \ C} \times \dfrac{1 \text{ mol C}}{12 \ \cancel{g \ C}} = 5 \text{ mol C}$

$\qquad$ 1 mol I and 1 mol S, so empirical formula is $C_5H_{10}SI$

$\quad$ **Check:** Molar mass of $C_5H_{10}SI = 5(12) + 10(1.0) + 32 + 127 = 229$ g/mol which is the mass given.

3.145   **Given:** Compound is 1/3 X by mass, atomic mass X is 3/4 atomic mass Y **Find:** empirical formula

Conceptual Plan: mass X and Y $\rightarrow$ mass ratio X:Y and then g X $\rightarrow$ mol X and g Y $\rightarrow$ mol Y and then

$$\frac{g\,X}{\text{atomic mass X}} \qquad \frac{g\,Y}{\text{atomic mass Y}}$$

mole ratio

Solution: $\dfrac{\text{mass X}}{\text{mass Y}} = \dfrac{\frac{1}{3}}{\frac{2}{3}} = \dfrac{1}{2}$ $\text{mol X} = \dfrac{1\,g}{\text{atomic mass X}}$ and $\text{mol Y} = \dfrac{2\,g}{\text{atomic mass Y}}$

But atomic mass X = 3/4 atomic mass Y so:

$$\text{mol X} = \frac{1\,g}{3/4(\text{atomic mass Y})} \text{ and } \text{mol Y} = \frac{2\,g}{\text{atomic mass Y}}$$

$$\frac{\text{mol X}}{\text{mol Y}} = \frac{\dfrac{1\,\cancel{g}}{3/4(\cancel{\text{atomic mass Y}})}}{\dfrac{2\,\cancel{g}}{\cancel{\text{atomic mass Y}}}} = \frac{2}{3} \qquad \text{Empirical Formula} = X_2Y_3$$

Conceptual Problems

3.147   The sphere in the molecular models represents the electron cloud of the atom. On this scale, the nucleus would be too small to see.

3.149   The statement is incorrect because a chemical formula is based on the ratio of atoms combined, not the ratio of grams combined. The statement should read the following: The chemical formula for ammonia (NH_3) indicates that ammonia contains three hydrogen atoms to each nitrogen atom.

3.151 H_2SO_4: Atomic mass S is approximately twice atomic mass O, both are much greater than atomic mass H. The order of % mass is % O > % S > % H.

4 Chemical Quantities and Aqueous Reactions

Review Questions

4.1 Reaction stoichiometry is the numerical relationships between chemical amounts in a balanced chemical equation. The coefficients in a chemical reaction specify the relative amounts in moles of each of the substances involved in the reaction.

4.3 No, the percent yield would not be different if the actual yield and theoretical yield were calculated in moles. The relationship between grams and moles is the molar mass. This would be the same value for the actual yield and the theoretical yield.

4.5 Molarity is a concentration term. It is the amount of solute (in moles) divided by the volume of solution (in liters). The molarity of a solution can be used as a conversion factor between moles of the solute and liters of the solution.

4.7 Acids are molecular compounds that ionize—form ions—when they dissolve in water. A strong acid is one that completely ionizes in solution. A weak acid is one that does not completely ionize in water. A solution of a weak acid is composed mostly of the non-ionized acid.

4.9 The solubility rules are a set of empirical rules that have been inferred from observations on many ionic compounds. The solubility rules allow us to predict if a compound is soluble or insoluble.

4.11 A precipitation reaction is one in which a solid or precipitate forms upon mixing two solutions. An example is $2 \, KI(aq) + Pb(NO_3)_2(aq) \rightarrow PbI_2(s) + 2 \, KNO_3(aq)$.

4.13 A molecular equation is an equation showing the complete neutral formulas for each compound in the reaction as if they existed as molecules. Equations that list individually all of the ions present as either reactants or products in a chemical reaction are complete ionic equation. Equations that show only the species that actually change during the reaction are net ionic equations.

4.15 When an acid and base are mixed, the $H^+(aq)$ from the acid combines with the OH^- from the base to form $H_2O(l)$. An example is $HCl(aq) + NaOH(aq) \rightarrow H_2O(l) + NaCl(aq)$.

4.17 Aqueous reactions that form a gas upon mixing two solutions are called gas-evolution reactions. An example is $H_2SO_4(aq) + Li_2S(aq) \rightarrow H_2S(g) + Li_2SO_4(aq)$.

4.19 Oxidation–reduction reactions or redox reactions are reactions in which electrons are transferred from one reactant to the other. An example is $4 \, Fe(s) + 3 \, O_2(g) \rightarrow 2 \, Fe_2O_3(s$

4.21 To identify redox reactions by using oxidation states, begin by assigning oxidation states to each atom in the reaction. A change in oxidation state for the atoms indicates a redox reaction.

4.23 A substance that causes the oxidation of another substance is called an oxidizing agent. A substance that causes the reduction of another substance is called a reducing agent.

Reaction Stoichiometry

4.25   **Given:** 7.2 moles C_6H_{14} **Find:** balanced reaction, moles O_2 required
Conceptual Plan: balance the equation then mol C_6H_{14} $\rightarrow$ mol O_2

$2\,C_6H_{14}(g) + 19\,O_2(g) \rightarrow 12\,CO_2(g) + 14\,H_2O(g)$ $\dfrac{19\text{ mol }O_2}{2\text{ mol }C_6H_{14}}$

Solution: $7.2\ \overline{mol\,C_6H_{14}} \times \dfrac{19\text{ mol }O_2}{2\ \overline{mol\,C_6H_{14}}} = 68.4\text{ mol }O_2 = 68\text{ mol }O_2$

Check: The units of the answer (mol O_2) are correct. The magnitude is reasonable because much more O_2 is needed than C_6H_{14}.

4.27   (a)   **Given:** 2.5 mol N_2O_5 **Find:** mol NO_2
Conceptual Plan: mol N_2O_5 $\rightarrow$ mol NO_2

$\dfrac{4\,NO_2}{2\,N_2O_5}$

Solution: $2.5\ \overline{mol\,N_2O_5} \times \dfrac{4\ \text{mol }NO_2}{2\ \overline{mol\,N_2O_5}} = 5.0\text{ mol }NO_2$

The units of the answer (mol NO_2) are correct. The magnitude is reasonable since it is greater than mol N_2O_5.

(b)   **Given:** 6.8 mol N_2O_5 **Find:** mol NO_2
Conceptual Plan: mol N_2O_5 $\rightarrow$ mol NO_2

$\dfrac{4\,NO_2}{2\,N_2O_5}$

Solution: $6.8\ \overline{mol\,N_2O_5} \times \dfrac{4\ \text{mol }NO_2}{2\ \overline{mol\,N_2O_5}} = 13.6\text{ mol }NO_2 = 14\text{ mol }NO_2$

Check: The units of the answer (mol NO_2) are correct. The magnitude is reasonable since it is greater than mol N_2O_5.

(c)   **Given:** 15.2 g N_2O_5 **Find:** mol NO_2
Conceptual Plan: g N_2O_5 $\rightarrow$ mol N_2O_5 $\rightarrow$ mol NO_2

$\dfrac{1\text{ mol }N_2O_5}{108.02\text{ g }N_2O_5}$ $\dfrac{4\,NO_2}{2\,N_2O_5}$

Solution: $15.2\ \overline{g\,N_2O_5} \times \dfrac{1\ \overline{mol\,N_2O_5}}{108.02\ \overline{g\,N_2O_5}} \times \dfrac{4\ \text{mol }NO_2}{2\ \overline{mol\,N_2O_5}} = 0.2814\text{ mol }NO_2 = 0.281\text{ mol }NO_2$

Check: The units of the answer (mol NO_2) are correct. The magnitude is reasonable since 15 g is about 0.13 mol N_2O_5 and the answer is greater than mol N_2O_5.

(d)   **Given:** 2.87 kg N_2O_5 **Find:** mol NO_2
Conceptual Plan: kg N_2O_5 $\rightarrow$ g N_2O_5 $\rightarrow$ mol N_2O_5 $\rightarrow$ mol NO_2

$\dfrac{1000\text{ g }N_2O_5}{\text{kg }N_2O_5}$ $\dfrac{1\text{ mol }N_2O_5}{108.02\text{ g }N_2O_5}$ $\dfrac{4\,NO}{2\,N_2O_5}$

Solution:

$2.87\ \overline{kg\,N_2O_5} \times \dfrac{1000\ \overline{g\,N_2O_5}}{\overline{kg\,N_2O_5}} \times \dfrac{1\ \overline{mol\,N_2O_5}}{108.02\ \overline{g\,N_2O_5}} \times \dfrac{4\ \text{mol }NO_2}{2\ \overline{mol\,N_2O_5}} = 53.14\text{ mol }NO_2 = 53.1\text{ mol }NO_2$

Check: The units of the answer (mol NO_2) are correct. The magnitude is reasonable since 2.87 kg is about 27 mol N_2O_5 and the answer is greater than mol N_2O_5.

4.29   **Given:** 3 mol SiO_2 **Find:** mol C, mol SiC, mol CO
Conceptual Plan: mol SiO_2 $\rightarrow$ $\rightarrow$ $\rightarrow$

$\dfrac{3\,C}{SiO_2}$ $\dfrac{SiC}{SiO_2}$ $\dfrac{2\,CO}{SiO_2}$

Solution: $3\ \overline{mol\,SiO_2} \times \dfrac{3\text{ mol }C}{\overline{mol\,SiO_2}} = 9\text{ mol }C$ $3\ \overline{mol\,SiO_2} \times \dfrac{\text{mol }SiC}{\overline{mol\,SiO_2}} = 3\text{ mol }SiC$

$3\ \overline{mol\,SiO_2} \times \dfrac{2\text{ mol }CO}{\overline{mol\,SiO_2}} = 6\text{ mol }CO$

Given: 6 mol C **Find:** mol SiO_2, mol SiC, mol CO

Conceptual Plan: mol C $\rightarrow$ mol SiO_2 $\rightarrow$ mol SiC $\rightarrow$ mol CO

$$\frac{SiO_2}{3\,C} \qquad \frac{SiC}{3\,C} \qquad \frac{2\,CO}{3\,C}$$

Solution: $6\ \overline{mol\,C} \times \dfrac{mol\ SiO_2}{3\ \overline{mol\,C}} = 2\ mol\ SiO_2 \qquad 6\ \overline{mol\,C} \times \dfrac{mol\ SiC}{3\ \overline{mol\,C}} = 2\ mol\ SiC$

$6\ \overline{mol\,C} \times \dfrac{2\ mol\ CO}{3\ \overline{mol\,C}} \qquad 4\ mol\ CO$

Given: 10 mol CO **Find:** mol SiO_2, mol C, mol SiC

Conceptual Plan: mol CO $\rightarrow$ mol SiO_2 $\rightarrow$ mol C $\rightarrow$ mol SiC

$$\frac{SiO_2}{2\,CO} \qquad \frac{3\,C}{2\,CO} \qquad \frac{SiC}{2\,CO}$$

Solution: $10\ \overline{mol\,CO} \times \dfrac{mol\ SiO_2}{2\ \overline{mol\,CO}} = 5.0\ mol\ SiO_2 \qquad 10\ \overline{mol\,C} \times \dfrac{3\ mol\ C}{2\ \overline{mol\,CO}} = 15\ mol\ C$

$10\ \overline{mol\,CO} \times \dfrac{mol\ SiC}{2\ \overline{mol\,CO}} = 5.0\ mol\ SiC$

Given: 2.8 mol SiO_2 **Find:** mol C, mol SiC, mol CO

Conceptual Plan: $_2$ $\rightarrow$ mol C $\rightarrow$ mol SiC $\rightarrow$ mol CO

$$\frac{3\,C}{SiO_2} \qquad \frac{SiC}{SiO_2} \qquad \frac{2\,CO}{SiO_2}$$

Solution: $2.8\ \overline{mol\,SiO_2} \times \dfrac{3\ mol\ C}{\overline{mol\,SiO_2}} = 8.4\ mol\ C \qquad 2.8\ \overline{mol\,SiO_2} \times \dfrac{mol\ SiC}{\overline{mol\,SiO_2}} = 2.8\ mol\ SiC$

$2.8\ \overline{mol\,SiO_2} \times \dfrac{2\ mol\ CO}{\overline{mol\,SiO_2}} = 5.6\ mol\ CO$

Given: 1.55 mol C **Find:** mol SiO_2, mol SiC, mol CO

Conceptual Plan: mol C $\rightarrow$ mol SiO_2 $\rightarrow$ mol SiC $\rightarrow$ mol CO

$$\frac{SiO_2}{3\,C} \qquad \frac{SiC}{3\,C} \qquad \frac{2\,CO}{3\,C}$$

Solution: $1.55\ \overline{mol\,C} \times \dfrac{1\ mol\ SiO_2}{3\ \overline{mol\,C}} = 0.517\ mol\ SiO_2 \qquad 1.55\ \overline{mol\,C} \times \dfrac{mol\ SiC}{3\ \overline{mol\,C}} = 0.517\ mol\ SiC$

$1.55\ \overline{mol\,C} \times \dfrac{2\ mol\ CO}{3\ \overline{mol\,C}} = 1.03\ mol\ CO$

SiO_2	C	SiC	CO
3	9	3	6
2	**6**	2	4
5.0	15	5.0	**10**
2.8	8.4	2.8	5.6
0.517	**1.55**	0.517	1.03

4.31 **Given:** 3.2 g Fe **Find:** g HBr; g H_2

Conceptual Plan: g Fe $\rightarrow$ mol Fe $\rightarrow$ mol HBr $\rightarrow$ g HBr

$$\frac{mol\ Fe}{55.8\ g\ Fe} \qquad \frac{2\ mol\ HBr}{mol\ Fe} \qquad \frac{80.9\ g\ HBr}{mol\ HBr}$$

g Fe $\rightarrow$ mol Fe $\rightarrow$ mol H_2 $\rightarrow$ g H_2

$$\frac{mol\ Fe}{55.8\ g\ Fe} \qquad \frac{1\ mol\ H_2}{mol\ Fe} \qquad \frac{2.02\ g\ H_2}{mol\ H_2}$$

Solution: $3.2\ \overline{g\,Fe} \times \dfrac{1\ \overline{mol\,Fe}}{55.8\ \overline{g\,Fe}} \times \dfrac{2\ \overline{mol\,HBr}}{1\ \overline{mol\,Fe}} \times \dfrac{80.9\ g\ HBr}{1\ \overline{mol\,HBr}} = 9.3\ g\ HBr$

$3.2\ \overline{g\,Fe} \times \dfrac{1\ \overline{mol\,Fe}}{55.8\ \overline{g\,Fe}} \times \dfrac{1\ \overline{mol\,H_2}}{1\ \overline{mol\,Fe}} \times \dfrac{2.02\ g\ H_2}{1\ \overline{mol\,H_2}} = 0.12\ g\ H_2$

Check: The units of the answers (g HBr, g H_2) are correct. The magnitude of the answers is reasonable because molar mass HBr is greater than Fe and molar mass H_2 is much less than Fe.

4.33   (a)   **Given:** 3.67 g Ba **Find:** g BaCl$_2$
               Conceptual Plan: g Ba → mol Ba → mol BaCl$_2$ → g BaCl$_2$

$$\frac{\text{mol Ba}}{137.33 \text{ g Ba}} \quad \frac{1 \text{ mol BaCl}_2}{1 \text{ mol Ba}} \quad \frac{208.23 \text{ g BaCl}_2}{1 \text{ mol BaCl}_2}$$

Solution: 3.67 g̶ ̶B̶a̶ × $\dfrac{1 \text{ m̶o̶l̶ ̶B̶a̶}}{137.33 \text{ g̶ ̶B̶a̶}}$ × $\dfrac{1 \text{ m̶o̶l̶ ̶B̶a̶C̶l̶}_2}{1 \text{ m̶o̶l̶ ̶B̶a̶}}$ × $\dfrac{208.23 \text{ g BaCl}_2}{1 \text{ m̶o̶l̶ ̶B̶a̶C̶l̶}_2}$ = 5.5647 g BaCl$_2$ = 5.56 g BaCl$_2$

Check: The units of the answer (g BaCl$_2$) are correct. The magnitude of the answer is reasonable because it is larger than grams Ba.

       (b)   **Given:** 3.67 g CaO **Find:** g CaCO$_3$
               Conceptual Plan: g CaO → mol CaO → mol CaCO$_3$ → g CaCO$_3$

$$\frac{\text{mol CaO}}{56.08 \text{ g CaO}} \quad \frac{\text{mol CaCO}_3}{1 \text{ mol CaO}} \quad \frac{100.09 \text{ g CaCO}_3}{\text{mol CaCO}_3}$$

Solution:

3.67 g̶ ̶C̶a̶O̶ × $\dfrac{1 \text{ m̶o̶l̶ ̶C̶a̶O̶}}{56.08 \text{ g̶ ̶C̶a̶O̶}}$ × $\dfrac{1 \text{ m̶o̶l̶ ̶C̶a̶C̶O̶}_3}{1 \text{ m̶o̶l̶ ̶C̶a̶O̶}}$ × $\dfrac{100.09 \text{ g CaCO}_3}{1 \text{ m̶o̶l̶ ̶C̶a̶C̶O̶}_3}$ = 6.550 g CaCO$_3$ = 6.55 g CaCO$_3$

Check: Units of answer (g CaCO$_3$) are correct. The magnitude of the answer is reasonable because it is larger than grams CaO.

       (c)   **Given:** 3.67 g Mg **Find:** g MgO
               Conceptual Plan: g Mg → mol Mg → mol MgO → g MgO

$$\frac{\text{mol Mg}}{24.30 \text{ g Mg}} \quad \frac{\text{mol MgO}}{\text{mol Mg}} \quad \frac{40.30 \text{ g MgO}}{\text{mol MgO}}$$

Solution: 3.67 g̶ ̶M̶g̶ × $\dfrac{1 \text{ m̶o̶l̶ ̶M̶g̶}}{24.30 \text{ g̶ ̶M̶g̶}}$ × $\dfrac{1 \text{ m̶o̶l̶ ̶M̶g̶O̶}}{1 \text{ m̶o̶l̶ ̶M̶g̶}}$ × $\dfrac{40.30 \text{ g MgO}}{1 \text{ m̶o̶l̶ ̶M̶g̶O̶}}$ = 6.086 g MgO = 6.09 g MgO

Check: The units of the answer (g MgO) are correct. The magnitude of the answer is reasonable because it is larger than grams Mg.

       (d)   **Given:** 3.67 g Al **Find:** g Al$_2$O$_3$
               Conceptual Plan: g Al → mol Al → mol Al$_2$O$_3$ → g Al$_2$O$_3$

$$\frac{\text{mol Al}}{26.98 \text{ g Al}} \quad \frac{2 \text{ mol Al}_2\text{O}_3}{4 \text{ mol Al}} \quad \frac{101.96 \text{ g Al}_2\text{O}_3}{\text{mol Al}_2\text{O}_3}$$

Solution: 3.67 g Al × $\dfrac{1 \text{ m̶o̶l̶ ̶A̶l̶}}{26.98 \text{ g̶ ̶A̶l̶}}$ × $\dfrac{2 \text{ m̶o̶l̶ ̶A̶l̶}_2\text{O̶}_3}{4 \text{ m̶o̶l̶ ̶A̶l̶}}$ × $\dfrac{101.96 \text{ g Al}_2\text{O}_3}{1 \text{ m̶o̶l̶ ̶A̶l̶}_2\text{O̶}_3}$ = 6.934 g Al$_2$O$_3$ = 6.93 g Al$_2$O$_3$

Check: The units of the answer (g Al$_2$O$_3$) are correct. The magnitude of the answer is reasonable because it is larger than grams Al.

4.35   (a)   **Given:** 4.85 g NaOH **Find:** g HCl
               Conceptual Plan: g NaOH → mol NaOH → mol HCl → g HCl

$$\frac{\text{mol NaOH}}{40.01 \text{ g NaOH}} \quad \frac{1 \text{ mol HCl}}{1 \text{ mol NaOH}} \quad \frac{36.46 \text{ g HCl}}{1 \text{ mol HCl}}$$

Solution: 4.85 g̶ ̶N̶a̶O̶H̶ × $\dfrac{1 \text{ m̶o̶l̶ ̶N̶a̶O̶H̶}}{40.01 \text{ g̶ ̶N̶a̶O̶H̶}}$ × $\dfrac{1 \text{ m̶o̶l̶ ̶H̶C̶l̶}}{1 \text{ m̶o̶l̶ ̶N̶a̶O̶H̶}}$ × $\dfrac{36.46 \text{ g HCl}}{1 \text{ m̶o̶l̶ ̶H̶C̶l̶}}$ = 4.42 g HCl

Check: The units of the answer (g HCl) are correct. The magnitude of the answer is reasonable since it is less than g NaOH.

       (b)   **Given:** 4.85 g Ca(OH)$_2$ **Find:** g HNO$_3$
               Conceptual Plan: g Ca(OH) →   →   → g HNO$_3$

$$\frac{\text{mol Ca(OH)}_2}{74.10 \text{ g Ca(OH)}_2} \quad \frac{2 \text{ mol HNO}_3}{1 \text{ mol Ca(OH)}_2} \quad \frac{63.02 \text{ g HNO}_3}{1 \text{ mol HNO}_3}$$

4.85 g̶ ̶C̶a̶(̶O̶H̶)̶$_2$ × $\dfrac{1 \text{ m̶o̶l̶ ̶C̶a̶(̶O̶H̶)̶}_2}{74.10 \text{ g̶ ̶C̶a̶(̶O̶H̶)̶}_2}$ × $\dfrac{2 \text{ m̶o̶l̶ ̶H̶N̶O̶}_3}{1 \text{ m̶o̶l̶ ̶C̶a̶(̶O̶H̶)̶}_2}$ × $\dfrac{63.02 \text{ g HNO}_3}{1 \text{ m̶o̶l̶ ̶H̶N̶O̶}_3}$ = 8.25 g HNO$_3$

Check: The units of the answer (g HNO$_3$) are correct. The magnitude of the answer is reasonable since it is more than g Ca(OH)$_2$.

(c)   **Given:** 4.85 g KOH **Find:** g H_2SO_4
       Conceptual Plan: g KOH   mol KOH   mol H_2SO_4 $\rightarrow$ g H_2SO_4

$$\frac{mol\ KOH}{56.11\ g\ KOH} \qquad \frac{1\ mol\ H_2SO_4}{2\ mol\ KOH} \qquad \frac{98.09\ g\ H_2SO_4}{1\ mol\ H_2SO_4}$$

Solution: $4.85\ \cancel{g\ NaOH} \times \dfrac{1\ \cancel{mol\ KOH}}{56.11\ \cancel{g\ KOH}} \times \dfrac{1\ \cancel{mol\ H_2SO_4}}{2\ \cancel{mol\ KOH}} \times \dfrac{98.09\ g\ H_2SO_4}{1\ \cancel{mol\ H_2SO_4}}\ =\ 4.24\ g\ H_2SO_4$

Check: The units of the answer (g H_2SO_4) are correct. The magnitude of the answer is reasonable since it is less than g KOH.

Limiting Reactant, Theoretical Yield, and Percent Yield

4.37   (a)   **Given:** 2 mol Na; 2 mol Br_2 **Find:** Limiting reactant
              Conceptual Plan: mol Na $\rightarrow$ mol NaBr

$$\frac{2\ mol\ NaBr}{2\ mol\ Na} \qquad \rightarrow \text{ smallest mol amount determines limiting reactant}$$

mol Br_2 $\rightarrow$ mol NaBr

$$\frac{2\ mol\ NaBr}{1\ mol\ Br_2}$$

Solution: $2\ \cancel{mol\ Na} \times \dfrac{2\ mol\ NaBr}{2\ \cancel{mol\ Na}}\ =\ 2\ mol\ NaBr$

$2\ \cancel{mol\ Br_2} \times \dfrac{2\ mol\ NaBr}{1\ \cancel{mol\ Br_2}}\ =\ 4\ mol\ NaBr$

Na is limiting reactant

Check: The answer is reasonable since Na produced the smallest amount of product.

(b)   **Given:** 1.8 mol Na; 1.4 mol Br_2 **Find:** Limiting reactant
       Conceptual Plan: mol Na $\rightarrow$ mol NaBr

$$\frac{2\ mol\ NaBr}{2\ mol\ Na} \qquad \rightarrow \text{ smallest mol amount determines limiting reactant}$$

mol Br_2 $\rightarrow$ mol NaBr

$$\frac{2\ mol\ NaBr}{1\ mol\ Br_2}$$

Solution: $1.8\ \cancel{mol\ Na} \times \dfrac{2\ mol\ NaBr}{2\ \cancel{mol\ Na}}\ =\ 1.8\ mol\ NaBr$

$1.4\ \cancel{mol\ Br_2} \times \dfrac{2\ mol\ NaBr}{1\ \cancel{mol\ Br_2}}\ =\ 2.8\ mol\ NaBr$

Na is limiting reactant

Check: The answer is reasonable since Na produced the smallest amount of product.

(c)   **Given:** 2.5 mol Na; 1 mol Br_2 **Find:** Limiting reactant
       Conceptual Plan: mol Na $\rightarrow$ mol NaBr

$$\frac{2\ mol\ NaBr}{2\ mol\ Na} \qquad \rightarrow \text{ smallest mol amount determines limiting reactant}$$

mol Br_2 $\rightarrow$ mol NaBr

$$\frac{2\ mol\ NaBr}{1\ mol\ Br_2}$$

Solution: $2.5\ \cancel{mol\ Na} \times \dfrac{2\ mol\ NaBr}{2\ \cancel{mol\ Na}}\ =\ 2.5\ mol\ NaBr$

$1\ \cancel{mol\ Br_2} \times \dfrac{2\ mol\ NaBr}{1\ \cancel{mol\ Br_2}}\ =\ 2\ mol\ NaBr$

Br_2 is limiting reactant

Check: The answer is reasonable since Br_2 produced the smallest amount of product.

(d)   **Given:** 12.6 mol Na; 6.9 mol Br_2 **Find:** Limiting reactant
        Conceptual Plan: mol Na → mol NaBr

$$\frac{2 \text{ mol NaBr}}{2 \text{ mol Na}}$$

→ **smallest mol amount determines limiting reactant**

        mol Br_2 → mol NaBr

$$\frac{2 \text{ mol NaBr}}{1 \text{ mol } Br_2}$$

Solution: $\underline{\hspace{1cm}}$ x $\dfrac{2 \text{ mol NaBr}}{2 \text{ mol Na}}$ = 12.6 mol NaBr

6.9 $\overline{\text{mol } Br_2}$ x $\dfrac{2 \text{ mol NaBr}}{1 \overline{\text{mol } Br_2}}$ = 13.8 mol NaBr

Na is limiting reactant

Check: The answer is reasonable since Na produced the smallest amount of product.

4.39   The greatest number of Cl_2 molecules will be formed from reaction mixture b and would be 3 molecules Cl_2.

(a)   **Given:** 7 molecules HCl, 1 molecule O_2 **Find:** Theoretical yield Cl_2
        Conceptual Plan: molecules HCl → molecules Cl_2

$$\frac{2 \text{ molecules } Cl_2}{4 \text{ molecules HCl}}$$

→ **smallest molecule amount determines limiting reactant**

        molecules O_2 → molecules Cl_2

$$\frac{2 \text{ molecules } Cl_2}{1 \text{ molecules } O_2}$$

Solution: 7 $\overline{\text{molecules HCl}}$ x $\dfrac{2 \text{ molecules } Cl_2}{4 \overline{\text{molecules HCl}}}$ = 3 molecules Cl_2

1 $\overline{\text{molecules } O_2}$ x $\dfrac{2 \text{ molecules } Cl_2}{1 \overline{\text{molecules } O_2}}$ = 2 molecules Cl_2

Theoretical Yield = 2 molecules Cl_2

(b)   **Given:** 6 molecules HCl, 3 molecules O_2 **Find:** Theoretical yield Cl_2
        Conceptual Plan: molecules HCl → molecules Cl_2

$$\frac{2 \text{ molecules } Cl_2}{4 \text{ molecules HCl}}$$

→ **smallest molecule amount determines limiting reactant**

        molecules O_2 → molecules Cl_2

$$\frac{2 \text{ molecules } Cl_2}{1 \text{ molecules } O_2}$$

Solution: 6 $\overline{\text{molecules HCl}}$ x $\dfrac{2 \text{ molecules } Cl_2}{4 \overline{\text{molecules HCl}}}$ = 3 molecules Cl_2

3 $\overline{\text{molecules } O_2}$ x $\dfrac{2 \text{ molecules } Cl_2}{1 \overline{\text{molecules } O_2}}$ = 6 molecules Cl_2

Theoretical Yield = 3 molecules Cl_2

(c)   **Given:** 4 molecules HCl, 5 molecules O_2 **Find:** Theoretical yield Cl_2
        Conceptual Plan: molecules HCl → molecules Cl_2

$$\frac{2 \text{ molecules } Cl_2}{4 \text{ molecules HCl}}$$

→ **smallest molecule amount determines limiting reactant**

        molecules O_2 → molecules Cl_2

$$\frac{2 \text{ molecules } Cl_2}{1 \text{ molecules } O_2}$$

Solution: 4 $\overline{\text{molecules HCl}}$ x $\dfrac{}{4 \overline{\text{molecules HCl}}}$ = 2 molecules Cl_2

5 $\overline{\text{molecules } O_2}$ x $\dfrac{2 \text{ molecules } Cl_2}{1 \overline{\text{molecules } O_2}}$ = 10 molecules Cl_2

Theoretical Yield = 2 molecules Cl_2

Check: The units of the answer (molecules Cl_2) are correct. The answer is reasonable based on the limiting reactant in each mixture.

4.41   (a)   **Given:** 4 mol Ti, 4 mol Cl_2 **Find:** Theoretical yield $TiCl_4$
               Conceptual Plan: mol Ti $\rightarrow$ mol $TiCl_4$

$$\frac{1 \text{ mol } TiCl_4}{1 \text{ mol } Ti}$$
$\rightarrow$ **smallest mol amount determines limiting reactant**

mol Cl_2 $\rightarrow$ mol $TiCl_4$

$$\frac{1 \text{ mol } TiCl_4}{2 \text{ mol } Cl_2}$$

Solution: $4 \text{ mol Ti} \times \dfrac{1 \text{ mol } TiCl_4}{1 \text{ mol Ti}} = 4 \text{ mol } TiCl_4$

$4 \text{ mol } Cl_2 \times \dfrac{1 \text{ mol } TiCl_4}{2 \text{ mol } Cl_2} = 2 \text{ mol } TiCl_4$

Theoretical Yield = 2 mol $TiCl_4$

Check: The units of the answer (mol $TiCl_4$) are correct. The answer is reasonable since Cl_2 produced the smallest amount of product and is the limiting reactant.

        (b)   **Given:** 7 mol Ti, 17 mol Cl_2 **Find:** Theoretical yield $TiCl_4$
               Conceptual Plan: mol Ti $\rightarrow$ mol $TiCl_4$

$$\frac{1 \text{ mol } TiCl_4}{1 \text{ mol } Ti}$$
$\rightarrow$ **smallest mol amount determines limiting reactant**

mol Cl_2 $\rightarrow$ mol $TiCl_4$

$$\frac{1 \text{ mol } TiCl_4}{2 \text{ mol } Cl_2}$$

Solution: $7 \text{ mol Ti} \times \dfrac{1 \text{ mol } TiCl_4}{1 \text{ mol Ti}} = 7 \text{ mol } TiCl_4$

$17 \text{ mol } Cl_2 \times \dfrac{1 \text{ mol } TiCl_4}{2 \text{ mol } Cl_2} = 8.5 \text{ mol } TiCl_4$

Theoretical Yield = 7 mol $TiCl_4$

Check: The units of the answer (mol $TiCl_4$) are correct. The answer is reasonable since Ti produced the smallest amount of product and is the limiting reactant.

        (c)   **Given:** 12.4 mol Ti, 18.8 mol Cl_2 **Find:** Theoretical yield $TiCl_4$
               Conceptual Plan: mol Ti $\rightarrow$ mol $TiCl_4$

$$\frac{1 \text{ mol } TiCl_4}{1 \text{ mol } Ti}$$
$\rightarrow$ **smallest mol amount determines limiting reactant**

mol Cl_2 $\rightarrow$ mol $TiCl_4$

$$\frac{1 \text{ mol } TiCl_4}{2 \text{ mol } Cl_2}$$

Solution: $12.4 \text{ mol Ti} \times \dfrac{1 \text{ mol } TiCl_4}{1 \text{ mol Ti}} = 12.4 \text{ mol } TiCl_4$

$18.8 \text{ mol } Cl_2 \times \dfrac{1 \text{ mol } TiCl_4}{2 \text{ mol } Cl_2} = 9.40 \text{ mol } TiCl_4$

Theoretical Yield = 9.40 mol $TiCl_4$

Check: The units of the answer (mol $TiCl_4$) are correct. The answer is reasonable since Cl_2 produced the smallest amount of product and is the limiting reactant.

4.43   **Given:** 4.2 mol ZnS, 6.8 mol O_2 **Find:** Mole amount of excess reactant left
        Conceptual Plan: mol ZnS $\rightarrow$ mol ZnO

$$\frac{2 \text{ mol ZnO}}{2 \text{ mol ZnS}}$$
$\rightarrow$ **smallest mol amount determines limiting reactant**

mol O_2 $\rightarrow$ mol ZnO

$$\frac{2 \text{ mol ZnO}}{3 \text{ mol } O_2}$$

then: mol limiting reactant $\rightarrow$ mol excess reactant required $\rightarrow$ mol excess reactant left

$$\frac{2 \text{ mol ZnS}}{3 \text{ mol } O_2}$$

Solution: $4.2 \ \cancel{\text{mol ZnS}} \times \dfrac{2 \text{ mol ZnO}}{2 \ \cancel{\text{mol ZnS}}} = 4.2 \text{ mol ZnO}$

$6.8 \ \cancel{\text{mol O}_2} \times \dfrac{2 \text{ mol ZnO}}{3 \ \cancel{\text{mol O}_2}} = 4.5 \text{ mol ZnO}$

ZnS is the limiting reactant, therefore, O_2 is the excess reactant.

$4.2 \ \cancel{\text{mol ZnS}} \times \dfrac{3 \text{ mol O}_2}{2 \ \cancel{\text{mol ZnS}}} = 6.3 \text{ mol O}_2 \text{ required}$

$6.8 \text{ mol O}_2 \ - \ 6.3 \text{ mol O}_2 = 0.5 \text{ mol O}_2 \text{ left}$

Check: The units of the answer (mol O_2) are correct and the magnitude is reasonable since it is less than the original amount of O_2.

4.45 (a) **Given:** 2.0 g Al, 2.0 g Cl_2 **Find:** Theoretical yield in g $AlCl_3$
          Conceptual Plan: g Al → **mol Al** → **mol AlCl₃**

$\dfrac{1 \text{ mol Al}}{26.98 \text{ g Al}} \qquad \dfrac{2 \text{ mol AlCl}_3}{2 \text{ mol Al}}$ → **smallest mol amount determines limiting reactant**

g Cl₂ → **mol Cl₂** → **mol AlCl₃**

$\dfrac{1 \text{ mol Cl}_2}{70.90 \text{ g Cl}_2} \qquad \dfrac{2 \text{ mol AlCl}_3}{3 \text{ mol Cl}_2}$

then: mol AlCl₃ → **g AlCl₃**

$\dfrac{133.3 \text{ g AlCl}_3}{\text{mol AlCl}_3}$

Solution: $2.0 \ \cancel{\text{g Al}} \times \dfrac{1 \ \cancel{\text{mol Al}}}{26.98 \ \cancel{\text{g Al}}} \times \dfrac{2 \text{ mol AlCl}_3}{2 \ \cancel{\text{mol Al}}} = 0.074 \text{ mol AlCl}_3$

$2.0 \ \cancel{\text{g Cl}_2} \times \dfrac{1 \ \cancel{\text{mol Cl}_2}}{70.90 \ \cancel{\text{g Cl}_2}} \times \dfrac{2 \text{ mol AlCl}_3}{\cancel{\phantom{3 \text{ mol}}}_2} = \underline{0.0188} \text{ mol AlCl}_3$

$\underline{0.0188} \text{ mol AlCl}_3 \times \dfrac{133.3 \text{ g AlCl}_3}{\text{mol AlCl}_3} = 2.5 \text{ g AlCl}_3$

Check: The units of the answer (g $AlCl_3$) are correct. The answer is reasonable since Cl_2 produced the smallest amount of product and is the limiting reactant.

(b) **Given:** 7.5 g Al, 24.8 g Cl_2 **Find:** Theoretical yield in g $AlCl_3$
    Conceptual Plan: g Al → **mol Al** → **mol AlCl₃**

$\dfrac{1 \text{ mol Al}}{26.98 \text{ g Al}} \qquad \dfrac{2 \text{ mol AlCl}_3}{2 \text{ mol Al}}$ → **smallest mol amount determines limiting reactant**

g Cl₂ → **mol Cl₂** → **mol AlCl₃**

$\dfrac{1 \text{ mol Cl}_2}{70.90 \text{ g Cl}_2} \qquad \dfrac{2 \text{ mol AlCl}_3}{2}$

then: mol AlCl₃ → **g AlCl₃**

$\dfrac{133.3 \text{ g AlCl}_3}{\text{mol AlCl}_3}$

Solution: $7.5 \ \cancel{\text{g Al}} \times \dfrac{1 \ \cancel{\text{mol Al}}}{26.98 \ \cancel{\text{g Al}}} \times \dfrac{2 \text{ mol AlCl}_3}{2 \ \cancel{\text{mol Al}}} = 0.2780 \text{ mol AlCl}_3$

$24.8 \ \cancel{\text{g Cl}_2} \times \dfrac{1 \ \cancel{\text{mol Cl}_2}}{70.90 \ \cancel{\text{g Cl}_2}} \times \dfrac{\phantom{2 \text{ mol}}^3}{3 \ \cancel{\text{mol Cl}}} = \underline{0.2332} \text{ mol AlCl}_3$

$\underline{0.2332} \text{ mol AlCl}_3 \times \dfrac{133.3 \text{ g AlCl}_3}{\text{mol AlCl}_3} = 31.1 \text{ g AlCl}_3$

Check: The units of the answer (g $AlCl_3$) are correct. The answer is reasonable since Cl_2 produced the smallest amount of product and is the limiting reactant.

(c) **Given:** 0.235 g Al, 1.15 g Cl_2 **Find:** Theoretical yield in g $AlCl_3$
Conceptual Plan: g Al → mol Al → mol $AlCl_3$

$$\frac{1 \text{ mol Al}}{26.98 \text{ g Al}} \quad \frac{2 \text{ mol AlCl}_3}{2 \text{ mol Al}} \quad → \textbf{ smallest mol amount determines limiting reactant}$$

g Cl_2 → mol Cl_2 → mol $AlCl_3$

$$\frac{1 \text{ mol Cl}_2}{70.90 \text{ g Cl}_2} \quad \frac{2 \text{ mol AlCl}_3}{3 \text{ mol Cl}_2}$$

then: mol $AlCl_3$ → g $AlCl_3$

$$\frac{133.34 \text{ g AlCl}_3}{\text{mol AlCl}_3}$$

Solution: $0.235 \text{ g Al} \times \frac{1 \text{ mol Al}}{26.98 \text{ g Al}} \times \frac{2 \text{ mol AlCl}_3}{2 \text{ mol Al}} = 0.008710 \text{ mol AlCl}_3$

$1.15 \text{ g Cl}_2 \times \frac{1 \text{ mol Cl}_2}{70.90 \text{ g Cl}_2} \times \frac{2 \text{ mol AlCl}_3}{3 \text{ mol Cl}_2} = 0.01081 \text{ mol AlCl}_3$

$0.008710 \text{ mol AlCl}_3 \times \frac{133.34 \text{ g AlCl}_3}{\text{mol AlCl}_3} = 1.16 \text{ g AlCl}_3$

Check: The units of the answer (g $AlCl_3$) are correct. The answer is reasonable since Al produced the smallest amount of product and is the limiting reactant.

4.47 **Given:** 22.55 Fe_2O_3, 14.78 g CO **Find:** Mole amount of excess reactant left
Conceptual Plan: g Fe_2O_3 → mol Fe_2O_3 → mol Fe

$$\frac{1 \text{ mol Fe}_2O_3}{159.7 \text{ g Fe}_2O_3} \quad \frac{2 \text{ mol Fe}}{1 \text{ mol Fe}_2O_3} \quad → \textbf{ smallest mol amount determines limiting reactant}$$

g CO → mol CO → mol Fe

$$\frac{1 \text{ mol CO}}{28.01 \text{ g CO}} \quad \frac{2 \text{ mol Fe}}{3 \text{ mol CO}}$$

then: mol limiting reactant → mol excess reactant required → mol excess reactant left → g excess reactant left

$$\frac{1 \text{ mol Fe}_2O_3}{3 \text{ mol CO}} \qquad \frac{159.7 \text{ g Fe}_2O_3}{1 \text{ mol Fe}_2O_3} \qquad \text{or } \frac{28.01 \text{ g CO}}{1 \text{ mol CO}}$$

Solution: $22.55 \text{ g Fe}_2O_3 \times \frac{1 \text{ mol Fe}_2O_3}{159.7 \text{ g Fe}_2O_3} \times \frac{2 \text{ mol Fe}}{1 \text{ mol Fe}_2O_3} = 0.2824 \text{ mol Fe}$

$14.78 \text{ g CO} \times \frac{1 \text{ mol CO}}{28.01 \text{ g CO}} \times \frac{2 \text{ mol Fe}}{3 \text{ mol CO}} = 0.3518 \text{ mol Fe}$

Fe_2O_3 is the limiting reactant, therefore, CO is the excess reactant.

$22.55 \text{ g Fe}_2O_3 \times \frac{1 \text{ mol Fe}_2O_3}{159.7 \text{ g Fe}_2O_3} \times \frac{3 \text{ mol CO}}{1 \text{ mol Fe}_2O_3} \times \frac{28.01 \text{ g CO}}{1 \text{ mol CO}} = 11.865 \text{ g CO required}$

$14.78 \text{ g CO} - 11.87 \text{ g CO} = 2.91 \text{ g CO left}$

Check: The units of the answer (g CO) is correct and the magnitude is reasonable since it is less than the original amount of CO.

4.49 **Given:** 28.5 g KCl; 25.7 g Pb^{2+}; 29.4 g $PbCl_2$ **Find:** limiting reactant, theoretical yield $PbCl_2$, % yield
Conceptual Plan: g KCl → mol KCl → mol $PbCl_2$

$$\frac{1 \text{ mol KCl}}{74.55 \text{ g KCl}} \quad \frac{1 \text{ mol PbCl}_2}{2 \text{ mol KCl}} \quad → \textbf{ smallest mol amount determines limiting reactant}$$

g Pb^{2+} → mol Pb^{2+} → mol $PbCl_2$

$$\frac{1 \text{ mol Pb}^{2+}}{207.2 \text{ g Pb}^{2+}} \quad \frac{1 \text{ mol PbCl}_2}{1 \text{ mol Pb}^{2+}}$$

then: mol $PbCl_2$ → g $PbCl_2$ **then: determine % yield**

$$\frac{278.1 \text{ g PbCl}_2}{\text{mol PbCl}_2} \qquad \frac{\text{actual yield g PbCl}_2}{\text{theoretical yield g PbCl}_2} \times 100$$

Solution: $28.5 \; \cancel{g \; KCl} \times \dfrac{1 \; \cancel{mol \; KCl}}{74.55 \; \cancel{g \; KCl}} \times \dfrac{1 \; mol \; PbCl_2}{2 \; \cancel{mol \; KCl}} = 0.19\underline{1}1 \; mol \; PbCl_2$

$25.7 \; \cancel{g \; Pb^{2+}} \times \dfrac{1 \; \cancel{mol \; Pb^{2+}}}{207.2 \; \cancel{g \; Pb^{2+}}} \times \dfrac{1 \; mol \; PbCl_2}{1 \; \cancel{mol \; Pb^{2+}}} = 0.1240 \; mol \; PbCl_2 \quad Pb^{2+}$ is the limiting reactant.

$0.12\underline{4}0 \; \cancel{mol \; PbCl_2} \times \dfrac{278.1 \; g \; PbCl_2}{1 \; \cancel{mol \; PbCl_2}} = 34.\underline{5} \; g \; PbCl_2$

$\dfrac{29.4 \; \cancel{g \; PbCl_2}}{34.\underline{5} \; \cancel{g \; PbCl_2}} \times 100 = 85.2\%$

Check: The theoretical yield has the correct units (g $PbCl_2$) and has a reasonable magnitude compared to the mass of Pb^{2+}, the limiting reactant. The % yield is reasonable, under 100%.

4.51 **Given:** 136.4 kg NH_3; 211.4 kg CO_2; 168.4 kg CH_4N_2O
Find: limiting reactant, theoretical yield CH_4N_2O, % yield
Conceptual Plan: kg $NH_3 \rightarrow$ g $NH_3 \rightarrow$ mol $NH_3 \rightarrow$ mol CH_4N_2O

$\dfrac{1000 \; g}{1 \; kg} \qquad \dfrac{1 \; mol \; NH_3}{17.03 \; g \; NH_3} \qquad \dfrac{1 \; mol \; CH_4N_2O}{2 \; mol \; NH_3}$

$\rightarrow$ **smallest   amount   determines limiting reactant**

kg $CO_2 \rightarrow$ g $CO_2 \rightarrow$ mol $CO_2 \rightarrow$ mol CH_4N_2O

$\dfrac{1000 \; g}{1 \; kg} \qquad \dfrac{1 \; mol \; CO_2}{44.01 \; g \; CO_2} \qquad \dfrac{1 \; mol \; CH_4N_2O}{1 \; mol \; CO_2}$

then: mol $CH_4N_2O \rightarrow$ **g** $CH_4N_2O \rightarrow$ **kg** CH_4N_2O **then: determine % yield**

$\dfrac{60.06 \; g \; CH_4N_2O}{1 \; mol \; CH_4N_2O} \qquad \dfrac{1 \; kg}{1000 \; g}$ $\dfrac{actual \; yield \; kg \; CH_4N_2O}{theoretical \; yield \; kg \; CH_4N_2O} \times 100$

Solution: $136.4 \; \cancel{kg \; NH_3} \times \dfrac{1000 \; \cancel{g}}{\cancel{kg}} \times \dfrac{1 \; \cancel{mol \; NH_3}}{17.03 \; \cancel{g \; NH_3}} \times \dfrac{1 \; mol \; CH_4N_2O}{2 \; \cancel{mol \; NH_3}} = 400\underline{4}.7 \; mol \; CH_4N_2O$

$211.4 \; \cancel{kg \; CO_2} \times \dfrac{1000 \; \cancel{g}}{\cancel{kg}} \times \dfrac{1 \; \cancel{mol \; CO_2}}{44.01 \; \cancel{g \; CO_2}} \times \dfrac{1 \; mol \; CH_4N_2O}{1 \; \cancel{mol \; CO_2}} = 480\underline{3}.4 \; mol \; CH_4N_2O$

NH_3 is the limiting reactant

$400\underline{4}.7 \; \cancel{mol \; CH_4N_2O} \times \dfrac{60.06 \; \cancel{g \; CH_4N_2O}}{1 \; \cancel{mol \; CH_4N_2O}} \times \dfrac{kg}{1000 \; \cancel{g}} = 240.\underline{5}2 \; kg \; CH_4N_2O$

$\dfrac{168.4 \; \cancel{kg \; CH_4N_2O}}{240.\underline{5}2 \; \cancel{kg \; CH_4N_2O}} \times 100 = 70.01\%$

Check: The theoretical yield has the correct units (kg CH_4N_2O) and has a reasonable magnitude compared to the mass of NH_3, the limiting reactant. The % yield is reasonable, under 100%.

Solution Concentration and Solution Stoichiometry

4.53 (a) **Given:** 3.25 mol LiCl; 2.78 L solution **Find:** Molarity LiCl
Conceptual Plan: mol LiCl, L solution $\rightarrow$ **Molarity**

$molarity \; (M) = \dfrac{amount \; of \; solute \; (in \; moles)}{volume \; of \; solution \; (in \; L)}$

Solution: $\dfrac{3.25 \; mol \; LiCl}{2.78 \; L \; solution} = 1.1\underline{6}9 \; M = 1.17 \; M$

Check: The units of the answer (M) are correct. The magnitude of the answer is reasonable. Concentrations are usually between 0 M and 18 M.

(b) **Given:** 28.33 g $C_6H_{12}O_6$; 1.28 L solution **Find:** Molarity $C_6H_{12}O_6$
Conceptual Plan: g $C_6H_{12}O_6 \rightarrow$ mol $C_6H_{12}O_6$, L solution $\rightarrow$ **Molarity**

$\dfrac{mol \; C_6H_{12}O_6}{180.16 \; g \; C_6H_{12}O_6} \qquad\qquad molarity \; (M) = \dfrac{amount \; of \; solute \; (in \; moles)}{volume \; of \; solution \; (in \; L)}$

Solution: $28.33 \, \overline{g \, C_6H_{12}O_6} \times \dfrac{1 \, mol \, C_6H_{12}O_6}{180.16 \, \overline{g \, C_6H_{12}O_6}} = 0.15724 \, mol \, C_6H_{12}O_6$

$\dfrac{0.15724 \, mol \, C_6H_{12}O_6}{1.28 \, L \, solution} = 0.1228 \, M = 0.123 \, M$

Check: The units of the answer (M) are correct. The magnitude of the answer is reasonable. Concentrations are usually between 0 M and 18 M.

(c)   **Given:** 32.4 mg NaCl; 122.4 mL solution **Find:** Molarity NaCl
      Conceptual Plan: mg NaCl → g NaCl → mol NaCl, and mL solution → L solution then Molarity

$\dfrac{g \, NaCl}{1000 \, mg \, NaCl} \qquad \dfrac{mol \, NaCl}{58.45 \, g \, NaCl} \qquad \dfrac{L \, solution}{1000 \, mL \, solution} \qquad molarity \, (M) = \dfrac{amount \, of \, solute \, (in \, moles)}{volume \, of \, solution \, (in \, L)}$

Solution: $32.4 \, \overline{mg \, NaCl} \times \dfrac{1 \, g}{1000 \, \overline{mg}} \times \dfrac{1 \, mol \, NaCl}{58.45 \, \overline{g \, NaCl}} = 5.543 \times 10^{-4} \, mol \, NaCl$

$122.4 \, \overline{mL \, solution} \times \dfrac{1 \, L}{1000 \, \overline{mL}} = 0.1224 \, L$

$\dfrac{5.543 \times 10^{-4} \, mol \, NaCl}{0.1224 \, L} = 0.0045287 \, M \, NaCl = 0.00453 \, M \, NaCl$

Check: The units of the answer (M) are correct. The magnitude of the answer is reasonable. Concentrations are usually between 0 M and 18 M.

4.55   (a)   **Given:** 0.556 L; 2.3 M KCl **Find:** mol KCl
             Conceptual Plan: volume solution x M = mol

$volume \, solution \, (L) \times M = mol$

Solution: $0.556 \, \overline{L \, solution} \times \dfrac{2.3 \, mol \, KCl}{\overline{L \, solution}} = 1.3 \, mol \, KCl$

Check: The units of the answer (mol KCl) are correct. The magnitude is reasonable since it is less than 1 L solution.

(b)   **Given:** 1.8 L; 0.85 M KCl **Find:** mol KCl
      Conceptual Plan: volume solution x M = mol

$volume \, solution \, (L) \times M = mol$

Solution: $1.8 \, \overline{L \, solution} \times \dfrac{0.85 \, mol \, KCl}{\overline{L \, solution}} = 1.5 \, mol \, KCl$

Check: The units of the answer (mol KCl) are correct. The magnitude is reasonable since it is less than 2 L solution.

(c)   **Given:** 114 mL; 1.85 M KCl **Find:** mol KCl
      Conceptual Plan: mL solution → L solution, then volume solution x M = mol

$\dfrac{1 \, L}{1000 \, mL} \qquad\qquad volume \, solution \, (L) \times M = mol$

$114 \, \overline{mL \, solution} \times \dfrac{1 \, L}{1000 \, \overline{mL}} \times \dfrac{1.85 \, mol \, KCl}{\overline{L \, solution}} = 0.211 \, mol \, KCl$

Check: The units of the answer (mol KCl) are correct. The magnitude is reasonable since it is less than 1 L solution.

4.57   **Given:** 400.0 mL; 1.1 M NaNO$_3$ **Find:** g NaNO$_3$
       Conceptual Plan: mL solution → L solution, then volume solution x M = mol NaNO$_3$

$\dfrac{L \, solution}{1000 \, mL \, solution} \qquad\qquad volume \, solution \, (L) \times M = mol$

then mol NaNO$_3$ → g NaNO$_3$

$\dfrac{85.01 \, g \, NaNO_3}{mol \, NaNO_3}$

Solution: $400.0 \ \overline{mL \ solution} \times \dfrac{1 \ \overline{L}}{1000 \ \overline{mL}} \times \dfrac{1.1 \ \overline{mol \ NaNO_3}}{\overline{L \ solution}} \times \dfrac{85.01 \ g}{\overline{mol \ NaNO_3}} = 37 \ g \ NaNO_3$

Check: The units of the answer (g $NaNO_3$) are correct. The magnitude is reasonable for the concentration and volume of solution.

4.59   **Given:** $V_1 = 123$ mL; $M_1 = 1.1$ M; $V_2 = 500.0$ mL **Find:** M_2

Conceptual Plan: mL $\rightarrow$ L then $V_1, M_1, V_2 \rightarrow M_2$

$$\dfrac{1 \ L}{1000 \ mL} \qquad\qquad V_1 M_1 = V_2 M_2$$

Solution: $123 \ \overline{mL} \times \dfrac{1 \ L}{1000 \ \overline{mL}} = 0.123 \ L \qquad 500.0 \ \overline{mL} \times \dfrac{1 \ L}{1000 \ \overline{mL}} = 0.5000 \ L$

$$M_2 = \dfrac{V_1 M_1}{V_2} = \dfrac{(0.123 \ \overline{L})(1.1 \ M)}{(0.5000 \ \overline{L})} = 0.27 \ M$$

Check: The units of the answer (M) are correct. The magnitude of the answer is reasonable since it is less than the original concentration.

4.61   **Given:** $V_1 = 50$ mL; $M_1 = 12$ M; $M_2 = 0.100$ M **Find:** V_2

Conceptual Plan: mL $\rightarrow$ L then $V_1, M_1, M_2 \rightarrow V_2$

$$\dfrac{1 \ L}{1000 \ mL} \qquad\qquad V_1 M_1 = V_2 M_2$$

Solution: $50 \ \overline{mL} \times \dfrac{1 \ L}{1000 \ \overline{mL}} = 0.050 \ L$

$$V_2 = \dfrac{V_1 M_1}{M_2} = \dfrac{(0.050 \ \overline{L})(12 \ M)}{(0.100 \ \overline{M})} = 6.0 \ L$$

Check: The units of the answer (L) are correct. The magnitude of the answer is reasonable since the new concentration is much less than the original; the volume must be larger.

4.63   **Given:** 95.4 mL, 0.102 M $CuCl_2$; 0.175 M Na_3PO_4 **Find:** volume Na_3PO_4

Conceptual Plan: mL $CuCl_2 \rightarrow$ L $CuCl_2 \rightarrow$ mol $CuCl_2 \rightarrow$ mol $Na_3PO_4 \rightarrow$ L $Na_3PO_4 \rightarrow$ mL Na_3PO_4

$$\dfrac{1 \ L}{1000 \ mL} \quad \dfrac{0.102 \ mol \ CuCl_2}{L} \quad \dfrac{2 \ mol \ Na_3PO_4}{3 \ mol \ CuCl_2} \quad \dfrac{1 \ L}{0.175 \ mol \ Na_3PO_4} \quad \dfrac{1000 \ mL}{L}$$

Solution: $95.4 \ \overline{mL \ CuCl_2} \times \dfrac{1 \ \overline{L}}{1000 \ \overline{mL}} \times \dfrac{0.102 \ \overline{mol \ CuCl_2}}{1 \ \overline{L}} \times \dfrac{2 \ \overline{mol \ Na_3PO_4}}{3 \ \overline{mol \ CuCl_2}} \times \dfrac{1 \ \overline{L}}{0.175 \ \overline{mol \ Na_3PO_4}} \times \dfrac{1000 \ mL}{1 \ \overline{L}}$

$= 37.1 \ mL \ Na_3PO_4$

Check: The units of the answer (mL Na_3PO_4) are correct. The magnitude of the answer is reasonable since the concentration of Na_3PO_4 is greater.

4.65   **Given:** 25.0 g H_2; 6.0 M H_2SO_4 **Find:** volume H_2SO_4

Conceptual Plan: g $H_2 \rightarrow$ mol $H_2 \rightarrow$ mol $H_2SO_4 \rightarrow$ L H_2SO_4

$$\dfrac{2.016 \ g \ H_2}{1 \ mol \ H_2} \quad \dfrac{3 \ mol \ H_2SO_4}{3 \ mol \ H_2} \quad \dfrac{1 \ L}{6.0 \ mol \ H_2SO_4}$$

Solution: $25.0 \ \overline{g \ H_2} \times \dfrac{1 \ \overline{mol \ H_2}}{2.016 \ \overline{g \ H_2}} \times \dfrac{3 \ \overline{mol \ H_2SO_4}}{3 \ \overline{mol \ H_2}} \times \dfrac{1 \ L}{6.0 \ \overline{mol \ H_2SO_4}} = 2.1 \ L \ H_2SO_4$

Check: The units of the answer (L H_2SO_4) are correct. The magnitude is reasonable since there are approximately 12 mol H_2 and the mole ratio is 1:1.

Types of Aqueous Solutions and Solubility

4.67   (a)   CsCl is an ionic compound. An aqueous solution is an electrolyte solution, so it conducts electricity.

(b) CH_3OH is a molecular compound that does not dissociate. An aqueous solution is a nonelectrolyte solution, so it does not conduct electricity.

(c) $Ca(NO_3)_2$ is an ionic compound. An aqueous solution is an electrolyte solution, so it conducts electricity.

(d) $C_6H_{12}O_6$ is a molecular compound that does not dissociate. An aqueous solution is a nonelectrolyte solution, so it does not conduct electricity.

4.69   (a) $AgNO_3$ is soluble. Compounds containing NO_3^- are always soluble with no exceptions. The ions in the solution are $Ag^+(aq)$ and $NO_3^-(aq)$.

         (b) $Pb(C_2H_3O_2)_2$ is soluble. Compounds containing $C_2H_3O_2^-$ are always soluble with no exceptions. The ions in the solution are $Pb^{2+}(aq)$ and $C_2H_3O_2^-(aq)$.

         (c) KNO_3 is soluble. Compounds containing K^+ are always soluble with no exceptions. The ions in solution are $K^+(aq)$ and $NO_3^-(aq)$.

         (d) $(NH_4)_2S$ is soluble. Compounds containing NH_4^+ are always soluble with no exceptions. The ions in solution are $NH_4^+(aq)$ and $S^{2-}(aq)$.

Precipitation Reactions

4.71   (a) $LiI(aq) + BaS(aq) \rightarrow$ Possible products: Li_2S and BaI_2. Li_2S is soluble. Compounds containing S^{2-} are normally insoluble but Li^+ is an exception. BaI_2 is soluble. Compounds containing I^- are normally soluble and Ba^{2+} is not an exception. $LiI(aq) + BaS(aq) \rightarrow$ No Reaction

         (b) $KCl(aq) + CaS(aq) \rightarrow$ Possible products: K_2S and $CaCl_2$. K_2S is soluble. Compounds containing S^{2-} are normally insoluble but K^+ is an exception. $CaCl_2$ is soluble. Compounds containing Cl^- are normally soluble and Ca^{2+} is not an exception. $KCl(aq) + CaS(aq) \rightarrow$ No Reaction

         (c) $CrBr_2(aq) + Na_2CO_3(aq) \rightarrow$ Possible products: $CrCO_3$ and $NaBr$. $CrCO_3$ containing CO_3^{2-} are normally insoluble and Cr^{2+} is not an exception. $NaBr$ is soluble. Compounds containing Br^- are normally soluble and Na^+ is not an exception.
$CrBr_2(aq) + Na_2CO_3(aq) \rightarrow CrCO_3(s) + 2\,NaBr(aq)$

         (d) $NaOH(aq) + FeCl_3(aq) \rightarrow$ Possible products $NaCl$ and $Fe(OH)_3$. $NaCl$ is soluble. Compounds containing Na^+ are normally soluble, no exceptions. $Fe(OH)_3$ is insoluble. Compounds containing OH^- are normally insoluble and Fe^{3+} is not an exception.
$3\,NaOH(aq) + FeCl_3(aq) \rightarrow 3\,NaCl(aq) + Fe(OH)_3(s)$

4.73   (a) $K_2CO_3(aq) + Pb(NO_3)_2(aq) \rightarrow$ Possible products: KNO_3 and $PbCO_3$. KNO_3 is soluble. Compounds containing K^+ are always soluble, no exceptions. $PbCO_3$ is insoluble. Compounds containing CO_3^{2-} are normally insoluble and Pb^{2+} is not an exception.
$K_2CO_3(aq) + Pb(NO_3)_2(aq) \rightarrow 2\,KNO_3(aq) + PbCO_3(s)$

         (b) $Li_2SO_4(aq) + Pb(C_2H_3O_2)_2(aq) \rightarrow$ Possible products: $LiC_2H_3O_2$ and $PbSO_4$. $LiC_2H_3O_2$ is soluble. Compounds containing Li^+ are always soluble, no exceptions. $PbSO_4$ is insoluble. Compounds containing SO_4^{2-} are normally soluble but, Pb^{2+} is an exception.
$Li_2SO_4(aq) + Pb(C_2H_3O_2)_2(aq) \rightarrow 2\,LiC_2H_3O_2(aq) + PbSO_4(s)$

         (c) $Cu(NO_3)_2(aq) + MgS(s) \rightarrow$ Possible products: CuS and $Mg(NO_3)_2$. CuS is insoluble. Compounds containing S^{2-} are normally insoluble and Cu^{2+} is not an exception. $Mg(NO_3)_2$ is soluble. Compounds containing NO_3^- are always soluble, no exceptions. $Cu(NO_3)_2(aq) + MgS(s) \rightarrow CuS(s) + Mg(NO_3)_2(aq)$

         (d) $Sr(NO_3)_2(aq) + KI(aq) \rightarrow$ Possible products: SrI_2 and KNO_3. SrI_2 is soluble. Compounds containing I^- are normally soluble and Sr^{2+} is not an exception. KNO_3 is soluble. Compounds containing K^+ are always soluble, no exceptions. $Sr(NO_3)_2(aq) + KI(aq) \rightarrow$ No Reaction

Ionic and Net Ionic Equations

4.75   (a) $H^+(aq) + \cancel{Cl^-}(aq) + \cancel{Li^+}(aq) + OH^-(aq) \rightarrow H_2O(l) + \cancel{Li^+}(aq) + \cancel{Cl^-}(aq)$
$H^+(aq) + OH^-(aq) \rightarrow H_2O(l)$

         (b) $\cancel{Mg^{2+}}(aq) + S^{2-}(aq) + Cu^{2+}(aq) + 2\,\cancel{Cl^-}(aq) \rightarrow CuS(s) + \cancel{Mg^{2+}}(aq) + 2\,\cancel{Cl^-}(aq)$
$Cu^{2+}(aq) + S^{2-}(aq) \rightarrow CuS(s)$

         (c) $\cancel{Na^+}(aq) + OH^-(aq) + H^+(aq) + \cancel{NO_3^-}(aq) \rightarrow H_2O(l) + \cancel{Na^+}(aq) + \cancel{NO_3^-}(aq)$
$H^+(aq) + OH^-(aq) + \rightarrow H_2O(l)$

(d) $6 \, \cancel{Na^+}(aq) + 2 \, PO_4{}^{3-}(aq) + 3 \, Ni^{2+}(aq) + 6 \, \cancel{Cl^-}(aq) \rightarrow Ni_3(PO_4)_2(s) + 6 \, \cancel{Na^+}(aq) + 6 \, \cancel{Cl^-}(aq)$

        $3 \, Ni^{2+}(aq) + 2 \, PO_4{}^{3-}(aq) \rightarrow Ni_3(PO_4)_2(s)$

4.77 $Hg_2{}^{2+}(aq) + \cancel{2NO_3^-}(aq) + \cancel{2Na^+}(aq) + 2 \, Cl^-(aq) \rightarrow Hg_2Cl_2(s) + \cancel{2Na^+}(aq) + \cancel{2NO_3^-}(aq)$

    $Hg_2{}^{2+}(aq) + 2 \, Cl^-(aq) \rightarrow Hg_2Cl_2(s)$

Acid-Base and Gas-Evolution Reactions

4.79   Skeletal reaction: $HBr(aq) + KOH(aq) \rightarrow H_2O(l) + KBr(aq)$

                        acid   base   water   salt

     Net ionic equation: $H^+(aq) + OH^-(aq) \rightarrow H_2O(l)$

4.81   (a)   Skeletal reaction: $H_2SO_4(aq) + Ca(OH)_2(aq) \rightarrow H_2O(l) + CaSO_4(s)$

                              acid   base   water   salt

       Balanced reaction: $H_2SO_4(aq) + Ca(OH)_2(aq) \rightarrow 2 \, H_2O(l) + CaSO_4(s)$

      (b)   Skeletal reaction: $HClO_4(aq) + KOH(aq) \rightarrow H_2O(l) + KClO_4(aq)$

                              acid   base   water   salt

       Balanced reaction: $HClO_4(aq) + KOH(aq) \rightarrow H_2O(l) + KClO_4(aq)$

      (c)   Skeletal reaction: $H_2SO_4(aq) + NaOH(aq \rightarrow {}_2O(l) + Na_2SO_4(aq)$

                              acid   base   water   salt

       Balanced reaction: $H_2SO_4(aq) + 2 \, NaOH(aq) \rightarrow 2 \, H_2O(l) + Na_2SO_4(aq)$

4.83   **Given:** 22.62 mL, 0.2000 M NaOH solution; 25.00 mL $HClO_4$ solution   **Find:** M $HClO_4$ solution

     Conceptual Plan: mL NaOH $\rightarrow$ L NaOH $\rightarrow$ mol NaOH $\rightarrow$ mol $HClO_4$

$$\frac{1 \, L}{1000 \, mL} \quad \frac{0.200 \, mol \, NaOH}{L \, NaOH} \quad \frac{1 \, mol \, HClO_4}{1 \, mol \, NaOH}$$

     mol $HClO_4$, volume $HClO_4$ solution $\rightarrow$ M

$$M = \frac{1 \, mol \, HClO_4}{L \, HClO_4 \, solution}$$

     Solution: $22.62 \, \cancel{mL \, NaOH} \times \dfrac{1 \, \cancel{L}}{1000 \, \cancel{mL}} \times \dfrac{0.2000 \, \cancel{mol \, NaOH}}{\cancel{L}} \times \dfrac{1 \, mol \, HClO_4}{1 \, \cancel{mol \, NaOH}} = 0.004524 \, mol \, HClO_4$

$$\frac{0.004524 \, mol \, HClO_4}{25.00 \, \cancel{mL} \, HClO_4} \times \frac{1000 \, \cancel{mL}}{1 \, L} = 0.18096 \, M \, HClO_4 = 0.1810 \, M \, HClO_4$$

     Check: The units of the answer (M $HClO_4$) are correct. The magnitude of the answer is reasonable since it is less than the M of NaOH.

4.85   (a)   Skeletal reaction: $HBr(aq) + NiS(s) \rightarrow NiBr_2(aq) + H_2S(g)$

                                                   gas

       Balanced reaction: $2 \, HBr(aq) + NiS(\,) \rightarrow NiBr_2(aq) + H_2S(g)$

      (b)   Skeletal reaction: $NH_4I(aq) + NaOH(aq) \rightarrow NH_4OH(aq) + NaI(aq) \rightarrow H_2O(l) + NH_3(g) + NaI(aq)$

                                    decomposes   gas

       Balanced reaction: $NH_4I(aq) + NaOH(aq) \rightarrow H_2O(l \quad (g) + NaI(aq)$

      (c)   Skeletal reaction: $HBr(aq) + Na_2S(aq) \rightarrow NaBr(aq) + H_2S(g)$

                                                 gas

       Balanced reaction: $2 \, HBr(aq) + Na_2S(aq) \rightarrow 2 \, NaBr(aq) + H_2S(g)$

      (d)   Skeletal reaction:

         $HClO_4(aq) + Li_2CO_3(aq) \rightarrow H \, CO_3(aq) + LiClO_4(aq) \rightarrow H_2O(l) + CO_2(g) + LiClO_4(aq)$

                              decomposes   gas

       Balanced reaction: $2 \, HClO_4(aq) + Li_2CO_3(aq) \rightarrow H_2O(l) + CO_2(g) + 2 \, LiClO_4(aq)$

Oxidation-Reduction and Combustion

4.87   (a)   Ag. The oxidation state of Ag = 0. The oxidation state of an atom in a free element is 0.

   (b) Ag^+. The oxidation state of Ag^+ = +1. The oxidation state of a monatomic ion is equal to its charge.

   (c) CaF_2. The oxidation state of Ca = +2, and the oxidation state of F = – 1. The oxidation state of a group 2A metal always has an oxidation state of +2, the oxidation of F is – 1 since the sum of the oxidation states in a neutral formula unit = 0.

   (d) H_2S. The oxidation state of H = + 1, and the oxidation state of S = – 2. The oxidation state of H when listed first is +1, the oxidation state of S is – 2 since S is in group 6A and the sum of the oxidation states in a neutral molecular unit = 0.

   (e) $CO_3{}^{2-}$. The oxidation state of C = +4, and the oxidation state of O = – 2. The oxidation state of O is normally – 2, and the oxidation state of C is deduced from the formula since the sum of the oxidation states must equal the charge on the ion. (C ox state) + 3(O ox state) = – 2; (C ox state) + 3(– 2) = – 2, so C ox state = + 4.

   (f) $CrO_4{}^{2-}$. The oxidation state of Cr = +6, and the oxidation state of O = – 2. The oxidation state of O is normally –2, and the oxidation state of Cr is deduced from the formula since the sum of the oxidation states must equal the charge on the ion. (Cr ox state) + 4(O ox state) = – 2; (Cr ox state) + 4(– 2) = – 2, so Cr ox state = + 6.

4.89   (a)   CrO. The oxidation state of Cr = +2, and the oxidation state of O = – 2. The oxidation state of O is normally – 2, and the oxidation state of Cr is deduced from the formula since the sum of the oxidation states must = 0.
(Cr ox state) + (O ox state) = 0; (Cr ox state) + (– 2) = 0, so Cr = +2.

   (b) CrO_3. The oxidation state of Cr = +6, and the oxidation state of O = – 2. The oxidation state of O is normally – 2, and the oxidation state of Cr is deduced from the formula since the sum of the oxidation states must = 0.
(Cr ox state) + 3(O ox state) = 0; (Cr ox state) +3 (– 2) = 0, so Cr = +6.

   (c) Cr_2O_3. The oxidation state of Cr = +3, and the oxidation state of O = – 2. The oxidation state of O is normally – 2, and the oxidation state of Cr is deduced from the formula since the sum of the oxidation states must = 0.
2(Cr ox state) +3 (O ox state) = 0; 2(Cr ox state) + 3(– 2) = 0, so Cr = +3.

4.91   (a) $$4\ Li(s) + O_2(g) \rightarrow 2\ Li_2O(s)$$
Oxidation states;   0   0   +1   – 2
This is a redox reaction since Li increases in oxidation number (oxidation) and O decreases in number (reduction). O_2 is the oxidizing agent, and Li is the reducing agent.

   (b) $$Mg(s) + Fe^{2+}(aq) \rightarrow Mg^{2+}(aq) + Fe(s)$$
Oxidation states;   0   +2   +2   0
This is a redox reaction since Mg increases in oxidation number (oxidation) and Fe decreases in number (reduction). Fe^{2+} is the oxidizing agent, and Mg is the reducing agent.

   (c) $$Pb(NO_3)_2(aq) + Na_2SO_4(aq) \rightarrow PbSO_4(s) + 2\ NaNO_3(aq)$$
Oxidation states;   +2 +5 – 2   +1 +6 – 2   +2 +6 –2   +1   +5 –2
This is a not a redox reaction since none of the atoms undergoes a change in oxidation number.

   (d) $$HBr(aq) + KOH(aq) \rightarrow H_2O(l) + KBr(aq)$$
Oxidation states;+1 – 1   +1 – 2 +1   +1 –2   +1 –2
This is a not a redox reaction since none of the atoms undergoes a change in oxidation number.

$$(g) \rightarrow SO_2(g)$$

Balanced reaction: $\quad S(s) + O_2(g) \rightarrow SO_2(g)$

(b) Skeletal reaction: $\quad C_3H_6(g) + O_2(g) \rightarrow CO_2(g) + H_2O(g)$

Balance C: $\quad C_3H_6(g) + O_2(g) \rightarrow 3CO_2(g) + H_2O(g)$

Balance H: $\quad C_3H_6(g) + O_2(g) \rightarrow 3CO_2(g) + 3H_2O(g)$

Balance O: $\quad C_3H_6(g) + 9/2\,O_2(g) \rightarrow 3CO_2(g) + 3H_2O(g)$

Clear fraction: $\quad 2C_3H_6(g) + 9O_2(g) \rightarrow 6CO_2(g) + 6H_2O(g)$

(c) Skeletal reaction: $\quad Ca(s) + O_2(g) \rightarrow CaO(s)$

Balance O: $\quad Ca(s) + O_2(g) \rightarrow 2CaO(s)$

Balance Ca: $\quad 2Ca(s) + O_2(g) \rightarrow 2CaO(s)$

(d) Skeletal reaction: $\quad C_5H_{12}S(l) + O_2(g) \rightarrow CO_2(g) + H_2O(g) + SO_2(g)$

Balance C: $\quad C_5H_{12}S(l) + O_2(g) \rightarrow 5CO_2(g) + H_2O(g) + SO_2(g)$

Balance H: $\quad C_5H_{12}S(l) + O_2(g) \rightarrow 5CO_2(g) + 6H_2O(g) + SO_2(g)$

Balance S: $\quad C_5H_{12}S(l) + O_2(g) \rightarrow 5CO_2(g) + 6H_2O(g) + SO_2(g)$

Balance O: $\quad C_5H_{12}S(l) + 9O_2(g) \rightarrow 5CO_2(g) + 6H_2O(g) + SO_2(g)$

Cumulative Problems

4.95 **Given:** In 100 g solution, 20.0 g $C_2H_6O_2$; density of solution = 1.03 g/mL **Find:** M of solution

Conceptual Plan: g $C_2H_6O_2 \rightarrow$ mol $C_2H_6O_2$ and g solution $\rightarrow$ mL solution $\rightarrow$ L solution

$$\frac{1\ \text{mol}\ C_2H_6O_2}{62.06\ \text{g}\ C_2H_6O_2} \qquad\qquad \frac{1.00\ \text{mL}}{1.03\ \text{g}} \qquad \frac{1\ \text{L}}{1000\ \text{mL}}$$

then M $C_2H_6O_2$

$$M = \frac{\text{mol}\ C_2H_6O_2}{\text{L solution}}$$

Solution:

$$20.0\ \cancel{\text{g}\ C_2H_6O_2} \times \frac{1\ \text{mol}\ C_2H_6O_2}{62.06\ \cancel{\text{g}\ C_2H_6O_2}} = 0.3222\ \text{mol}\ C_2H_6O_2$$

$$100.0\ \cancel{\text{g solution}} \times \frac{1.00\ \cancel{\text{mL solution}}}{1.03\ \cancel{\text{g solution}}} \times \frac{1\ \text{L}}{1000\ \cancel{\text{mL}}} = 0.09708\ \text{L}$$

$$M = \frac{0.3222\ \text{mol}\ C_2H_6O_2}{0.09708\ \text{L}} = 3.32\ \text{M}$$

Check: The units of the answer (M $C_2H_6O_2$) are correct. The magnitude of the answer is reasonable since the concentration of solutions is usually between 0 and 18 M.

4.97 **Given:** 2.5 g $NaHCO_3$ **Find:** g HCl

Conceptual Plan: g $NaHCO_3 \rightarrow$ mol $NaHCO_3 \rightarrow$ mol HCl $\rightarrow$ g HCl

$$\frac{1\ \text{mol}\ NaHCO_3}{84.02\ \text{g}\ NaHCO_3} \qquad \frac{1\ \text{mol}\ HCl}{1\ \text{mol}\ NaHCO_3} \qquad \frac{36.46\ \text{g}\ HCl}{1\ \text{mol}\ HCl}$$

Solution: $HCl(aq) + NaHCO_3(aq) \rightarrow H_2O(l) + CO_2(g) + NaCl(aq)$

$$2.5\ \cancel{\text{g}\ NaHCO_3} \times \frac{1\ \cancel{\text{mol}\ NaHCO_3}}{84.02\ \cancel{\text{g}\ NaHCO_3}} \times \frac{1\ \cancel{\text{mol}\ HCl}}{1\ \cancel{\text{mol}\ NaHCO_3}} \times \frac{36.46\ \text{g}\ HCl}{1\ \cancel{\text{mol}\ HCl}} = 1.1\ \text{g}\ HCl$$

Check: The units of the answer (g HCl) are correct. The magnitude of the answer is reasonable since the molar mass of HCl is less than the molar mass of $NaHCO_3$.

4.99 **Given:** 1.0 kg C_8H_{18} **Find:** kg CO_2

Conceptual Plan: kg $C_8H_{18} \rightarrow$ g $C_8H_{18} \rightarrow$ mol $C_8H_{18} \rightarrow$ mol $CO_2 \rightarrow$ g $CO_2 \rightarrow$ kg CO_2

$$\frac{1000\ \text{g}}{\text{kg}} \qquad \frac{1\ \text{mol}\ C_8H_{18}}{114.22\ \text{g}\ C_8H_{18}} \qquad \frac{16\ \text{mol}\ CO_2}{2\ \text{mol}\ C_8H_{18}} \qquad \frac{44.01\ \text{g}\ CO_2}{1\ \text{mol}\ CO_2} \qquad \frac{\text{kg}}{1000\ \text{g}}$$

Solution:
$$2\,C_8H_{18}(g) + 25\,O_2(g) \rightarrow 16\,CO_2(g) + 18\,H_2O(g)$$

$$1.0\ \cancel{kg\ C_8H_{18}} \times \frac{1000\ \cancel{g}}{\cancel{kg}} \times \frac{1\ \cancel{mol\ C_8H_{18}}}{114.22\ \cancel{g\ C_8H_{18}}} \times \frac{16\ \cancel{mol\ CO_2}}{2\ \cancel{mol\ C_8H_{18}}} \times \frac{44.01\ \cancel{g\ CO_2}}{1\ \cancel{mol\ CO_2}} \times \frac{kg}{1000\ \cancel{g}} = 3.1\ kg\ CO_2$$

Check: The units of the answer (kg CO_2) are correct. The magnitude of the answer is reasonable since the ratio of CO_2 to C_8H_{18} is 8:1.

4.101 **Given:** 3.00 mL $C_4H_6O_3$, d = 1.08 g/mL; 1.25 g $C_7H_6O_3$; 1.22 g $C_9H_8O_4$ **Find:** limiting reactant, theoretical yield $C_9H_8O_4$ and % yield $C_9H_8O_4$

Conceptual Plan: mL $C_4H_6O_3 \rightarrow$ g $C_4H_6O_3 \rightarrow$ mol $C_4H_6O_3 \rightarrow$ mol $C_9H_8O_4$

$$\frac{1.08\ g\ C_4H_6O_3}{1.00\ mL\ C_4H_6O_3} \qquad \frac{1\ mol\ C_4H_6O_3}{102.09\ g\ C_4H_6O_3} \qquad \frac{1\ mol\ C_9H_8O_4}{1\ mol\ C_4H_6O_3}$$

$\rightarrow$ smallest amount determines limiting reactant

g $C_7H_6O_3 \rightarrow$ mol $C_7H_6O_3 \rightarrow$ mol $C_9H_8O_4$

$$\frac{1\ mol\ C_7H_6O_3}{138.12\ g\ C_7H_6O_3} \qquad \frac{1\ mol\ C_9H_8O_4}{1\ mol\ C_7H_6O_3}$$

then: mol $C_9H_8O_4 \rightarrow$ g $C_9H_8O_4$ then: determine % yield

$$\frac{180.1\ g\ C_9H_8O_4}{mol\ C_9H_8O_4} \qquad\qquad \frac{actual\ yield\ g\ C_9H_8O_4}{theoretical\ yield\ g\ C_9H_8O_4} \times 100$$

Solution:

$$3.00\ \cancel{mL\ C_4H_6O_3} \times \frac{1.08\ \cancel{g\ C_4H_6O_3}}{\cancel{mL\ C_4H_6O_3}} \times \frac{1\ \cancel{mol\ C_4H_6O_3}}{102.09\ \cancel{g\ C_4H_6O_3}} \times \frac{1\ mol\ C_9H_8O_4}{1\ \cancel{mol\ C_4H_6O_3}} = 0.03174\ mol\ C_9H_8O_4$$

$$1.25\ \cancel{g\ C_7H_6O_3} \times \frac{1\ \cancel{mol\ C_7H_6O_3}}{138.12\ \cancel{g\ C_7H_6O_3}} \times \frac{1\ mol\ C_9H_8O_4}{1\ \cancel{mol\ C_7H_6O_3}} = 0.009050\ mol\ C_9H_8O_4$$

Salicylic acid is the limiting reactant.

$$0.009050\ \cancel{mol\ C_9H_8O_4} \times \frac{180.1\ g\ C_9H_8O_4}{1\ \cancel{mol\ C_9H_8O_4}} = 1.630\ g\ C_9H_8O_4$$

$$\frac{1.22\ \cancel{g\ C_9H_8O_4}}{1.630\ \cancel{g\ C_9H_8O_4}} \times 100 = 74.8\%$$

Check: The theoretical yield has the correct units (g $C_9H_8O_4$) and has a reasonable magnitude compared to the mass of $C_7H_6O_3$, the limiting reactant. The % yield is reasonable, under 100%.

4.103 **Given:** (a) 11 molecules H_2, 2 molecules O_2; (b) 8 molecules H_2, 4 molecules O_2; (c) 4 molecules H_2, 5 molecules O_2; (d) 3 molecules H_2, 6 molecules O_2 **Find:** loudest explosion based on equation

Conceptual Plan: loudest explosion will occur in the balloon with the mol ratio closest to the balanced equation and that contains the most H_2

Solution: $2H_2(g) + O_2(g) \rightarrow H_2O(l)$

Balloon (a) has enough O_2 to react with 4 molecules H_2; balloon (b) has enough O_2 to react with 8 molecules H_2; balloon (c) has enough O_2 to react with 10 molecules H_2; and balloon (d) has enough O_2 for 3 molecules of H_2 to react. Therefore, balloon (b) will have the loudest explosion because it has the most H_2 that will react.

Check: Answer seems correct since it has the most H_2 with enough O_2 in the balloon to completely react.

4.105   (a)   Skeletal reaction: $HCl(aq) + Hg_2(NO_3)_2(aq) \rightarrow Hg_2Cl_2(s) + HNO_3(aq)$

     Balance Cl: $2HCl(aq) + Hg_2(NO_3)_2(aq) \rightarrow Hg_2Cl_2(s) + 2HNO_3(aq)$

     (b)   Skeletal reaction: $KHSO_3(aq) + HNO_3(aq) \rightarrow H_2O(l) + SO_2(g) + KNO_3(aq)$

     Balanced reaction: $KHSO_3(aq) + HNO_3(aq) \rightarrow H_2O(l) + SO_2(g) + KNO_3(aq)$

     (c)   Skeletal reaction: $NH_4Cl(aq) + Pb(NO_3)_2(aq) \rightarrow PbCl_2(s) + NH_4NO_3(aq)$

     Balance Cl: $2NH_4Cl(aq) + Pb(NO_3)_2(aq) \rightarrow PbCl_2(s) + NH_4NO_3(aq)$

     Balance N: $2NH_4Cl(aq) + Pb(NO_3)_2(aq) \rightarrow PbCl_2(s) + 2NH_4NO_3(aq)$

(d)   Skeletal reaction: $NH_4Cl(aq) + Ca(OH)_2(aq) \rightarrow NH_3(g) + H_2O(l) + CaCl_2(aq)$

Balance Cl: $2NH_4Cl(aq) + Ca(OH)_2(aq) \rightarrow NH_3(g) + H_2O(l) + CaCl_2(aq)$

Balance N: $2NH_4Cl(aq) + Ca(OH)_2(aq) \rightarrow 2NH_3(g) + H_2O(l) + CaCl_2(aq)$

Balance H: $2NH_4Cl(aq) + Ca(OH)_2(aq) \rightarrow 2NH_3(g) + 2H_2O(l) + CaCl_2(aq)$

4.107   **Given:** 1.5 L solution, 0.050 M $CaCl_2$, 0.085 M $Mg(NO_3)_2$ **Find:** g Na_3PO_4

Conceptual Plan: V,M $CaCl_2$ → mol $CaCl_2$ and V,M $Mg(NO_3)_2$ → mol $Mg(NO_3)_2$

$$V \times M = mol \qquad\qquad V \times M = mol$$

then (mol $CaCl_2$ + mol $Mg(NO_3)_2$) → Na_3PO_4 → g Na_3PO_4

$$\frac{2\text{ mol } Na_3PO_4}{3\text{ mol } (CaCl_2 + Mg(NO_3)_2)} \qquad \frac{163.97\text{ g } Na_3PO_4}{1\text{ mol } Na_3PO_4}$$

Solution: $3CaCl_2(aq) + 2Na_3PO_4(aq) \rightarrow Ca_3(PO_4)_2(s) + 6\,NaCl(aq)$

$3\,Mg(NO_3)_2(aq) + 2Na_3PO_4(aq) \rightarrow Mg_3(PO_4)_2(s) + 6\,NaCl(aq)$

$1.5\text{ L} \times 0.050\text{ M } CaCl_2 = 0.07\underline{5}\text{ mol } CaCl_2$

$1.5\text{ L} \times 0.085\text{ M } Mg(NO_3)_2 = 0.1\underline{2}75\text{ mol } Mg(NO_3)_2$

$$0.2025 \text{ mol } CaCl_2 \text{ and } Mg(NO_3)_2 \times \frac{2\text{ mol } Na_3PO_4}{3\text{ mol } CaCl_2 \text{ and } Mg(NO_3)_2} \times \frac{163.97\text{ g mol } Na_3PO_4}{\text{mol } Na_3PO_4} = 22\text{ g mol } Na_3PO_4$$

Check: The units of the answer (g Na_3PO_4) are correct. The magnitude of the answer is reasonable since it is needed to remove both the Ca and Mg ions.

4.109   **Given:** 1.0 L, 0.10 M OH^- **Find:** g Ba

Conceptual Plan: VM → mol OH^- → mol $Ba(OH)_2$ → mol BaO → mol Ba → g Ba

$$V \times M = mol \quad \frac{1\text{ mol } Ba(OH)_2}{2\text{ mol } OH} \quad \frac{1\text{ mol } BaO}{1\text{ mol } Ba(OH)_2} \quad \frac{1\text{ mol } Ba}{1\text{ mol } BaO} \quad \frac{137.3\text{ g } Ba}{1\text{ mol } Ba}$$

Solution: $BaO(s) + H_2O(l) \rightarrow Ba(OH)_2(aq)$

$$1.0\text{ L} \times \frac{0.10\text{ mol } OH^-}{\text{L}} \times \frac{1\text{ mol } Ba(OH)_2}{2\text{ mol } OH^-} \times \frac{1\text{ mol } BaO}{1\text{ mol } Ba(OH)_2} \times \frac{1\text{ mol } Ba}{1\text{ mol } BaO} \times \frac{137.3\text{ g } Ba}{1\text{ mol } Ba} = 6.9\text{ g Ba}$$

Check: The units of the answer (g Ba) are correct. The magnitude is reasonable since the molar mass of Ba is large and there are 2 moles hydroxide per mole Ba.

4.111   **Given:** 30.0% $NaNO_3$, \$9.00/ 100 lb; 20.0 % $(NH_4)_2SO_4$, \$8.10/ 100 lb   **Find:** cost / lb N

Conceptual Plan: mass fertilizer → mass $NaNO_3$ → mass N → cost/lb N

$$\frac{30.0\text{ lb } NaNO_3}{100\text{ lb fertilizer}} \quad \frac{16.48\text{ lb N}}{100\text{ lb } NaNO_3} \quad \frac{\$9.00}{100\text{ lb fertilizer}}$$

and: mass fertilizer → mass $(NH_4)_2SO_4$ → mass N → cost/lb N

$$\frac{20.0\text{ lb } (NH_4)_2SO_4}{100\text{ lb fertilizer}} \quad \frac{21.2\text{ lb N}}{100\text{ lb } (NH_4)_2SO_4} \quad \frac{\$8.10}{100\text{ lb fertilizer}}$$

Solution:

$$100\text{ lb fertilizer} \times \frac{30.0\text{ lb } NaNO_3}{100\text{ lb fertilizer}} \times \frac{16.48\text{ lb N}}{100\text{ lb } NaNO_3} = 4.9\underline{4}4\text{ lb N}$$

$$\frac{\$9.00}{100\text{ lb fertilizer}} \times \frac{100\text{ lb fertilizer}}{4.944\text{ lb N}} = \$1.8\underline{2}/\text{ lb N}$$

$$100\text{ lb fertilizer} \times \frac{20.0\text{ lb } (NH_4)_2SO_4}{100\text{ lb fertilizer}} \times \frac{21.2\text{ lb N}}{100\text{ lb } (NH_4)_2SO_4} = 4.2\underline{4}0\text{ lb N}$$

$$\frac{\$8.10}{100\text{ lb fertilizer}} \times \frac{100\text{ lb fertilizer}}{4.24\text{ lb N}} = \$1.9\underline{1}/\text{ lb N}$$

The more economical fertilizer is the $NaNO_3$ because it costs less/ lb N.

Check: The units of the cost (\$/lb N) are correct. The answer is reasonable because you compare the cost/lb N directly.

4.113   **Given:** 24.5 g Au, 24.5 g BrF_3, 24.5 g KF **Find:** g $KAuF_4$
Conceptual Plan: g Au → mol Au → mol $KAuF_4$

$$\frac{1 \text{ mol Au}}{196.97 \text{ g Au}} \quad \frac{2 \text{ mol } KAuF_4}{2 \text{ mol Au}}$$

g BrF_3 → mol BrF_3 → mol $KAuF_4$ → **smallest mol amount determines limiting reactant**

$$\frac{1 \text{ mol } BrF_3}{136.9 \text{ g } BrF_3} \quad \frac{2 \text{ mol } KAuF_4}{2 \text{ mol } BrF_3}$$

g KF → mol KF → mol $KAuF_4$

$$\frac{1 \text{ mol KF}}{58.10 \text{ g KF}} \quad \frac{2 \text{ mol } KAuF_4}{2 \text{ mol KF}}$$

then: mol $KAuF_4$ → g $KAuF_4$

$$\frac{312.07 \text{ g } KAuF_4}{\text{mol } KAuF_4}$$

$$2 \text{ Au}(s) + 2BrF_3(l) + 2KF(s) \rightarrow Br_2(l) + 2KAuF_4(s)$$

Oxidation states;   0   + 3– 1   +1– 1   0   +1 +3 – 1

This is a redox reaction since Au increases in oxidation number (oxidation) and Br decreases in number (reduction). BrF_3 is the oxidizing agent, and Au is the reducing agent.
Solution:

$$24.5 \text{ g Au} \times \frac{1 \text{ mol Au}}{196.97 \text{ g Au}} \times \frac{2 \text{ mol } KAuF_4}{2 \text{ mol Au}} = 0.1244 \text{ mol } KAuF_4$$

$$24.5 \text{ g } BrF_3 \times \frac{1 \text{ mol } BrF_3}{136.90 \text{ g } BrF_3} \times \frac{2 \text{ mol } KAuF_4}{2 \text{ mol } BrF_3} = 0.1790 \text{ mol } KAuF$$

$$24.5 \text{ g KF} \times \frac{1 \text{ mol KF}}{58.10 \text{ g KF}} \times \frac{2 \text{ mol } KAuF_4}{2 \text{ mol KF}} = 0.4217 \text{ mol } KAuF_4$$

$$0.1244 \text{ mol } KAuF_4 \times \frac{312.07 \text{ g } KAuF_4}{1 \text{ mol } KAuF_4} = 38.8 \text{ g } KAuF_4$$

Check: Units of the answer (g $KAuF_4$) are correct. The magnitude of the answer is reasonable compared to the mass of the limiting reactant Au.

4.115   **Given:** solution may contain Ag^+, Ca^{2+}, and Cu^{2+} **Find:** determine which ions are present
Conceptual Plan: test the solution sequentially with NaCl, Na_2SO_4, and Na_2CO_3 and see if precipitates form
Solution: Original solution + NaCl yields no reaction: Ag^+ is not present since chlorides are normally soluble, but Ag^+ is an exception.
Original solution with Na_2SO_4 yields a precipitate and solution 2. The precipitate is $CaSO_4$, so Ca^{2+} is present. Sulfates are normally soluble but Ca^{2+} is an exception.
Solution 2 with Na_2CO_3 yields a precipitate. The precipitate is $CuCO_3$, so Cu^{2+} is present. All carbonates are insoluble.
NET IONIC EQUATIONS:

$$Ca^{2+}(aq) + SO_4{}^{2-}(aq) \rightarrow CaSO_4(s)$$
$$Cu^{2+}(aq) + CO_3{}^{2-}(aq) \rightarrow CuCO_3(s)$$

Check: The answer is reasonable since two different precipitates formed and all the Ca^{2+} was removed before the carbonate was added.

4.117   **Given:** 1.00 g NH_3 **Find:** g PH_3
Conceptual Plan: Determine reaction sequence, then g NH_3 → mol NH_3 → mol PH_3 → g PH_3

$$\frac{1 \text{ mol } NH_3}{17.04 \text{ g } NH_3} \qquad \frac{34.00 \text{ g } PH_3}{1 \text{ mol } PH_3}$$

Solution: Balance the reaction sequence:

$$6NH_3 + 71/2 \, O_2 \rightarrow \cancel{6NO} + 9H_2O$$
$$\cancel{6NO} + P_4 \rightarrow \cancel{P_4O_6} + 3 \, N_2$$
$$\cancel{P_4O_6} + 6H_2O \rightarrow \cancel{4H_3PO_3}$$
$$\cancel{4H_3PO_3} \rightarrow PH_3 + 3H_3PO_4$$

Therefore, 6 mol NH_3 produces 1 mol PH_3

$$1.00 \text{ g } NH_3 \times \frac{1 \text{ mol } NH_3}{17.04 \text{ g } NH_3} \times \frac{1 \text{ mol } PH_3}{6 \text{ mol } NH_3} \times \frac{34.00 \text{ g } PH_3}{1 \text{ mol } PH_3} = 0.333 \text{ g } PH_3$$

Check: The answer is g PH_3, which is correct. The magnitude is reasonable. Even though the molar mass of PH_3 is greater than NH_3, 6 mol of NH_3 are required to produce 1 mol PH_3.

4.119   **Given:** 10.0 kg mixture, 30.35% hexane, 15.85% heptane, 53.80% octane **Find:** Total mass CO_2
Conceptual Plan: kg hexane $\rightarrow$ **kmol hexane** $\rightarrow$ **kmol CO_2** $\rightarrow$ **kg CO_2**

$$\frac{1\ kmol\ C_6H_{14}}{86.20\ kg\ C_6H_{14}} \qquad \frac{12\ kmol\ CO_2}{2\ kmol\ C_6H_{14}} \qquad \frac{44.01\ kg\ CO_2}{1\ kmol\ CO_2}$$

kg heptane $\rightarrow$ **kmol heptane** $\rightarrow$ **kmol CO_2** $\rightarrow$ **kg CO_2**

$$\frac{1\ kmol\ C_7H_{16}}{100.23\ kg\ C_7H_{16}} \qquad \frac{7\ kmol\ CO_2}{1\ kmol\ C_7H_{16}} \qquad \frac{44.01\ kg\ CO_2}{1\ kmol\ CO_2}$$

kg octane $\rightarrow$ **kmol octane** $\rightarrow$ **kmol CO_2** $\rightarrow$ **kg CO_2**

$$\frac{1\ kmol\ C_8H_{18}}{114.26\ kg\ C_8H_{18}} \qquad \frac{16\ kmol\ CO_2}{2\ kmol\ C_8H_{18}} \qquad \frac{44.01\ kg\ CO_2}{1\ kmol\ CO_2}$$

Solution: Balanced Reactions:

$$2C_6H_{14}(l) + 19O_2(g) \rightarrow 12CO_2(g) + 14H_2O(l)$$
$$C_7H_{16}(l) + 11O_2(g) \rightarrow 7CO_2(g) + 8H_2O(l)$$
$$2C_8H_{18}(l) + 25O_2(g) \rightarrow 16CO_2(g) + 18H_2O(l)$$

$$10.0\ kg\ mix \times \frac{30.35\ kg\ C_6H_{14}}{100.0\ kg\ mix} \times \frac{1\ kmol\ C_6H_{14}}{86.20\ kg\ C_6H_{14}} \times \frac{12\ kmol\ CO_2}{2\ kmol\ C_6H_{14}} \times \frac{44.01\ kg\ CO_2}{1\ kmol\ CO_2} = 9.29\underline{7}\ kg\ CO_2$$

$$10.0\ kg\ mix \times \frac{15.85\ kg\ C_7H_{16}}{100.0\ kg\ mix} \times \frac{1\ kmol\ C_7H_{16}}{100.23\ kg\ C_7H_{16}} \times \frac{7\ kmol\ CO_2}{1\ kmol\ C_7H_{16}} \times \frac{44.01\ kg\ CO_2}{1\ kmol\ CO_2} = 4.87\underline{1}\ kg\ CO_2$$

$$10.0\ kg\ mix \times \frac{53.80\ kg\ C_8H_{18}}{100.0\ kg\ mix} \times \frac{1\ kmol\ C_8H_{18}}{114.26\ kg\ C_8H_{18}} \times \frac{16\ kmol\ CO_2}{2\ kmol\ C_8H_{18}} \times \frac{44.01\ kg\ CO_2}{1\ kmol\ CO_2} = \underline{}78\ kg\ CO_2$$

Total CO_2 = 9.30 kg + 4.87 kg + 16.6 kg = 30.8 kg CO_2
Check: The units of the answer (kg CO_2) are correct. The magnitude of the answer is reasonable since a large amount of CO_2 is produced per mole of hydrocarbon.

Challenge Problems

4.121   **Given:** g C_3H_8 + C_2H_2 = 2.0 g; mol CO_2 = 1.5 mol H_2O **Find:** original g C_2H_2
Conceptual Plan: mol C_3H_8 $\rightarrow$ **mol CO_2 and mol H_2O and mol C_2H_2** $\rightarrow$ **mol CO_2 and mol H_2O**
Solution: Let a = mol C_3H_8 and b = mol C_2H_2

$$C_3H_8 + 5O_2 \rightarrow 3CO_2 + 4H_2O \qquad\qquad C_2H_2 + 3/2O_2 \rightarrow 2CO_2 + H_2O$$
$$\ \ a \qquad\qquad\quad 3a \quad\ 4a \qquad\qquad\qquad\quad b \qquad\qquad\quad 2b \quad\ b$$

Total mol CO_2 = 3a + 2b   and total mol H_2O = 4a + b
mol CO_2 = 1.5(mol H_2O)
So: 3a + 2b = 1.5(4a + b)

And $\left(a\ mol\ C_3H_8 \times \dfrac{44.11\ C_3H_8}{1\ mol\ C_3H_8} \right) + \left(b\ mol\ C_2H_2 \times \dfrac{26.01\ C_2H_2}{mol\ C_2H_2} \right) = 2.0\ g$

Solve simultaneous equations: a = 9.9$\underline{8}$ × 10^{-3} mol C_3H_8 and b = 0.059$\underline{9}$ mol C_2H_2
Substitute for b and solve for grams C_2H_2.

$$0.06\underline{0}\ mol\ C_2H_2 \times \frac{26.01\ C_2H_2}{mol\ C_2H_2} = 1.5\underline{6}\ g\ C_2H_2 = 1.6\ g\ C_2H$$

Check: The units of the answer (g C_2H_2) are correct. The magnitude is reasonable since it is less than the total mass.

4.123   **Given:** 0.100L, 1.22M NaI; total mass = 28.1 g **Find:** g AgI
Conceptual Plan: vol, M $\rightarrow$ **mol NaI** $\rightarrow$ **mol I^- ; total mol I^-** $\rightarrow$ **mol AgI and HgI_2**

Solution: $0.100 \text{ L soln} \times \dfrac{1.22 \text{ mol NaI}}{\text{L soln}} \times \dfrac{1 \text{ mol I}^-}{\text{mol NaI}} = 0.122 \text{ mol I}^-$

Let $x = \text{mol AgI}$ and $y = \text{mol HgI}_2$

$x + 2y = 0.122 \text{ mol I}^-$ so $y = 0.061 - 0.5x$

$\left(x \text{ mol AgI} \times \dfrac{234.77 \text{ g AgI}}{1 \text{ mol AgI}} \right) + \left(y \text{ mol HgI}_2 \times \dfrac{454.39 \text{ g HgI}_2}{\text{mol HgI}_2} \right) = 28.1 \text{ g}$

Solve the simultaneous equations and $x = 0.0504 \text{ mol AgI}$

$0.0504 \text{ mol AgI} \times \dfrac{234.77 \text{ g AgI}}{1 \text{ mol AgI}} = 11.8 \text{ g AgI}$

Check: The units of the answer (g AgI) are correct. The magnitude is reasonable since it is less than the total mass.

4.125 **Given:** 3.5×10^{-3} M Ca^{2+}. 1.1×10^{-3} M Mg^{2+}, 19.5 gal H$_2$O; 0.65 kg detergent/load **Find:** % by mass Na$_2$CO$_3$
Conceptual Plan: gal H$_2$O $\rightarrow$ **L H$_2$O then VM** $\rightarrow$ **mol Ca^{2+} and VM** $\rightarrow$ **mol Mg^{2+}**

$$\dfrac{3.785 \text{ L}}{1 \text{ gal}} \qquad \text{vol} \times \text{M} = \text{mol} \qquad \text{vol} \times \text{M} = \text{mol}$$

Then total moles ions $\rightarrow$ **mol CO$_3^{2-}$** $\rightarrow$ **mol Na$_2$CO$_3$** $\rightarrow$ **g Na$_2$CO$_3$** $\rightarrow$ **kg Na$_2$CO$_3$** $\rightarrow$ **% Na$_2$CO$_3$**

$$\dfrac{1 \text{ mol CO}_3^{2-}}{1 \text{ mol ion}} \quad \dfrac{1 \text{ mol Na}_2\text{CO}_3}{1 \text{ mol CO}_3^{2-}} \quad \dfrac{106.01 \text{ g Na}_2\text{CO}_3}{1 \text{ mol Na}_2\text{CO}_3} \quad \dfrac{\text{kg}}{1000 \text{ g}} \quad \dfrac{\text{kg Na}_2\text{CO}_3}{\text{kg detergent} \times 100}$$

Solution: $19.5 \text{ gal} \times \dfrac{3.785 \text{ L}}{1 \text{ gal}} \times \dfrac{3.5 \times 10^{-3} \text{ mol Ca}^{2+}}{\text{L}} = 0.258 \text{ mol Ca}^{2+}$

$19.5 \text{ gal} \times \dfrac{3.785 \text{ L}}{1 \text{ gal}} \times \dfrac{1.1 \times 10^{-3} \text{ mol Mg}^{2+}}{\text{L}} = 0.08119 \text{ mol Mg}^{2+}$

$0.3392 \text{ mol ions} \times \dfrac{1 \text{ mol CO}_3^{2-}}{\text{mol ions}} \times \dfrac{1 \text{ mol Na}_2\text{CO}_3}{\text{mol CO}_3^{2-}} \times \dfrac{106.01 \text{ g Na}_2\text{CO}_3}{1 \text{ mol Na}_2\text{CO}_3} \times \dfrac{\text{kg Na}_2\text{CO}_3}{1000 \text{ g Na}_2\text{CO}_3} = 0.03596 \text{ kg Na}_2\text{CO}_3$

$\dfrac{0.03596 \text{ kg Na}_2\text{CO}_3}{0.65 \text{ kg detergent}} \times 100 = 5.5 \text{ % Na}_2\text{CO}_3$

Check: The units of the answer (% Na$_2$CO$_3$) are correct. The magnitude of the answer is reasonable. The percent is less than 100 %.

4.127 In designing the unit you would need to consider the theoretical yield and % yield of the reaction, how changing the limiting reactant would affect the reaction, and the stoichiometry between KO$_2$ and O$_2$ in order to determine the mass of KO$_2$ required to produce enough O$_2$ for 10 minutes. You might also consider the speed of the reaction and whether or not the reaction produced heat. Additionally, because your body does not use 100% of the oxygen taken in with each breath, the apparatus would only need to replenish the oxygen used. The percentage of oxygen in air is about 20% and the percentage in exhaled air is about 16%, so we will assume that 4% of the air would need to be replenished with oxygen. (NOTE: The problem can also be solved by finding the amount of KO$_2$ that would be required to react with all of the exhaled CO$_2$.)
Given: air = 4% O$_2$ **Find:** O$_2$ for 10 min breathing time
Conceptual Plan: 10 min $\rightarrow$ **vol air** $\rightarrow$ **vol O2** $\rightarrow$ **mol O2** $\rightarrow$ **mol KO2** $\rightarrow$ **g KO2**

$$\dfrac{8 \text{ L air}}{1 \text{ min}} \quad \dfrac{4 \text{ L O}_2}{100 \text{ L air}} \quad \dfrac{1 \text{ mol O}_2}{22.4 \text{ L O}_2} \quad \dfrac{4 \text{ mol KO}_2}{3 \text{ mol O}_2} \quad \dfrac{71.10 \text{ g KO}_2}{2}$$

Solution: $10 \text{ min.} \times \dfrac{8 \text{ L air}}{\text{min}} \times \dfrac{4 \text{ L O}_2}{100 \text{ L air}} \times \dfrac{1 \text{ mol O}_2}{22.4 \text{ L O}_2} \times \dfrac{4 \text{ mol KO}_2}{3 \text{ mol O}_2} \times \dfrac{71.10 \text{ g KO}_2}{1 \text{ mol KO}_2} = 14 \text{ g KO}_2$

Check: The units of the answer (g KO$_2$) are correct. The magnitude of the answer is reasonable since it is an amount that could be carried in a portable device.

4.129 **Given:** 151 g Na$_2$B$_4$O$_7$ **Find:** g B$_5$H$_9$
Conceptual Plan: g Na$_2$B$_4$O$_7$ $\rightarrow$ **mol Na$_2$B$_4$O$_7$** $\rightarrow$ **mol B$_5$H$_9$** $\rightarrow$ **g B$_5$H$_9$**

$$\dfrac{\text{mol Na}_2\text{B}_4\text{O}_7}{201.22 \text{ g Na}_2\text{B}_4\text{O}_7} \quad \dfrac{4 \text{ mol B}_5\text{H}_9}{5 \text{ mol Na}_2\text{B}_4\text{O}_7} \quad \dfrac{63.13 \text{ g B}_5\text{H}_9}{\text{mol B}_5\text{H}_9}$$

Solution: All the B in B_5H_9 goes to the $Na_2B_4O_7$ so the mole ratio between the two can be used.

$$151 \text{ g Na}_2\text{B}_4\text{O}_7 \times \frac{1 \text{ mol Na}_2\text{B}_4\text{O}_7}{201.22 \text{ g Na}_2\text{B}_4\text{O}_7} \times \frac{4 \text{ mol B}_5\text{H}_9}{5 \text{ mol Na}_2\text{B}_4\text{O}_7} \times \frac{63.13 \text{ g B}_5\text{H}_9}{1 \text{ mol B}_5\text{H}_9} = 37.9 \text{ g B}_5\text{H}_9$$

Check: The units of the answer (g B_5H_9) are correct. The magnitude of the answer is reasonable since the molar mass of B_5H_9 is less than the molar mass of $Na_2B_4O_7$.

4.131   **Given:** 5 mol NO, 10 mol H_2 **Find:** conditions of product mixture
     Conceptual Plan: mol H_2 → mol NO and mol H_2 → mol NH_3 and mol H_2 → mol H_2O
     Solution: The correct answer is a. Since the mol ratio of H_2 to NO is 5:2, the 10 mol of H_2 will require 4 mol NO and H_2 is the limiting reactant. This eliminates answers b and c. Since there is excess NO, this eliminates d, leaving answer a.

4.133   **Given:** 6 molecules N_2H_4; 4 molecules N_2O_4; (a) contains 9 molecules N_2, 12 molecules H_2O, and 1 molecule N_2O_4; solution (b) contains 12 molecules N_2, 16 molecules H_2O, and 2 molecules N_2O_4; solution (c) contains 9 molecules N_2, 12 molecules H_2O **Find:** theoretical yield N_2, H_2O
     Conceptual Plan: molecules N_2H_4 → molecules N_2

$$\frac{3 \text{ molecules N}_2}{2 \text{ molecules N}_2\text{H}_4} \quad \rightarrow \textbf{ smallest molecules amount determines}$$

limiting reactant

molecules N_2O_4 → molecules N_2

$$\frac{3 \text{ molecules N}_2}{1 \text{ molecules N}_2\text{O}_4}$$

molecules N_2H_4 → molecules H_2O

$$\frac{4 \text{ molecules H}_2\text{O}}{2 \text{ molecules N}_2\text{H}_4}$$

molecules N_2H_4 → molecules N_2O_4

$$\frac{1 \text{ molecules N}_2\text{O}_4}{2 \text{ molecules N}_2\text{H}_4}$$

Solution: $6 \text{ molecules N}_2\text{H}_4 \times \dfrac{3 \text{ molecules N}_2}{2 \text{ molecules N}_2\text{H}_4} = 9 \text{ molecules N}_2$

$6 \text{ molecules N}_2\text{O}_4 \times \dfrac{3 \text{ molecules N}_2}{1 \text{ molecules N}_2\text{O}_4} = 18 \text{ molecules N}_2$

Limiting reactant = N_2H_4 because it produced the least molecules of N_2

$6 \text{ molecules N}_2\text{H}_4 \times \dfrac{4 \text{ molecules H}_2\text{O}}{2 \text{ molecules N}_2\text{H}_4} = 12 \text{ molecules H}_2\text{O}$

$6 \text{ molecules N}_2\text{H}_4 \times \dfrac{1 \text{ molecules N}_2\text{O}_4}{2 \text{ molecules N}_2\text{H}_4} = 3 \text{ molecules N}_2\text{O}_4 \text{ used}$

Reaction mixture should contain 9 molecules N_2, 12 molecules H_2O, and 1 molecule N_2O_4; this is best represented by (a).

5 Gases

Review Questions

5.1   Pressure is the force exerted per unit area by gas molecules as they strike the surfaces around them. Pressure is caused by collisions of gas molecules with surfaces or other gas molecules.

5.3   When you exhale, you reverse the process of inhalation. The chest cavity muscles relax, which decreases the lung volume, increasing the pressure within the lungs and forcing the air out of the lungs.

5.5   A manometer is a U-shaped tube containing a dense liquid, usually mercury. In an open-ended manometer, one end of the tube is open to atmospheric pressure and the other is attached to a flask containing the gas sample. If the pressure of the gas sample is exactly equal to atmospheric pressure, then the mercury levels on both sides of the tube are the same. If the pressure of the sample is greater than atmospheric pressure, the mercury level on the sample side of the tube is lower than on the side open to the atmosphere. If the pressure of the sample is less than atmospheric pressure, the mercury level on the sample side is higher than on the side open to the atmosphere. This type of manometer always measures the pressure of the gas sample relative to atmospheric pressure. The difference in height between the two levels is equal to the pressure difference from atmospheric pressure.

5.7   This pain is caused by air-containing cavities within your ear. When you ascend a mountain, the external pressure (the pressure that surrounds you) drops, while the pressure within your ear cavities (the internal pressure) remains the same. This creates an imbalance—the greater internal pressure forces your eardrum to bulge outward, causing pain. With time, and the help of a yawn or two, the excess air within your ear cavities escapes, equalizing the internal and external pressure and relieving the pain.

5.9   When we breathe, we expand the volume of our chest cavity, reducing the pressure on the outer surface of the lungs to less than 1 atm (Boyle's law). Because of this pressure differential, the lungs expand, the pressure in them falls, and air from outside our lungs then flows into them. Extra-long snorkels do not work because of the pressure exerted by water at an increased depth. A diver at 10 m experiences an external pressure of 2 atm. This is more than the muscles of the chest cavity can overcome—the chest cavity and lungs are compressed, resulting in an air pressure within them of more than 1 atm. If the diver had a snorkel that went to the surface—where the air pressure is 1 atm—air would flow out of his lungs, not into them. It would be impossible to breathe.

5.11   The ideal gas law ($PV = nRT$) combines all of the relationships between the four variables relevent to gases (pressure, volume, number of moles, and temperature (in kelvin's)) in one simple expression.

5.13   The molar volume of an ideal gas is the volume occupied by one mole of gas at T = 0 °C (273 K) and P = 1.00 atm. Substituting these values into the ideal gas law, one can calculate this value as 22.414 L.

5.15   The pressure due to any individual component in a gas mixture is called the partial pressure (P_n) of that component and can be calculated from the ideal gas law by assuming that each gas component acts independently. The sum of the partial pressures of the components in a gas mixture must equal the total pressure: $P_{total} = P_a + P_b + P_c + \ldots$ where P_{total} is the total pressure and P_a, P_b, $P_c \ldots$ are the partial pressures of the components.

5.17   No, when collecting a gas over water, it will contain some water molecules. The vapor pressure of water can be gotten from Table 5.4. Therefore, $P_{Gas} = P_{Total} - P_{H_2O}$.

5.19   The basic postulates of kinetic molecular theory are as follows: (1) The size of a particle is negligibly small, (2) the average kinetic energy of a particle is proportional to the temperature in kelvins, and (3) the collision of one particle with another (or with the walls) is completely elastic. Pressure is defined as force divided by area. According to kinetic molecular theory, a gas is a collection of particles in constant motion. The motion results in collisions between the particles and the surfaces around them. As each particle collides with a surface, it exerts a force upon that surface. The result of many particles in a gas sample exerting forces on the surfaces around them is constant pressure.

5.21   Postulate 2 of kinetic molecular theory states that the average kinetic energy is proportional to the temperature in kelvins. The root mean square velocity of a collection of gas particles is inversely proportional to the square root of the molar mass of the particles in kilograms per mole.

5.23   The process by which gas molecules spread out in response to a concentration gradient is called diffusion. Effusion is the process by which a gas escapes from a container into a vacuum through a small hole. The rate of effusion is inversely proportional to the square root of the molar mass of the gas.

5.25   Sulfur oxides (SO_x): Sulfur oxides include SO_2 and SO_3, which are produced chiefly during coal-fired electricity generation and industrial metal refining. Carbon monoxide (CO): Carbon monoxide is formed by the incomplete combustion of fossil fuels (petroleum, natural gas, and coal). It is emitted mainly by motor vehicles. Nitrogen oxides (NO_x): Nitrogen oxides include NO and NO_2, which are emitted by motor vehicles, by fossil-fuel based electricity generation plants, and by any high temperature combustion process that occurs in air. Ozone (O_3): Ozone is produced when some of the products of fossil-fuel combustion, especially nitrogen oxides and unburned volatile organic compounds (VOCs), react in the presence of sunlight. The levels of all of these pollutants are decreasing over U.S. cities.

5.27   Chlorofluorocarbons (CFCs) are blamed for destroying stratospheric ozone. When CFCs reach the stratosphere, UV light (which is less abundant below the ozone layer because the ozone absorbs it) breaks a carbon-chlorine bond in the CFC, generating a very reactive chlorine atom. This chlorine atom then reacts with ozone in a cyclic reaction that destroys two ozone molecules and regenerates itself to repeat the process. In this way, a single chlorine atom can destroy hundreds of ozone molecules. Legislation has been passed in many nations calling for a complete ban on CFC production beginning in 1996.

Converting Between Pressure Units

5.29   (a)   **Given:** 24.9 in Hg   **Find:** atm
        Conceptual Plan: in Hg $\rightarrow$ atm
        $$\frac{1\,atm}{29.92\,in\,Hg}$$
        Solution: $24.9\,\cancel{in\,Hg} \times \dfrac{1\,atm}{29.92\,\cancel{in\,Hg}} = 0.832\,atm$
        Check: The units (atm) are correct. The magnitude of the answer (<1) makes physical sense because we started with less than 29.92 in Hg.

        (b)   **Given:** 24.9 in Hg   **Find:** mmHg
        Conceptual Plan: Use answer from part (a) then convert atm $\rightarrow$ mmHg
        $$\frac{760\,mm\,Hg}{1\,atm}$$
        Solution: $0.832\,\cancel{atm} \times \dfrac{760\,mm\,Hg}{1\,\cancel{atm}} = 632\,mmHg$
        Check: The units (mmHg) are correct. The magnitude of the answer (< 760 mmHg) makes physical sense because we started with less than 1 atm.

(c)   **Given:** 24.9 in Hg   **Find:** psi
Conceptual Plan: Use answer from part (a) then convert atm → psi

$$\frac{14.7\,\text{psi}}{1\,\text{atm}}$$

Solution: $0.832\,\cancel{\text{atm}} \times \dfrac{14.7\,\text{psi}}{1\,\cancel{\text{atm}}} = 12.2\,\text{psi}$

Check: The units (psi) are correct. The magnitude of the answer (< 14.7 psi) makes physical sense because we started with less than 1 atm.

(d)   **Given:** 24.9 in Hg   **Find:** Pa
Conceptual Plan: Use answer from part (a) then convert atm → Pa

$$\frac{101{,}325\,\text{Pa}}{1\,\text{atm}}$$

Solution: $0.832\,\cancel{\text{atm}} \times \dfrac{101{,}325\,\text{Pa}}{1\,\cancel{\text{atm}}} = 8.43 \times 10^4\,\text{Pa}$

Check: The units (mmHg) are correct. The magnitude of the answer (< 101,325 Pa) makes physical sense because we started with less than 1 atm.

5.31   (a)   **Given:** 31.85 in Hg   **Find:** mmHg
Conceptual Plan: in Hg → mmHg

$$\frac{25.4\,\text{mmHg}}{1\,\text{in Hg}}$$

Solution: $31.85\,\cancel{\text{in Hg}} \times \dfrac{25.4\,\text{mmHg}}{1\,\cancel{\text{in Hg}}} = 809.0\,\text{mmHg}$

Check: The units (mmHg) are correct. The magnitude of the answer (809) makes physical sense because inches are larger than mm.

(b)   **Given:** 31.85 in Hg   **Find:** atm
Conceptual Plan: Use answer from part (a) then convert mmHg → atm

$$\frac{1\,\text{atm}}{760\,\text{mmHg}}$$

Solution: $809.0\,\cancel{\text{mmHg}} \times \dfrac{1\,\text{atm}}{760\,\cancel{\text{mmHg}}} = 1.064\,\text{atm}$

Check: The units (atm) are correct. The magnitude of the answer (>1) makes physical sense because we started with more than 760 mmHg.

(c)   **Given:** 31.85 in Hg   **Find:** torr
Conceptual Plan: Use answer from part (a) then convert mmHg → torr

$$\frac{1\,\text{torr}}{1\,\text{mmHg}}$$

Solution: $809.0\,\cancel{\text{mmHg}} \times \dfrac{1\,\text{torr}}{1\,\cancel{\text{mmHg}}} = 809.0\,\text{torr}$

Check: The units (torr) are correct. The magnitude of the answer (809) makes physical sense because both units are of the same size.

(d)   **Given:** 31.85 in Hg   **Find:** kPa
Conceptual Plan: Use answer from part b) then convert atm → Pa → kPa

$$\frac{101{,}325\,\text{Pa}}{1\,\text{atm}}\quad\frac{1\,\text{kPa}}{1000\,\text{Pa}}$$

Solution: $1.064\,\cancel{\text{atm}} \times \dfrac{101{,}325\,\cancel{\text{Pa}}}{1\,\cancel{\text{atm}}} \times \dfrac{1\,\text{kPa}}{1000\,\cancel{\text{Pa}}} = 107.8\,\text{kPa}$

Check: The units (kPa) are correct. The magnitude of the answer (108) makes physical sense because we started with more than 1 atm and there are ~101 kPa in an atm.

5.33   (a)   **Given:** $P_{bar} = 762.4$ mm Hg and figure   **Find:** P_{gas}
Conceptual plan: Measure height difference then convert cm Hg → mm Hg → mm Hg

$$\frac{10\,\text{mm Hg}}{1\,\text{cm Hg}}\qquad P_{gas} = h + P_{bar}$$

Solution:

$h = 7.0\,\cancel{\text{cm Hg}} \times \dfrac{10\,\text{mm Hg}}{1\,\cancel{\text{cm Hg}}} = 70.\ \text{mm Hg}$ $P_{gas} = 70.\ \text{mm Hg} + 762.4\ \text{mm Hg} = 832\ \text{mm Hg}$

Check: The units (mm Hg) are correct. The magnitude of the answer (832 mm Hg) makes physical sense because the mercury column is higher on the right, indicating that the pressure is above barometric pressure. No significant figures to the right of the decimal point can be reported since the mercury height is known only to the 1's place.

(b)   **Given**: $P_{bar} = 762.4$ mm Hg and figure   **Find**: P_{gas}
     Conceptual plan: Measure height difference then convert cm Hg $\rightarrow$ **mm Hg** $\rightarrow$ **mm Hg**

$$\frac{10\,\text{mm Hg}}{1\,\text{cm Hg}} \qquad P_{gas} = h + P_{bar}$$

     Solution:

$$h = -4.4\,\overline{\text{cm Hg}} \times \frac{10\,\text{mm Hg}}{1\,\overline{\text{cm Hg}}} = -44 \text{ mm Hg} \quad P_{gas} = -44 \text{ mm Hg} + 762.4 \text{ mm Hg} = 718 \text{ mm Hg}$$

     Check: The units (mm Hg) are correct. The magnitude of the answer (718 mm Hg) makes physical sense because the mercury column is higher on the left, indicating that the pressure is below barometric pressure. No significant figures to the right of the decimal point can be reported since the mercury height is known only to the 1's place.

Simple Gas Laws

5.35   **Given**: $V_1 = 5.6$ L, $P_1 = 735$ mmHg, and $V_2 = 9.4$ L   **Find**: P_2
     Conceptual Plan: $V_1, P_1, V_2 \rightarrow P_2$

$$P_1 V_1 = P_2 V_2$$

     Solution:
     $P_1 V_1 = P_2 V_2$ Rearrange to solve for P_2.

$$P_2 = P_1 \frac{V_1}{V_2} = 735 \text{ mmHg} \times \frac{5.6\,\cancel{\text{L}}}{9.4\,\cancel{\text{L}}} = 437.872 \text{ mmHg} = 4.4 \times 10^2$$

     Check: The units (mmHg) are correct. The magnitude of the answer (440 mmHg) makes physical sense because Boyle's Law indicates that as the volume increases, the pressure decreases.

5.37   **Given**: $V_1 = 48.3$ mL, $T_1 = 22\,°C$, and $T_2 = 87\,°C$ **Find**: V_2
     Conceptual Plan: $°C \rightarrow K$ then $V_1, T_1, T_2 \rightarrow V_2$

$$K = °C + 273.15 \qquad \frac{V_1}{T_1} = \frac{V_2}{T_2}$$

     Solution: $T_1 = 22\,°C + 273.15 = 295$ K and $T_2 = 87\,°C + 273.15 = 360.$ K

$$\frac{V_1}{T_1} = \frac{V_2}{T_2} \text{ Rearrange to solve for } V_2.\ V_2 = V \frac{T_2}{T_1} = 48.3 \text{ mL} \times \frac{360 \text{ K}}{295 \text{ K}} = 58.9 \text{ mL}$$

     Check: The units (mL) are correct. The magnitude of the answer (59 mL) makes physical sense because Charles's Law indicates that as the volume increases, the temperature increases.

5.39   **Given**: $V_1 = 2.46$ L, $n_1 = 0.158$ mol, and $\Delta n = 0.113$ mol   **Find**: V_2
     Conceptual Plan: $n_1 \rightarrow n_2$ then $V_1, n_1, n_2 \rightarrow V_2$

$$n_1 + \Delta n = n_2 \qquad \frac{V_1}{n_1} = \frac{V_2}{n_2}$$

     Solution: $n_2 = 0.158$ mol $+ 0.113$ mol $= 0.271$ mol

$$\frac{V_1}{n_1} = \frac{V_2}{n_2} \text{ Rearrange to solve for } V_2.\ V_2 = {}_1\frac{n_2}{n_1} = 2.46 \text{ L} \times \frac{0.271\,\cancel{\text{mol}}}{0.158\,\cancel{\text{mol}}} = 4.21937 \text{ L} = 4.22 \text{ L}$$

     Check: The units (L) are correct. The magnitude of the answer (4 L) makes physical sense because Avogadro's Law indicates that as the number of moles increases, the volume increases.

Ideal Gas Law

5.41   **Given**: $n = 0.118$ mol, $P = 0.97$ atm, and $T = 305$ K   **Find**: V
     Conceptual Plan: $n, P, T \rightarrow V$

$$PV = nRT$$

     Solution: $PV = nRT$ Rearrange to solve for V. $V = \dfrac{nRT}{P} = \dfrac{0.118\,\cancel{\text{mol}} \times 0.08206 \dfrac{\text{L} \cdot \cancel{\text{atm}}}{\cancel{\text{mol}} \cdot \cancel{\text{K}}} \times 305\,\cancel{\text{K}}}{0.97\,\cancel{\text{atm}}} = 3.0 \text{ L}$

The volume would be the same for argon gas because the ideal gas law does not care about the mass of the gas, only the number of moles of gas.

Check: The units (L) are correct. The magnitude of the answer (3 L) makes sense because, as you will see in the next section, one mole of an ideal gas under standard conditions (273 K and 1 atm) occupies 22.4 L. Although these are not standard conditions, they are close enough for a ballpark check of the answer. Since this gas sample contains 0.118 moles, a volume of 3 L is reasonable.

5.43   **Given:** $V = 10.0$ L, $n = 0.448$ mol, and $T = 315$ K   **Find:** P
       Conceptual Plan: $n, V, T \rightarrow P$
$$PV = nRT$$
Solution:

$PV = nRT$ Rearrange to solve for P. $P = \dfrac{nRT}{V} = \dfrac{0.448 \text{ mol} \times 0.08206 \dfrac{\text{L} \cdot \text{atm}}{\text{mol} \cdot \text{K}} \times 315 \text{ K}}{10.0 \text{ L}} = 1.16$ atm

Check: The units (atm) are correct. The magnitude of the answer (~1 atm) makes sense because, as you will see in the next section, one mole of an ideal gas under standard conditions (273 K and 1 atm) occupies 22.4 L. Although these are not standard conditions, they are close enough for a ballpark check of the answer. Since this gas sample contains 0.448 moles in a volume of 10 L, a pressure of 1 atm is reasonable.

5.45   **Given:** $V = 28.5$ L, $P = 1.8$ atm, and $T = 298$ K   **Find:** n
       Conceptual Plan: $V, P, T \rightarrow n$
$$PV = nRT$$
Solution: $PV = nRT$ Rearrange to solve for n. $n = \dfrac{PV}{RT} = \dfrac{1.8 \text{ atm} \times 28.5 \text{ L}}{0.08206 \dfrac{\text{L} \cdot \text{atm}}{\text{mol} \cdot \text{K}} \times 298 \text{ K}} = 2.1$ mol

Check: The units (mol) are correct. The magnitude of the answer (2 mol) makes sense because, as you will see in the next section, one mole of an ideal gas under standard conditions (273 K and 1 atm) occupies 22.4 L. Although these are not standard conditions, they are close enough for a ballpark check of the answer. Since this gas sample has a volume of 28.5 L, and a pressure of 1.8 atm, ~ 2 mol is reasonable.

5.47   **Given:** $P_1 = 36.0$ psi (gauge P), $V_1 = 11.8$ L, $T_1 = 12.0$ °C, $V_2 = 12.2$ L, and $T_2 = 65.0$ °C
       Find: P_2 and compare to $P_{max} = 38.0$ psi (gauge P)
       Conceptual Plan: °C $\rightarrow$ K and gauge P $\rightarrow$ psi $\rightarrow$ atm then $P_1, V_1, T_1, V_2, T_2 \rightarrow P_2$
$$K = \text{°C} + 273.15 \qquad \text{psi} = \text{gauge P} + 14.7 \quad \frac{1 \text{ atm}}{14.7 \text{ psi}} \qquad\qquad \frac{P_1 V_1}{T_1} = \frac{P_2 V_2}{T_2}$$
Solution: $T_1 = 12.0$ °C $+ 273.15 = 285.2$ K and $T_2 = 65.0$ °C $+ 273.15 = 338.2$ K

$P_1 = 36.0$ psi (gauge P) $+ 14.7 = 50.7 \text{ psi} \times \dfrac{1 \text{ atm}}{14.7 \text{ psi}} = 3.44898$ atm

$P_{max} = 38.0$ psi (gauge P) $+ 14.7 = 52.7 \text{ psi} \times \dfrac{1 \text{ atm}}{14.7 \text{ psi}} = 3.59$ atm

$\dfrac{P_1 V_1}{T_1} = \dfrac{P_2 V_2}{T_2}$ Rearrange to solve for P_2. $P_2 = P_1 \dfrac{V_1}{V_2} \dfrac{T_2}{T_1} = 3.44898$ atm $\times \dfrac{11.8 \text{ L}}{12.2 \text{ L}} \times \dfrac{338.2 \text{ K}}{285.2 \text{ K}} = 3.96$ atm

This exceeds the maximum tire rating of 3.59 atm or 38.0 psi (gauge P).
Check: The units (atm) are correct. The magnitude of the answer (3.95 atm) makes physical sense because the relative increase in T is greater than the relative increase in V, so P should increase.

5.49   **Given:** m (CO_2) $= 28.8$ g, $P = 742$ mmHg, and $T = 22$ °C   **Find:** V
       Conceptual Plan: °C $\rightarrow$ K and mmHg $\rightarrow$ atm and g $\rightarrow$ mol then $n, P, T \rightarrow V$
$$K = \text{°C} + 273.15 \qquad \frac{1 \text{ atm}}{760 \text{ mm Hg}} \qquad \frac{1 \text{ mol}}{44.01 \text{ g}} \qquad\qquad PV = nRT$$
Solution: $T_1 = 22$ °C $+ 273.15 = 295$ K, $P = 742 \text{ mmHg} \times \dfrac{1 \text{ atm}}{760 \text{ mmHg}} = 0.976316$ atm,

$n = 28.8 \text{ g} \times \dfrac{1 \text{ mol}}{44.01 \text{ g}} = 0.654397$ mol $PV = nRT$ Rearrange to solve for V.

$V = \dfrac{nRT}{P} = \dfrac{0.654397 \text{ mol} \times 0.08206 \dfrac{\text{L} \cdot \text{atm}}{\text{mol} \cdot \text{K}} \times 295 \text{ K}}{0.976316 \text{ atm}} = 16.2$ L

Check: The units (L) are correct. The magnitude of the answer (16 L) makes sense because one mole of an ideal gas under standard conditions (273 K and 1 atm) occupies 22.4 L. Although these are not standard conditions, they are close enough for a ballpark check of the answer. Since this gas sample contains 0.65 moles, a volume of 16 L is reasonable.

Molar Volume, Density, and Molar Mass of a Gas

5.51 **Given**: 26.0 g argon, $V = 55.0$ mL, and $T = 295$ K **Find**: P
Conceptual Plan: $g \rightarrow n$ and $mL \rightarrow L$ then $n, V, T \rightarrow P$

$$\frac{1 \, mol}{39.95 \, g} \qquad \frac{1 \, L}{1000 \, mL} \qquad P V = nRT$$

Solution: $26.0 \, \text{g Ar} \times \dfrac{1 \, mol \, Ar}{39.95 \, \text{g Ar}} = 0.6508135 \, mol \, Ar \quad 55.0 \, \text{mL} \times \dfrac{1 \, L}{1000 \, mL} = 0.0550 \, L$

$P V = nRT$ Rearrange to solve for P.

$$P = \frac{nRT}{V} = \frac{0.6508135 \, \text{mol} \times 0.08206 \, \frac{\text{L} \cdot \text{atm}}{\text{mol} \cdot \text{K}} \times 295 \, \text{K}}{0.0550 \, \text{L}} = 286.44906 \, atm = 286 \, atm$$

Check: The units (atm) are correct. The magnitude of the answer (300 atm) makes sense because, as you will see in the next section, one mole of an ideal gas under standard conditions (273 K and 1 atm) occupies 22.4 L. Although these are not standard conditions, they can be used for a ballpark check of the answer. Since the volume is ~ $1/400^{th}$ the molar volume and we have ~2/3 of a mole, the resulting pressure should be $(400)(2/3) = 270$ atm.

Given: $V_1 = 55.0$ mL, $P_1 = 286$ atm, and $P_2 = 1.20$ atm **Find**: V_2 (number of 750 mL-bottles)
Conceptual Plan: $V_1, P_1, P_2 \rightarrow V_2$

$$P_1 V_1 = P_2 V_2$$

Solution: $P_1 V_1 = P_2 V_2$ Rearrange to solve for V_2.

$$V_2 = V_1 \frac{P_1}{P_2} = 55.0 \, mL \times \frac{286.44906 \, \text{atm}}{1.20 \, \text{atm}} = 1.31289 \times 10^4 \, \text{mL} \times \frac{1 \, bottle}{750.0 \, mL} = 17.5 \, bottles$$

Check: The units (bottles) are correct. The magnitude of the answer (18 bottles) makes physical sense because Boyle's Law indicates that as the volume decreases, the pressure increases. The pressure is decreasing by a factor of ~ 250 and so the volume should increase by this factor.

5.53 **Given**: sample a = 5 gas particles, sample b = 10 gas particles, and sample c = 8 gas particles, with all temperatures and volumes the same **Find**: sample with largest P
Conceptual Plan: $n, V, T \rightarrow P$

$$P V = nRT$$

Solution: $P V = nRT$ Since V and T are constant, this means that $P \propto n$. The sample with the largest number of particles will have the largest P. $P_b > P_c > P_a$.

5.55 **Given**: $P_1 = 755$ mmHg, $T_1 = 25 \, °C$, and $T_2 = 1155 \, °C$ **Find**: P_2
Conceptual Plan: $°C \rightarrow K$ and $mmHg \rightarrow atm$ then $P_1, T_1, T_2 \rightarrow P_2$

$$K = °C + 273.15 \qquad \frac{1 \, atm}{760 \, mmHg} \qquad \frac{P_1}{T_1} = \frac{P_2}{T_2}$$

Solution: $T_1 = 25 \, °C + 273.15 = 298$ K and $T_2 = 1155 \, °C + 273.15 = 1428$ K

$P = 755 \, \text{mmHg} \times \dfrac{1 \, atm}{760 \, \text{mmHg}} = 0.993421 \, atm \quad \dfrac{P_1}{T_1} = \dfrac{P_2}{T_2}$ Rearrange to solve for P_2.

$$P_2 = P_1 \frac{T_2}{T_1} = 0.993421 \, atm \times \frac{1428 \, K}{298 \, K} = 4.76 \, atm$$

Check: The units (atm) are correct. The magnitude of the answer (5 atm) makes physical sense because there is a significant increase in T, which will increase P significantly.

5.57 **Given**: STP and m (Ne) = 33.6 g **Find**: V
Conceptual Plan: $g \rightarrow mol \rightarrow V$

$$\frac{1 \, mol}{20.18 \, g} \qquad \frac{22.414 \, L}{1 \, mol}$$

Solution: $33.6 \, \text{g} \times \dfrac{1 \, mol}{20.18 \, \text{g}} \times \dfrac{22.414 \, L}{1 \, mol} = 37.3 \, L$

Check: The units (L) are correct. The magnitude of the answer (37 L) makes sense because one mole of an ideal gas under standard conditions (273 K and 1 atm) occupies 22.4 L and we have about 1.7 mol.

5.59 **Given:** H_2, $P = 1655$ psi, and $T = 20.0$ °C **Find:** d
Conceptual Plan: °C → K and psi → atm then $P, T, \mathcal{M} \rightarrow d$

$$K = °C + 273.15 \qquad \frac{1\,\text{atm}}{14.70\,\text{psi}} \qquad\qquad d = \frac{P\mathcal{M}}{RT}$$

Solution: $T = 20.0$ °C $+ 273.15 = 293.2$ K $\qquad P = 1655\,\cancel{\text{psi}} \times \dfrac{1\,\text{atm}}{14.70\,\cancel{\text{psi}}} = 112.\underline{5}85$ atm

$$d = \frac{P\mathcal{M}}{RT} = \frac{112.\underline{5}85\,\cancel{\text{atm}} \times 2.016\,\dfrac{\text{g}}{\cancel{\text{mol}}}}{0.08206\dfrac{\text{L}\cdot\cancel{\text{atm}}}{\cancel{\text{K}}\cdot\cancel{\text{mol}}} \times 293.2\,\cancel{\text{K}}} = 9.434\,\frac{\text{g}}{\text{L}}$$

Check: The units (g/L) are correct. The magnitude of the answer (9 g/L) makes physical sense because this is a high pressure, so the gas density will be on the high side.

5.61 **Given:** $V = 248$ mL, $m = 0.433$ g, $P = 745$ mmHg, and $T = 28$ °C **Find:** $\mathcal{M}$
Conceptual Plan: °C → K mmHg → atm mL → L then $V, m \rightarrow d$ then $d, P, T \rightarrow \mathcal{M}$

$$K = °C + 273.15 \quad \frac{1\,\text{atm}}{760\,\text{mmHg}} \quad \frac{1\,\text{L}}{1000\,\text{mL}} \qquad d = \frac{m}{V} \qquad d = \frac{P\mathcal{M}}{RT}$$

Solution: $T = 28$ °C $+ 273.15 = 301$ K $\quad P = 745\,\cancel{\text{mmHg}} \times \dfrac{1\,\text{atm}}{760\,\cancel{\text{mmHg}}} = 0.980263$ atm

$V = 248\,\cancel{\text{mL}} \times \dfrac{1\,\text{L}}{1000\,\cancel{\text{mL}}} = 0.248$ L $\quad d = \dfrac{m}{V} = \dfrac{0.433\,\text{g}}{0.248\,\text{L}} = 1.7\underline{4}597$ g/L $\quad d = \dfrac{P\mathcal{M}}{RT}$ Rearrange to solve for $\mathcal{M}$.

$$\mathcal{M} = \frac{dRT}{P} = \frac{1.7\underline{4}597\,\dfrac{\text{g}}{\cancel{\text{L}}} \times 0.08206\dfrac{\cancel{\text{L}}\cdot\cancel{\text{atm}}}{\cancel{\text{K}}\cdot\text{mol}} \times 301\,\cancel{\text{K}}}{0.980263\,\cancel{\text{atm}}} = 44.0\,\text{g/mol}$$

Check: The units (g/mol) are correct. The magnitude of the answer (44 g/mol) makes physical sense because this is a reasonable number for a molecular weight of a gas.

5.63 **Given:** $m = 38.8$ mg, $V = 224$ mL, $T = 55$ °C, and $P = 886$ torr **Find:** $\mathcal{M}$
Conceptual Plan: mg → g mL → L °C → K torr → atm then $V, m \rightarrow d$ then $d, P, T \rightarrow \mathcal{M}$

$$\frac{1\,\text{g}}{1000\,\text{mg}} \quad \frac{1\,\text{L}}{1000\,\text{mL}} \quad K = °C + 273.15 \quad \frac{1\,\text{atm}}{760\,\text{torr}} \qquad d = \frac{m}{V} \qquad d = \frac{P\mathcal{M}}{RT}$$

Solution: $m = 38.8\,\cancel{\text{mg}} \times \dfrac{1\,\text{g}}{1000\,\cancel{\text{mg}}} = 0.0388$ g $\quad V = 224\,\cancel{\text{mL}} \times \dfrac{1\,\text{L}}{1000\,\cancel{\text{mL}}} = 0.224$ L $\quad T = 55$ °C $+ 273.15 = 328$ K

$P = 886\,\cancel{\text{torr}} \times \dfrac{1\,\text{atm}}{760\,\cancel{\text{torr}}} = 1.165789$ atm $\quad d = \dfrac{m}{V} = \dfrac{0.0388\,\text{g}}{0.224\,\text{L}} = 0.17\underline{3}214$ g/L $\quad d = \dfrac{P\mathcal{M}}{RT}$

Rearrange to solve for $\mathcal{M}$. $\quad \mathcal{M} = \dfrac{dRT}{P} = \dfrac{0.17\underline{3}214\,\dfrac{\text{g}}{\cancel{\text{L}}} \times 0.08206\dfrac{\cancel{\text{L}}\,\cancel{\text{atm}}}{\cancel{\text{K}}\,\text{mol}} \times 328\,\cancel{\text{K}}}{1.165789\,\cancel{\text{atm}}} = 4.00\,\text{g/mol}$

Check: The units (g/mol) are correct. The magnitude of the answer (4 g/mol) makes physical sense because this is a reasonable number for a molecular weight of a gas, especially since the density is on the low side.

Partial Pressure

5.65 **Given:** $P_{N_2} = 215$ torr, $P_{O_2} = 102$ torr, $P_{He} = 117$ torr, $V = 1.35$ L, and $T = 25.0$ °C
Find: P_{Total}, m_{N_2}, m_{O_2}, m_{He}
Conceptual Plan: °C → K and torr → atm and $P, V, T \rightarrow n$ then mol → g

$$K = °C + 273.15 \qquad \frac{1\,\text{atm}}{760\,\text{torr}} \qquad PV = nRT \qquad \mathcal{M}$$

and $P_{N_2}, P_{O_2}, P_{He} \rightarrow P_{Total}$

$$P_{Total} = P_{N_2} + P_{O_2} + P_{He}$$

Solution: $T_1 = 25.0$ °C $+ 273.15 = 298.2$ K, $\quad PV = nRT$ Rearrange to solve for n.

$n = \dfrac{PV}{RT} \quad P_{N_2} = 215\,\cancel{\text{torr}} \times \dfrac{1\,\text{atm}}{760\,\cancel{\text{torr}}} = 0.2828947$ atm $\quad n_{N_2} = \dfrac{0.2828947\,\cancel{\text{atm}} \times 1.35\,\cancel{\text{L}}}{0.08206\,\dfrac{\cancel{\text{L}}\cdot\cancel{\text{atm}}}{\text{mol}\cdot\cancel{\text{K}}} \times 298.2\,\cancel{\text{K}}} = 0.01560700$ mol

$0.01560700\,\cancel{\text{mol}} \times \dfrac{28.02\,\text{mol}}{1\,\cancel{\text{mol}}} = 0.437\,\text{g}\,N_2$

$P_{O_2} = 102\,\cancel{\text{torr}} \times \dfrac{1\,\text{atm}}{760\,\cancel{\text{torr}}} = 0.1342105$ atm $\quad n_{O_2} = \dfrac{0.1342105\,\cancel{\text{atm}} \times 1.35\,\cancel{\text{L}}}{0.08206\,\dfrac{\cancel{\text{L}}\cdot\cancel{\text{atm}}}{\text{mol}\cdot\cancel{\text{K}}} \times 298.2\,\cancel{\text{K}}} = 0.007404252$ mol

$$0.007404252 \; \cancel{mol} \; \times \; \frac{32.00 \; mol}{1 \; \cancel{mol}} = 0.237 \; g \; O_2$$

$$P_{He} = 117 \; \cancel{torr} \times \frac{1 \; atm}{760 \; \cancel{torr}} = 0.1539474 \; atm \quad n_{He} = \frac{0.1539474 \; \cancel{atm} \times 1.35 \; \cancel{L}}{0.08206 \; \frac{\cancel{L} \cdot \cancel{atm}}{mol \cdot \cancel{K}} \times 298.2 \; \cancel{K}} = 0.008493113 \; mol$$

$$0.008493113 \; \cancel{mol} \; \times \; \frac{4.003 \; mol}{1 \; \cancel{mol}} = 0.0340 \; g \; He \; and$$

$P_{Total} = P_{N_2} + P_{O_2} + P_{He} = 0.283 \; atm + 0.134 \; atm + 0.154 \; atm = 0.571 \; atm \; or$

$P_{Total} = P_{N_2} + P_{O_2} + P_{He} = 215 \; torr + 102 \; torr + 117 \; torr = 434 \; torr$

Check: The units (g and atm) are correct. The magnitude of the answer (1 g) makes sense because gases are not very dense and these pressures are < 1 atm. Since all of the pressures are small, the total is < 1 atm.

5.67   **Given:** $m \; (CO_2) = 1.20 \; g$, $V = 755 \; mL$, $P_{N_2} = 725 \; mmHg$, and $T = 25.0 \; °C$ **Find:** P_{Total}

Conceptual Plan: mL $\rightarrow$ L and °C $\rightarrow$ K and g $\rightarrow$ mol and $n, P, T \rightarrow V$ then atm $\rightarrow$ mmHg

$$\frac{1 \; L}{1000 \; mL} \qquad K = °C + 273.15 \qquad \frac{1 \; mol}{44.01 \; g} \qquad\qquad PV = nRT \qquad \frac{760 \; mmHg}{1 \; atm}$$

finally $P_{CO_2}, P_{N_2} \rightarrow P_{Total}$

$$P_{Total} = P_{CO_2} + P_{N_2}$$

Solution: $V = 755 \; \cancel{mL} \times \dfrac{L}{1000 \; \cancel{mL}} = 0.755 \; L \quad T = 25.0 \; °C + 273.15 = 298.2 \; K,$

$n = 1.20 \; \cancel{g} \times \dfrac{1 \; mol}{44.01 \; \cancel{g}} = 0.0272665 \; mol, \quad PV = nRT$ Rearrange to solve for P.

$$P = \frac{nRT}{V} = \frac{0.0272665 \; \cancel{mol} \times 0.08206 \; \frac{\cancel{L} \cdot atm}{\cancel{mol} \cdot \cancel{K}} \times 298.2 \; \cancel{K}}{0.755 \; \cancel{L}} = 0.883735 \; atm$$

$$P_{CO_2} = 0.883735 \; \cancel{atm} \times \frac{760 \; mmHg}{1 \; \cancel{atm}} = 672 \; mmHg$$

$$P_{Total} = P_{CO_2} + P_{N_2} = 672 \; mmHg + 725 \; mmHg = 1397 \; mmHg \; or \; 1397 \cancel{torr} \times \frac{1 \; atm}{760 \; \cancel{torr}} = 1.84 \; atm$$

Check: The units (mmHg) are correct. The magnitude of the answer (1400 mmHg) makes sense because it must be greater than 725 mmHg.

5.69   **Given:** $m \; (N_2) = 1.25 \; g$, $m \; (O_2) = 0.85 \; g$, $V = 1.55 \; L$, and $T = 18 \; °C$ **Find:** $\chi_{N_2}, \; _{O_2}, \; P_{N_2}, \; P_{O_2}$

Conceptual Plan: g $\rightarrow$ mol then $n_{N_2}, \; n_{O_2} \rightarrow \chi_{N_2}$ and $n_{N_2}, \; n_{O_2} \rightarrow \chi_{O_2}$ °C $\rightarrow$ K

$$\mathcal{M} \qquad\qquad \chi_{N_2} = \frac{n_{N_2}}{n_{N_2} + n_{O_2}} \qquad \chi_{O_2} = \frac{O_2}{n_{N_2} + n_{O_2}} \qquad K = °C + 273.15$$

then $n, V, T \rightarrow P$

$$PV = nRT$$

Solution: $n_{N_2} = 1.25 \; \cancel{g} \times \dfrac{1 \; mol}{28.02 \; \cancel{g}} = 0.0446110 \; mol, \; n_{O_2} = 0.85 \; \cancel{g} \times \dfrac{1 \; mol}{32.00 \; \cancel{g}} = 0.026563 \; mol,$

$T = 18 \; °C + 273.15 = 291 \; K, \; \chi_{N_2} = \dfrac{n_{N_2}}{n_{N_2} + n_{O_2}} = \dfrac{0.0446110 \; mol}{0.0446110 \; mol + 0.026563 \; mol} = 0.626792 = 0.627,$

$\chi_{O_2} = \dfrac{n_{O_2}}{n_{N_2} + n_{O_2}} = \dfrac{0.026563}{0.0446110 \; mol + 0.026563 \; mol} = 0.373212$ We can also calculate this as

$\chi_{O_2} = 1 - \chi_{N_2} = 1 - 0.626792 = 0.373208 = 0.373 \; PV = nRT$ Rearrange to solve for P. $P = \dfrac{nRT}{V}$

$$P_{N_2} = \frac{0.044611 \; \cancel{mol} \times 0.08206 \frac{\cancel{L} \cdot atm}{\cancel{mol} \cdot \cancel{K}} \times 291 \cancel{K}}{1.55 \; \cancel{L}} = 0.687 \; atm$$

$$P_{O_2} = \frac{0.026563 \; \cancel{mol} \times 0.08206 \frac{\cancel{L} \cdot atm}{\cancel{mol} \cdot \cancel{K}} \times 291 \cancel{K}}{1.55 \; \cancel{L}} = 0.409 \; atm$$

Check: The units (none and atm) are correct. The magnitude of the answers makes sense because the mole fractions should total 1 and since the weight of N_2 is greater than O_2, its mole fraction is larger. The number of moles is <<1, so we expect the pressures to be <1 atm, given the V (1.55 L).

5.71   **Given:** $T = 30.0\ °C$, $P_{Total} = 732$ mmHg, and $V = 722$ mL   **Find:** P_{H_2} and m_{H_2}

Conceptual Plan: $T \rightarrow P_{H_2O}$ then $P_{Total}, P_{H_2O} \rightarrow P_{H_2}$ then mmHg $\rightarrow$ atm and mL $\rightarrow$ L

$$\underset{\text{Table 5.4}}{} \qquad \underset{P_{Total} = P_{H_2O} + P_{H_2}}{} \qquad \frac{1\,\text{atm}}{760\,\text{mmHg}} \qquad \frac{1\,\text{L}}{1000\,\text{mL}}$$

and $°C \rightarrow K$ $P, V, T \rightarrow n$ **then** mol $\rightarrow$ g

$$\underset{K = °C + 273.15}{} \qquad \underset{PV = nRT}{} \qquad \frac{2.016\,\text{g}}{1\,\text{mol}}$$

Solution: Table 5.4 states that at 30° C, $P_{H_2O} = 31.86$ mmHg $P_{Total} = P_{H_2O} + P_{H_2}$

Rearrange to solve for P_{H_2}. $P_{H_2} = P_{Total} - P_{H_2O} = 732$ mmHg $-$ 31.86 mmHg $=$ 700. mmHg

$$P_{H_2} = 700.\ \cancel{\text{mmHg}} \times \frac{1\ \text{atm}}{760\ \cancel{\text{mmHg}}} = 0.92\underline{1}052\ \text{atm} \quad V = 722\ \cancel{\text{mL}} \times \frac{1\ \text{L}}{1000\ \cancel{\text{mL}}} = 0.722\ \text{L,}$$

$$T = 30.0\ °C + 273.15 = 303.2\ K, \quad P\,V = nRT \quad \text{Rearrange to solve for } n. \quad n = \frac{PV}{RT}$$

$$n_{H_2} = \frac{0.92\underline{1}052\ \cancel{\text{atm}} \times 0.722\ \cancel{\text{L}}}{0.08206\ \dfrac{\cancel{\text{L}} \cdot \cancel{\text{atm}}}{\text{mol} \cdot \cancel{\text{K}}} \times 303.2\ \cancel{\text{K}}} = 0.026\underline{7}277\ \text{mol} \quad \text{then } 0.026\underline{7}277\ \cancel{\text{mol}} \times \frac{2.016\ \text{g}}{1\ \cancel{\text{mol}}} = 0.0539\ \text{g H}_2$$

Check: The units (g) are correct. The magnitude of the answer ($<<$ 1 g) makes sense because gases are not very dense, hydrogen is light, the volume is small, and the pressure is ~1 atm.

5.73   **Given:** $T = 25\ °C$, $P_{Total} = 748$ mmHg, and $V = 0.951$ L   **Find:** P_{H_2} and m_{H_2}

Conceptual Plan: $T \rightarrow P_{H_2O}$ then $P_{Total}, P_{H_2O} \rightarrow P_{H_2}$ then mmHg $\rightarrow$ atm and mL $\rightarrow$ L

$$\underset{\text{Table 5.4}}{} \qquad \underset{P_{Total} = P_{H_2O} + P_{H_2}}{} \qquad \frac{1\,\text{atm}}{760\,\text{mmHg}} \qquad \frac{1\,\text{L}}{1000\,\text{mL}}$$

and $°C \rightarrow K$ $P, V, T \rightarrow n$ **then** mol $\rightarrow$ g

$$\underset{K = °C + 273.15}{} \qquad \underset{PV = nRT}{} \qquad \frac{2.016\,\text{g}}{1\,\text{mol}}$$

Solution: Table 5.4 states that at 25° C, $P_{H_2O} = 23.78$ mmHg $P_{Total} = P_{H_2O} + P_{H_2}$

Rearrange to solve for P_{H_2}. $P_{H_2} = P_{Total} - P_{H_2O} = 748$ mmHg $-$ 23.78 mmHg $=$ 724 mmHg

$$P_{H_2} = 724\ \cancel{\text{mmHg}} \times \frac{1\ \text{atm}}{760\ \cancel{\text{mmHg}}} = 0.95\underline{2}632\ \text{atm} \quad T = 25\ °C + 273.15 = 298\ K, \quad P\,V = nRT$$

Rearrange to solve for n. $n_{H_2} = \dfrac{PV}{RT} = \dfrac{0.95\underline{2}632\ \cancel{\text{atm}} \times 0.951\ \cancel{\text{L}}}{0.08206\ \dfrac{\cancel{\text{L}} \cdot \cancel{\text{atm}}}{\text{mol} \cdot \cancel{\text{K}}} \times 298\ \cancel{\text{K}}} = 0.037\underline{0}474\ \text{mol}$

$$0.037\underline{0}474\ \cancel{\text{mol}} \times \frac{2.016\ \text{g}}{1\ \cancel{\text{mol}}} = 0.0747\ \text{g H}_2$$

Check: The units (g) are correct. The magnitude of the answer ($<<$ 1 g) makes sense because gases are not very dense, hydrogen is light, the volume is small, and the pressure is ~1 atm.

Reaction Stoichiometry Involving Gases

5.75   **Given:** $m\ (C) = 15.7$ g, $P = 1.0$ atm, and $T = 355$ K **Find:** V

Conceptual Plan: g C $\rightarrow$ mol C $\rightarrow$ mol H_2 then n (mol H_2), $P, T \rightarrow V$

$$\frac{1\,\text{mol}}{12.01\,\text{g C}} \quad \frac{1\,\text{mol}\,H_2}{1\,\text{mol C}} \qquad\qquad PV = nRT$$

Solution: $15.7\ \cancel{\text{g C}} \times \dfrac{1\ \cancel{\text{mol C}}}{12.01\ \cancel{\text{g C}}} \times \dfrac{1\ \text{mol }H_2}{1\ \cancel{\text{mol C}}} = 1.3\underline{0}724\ \text{mol }H_2, \quad P\,V = nRT$ Rearrange to solve for V.

$$V = \frac{nRT}{P} = \frac{1.3\underline{0}724\ \cancel{\text{mol}} \times 0.08206\ \dfrac{\text{L} \cdot \cancel{\text{atm}}}{\cancel{\text{mol}} \cdot \cancel{\text{K}}} \times 355\ \cancel{\text{K}}}{1.0\ \cancel{\text{atm}}} = 38\ \text{L}$$

Check: The units (L) are correct. The magnitude of the answer (38 L) makes sense because we have more than one mole of gas, and so we expect more than 22 L.

5.77   **Given:** P = 748 mmHg, T = 86 °C, and m (CH$_3$OH) = 25.8 g, and   **Find:** V_{H_2} and V_{CO}
       Conceptual Plan: g CH$_3$OH → mol CH$_3$OH → mol H$_2$ and mmHg → atm and °C → K

$$\frac{1\,mol\,CH_3OH}{32.04\,g\,CH_3OH} \qquad \frac{2\,mol\,H_2}{1\,mol\,CH_3OH} \qquad \frac{1\,atm}{760\,mmHg} \qquad K = °C + 273.15$$

then n (mol H$_2$), P, T → V and mol H$_2$ → mol CO then n (mol CO), P, T → V

$$PV = nRT \qquad \frac{1\,mol\,CO}{2\,mol\,H_2} \qquad PV = nRT$$

Solution: $25.8 \; \cancel{g\,CH_3OH} \times \dfrac{1 \; \cancel{mol\,CH_3OH}}{32.04 \; \cancel{g\,CH_3OH}} \times \dfrac{2 \; mol\,H_2}{1 \; \cancel{mol\,CH_3OH}} = 1.61049 \; mol\,H_2,$

$P_{H_2} = 748 \; \cancel{mmHg} \times \dfrac{1\,atm}{760 \; \cancel{mmHg}} = 0.984211 \; atm, \; T = 86 °C + 273.15 = 359 \; K, \; PV = nRT$

Rearrange to solve for V. $V = \dfrac{nRT}{P} \qquad V_{H_2} = \dfrac{1.61049 \; \cancel{mol} \times 0.08206 \dfrac{L \cdot \cancel{atm}}{\cancel{mol} \cdot \cancel{K}} \times 359 \; \cancel{K}}{0.984211 \; \cancel{atm}} = 48.2 \; L\,H_2$

$1.61049 \; \cancel{mol\,H_2} \times \dfrac{1\,mol\,CO}{2 \; \cancel{mol\,H_2}} = 0.80525 \; mol\,CO, \; V_{CO} = \dfrac{0.80525 \; \cancel{mol} \times 0.08206 \dfrac{L \cdot \cancel{atm}}{\cancel{mol} \cdot \cancel{K}} \times 359 \; \cancel{K}}{0.984211 \; \cancel{atm}} = 24.1 \; L\,CO$

Check: The units (L) are correct. The magnitude of the answer (48 L and 24 L) makes sense because we have more than one mole of hydrogen gas and half that of CO and so we expect significantly more than 22 L for hydrogen and half that for CO.

5.79   **Given:** V = 11.8 L, and STP   **Find:** m (NaN$_3$)
       Conceptual Plan: V_{N_2} → mol N$_2$ → mol NaN$_3$ → g NaN$_3$

$$\frac{1\,mol\,N_2}{22.414\,L\,N_2} \qquad \frac{2\,mol\,NaN_3}{3\,mol\,N_2} \qquad \frac{65.03\,g\,NaN_3}{1\,mol\,NaN_3}$$

Solution: $11.8 \; \cancel{L\,N_2} \times \dfrac{1 \; \cancel{mol\,N_2}}{22.414 \; \cancel{L\,N_2}} \times \dfrac{2 \; \cancel{mol\,NaN_3}}{3 \; \cancel{mol\,N_2}} \times \dfrac{65.03 \; g\,NaN_3}{1 \; \cancel{mol\,NaN_3}} = 22.8 \; g\,NaN_3$

Check: The units (g) are correct. The magnitude of the answer (23 g) makes sense because, we have about a half a mole of nitrogen gas, which translates to even fewer moles of NaN$_3$ and so we expect significantly less than 65 g.

5.81   **Given:** V_{CH_4} = 25.5 L, P_{CH_4} = 732 torr, and T = 25 °C; mixed with V_{H_2O} = 22.8 L, P_{H_2O} = 702 torr, and T = 125 °C; forms P_{H_2} = 26.2 L at STP   **Find:** % Yield
       Conceptual Plan: CH$_4$: torr → atm and °C → K and P, V, T → n_{CH_4} → n_{H_2}

$$\frac{1\,atm}{760\,torr} \qquad K = °C + 273.15 \qquad PV = nRT \qquad \frac{3\,mol\,H_2}{1\,mol\,CH_4}$$

H$_2$O: torr → atm and °C → K and P, V, T → n_{H_2O} → n_{H_2}

$$\frac{1\,atm}{760\,torr} \qquad K = °C + 273.15 \qquad PV = nRT \qquad \frac{3\,mol\,H_2}{1\,mol\,CH_4}$$

Select smaller n_{H_2} as theoretical yield,
then L_{H_2} → mol H$_2$ (actual yield) finally actual yield, theoretical yield → % Yield

$$\frac{1\,mol\,H_2}{22.414\,L\,H_2} \qquad\qquad\qquad \% \; Yield = \frac{actual\;yield}{theoretical\;yield} \times 100\%$$

Solution: CH$_4$: $P_{CH_4} = 732 \; \cancel{torr} \times \dfrac{1\,atm}{760 \; \cancel{torr}} = 0.963158 \; atm, \; T = 25 °C + 273.15 = 298 \; K, \; PV = nRT$

Rearrange to solve for n. $n = \dfrac{PV}{RT} \qquad n_{CH_4} = \dfrac{0.963158 \; \cancel{atm} \times 25.5 \; \cancel{L}}{0.08206 \dfrac{\cancel{L} \cdot \cancel{atm}}{mol \cdot \cancel{K}} \times 298 \; \cancel{K}} = 1.00436 \qquad CH_4$

$1.00436 \; \cancel{mol\,CH_4} \times \dfrac{3\,mol\,H_2}{1 \; \cancel{mol\,CH_4}} = 3.01308 \; mol\,H_2$

H$_2$O: $P_{H_2O} = 702 \; \cancel{torr} \times \dfrac{1\,atm}{760 \; \cancel{torr}} = 0.923684 \; atm, \; T = 125 °C + 273.15 = 398 \; K, \; n = \dfrac{PV}{RT}$

$n_{H_2O} = \dfrac{0.923684 \; \cancel{atm} \times 22.8 \; \cancel{L}}{0.08206 \dfrac{\cancel{L} \cdot \cancel{atm}}{mol \cdot \cancel{K}} \times 398 \; \cancel{K}} = 0.644828 \; mol\,H_2O \quad 0.644828 \; \cancel{mol\,H_2O} \times \dfrac{3\,mol\,H_2}{1 \; \cancel{mol\,H_2O}} = 1.93448 \; mol\,H_2$

Water is the limiting reagent since the moles of hydrogen generated is lower.

Theoretical yield = 1.9$\underline{3}$448 mol H_2

$26.2 \; \cancel{L \, H_2} \times \dfrac{1 \; mol \; H_2}{22.414 \; \cancel{L \, H_2}} = 1.1\underline{6}891 \; mol \; H_2 = $ actual yield

$\% \; Yield \; = \; \dfrac{actual \; yield}{theoretical \; yield} \times 100 \; \% \; = \; \dfrac{1.16891 \; \cancel{mol \, H_2}}{1.93448 \; \cancel{mol \, H_2}} \times 100 \; \% \; = \; 60.4 \; \%$

Check: The units (%) are correct. The magnitude of the answer (60 %) makes sense because it is between 0 and 100 %.

Kinetic Molecular Theory

5.83   (a)   Yes, since the average kinetic energy of a particle is proportional to the temperature in kelvins and the two gases are at the same temperature, they have the same average kinetic energy.

(b)   No, since the helium atoms are lighter, they must move faster to have the same kinetic energy as argon atoms.

(c)   No, since the Ar atoms are moving slower to compensate for their larger mass, they will exert the same pressure on the walls of the container.

(d)   Since He is lighter, it will have the faster rate of effusion.

5.85   **Given:** F_2, Cl_2, Br_2, and $T = 298$ K   **Find:** u_{rms} KE_{avg} for each gas and relative rates of effusion

Conceptual Plan: $\mathcal{M}, T \rightarrow u_{rms} \rightarrow KE_{avg}$

$$u_{rms} = \sqrt{\dfrac{3RT}{\mathcal{M}}} \qquad KE_{avg} = \tfrac{1}{2} N_A m u_{rms}^2 = \tfrac{3}{2} RT$$

Solution:

$F_2 \text{:} \; \mathcal{M} = \dfrac{38.00 \; \cancel{g}}{1 \; mol} \times \dfrac{1 \; kg}{1000 \; \cancel{g}} = 0.03800 \; kg/mol, \; u = \sqrt{\dfrac{3RT}{\mathcal{M}}} = \sqrt{\dfrac{3 \times 8.314 \dfrac{J}{\cancel{K} \cdot \cancel{mol}} \times 298 \; \cancel{K}}{0.03800 \; \dfrac{kg}{\cancel{mol}}}} = 442 \; m/s$

$Cl_2 \text{:} \; \mathcal{M} = \dfrac{70.90 \; \cancel{g}}{1 \; mol} \times \dfrac{1 \; kg}{1000 \; \cancel{g}} = 0.07090 \; kg/mol, \; u_{rms} = \sqrt{\dfrac{3RT}{\mathcal{M}}} = \sqrt{\dfrac{3 \times 8.314 \dfrac{J}{\cancel{K} \cdot \cancel{mol}} \times 298 \; \cancel{K}}{0.07090 \; \dfrac{kg}{\cancel{mol}}}} = 324 \; m/s$

$Br_2 \text{:} \; \mathcal{M} = \dfrac{159.80 \; \cancel{g}}{1 \; mol} \times \dfrac{1 \; kg}{1000 \; \cancel{g}} = 0.15980 \; kg/mol, \; u_{rms} = \sqrt{\dfrac{3RT}{\mathcal{M}}} = \sqrt{\dfrac{3 \times 8.314 \dfrac{J}{\cancel{K} \cdot \cancel{mol}} \times 298 \; \cancel{K}}{0.15980 \; \dfrac{kg}{\cancel{mol}}}} = 216 \; m/s$

All molecules have the same kinetic energy:

$KE_{avg} \; = \; \dfrac{3}{2} RT = \dfrac{3}{2} \times 8.314 \; \dfrac{J}{K \cdot mol} \times 298 \; K = 3.72 \times 10^3 \; J/mol$

Since rate of effusion is proportional to $\sqrt{\dfrac{1}{\mathcal{M}}}$, F_2 will have the fastest rate and Br_2 will have the slowest rate.

Check: The units (m/s) are correct. The magnitude of the answer (200 – 450 m/s) makes sense because it is consistent with what was seen in the text, and the heavier the molecule, the slower the molecule.

5.87   **Given:** $^{238}UF_6$ and $^{235}UF_6$ U-235 = 235.054 amu, U-238 = 238.051 amu

Find: ratio of effusion rates $^{238}UF_6$ / $^{235}UF_6$

Conceptual Plan: $\mathcal{M}(^{238}UF_6), \mathcal{M}(^{235}UF_6) \rightarrow$ **Rate** $(^{238}UF_6)$/**Rate** $(^{235}UF_6)$

$$\dfrac{Rate\,(^{238}UF_6)}{Rate\,(^{235}UF_6)} = \sqrt{\dfrac{\mathcal{M}(^{235}UF_6)}{\mathcal{M}(^{238}UF_6)}}$$

Solution: $^{238}UF_6$: $\mathcal{M} = \dfrac{352.05 \text{ g}}{1 \text{ mol}} \times \dfrac{1 \text{ kg}}{1000 \text{ g}} = 0.35205 \text{ kg/mol}$,

$^{235}UF_6$: $\mathcal{M} = \dfrac{349.05 \text{ g}}{1 \text{ mol}} \times \dfrac{1 \text{ kg}}{1000 \text{ g}} = 0.34905 \text{ kg/mol}$,

$\dfrac{Rate\,(^{238}UF_6)}{Rate\,(^{235}UF_6)} = \sqrt{\dfrac{\mathcal{M}(^{235}UF_6)}{\mathcal{M}(^{238}UF_6)}} = \sqrt{\dfrac{0.34905 \text{ kg/mol}}{0.35205 \text{ kg/mol}}} = 0.99574$

Check: The units (none) are correct. The magnitude of the answer (<1) makes sense because the heavier molecule has the lower effusion rate since it moves slower.

5.89   **Given:** Ne and unknown gas; and Ne effusion in 76 s and unknown in 155 s
Find: identify unknown gas
Conceptual Plan: $\mathcal{M}(\text{Ne})$, **Rate (Ne), Rate (Unk)** $\rightarrow$ $\mathcal{M}(\text{Kr})$

$$\frac{Rate\,(Ne)}{Rate\,(Unk)} = \sqrt{\frac{\mathcal{M}(Unk)}{\mathcal{M}(Ne)}}$$

Solution: Ne: $\mathcal{M} = \dfrac{20.18 \text{ g}}{1 \text{ mol}} \times \dfrac{1 \text{ kg}}{1000 \text{ g}} = 0.02018 \text{ kg/mol}$, $\dfrac{Rate\,(Ne)}{Rate\,(Unk)} = \sqrt{\dfrac{\mathcal{M}(Unk)}{\mathcal{M}(\ \ )}}$ Rearrange to solve for

$\mathcal{M}(Unk)$. $\mathcal{M}(Unk) = \mathcal{M}(Ne)\left(\dfrac{Rate\,(Ne)}{Rate\,(Unk)}\right)^2$ Since Rate α 1/(effusion time),

$\mathcal{M}(Unk) = \mathcal{M}(Ne\left(\dfrac{Time\,(Unk)}{Time\,(Ne)}\right)^2 = 0.02018 \dfrac{\text{kg}}{\text{mol}} \times \left(\dfrac{155 \text{ s}}{76 \text{ s}}\right)^2 = 0.084 \dfrac{\text{kg}}{\text{mol}} \times \dfrac{1000 \text{ g}}{1 \text{ kg}} = 84 \text{ g/mol or Kr.}$

Check: The units (g/mol) are correct. The magnitude of the answer (>Ne) makes sense because, Ne effused faster and so must be lighter.

5.91   Gas A has the higher molar mass, since it has the slower average velocity. Gas B will have the higher effusion rate, since it has the higher velocity.

Real Gases

5.93   The postulate that the volume of the gas particles is small compared to the space between them breaks down at high pressure. At high pressures the number of molecules per unit volume increases, so the volume of the gas particles becomes more significant. Since the spacing between the particles is reduced, the molecules themselves occupy a significant portion of the volume.

5.95   **Given:** Ne, $n = 1.000$ mol, $P = 500.0$ atm, and $T = 355.0$ K **Find:** V(ideal) and V(van der Waals)
Conceptual Plan: $n, P, T \rightarrow V$ **and** $n, P, T \rightarrow V$

$$PV = nRT \qquad \left(P + \frac{an^2}{V^2}\right)(V - nb) = nRT$$

Solution: $PV = nRT$ Rearrange to solve for V.

$V = \dfrac{nRT}{P} = \dfrac{1.000 \text{ mol} \times 0.08206 \dfrac{\text{L} \cdot \text{atm}}{\text{mol} \cdot \text{K}} \times 355.0 \text{ K}}{500.0 \text{ atm}} = 0.05826 \text{ L}$

$\left(P + \dfrac{an^2}{V^2}\right)(V - nb) = nRT$ Rearrange to solve to $V = \dfrac{nRT}{\left(P + \dfrac{an^2}{V^2}\right)} + nb$

Using $a = 0.211$ L^2 atm/mol^2 and $b = 0.0171$ L/mol from Table 5.5, and the V from the ideal gas law calculation above, solve for V by successive approximations.

$V = \dfrac{1.000 \text{ mol} \times 0.08206 \dfrac{\text{L} \cdot \text{atm}}{\text{mol} \cdot \text{K}} \times 355.0 \text{ K}}{500.0 \text{ atm} + \dfrac{0.211 \dfrac{\text{L}^2 \cdot \text{atm}}{\text{mol}^2} \times (1.000 \text{ mol})^2}{(0.05826 \text{ L})^2}} + \left(1.000 \text{ mol} \times 0.0171 \dfrac{\text{L}}{\text{mol}}\right) = 0.068915 \text{ L}$

Plug in this new value.

$$V = \frac{1.000 \text{ mol} \times 0.08206 \frac{L \cdot atm}{mol \cdot K} \times 355.0\,K}{500.0\,atm + \frac{0.211 \frac{L^2 \cdot atm}{mol^2} \times (1.000\,mol)^2}{(0.068915\,L)^2}} + \left(1.000\,mol \times 0.0171\frac{L}{mol}\right) = 0.070609\,L$$

Plug in this new value.

$$V = \frac{1.000 \text{ mol} \times 0.08206 \frac{L \cdot atm}{mol \cdot K} \times 355.0\,K}{500.0\,atm + \frac{0.211 \frac{L^2 \cdot atm}{mol^2} \times (1.000\,mol)^2}{(0.070609\,L)^2}} + \left(1.000\,mol \times 0.0171\frac{L}{mol}\right) = 0.070817\,L$$

Plug in this new value.

$$V = \frac{1.000 \text{ mol} \times 0.08206 \frac{L \cdot atm}{mol \cdot K} \times 355.0\,K}{500.0\,atm + \frac{0.211 \frac{L^2 \cdot atm}{mol^2} \times (1.000\,mol)^2}{(0.070817\,L)^2}} + \left(1.000\,mol \times 0.0171\frac{L}{mol}\right) = 0.070842\,L = 0.0708\,L$$

The two values are different because we are at very high pressures. The pressure is corrected from 500.0 atm to 542.1 atm and the final volume correction is 0.0171 L.

Check: The units (L) are correct. The magnitude of the answer (~0.06 L) makes sense because we are at such a high pressure and have one mole of gas.

Cumulative Problems

5.97 **Given:** m (penny) = 2.482 g, T = 25 °C, V = 0.899 L, and P_{Total} = 791 mmHg **Find:** % Zn in penny
Conceptual Plan: $T \rightarrow P_{H_2O}$ then $P_{Total}, P_{H_2O} \rightarrow P_{H_2}$ then mmHg $\rightarrow$ atm and °C $\rightarrow$ K

$$\text{Table 5.3} \qquad P_{Total} = P_{H_2O} + P_{H_2} \qquad \frac{1\,atm}{760\,mmHg} \qquad K = °C + 273.15$$

and $P, V, T \rightarrow n_{H_2} \rightarrow n_{Zn} \rightarrow g_{Zn} \rightarrow$ **% Zn**

$$PV = nRT \qquad \frac{1\,mol\,Zn}{1\,mol\,H_2} \frac{65.39\,g\,Zn}{1\,mol\,Zn} \qquad \%Zn = \frac{g_{Zn}}{g_{penny}} \times 100\%$$

Solution: Table 5.4 states that P_{H_2O} = 23.78 mmHg at 25 °C $\quad P_{Total} = P_{H_2O} + P_{H_2}$ Rearrange to solve for P_{H_2}.

$$P_{H_2} = P_{Total} - P_{H_2O} = 791\,mmHg - 23.78\,mmHg = 767\,mmHg \quad P_{H_2} = 767\,mmHg \times \frac{1\,atm}{760\,mmHg} = 1.0095\,atm$$

then T = 25 °C + 273.15 = 298 K, $PV = nRT$

Rearrange to solve for n. $n_{H_2} = \frac{PV}{RT} = \frac{1.0095\,atm \times 0.899\,L}{0.08206 \frac{L \cdot atm}{mol \cdot K} \times 298\,K} = 0.0371123\,mol$

$$0.0371123\,mol\,H_2 \times \frac{1\,mol\,Zn}{1\,mol\,H_2} \times \frac{65.39\,g\,Zn}{1\,mol\,Zn} = 2.42677\,g\,Zn$$

$$\%Zn = \frac{g_{Zn}}{g_{penny}} \times 100\% = \frac{2.42677\,g}{2.482\,g} \times 100\% = 97.8\%\,Zn$$

Check: The units (% Zn) are correct. The magnitude of the answer (98 %) makes sense because it should be between 0 and 100 %. We expect about 1/22 a mole of gas, since our conditions are close to STP and we have ~ 1 L of gas.

5.99 **Given:** V = 255 mL, m (flask) = 143.187 g, m (flask + gas) = 143.289 g, P = 267 torr, and T = 25 °C **Find:** $\mathcal{M}$
Conceptual Plan: °C $\rightarrow$ K torr $\rightarrow$ atm mL $\rightarrow$ L m (flask), m (flask + gas) $\rightarrow$ m (gas)

$$K = °C + 273.15 \quad \frac{1\,atm}{760\,torr} \qquad \frac{1\,L}{1000\,mL} \qquad m\,(gas) = m\,(flask + gas) - m\,(flask)$$

then $V, m \rightarrow d$ **then** $d, P, T, \rightarrow \mathcal{M}$

$$d = \frac{m}{V} \qquad d = \frac{P\mathcal{M}}{RT}$$

Solution: $T = 25\ °C + 273.15 = 298\ K$, $P = 267\ \cancel{torr} \times \dfrac{1\ atm}{760\ \cancel{torr}} = 0.35\underline{1}316\ atm$,

$V = 255\ \cancel{mL} \times \dfrac{1\ L}{1000\ \cancel{mL}} = 0.255\ L$,

$m\ (gas) = m\ (flask + gas) - m\ (flask) = 143.289\ g - 143.187\ g = 0.102\ g$,

$d = \dfrac{m}{V} = \dfrac{0.102\ g}{0.255\ L} = 0.400\ g/L$, $d = \dfrac{P\mathcal{M}}{RT}$ Rearrange to solve for $\mathcal{M}$.

$\mathcal{M} = \dfrac{dRT}{P} = \dfrac{0.400\ \dfrac{g}{\cancel{L}} \times 0.08206 \dfrac{\cancel{L}\ \cancel{atm}}{K\ mol} \times 298\ \cancel{K}}{0.351316\ \cancel{atm}} = 27.8\ g/mol$

Check: The units (g/mol) are correct. The magnitude of the answer (28 g/mol) makes physical sense because this is a reasonable number for a molecular weight of a gas.

5.101   **Given:** $V = 158\ mL$, $m\ (gas) = 0.275\ g$, $P = 556\ mmHg$, $T = 25\ °C$, gas = 82.66 % C and 17.34 % H
        Find: Molecular formula
        Conceptual Plan: °C $\rightarrow$ K mmHg $\rightarrow$ atm mL $\rightarrow$ L then V, m $\rightarrow$ d

            $K = °C + 273.15$ $\dfrac{1\ atm}{760\ mmHg}$ $\dfrac{1\ L}{1000\ mL}$ $d = \dfrac{m}{V}$

        then $d, P, T,$ $\rightarrow$ $\mathcal{M}$ **then** % C, % H, $\mathcal{M}$ $\rightarrow$ **formula**

           $d = \dfrac{P\mathcal{M}}{RT}$ $\#C = \dfrac{\mathcal{M}\ 0.8266\ g\ C}{12.01\dfrac{g\ C}{mol\ C}}$ $\#H = \dfrac{\mathcal{M}\ 0.1734\ g\ H}{1.008\dfrac{g\ H}{mol\ H}}$

Solution: $T = 25\ °C + 273.15 = 298\ K$, $P = 556\ \cancel{mmHg} \times \dfrac{1\ atm}{760\ \cancel{mmHg}} = 0.731579\ atm$,

$V = 158\ \cancel{mL} \times \dfrac{1\ L}{1000\ \cancel{mL}} = 0.158\ L$, $d = \dfrac{m}{V} = \dfrac{0.275\ g}{0.158\ L} = 1.7\underline{4}051\ g/L$, $d = \dfrac{P\mathcal{M}}{RT}$ Rearrange to solve for $\mathcal{M}$.

$\mathcal{M} = \dfrac{dRT}{P} = \dfrac{1.7\underline{4}051\ \dfrac{g}{\cancel{L}} \times 0.08206\dfrac{\cancel{L}\ \cancel{atm}}{K\ mol} \times 298\ \cancel{K}}{0.731579\ \cancel{atm}} = 58.2\ g/mol$,

$\#C = \dfrac{\mathcal{M} \times 0.8266\ g\ C}{12.01\ \dfrac{g\ C}{mol\ C}} = \dfrac{58.2\ \dfrac{\cancel{g\ HC}}{mol\ HC} \times \dfrac{0.8266\ \cancel{g\ C}}{1\ \cancel{g\ HC}}}{12.01\ \dfrac{\cancel{g\ C}}{mol\ C}} = 4.00\ \dfrac{mol\ C}{mol\ HC}$

$\#H = \dfrac{\mathcal{M} \times 0.1734\ g\ H}{1.008\ \dfrac{g\ H}{mol\ H}} = \dfrac{58.2\ \dfrac{\cancel{g\ HC}}{mol\ HC} \times \dfrac{0.1734\ \cancel{g\ H}}{1\ \cancel{g\ HC}}}{1.008\ \dfrac{\cancel{g\ H}}{mol\ H}} = 10.0\ \dfrac{mol\ H}{mol\ HC}$ Formula is C_4H_{10} or butane.

Check: The answer came up with integer number of C and H atoms in the formula and a molecular weight (58 g/mol) that is reasonable for a gas.

5.103   **Given:** $m\ (NiO) = 24.78\ g$, $T = 40.0\ °C$, and $P_{Total} = 745\ mmHg$ **Find:** V_{O_2}
        Conceptual Plan: T $\rightarrow$ P_{H_2O} then P_{Total}, P_{H_2O} $\rightarrow$ P_{O_2} then mmHg $\rightarrow$ atm and °C $\rightarrow$ K

            Table 5.4 $P_{Total} = P_{H_2O} + P_{O_2}$ $\dfrac{1\ atm}{760\ mmHg}$ $K = °C + 273.15$

        and g $_{NiO}$ $\rightarrow$ n_{NiO} $\rightarrow$ n_{O_2} **then** P, V, T $\rightarrow$ n_{O_2}

           $\dfrac{1\ mol\ NiO}{74.69\ g\ NiO}$ $\dfrac{1\ mol\ O_2}{2\ mol\ NiO}$ $PV = nRT$

Solution: Table 5.4 states that $P_{H_2O} = 55.40\ mmHg$ at 40°C $P_{Total} = P_{H_2O} + P_{O_2}$ Rearrange to solve for P_{O_2}.
$P_{O_2} = P_{Total} - P_{H_2O} = 745\ mmHg - 55.40\ mmHg = 689.\underline{6}\ mmHg$

$P_{O_2} = 689.\underline{6}\ \cancel{mmHg} \times \dfrac{1\ atm}{760\ \cancel{mmHg}} = 0.907368\ atm$ $T = 40.0\ °C + 273.15 = 313.2\ K$,

$24.78\ \cancel{g\ NiO} \times \dfrac{1\ \cancel{mol\ NiO}}{74.69\ \cancel{mol\ NiO}} \times \dfrac{1\ mol\ O_2}{2\ \cancel{mol\ NiO}} = 0.165\underline{8}857\ mol\ O_2$ $PV = nRT$

Rearrange to solve for V. $V_{O_2} = \dfrac{nRT}{P} = \dfrac{0.165\underline{8}857\ \cancel{mol} \times 0.08206\ \dfrac{L \cdot \cancel{atm}}{\cancel{mol} \cdot K} \times 313.2\ K}{0.907368\ \cancel{atm}} = 4.70\ L$

Check: The units (L) are correct. The magnitude of the answer (5 L) makes sense because we have much less than 0.5 mole of NiO, so we get less than a mole of oxygen. Thus we expect a volume much less than 22 L.

5.105   **Given**: HCl, K_2S to H_2S, V_{H_2S} = 42.9 mL, P_{H_2S} = 752 mmHg, and T = 25.8 °C **Find**: $m(K_2S)$
Conceptual Plan: read description of reaction and convert words to equation then °C $\rightarrow$ K

$$K = °C + 273.15$$

and mmHg $\rightarrow$ atm and mL $\rightarrow$ L then $P, V, T \rightarrow n_{H_2S} \rightarrow n_{K_2S} \rightarrow g_{K_2S}$

$$\frac{1\,atm}{760\,mmHg} \qquad \frac{1\,L}{1000\,mL} \qquad PV = nRT \qquad \frac{1\,mol\,K_2S}{1\,mol\,H_2S} \quad \frac{1\,mol\,K_2S}{110.27\,g\,K_2S}$$

Solution: 2 HCl (aq) + K_2S (s) $\rightarrow$ H_2S (g) + 2 KCl (aq)

$$T = 25.8\ °C + 273.15 = 299.0\ K,\ P_{H_2S} = 752\ \cancel{mmHg} \times \frac{1\ atm}{760\ \cancel{mmHg}} = 0.989474\ atm,$$

$$V_{H_2S} = 42.9\ \cancel{mL} \times \frac{1\ L}{1000\ \cancel{mL}} = 0.0429\ L \qquad PV = nRT\quad \text{Rearrange to solve for } n_{H_2S}.$$

$$n_{H_2S} = \frac{PV}{RT} = \frac{0.989474\ \cancel{atm} \times 0.0429\ \cancel{L}}{0.08206\ \dfrac{\cancel{L} \cdot \cancel{atm}}{mol \cdot \cancel{K}} \times 299.0\ \cancel{K}} = 0.00173005\ mol$$

$$0.00173005\ \cancel{mol\,H_2S} \times \frac{1\ \cancel{mol\,K_2S}}{1\ \cancel{mol\,H_2S}} \times \frac{110.27\ g\ K_2S}{1\ \cancel{mol\,K_2S}} = 0.191\ g\ K_2S$$

Check: The units (g) are correct. The magnitude of the answer (0.1 g) makes sense because we have such a small volume of gas generated.

5.107   **Given**: T = 22 °C, P = 1.02 atm, and m = 11.83 g **Find**: V_{Total}
Conceptual Plan: °C $\rightarrow$ K and $g_{(NH_4)_2CO_3} \rightarrow n_{(NH_4)_2CO_3} \rightarrow n_{Gas}$ then $P, n, T \rightarrow V$

$$K = °C + 273.15 \qquad \frac{1\,mol\,(NH_4)_2CO_3}{96.09\,g\,(NH_4)_2CO_3} \quad \frac{(2 + 1 + 1 = 4)\,mol\,gas}{1\,mol\,NH_4CO_3} \qquad PV = nRT$$

Solution: T = 22 °C + 273.15 = 295 K,

$$11.83\ \cancel{g\,NH_4CO_3} \times \frac{1\ \cancel{mol\ (NH_4)_2CO_3}}{96.09\ \cancel{g\ (NH_4)_2CO_3}} \times \frac{4\ mol\ gas}{1\ \cancel{mol\ (NH_4)_2CO_3}} = 0.492455\ mol\ gas$$

$PV = nRT$ Rearrange to solve for V_{Gas}.

$$V_{Gas} = \frac{nRT}{P} = \frac{0.492455\ \cancel{mol\ gas} \times 0.08206\ \dfrac{L \cdot \cancel{atm}}{\cancel{mol} \cdot \cancel{K}} \times 295\ \cancel{K}}{1.02\ \cancel{atm}} = 11.7\ L$$

Check: The units (L) are correct. The magnitude of the answer (12 L) makes sense because we have about a half a mole of gas generated.

Given: He and air; V = 855 mL, P = 125 psi, T = 25 °C, $\rightarrow$ (air) = 28.8 g/mol **Find**: $\Delta = m(air) - m(He)$
Conceptual Plan: mL $\rightarrow$ L and psi $\rightarrow$ atm and °C $\rightarrow$ K then $P, T, \mathcal{M} \rightarrow d$

$$\frac{1\,L}{1000\,mL} \qquad \frac{1\,atm}{14.7\,psi} \qquad K = °C + 273.15 \qquad d = \frac{P\mathcal{M}}{RT}$$

then $d, V \rightarrow m$ then $m(air), m(He) \rightarrow \Delta$

$$d = \frac{m}{V} \qquad\qquad \Delta = m(air) - m(He)$$

Solution: $V = 855\ \cancel{mL} \times \dfrac{1\ L}{1000\ \cancel{mL}} = 0.855\ L,\ P = 125\ \cancel{psi} \times \dfrac{1\ atm}{14.7\ \cancel{psi}} = 8.50340\ atm,$

$$T = 25\ °C + 273.15 = 298\,K,\ d_{air} = \frac{P\mathcal{M}}{RT} = \frac{8.50340\ \cancel{atm} \times 28.8\ \dfrac{g\ air}{\cancel{mol\ air}}}{0.08206\ \dfrac{L \cdot \cancel{atm}}{\cancel{K} \cdot \cancel{mol}} \times 298\ \cancel{K}} = 10.0147\ \frac{g\ air}{L},\ d = \frac{m}{V}$$

Rearrange to solve for m. $m = dV$

$$m_{air} = 10.0147\ \frac{g\ air}{\cancel{L}} \times 0.8554\ \cancel{L} = 8.56657\ g\ air,\ d_{He} = \frac{P\mathcal{M}}{RT} = \frac{8.50340\ \cancel{atm} \times 4.03\ \dfrac{g\ He}{\cancel{mol\ He}}}{0.08206\ \dfrac{L \cdot \cancel{atm}}{\diagdown \cdot \cancel{mol}} \times 298\ \cancel{K}} = 1.40136\ \frac{g\ He}{L},$$

$$m_{He} = 1.40136\ \frac{g\ He}{\cancel{L}} \times 0.855\ \cancel{L} = 1.19816\ g\ He,$$

$$\Delta = m(air) - m(He) = 8.56657\ g\ air - 1.19816\ g\ He = 7.37\ g$$

Check: The units (g) are correct. We expect the difference to be less than the difference in the molecular weights since we have less than a mole of gas.

5.111   **Given:** flow = 335 L/s, P_{NO} = 22.4 torr, T_{NO} = 955 K, P_{NH_3} = 755 torr, and T_{NO} = 298 K, and NH_3 purity = 65.2 %   **Find:** $Flow_{NH_3}$

Conceptual Plan: torr $\rightarrow$ atm then P_{NO}, V_{NO}/s, T_{NO} $\rightarrow$ n_{NO}/s $\rightarrow$ n_{NH_3}/s (pure)

$$\frac{1\,atm}{760\,torr} \qquad\qquad PV = nRT \qquad \frac{4\,mol\,NH_3}{4\,mol\,NO}$$

then n_{NH_3}/s (pure) $\rightarrow$ n_{NH_3}/s (impure) then n_{NH_3}/s (impure), P_{NH_3}, T_{NH_3} $\rightarrow$ V_{NH_3}/s

$$\frac{100\,mol\,NH_3\,impure}{65.2\,mol\,NH_3\,pure} \qquad\qquad PV = nRT$$

Solution: P_{NO} = 22.4 torr $\times \dfrac{1\,atm}{760\,torr}$ = 0.0294737 atm, P_{NH_3} = 755 torr $\times \dfrac{1\,atm}{760\,torr}$ = 0.993421 atm

$PV = nRT$ Rearrange to solve for n_{NO}. Note that we can substitute V/s for V and get n/s as a result.

$$\frac{n_{NO}}{s} = \frac{PV}{RT} = \frac{0.0294737\,atm \times 335\,L/s}{0.08206\,\dfrac{L\cdot atm}{mol\cdot K} \times 955\,K} = 0.125992\,\frac{mol\,NO}{s}$$

$$0.125992\,\frac{mol\,NO}{s} \times \frac{4\,mol\,NH_3}{4\,mol\,NO} \times \frac{100\,mol\,NH_3\,impure}{65.2\,mol\,NH_3\,pure} = 0.193240\,\frac{mol\,NH_3\,impure}{s} \qquad PV = nRT$$

Rearrange to solve for V_{NH_3}. Note that we can substitute n/s for n and get V/s as a result.

$$\frac{V_{NH_3}}{s} = \frac{nRT}{P} = \frac{0.193240\,\dfrac{mol\,NH_3\,impure}{s} \times 0.08206\,\dfrac{L\cdot atm}{mol\cdot K} \times 298\,K}{0.993421\,atm} = 4.76\,\frac{L}{s}\,impure\,NH_3$$

Check: The units (L) are correct. The magnitude of the answer (5 L/s) makes sense because we expect it to be less than for the NO. The NO is at a very low concentration and a high temperature, when this converts to a much higher pressure and lower temperature this will go down significantly, even though the ammonia is impure. From a practical standpoint, you would like a low flow rate to make it economical.

5.113   **Given:** l = 30.0 cm, w = 20.0 cm, h = 15.0 cm, 14.7 psi **Find:** Force (lbs)

Conceptual Plan: l, w, h $\rightarrow$ Surface Area, SA (cm^2) $\rightarrow$ Surface Area(in^2) $\rightarrow$ Force

$$SA = 2(lh) + 2(wh) + 2(lw) \qquad\qquad \frac{(1\,in)^2}{(2.54\,cm)^2} \qquad\qquad \frac{14.7\,lbs}{1\,in^2}$$

Solution: $SA = 2(lh) + 2(wh) + 2(lw) = 2(30.0\,cm \times 15.0\,cm) + 2(20.0\,cm \times 15.0\,cm)$

$+ \; 2(30.0\,cm \times 20.0\,cm) = 2700\,cm^2$

$$2700\,cm^2 \times \frac{(1\,in)^2}{(2.54\,cm)^2} = 418.50\,in^2, \; 418.50\,in^2 \times \frac{14.7\,lbs}{1\,in^2} = 6150\,lbs.\;\text{The can would be crushed.}$$

Check: The units (lbs) are correct. The magnitude of the answer (6150 lbs) is not unreasonable since there is a large surface area.

5.115   **Given:** V_1 = 160.0 L, P_1 = 1855 psi, 3.5 L/balloon, P_2 = 1.0 atm = 14.7 psi, and T = 298 K **Find:** # balloons

Conceptual Plan: V_1, P_1, P_2 V_2 then L $\rightarrow$ # balloons

$$P_1V_1 = P_2V_2 \qquad \frac{1\,balloon}{3.5\,L}$$

Solution: $P_1V_1 = P_2V_2$ Rearrange to solve for V_2. $V_2 = \dfrac{P_1}{P_2}V_1 = \dfrac{1855\,psi}{14.7\,psi} \times 160.0\,L = 20190.5\,L,$

$20190.5\,L \times \dfrac{1\,balloon}{3.5\,L} = 5800\,balloons$

Check: The units (balloons) are correct. The magnitude of the answer (5800) is reasonable since a store does not want to buy a new helium tank very often.

5.117   **Given:** r_1 = 2.5 cm, P_1 = 4.00 atm, T = 298 K, and P_2 = 1.00 atm **Find:** r_2

Conceptual Plan: r_1 $\rightarrow$ V_1 V_1, P_1, P_2 $\rightarrow$ V_2 then V_2 $\rightarrow$ r_2

$$V = \frac{4}{3}\pi r^3 \qquad\qquad P_1V_1 = P_2V_2 \qquad\qquad V = \frac{4}{3}\pi r^3$$

$$V = \frac{4}{3}\pi r^3 = \frac{4}{3} \times \pi \times (2.5 \text{ cm})^3 = 65.450 \text{ cm}^3 \quad P_1 V_1 = P_2 V_2 \quad \text{Rearrange to solve for } V_2.$$

$$V_2 = \frac{P_1}{P_2} V_1 = \frac{4.00 \text{ atm}}{1.00 \text{ atm}} \times 65.450 \text{ cm}^3 = 261.80 \text{ cm}^3, V = \frac{4}{3}\pi r^3$$

Rearrange to solve for r. $\quad r = \sqrt[3]{\dfrac{3V}{4\pi}} = \sqrt[3]{\dfrac{3 \times 261.80 \text{ cm}^3}{4 \times \pi}} = 4.0 \text{ cm}$

Check: The units (cm) are correct. The magnitude of the answer (4 cm) is reasonable since the bubble will expand as the pressure is decreased.

5.119　**Given:** 2.0 mol CO : 1.0 mol O_2, $V = 2.45$ L, $P_1 = 745$ torr, $P_2 = 552$ torr, and $T = 552$ °C
Find: % reacted
Conceptual Plan: from $PV = nRT$ we know that $P \propto n$, looking at the chemical reaction we see that 2 + 1 = 3 moles of gas gets converted to 2 moles of gas. If all the gas reacts, $P_2 = 2/3\ P_1$.
Calculate $-\Delta P$ for 100 % reacted and for actual case. Then calculate % reacted.

$$-\Delta P\ 100\text{ % reacted} = P_1 - \frac{2}{3}P_1 \quad -\Delta P\ actual = P_1 - P_2 \quad \text{% reacted} = \frac{\Delta P\ actual}{\Delta P\ 100\text{ % reacted}} \times 100\text{ %}$$

Solution: $-\Delta P\ 100\text{ % reacted} = P_1 - \dfrac{2}{3}P_1 = 745 \text{ torr} - \dfrac{2}{3} 745 \text{ torr} = 248.333 \text{ torr}$,

$-\Delta P\ actual = P_1 - P_2 = 745 \text{ torr} - 552 \text{ torr} = 193 \text{ torr}$,

$\text{% reacted} = \dfrac{\Delta P\ actual}{\Delta P\ 100\text{ % reacted}} \times 100\% = \dfrac{193 \text{ torr}}{248.333 \text{ torr}} \times 100\% = 77.7\text{ %}$

Check: The units (%) are correct. The magnitude of the answer (78 %) makes sense because the pressure dropped most of the way to the pressure if all of the reactants had reacted. **Note: There are many ways to solve this problem, including calculating the moles of reactants and products using $PV = nRT$.**

5.121　**Given:** $P(\text{Total})_1 = 2.2$ atm $= CO + O_2$, $P(\text{Total})_2 = 1.9$ atm $= CO + O_2 + CO_2$, $V = 1.0$ L, $T = 1.0 \times 10^3$ K
Find: mass CO_2 made
Conceptual Plan: $P(\text{Total})_1 = 2.2$ atm $= P(CO)_1 + P(O_2)_1$, $P(\text{Total})_2 = 1.9$ atm $= P(CO)_2 + P(O_2)_2 + P(CO_2)_2$. Let x = amount of $P(O_2)$ reacted. From stoichiometry: $P(CO)_2 = P(CO)_1 - 2x$, $P(O_2)_2 = P(O_2)_1 - x$, $P(CO_2)_2 = 2x$. Thus $P(\text{Total})_2 = 1.9$ atm $= P(CO)_1 - 2x + P(O_2)_1 - x + 2x = P(\text{Total})_1 - x$. Using the initial conditions: 1.9 atm = 2.2 atm – x. So x = 0.3 atm and since 2x = $P(CO_2)_2$ = 0.6 atm, then $P, V, T \rightarrow n \rightarrow$ g.

$$PV = nRT \quad \frac{44.01 \text{ g}}{1 \text{ mol}}$$

Solution: $PV = nRT$ Rearrange to solve for n.

$$n = \frac{PV}{RT} = \frac{0.6 \text{ atm} \times 1.0 \text{ L}}{0.08206 \dfrac{\text{L} \cdot \text{atm}}{\text{mol} \cdot \text{K}} \times 1000 \text{ K}} = 0.0073117 \text{ mol}$$

$0.0073117 \text{ mol} \times \dfrac{44.01 \text{ g}}{1 \text{ mol}} = 0.321789 \text{ g } CO_2 = 0.3 \text{ g } CO_2$

Check: The units (g) are correct. The magnitude of the answer (0.3 g) makes sense because we have such a small volume, at a very high temperature and such a small pressure. This leads us to expect a very small number of moles.

5.123　**Given:** $h_1 = 22.6$ m, $T_1 = 22$ °C, and $h_2 = 23.8$ m　**Find:** T_2
Conceptual Plan: °C $\rightarrow$ K since $V_{\text{cylinder}} \propto h$ **we do not need to know** r **to use** $V_1, T_1, T_2 \rightarrow V_2$

$$K = °C + 273.15 \qquad V = \pi r^2 h \qquad \qquad \frac{V_1}{T_1} = \frac{V_2}{T_2}$$

Solution: $T_1 = 22$ °C + 273.15 = 295K, $\dfrac{V_1}{T_1} = \dfrac{V_2}{T_2}$ Rearrange to solve for T_2.

$$T_2 = T_1 \times \frac{V_2}{V_1} = T_1 \times \frac{\pi r^2 h_2}{\pi r^2 h_1} = 295 \text{ K} \times \frac{23.8 \text{ m}}{22.6 \text{ m}} = 311 \text{ K}$$

Check: The units (K) are correct. We expect the temperature to increase since the volume increased.

5.125　**Given:** He, $V = 0.35$ L, $P_{\text{max}} = 88$ atm, and $T = 299$ K　**Find:** m_{He}
Conceptual Plan: $P, V, T \rightarrow n$ then mol $\rightarrow$ g

$$PV = nRT \qquad \qquad \mathcal{M}$$

Solution: $PV = nRT$ Rearrange to solve for n.

$$n_{He} = \frac{PV}{RT} = \frac{88 \text{ atm} \times 0.35 \text{ L}}{0.08206 \frac{\text{L} \cdot \text{atm}}{\text{mol} \cdot \text{K}} \times 299 \text{ K}} = 1.2553 \text{ mol}, \quad 1.2553 \text{ mol} \times \frac{4.003 \text{ g}}{1 \text{ mol}} = 5.0 \text{ g He}$$

Check: The units (g) are correct. The magnitude of the answer (5 g) makes sense because the high pressure and the low volume cancel out (remember 22 L / mol at STP) and so we expect ~ 1 mol and so ~ 4 g.

5.127   **Given:** 15.0 mL HBr in 1.0 min; and 20.3 mL unknown hydrocarbon gas in 1.0 min
       Find: formula of unknown gas
       Conceptual Plan: Since these are gases under the same conditions $V \alpha n$, V, time $\rightarrow$ Rate then

$$Rate = \frac{V}{time}$$

       (HBr), Rate (HBr), Rate (Unk) $\rightarrow$ $\mathcal{M}$(Unk)

$$\frac{Rate(HBr)}{Rate(U)} = \sqrt{\frac{\mathcal{M}(U)}{\mathcal{M}(HBr)}}$$

       Solution: $Rate(HBr) = \dfrac{V}{time} = \dfrac{15.0 \text{ mL}}{1.0 \text{ min}} = 15.0 \dfrac{\text{mL}}{\text{min}}$, $Rate(Unk) = \dfrac{V}{time} = \dfrac{20.3 \text{ mL}}{1.0 \text{ min}} = 20.3 \dfrac{\text{mL}}{\text{min}}$,

$\dfrac{Rate(HBr)}{Rate(Unk)} = \sqrt{\dfrac{\mathcal{M}(Unk)}{\mathcal{M}(HBr)}}$ Rearrange to solve for $\mathcal{M}(Unk)$.

$$\mathcal{M}(Unk) = \mathcal{M}(HBr)\left(\frac{Rate(HBr)}{Rate(Unk)}\right)^2 = 80.91 \frac{g}{mol} \times \left(\frac{15.0 \frac{mL}{min}}{20.3 \frac{mL}{min}}\right)^2 = 44.2 \frac{g}{mol} \text{ The formula is } C_3H_8, \text{ propane.}$$

Check: The units (g/mol) are correct. The magnitude of the answer (< HBr) makes sense because the unknown diffused faster and so must be lighter.

5.129   **Given:** 0.583 g neon, $V = 8.00 \times 10^2 \text{ cm}^3$, $P_{Total} = 1.17$ atm, and $T = 295$ K   **Find:** g argon
       Conceptual Plan: g $\rightarrow$ n and mL $\rightarrow$ L then n, V, T $\rightarrow$ P_{Ne} then P_{Ne}, P_{Total} $\rightarrow$ P_{Ar} then

$$\frac{1 \text{ mol}}{20.18 \text{ g}} \qquad \frac{1 \text{ L}}{1000 \text{ mL}} \qquad PV = nRT \qquad P_{Total} = P_{Ne} + P_{Ar}$$

P_{Ar}, V, T $\rightarrow$ n $\rightarrow$ g

$$PV = nRT \quad \frac{39.95 \text{ g}}{1 \text{ mol}}$$

Solution: $0.583 \text{ g Ne} \times \dfrac{1 \text{ mol Ne}}{20.18 \text{ g Ne}} = 0.02888999 \text{ mol Ne} \quad 8.00 \times 10^2 \text{ mL} \times \dfrac{1 \text{ L}}{1000 \text{ mL}} = 0.800 \text{ L}$

$PV = nRT$ Rearrange to solve for P.

$$P = \frac{nRT}{V} = \frac{0.02888999 \text{ mol} \times 0.08206 \frac{\text{L} \cdot \text{atm}}{\text{mol} \cdot \text{K}} \times 295 \text{ K}}{0.800 \text{ L}} = 0.874200 \text{ atm Ne}$$

$P_{Total} = P_{Ne} + P_{Ar}$ Rearrange to solve for P_{Ar}. $P_{Ar} = P_{Total} - P_{Ne} = 1.17 \text{ atm} - 0.874200 \text{ atm} = 0.295800 \text{ atm}$

$PV = nRT$ Rearrange to solve for n. $n_{Ar} = \dfrac{PV}{RT} = \dfrac{0.295800 \text{ atm} \times 0.800 \text{ L}}{0.08206 \frac{\text{L} \cdot \text{atm}}{\text{mol} \cdot \text{K}} \times 295 \text{ K}} = 0.00977539 \text{ mol Ar}$

$0.00977539 \text{ mol Ar} \times \dfrac{39.95 \text{ g Ar}}{1 \text{ mol Ar}} = 0.390527 \text{ g Ar} = 0.39 \text{ g Ar}$

Check: The units (g) are correct. The magnitude of the answer (0.4 g) makes sense because the pressure and volume are small.

5.131   **Given:** 75.2 % by mass nitrogen + 24.8 % by mass krypton, $P_{Total} = 745$ mmHg   **Find:** P_{Kr}
       Solution: Assume 100 g total, so we have 75.2 g N_2 and 24.8 g Kr. Converting these masses to moles,

$75.2 \text{ g N}_2 \times \dfrac{1 \text{ mol N}_2}{28.02 \text{ g N}_2} = 2.683797 \text{ mol N}_2$ and $24.8 \text{ g Kr} \times \dfrac{1 \text{ mol Kr}}{83.80 \text{ g Kr}} = 0.2959427 \text{ mol Kr.}$

$$P_{Kr} = \chi_{Kr} P_{Total} = \frac{0.2959427 \text{ mol Kr}}{2.683797 \text{ mol N}_2 + 0.2959427 \text{ mol Kr}} \quad 745 \text{ mmHg Kr} = 74.0 \text{ mmHg Kr}$$

Check: The units (mmHg) are correct. The magnitude of the answer (74 mmHg) makes sense because, the mixture is mostly nitrogen by mass, and this dominance is magnified since the molar mass of krypton is larger than the molar mass of nitrogen.

Challenge Problems

5.133   **Given:** $2\,NH_3\,(g) \rightarrow N_2\,(g) + 3\,H_2\,(g)$; $N_2H_4\,(g) \rightarrow N_2\,(g) + 2\,H_2\,(g)$; initially $P = 0.50$ atm, $T = 300$ K, finally $P = 4.5$ atm, $T = 1200$ K   **Find:** N_2H_4 percent initially

Conceptual Plan: $P_{\text{initial}}, T_{\text{initial}}, T_{\text{final}} \rightarrow P_{\text{final}}$ **then determine change in moles of gas**

$$\frac{P_{\text{initial}}}{T_{\text{initial}}} = \frac{P_{\text{final}}}{T_{\text{final}}} \qquad \frac{3\text{ atm added gas}}{1\text{ atm }NH_3\text{ reacted}} \text{ and } \frac{2\text{ atm added gas}}{N_2H_4\text{ reacted}}$$

$P_1, P_2 \rightarrow \Delta P$ **write expression for** ΔP **then solve for** $P_{1N_2H_4}$ **and** P_{1NH_3} **finally** $P_{1N_2H_4}, P_{1NH_3} \rightarrow \% N_2H_4$

$$\Delta P = P_2 - P_1 \quad \Delta P = P_{1NH_3}\frac{3\text{ atm added gas}}{2\text{ atm reacted}} + P_{1N_2H_4}\frac{2\text{ atm added gas}}{1\text{ atm reacted}} \text{ where } P_{1,1200K} = P_{1NH_3} + P_{1N_2H_4} \quad \% N_2H_4 = \frac{P_{N_2H_4}}{P_{N_2H_4} + P_{NH_3}} \times 100\%$$

Solution: $\dfrac{P_{\text{initial}}}{T_{\text{initial}}} = \dfrac{P_{\text{final}}}{T_{\text{final}}}$ Rearrange to solve for P_{final}. $P_2 = P_1 \times \dfrac{T_2}{T_1} = 0.50\text{ atm} \times \dfrac{1200\,\text{K}}{300\,\text{K}} = 2.0\,\text{atm}$ if no reaction occurred.

$\Delta P = P_{\text{final}} - P_{\text{initial}} = 4.5\,\text{atm} - 2.0\,\text{atm} = 2.5\,\text{atm}$, and $P_{1,1200K} = 2.0\,\text{atm} = P_{1NH_3} + P_{1N_2H_4}$ or

$P_{1NH_3} = 2.0\,\text{atm} - P_{1N_2H_4}$.

Substitute this into $\Delta P = P_{1NH_3}\dfrac{3\text{ atm added gas}}{2\text{ atm reacted}} + P_{1N_2H_4}\dfrac{2\text{ atm added gas}}{1\text{ atm reacted}}$ and solve for $P_{1N_2H_4}$.

$\Delta P = 2.5\,\text{atm} = (2.0\,\text{atm} - P_{1N_2H_4})\dfrac{3\text{ atm added gas}}{2\text{ atm reacted}} + P_{1N_2H_4}\dfrac{2\text{ atm added gas}}{1\text{ atm reacted}} \rightarrow$

$P_{1N_2H_4} = 3.0\,\text{atm} - 2.5\,\text{atm} = 0.5\,\text{atm}$ and $P_{NH_3} = 2.0\,\text{atm} - 0.5\,\text{atm} = 1.5\,\text{atm}$ finally

$\% N_2H_4 = \dfrac{P_{N_2H_4}}{P_{N_2H_4} + P_{NH_3}} \times 100\% = \dfrac{0.5\,\text{atm}}{0.5\,\text{atm} + 1.5\,\text{atm}} \times 100\% = \underline{25}\% \, N_2H_4 = 30\% \, N_2H_4$

Check: The units (%) are correct. The magnitude of the answer (30 %) makes sense because if it were all N_2H_4 the final pressure would have been 6 atm. Since we are closer to the initial pressure than this maximum pressure, less than half of the gas is N_2H_4.

5.135   **Given:** $2\,CO_2\,(g) \rightarrow 2\,CO\,(g) + O_2\,(g)$; initially $P = 10.0$ atm, $T = 701$ K, finally $P = 22.5$ atm, $T = 1401$ K
Find: mole percent decomposed

Conceptual Plan: $P_{\text{initial}}, T_{\text{initial}}, T_{\text{final}} \rightarrow P_{\text{final}}$ **then determine change in moles of gas**

$$\frac{P_{\text{initial}}}{T_{\text{initial}}} = \frac{P_{\text{final}}}{T_{\text{final}}} \qquad \frac{1\text{ atm added gas}}{2\text{ atm }CO_2\text{ reacted}}$$

$P_1, P_2 \rightarrow \Delta P$ **write expression for** ΔP **then solve for** $P_{CO_2\text{ reacted}}$ **finally**

$$\Delta P = P_2 - P_1 \qquad \Delta P = P_{CO_2\text{ reacted}}\frac{1\text{ atm added gas}}{2\text{ atm }CO_2\text{ reacted}}$$

$P_{\text{final}}, P_{CO2\text{ reacted}} \rightarrow \% \, CO_2$ **decomposed**

$$\% CO_2 \text{ decomposed} = \frac{P_{CO_2\text{ reacted}}}{P_{\text{final}}} \times 100\%$$

Solution: $\dfrac{P_{\text{initial}}}{T_{\text{initial}}} = \dfrac{P_{\text{final}}}{T_{\text{final}}}$ Rearrange to solve for P. $P_2 = P_1 \times \dfrac{T_2}{T_1} = 10.0\,\text{atm} \times \dfrac{1401\,\text{K}}{701\,\text{K}} = 19.\underline{9}85735\,\text{atm}$

$\Delta P = P_{\text{final}} - P_{\text{initial}} = 22.5\,\text{atm} - 19.\underline{9}85735\,\text{atm} = 2.\underline{5}14265\,\text{atm}$,

$\Delta P = P_{CO_2\text{ reacted}}\dfrac{1\text{ atm added gas}}{2\text{ atm }CO_2\text{ reacted}}$ or the pressure increases 1 atm for each 2 atm of gas decomposed, so $5.\underline{0}2853$ atm decomposes and then

$\% CO_2 \text{ decomposed} = \dfrac{P_{CO_2\text{ reacted}}}{P_{\text{final}}} \times 100\% = \dfrac{5.\underline{0}2853\text{ atm}}{19.\underline{8}75735\text{ atm}} \times 100\% = 25.\underline{1}606\% \, CO_2 \text{ decomposed} =$

25% CO_2 decomposed

Check: The units (%) are correct. The magnitude of the answer (11 %) makes sense because if all of the gas decomposed the final pressure would have been 40 atm. Since we are much closer to the initial pressure than this maximum pressure, much less than half of the gas decomposed.

5.137   **Given:** CH_4: $V = 155$ mL at STP; O_2: $V = 885$ mL at STP; NO: $V = 55.5$ mL at STP; mixed in a flask: $V = 2.0$ L, $T = 275$ K, and 90.0 % of limiting reagent used.   **Find:** Ps of all components and P_{Total}.

Conceptual Plan: CH_4: $mL \rightarrow L \rightarrow mol_{CO_4} \rightarrow mol_{CO_2}$ and

$$\frac{1\,L}{1000\,mL} \quad \frac{1\,mol}{22.414\,L} \quad \frac{1\,mol\,CO_2}{5\,mol\,NO}$$

O_2: $mL \rightarrow L \rightarrow mol_{O_2} \rightarrow mol_{CO_2}$ and NO: $mL \rightarrow L \rightarrow mol_{NO} \rightarrow mol_{CO_2}$

$$\frac{1\,L}{1000\,mL} \quad \frac{1\,mol}{22.414\,L} \quad \frac{1\,mol\,CO_2}{5\,mol\,O_2} \qquad\qquad \frac{1\,L}{1000\,mL} \quad \frac{1\,mol}{22.414\,L} \quad \frac{1\,mol\,CO_2}{5\,mol\,NO}$$

the smallest yield determines the limiting reagent then initial $mol_{NO} \rightarrow$ reacted $mol_{NO} \rightarrow$ final mol_{NO}

NO is the limiting reagent   90.0%   0.100 x initial mol_{no}

reacted $mol_{NO} \rightarrow$ reacted mol_{CH_4} then initial mol_{CH_4}, reacted $mol_{CH_4} \rightarrow$ final mol_{CH_4} then

$$\frac{1\,mol\,CH_4}{5\,mol\,NO}$$

initial mol_{CH_4} – reacted mol_{CH_4} = final mol_{CH_4}

final mol_{CH_4}, $V, T \rightarrow$ final P_{CH_4} and reacted $mol_{NO} \rightarrow$ reacted mol_{O_2} then

$$PV = nRT \qquad\qquad \frac{5\,mol\,O_2}{5\,mol\,NO}$$

initial mol_{O_2}, reacted $mol_{O_2} \rightarrow$ final mol_{O_2} then final mol_{O_2}, $V, T \rightarrow$ final P_{O_2} and

initial mol_{O_2} – reacted mol_{O_2} = final mol_{O_2} $PV = nRT$

final mol_{NO}, $V, T \rightarrow$ final P_{NO} and theoretical mol_{CO_2} from NO $\rightarrow$ final mol_{CO_2}

$$PV = nRT \qquad\qquad\qquad 90.0\%$$

final mol_{CO_2}, $V, T \rightarrow P_{CO_2}$ then final $mol_{CO_2} \rightarrow mol_{H_2O}$ then mol_{H_2O}, $V, T \rightarrow P_{H_2O}$ and

$$PV = nRT \qquad\qquad \frac{1\,mol\,H_2O}{1\,mol\,CO_2} \qquad\qquad PV = nRT$$

final $mol_{CO_2} \rightarrow mol_{NO_2}$ then mol_{NO_2}, $V, T \rightarrow P_{NO_2}$ and final $mol_{CO_2} \rightarrow mol_{OH}$ then

$$\frac{1\,mol\,NO_2}{1\,mol\,CO_2} \qquad\qquad PV = nRT \qquad\qquad \frac{2\,mol\,OH}{1\,mol\,CO_2}$$

mol_{OH}, $V, T \rightarrow P_{OH}$ finally $P_{CH_4}, P_{O_2}, P_{NO}, P_{CO_2}, P_{H_2O}, P_{NO_2}, P_{OH} \rightarrow P_{Ttotal}$

$$PV = nRT \qquad\qquad\qquad\qquad P_{Total} = \sum P$$

Solution: CH_4: $155\,\cancel{mL} \times \dfrac{1\,\cancel{L}}{1000\,\cancel{mL}} \times \dfrac{1\,\cancel{mol\,CH_4}}{22.414\,\cancel{L}} \times \dfrac{1\,mol\,CO_2}{1\,\cancel{mol\,CH_4}} = 0.00691\underline{5}32\ mol\,CO_2$,

O_2: $885\,\cancel{mL} \times \dfrac{1\,\cancel{L}}{1000\,\cancel{mL}} \times \dfrac{1\,\cancel{mol\,O_2}}{22.414\,\cancel{L}} = 0.039\underline{4}842\ mol\,O_2 \dfrac{1\,\cancel{mol\,CO_2}}{5\,\cancel{mol\,O_2}} = 0.00789\underline{6}85\ mol\,CO_2$

NO: $55.5\,\cancel{mL} \times \dfrac{1\,\cancel{L}}{1000\,\cancel{mL}} \times \dfrac{1\,\cancel{mol\,NO}}{22.414\,\cancel{L}} \times \dfrac{1\,mol\,CO_2}{5\,\cancel{mol\,NO}} = 0.000495\underline{2}26\ mol\,CO_2$.

$0.000495\underline{2}26\ mol\,CO_2$ is the smallest yield, so NO is the limiting reagent.

$55.5\,\cancel{mL} \times \dfrac{1\,\cancel{L}}{1000\,\cancel{mL}} \times \dfrac{1\,mol\,NO}{22.414\,\cancel{L}} = 0.00247\underline{6}13\ mol\,NO$

reacted mol NO $= 0.900 \times mol\,NO = 0.900 \times 0.00247\underline{6}13\ mol\,NO = 0.00222\underline{8}52\ mol\,NO$,

unreacted mol NO $= 0.100 \times mol\,NO = 0.100 \times 0.00247\underline{6}13\ mol\,NO = 0.000247\underline{6}13\ mol\,NO$,

$0.00222\underline{8}52\,\cancel{mol\,NO} \times \dfrac{1\,mol\,CH_4}{5\,\cancel{mol\,NO}} = 0.000445\underline{7}04\ mol\,CH_4$ reacted,

$0.00691\underline{5}32\ mol\,CH_4 - 0.000445\underline{7}04\ mol\,CH_4$ reacted $= 0.00646\underline{9}62\ mol\,CH_4$ then $PV = nRT$

Rearrange to solve for P. $P = \dfrac{nRT}{V} = \dfrac{0.00646\underline{9}62\,\cancel{mol} \times 0.08206\,\frac{\cancel{L}\cdot atm}{\cancel{mol}\cdot\cancel{K}} \times 275\,\cancel{K}}{2.0\,\cancel{L}} = 0.0730\ atm\,CH_4$ remaining

$0.00222\underline{8}52\,\cancel{mol\,NO} \times \dfrac{5\,mol\,O_2}{5\,\cancel{mol\,NO}} = 0.00222\underline{8}52\ mol\,O_2$ reacted,

$0.039\underline{4}842\ mol\,O_2 - 0.00222\underline{8}52\ mol\,O_2$ reacted $= 0.037\underline{2}557\ mol\,O_2$

$P = \dfrac{nRT}{V} = \dfrac{0.037\underline{2}557\,\cancel{mol} \times 0.08206\,\frac{\cancel{L}\cdot atm}{\cancel{mol}\cdot\cancel{K}} \times 275\,\cancel{K}}{2.0\,\cancel{L}} = 0.420\ atm\,O_2$ remaining

$P = \dfrac{nRT}{V} = \dfrac{0.000247\underline{6}13\,\cancel{mol} \times 0.08206\,\frac{\cancel{L}\cdot atm}{\cancel{mol}\cdot\cancel{K}} \times 275\,\cancel{K}}{2.0\,\cancel{L}} = 0.00279\ atm\,NO$ remaining

$0.00222\underline{8}52\,\cancel{mol\,NO} \times \dfrac{1\,mol\,CO_2}{5\,\cancel{mol\,NO}} = 0.000445\underline{7}04\ mol\,CO_2$

$$P = \frac{nRT}{V} = \frac{0.000445704 \; \text{mol} \times 0.08206 \frac{\text{L} \cdot \text{atm}}{\text{mol} \cdot \text{K}} \times 275 \; \text{K}}{2.0 \; \text{L}} = 0.00503 \; \text{atm CO}_2 \; \text{produced}$$

$$0.00222852 \; \text{mol NO} \times \frac{1 \; \text{mol H}_2\text{O}}{5 \; \text{mol NO}} = 0.000445704 \; \text{mol H}_2\text{O}$$

$$P = \frac{nRT}{V} = \frac{0.000445704 \; \text{mol} \times 0.08206 \frac{\text{L} \cdot \text{atm}}{\text{mol} \cdot \text{K}} \times 275 \; \text{K}}{2.0 \; \text{L}} = 0.00503 \; \text{atm H}_2\text{O} \; \text{produced}$$

$$0.00222852 \; \text{mol NO} \times \frac{5 \; \text{mol NO}_2}{5 \; \text{mol NO}} = 0.00222852 \; \text{mol NO}_2$$

$$P = \frac{nRT}{V} = \frac{0.00222852 \; \text{mol} \times 0.08206 \frac{\text{L} \cdot \text{atm}}{\text{mol} \cdot \text{K}} \times 275 \; \text{K}}{2.0 \; \text{L}} = 0.0251 \; \text{atm NO}_2 \; \text{produced}$$

$$0.00222852 \; \text{mol NO} \times \frac{2 \; \text{mol OH}}{5 \; \text{mol NO}} = 0.000891408 \; \text{mol OH}$$

$$P = \frac{nRT}{V} = \frac{0.000891408 \; \text{mol} \times 0.08206 \frac{\text{L} \cdot \text{atm}}{\text{mol} \cdot \text{K}} \times 275 \; \text{K}}{2.0 \; \text{L}} = 0.0101 \; \text{atm OH} \; \text{produced}$$

$$\text{Total} = \sum P$$

$$= 0.0730 \, \text{atm} + 0.420 \, \text{atm} + 0.00279 \, \text{atm} + 0.00503 \, \text{atm} + 0.00503 \, \text{atm} + 0.0251 \, \text{atm} + 0.0101 \, \text{atm}$$

$$= 0.541 \; \text{atm}$$

Check: The units (atm) are correct. The magnitude of the answers is reasonable. The limiting reagent has the lowest pressure. The product pressures are in line with the ratios of the stoichiometric coefficients.

5.139   **Given:** $P_{CH_4} + P_{C_2H_6} = 0.53$ atm, $P_{CO_2} + P_{H_2O} = 2.2$ atm   **Find:** χ_{CH_4}

     Conceptual Plan: Write balanced reactions to determine change in moles of gas for CH$_4$ and C$_2$H$_6$.

$$2 \, CH_4 \, (g) + 4 \, O_2 \, (g) \rightarrow 4 \, H_2O \, (g) + 2 \, CO_2 \, (g) \text{ and } 2 \, C_2H_6 \, (g) + 7 \, O_2 \, (g) \rightarrow 6 \, H_2O \, (g) + 4 \, CO_2 \, (g) \text{ thus } \quad \frac{6 \text{ mol gases}}{2 \text{ mol } CH_4} \quad \frac{10 \text{ mol gases}}{2 \text{ mol } C_2H_6}$$

     write expression for final pressure, substituting in data given $\rightarrow \chi_{CH_4}$

$$\chi_{CH_4} = \frac{n_{CH_4}}{n_{CH_4} + n_{C_2H_6}} \text{ and } \chi_{C_2H_6} = 1 - \chi_{CH_4}$$

$$P_{CH_4} = \chi_{CH_4} P_{Total} \quad P_{C_2H_6} = \chi_{C_2H_6} P_{Total} \quad P_{Final} = \left(\chi_{CH_4} P_{Total} \times \frac{6 \text{ mol gases}}{2 \text{ mol } CH_4} \right) + \left((1 - \chi_{CH_4}) P_{Total} \times \frac{10 \text{ mol gases}}{2 \text{ mol } C_2H_6} \right)$$

     Solution:

$$P_{Final} = \left(\chi_{CH_4} \times 0.53 \, \text{atm} \times \frac{6 \text{ mol gases}}{2 \text{ mol } CH_4} \right) + \left((1 - \chi_{CH_4}) \times 0.53 \, \text{atm} \times \frac{10 \text{ mol gases}}{2 \text{ mol } C_2H_6} \right) = 2.2 \, \text{atm}$$

     Substitute as above for $\chi_{C_2H_6}$, then to solve for $\chi_{CH_4} = 0.42$.

     Check: The units (none) are correct. The magnitude of the answer (0.42) makes sense because if it were all methane the final pressure would have been 1.59 atm, and if it were all ethane the final pressure would have been 2.65 atm. Since we are closer to the latter pressure, we expect the mole fraction of methane to be less than 0.5.

Conceptual Problems

5.141   Since the passengers have more mass than the balloon, they have more momentum than the balloon. The passengers will continue to travel in their original direction longer. The car is slowing so the relative position of the passengers is to move forward and the balloon to move backwards. The opposite happens upon acceleration.

5.143   B is the limiting reactant (2.0 L of B requires 1.0 L A to completely react). The final container will have 0.5 L A and 2.0 L C, so the final volume will be 2.5 L. The change will be $((2.5 \, \text{L}/3.5 \, \text{L}) \times 100 \, \%) - 100 \, \% = -29 \, \%$.

5.145   (a)   False – All gases have the same average kinetic energy at the same temperature.

       (b)   False – The gases will have the same partial pressures since we have the same number of moles of each.

       (c)   False – The average velocity of the B molecules will be less than that of the A molecules since the Bs are heavier.

       (d)   True – Since B molecules are heavier they will contribute more to the density ($d = m/V$).

6 Thermochemistry

Review Questions

6.1 Thermochemistry is the study of the relationship between chemistry and energy. It is important because energy and its uses are critical to our society. It is important to understand how much energy is required or released in a process.

6.3 Kinetic energy is energy associated with the motion of an object. Potential energy is energy associated with the position or composition of an object. Examples of kinetic energy are a moving billiard ball, gas molecules, and a raging river. Examples of potential energy are a billiard ball raised above the surface of a billiard table, a compressed spring, and molecules.

6.5 The SI unit of energy is $kg\frac{m^2}{s^2}$, defined as the joule (J), named after the English scientist James Joule. Other units of energy are the kilojoule (kJ), the calorie (cal), the Calorie (Cal), and the kilowatt-hour (kWh).

6.7 According to the first law, a device that would continually produce energy with no energy input, sometimes known as a perpetual motion machine, cannot exist because the best we can do with energy is break even.

6.9 The internal energy (E) of a system is the sum of the kinetic and potential energies of all of the particles that compose the system. Internal energy is a state function.

6.11 If the reactants have a lower internal energy than the products, ΔE_{sys} is positive and energy flows into the system from the surroundings.

6.13 The internal energy (E) of a system is the sum of the kinetic and potential energies of all of the particles that compose the system. The change in the internal energy of the system (ΔE) must be the sum of the heat transferred (q) and the work done (w): $\Delta E = q + w$.

6.15 The heat capacity of a system is usually defined as the quantity of heat required to change its temperature by 1 °C. Heat capacity (C) is a measure of the system's ability to hold thermal energy without undergoing a large change in temperature. The difference between heat capacity (C) and specific heat capacity (C_s) is that the specific heat capacity is the amount of heat required to raise the temperature of *1 gram* of the substance by 1 °C.

6.17 When two objects of different temperatures come in direct contact heat flows from the higher temperature object to the lower temperature object. The amount of heat lost by the warmer object is equal to the amount of heat gained by the cooler object. The warmer object's temperature will drop and the cooler object's temperature will rise until they reach the same temperature. The magnitude of these temperature changes depends on the mass and heat capacities of the two objects.

6.19   In calorimetry, the thermal energy exchanged between the reaction (defined as the system) and the surroundings is measured by observing the change in temperature of the surroundings. A bomb calorimeter is used to measure the ΔE_{rxn} for combustion reactions. The calorimeter includes a tight fitting, sealed container that forces the reaction to occur at constant volume. A coffee-cup calorimeter is used to measure ΔH_{rxn} for many aqueous reactions. The calorimeter consists of two Styrofoam® coffee cups, one inserted into the other, to provide insulation from the laboratory environment. Since the reaction happens under conditions of constant pressure (open to the atmosphere), $q_{rxn} = q_p = \Delta H_{rxn}$.

6.21   An endothermic reaction has a positive ΔH and absorbs heat from the surroundings. An endothermic reaction feels cold to the touch. An exothermic reaction has a negative ΔH and gives off heat to the surroundings. An exothermic reaction feels warm to the touch.

6.23   The internal energy of a chemical system is the sum of its kinetic energy and its potential energy. It is this potential energy that absorbs the energy in an endothermic chemical reaction. In an endothermic reaction, as some bonds break and others form, the protons and electrons go from an arrangement of lower potential energy to one of higher potential energy, absorbing thermal energy in the process. This absorption of thermal energy reduces the kinetic energy of the system. This is detected as a drop in temperature.

6.25   (a) If a reaction is multiplied by a factor, the ΔH is multiplied by the same factor.

(b) If a reaction is reversed, the sign of ΔH is reversed.

The relationships hold because H is a state function. Twice as much energy is contained in twice the quantity of reactants or products. If the reaction is reversed, the final and initial states have been switched and the direction of heat flow is reversed.

6.27   The standard state is defined as follows: for a gas, the pure gas at a pressure of exactly 1 atmosphere; for a liquid or solid, the pure substance in its most stable form at a pressure of 1 atm and the temperature of interest (often taken to be 25 °C); and for a substance in solution, a concentration of exactly 1 M. The standard enthalpy change ($\Delta H°$) is the change in enthalpy for a process when all reactants and products are in their standard states. The superscript degree sign indicates standard states.

6.29   To calculate $\Delta H_{rxn}°$, subtract the heats of formations of the reactants multiplied by their stoichiometric coefficients from the heats of formation of the products multiplied by their stoichiometric coefficients. In the form of an equation:

$$\Delta H_{rxn}° = \sum n_p \Delta H_f°(\text{products}) - \sum n_R \Delta H_f°(\text{reactants})$$

6.31   One of the main problems associated with the burning of fossil fuels is that, even though they are abundant in the Earth's crust, they are a finite and non-renewable energy source. The other major problems associated with fossil fuel use are related to the products of combustion. Three major environmental problems associated with the emissions of fossil fuel combustion are air pollution, acid rain, and global warming. One of the main products of fossil fuel combustion is carbon dioxide (CO_2), which is a greenhouse gas.

Energy Units

6.33   (a)   **Given:** 534 kWh   **Find:** J
Conceptual Plan: kWh $\rightarrow$ J

$$\frac{3.60 \times 10^6 \, J}{1 \, kWh}$$

Solution: $534 \, \cancel{kWh} \times \dfrac{3.60 \times 10^6 \, J}{1 \, \cancel{kWh}} = 1.92 \times 10^9 \, J$

Check: The units (J) are correct. The magnitude of the answer (10^9) makes physical sense because a kWh is much larger than a Joule, so the answer increases.

(b)   **Given:** 215 kJ   **Find:** Cal
Conceptual Plan: kJ $\rightarrow$ J $\rightarrow$ Cal

$$\frac{1000 \, J}{1 \, kJ} \quad \frac{1 \, Cal}{4184 \, J}$$

Solution: $215 \text{ kJ} \times \dfrac{1000 \text{ J}}{1 \text{ kJ}} \times \dfrac{1 \text{ Cal}}{4184 \text{ J}} = 51.4 \text{ Cal}$

Check: The units (Cal) are correct. The magnitude of the answer (51) makes physical sense because a Calorie is about $\frac{1}{4}$ of a kJ, so the answer decreases by a factor of about four.

(c) **Given:** 567 Cal **Find:** J
    Conceptual Plan: Cal → J

$$\dfrac{4184 \text{ J}}{1 \text{ Cal}}$$

Solution: $567 \text{ Cal} \times \dfrac{4184 \text{ J}}{1 \text{ Cal}} = 2.37 \times 10^6 \text{ J}$

Check: The units (J) are correct. The magnitude of the answer (10^6) makes physical sense because a Calorie is much larger than a Joule, so the answer increases.

(d) **Given:** 2.85×10^3 J **Find:** cal
    Conceptual Plan: J → cal

$$\dfrac{1 \text{ cal}}{4.184 \text{ J}}$$

Solution: $2.85 \times 10^3 \text{ J} \times \dfrac{1 \text{ cal}}{4.184 \text{ J}} = 681 \text{ cal}$

Check: The units (cal) are correct. The magnitude of the answer (680) makes physical sense because a J is about $\frac{1}{4}$ the size of a calorie, so the answer decreases by a factor of about four.

6.35 (a) **Given:** 2387 Cal **Find:** J
        Conceptual Plan: Cal → J

$$\dfrac{4184 \text{ J}}{1 \text{ Cal}}$$

Solution: $2387 \text{ Cal} \times \dfrac{4184 \text{ J}}{1 \text{ Cal}} = 9.987 \times 10^6 \text{ J}$

Check: The units (J) are correct. The magnitude of the answer (10^7) makes physical sense because a Calorie is much larger than a Joule, so the answer increases.

(b) **Given:** 2387 Cal **Find:** kJ
    Conceptual Plan: Cal → J → kWh

$$\dfrac{4184 \text{ J}}{1 \text{ Cal}} \quad \dfrac{1 \text{ kJ}}{1000 \text{ J}}$$

Solution: $2387 \text{ Cal} \times \dfrac{4184 \text{ J}}{1 \text{ Cal}} \times \dfrac{1 \text{ kJ}}{1000 \text{ J}} = 9.987 \times 10^3 \text{ kJ}$

Check: The units (kJ) are correct. The magnitude of the answer (10^4) makes physical sense because a Calorie is larger than a kJ, so the answer increases.

(c) **Given:** 2387 Cal **Find:** kWh
    Conceptual Plan: Cal → J → kWh

$$\dfrac{4184 \text{ J}}{1 \text{ Cal}} \quad \dfrac{1 \text{ kWh}}{3.60 \times 10^6 \text{ J}}$$

Solution: $2387 \text{ Cal} \times \dfrac{4184 \text{ J}}{1 \text{ Cal}} \times \dfrac{1 \text{ kWh}}{3.60 \times 10^6 \text{ J}} = 2.774 \text{ kWh}$

Check: The units (kWh) are correct. The magnitude of the answer (3) makes physical sense because a Calorie is much smaller than a kWh, so the answer decreases.

Internal Energy, Heat, and Work

6.37 (d) $\Delta E_{\text{sys}} = -\Delta E_{\text{surr}}$ If energy change of the system is negative, energy is being transferred from the system to the surroundings, decreasing the energy of the system and increasing the energy of the surroundings. The amount of energy lost by the system must go somewhere, so the amount gained by the surroundings is equal and opposite to that lost by the system.

6.39 (a) The energy exchange is primarily heat since the skin (part of the surroundings) is cooled. There is a small expansion (work) since water is being converted from a liquid to a gas. The sign of ΔE_{sys} is positive since the surroundings cool.

(b) The energy exchange is primarily work. The sign of ΔE_{sys} is negative since the system is expanding (doing work on the surroundings).

(c) The energy exchange is primarily heat. The sign of ΔE_{sys} is positive since the system is being heated by the flame.

6.41 **Given:** 622 kJ heat released; 105 kJ work done on surroundings **Find:** ΔE_{sys}
Conceptual Plan: interpret language to determine the sign of the two terms then $q, w \rightarrow \Delta E_{sys}$
$$\Delta E = q + w$$
Solution: Since heat is released from the system to the surroundings, $q = -622$ kJ; since the system is doing work on the surroundings, $w = -105$ kJ. $\Delta E = q + w = -622$ kJ $- 105$ kJ $= -727$ kJ $= -7.27 \times 10^2$ kJ
Check: The units (kJ) are correct. The magnitude of the answer (-730) makes physical sense because both terms are negative.

6.43 **Given:** 655 J heat absorbed; 344 J work done on surroundings **Find:** ΔE_{sys}
Conceptual Plan: interpret language to determine the sign of the two terms then $q, w \rightarrow \Delta E_{sys}$
$$\Delta E = q + w$$
Solution: Since heat is absorbed by the system, $q = +655$ J; since the system is doing work on the surroundings, $w = -344$ J. $\Delta E = q + w = 655$ J $- 344$ J $= 311$ J.
Check: The units (J) are correct. The magnitude of the answer ($+300$) makes physical sense because heat term dominates over the work term.

Heat, Heat Capacity, and Work

6.45 Cooler A had more ice after 3 hours because most of the ice in cooler B was melted in order to cool the soft drinks that started at room temperature. In cooler A the drinks were already cold and so the ice only needed to maintain this cool temperature.

6.47 **Given:** 1.50 L water, $T_i = 25.0$ °C, $T_f = 100.0$ °C, d $= 1.0$ g/mL **Find:** q
Conceptual Plan: L $\rightarrow$ mL $\rightarrow$ g and pull C_s from Table 6.4 and $T_i, T_f \rightarrow \Delta T$ then $m, C_s, \Delta T \rightarrow q$
$$\frac{1000 \text{ mL}}{1 \text{ L}} \quad \frac{1.0 \text{ g}}{1.0 \text{ mL}} \qquad 4.18 \frac{\text{J}}{\text{g} \cdot \text{°C}} \qquad \Delta T = T_f - T_i \qquad q = mC_s\Delta T$$
Solution: $1.50 \text{ L} \times \dfrac{1000 \text{ mL}}{1 \text{ L}} \times \dfrac{1.0 \text{ g}}{1.0 \text{ mL}} = 1500$ g and $\Delta T = T_f - T_i = 100.0$ °C $- 25.0$ °C $= 75.0$ °C

then $q = mC_s\Delta T = 1500 \text{ g} \times 4.18\dfrac{\text{J}}{\text{g} \cdot \text{°C}} \times 75.0 \text{ °C} = 4.7 \times 10^5$ J

Check: The units (J) are correct. The magnitude of the answer (10^6) makes physical sense because there is such a large mass, a significant temperature change, and a high specific heat capacity material.

6.49 (a) **Given:** 25 g gold, $T_i = 27.0$ °C, $q = 2.35$ kJ **Find:** T_f
Conceptual Plan: kJ $\rightarrow$ J and pull C_s from Table 6.4 then $m, C_s, q \rightarrow \Delta T$ then $T_i, \Delta T \rightarrow T_f$
$$\frac{1000 \text{ J}}{1 \text{ kJ}} \qquad 0.128 \frac{\text{J}}{\text{g} \cdot \text{°C}} \qquad q = mC_s\Delta T \qquad \Delta T = T_f - T_i$$
Solution: $2.35 \text{ kJ} \times \dfrac{1000 \text{ J}}{1 \text{ kJ}} = 2350$ J then $q = mC_s\Delta T$. Rearrange to solve for ΔT.

$\Delta T = \dfrac{q}{mC_s} = \dfrac{2350 \text{ J}}{25 \text{ g} \times 0.128\dfrac{\text{J}}{\text{g} \cdot \text{°C}}} = 734.375$ °C finally $\Delta T = T_f - T_i$. Rearrange to solve for T_f.

$T_f = \Delta T + T_i = 734.375$ °C $+ 27.0$ °C $= 760$ °C
Check: The units (°C) are correct. The magnitude of the answer (760) makes physical sense because there is such a large amount of heat absorbed, such a small mass, and specific heat capacity. The temperature change should be very large.

(b) **Given:** 25 g silver, $T_i = 27.0\ °C$, $q = 2.35$ kJ **Find:** T_f
 Conceptual Plan: kJ $\rightarrow$ J and pull C_s from Table 6.4 then m, C_s, q $\rightarrow$ ΔT then T_i, ΔT $\rightarrow$ T_f

$$\frac{1000\ J}{1\ kJ} \qquad 0.235\frac{J}{g\cdot °C} \qquad q = mC_s\Delta T \qquad \Delta T = T_f - T_i$$

Solution: $2.35\ kJ \times \dfrac{1000\ J}{1\ kJ} = 2350\ J$ then $= mC_s\Delta T$. Rearrange to solve for ΔT.

$$\Delta T = \frac{q}{mC_s} = \frac{2350\ J}{25\ g \times 0.235\dfrac{J}{g\cdot °C}} = 400\ °C \text{ finally } \Delta T = T_f - T_i. \text{ Rearrange to solve for } T_f.$$

$T_f = \Delta T + T_i = 400\ °C + 27.0\ °C = 430\ °C$

Check: The units (°C) are correct. The magnitude of the answer (430) makes physical sense because there is such a large amount of heat absorbed, such a small mass, and specific heat capacity. The temperature change should be very large. The temperature change should be less than that of the gold because the specific heat capacity is greater.

(c) **Given:** 25 g aluminum, $T_i = 27.0\ °C$, $q = 2.35$ kJ **Find:** T_f
 Conceptual Plan: kJ $\rightarrow$ J and pull C_s from Table 6.4 then m, C_s, q $\rightarrow$ ΔT then T_i, ΔT $\rightarrow$ T_f

$$\frac{1000\ J}{1\ kJ} \qquad 0.903\frac{J}{g\cdot °C} \qquad q = mC_s\Delta T \qquad \Delta T = T_f - T_i$$

Solution: $2.35\ kJ \times \dfrac{1000\ J}{1\ kJ} = 2350\ J$ then $q = mC_s\Delta T$. Rearrange to solve for ΔT.

$$\Delta T = \frac{q}{mC_s} = \frac{2350\ J}{25 g \times 0.903\dfrac{J}{g\cdot °C}} = 104.10°C \text{ finally } \Delta T = T_f - T_i. \text{ Rearrange to solve for } T_f.$$

$T_f = \Delta T + T_i = 104.10\ °C + 27.0\ °C = 130\ °C$

Check: The units (°C) are correct. The magnitude of the answer (130) makes physical sense because there is such a large amount of heat absorbed, and such a small mass. The temperature change should be less than that of the silver because the specific heat capacity is greater.

(d) **Given:** 25 g water, $T_i = 27.0\ °C$, $q = 2.35$ kJ **Find:** T_f
 Conceptual Plan: kJ $\rightarrow$ J and pull C_s from Table 6.4 then m, C_s, q $\rightarrow$ ΔT then T_i, ΔT $\rightarrow$ T_f

$$\frac{1000\ J}{1\ kJ} \qquad 4.18\frac{J}{g\cdot °C} \qquad q = mC_s\Delta T \qquad \Delta T = T_f - T_i$$

Solution: $2.35\ kJ \times \dfrac{1000\ J}{1\ kJ} = 2350\ J$ then $q = mC_s\Delta T$. Rearrange to solve for ΔT.

$$\Delta T = \frac{q}{mC_s} = \frac{2350\ J}{25\ g \times 4.18\dfrac{J}{g\cdot °C}} = 22.488°C \text{ finally } \Delta T = T_f - T_i. \text{ Rearrange to solve for } T_f.$$

$T_f = \Delta T + T_i = 22.488\ °C + 27.0\ °C = 49\ °C$

Check: The units (°C) are correct. The magnitude of the answer (130) makes physical sense because there is such a large amount of heat absorbed, and such a small mass. The temperature change should be less than that of the aluminum because the specific heat capacity is greater.

6.51 **Given:** $V_i = 0.0$ L, $V_f = 2.5$ L, $P = 1.1$ atm **Find:** w (J)
 Conceptual Plan: V_i, V_f $\rightarrow$ ΔV then P, ΔV $\rightarrow$ w (L atm) $\rightarrow$ w

$$\Delta V = V_f - V_i \qquad w = -P\Delta V \qquad \frac{101.3\ J}{1\ L\cdot atm}$$

Solution: $\Delta V = V_f - V_i = 2.5L - 0.0L = 2.5L$ then

$$w = -P\Delta V = -1.1\ atm \times 2.5\ L \times \frac{101.3\ J}{1\ L\cdot atm} = -280\ J$$

Check: The units (J) are correct. The magnitude of the answer (−280) makes physical sense because this is an expansion (negative work) and we have ~ atmospheric pressure and a small volume of expansion.

6.53   **Given:** $q = 565$ J absorbed, $V_i = 0.10$ L, $V_f = 0.85$ L, $P = 1.0$ atm   **Find:** ΔE_{sys}
         Conceptual Plan: $V_i, V_f \rightarrow \Delta V$ **and interpret language to determine the sign of the heat**

$$\Delta V = V_f - V_i \qquad\qquad\qquad q = +565 \text{ J}$$

         then $P, \Delta V \rightarrow w$ **(L atm)** $\rightarrow w$ **(J) finally** $q, w \rightarrow \Delta E_{sys}$

$$w = -P\Delta V \qquad \frac{101.3 \text{ J}}{1 \text{ L atm}} \qquad\qquad \Delta E = q + w$$

         Solution: $\Delta V = V_f - V_i = 0.85 \text{ L} - 0.10 \text{ L} = 0.75 \text{ L}$ then

$$w = -P\Delta V = -1.0 \text{ atm} \times 0.75 \text{ L} \times \frac{101.3 \text{ J}}{1 \text{ L} \cdot \text{atm}} = -75.975 \text{ J} \quad \Delta E = q + w = +565 \text{ J} - 75.975 \text{ J} = 489 \text{ J}$$

         Check: The units (J) are correct. The magnitude of the answer (500) makes physical sense because the heat absorbed dominated the small expansion work (negative work).

Enthalpy and Thermochemical Stoichiometry

6.55   **Given:** 1 mol fuel, 3452 kJ heat produced; 11 kJ work done on surroundings   **Find:** $\Delta E_{sys}, \Delta H$
         Conceptual Plan: interpret language to determine the sign of the two terms
         then $q \rightarrow \Delta H$ **and** $q, w \rightarrow \Delta E_{sys}$

$$\Delta H = q_p \qquad\qquad \Delta E = q + w$$

         Solution: Since heat is produced by the system to the surroundings, $q = -3452$ kJ; since the system is doing work on the surroundings, $w = -11$ kJ. $\Delta H = q_p = -3452$ kJ and
         $\Delta E = q + w = -3452 \text{ kJ} - 11 \text{ kJ} = -3463 \text{ kJ}$.
         Check: The units (kJ) are correct. The magnitude of the answer (–3500) makes physical sense because both terms are negative. We expect significant amounts of energy from fuels.

6.57   (a)   Combustion is an exothermic process; ΔH is negative.

         (b)   Evaporation requires an input of energy, so it is endothermic; ΔH is positive.

         (c)   Condensation is the reverse of evaporation, so it is exothermic; ΔH is negative.

6.59   **Given:** 177 mL acetone (C_3H_6O), $\Delta H^\circ_{rxn} = -1790$ kJ; d = 0.788 g/mL   **Find:** q
         Conceptual Plan: mL acetone $\rightarrow$ **g acetone** $\rightarrow$ **mol acetone** $\rightarrow$ q

$$\frac{0.788 \text{ g}}{1 \text{ mL}} \qquad \frac{1 \text{ mol}}{58.08 \text{ g}} \qquad \frac{-1790 \text{ kJ}}{1 \text{ mol}}$$

         Solution: $177 \text{ mL} \times \dfrac{0.788 \text{ g}}{1 \text{ mL}} \times \dfrac{1 \text{ mol}}{58.08 \text{ g}} \times \dfrac{-1790 \text{ kJ}}{1 \text{ mol}} = -4.30 \times 10^3$ kJ or 4.30×10^3 kJ released

         Check: The units (kJ) are correct. The magnitude of the answer (-10^3) makes physical sense because the enthalpy change is negative and we have more than a mole of acetone. We expect more than 1790 kJ to be released.

6.61   **Given:** pork roast, $\Delta H^\circ_{rxn} = -2217$ kJ; q needed $= 1.6 \times 10^3$ kJ, 10 % efficiency   **Find:** $m(CO_2)$
         Conceptual Plan: q **used** $\rightarrow$ q **generated** $\rightarrow$ **mol** CO_2 $\rightarrow$ **g** CO_2

$$\frac{100 \text{ kJ generated}}{10 \text{ kJ used}} \qquad \frac{3 \text{ mol}}{2217 \text{ kJ}} \qquad \frac{44.01 \text{ g}}{1 \text{ mol}}$$

         Solution: $1.6 \times 10^3 \text{ kJ} \times \dfrac{100 \text{ kJ generated}}{10 \text{ kJ used}} \times \dfrac{3 \text{ mol } CO_2}{2217 \text{ kJ}} \times \dfrac{44.01 \text{ g } CO_2}{1 \text{ mol } CO_2} = 950 \text{ g } CO_2$

         Check: The units (g) are correct. The magnitude of the answer (~1000) makes physical sense because the process is not very efficient and a lot of energy is needed.

Thermal Energy Transfer

6.63   **Given:** silver block, $T_{Agi} = 58.5$ °C, 100.0 g water, $T_{H_2Oi} = 24.8$ °C, $T_f = 26.2$ °C   **Find:** mass of silver block
         Conceptual Plan: pull C_s **values from table then** H_2O: $m, C_s, T_i, T_f \rightarrow q$ Ag: $C_s, T_i, T_f \rightarrow m$

$$\text{Ag: } 0.235 \frac{\text{J}}{\text{g} \cdot \text{°C}} \quad H_2O: 4.18 \frac{\text{J}}{\text{g} \cdot \text{°C}} \qquad q = mC_s(T_f - T_i) \text{ then set } q_{Ag} = -q_{H_2O}$$

Solution: $q = mC_s(T_f - T_i)$ substitute in values and set $q_{Ag} = -q_{H_2O}$.

$$q_{Ag} = m_{Ag}C_{Ag}(T_f - T_{Agi}) = m_{Ag} \times 0.235 \frac{J}{g \cdot °C} \times (26.2 °C - 58.5 °C) =$$

$$-q_{H_2O} = -m_{H_2O}C_{H_2O}(T_f - T_{H_2Oi}) = -100.0 \text{ g} \times 4.18 \frac{J}{g \cdot °C} \times (26.2 °C - 24.8 °C)$$

Rearrange to solve for m_{Ag}.

$$m_{Ag} \times \left(-7.5\underline{9}05 \frac{J}{g}\right) = -585.2 \text{ J} \rightarrow m_{Ag} = \frac{-585.2 \text{ J}}{-7.5\underline{9}05 \frac{J}{g}} = 77.0\underline{9}64 \text{ g Ag} = 77.1 \text{ g Ag}$$

Check: The units (g) are correct. The magnitude of the answer (77 g) makes physical sense because the heat capacity of water is much greater than the heat capacity of silver.

6.65   **Given:** 31.1 g gold, $T_{Aui} = 69.3 °C$, 64.2 g water, $T_{H_2Oi} = 27.8 °C$ **Find:** T_f
    Conceptual Plan: pull C_s values from table then $m, C_s, T_i \rightarrow T_f$

$$\text{Au: } 0.128 \frac{J}{g \cdot °C} \quad H_2O: 4.18 \frac{J}{g \cdot °C} \qquad\qquad q = mC_s(T_f - T_i) \text{ then set } q_{Au} = -q_{H_2O}$$

    Solution: $q = mC_s(T_f - T_i)$ substitute in values and set $q_{Au} = -q_{H_2O}$.

$$q_{Au} = m_{Au}C_{Au}(T_f - T_{Aui}) = 31.1 \text{ g} \times 0.128 \frac{J}{g \cdot °C} \times (T_f - 69.3 °C) =$$

$$-q_{H_2O} = -m_{H_2O}C_{H_2O}(T_f - T_{H_2Oi}) = -64.2 \text{ g} \times 4.18 \frac{J}{g \cdot °C} \times (T_f - 27.8 °C)$$

Rearrange to solve for T_f.

$$3.9808 \frac{J}{°C} \times (T_f - 69.3 °C) = -268.356 \frac{J}{°C} \times (T_f - 27.8 °C) \rightarrow$$

$$3.9\underline{8}08 \frac{J}{°C} T_f - 275.8694 \text{ J} = -268.356 \frac{J}{°C} T_f + 74\underline{6}0.2967 \text{ J} \rightarrow$$

$$268.356 \frac{J}{°C} T_f + 3.9\underline{8}08 \frac{J}{°C} T_f = 275.8694 \text{ J} + 74\underline{6}0.2967 \text{ J} \rightarrow 272.3\underline{3}68 \frac{J}{°C} T_f = 77\underline{3}6.1661 \text{ J} \rightarrow$$

$$T_f = \frac{77\underline{3}6.1661 \text{ J}}{272.3\underline{3}68 \frac{J}{°C}} = 28.4 °C$$

Check: The units (°C) are correct. The magnitude of the answer (28) makes physical sense because the heat transfer is dominated by the water (larger mass and larger specific heat capacity). The final temperature should be closer to the initial temperature of water than of gold.

6.67   **Given:** 6.15 g substance A, $T_{Ai} = 20.5 °C$, 25.2 g substance B, $T_{Bi} = 52.7 °C$, $C_s = 1.17 \text{ J/g} \cdot °C$, $T_f = 46.7 °C$
    Find: specific heat capacity of substance A
    Conceptual Plan: A: $m, T_i, T_f \rightarrow q$ B: $m, C_s, T_i, T_f \rightarrow q$ and solve for C

$$q = mC_s(T_f - T_i) \quad \text{then set } q_A = -q_B$$

    Solution: $q = mC_s(T_f - T_i)$ substitute in values and set $q_A = -q_B$.

$$A = m_A C_A(T_f - T_{Ai}) = 6.15 \text{ g} \times C_A \times (46.7 °C - 20.5 °C) =$$

$$-q_B = -m_B C_B(T_f - T_{Bi}) = -25.2 \text{ g} \times 1.17 \frac{J}{g \cdot °C} \times (46.7 °C - 52.7 °C)$$

Rearrange to solve for C_A.

$$C_A \times (161.13 \text{ g} \cdot °C) = 176.904 \text{ J} \rightarrow C_A = \frac{176.904 \text{ J}}{16\underline{1}.13 \text{ g} \cdot °C} = 1.09\underline{7}896 \frac{J}{g \cdot °C} = 1.10 \frac{J}{g \cdot °C}$$

Check: The units (J/g ·°C) are correct. The magnitude of the answer (1 J/g ·°C) makes physical sense because the mass of substance B is greater than the mass of substance A by a factor of ~4.1, and the temperature change for substance A is greater than the temperature change of substance B by a factor of ~4.4, so the heat capacity of substance A will be a little smaller.

Calorimetry

6.69 $\Delta H_{rxn} = q_p$ and $\Delta E_{rxn} = q_V = \Delta H - P\Delta V$. Since combustions always involve expansions, expansions do work and therefore have a negative value. Combustions are always exothermic and therefore have a negative value. This means that ΔE_{rxn} is more negative than ΔH°_{rxn} and so A (– 25.9 kJ) is the constant volume process and B (– 23.3 kJ) is the constant pressure process.

6.71   **Given:** 0.514 g biphenyl ($C_{12}H_{10}$), bomb calorimeter, $T_i = 25.8$ °C, $T_f = 29.4$ °C, $C_{cal} = 5.86$ kJ/°C   **Find:** ΔE_{rxn}

Conceptual Plan: $T_i, T_f \rightarrow \Delta T$ then $\Delta T, C_{cal} \rightarrow q_{cal} \rightarrow q_{rxn}$ then g $C_{12}H_{10} \rightarrow$ mol $C_{12}H_{10}$

$$\Delta T = T_f - T_i \qquad\qquad q_{cal} = C_{cal}\Delta T \quad q_{cal} = -q_{rxn} \qquad\qquad \frac{1\ mol}{154.20\ g}$$

then q_{rxn}, mol $C_{12}H_{10} \rightarrow \Delta E_{rxn}$

$$\Delta E_{rxn} = \frac{q_V}{mol\ C_{12}H_{10}}$$

Solution: $\Delta T = T_f - T_i = 29.4$ °C $- 25.8$ °C $= 3.6$ °C then $q_{cal} = C_{cal}\Delta T = 5.86\ \dfrac{kJ}{°C} \times 3.6\ °C = 21.096$ kJ

then $q_{cal} = -q_{rxn} = -21.096$ kJ and $0.514\ \bcancel{g\ C_{12}H_{10}} \times \dfrac{1\ mol\ C_{12}H_{10}}{154.20\ \bcancel{g\ C_{12}H_{10}}} = 0.00333333$ mol $C_{12}H_{10}$ then

$$\Delta E_{rxn} = \frac{q_V}{mol\ C_{12}H_{10}} = \frac{-21.096\ kJ}{0.00333333\ mol\ C_{12}H_{10}} = -6.3 \times 10^3\ kJ/mol$$

Check: The units (kJ/mol) are correct. The magnitude of the answer (– 6000) makes physical sense because there is such a large heat generated from a very small amount of biphenyl.

6.73   **Given:** 0.103 g zinc, coffee-cup calorimeter, $T_i = 22.5$ °C, $T_f = 23.7$ °C, 50.0 mL solution, d (solution) = 1.0 g/mL, $C_{soln} = 4.18$ kJ/g °C   **Find:** ΔH_{rxn}

Conceptual Plan: $T_i, T_f \rightarrow \Delta T$ and mL soln $\rightarrow$ g soln then $\Delta T, C_{cal} \rightarrow q_{cal} \rightarrow q_{rxn}$ then

$$\Delta T = T_f - T_i \qquad\qquad \frac{1.0\ g}{1.0\ mL} \qquad\qquad q_{cal} = m\,C_{soln}\Delta T \quad q_{soln} = -q_{rxn}$$

g Zn $\rightarrow$ mol Zn then q_{rxn}, mol Zn $\rightarrow \Delta H_{rxn}$

$$\frac{1\ mol}{65.37\ g} \qquad\qquad \Delta H_{rxn} = \frac{q_p}{mol\ Zn}$$

Solution: $\Delta T = T_f - T_i = 23.7$ °C $- 22.5$ °C $= 1.2$ °C and $50.0\ \bcancel{mL} \times \dfrac{1.0\ g}{1.0\ \bcancel{mL}} = 50.0$ g then

$q_{soln} = m\,C_{soln}\Delta T = 50.0\ \bcancel{g} \times 4.18\ \dfrac{J}{\bcancel{g} \cdot \bcancel{°C}} \times 1.2\ \bcancel{°C} = 250.8$ J then $q_{soln} = -q_{rxn} = -250.8$ J and

$0.103\ \bcancel{g\ Zn} \times \dfrac{1\ mol\ Zn}{65.37\ \bcancel{g\ Zn}} = 0.00157565$ mol Zn then

$$\Delta H_{rxn} = \frac{q_p}{mol\ Zn} = \frac{-250.8\ J}{0.00157565\ mol\ Zn} = -1.6 \times 10^5\ J/mol = -1.6 \times 10^2\ kJ/mol$$

Check: The units (kJ/mol) are correct. The magnitude of the answer (–160) makes physical sense because there is such a large heat generated from a very small amount of zinc.

Quantitative Relationships Involving ΔH and Hess's Law

6.75   (a)   Since A + B $\rightarrow$ 2 C has ΔH_1 then 2 C $\rightarrow$ A + B will have a $\Delta H_2 = -\Delta H_1$. When the reaction direction is reversed, it changes from exothermic to endothermic (or vice versa), so the sign of ΔH changes.

(b)   Since A + $\frac{1}{2}$ B $\rightarrow$ C has ΔH_1 then 2 A + B $\rightarrow$ 2 C will have a $\Delta H_2 = 2\,\Delta H_1$. When the reaction amount doubles, the amount of heat (or ΔH) doubles.

(c)   Since A $\rightarrow$ B + 2 C has ΔH_1 then $\frac{1}{2}$ A $\rightarrow$ $\frac{1}{2}$ B + C will have a $\Delta H_{1'} = \frac{1}{2}\,\Delta H_1$. When the reaction amount is cut in half, the amount of heat (or ΔH) is cut in half. Then $\frac{1}{2}$ B + C $\rightarrow$ $\frac{1}{2}$ A will have a $\Delta H_2 = -\Delta H_{1'} = -\frac{1}{2}\,\Delta H_1$

so the sign of ΔH changes.

6.77   Since the first reaction has Fe_2O_3 as a product and the reaction of interest has it as a reactant, we need to reverse the first reaction. When the reaction direction is reversed, ΔH changes.

$Fe_2O_3 (s) \rightarrow 2\ Fe\ (s) + 3/2\ O_2 (g)$ $\Delta H = +824.2$ kJ

Since the second reaction has 1 mole CO as a reactant and the reaction of interest has 3 moles of CO as a reactant, we need to multiply the second reaction and the ΔH by 3.

$3[CO\ (g) + 1/2\ O_2 (g) \rightarrow CO_2 (g)]$ $\Delta H = 3(-282.7$ kJ$) = -848.1$ kJ

Hess's Law states the ΔH of the net reaction is the sum of the ΔH of the steps.

The rewritten reactions are as follows:

$Fe_2O_3 (s) \rightarrow 2\ Fe\ (s) + \cancel{3/2\ O_2 (g)}$ $\Delta H = +824.2$ kJ
$3\ CO\ (g) + \cancel{3/2\ O_2 (g)} \rightarrow 3\ CO_2 (g)$ $\Delta H = -848.1$ kJ

$Fe_2O_3 (s) + 3\ CO\ (g) \rightarrow 2\ Fe\ (s) + 3\ CO_2 (g)$ $\Delta H_{rxn} = -23.9$ kJ

6.79   Since the first reaction has C_5H_{12} as a reactant and the reaction of interest has it as a product, we need to reverse the first reaction. When the reaction direction is reversed, ΔH changes.

$5\ CO_2 (g) + 6\ H_2O\ (g) \rightarrow C_5H_{12} (l) + 8\ O_2 (g)$ $\Delta H = +3505.8$ kJ

Since the second reaction has 1 mole C as a reactant and the reaction of interest has 5 moles of C as a reactant, we need to multiply the second reaction and the ΔH by 5.

$5[C\ (s) + O_2 (g) \rightarrow CO_2 (g)]$ $\Delta H = 5(-393.5$ kJ$) = -1967.5$ kJ

Since the third reaction has 2 moles H_2 as a reactant and the reaction of interest has 6 moles of H_2 as a reactant, we need to multiply the third reaction and the ΔH by 3.

$3[2\ H_2 (g) + O_2 (g) \rightarrow 2\ H_2O\ (g)]$ $\Delta H = 3(-483.5$ kJ$) = -1450.5$ kJ

Hess's Law states the ΔH of the net reaction is the sum of the ΔH of the steps.

The rewritten reactions are as follows:

$\cancel{5\ CO_2 (g)} + \cancel{6\ H_2O\ (g)} \rightarrow C_5H_{12} (l) + \cancel{8\ O_2 (g)}$ $\Delta H = +3505.8$ kJ
$5\ C\ (s) + \cancel{5\ O_2 (g)} \rightarrow \cancel{5\ CO_2 (g)}$ $\Delta H = -1967.5$ kJ
$6\ H_2 (g) + \cancel{3\ O_2 (g)} \rightarrow \cancel{6\ H_2O\ (g)}$ $\Delta H = -1450.5$ kJ

$5\ C\ (s) + 6\ H_2 (g) \rightarrow C_5H_{12} (l)$ $\Delta H_{rxn} = +87.8$ kJ

6.81   (a) $\dfrac{1}{2} N_2 (g) + \dfrac{3}{2} H_2 (g) \rightarrow NH_3 (g)$ $\Delta H_f^\circ = -45.9$ kJ/mol

        (b) $C\ (s) + O_2 (g) \rightarrow CO_2 (g)$ $\Delta H_f^\circ = -393.5$ kJ/mol

        (c) $2\ Fe\ (s) + \dfrac{3}{2} O_2 (g) \rightarrow Fe_2O_3 (s)$ $\Delta H_f^\circ = -824.2$ kJ/mol

        (d) $C\ (s) + 2\ H_2 (g) \rightarrow CH_4 (g)$ $\Delta H_f^\circ = -74.6$ kJ/mol

6.83   **Given:** $N_2H_4 (l) + N_2O_4 (g) \rightarrow 2\ N_2O\ (g) + 2\ H_2O\ (g)$ **Find:** ΔH_{rxn}°

        Conceptual Plan: $\Delta H_{rxn}^\circ = \sum n_P \Delta H_f^\circ (products) - \sum n_R \Delta H_f^\circ (reactants)$

        Solution:

Reactant/Product	ΔH_f°(kJ/mol from Appendix IIB)
$N_2H_4 (l)$	50.6
$N_2O_4 (g)$	11.1
$N_2O\ (g)$	81.6
$H_2O\ (g)$	-241.8

Be sure to pull data for the correct formula and phase.

$\Delta H_{rxn}^\circ = \sum n_P \Delta H_f^\circ (products) - \sum n_R \Delta H_f^\circ (reactants)$

$= [2(\Delta H_f^\circ(N_2O\ (g))) + 2(\Delta H_f^\circ(H_2O\ (g)))] - [1(\Delta H_f^\circ(N_2H_4 (l))) + 1(\Delta H_f^\circ(N_2O_4 (g)))]$

$= [2(81.6$ kJ$) + 2(-241.8$ kJ$)] - [1(50.6$ kJ$) + 1(11.1$ kJ$)]$

$= [-320.4$ kJ$] - [61.7$ kJ$]$

$= -382.1$ kJ

Check: The units (kJ) are correct. The answer is negative, which means that the reaction is exothermic. The answer is dominated by the negative heat of formation of water.

6.85   (a)   **Given:** $C_2H_4\ (g) + H_2\ (g) \rightarrow C_2H_6\ (g)$ **Find:** ΔH°_{rxn}

Conceptual Plan: $\Delta H^\circ_{rxn} = \sum n_P \Delta H^\circ_f(products) - \sum n_R \Delta H^\circ_f(reactants)$

Solution:

Reactant/Product	ΔH°_f(kJ/mol from Appendix IIB)
$C_2H_4\ (g)$	52.4
$H_2\ (g)$	0.0
$C_2H_6\ (g)$	-84.68

Be sure to pull data for the correct formula and phase.

$\Delta H^\circ_{rxn} = \sum n_P \Delta H^\circ_f(products) - \sum n_R \Delta H^\circ_f(reactants)$

$= [1(\Delta H^\circ_f(C_2H_6\ (g)))] - [1(\Delta H^\circ_f(C_2H_4\ (g))) + 1(\Delta H^\circ_f(H_2\ (g)))]$

$= [1(-84.68\ \text{kJ})] - [1(52.4\ \text{kJ}) + 1(0.0\ \text{kJ})]$

$= [-84.68\ \text{kJ}] - [52.4\ \text{kJ}]$

$= -137.1\ \text{kJ}$

Check: The units (kJ) are correct. The answer is negative, which means that the reaction is exothermic. Both hydrocarbon terms are negative, so the final answer is negative.

    (b)   **Given:** $CO\ (g) + H_2O\ (g) \rightarrow H_2\ (g) + CO_2\ (g)$ **Find:** ΔH°_{rxn}

Conceptual Plan: $\Delta H^\circ_{rxn} = \sum n_P \Delta H^\circ_f(products) - \sum n_R \Delta H^\circ_f(reactants)$

Solution:

Reactant/Product	ΔH°_f(kJ/mol from Appendix IIB)
$CO\ (g)$	-110.5
$H_2O\ (g)$	-241.8
$H_2\ (g)$	0.0
$CO_2\ (g)$	-393.5

Be sure to pull data for the correct formula and phase.

$\Delta H^\circ_{rxn} = \sum n_P \Delta H^\circ_f(products) - \sum n_R \Delta H^\circ_f(reactants)$

$= [1(\Delta H^\circ_f(H_2\ (g))) + 1(\Delta H^\circ_f(CO_2\ (g)))] - [1(\Delta H^\circ_f(CO\ (g))) + 1(\Delta H^\circ_f(H_2O\ (g)))]$

$= [1(0.0\ \text{kJ}) + 1(-393.5\ \text{kJ})] - [1(-110.5\ \text{kJ}) + 1(-241.8\ \text{kJ})]$

$= [-393.5\ \text{kJ}] - [-352.3\ \text{kJ}]$

$= -41.2\ \text{kJ}$

Check: The units (kJ) are correct. The answer is negative, which means that the reaction is exothermic.

    (c)   **Given:** $3\ NO_2\ (g) + H_2O\ (l) \rightarrow 2\ HNO_3\ (aq) + NO\ (g)$ **Find:** ΔH°_{rxn}

Conceptual Plan: $\Delta H^\circ_{rxn} = \sum n_P \Delta H^\circ_f(products) - \sum n_R \Delta H^\circ_f(reactants)$

Solution:

Reactant/Product	ΔH°_f(kJ/mol from Appendix IIB)
$NO_2\ (g)$	33.2
$H_2O\ (l)$	-285.8
$HNO_3\ (aq)$	-207
$NO\ (g)$	91.3

Be sure to pull data for the correct formula and phase.

$\Delta H^\circ_{rxn} = \sum n_P \Delta H^\circ_f(products) - \sum n_R \Delta H^\circ_f(reactants)$

$= [2(\Delta H^\circ_f(HNO_3\ (aq))) + 1(\Delta H^\circ_f(NO\ (g)))] - [3(\Delta H^\circ_f(NO_2\ (g))) + 1(\Delta H^\circ_f(H_2O\ (l)))]$

$= [2(-207\ \text{kJ}) + 1(91.3\ \text{kJ})] - [3(33.2\ \text{kJ}) + 1(-285.8\ \text{kJ})]$

$= [-322.7\ \text{kJ}] - [-186.2\ \text{kJ}]$

$= -137\ \text{kJ}$

Check: The units (kJ) are correct. The answer is negative, which means that the reaction is exothermic.

(d) **Given:** Cr_2O_3 (s) + 3 CO (g) → 2 Cr (s) + 3 CO_2 (g) **Find:** ΔH°_{rxn}

Conceptual Plan: $\Delta H^\circ_{rxn} = \sum n_P \Delta H^\circ_f(products) - \sum n_R \Delta H^\circ_f(reactants)$

Solution:

Reactant/Product	ΔH°_f(kJ/mol from Appendix IIB)
Cr_2O_3 (s)	− 1139.7
CO (g)	− 110.5
Cr (s)	0.0
CO_2 (g)	− 393.5

Be sure to pull data for the correct formula and phase.

$\Delta H^\circ_{rxn} = \sum n_P \Delta H^\circ_f(products) - \sum n_R \Delta H^\circ_f(reactants)$

$= [2(\Delta H^\circ_f(Cr\ (s))) + 3(\Delta H^\circ_f(CO_2\ (g)))] - [1(\Delta H^\circ_f(Cr_2O_3\ (s))) + 3(\Delta H^\circ_f(CO\ (g)))]$

$= [2(0.0\ kJ) + 3(- 393.5\ kJ)] - [1(- 1139.7\ kJ) + 3(- 110.5\ kJ)]$

$= [- 1180.5\ kJ] - [- 1471.2\ kJ]$

$= 290.7\ kJ$

Check: The units (kJ) are correct. The answer is positive, which means that the reaction is endothermic.

6.87 **Given:** form glucose ($C_6H_{12}O_6$) and oxygen from sunlight, carbon dioxide, and water **Find:** ΔH°_{rxn}

Conceptual Plan: write balanced reaction then $\Delta H^\circ_{rxn} = \sum n_P \Delta H^\circ_f(products) - \sum n_R \Delta H^\circ_f(reactants)$

Solution: 6 CO_2 (g) + 6 H_2O (l) → $C_6H_{12}O_6$ (s) + 6 O_2 (g)

Reactant/Product	ΔH°_f(kJ/mol from Appendix IIB)
CO_2 (g)	− 393.5
H_2O (l)	− 285.8
$C_6H_{12}O$ (s)	− 1273.3
O_2 (g)	0.0

Be sure to pull data for the correct formula and phase.

$\Delta H^\circ_{rxn} = \sum n_P \Delta H^\circ_f(products) - \sum n_R \Delta H^\circ_f(reactants)$

$= [1(\Delta H^\circ_f(C_6H_{12}O\ (s))) + 6(\Delta H^\circ_f(O_2\ (g)))] - [6(\Delta H^\circ_f(CO_2\ (g))) + 6(\Delta H^\circ_f(H_2O\ (l)))]$

$= [1(- 1273.3\ kJ) + 6(0.0\ kJ)] - [6(- 393.5\ kJ) + 6(- 285.8\ kJ)]$

$= [- 1273.3\ kJ] - [- 4075.6\ kJ]$

$= + 2802.5\ kJ$

Check: The units (kJ) are correct. The answer is positive, which means that the reaction is endothermic. The reaction requires the input of light energy, so we expect that this will be an endothermic reaction.

6.89 **Given:** 2 CH_3NO_2 (l) + 3/2 O_2 (g) → 2 CO_2 (g) + 3 H_2O (g) + N_2 (g) and $\Delta H^\circ_{rxn} = - 709.2\ kJ/mol$

Find: ΔH°_f (CH_3NO_2 (l))

Conceptual Plan: fill known values into $\Delta H^\circ_{rxn} = \sum n_P \Delta H^\circ_f(products) - \sum n_R \Delta H^\circ_f(reactants)$ **and rearrange to solve for** ΔH°_f (CH_3NO_2 (l))

Solution:

Reactant/Product	ΔH°_f(kJ/mol from Appendix IIB)
O_2 (g)	0.0
CO_2 (g)	− 393.5
H_2O (g)	− 241.8
N_2 (g)	0.0

Be sure to pull data for the correct formula and phase.

$\Delta H^\circ_{rxn} = \sum n_P \Delta H^\circ_f(products) - \sum n_R \Delta H^\circ_f(reactants)$

$= [2(\Delta H^\circ_f(CO_2\ (g))) + 3(\Delta H^\circ_f(H_2O\ (g))) + 1(\Delta H^\circ_f(N_2\ (g)))] - [2(\Delta H^\circ_f(CH_3NO_2\ (l))) + 3/2(\Delta H^\circ_f(O_2\ (g)))]$

$2(- 709.2\ kJ) = [2(- 393.5\ kJ) + 3(- 241.8\ kJ) + 1(0.0\ kJ)] - [2(\Delta H^\circ_f(CH_3NO_2(l)) + 3/2(0.0\ kJ)]$

$- 1418.4\ kJ = [- 1512.4\ kJ] - [2(\Delta H^\circ_f\ (CH_3NO_2(l))]$

$\Delta H^\circ_f(CH_3NO_2(l)) = - 94.0\ kJ/mol$

Check: The units (kJ/mol) are correct. The answer is negative (but not as negative as water and carbon dioxide), which is consistent with an exothermic combustion reaction.

Energy Use and the Environment

6.91   (a)   **Given:** methane, $H_{rxn}^{\circ} = -802.3$ kJ; $q = 1.00 \times 10^2$ kJ   **Find:** $m(CO_2)$
              Conceptual Plan: $q \rightarrow$ **mol CO_2** $\rightarrow$ **g CO_2**

$$\frac{1 \text{ mol}}{-802.3 \text{ kJ}} \qquad \frac{44.01 \text{ g}}{1 \text{ mol}}$$

              Solution: $-1.00 \times 10^2 \text{ kJ} \times \dfrac{1 \text{ mol } CO_2}{-802.3 \text{ kJ}} \times \dfrac{44.01 \text{ g } CO_2}{1 \text{ mol } CO_2} = 5.49 \text{ g } CO_2$

              Check: The units (g) are correct. The magnitude of the answer (~5) makes physical sense because less than a mole of fuel is used.

  (b)   **Given:** propane, $\Delta H_{rxn}^{\circ} = -2217$ kJ; $q = 1.00 \times 10^2$ kJ   **Find:** $m(CO_2)$
              Conceptual Plan: $q \rightarrow$ **mol CO_2** $\rightarrow$ **g CO_2**

$$\frac{3 \text{ mol}}{-2217 \text{ kJ}} \qquad \frac{44.01 \text{ g}}{1 \text{ mol}}$$

              Solution: $-1.00 \times 10^2 \text{ kJ} \times \dfrac{3 \text{ mol } CO_2}{-2217 \text{ kJ}} \times \dfrac{44.01 \text{ g } CO_2}{1 \text{ mol } CO_2} = 5.96 \text{ g } CO_2$

              Check: The units (g) are correct. The magnitude of the answer (~6) makes physical sense because less than a mole of fuel is used.

  (c)   **Given:** octane, $\Delta H_{rxn}^{\circ} = -5074.1$ kJ; $q = 1.00 \times 10^2$ kJ   **Find:** $m(CO_2)$
              Conceptual Plan: $q \rightarrow$ **mol CO_2** $\rightarrow$ **g CO_2**

$$\frac{8 \text{ mol}}{-5074.1 \text{ kJ}} \qquad \frac{44.01 \text{ g}}{1 \text{ mol}}$$

              Solution: $-1.00 \times 10^2 \text{ kJ} \times \dfrac{8 \text{ mol } CO_2}{-5074.1 \text{ kJ}} \times \dfrac{44.01 \text{ g } CO_2}{1 \text{ mol } CO_2} = 6.94 \text{ g } CO_2$

              Check: The units (g) are correct. The magnitude of the answer (~7) makes physical sense because less than a mole of fuel is used.
              The methane generated the least carbon dioxide for the given amount of heat, while the octane generated the most carbon dioxide for the given amount of heat.

6.93   **Given:** 7×10^{12} kg/yr octane (C_8H_{18}), $\Delta_{rxn}^{\circ} = -5074.1$ kJ (using Problem 91), 3×10^{15} kg CO_2 in the atmosphere,
             Find: $m(CO_2)$ in kg and time to double atmospheric CO_2
             Conceptual Plan: use reaction from Problem 91 C_8H_{18} *(l)* + 25/2 O_2 *(g)* $\rightarrow$ 8 CO_2 *(g)* + 9 H_2O *(g)*
             kg (C_8H_{18}) $\rightarrow$ **g (C_8H_{18})** $\rightarrow$ **mol (C_8H_{18})** $\rightarrow$ **mol CO_2** $\rightarrow$ **g CO_2** $\rightarrow$ **kg CO_2 produced**

$$\frac{1000 \text{ g}}{1 \text{ kg}} \qquad \frac{1 \text{ mol } C_8H_{18}}{114.22 \text{ g}} \qquad \frac{8 \text{ mol } CO_2}{1 \text{ mol } C_8H_{18}} \qquad \frac{44.01 \text{ g}}{1 \text{ mol}} \qquad \frac{1 \text{ kg}}{1000 \text{ g}}$$

             then kg CO_2 $\rightarrow$ **yr**

$$\frac{3 \times 10^{15} \text{ kg } CO_2}{\left(\dfrac{\text{kg } CO_2 \text{ produced}}{\text{yr}}\right)}$$

            Solution:

$$7 \times 10^{12} \text{ kg} \times \frac{1000 \text{ g}}{1 \text{ kg}} \times \frac{1 \text{ mol } C_8H_{18}}{114.22 \text{ g}} \times \frac{8 \text{ mol } CO_2}{1 \text{ mol } C_8H_{18}} \times \frac{44.01 \text{ g } CO_2}{1 \text{ mol } CO_2} \times \frac{1 \text{ kg}}{1000 \text{ g}} = \underline{2.158 \times 10^{13}} \text{ kg } CO_2$$

$$= \underline{2 \times 10^{13}} \text{ kg } CO_2 \text{ per year}$$

$$\frac{3 \times 10^{15} \text{ kg } CO_2}{\left(\dfrac{\underline{2.158 \times 10^{13}} \text{ kg } CO_2 \text{ produced}}{\text{yr}}\right)} = \underline{139} \text{ yr} = \underline{100} \text{ yr}$$

             Check: The units (kg and yr) are correct. The magnitude of the answer (10^{13} kg) makes physical sense because the mass of CO_2 is larger than the hydrocarbon mass in a combustion (since O is much heavier than

             generated each year.

Cumulative Problems

6.95 **Given:** billiard ball$_A$ = system: $m_A = 0.17$ kg, $v_{A1} = 4.5$ m/s slows to $v_{A2} = 3.8$ m/s and $v_{A3} = 0$; ball$_B$: $m_B = 0.17$ kg, $v_{B1} = 0$ and $v_{B2} = 3.8$ m/s, and $KE = \frac{1}{2}mv^2$ **Find:** w, q, ΔE_{sys}

Conceptual Plan: $m, v \rightarrow KE$ then $KE_{A3}, KE_{A1} \rightarrow \Delta E_{sys}$ and $KE_{A2}, KE_{A1} \rightarrow q$ and $KE_{B2}, KE_{B1} \rightarrow w_B$

$$KE = \frac{1}{2}mv^2 \qquad \Delta E_{sys} = KE_{A3} - KE_{A1} \qquad q = KE_{A2} - KE_{A1} \qquad w_B = KE_{B2} - KE_{B1}$$

$\Delta E_{sys}, q \rightarrow w_A$ verify that $w_A = -w_B$ so that no heat is transferred to ball$_B$

$$\Delta E = q + w$$

Solution: $KE = \frac{1}{2}mv^2$ since m is in kg and v is in m/s, KE will be in kg·m^2/s^2, which is joule.

$$KE_{A1} = \frac{1}{2}(0.17 \text{ kg})\left(4.5 \frac{m}{s}\right)^2 = 1.7213 \frac{kg \cdot m^2}{s^2} = 1.7213 \text{ J,}$$

$$KE_{A2} = \frac{1}{2}(0.17 \text{ kg})\left(3.8 \frac{m}{s}\right)^2 = 1.2274 \frac{kg \cdot m^2}{s^2} = 1.2274 \text{ J,}$$

$$KE_{A3} = \frac{1}{2}(0.17 \text{ kg})\left(0 \frac{m}{s}\right)^2 = 0 \frac{kg \cdot m^2}{s^2} = 0 \text{ J,} \quad KE_{B1} = \frac{1}{2}(0.17 \text{ kg})\left(0 \frac{m}{s}\right)^2 = 0 \frac{kg \cdot m^2}{s^2} = 0 \text{ J and}$$

$$KE_{B2} = \frac{1}{2}(0.17 \text{ kg})\left(3.8 \frac{m}{s}\right)^2 = 1.2274 \frac{kg \cdot m^2}{s^2} = 1.2274 \text{ J.}$$

$\Delta E_{sys} = KE_{A3} - KE_{A1} = 0 \text{ J} - 1.7213 \text{ J} = -1.7213 \text{ J} = -1.7 \text{ J,}$

$q = KE_{A2} - KE_{A1} = 1.2274 \text{ J} - 1.7213 \text{ J} = -0.4939 \text{ J} = -0.5 \text{ J,}$

$w_B = KE_{B2} - KE_{B1} = 1.2274 \text{ J} - 0 \text{ J} = 1.2274 \text{ J and}$

$w = \Delta E - \quad = -1.7213 \text{ J} - -0.4939 \text{ J} = -1.2274 \text{ J} = -1.2 \text{ J.}$

Since $w_A = -w_B$ no heat is transferred to ball$_B$.

Check: The units (J) are correct. Since the ball is initially moving and is stopped at the end, it has lost energy (negative ΔE_{sys}). As the ball slows due to friction, it is releasing heat (negative q). The kinetic energy is transferred to a second ball, so it does work (w negative).

6.97 **Given:** H_2O (l) $\rightarrow H_2O$ (g) $\Delta H_{rxn}^{\circ} = +44.01$ kJ/mol; $\Delta T_{body} = -0.50$ °C, $m_{body} = 95$ kg, $C_{body} = 4.0$ J/g °C **Find:** m_{H_2O}

Conceptual Plan: kg $\rightarrow$ g then $m_{body}, \Delta T, C_{body} \rightarrow q_{body} \rightarrow q_{rxn}$ (J) $\rightarrow q_{rxn}$ (kJ) $\rightarrow$ mol $H_2O \rightarrow$ g H_2O

$$\frac{1000 \text{ g}}{1 \text{ kg}} \qquad q_{body} = m_{body}C_{body}\Delta T_{body} \quad q_{rxn} = -q_{body} \qquad \frac{1 \text{ kJ}}{1000 \text{ J}} \qquad \frac{1 \text{ mol}}{44.01 \text{ kJ}} \qquad \frac{18.01 \text{ g}}{1 \text{ mol}}$$

Solution: 95 kg $\times \dfrac{1000 \text{ g}}{1 \text{ kg}} = 95000$ g then

$$q_{body} = m_{body}C_{body}\Delta T_{body} = 95000 \text{ g} \times 4.0 \frac{J}{g \cdot ^{\circ}C} \times (-0.50 ^{\circ}C) = -190000 \text{ J then}$$

$$q_{rxn} = -q_{body} = 190000 \text{ J} \times \frac{1 \text{ kJ}}{1000 \text{ J}} \times \frac{1 \text{ mol}}{44.01 \text{ kJ}} \times \frac{18.01 \text{ g}}{1 \text{ mol}} = 78 \text{ g } H_2O$$

Check: The units (g) are correct. The magnitude of the answer (78) makes physical sense because a person can sweat this much on a hot day.

6.99 **Given:** H_2O (s) $\rightarrow H_2O$ (l) ΔH_f° (H_2O (s)) $= -291.8$ kJ/mol; 355 mL beverage $T_{Bevi} = 25.0$ °C, $T_{Bevf} = 0.0$ °C, $C_{Bev} = 4.184$ J/g °C, $d_{Bev} = 1.0$ g/mL **Find:** ΔH_{rxn}° (ice melting) and m_{ice}

Conceptual Plan: $\Delta H_{rxn}^{\circ} = \sum n_P \Delta H_f^{\circ}(products) - \sum n_R \Delta H_f^{\circ}(reactants)$ mL $\rightarrow$ g and $T_i, T_f \rightarrow \Delta T$ then

$$\frac{1.0 \text{ g}}{1.0 \text{ mL}} \qquad T = T_f - T_i$$

$m_{H_2O}, \Delta T_{H_2O}, C_{H_2O} \rightarrow q_{H_2O} \rightarrow q_{rxn}$ (J) $\rightarrow q_{rxn}$ (kJ) $\rightarrow$ mol ice $\rightarrow$ g ice

$$q_{Bev} = m_{Bev}C_{Bev}\Delta T_{Bev} \quad q_{rxn} = -q_{Bev} \qquad \frac{1 \text{ kJ}}{1000 \text{ J}} \qquad \frac{1 \text{ mol}}{\Delta H_{rxn}^{\circ}} \qquad \frac{18.01 \text{ g}}{1 \text{ mol}}$$

Solution:

Reactant/Product	ΔH_f°(kJ/mol from Appendix IIB)
H_2O (s)	-291.8
H_2O (l)	-285.8

$$\Delta H_{rxn}^\circ = \sum n_P \Delta H_f^\circ(products) - \sum n_R \Delta H_f^\circ(reactants)$$
$$= [1(\Delta H_f^\circ(H_2O\ (l)))] - [1(\Delta H_f^\circ(H_2O\ (s)))]$$
$$= [1(-285.8\ kJ)] - [1(-291.8\ kJ)]$$
$$= +6.0\ kJ$$

$355\ \cancel{mL} \times \dfrac{1.0\ g}{1.0\ \cancel{mL}} = 355\ g$ and $\Delta T = T_f - T_i = 0.0\ °C - 25.0\ °C = -25.0\ °C$ then

$q_{Bev} = m_{Bev}C_{Bev}\Delta T_{Bev} = 355\ \cancel{g} \times 4.184\ \dfrac{J}{\cancel{g} \cdot \cancel{°C}} \times (-25.0\ \cancel{°C}) = -37133\ J$ then

$q_{rxn} = -q_{Bev} = -37133\ \cancel{J} \times \dfrac{1\ \cancel{kJ}}{1000\ \cancel{J}} \times \dfrac{1\ \cancel{mol}}{-6.0\ \cancel{kJ}} \times \dfrac{18.01\ g}{1\ \cancel{mol}} = 110\ g\ ice$

Check: The units (kJ and g) are correct. The answer is positive, which means that the reaction is endothermic. We expect an endothermic reaction because we know that heat must be added to melt ice. The magnitude of the answer (110 g) makes physical sense because it is much smaller than the weight of the beverage and it would fit in a glass with the beverage.

6.101   **Given:** 25.5 g aluminum, $T_{Ali} = 65.4\ °C$, 55.2 g water, $T_{H_2Oi} = 22.2\ °C$ **Find:** T_f
       Conceptual Plan: pull C_s values from table then m, C_s, $_i \to T_f$

                  Al: $0.903\ \dfrac{J}{g \cdot °C}$ H_2O: $4.18\ \dfrac{J}{g \cdot °C}$ $q = mC_s(T_f - T_i)$ then set $q_{Al} = -q_{H_2O}$

       Solution: $q = mC_s(T_f - T_i)$ substitute in values and set $q_{Al} = -q_{H_2O}$.

$$q_{Al} = m_{Al}C_{Al}(T_f - T_{Ali}) = 25.5\ \cancel{g} \times 0.903\ \dfrac{J}{\cancel{g} \cdot °C} \times (T_f - 65.4\ °C) =$$

$$-q_{H_2O} = -m_{H_2O}C_{H_2O}(T_f - T_{H_2Oi}) = -55.2\ \cancel{g} \times 4.18\ \dfrac{J}{\cancel{g} \cdot °C} \times (T_f - 22.2\ °C)$$

Rearrange to solve for T_f.

$$23.\underline{0}265\ \dfrac{J}{°C} \times (T_f - 65.4\ °C) = -230.\underline{7}36\ \dfrac{J}{°C} \times (T_f - 22.2\ °C) \to$$

$$23.\underline{0}265\ \dfrac{J}{°C}T_f - 1505.93\ J = -230.\underline{7}36\ \dfrac{J}{°C}T_f + 5122.34\ J \to$$

$$-5122.34\ J - 1505.93\ J = -230.\underline{7}36\ \dfrac{J}{°C}T_f - 23.\underline{0}265\ \dfrac{J}{°C}T_f \to 6628.27\ J = 253.\underline{7}625\ \dfrac{J}{°C}T_f \to$$

$$T_f = \dfrac{6628.27\ \cancel{J}}{253.\underline{7}625\dfrac{\cancel{J}}{°C}} = 26.1°C$$

Check: The units (°C) are correct. The magnitude of the answer (26) makes physical sense because the heat transfer is dominated by the water (larger mass and larger specific heat capacity). The final temperature should be closer to the initial temperature of water than of aluminum.

6.103   **Given:** palmitic acid ($C_{16}H_{32}O_2$) combustion ΔH_f° ($C_{16}H_{32}O_2$ (s)) $= -208$ kJ/mol; sucrose ($C_{12}H_{22}O_{11}$
       bustion ΔH_f° ($C_{12}H_{22}O_{11}$ (s)) $= -2226.1$ kJ/mol **Find:** ΔH_{rxn}° in kJ/mol and Cal/g
       Conceptual Plan: write balanced reaction then $\Delta H_{rxn}^\circ = \sum n_P \Delta H_f^\circ(products) - \sum n_R \Delta H_f^\circ(reactants)$
       kJ/mol $\to$ J/mol $\to$ Cal/mol $\to$ Cal/g

          $\dfrac{1000\ J}{1\ kJ}$ $\dfrac{1\ Cal}{4184\ J}$ PA: $\dfrac{1\ mol}{256.42\ g}$ S: $\dfrac{1\ mol}{342.30\ g}$

       Solution: Combustion is the combination with oxygen to form carbon dioxide and water (l):
       $C_{16}H_{32}O_2$ (s) $+ 23\ O_2$ (g) $\to 16\ CO_2$ (g) $+ 16\ H_2O$ (l)

Reactant/Product	ΔH_f°(kJ/mol from Appendix IIB)
$C_{16}H_{32}O_2$ (s)	-208
O_2 (g)	0.0
CO_2 (g)	-393.5
H_2O (l)	-285.8

Be sure to pull data for the correct formula and phase.

$\Delta H_{rxn}^{\circ} = \sum n_P \Delta H_f^{\circ}(products) - \sum n_R \Delta H_f^{\circ}(reactants)$

$= [16(\Delta H_f^{\circ}(CO_2(g))) + 16(\Delta H_f^{\circ}(H_2O(l)))] - [1(\Delta H_f^{\circ}(C_{16}H_{32}O_2(s))) + 23(\Delta H_f^{\circ}(O_2(g)))]$

$= [16(-393.5 \text{ kJ}) + 16(-285.8 \text{ kJ})] - [1(-208 \text{ kJ}) + 23(0.0 \text{ kJ})]$

$= [-10868.8 \text{ kJ}] - [-208 \text{ kJ}]$

$= -10,660.8 \text{ kJ/mol} = -10,661 \text{ kJ/mol}$

$-10,660.8 \dfrac{\text{kJ}}{\text{mol}} \times \dfrac{1000 \text{ J}}{1 \text{ kJ}} \times \dfrac{1 \text{ Cal}}{4184 \text{ J}} \times \dfrac{1 \text{ mol}}{256.42 \text{ g}} = -9.9378 \text{ Cal/g}$

$C_{12}H_{22}O_{11}(s) + 12\,O_2(g) \rightarrow 12\,CO_2(g) + 11\,H_2O(l)$

Reactant/Product	ΔH_f°(kJ/mol from Appendix IIB)
$C_{12}H_{22}O_{11}(s)$	-2226.1
$O_2(g)$	0.0
$CO_2(g)$	-393.5
$H_2O(l)$	-285.8

Be sure to pull data for the correct formula and phase.

$\Delta H_{rxn}^{\circ} = \sum n_P \Delta H_f^{\circ}(products) - \sum n_R \Delta H_f^{\circ}(reactants)$

$= [12(\Delta H_f^{\circ}(CO_2(g))) + 11(\Delta H_f^{\circ}(H_2O(l)))] - [1(\Delta H_f^{\circ}(C_{12}H_{22}O_{11}(s))) + 12(\Delta H_f^{\circ}(O_2(g)))]$

$= [12(-393.5 \text{ kJ}) + 11(-285.8 \text{ kJ})] - [1(-2226.1 \text{ kJ}) + 12(0.0 \text{ kJ})]$

$= [-7865.8 \text{ kJ}] - [-2226.1 \text{ kJ}]$

$= -5639.7 \text{ kJ/mol}$

$-5639.7 \dfrac{\text{kJ}}{\text{mol}} \times \dfrac{1000 \text{ J}}{1 \text{ kJ}} \times \dfrac{1 \text{ Cal}}{4184 \text{ J}} \times \dfrac{1 \text{ mol}}{342.30 \text{ g}} = -3.938 \text{ Cal/g}$

Check: The units (kJ/mol and Cal/g) are correct. The magnitudes of the answers are consistent with the food labels we see every day. Palmitic acid gives more Cal/g than sucrose.

6.105   At constant P $\Delta H_{rxn} = q_P$ and at constant V $\Delta E_{rxn} = q_V = \Delta H_{rxn} - P\Delta V$. $PV = nRT$ at constant P, and a constant number of moles of gas, as we change the T the only variable that can change is V, so $P\Delta V = nR\Delta T$. Substituting into the equation for ΔE_{rxn} we get $\Delta E_{rxn} = \Delta H_{rxn} - nR\Delta T$ or $\Delta H_{rxn} = \Delta E_{rxn} + nR\Delta T$.

6.107   **Given:** 16 g peanut butter, bomb calorimeter, $T_i = 22.2$ °C, $T_f = 25.4$ °C, $C_{cal} = 120.0$ kJ/°C
Find: calories in peanut butter
Conceptual Plan: $T_i, T_f \rightarrow \Delta T$ then $\Delta T, C_{cal} \rightarrow q_{cal} \rightarrow q_{rxn}$ (kJ) $\rightarrow q_{rxn}$ (kJ) $\rightarrow q_{rxn}$ (Cal)

$\Delta T = T_f - T_i$ $q_{cal} = -C_{cal}\Delta T$ $q_{rxn} = -q_{cal}$ $\dfrac{1000 \text{ J}}{1 \text{ kJ}}$ $\dfrac{1 \text{ Cal}}{4184 \text{ J}}$

then q_{rxn} (Cal) $\rightarrow$ **Cal/g**

$\div$ 16 g peanut butter

Solution: $\Delta T = T_f - T_i = 25.4$ °C $- 22.2$ °C $= 3.2$ °C then $q_{cal} = C_{cal}\Delta T = 120.0 \dfrac{\text{kJ}}{°C} \times 3.2 °C = 384 \text{ kJ}$

then $q_{rxn} = -q_{cal} = -384 \text{ kJ} \times \dfrac{1000 \text{ J}}{1 \text{ kJ}} \times \dfrac{1 \text{ Cal}}{4184 \text{ J}} = 91.778 \text{ Cal}$ then $\dfrac{91.778 \text{ Cal}}{16 \text{ g}} = 5.7 \text{ Cal/g}$

Check: The units (Cal/g) are correct. The magnitude of the answer (6) makes physical sense because there is a significant percentage of fat and sugar in peanut butter. The answer is in line with the answers in Problem 103.

6.109   **Given:** $V_1 = 20.0$ L at $P_1 = 3.0$ atm; $P_2 = 1.5$ atm let expand at constant T **Find:** $w, q, \Delta E_{sys}$
Conceptual Plan: $V_1, P_1, P_2 \rightarrow V_2$ then $V_1, V_2 \rightarrow \Delta V$ then $P, \Delta V \rightarrow w$ (L atm) $\rightarrow w$ (J)

$P_1V_1 = P_2V_2$ $\Delta V = V_2 - V_1$ $w = -P\Delta V$ $\dfrac{101.3 \text{ J}}{1 \text{ L atm}}$

for an ideal gas $\Delta E_{sys} \propto T$, so since this is a constant temperature process $\Delta E_{sys} = 0$ finally $\Delta E_{sys}, w \rightarrow q$

$\Delta E = q + w$

Solution: $P_1V_1 = P_2V_2$. Rearrange to solve for V_2. $V_2 = V_1 \dfrac{P_1}{P_2} = (20.0 \text{ L}) \times \dfrac{3.0 \text{ atm}}{1.5 \text{ atm}} = 40. \text{ L}$ and

$\Delta V = V_2 - V_1 = 40. \text{ L} - 20.0 \text{ L} = 20. \text{ L}$ then

$w = -P\Delta V = -1.5 \text{ atm} \times 20. \text{ L} \times \dfrac{101.3 \text{ J}}{1 \text{ L} \cdot \text{atm}} = -3039 \text{ J} = -3.0 \times 10^3 \text{ J}$ $\Delta E = q + w$

Rearrange to solve for q. $q = \Delta E_{sys} - w = +0\,J - (-3039\,J) = 3.0 \times 10^3\,J$

Check: The units (J) are correct. Since there is no temperature change, we expect no energy change ($\Delta E_{sys} = 0$). The piston expands and so does work (negative work) and so heat is absorbed (positive q).

6.111   The oxidation of S (g) to SO_3 can be written as follows:
$S\,(g) + 3/2\,O_2\,(g) \rightarrow SO_3\,(g)$ $\Delta H = -204\,kJ$
The oxidation of SO_2 (g) to SO_3 can be written as follows:
$SO_2\,(g) + 1/2\,O_2\,(g) \rightarrow SO_3\,(g)$ $\Delta H = +89.5\,kJ$
The enthalpy of formation reaction for SO_2 (g) under these conditions can be written as follows:
$S\,(g) + O_2\,(g) \rightarrow SO_2\,(g)$ $\Delta H =$??
Since the second reaction has 1 mole SO_2 as a reactant and the reaction of interest has 1 mole of SO_2 as a product, we need to reverse the second reaction. When the reaction direction is reversed, ΔH changes sign.
$SO_3\,(g) \rightarrow SO_2\,(g) + 1/2\,O_2\,(g)$ $\Delta H = -89.5\,kJ$
Hess's Law states the ΔH of the net reaction is the sum of the ΔH of the steps.
The rewritten reactions are as follows:

$S\,(g) + \cancel{3/2\,O_2\,(g)} \rightarrow \cancel{SO_3\,(g)}$	$\Delta H = -204\,kJ$
$\cancel{SO_3\,(g)} \rightarrow SO_2\,(g) + \cancel{1/2\,O_2\,(g)}$	$\Delta H = -89.5\,kJ$
$S\,(g) + O_2\,(g) \rightarrow SO_2\,(g)$	$\Delta H = -294\,kJ = \Delta H_f$

Note that this is not under standard conditions, since S is not a solid.

6.113   **Given:** 25.3% methane (CH_4), 38.2% ethane (C_2H_6), and the rest propane (C_3H_8) by volume; $V = 1.55$ L tank, $P = 755$ mmHg, and $T = 298$ K   **Find:** heat for combustion
Conceptual Plan: percent composition $\rightarrow$ mmHg $\rightarrow$ atm then $P, V, T \rightarrow n$ then

$\quad\quad\quad$ Dalton's Law of Partial Pressures $\quad \dfrac{1\,atm}{760\,mmHg} \quad\quad\quad PV = nRT$

use data in Problem 91 for methane, and calculate heat of combustion for ethane and propane

$\Delta H^{\circ}_{rxn}\,(CH_4) = -802.3\,kJ;\quad \Delta H^{\circ}_{rxn}\,(C_3H_8) = -2217\,kJ$ write balanced reaction then $\Delta H^{\circ}_{rxn} = \sum n_P \Delta H^{\circ}_f(products) - \sum n_R \Delta H^{\circ}_f(reactants)$
then $n, \Delta H \rightarrow q$

Solution: $P_{CH_4} = \dfrac{25.3\,\text{mmHg } CH_4}{100\,\text{mmHg gas}} \times 755\,\text{mmHg gas} \times \dfrac{1\,atm\,CH_4}{760\,\text{mmHg}} = 0.2513355\,atm\,CH_4,$

$C_2H_6 = \dfrac{38.2\,\text{mmHg } C_2H_6}{100\,\text{mmHg gas}} \times 755\,\text{mmHg gas} \times \dfrac{1\,atm\,C_2H_6}{760\,\text{mmHg}} = 0.37948684\,atm\,C_2H_6,$

$P_{C_3H_8} = \dfrac{100 - (25.3 + 38.2)\,\text{mmHg } C_3H_8}{100\,\text{mmHg gas}} \times 755\,\text{mmHg gas} \times \dfrac{1\,atm\,C_3H_8}{760\,\text{mmHg}} = 0.36259868\,atm\,C_3H_8$

$PV = nRT$ Rearrange to solve for n.

$n_{CH_4} = \dfrac{PV}{RT} = \dfrac{0.2513355\,\text{atm } CH_4 \times 1.55\,L}{0.08206\,\dfrac{L \cdot atm}{mol \cdot K} \times 298\,K} = 0.01593081\,mol\,CH_4,$

$n_{C_2H_6} = \dfrac{PV}{RT} = \dfrac{0.37948684\,\text{atm } C_2H_6 \times 1.55\,L}{0.08206\,\dfrac{L \cdot atm}{mol \cdot K} \times 298\,K} = 0.02405363\,mol\,C_2H_6$

$n_{C_2H_6} = \dfrac{PV}{RT} = \dfrac{0.36259868\,\text{atm } C_3H_8 \times 1.55\,L}{0.08206\,\dfrac{L \cdot atm}{mol \cdot K} \times 298\,K} = 0.022983181\,mol\,C_3H_8$

$C_2H_6\,(g) + 7/2\,O_2\,(g) \rightarrow 2\,CO_2\,(g) + 3\,H_2O\,(g)$

Reactant/Product	ΔH°_f(kJ/mol from Appendix IIB)
C_2H_6 (g)	-84.68
O_2 (g)	0.0
CO_2 (g)	-393.5
H_2O (g)	-241.8

Be sure to pull data for the correct formula and phase.

$\Delta H^{\circ}_{rxn} = \sum n_P \Delta H^{\circ}_f(products) - \sum n_R \Delta H^{\circ}_f(reactants)$

$= [2(\Delta H^{\circ}_f(CO_2\,(g))) + 3(\Delta H^{\circ}_f(H_2O\,(g)))] - [1(\Delta H^{\circ}_f(C_2H_6\,(g))) + 7/2(\Delta H^{\circ}_f(O_2\,(g)))]$

$= [2(-393.5\,kJ) + 3(-241.8\,kJ)] - [1(-84.68\,kJ) + 7/2(0.0\,kJ)]$

$= [-1512.4\,kJ] - [-84.68\,kJ]$

$= -1427.7\,kJ$

$C_3H_8\,(g) + 5\,O_2\,(g) \rightarrow 3\,CO_2\,(g) + 4\,H_2O\,(g)$

Reactant/Product	ΔH°_f(kJ/mol from Appendix IIB)
$C_3H_8\,(g)$	-103.85
$O_2\,(g)$	0.0
$CO_2\,(g)$	-393.5
$H_2O\,(g)$	-241.8

Be sure to pull data for the correct formula and phase.

$\Delta H^{\circ}_{rxn} = \sum n_P \Delta H^{\circ}_f(products) - \sum n_R \Delta H^{\circ}_f(reactants)$

$= [3(\Delta H^{\circ}_f(CO_2\,(g))) + 4(\Delta H^{\circ}_f(H_2O\,(g)))] - [1(\Delta H^{\circ}_f(C_3H_8\,(g))) + 5(\Delta H^{\circ}_f(O_2\,(g)))]$

$= [3(-393.5\,kJ) + 4(-241.8\,kJ)] - [1(-103.85\,kJ) + 5(0.0\,kJ)]$

$= [-2147.7\,kJ] - [-103.85\,kJ]$

$= -2043.9\,kJ$

$0.01\underline{5}93081\ \overline{mol\,CH_4} \times \dfrac{-802.3\,kJ}{1\ \overline{mol\,CH_4}} = -12.\underline{7}81289\,kJ,$

$0.02\underline{4}05363\ \overline{mol\,C_2H_6} \times \dfrac{-1427.7\,kJ}{1\ \overline{mol\,C_2H_6}} = -34.\underline{3}4137\,kJ,\ \text{and}$

$0.022\underline{9}83181\ \overline{mol\,C_3H_8} \times \dfrac{-2043.9\,kJ}{1\ \overline{mol\,C_3H_8}} = -46.\underline{9}7417\,kJ$

The total heat is $-12.\underline{7}81289\,kJ - 34.\underline{3}4137\,kJ - 46.\underline{9}7417\,kJ = -94.\underline{0}9683\,kJ = -94.0\,kJ$

Check: The units (kJ) are correct. The magnitude of the answer (–100 kJ) makes sense because heats of combustion are typically large and negative.

6.115   **Given:** 1.55 cm copper cube and 1.62 cm aluminum cube, $T_{Metalsi} = 55.0\,°C$, 100.0 mL water, $T_{H_2Oi} = 22.2\,°C$
Other: density (water) = 0.998 g/mL   **Find:** T_f
Conceptual Plan: pull d values from Table 1.4 then edge length $\rightarrow V \rightarrow m$ then

Cu: 8.96 g/mL Al: 2.70 g/mL $V = l^3$ $d = m/V$

pull C_s values from Table 6.4   then $m,\ C_s,\ T_i \rightarrow T_f$

Cu: 0.385 $\dfrac{J}{g\cdot°C}$ Al: 0.903 $\dfrac{J}{g\cdot°C}$ H$_2$O: 4.18 $\dfrac{J}{g\cdot°C}$ $q = mC_s(T_f - T_i)$ then set $q_{Cu} + q_{Al} = -q_{H_2O}$

Solution: $V_{Cu} = l^3 = (1.55\,cm)^3 = 3.723875\,cm^3 = 3.723875\,mL$ and

$V_{Al} = l^3 = (1.62\,cm)^3 = 4.2\underline{5}1528\,cm^3 = 4.2\underline{5}1528\,mL$ then $d = m/V$. Rearange to solve for m. $m = d\,V$

$m_{Cu} = 8.96\,\dfrac{g}{mL} \times 3.723875\,mL = 33.\underline{3}6592\,g\ Cu,$

$m_{Al} = 2.70\,\dfrac{g}{mL} \times 4.251528\,mL = 11.\underline{4}791256\,g\ Al$ and $m_{H_2O} = 0.998\,\dfrac{g}{mL} \times 100.0\,mL = 99.8\,g\ H_2O$

$q = mC_s(T_f - T_i)$ substitute in values and set $q_{Cu} + q_{Al} = -q_{H_2O}$.

$q_{Cu} + q_{Al} = m_{Cu}C_{Cu}(T_f - T_{Cui}) + m_{Al}C_{Al}(T_f - T_{Ali}) =$

$33.\underline{3}6592\,g \times 0.385\,\dfrac{J}{g\cdot°C} \times (T_f - 55.0\,°C) + 11.\underline{4}791256\,g \times 0.903\,\dfrac{J}{g\cdot°C} \times (T_f - 55.0\,°C) =$

$-q_{H_2O} = -m_{H_2O}C_{H_2O}(T_f - T_{H_2Oi}) = -99.8\,g \times 4.18\,\dfrac{J}{g\cdot°C} \times (T_f - 22.2\,°C)$

Rearrange to solve for T_f.

$$12.84588 \frac{J}{^\circ C} \times (T_f - 55.0\ ^\circ C) + 10.36565 \frac{J}{^\circ C} \times (T_f - 55.0\ ^\circ C) = -417.164 \frac{J}{^\circ C} \times (T_f - 22.2\ ^\circ C) \rightarrow$$

$$12.84588 \frac{J}{^\circ C} T_f - 706.5234\ J + 10.36565 \frac{J}{^\circ C} T_f - 570.1108\ J = -417.164 \frac{J}{^\circ C} T_f + 9261.041\ J \rightarrow$$

$$12.84588 \frac{J}{^\circ C} T_f + 10.36565 \frac{J}{^\circ C} T_f + 417.164 \frac{J}{^\circ C} T_f = +706.5234\ J + 570.1108\ J + 9261.041\ J \rightarrow$$

$$440.3755 \frac{J}{^\circ C} T_f = 10537.675\ J \rightarrow T_f = \frac{10537.675\ J}{440.3755\ \frac{J}{^\circ C}} = 23.92884\ ^\circ C = 23.9\ ^\circ C$$

Check: The units ($^\circ C$) are correct. The magnitude of the answer (24) makes physical sense because the heat transfer is dominated by the water (larger mass and larger specific heat capacity). The final temperature should be closer to the initial temperature of water than of copper and aluminum.

Challenge Problems

6.117   **Given:** 655 kWh/yr, coal is 3.2 % S, remainder is C, S emitted as SO_2 (g) and gets converted to H_2SO_4 when reacting with water   **Find:** m (H_2SO_4)/yr
Conceptual Plan: write balanced reaction then $\Delta H^\circ_{rxn} = \sum n_P \Delta H^\circ_f(products) - \sum n_R \Delta H^\circ_f(reactants)$
(since the form of sulfur is not given, assume all heat is from combustion of only carbon) then
kWh $\rightarrow$ J $\rightarrow$ kJ $\rightarrow$ mol (C) $\rightarrow$ g (C) $\rightarrow$ g (S) $\rightarrow$ mol (H_2SO_4) $\rightarrow$ mol (H_2SO_4) $\rightarrow$ g (H_2SO_4)

$$\frac{3.60 \times 10^6 J}{1\ kWh} \quad \frac{1\ kJ}{1000\ J} \quad \frac{mol\ C}{\Delta H^\circ_f(CO_2\,(g))} \quad \frac{12.01\ g}{1\ mol} \quad \frac{3.2\ g\ S}{(100.0 - 3.2)\ g\ C} \quad \frac{1\ mol}{32.06\ g} \quad \frac{1\ mol\ H_2SO_4}{1\ mol\ S} \quad \frac{98.09\ g}{1\ mol}$$

Solution: C (s) + O_2 (g) $\rightarrow$ CO_2 (g). This reaction is the heat of formation of CO_2 (g), so
$\Delta H^\circ_{rxn} = \Delta H^\circ_f(CO_2\,(g)) = -393.5$ kJ/mol then

$$655\ kWh \times \frac{3.60 \times 10^6\ J}{1\ kWh} \times \frac{1\ kJ}{1000\ J} \times \frac{mol\ C}{393.5\ kJ} \times \frac{12.01\ g\ C}{1\ mol\ C} \times \frac{3.2\ g\ S}{(100.0 - 3.2)\ g\ C} \times \frac{1\ mol\ S}{32.07\ g\ S} \times$$

$$\times \frac{1\ mol\ H_2SO_4}{1\ mol\ S} \times \frac{98.09\ g\ H_2SO_4}{1\ mol\ H_2SO_4} = 7.3 \times 10^3\ g\ H_2SO_4$$

Check: The units (g) are correct. The magnitude (7300) is reasonable, considering this is just 1 home.

6.119   **Given:** methane combustion, 100 % efficiency, $\Delta T = 10.0\ ^\circ C$, house = 30.0 m x 30.0 m x 3.0 m, C_s (air) = 30 J/K·mol, 1.00 mol air = 22.4 L   **Find:** m (CH_4)
Conceptual Plan: $l, w, h \rightarrow V(m^3) \rightarrow V(cm^3) \rightarrow V(L) \rightarrow$ mol (air) then $m, C_s, \Delta T \rightarrow q_{air}$ (J)

$$V = lwh \qquad \frac{(100\ cm)^3}{(1\ m)^3} \qquad \frac{1\ L}{1000\ cm^3} \qquad \frac{1\ mol\ air}{22.4\ L} \qquad\qquad q = mC_s\Delta T$$

then q_{air} (J) $\rightarrow$ q_{rxn} (J) $\rightarrow$ q(kJ), then write balanced reaction for methane combustion,

$$q_{rxn} = -q_{air} \qquad \frac{1\ kJ}{1000\ J}$$

then $\Delta H^\circ_{rxn} = \sum n_P \Delta H^\circ_f(products) - \sum n_R \Delta H^\circ_f(reactants)$, and then q(kJ) $\rightarrow$ mol (CH_4) $\rightarrow$ g (CH_4)

$$\Delta H^\circ_{rxn} \qquad \frac{16.04 g}{1\ mol}$$

Solution: $V = lwh = 30.0$ m x 30.0 m x 3.0 m = 2700 m^3, then

$$2700\ m^3 \times \frac{(100\ cm)^3}{(1\ m)^3} \times \frac{1\ L}{1000\ cm^3} \times \frac{1\ mol\ air}{22.4\ L} = 1.20536 \times 10^5\ mol\ air, \text{ and then}$$

$$q = mC_s\Delta T = 1.20536 \times 10^5\ mol \times 30 \frac{J}{mol \cdot ^\circ C} \times 10.0\ ^\circ C = 3.6161 \times 10^7\ J \times \frac{1\ kJ}{1000\ J} = 3.6161 \times 10^4\ J\ \text{needed}$$

CH_4 (g) + 2 O_2 (g) $\rightarrow$ CO_2 (g) + 2 H_2O (g)

Reactant/Product	ΔH°_f(kJ/mol from Appendix IIB)
CH_4 (g)	-74.6
O_2 (g)	0.0
CO_2 (g)	-393.5
H_2O (g)	-241.8

Be sure to pull data for the correct formula and phase.

$$\Delta H^\circ_{rxn} = \sum n_P \Delta H^\circ_f (products) - \sum n_R \Delta H^\circ_f (reactants)$$
$$= [1(\Delta H^\circ_f(CO_2\,(g))) + 2(\Delta H^\circ_f(H_2O\,(g)))] - [1(\Delta H^\circ_f(CH_4\,(g))) + 2(\Delta H^\circ_f(O_2\,(g)))]$$
$$= [(-393.5\ kJ) + 2(-241.8\ kJ)] - [1(-74.6\ kJ) + 2(0.0\ kJ)]$$
$$= [-877.1\ kJ] - [-74.6\ kJ]$$
$$= -802.5\ kJ$$

$$q_{rxn} = -q_{air} = -3.6161 \times 10^4\ \cancel{kJ} \times \frac{1\ \cancel{mol\ CH_4}}{-802.5\ \cancel{kJ}} \times \frac{16.04\ g\ CH_4}{1\ \cancel{mol\ CH_4}} = 722.8\ g\ CH_4 = 700\ g\ CH_4$$

Check: The units (g) are correct. The magnitude (700) is not surprising since the volume of a house is large.

6.121 **Given:** m (ice) = 9.0 g; coffee: T_1 = 90.0 °C, m = 120.0 g, $C_s = C_{H_2O}$, ΔH°_{fus} = 6.0 kJ/mol **Find:** T_f of coffee
Conceptual Plan: $q_{ice} = -q_{coffee}$ so g (ice) $\rightarrow$ mol (ice) $\rightarrow$ q_{fus}(kJ) $\rightarrow$ q_{fus} (J) $\rightarrow$ q_{coffee} (J) then

$$\frac{1\ mol}{18.01\ g} \qquad \frac{6.0\ kJ}{1\ mol} \qquad \frac{1000\ J}{1\ kJ} \qquad q_{coffee} = -q_{ice}$$

$q, m, C_s \rightarrow \Delta T$ then T_i, $\Delta T \rightarrow T_2$ now we have slightly cooled coffee in contact with 0.0 °C water

$$q = mC_s\Delta T \qquad\qquad \Delta T = T_2 - T_i$$

so $q_{ice} = -q_{coffee}$ with m, C_s, $T_i \rightarrow T_f$

$$q = mC_s(T_f - T_i) \text{ then set } q_{ice} = -q_{coffee}$$

Solution: $9.0\ \cancel{g} \times \dfrac{1\ \cancel{mol}}{18.01\ \cancel{g}} \times \dfrac{6.0\ \cancel{kJ}}{1\ mol} \times \dfrac{1000\ J}{1\ \cancel{kJ}} = 2.9983 \times 10^3\ J$, $\quad q_{coffee} = -q_{ice} = -2.9983 \times 10^3\ J$

$q = mC_s\Delta T$ Rearrange to solve for ΔT. $\Delta T = \dfrac{q}{mC_s} = \dfrac{-2.9983 \times 10^3\ \cancel{J}}{120.0\ \cancel{g} \times 4.18\ \dfrac{\cancel{J}}{\cancel{g}\cdot °C}} = -5.9775\ °C$ then

$\Delta T = T_2 - T_i$. Rearrange to solve for T_2. $T_2 = \Delta T + T_i = -5.9775\ °C + 90.0\ °C = 84.0225\ °C$
$q = mC_s(T_f - T_i)$ substitute in values and set $q_{H_2O} = -q_{coffee}$.

$$q_{H_2O} = m_{H_2O}C_{H_2O}(T_f - T_{H_2Oi}) = 9.0\ g \times \cancel{4.18\ \frac{J}{g\cdot°C}} \times (T_f - 0.0\ °C) =$$

$$-q_{coffee} = -m_{coffee}C_{coffee}(T_f - T_{coffee2}) = -120.0\ g \times \cancel{4.18\ \frac{J}{g\cdot°C}} \times (T_f - 84.0225\ °C)$$

Rearrange to solve for T_f.
$9.0\ g\ T_f = -120.0\ g\ (T_f - 84.0225\ °C) \rightarrow 9.0\ g\ T_f = -120.0\ g\ T_f + 10082.7\ g \rightarrow$

$-10082.7\ g = -129.0\ \dfrac{g}{°C}\ T_f \rightarrow T_f = \dfrac{-10082.7\ \cancel{g}}{-129.0\ \dfrac{\cancel{g}}{°C}} = 78.2\ °C$

Check: The units (°C) are correct. The temperature is closer to the original coffee temperature since the mass of coffee is so much larger than the ice mass.

6.123 $KE = \dfrac{1}{2}mv^2$, for an ideal gas $v = u_{rms} = \sqrt{\dfrac{3RT}{\mathcal{M}}}$ and so $KE_{avg} = \dfrac{1}{2}N_A mu^2_{rms} = \dfrac{3}{2}RT$ then

$\Delta E_{sys} = KE_2 - KE_1 = \dfrac{3}{2}RT_2 - \dfrac{3}{2}RT_1 = \dfrac{3}{2}R\Delta T$. At constant V $\Delta E_{sys} = C_V\Delta T$ so $C_V = \dfrac{3}{2}R$.

At constant P, $\Delta E_{sys} = q + w = q_P - P\Delta V = \Delta H - P\Delta V$, but since $PV = nRT$, for one mole of an ideal gas at constant P $P\Delta V = R\Delta T$, so $\Delta E_{sys} = q + w = q_P - P\Delta V = \Delta H - P\Delta V = \Delta H - R\Delta T$ then

$\dfrac{3}{2}R\Delta T = \Delta H - R\Delta T$ or $\Delta H = \dfrac{5}{2}R\Delta T = C_P\Delta T$ so $C_P = \dfrac{5}{2}R$.

6.125 $q = \Delta H = 454\ \cancel{g} \times \dfrac{1\ \cancel{mol}}{18.02\ \cancel{g}} \times \dfrac{40.7\ kJ}{1\ \cancel{mol}} = 1025.405\ kJ = 1030\ kJ$ and $w = -P\Delta V$. Assume that $P = 1$ atm

(exactly) and $\Delta V = V_G - V_L$, where $V_L = 454\ \cancel{g} \times \dfrac{1\ \cancel{mL}}{0.9998\ \cancel{g}} \times \dfrac{1\ L}{1000\ \cancel{mL}} = 0.4540908\ L$ and $PV = nRT$.

Rearrange to solve for V_G. $V_G = \dfrac{nRT}{P} = \dfrac{454 \, \text{g} \times \dfrac{1 \, \text{mol}}{18.02 \, \text{g}} \times 0.08206 \dfrac{\text{L} \cdot \text{atm}}{\text{mol} \cdot \text{K}} \times 373 \, \text{K}}{1 \, \text{atm}} = 771.1545 \, \text{L}$

$\Delta V = V_G - V_L = 771.1545 \, \text{L} - 0.4540908 \, \text{L} = 770.7004 \, \text{L}$ and so

$w = -P\Delta V = -1.0 \, \text{atm} \times 770.7004 \, \text{L} \times \dfrac{101.3 \, \text{J}}{1 \, \text{L} \cdot \text{atm}} = -78071.9539 \, \text{J} = -7.81 \times 10^4 \, \text{J} = -78.1 \, \text{kJ}.$

Finally $\Delta E = q + w = 1025.405 \, \text{kJ} - 78.0719539 \, \text{kJ} = 947.333 \, \text{kJ} = 950 \, \text{kJ}.$

6.127 $C_8H_{18} \, (l) + 25/2 \, O_2 \, (g) \rightarrow 8 \, CO_2 \, (g) + 9 \, H_2O \, (l)$; $q = \Delta H = -1303 \, \text{kJ/mol}$, and $w = -P\Delta V$. Assume that $P = 1$ atm (exactly) and $\Delta V = \Delta V_G$ since the gas volumes are so much larger than the liquid volumes. The

change in the number of moles of gas $\Delta n_G = 8 \, \text{mol} - \dfrac{25}{2}\text{mol} = -4.5 \, \text{mol}$ and $P\Delta V = \Delta nRT$. Rearrange to

solve for ΔV_G. $\Delta V_G = \dfrac{\Delta nRT}{P} = \dfrac{-4.5 \, \text{mol} \times 0.08206 \dfrac{\text{L} \cdot \text{atm}}{\text{mol} \cdot \text{K}} \times 298 \, \text{K}}{1 \, \text{atm}} = -110.0425 \, \text{L}$ and so

$w = -P\Delta V = -1.0 \, \text{atm} \times (-110.0425 \, \text{L}) \times \dfrac{101.3 \, \text{J}}{1 \, \text{L} \cdot \text{atm}} = +11147.30 \, \text{J} = +11000 \, \text{J} = +11 \, \text{kJ}.$

Finally $\Delta E = q + w = -1303 \, \text{kJ} + 11.14730 \, \text{kJ} = -1291.8527 \, \text{kJ} = -1292 \, \text{kJ}.$

Conceptual Problems

6.129   (d)   Only one answer is possible. $\Delta E_{\text{sys}} = -\Delta E_{\text{surr}}.$

6.131   (a)   At constant P, $\Delta E_{\text{sys}} = q + w = q_P + w = \Delta H + w$ so $\Delta E_{\text{sys}} - w = \Delta H = q.$

6.133   The aluminum cylinder will be cooler after 1 hour because it has a lower heat capacity than water (less heat needs to be pulled out for every °C temperature change).

6.135   **Given:** 2418 J heat produced; 5 J work done on surroundings at constant P **Find:** ΔE, ΔH, q, and w
           Conceptual Plan: interpret language to determine the sign of the two terms then $q, w \rightarrow \Delta E_{\text{sys}}$
                                                                                 $\Delta E = q + w$
           Solution: Since heat is released from the system to the surroundings, $q = -2418 \, \text{J}$
           since the system is doing work on the surroundings, $w = -5 \, \text{kJ}$. At constant P, $\Delta H = q = -2.418 \, \text{kJ}$;
           $\Delta E = q + w = -2418 \, \text{J} - 5 \, \text{J} = -2423 \, \text{J} = -2 \, \text{kJ}.$
           Check:
           terms are negative and the amount of work done is negligibly small.

6.137   (b)   If ΔV is positive then $w = -P\Delta V < 0$. Since $\Delta E_{\text{sys}} = q + w = q_P + w = \Delta H + w$ if w is negative then $\Delta H > \Delta E_{\text{sys}}.$

7 The Quantum-Mechanical Model of the Atom

Review Questions

7.1   When a particle is absolutely small it means that you cannot observe it without disturbing it. When you observe the particle, it behaves differently than when you do not observe it. Electrons fit this description.

7.3   The quantum-mechanical model of the atom is important because it explains how electrons exist in atoms and how those electrons determine the chemical and physical properties of elements.

7.5   The wavelength (λ) of the wave is the distance in space between adjacent crests and is measured in units of distance. The amplitude of the wave is the vertical height of a crest. The more closely spaced the waves, that is, the shorter the wavelength, the more energy there is. The amplitude of the electric and magnetic field waves in light determine the intensity or brightness of the light. The higher the amplitude, the more energy the wave has.

7.7   For visible light, wavelength determines the color. Red light has a wavelength of 750 nm, the longest wavelength of visible light, and blue has a wavelength of 500 nm.

7.9   (a)   Gamma rays(γ) – the wavelength range is 10^{-11} to 10^{-15} m. Gamma rays are produced by the sun, other stars, and certain unstable atomic nuclei on Earth. Human exposure to gamma rays is dangerous because the high energy of gamma rays can damage biological molecules.

   (b)   X-rays – the wavelength range is 10^{-8} to 10^{-11} m. X-rays are used in medicine. X-rays pass through many substances that block visible light and are therefore used to image bones and internal organs. X-rays are sufficiently energetic to damage biological molecules so, while several yearly exposures to X-rays are harmless, excessive exposure increases cancer risk.

   (c)   Ultraviolet radiation (UV) – the wavelength range is 0.4×10^{-6} to 10^{-8} m. Ultraviolet radiation is most familiar as the component of sunlight that produces a sunburn or suntan. While not as energetic as gamma rays or X-rays, ultraviolet light still carries enough energy to damage biological molecules. Excessive exposure to ultraviolet light increases the risk of skin cancer and cataracts and causes premature wrinkling of the skin.

   (d)   Visible light – the wavelength range is 0.75×10^{-6} to 0.4×10^{-6} m (750 nm to 400 nm). Visible light, as long as the intensity is not too high, does not carry enough energy to damage biological molecules. It does, however, cause certain molecules in our eyes to change their shape, sending a signal to brains that results in vision.

   (e)   Infrared radiation (IR) – the wavelength range is 0.75×10^{-6} to 10^{-3} m. The heat you feel when you place your hand near a hot object is infrared radiation. All warm objects, including human bodies, emit infrared light. Although infrared light is invisible to our eyes, infrared sensors can detect it and are often used in night vision technology to "see" in the dark.

(f)   Microwave radiation – the wavelength range is 10^{-3} to 10^{-1} m. Microwave radiation is used in radar and in microwave ovens. Microwave radiation is efficiently absorbed by water and can therefore heat substances that contain water.

(g)   Radio waves – the wavelength range is 10^{-1} to 10^5 m. Radio waves are used to transmit the signals responsible for AM and FM radio, cellular telephones, television, and other forms of communication.

7.11   Diffraction occurs when a wave encounters an obstacle or a slit that is comparable in size to its wavelength. The wave bends around the slit. The diffraction of light through two slits separated by a distance comparable to the wavelength of the light results in an interference pattern. Each slit acts as a new wave source, and the two new waves interfere with each other. This results in a pattern of bright and dark lines.

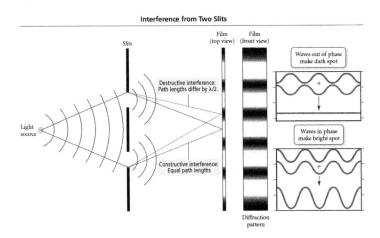

7.13   Because of the results of the experiments with the photoelectric effect, Einstein proposed that light energy must come in packets. The amount of energy in a light packet depends on its frequency (wavelength). The emission of electrons depends on whether or not a single photon has sufficient energy to dislodge a single electron.

7.15   An emission spectrum occurs when an atom absorbs energy and re-emits that energy as light. The light emitted contains distinct wavelengths for each element. The emission spectrum of a particular element is always the same and can be used to identify the element. A white light spectrum is continuous, meaning that there are no sudden interruptions in the intensity of the light as a function of wavelengths. It consists of all wavelengths. Emission spectra are not continuous. They consist of bright lines at specific wavelengths, with complete darkness in between.

7.17   Electron diffraction occurs when an electron beam is aimed at two closely spaced slits, and a series of detectors is arranged to detect the electrons after they pass through the slits. An interference pattern similar to that observed for light is recorded behind the slits. Electron diffraction is evidence of the wave nature of electrons.

7.19   Complementary properties are those that exclude one another. The more you know about one, the less you know about the other. Which of two complementary properties you observe depends on the experiment you perform. In electron diffraction, when you try to observe which hole the electron goes through (particle nature) you lose the interference pattern (wave nature). When you try to observe the interference pattern, you cannot determine which hole the electron goes through.

7.21   A trajectory is a path that is determined by the particle's velocity (the speed and direction of travel), its position, and the forces acting on it. Both position and velocity are required to predict a trajectory.

7.23   Deterministic means that the present determines the future. That means that under the identical condition, identical results will occur.

7.25   A probability distribution map is a statistical map that shows where an electron is likely to be found under a given set of conditions.

7.27   An orbital is a probability distribution map showing where the electron is likely to be found.

7.29   The principal quantum number (n) is an integer and has possible values of 1,2,3, etc. The principal quantum number determines the overall size and energy of an orbital.

7.31   The magnetic quantum number (m_l) is an integer ranging from $-l$ to $+l$. For example, if $l = 1$, $m_l = -1, 0, +1$. The magnetic quantum number specifies the orientation of the orbital.

7.33   The probability density is the probability per unit volume of finding the electron at a point in space. The radial distribution function represents the total probability of finding the electron within a thin spherical shell at a distance r from the nucleus. In contrast to probability density, which has a maximum at the nucleus for an s orbital, the radial distribution function has a value of zero at the nucleus. It increases to a maximum and then decreases again with increasing r.

7.35   The sublevels are s ($l=0$), which can hold a maximum of 2 electrons; p ($l = 1$), which can hold a maximum of 6 electrons; d ($l = 2$), which can hold a maximum of 10 electrons; and f ($l = 3$), which can hold a maximum of 14 electrons.

Problems by Topic

Electromagnetic Radiation

7.37   **Given:** distance to sun = 1.496×10^8 km **Find:** time for light to travel from sun to Earth
        Conceptual Plan: distance km $\rightarrow$ distance m $\rightarrow$ time
$$\frac{1000 \text{ m}}{\text{km}} \qquad \text{time} = \frac{\text{distance}}{3.00 \times 10^8 \text{ m/s}}$$
        Solution: $1.496 \times 10^8 \, \cancel{\text{km}} \times \dfrac{1000 \, \cancel{\text{m}}}{\cancel{\text{km}}} \times \dfrac{\text{s}}{3.00 \times 10^8 \, \cancel{\text{m}}} = 499$ s
        Check: The units of the answer, seconds, are correct. The magnitude of the answer is reasonable, since it corresponds to about 8 min.

7.39   (i)   By increasing wavelength the order is d) ultraviolet < c) infrared < b) microwave < a) radio waves.

        (ii)   By increasing energy the order is a) radio waves < b) microwaves < c) infrared < d) ultraviolet.

7.41   (a)   **Given:** $\lambda = 632.8$ nm **Find:** frequency (ν)
               Conceptual Plan: nm $\rightarrow$ m $\rightarrow$ ν
$$\frac{\text{m}}{10^9 \text{ nm}} \qquad \nu = \frac{c}{\lambda}$$
               Solution: $632.8 \, \cancel{\text{nm}} \times \dfrac{\text{m}}{10^9 \, \cancel{\text{nm}}} = 6.328 \times 10^{-7}$ m $\quad \nu = \dfrac{3.00 \times 10^8 \, \cancel{\text{m}}}{\text{s}} \times \dfrac{1}{6.328 \times 10^{-7} \, \cancel{\text{m}}} = 4.74 \times 10^{14} \, \text{s}^{-1}$
               Check: The units of the answer, s^{-1}, are correct. The magnitude of the answer seems reasonable since wavelength and frequency are inversely proportional.

        (b)   **Given:** $\lambda = 503$ nm **Find:** frequency (ν)
               Conceptual Plan: nm $\rightarrow$ m $\rightarrow$ ν
$$\frac{\text{m}}{10^9 \text{ nm}} \qquad \nu = \frac{c}{\lambda}$$
               Solution: $503 \, \cancel{\text{nm}} \times \dfrac{\text{m}}{10^9 \, \cancel{\text{nm}}} = 5.03 \times 10^{-7}$ m $\quad \nu = \dfrac{3.00 \times 10^8 \, \cancel{\text{m}}}{\text{s}} \times \dfrac{1}{5.03 \times 10^{-7} \, \cancel{\text{m}}} = 5.96 \times 10^{14} \, \text{s}^{-1}$
               Check: The units of the answer, s^{-1}, are correct. The magnitude of the answer seems reasonable since wavelength and frequency are inversely proportional.

        (c)   **Given:** $\lambda = 0.052$ nm **Find:** frequency (ν)
               Conceptual Plan: nm $\rightarrow$ m $\rightarrow$ ν
$$\frac{\text{m}}{10^9 \text{ nm}} \qquad \nu = \frac{c}{\lambda}$$
               Solution: $0.052 \, \cancel{\text{nm}} \times \dfrac{\text{m}}{10^9 \, \cancel{\text{nm}}} = 5.2 \times 10^{-9}$ m $\quad \nu = \dfrac{3.00 \times 10^8 \, \cancel{\text{m}}}{\text{s}} \times \dfrac{1}{5.2 \times 10^{-9} \, \cancel{\text{m}}} = \qquad {}^{18} \, \text{s}^{-1}$

Check: The units of the answer, s^{-1}, are correct. The magnitude of the answer seems reasonable since wavelength and frequency are inversely proportional.

7.43   (a)   **Given:** frequency (ν) from 5 a. = $4.74 \times 10^{14} \, s^{-1}$ **Find:** Energy

Conceptual Plan: $\nu \rightarrow E$

$$E = h\nu \quad h = 6.626 \times 10^{-34} \, J \, s$$

Solution: $6.626 \times 10^{-34} \, J \, s \times \dfrac{4.74 \times 10^{14}}{s} = 3.14 \times 10^{-19} \, J$

Check: The units of the answer, J, are correct. The magnitude of the answer is reasonable since we are talking about the energy of one photon.

(b)   **Given:** frequency (ν) from 5 b. = $5.96 \times 10^{14} \, s^{-1}$ **Find:** Energy

Conceptual Plan: $\nu \rightarrow E$

$$E = h\nu \quad h = 6.626 \times 10^{-34} \, J \, s$$

Solution: $6.626 \times 10^{-34} \, J \, s \times \dfrac{5.96 \times 10^{14}}{s} = 3.95 \times 10^{-19} \, J$

Check: The units of the answer, J, are correct. The magnitude of the answer is reasonable since we are talking about the energy of one photon.

(c)   **Given:** frequency (ν) from 5 c. = $5.8 \times 10^{18} \, s^{-1}$ **Find:** Energy

Conceptual Plan: $\nu \rightarrow E$

$$E = h\nu \quad h = 6.626 \times 10^{-34} \, J \, s$$

Solution: $6.626 \times 10^{-34} \, J \, s \times \dfrac{5.8 \times 10^{18}}{s} = 3.8 \times 10^{-15} \, J$

Check: The units of the answer, J, are correct. The magnitude of the answer is reasonable since we are talking about the energy of one photon.

7.45   **Given:** $\lambda = 532 \, nm$ and $E_{pulse} = 3.85 \, mJ$ **Find:** number of photons

Conceptual Plan: $nm \rightarrow m \rightarrow E_{photon} \rightarrow$ number of photons

$$\dfrac{m}{10^9 nm} \quad E = \dfrac{hc}{\lambda}; \, h = 6.626 \times 10^{-34} \, J \, s \quad \dfrac{E_{pulse}}{E_{photon}}$$

Solution: $532 \, nm \times \dfrac{m}{10^9 \, nm} = 5.32 \times 10^{-7} \, m \quad E = \dfrac{6.626 \times 10^{-34} \, J \, s \times \dfrac{3.00 \times 10}{s}}{5.32 \times 10^{-7} \, m} = 3.7364 \times 10^{-19} \, J/photon$

$3.85 \, mJ \times \dfrac{J}{1000 \, mJ} \times \dfrac{1 \, photon}{3.7364 \times 10^{-19} \, J} = 1.03 \times 10^{16} \, photons$

Check: The units of the answer, number of photons, are correct. The magnitude of the answer is reasonable for the amount of energy involved.

7.47   (a)   **Given:** $\lambda = 1500 \, nm$ **Find:** E for 1 mol photons

Conceptual Plan: $nm \rightarrow m \rightarrow E_{photon} \rightarrow E(J)_{mol} \rightarrow E(kJ)_{mol}$

$$\dfrac{m}{10^9 \, nm} \quad E = \dfrac{hc}{\lambda}; \, h = 6.626 \times 10^{-34} \, J \, s \quad \dfrac{mol}{6.022 \times 10^{23} \, photons} \quad \dfrac{kJ}{1000 \, J}$$

Solution:

$1500 \, nm \times \dfrac{m}{10^9 \, nm} = 1.500 \times 10^{-6} \, m \quad E = \dfrac{6.626 \times 10^{-34} \, J \, s \times \dfrac{3.00 \times 10^8 \, m}{s}}{1.500 \times 10^{-6} \, m} = 1.3252 \times 10^{-19} \, J/photon$

$\dfrac{1.3252 \times 10^{-19} \, J}{photon} \times \dfrac{6.022 \times 10^{23} \, photons}{mol} \times \dfrac{kJ}{1000 \, J} = 79.8 \, kJ/mol$

Check: The units of the answer, kJ/mol, are correct. The magnitude of the answer is reasonable for a wavelength in the infrared region.

(b)   **Given:** $\lambda = 500 \, nm$ **Find:** E for 1 mol photons

Conceptual Plan: $nm \rightarrow m \rightarrow E_{photon} \rightarrow E_{mol} \rightarrow E(kJ)_{mol}$

$$\dfrac{m}{10^9 \, nm} \quad E = \dfrac{hc}{\lambda}; \, h = 6.626 \times 10^{-34} \, J \, s \quad \dfrac{mol}{6.022 \times 10^{23} \, photons} \quad \dfrac{kJ}{1000 \, J}$$

Solution:

$$500 \, \text{nm} \times \frac{m}{10^9 \, \text{nm}} = 5.00 \times 10^{-7} \, m \qquad E = \frac{6.626 \times 10^{-34} \, \text{J} \, \text{s} \times \frac{3.00 \times 10^8 \, m}{\text{s}}}{5.00 \times 10^{-7} \, m} = 3.9\underline{7}56 \times 10^{-19} \, \text{J/photon}$$

$$\frac{3.9\underline{7}56 \times 10^{-19} \, \text{J}}{\text{photon}} \times \frac{6.022 \times 10^{23} \, \text{photons}}{\text{mol}} \times \frac{\text{kJ}}{1000 \, \text{J}} = 239 \, \text{kJ/mol}$$

Check: The units of the answer, kJ/mol, are correct. The magnitude of the answer is reasonable for a wavelength in the visible region.

(c)   **Given:** λ = 150 nm **Find:** E for 1 mol photons
   Conceptual Plan: nm $\rightarrow$ m $\rightarrow$ E$_{\text{photon}}$ $\rightarrow$ E$_{\text{mol}}$ $\rightarrow$ E(kJ)$_{\text{mol}}$

$$\frac{m}{10^9 \text{nm}} \qquad E = \frac{hc}{\lambda}; \, h = 6.626 \times 10^{-34} \, \text{J s} \qquad \frac{\text{mol}}{6.022 \times 10^{23} \, \text{photons}} \qquad \frac{\text{kJ}}{1000 \, \text{J}}$$

Solution:

$$1.50 \, \text{nm} \times \frac{m}{10^9 \, \text{nm}} = 1.50 \times 10^{-7} \, m \qquad E = \frac{6.626 \times 10^{-34} \, \text{J} \, \text{s} \times \frac{3.00 \times 10^8 \, m}{\text{s}}}{1.50 \times 10^{-7} \, m} = 1.3\underline{2}52 \times 10^{-18} \, \text{J/photon}$$

$$\frac{1.3\underline{2}52 \times 10^{-18} \, \text{J}}{\text{photon}} \times \frac{6.022 \times 10^{23} \, \text{photons}}{\text{mol}} \times \frac{\text{kJ}}{1000 \, \text{J}} = 798 \, \text{kJ/mol}$$

Check: The units of the answer, kJ/mol, are correct. The magnitude of the answer is reasonable for a wavelength in the ultraviolet region. Note: The energy increases from the IR to the Vis to the UV as expected.

The Wave Nature of Matter and the Uncertainty Principle

7.49   The interference pattern would be a series of light and dark lines.

7.51   **Given:** m = 9.109 x 10^{-31} kg, λ = 0.20nm **Find:** v
   Conceptual Plan: m, $\rightarrow$ v

$$v = \frac{h}{m\lambda}$$

Solution: $\dfrac{6.626 \times 10^{-34} \dfrac{\text{kg} \cdot m^2}{s^2} \cdot \text{s}}{(9.109 \times 10^{-31} \, \text{kg})(0.20 \, \text{nm}) \left(\dfrac{1m}{1 \times 10^9 \, \text{nm}} \right)} = 3.6 \times 10^6 \, \text{m/s}$

Check: The units of the answer, m/s are correct. The magnitude of the answer is large as would be expected for the speed of the electron.

7.53   **Given:** m = 9.109 x 10^{-31} kg; v = 1.35 x 10^5 m/s **Find:** λ
   Conceptual Plan: m,v $\rightarrow$ λ

$$\lambda = \frac{h}{mv}$$

Solution: $\dfrac{6.626 \times 10^{-34} \dfrac{\text{kg} \cdot m^2}{s^2} \cdot \text{s}}{(9.109 \times 10^{-31} \, \text{kg}) \left(\dfrac{1.35 \times 10^5 \, m}{\text{s}} \right)} = 5.39 \times 10^{-9} \, m = 5.39 \, \text{nm}$

Check: The units of the answer, m, are correct. The magnitude is reasonable since we are looking at an electron.

7.55   **Given:** m = 143 g; v = 95 mph **Find:** λ
   Conceptual Plan: m,v $\rightarrow$ λ

$$\lambda = \frac{h}{mv}$$

Solution: $$\dfrac{6.626 \times 10^{-34}\, \frac{kg \cdot m^2}{s^2} \cdot s}{(143\,g)\left(\frac{kg}{1000\,g}\right)\left(\frac{95\,mi}{hr}\right)\left(\frac{1.609\,km}{mi}\right)\left(\frac{1000\,m}{km}\right)\left(\frac{hr}{3600\,s}\right)} = 1.1 \times 10^{-34}\, m$$

The value of the wavelength, 1.1×10^{-34} m, is so small it will not have an effect on the trajectory of the baseball.

Check: The units of the answer, m, are correct. The magnitude of the answer is very small as would be expected for the de Broglie wavelength of a baseball.

7.57   **Given:** $\Delta x = 552\,pm$, $m = 9.109 \times 10^{-31}$ kg **Find:** Δv
        Conceptual Plan: $\Delta x, m \rightarrow \Delta v$

$$\Delta x \times m \Delta v \geq \dfrac{h}{4\pi}$$

Solution: $$\dfrac{6.626 \times 10^{-34}\, \frac{kg \cdot m^2}{s^2} \cdot s}{4(3.141)(9.109 \times 10^{-31}\, kg)(552\, pm)\left(\frac{m}{1 \times 10^{12}\, pm}\right)} = 1.05 \times 10^5\, m/s$$

Check: The units of the answer, m/s, are correct. The magnitude is reasonable for the uncertainty in the speed of an electron.

Orbitals and Quantum Numbers

7.59   Since the size of the orbital is determined by the n quantum, with the size increasing with increasing n, an electron in a $2s$ orbital is closer, on average, to the nucleus than an electron in a $3s$ orbital.

7.61   The value of l is an integer that lies between 0 and $n - 1$.

        (a)   When $n = 1$, l can only be $l = 0$.

        (b)   When $n = 2$, l can be $l = 0$ or $l = 1$.

        (c)   When $n = 3$, l can be $l = 0$, $l = 1$, or $l = 2$.

        (d)   When $n = 4$, l can be $l = 0$, $l = 1$, $l = 2$, or $l = 3$.

7.63   Set c cannot occur together as a set of quantum numbers to specify an orbital. l must lie between 0 and $n - 1$, so for $n = 3$, l can only be as high as 2.

7.65   The 2 orbital would be the same shape as the $1s$ orbital but would be larger in size and the $3p$ orbitals would have the same shape as the $2p$ orbitals but would be larger in size. Also, the $2s$ and $3p$ orbitals would have more nodes.

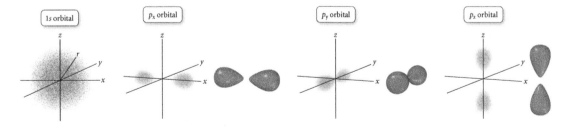

Atomic Spectroscopy

7.67   When the atom emits the photon of energy that was needed to raise the electron to the $n = 2$ level, the photon has the same energy as the energy absorbed to move the electron to the excited state. Therefore, the electron has to be in $n = 1$ (the ground state) following the emission of the photon.

7.69   According to the quantum-mechanical model, the higher the n level the higher the energy. So, the transition from $3p \rightarrow 1s$ would be a greater energy difference than a transition from $2p \rightarrow 1s$. The lower energy transition would have the longer wavelength. Therefore, the $2p \rightarrow 1s$ transition would produce a longer wavelength.

7.71   (a)   **Given:** $n = 2 \rightarrow n = 1$ **Find:** λ

   Conceptual Plan: $n = 1, n = 2 \rightarrow \Delta E_{atom} \rightarrow \Delta E_{photon} \rightarrow \lambda$

$$\Delta E_{atom} = E_1 - E_2 \qquad \Delta E_{atom} \rightarrow -\Delta E_{photon} \qquad E = \frac{hc}{\lambda}$$

   Solution:

$$\Delta E = E_1 - E_2$$

$$= -2.18 \times 10^{-18} J\left(\frac{1}{1^2}\right) - \left[-2.18 \times 10^{-18}\left(\frac{1}{2^2}\right)\right] = -2.18 \times 10^{-18}\ J\left[\left(\frac{1}{1^2}\right) - \left(\frac{1}{2^2}\right)\right] = -1.6\underline{3}5 \times 10^{-18} J$$

$$\Delta E_{photon} = -\Delta E_{atom} = 1.6\underline{3}5 \times 10^{-18} J \qquad \lambda = \frac{hc}{E} = \frac{(6.626 \times 10^{-34} J \cdot s)(3.00 \times 10^8 m/s)}{1.6\underline{3}5 \times 10^{-18} J} = 1.22 \times 10^{-7} m$$

   This transition would produce a wavelength in the UV region.

   Check: The units of the answer, m, are correct. The magnitude of the answer is reasonable since it is in the region of UV radiation.

   (b)   **Given:** $n = 3 \rightarrow n = 1$ **Find:** λ

   Conceptual Plan: $n = 1, n = 3 \rightarrow \Delta E_{atom} \rightarrow \Delta E_{photon} \rightarrow \lambda$

$$\Delta E_{atom} = E_1 - E_3 \qquad \Delta E_{atom} \rightarrow -\Delta E_{photon} \qquad E = \frac{hc}{\lambda}$$

   Solution:

$$\Delta E = E_1 - E_3$$

$$= -2.18 \times 10^{-18} J\left(\frac{1}{1^2}\right) - \left[-2.18 \times 10^{-18}\left(\frac{1}{3^2}\right)\right] = -2.18 \times 10^{-18}\ J\left[\left(\frac{1}{1^2}\right) - \left(\frac{1}{3^2}\right)\right] = -1.9\underline{3}8 \times 10^{-18}\ J$$

$$\Delta E_{photon} = -\Delta E_{atom} = 1.9\underline{3}8 \times 10^{-18} J \qquad \lambda = \frac{hc}{E} = \frac{(6.626 \times 10^{-34}\ J \cdot s)(3.00 \times 10^8\ m/s)}{1.9\underline{3}8 \times 10^{-18}\ J} = 1.03 \times 10^{-7}\ m$$

   This transition would produce a wavelength in the UV region.

   Check: The units of the answer, m, are correct. The magnitude of the answer is reasonable since it is in the region of UV radiation.

   (c)   **Given:** $n = 4 \rightarrow n = 2$ **Find:** λ

   Conceptual Plan: $n = 2, n = 4 \rightarrow \Delta E_{atom} \rightarrow \Delta E_{photon} \rightarrow \lambda$

$$\Delta E_{atom} = E_2 - E_4 \qquad \Delta E_{atom} \rightarrow -\Delta E_{photon} \qquad E = \frac{hc}{\lambda}$$

   Solution:

$$\Delta E = E_2 - E_4$$

$$= -2.18 \times 10^{-18} J\left(\frac{1}{2^2}\right) - \left[-2.18 \times 10^{-18}\left(\frac{1}{4^2}\right)\right] = -2.18 \times 10^{-18} J\left[\left(\frac{1}{2^2}\right) - \left(\frac{1}{4^2}\right)\right] = -4.0\underline{8}7 \times 10^{-19} J$$

$$\Delta E_{photon} = -\Delta E_{atom} = 4.0\underline{8}7 \times 10^{-19} J \qquad \lambda = \frac{hc}{E} = \frac{(6.626 \times 10^{-34}\ J \cdot s)(3.00 \times 10^8\ m/s)}{4.0\underline{8}7 \times 10^{-19}\ J} = 4.86 \times 10^{-7}\ m$$

   This transition would produce a wavelength in the visible region.

   Check: The units of the answer, m, are correct. The magnitude of the answer is reasonable since it is in the region of visible light.

   (d)   **Given:** $n = 5 \rightarrow n = 2$ **Find:** λ

   Conceptual Plan: $n = 2, n = 5 \rightarrow \Delta E_{atom} \rightarrow \Delta E_{photon} \rightarrow \lambda$

$$\Delta E_{atom} = E_2 - E_5 \qquad \Delta E_{atom} \rightarrow -\Delta E_{photon} \qquad E = \frac{hc}{\lambda}$$

   Solution:

$$\Delta E = E_2 - E_5$$

$$= -2.18 \times 10^{-18} J\left(\frac{1}{2^2}\right) - \left[-2.18 \times 10^{-18}\left(\frac{1}{5^2}\right)\right] = -2.18 \times 10^{-18} J\left[\left(\frac{1}{2^2}\right) - \left(\frac{1}{5^2}\right)\right] = -4.5\underline{7}8 \times 10^{-19} J$$

$$\Delta E_{photon} = -\Delta E_{atom} = 4.5\underline{7}8 \times 10^{-19} J \qquad \lambda = \frac{hc}{E} = \frac{(6.626 \times 10^{-34}\ J \cdot s)(3.00 \times 10^8\ m/s)}{4.5\underline{7}8 \times 10^{-19}\ J} = 4.34 \times 10^{-7}\ m$$

   This transition would produce a wavelength in the visible region.

Check: The units of the answer, m, are correct. The magnitude of the answer is reasonable since it is in the region of visible light.

7.73   **Given:** n(initial) = 7 λ = 397 nm **Find:** n(final)
Conceptual Plan: $\lambda \rightarrow \Delta E_{photon} \rightarrow \Delta E_{atom} \rightarrow n = x, n = 7$

$$E = \frac{hc}{\lambda} \qquad \Delta E_{photon} \rightarrow -\Delta E_{atom} \qquad \Delta E_{atom} = E_x - E_7$$

Solution: $E = \dfrac{hc}{\lambda} = \dfrac{(6.626 \times 10^{-34}\,\text{J}\cdot\text{s})(3.00 \times 10^8\,\text{m/s})}{(397\,\cancel{\text{nm}})\left(\dfrac{\cancel{\text{m}}}{10^9\,\cancel{\text{nm}}}\right)} = 5.00\underline{7} \times 10^{-19}\,\text{J}$

$\Delta E_{atom} = -\Delta E_{photon} = -5.00\underline{7} \times 10^{-19}\,\text{J}$

$\Delta E = E_x - E_7 = -5.00\underline{7} \times 10^{-19} = -2.18 \times 10^{-18}\,\text{J}\left(\dfrac{1}{x^2}\right) - \left[-2.18 \times 10^{-18}\left(\dfrac{1}{7^2}\right)\right] = -2.18 \times 10^{-18}\,\text{J}\left[\left(\dfrac{1}{x^2}\right) - \left(\dfrac{1}{7^2}\right)\right]$

$0.2297 = \left(\dfrac{1}{x^2}\right) - \left(\dfrac{1}{7^2}\right) \qquad\qquad 0.25229 = \left(\dfrac{1}{x^2}\right) \qquad x^2 = 3.998 \quad x = 2$

Check: The answer is reasonable since it is an integer less than the initial value of 7.

Cumulative Problems

7.75   **Given:** 348 kJ/mol **Find:** λ
Conceptual Plan: kJ/mol $\rightarrow$ kJ/molec $\rightarrow$ J/molec $\rightarrow$ λ

$$\frac{6.022 \times 10^{23}\,\text{C} - \text{C bonds}}{\text{mol C} - \text{C bonds}} \quad \frac{1000\,\text{J}}{\text{kJ}} \qquad E = \frac{hc}{\lambda}$$

Solution: $\dfrac{348\,\cancel{\text{kJ}}}{\cancel{\text{mol C} - \text{C bonds}}} \times \dfrac{\cancel{\text{mol C} - \text{C bonds}}}{6.022 \times 10^{23}\,\cancel{\text{C} - \text{C bonds}}} \times \dfrac{1000\,\text{J}}{\cancel{\text{kJ}}} = 5.77\underline{9} \times 10^{-19}\,\text{J}$

$\lambda = \dfrac{(6.626 \times 10^{-34}\,\cancel{\text{J}}\cdot\text{s})(3.00 \times 10^8\,\text{m/s})}{5.77\underline{9} \times 10^{-19}\,\cancel{\text{J}}} = 3.44 \times 10^{-7}\,\text{m} = 344\,\text{nm}$

Check: The units of the answer, m or nm, are correct. The magnitude of the answer is reasonable since this wavelength is in the UV region.

7.77   **Given:** E_{pulse} = 5.0 watts; d = 5.5 mm; hole = 1.2 mm; λ = 532 nm **Find:** photons/s
Conceptual Plan: fraction of beam through hole $\rightarrow$ fraction of power and then $E_{photon} \rightarrow$ number photons/s

$$\frac{\text{area hole}}{\text{area beam}} \qquad \text{fraction x power} \qquad E = \frac{hc}{\lambda} \qquad \frac{\text{power/s}}{\text{E/photon}}$$

Solution: $A = \pi r^2 \dfrac{\pi(0.60\,\text{mm})^2}{\pi(2.75\,\text{mm})^2} = 0.0476 \qquad 0.0476 \times 5.0\,\text{watts} \times \dfrac{\text{J/s}}{\text{watt}} = 0.2\underline{3}8\,\text{J/s}$

$E_{photon} = \dfrac{(6.626 \times 10^{-34}\,\text{J}\cdot\text{s})(3.00 \times 10^8\,\text{m/s})}{(532\,\cancel{\text{nm}})\left(\dfrac{\cancel{\text{m}}}{10^9\,\cancel{\text{nm}}}\right)} = 3.7\underline{3}6 \times 10^{-19}\,\text{J/photon}$

$\dfrac{0.2\underline{3}8\,\cancel{\text{J}}/\text{s}}{3.7\underline{3}6 \times 10^{-19}\,\cancel{\text{J}}/\text{photon}} = 6.4 \times 10^{17}\,\text{photons/s}$

Check: The units of the answer, number of photons/s, are correct. The magnitude of the answer is reasonable.

7.79   **Given:** KE = 506 eV **Find:** λ
Conceptual Plan: $KE_{ev} \rightarrow KE_J \rightarrow v \rightarrow \lambda$

$$\frac{1.602 \times 10^{-19}\,\text{J}}{\text{eV}} \quad KE = 1/2\,mv^2 \quad \lambda = \frac{h}{mv}$$

Solution:

$506\,\text{eV}\left(\dfrac{1.602 \times 10^{-19}\,\text{J}}{\text{eV}}\right)\left(\dfrac{\frac{\text{kg}\cdot\text{m}^2}{\text{s}^2}}{\text{J}}\right) = \dfrac{1}{2}(9.11 \times 10^{-31}\,\text{kg})\,v^2$

$$v^2 = \frac{506\,\cancel{eV}\left(\frac{1.602 \times 10^{-19}\,\cancel{J}}{\cancel{eV}}\right)\left(\frac{kg \cdot m^2}{s^2}\right)}{\frac{1}{2}(9.11 \times 10^{-31}\,\cancel{kg})} = 1.7796 \times 10^{14}\,\frac{m^2}{s^2}$$

$$v = 1.33 \times 10^7\,m/s \qquad \lambda = \frac{h}{mv} = \frac{6.626 \times 10^{-34}\,\frac{kg \cdot m^2}{\cancel{s}} \cdot \cancel{s}}{(9.11 \times 10^{-31}\,\cancel{kg})(1.33 \times 10^7\,\cancel{m}/\cancel{s})} = 5.47 \times 10^{-11}\,m = 0.0547\,nm$$

Check: The units of the answer, m or nm, are correct. The magnitude of the answer is reasonable because a de Broglie wavelength is usually a very small number.

7.81   **Given:** $n = 1 \rightarrow n = \infty$ **Find:** E; λ

Conceptual Plan: $n = \infty$, $n = 1 \rightarrow \Delta E_{atom} \rightarrow \Delta E_{photon} \rightarrow \lambda$

$$\Delta E_{atom} = E_\infty - E_1 \qquad \Delta E_{atom} \rightarrow \Delta E_{photon} \qquad E = \frac{hc}{\lambda}$$

Solution: $\Delta E = E_\infty - E_1 = 0 - \left[-2.18 \times 10^{-18}\left(\frac{1}{1^2}\right)\right] = +2.18 \times 10^{-18}\,J$

$$\Delta E_{photon} = -\Delta E_{atom} = +2.18 \times 10^{-18}\,J$$

$$\lambda = \frac{hc}{E} = \frac{(6.626 \times 10^{-34}\,\cancel{J} \cdot \cancel{s})(3.00 \times 10^8\,m/\cancel{s})}{2.18 \times 10^{-18}\,\cancel{J}} = 9.12 \times 10^{-8}\,m = 91.2\,nm$$

Check: The units of the answers, J for E and m or nm for part 1, are correct. The magnitude of the answer is reasonable because it would require more energy to completely remove the electron than just moving it to a higher n level. This results in a shorter wavelength.

7.83   (a)   **Given:** $n = 1$ **Find:** number of orbitals if $l = 0 \rightarrow n$

Conceptual Plan: value n $\rightarrow$ values l $\rightarrow$ values m_l $\rightarrow$ number of orbitals

$$l = 0 \rightarrow n \qquad\qquad m_l = -1 \rightarrow +1\ \text{total}\ m_l$$

Solution:			
$n =$	1		
$l =$	0	1	
$m_l =$	0	-1, 0, +1	

total 4 orbitals

Check: The total orbitals will be equal to the number of l sublevels[2].

(b)   **Given:** $n = 2$ **Find:** number of orbitals if $l = 0 \rightarrow n$

Conceptual Plan: value n $\rightarrow$ values l $\rightarrow$ values m_l $\rightarrow$ number of orbitals

$$l = 0 \rightarrow n \qquad\qquad m_l = -1 \rightarrow +1\ \text{total}\ m_l$$

Solution:			
$n =$	2		
$l =$	0	1	2
$m_l =$	0	-1, 0, +1	-2,-1,0,1,2

total 9 orbitals

Check: l sublevels[2].

(c)   **Given:** $n = 3$ **Find:** number of orbitals if $l = 0 \rightarrow n$

Conceptual Plan: value n $\rightarrow$ values l $\rightarrow$ values m_l $\rightarrow$ number of orbitals

$$l = 0 \rightarrow n \qquad\qquad m_l = -1 \rightarrow +1\ \text{total}\ m_l$$

Solution:				
$n =$	3			
$l =$	0	1	2	3
$m_l =$	0	-1, 0, +1	-2,-1,0,1,2	-3,-2,-1,0,1,2,3

total 16 orbitals

Check: The total orbitals will be equal to the number of l sublevels[2].

7.85 **Given:** $\lambda = 1875$ nm; 1282 nm; 1093 nm **Find:** equivalent transitions

Conceptual Plan: $\lambda \rightarrow E_{photon} \rightarrow E_{atom} \rightarrow n$

$$E = \frac{hc}{\lambda} \qquad E_{photon} = \qquad -E_{atom} \qquad E = -2.18 \times 10^{-18} J\left(\frac{1}{n_f^2} - \frac{1}{n_i^2}\right)$$

Solution: Since the wavelength of the transitions are longer wavelengths than those obtained in the visual region, the electron must relax to a higher n level. Therefore, we can assume that the electron returns to the n = 3 level.

For $\lambda = 1875$ nm: $E = \dfrac{(6.626 \times 10^{-34} J \cdot s)(3.00 \times 10^8 m/s)}{1875 \, nm\left(\dfrac{m}{10^9 \, nm}\right)} = 1.060 \times 10^{-19} J \quad 1.060 \times 10^{-19} J = -1.060 \times 10^{-19} J$

$$-1.060 \times 10^{-19} J = -2.18 \times 10^{-18}\left(\frac{1}{3^2} - \frac{1}{n^2}\right); n = 4$$

For $\lambda = 1282$ nm: $E = \dfrac{(6.626 \times 10^{-34} J \cdot s)(3.00 \times 10^8 m/s)}{1282 \, nm\left(\dfrac{m}{10^9 \, nm}\right)} = 1.551 \times 10^{-19} J \quad 1.551 \times 10^{-19} J = -1.551 \times 10^{-19} J$

$$-1.551 \times 10^{-19} = -2.18 \times 10^{-18}\left(\frac{1}{3^2} - \frac{1}{n^2}\right); n = 5$$

For $\lambda = 1093$ nm: $E = \dfrac{(6.626 \times 10^{-34} J \cdot s)(3.00 \times 10^8 m/s)}{1093 \, nm\left(\dfrac{m}{10^9 \, nm}\right)} = 1.819 \times 10^{-19} J \quad 1.819 \times 10^{-19} J = -1.819 \times 10^{-19} J$

$$-1.819 \times 10^{-19} J = -2.18 \times 10^{-18}\left(\frac{1}{3^2} - \frac{1}{n^2}\right); n = 6$$

Check: The values obtained are all integers, which is correct. The values of n: 4,5,6, are reasonable. The values of n increase as the wavelength decreases because the two n levels involved are further apart and more energy is released as the electron relaxes to the $n = 3$ level.

7.87 **Given:** $\Phi = 193$ kJ/mol **Find:** threshold frequency(ν)

Conceptual Plan: Φ **kJ/ mol** $\rightarrow$ Φ **kJ/ atom** $\rightarrow \Phi$ **J/ atom** $\rightarrow$ ν

$$\frac{6.022 \times 10^{23} atoms}{mol} \qquad \frac{1000 J}{kJ} \qquad \Phi = h\nu$$

Solution: $\nu = \dfrac{\Phi}{h} = \dfrac{\left(\dfrac{193 \, kJ}{mol}\right)\left(\dfrac{mol}{6.022 \times 10^{23} atoms}\right)\left(\dfrac{1000 J}{kJ}\right)}{6.626 \times 10^{-34} J \cdot s} = 4.84 \times 10^{14} \, s^{-1}$

Check: The units of the answer, s^{-1}, are correct. The magnitude of the answer puts the frequency in the infrared range and is a reasonable answer.

7.89 **Given:** $\nu_{low} = 30 s^{-1}$ $\nu_{hi} = 1.5 \times 10^4 \, s^{-1}$; speed = 344 m/s **Find:** $\lambda_{low} - \lambda_{hi}$

Conceptual Plan: $\nu_{low} \rightarrow \lambda_{low}$ and $\nu_{hi} = \lambda_{hi}$ then $\lambda_{low} - \lambda_{hi}$

$$\lambda\nu = speed$$

Solution: $\lambda = \dfrac{speed}{\nu} \lambda \quad_{low} = \dfrac{344 \, m/s}{30 \, s^{-1}} = 11 \, m \quad \lambda_{hi} = \dfrac{344 \, m/s}{1.5 \times 10^4 \, s^{-1}} = 0.023 \, m \quad 11 \, m - 0.023 \, m = 11 \, m$

Check: The units of the answer, m, are correct. The magnitude is reasonable since the value is only determined by the low frequency value because of significant figures.

7.91 **Given:** $\lambda = 792$ nm, V = 100.0 mL, P = 55.7 mtorr, T = 25°C **Find:** E to dissociate 15.0%

Conceptual Plan: $\lambda \rightarrow$ **E/molecule** and then **P.V.T** $\rightarrow$ **n** $\rightarrow$ **molecules**

$$E = \frac{hc}{\lambda} \qquad\qquad n = \frac{PV}{RT} \qquad \frac{6.022 \times 10^{23} \, molecules}{mole}$$

Solution: $E = \dfrac{(6.626 \times 10^{-34} J \cdot s)(3.00 \times 10^8 m/s)}{792 \, nm\left(\dfrac{m}{10^9 \, nm}\right)} = 2.51 \times 10^{-19} J/molecule$

$$\dfrac{(55.7\ \cancel{\text{mtorr}})\left(\dfrac{1\ \cancel{\text{torr}}}{1000\ \cancel{\text{mtorr}}}\right)\left(\dfrac{1\ \text{atm}}{760\ \cancel{\text{torr}}}\right)(100.0\ \cancel{\text{mL}})\left(\dfrac{\cancel{\text{L}}}{1000\ \cancel{\text{mL}}}\right)\left(\dfrac{6.022\times 10^{23}\ \text{molecules}}{\cancel{\text{mol}}}\right)}{\left(\dfrac{0.0821\ \cancel{\text{L}}\,\text{atm}}{\cancel{\text{mol}}\,\text{K}}\right)(298\ \text{K})} = 1.80\times 10^{17}\ \text{molecules}$$

$(1.80 \times 10^{17}\ \text{molecules})(0.15\%) = 2.70 \times 10^{16}\ \text{molecules dissociated}$

$(2.51 \times 10^{-19}\ \text{J/molecule})(2.70 \times 10^{16}\ \text{molecules}) = 6.777 \times 10^{-3}\,\text{J} = 6.78 \times 10^{-3}\,\text{J}$

Check: The units of the answer, J, are correct. The magnitude is reasonable since it is for a part of a mole of molecules.

7.93   **Given:** 20.0 mW, 1.00 hr., 2.29×10^{20} photons **Find:** λ

Conceptual Plan: mW $\rightarrow$ W $\rightarrow$ J $\rightarrow$ J/photon $\rightarrow$ λ

$$\dfrac{\text{W}}{1000\ \text{mW}} \qquad E = W\times s \qquad \dfrac{E}{\text{number of photons}} \qquad \lambda = \dfrac{hc}{E}$$

Solution: $(20.0\ \cancel{\text{mW}})\left(\dfrac{1\ \cancel{\text{W}}}{1000\ \cancel{\text{mW}}}\right)\left(\dfrac{\frac{\text{J}}{\text{s}}}{\cancel{\text{W}}}\right)\left(\dfrac{3600\ \cancel{\text{s}}}{2.29\times 10^{20}\ \text{photons}}\right) = 3.14\times 10^{-19}\,\text{J/photon}$

$$\dfrac{(6.626\times 10^{-34}\ \cancel{\text{J}}\cdot\cancel{\text{s}})(3.00\times 10^{8}\ \cancel{\text{m}}/\cancel{\text{s}})\left(\dfrac{10^{9}\ \text{nm}}{\cancel{\text{m}}}\right)}{3.14\times 10^{-19}\ \cancel{\text{J}}} = 632\ \text{nm}$$

Check: The units of the answer, nm, are correct. The magnitude is reasonable because it is in the red range.

Challenge Problems

7.95   (a)   **Given:** $n = 1$, $n = 2$, $n = 3$, L = 155 pm **Find:** E_1, E_2, E_3

Conceptual Plan: $n \rightarrow E$

$$E_n = \dfrac{n^2 h^2}{8\,m\,L^2}$$

Solution:

$$E_1 = \dfrac{1^2(6.626\times 10^{-34}\ \text{J}\cdot\text{s})^2}{8(9.11\times 10^{-31}\ \text{kg})(155\ \cancel{\text{pm}})^2\left(\dfrac{\text{m}}{10^{12}\ \cancel{\text{pm}}}\right)^2} = \dfrac{1(6.626\times 10^{-34})^2\,\text{J}^2\,\text{s}^2}{8(9.11\times 10^{-31}\ \text{kg})(155\times 10^{-12})^2\,\text{m}^2}$$

$$= \dfrac{1(6.626\times 10^{-34})^2\left(\dfrac{\text{kg}\cdot\cancel{\text{m}^2}}{\cancel{\text{s}^2}}\right)\text{J}\,\cancel{\text{s}^2}}{8(9.11\times 10^{-31}\ \cancel{\text{kg}})(155\times 10^{-12})^2\,\cancel{\text{m}^2}} = 2.51\times 10^{-18}\,\text{J}$$

$$E_2 = \dfrac{2^2(6.626\times 10^{-34}\ \text{J}\cdot\text{s})^2}{8(9.11\times 10^{-31}\ \text{kg})(155\ \cancel{\text{pm}})^2\left(\dfrac{\text{m}}{10^{12}\ \cancel{\text{pm}}}\right)^2} = \dfrac{4(6.626\times 10^{-34})^2\,\text{J}^2\,\text{s}^2}{8(9.11\times 10^{-31}\ \text{kg})(155\times 10^{-12})^2\,\text{m}^2}$$

$$= \dfrac{4(6.626\times 10^{-34})^2\left(\dfrac{\text{kg}\cdot\cancel{\text{m}^2}}{\cancel{\text{s}^2}}\right)\text{J}\,\cancel{\text{s}^2}}{8(9.11\times 10^{-31}\cancel{\text{kg}})(155\times 10^{-12})^2\,\cancel{\text{m}^2}} = 1.00\times 10^{-17}\,\text{J}$$

$$E_3 = \dfrac{3^2(6.626\times 10^{-34}\ \text{J}\cdot\text{s})^2}{8(9.11\times 10^{-31}\ \text{kg})(155\ \cancel{\text{pm}})^2\left(\dfrac{\text{m}}{10^{12}\ \cancel{\text{pm}}}\right)^2} = \dfrac{9(6.626\times 10^{-34})^2\,\text{J}^2\,\text{s}^2}{8(9.11\times 10^{-31}\ \text{kg})(155\times 10^{-12})^2\,\text{m}^2}$$

$$= \dfrac{9(6.626\times 10^{-34})^2\left(\dfrac{\text{kg}\cdot\cancel{\text{m}^2}}{\cancel{\text{s}^2}}\right)\text{J}\,\cancel{\text{s}^2}}{8(9.11\times 10^{-31}\ \cancel{\text{kg}})(155\times 10^{-12})^2\,\cancel{\text{m}^2}} = 2.26\times 10^{-17}$$

Check: The units of the answers, J, are correct. The answers seem reasonable since the energy is increasing with increasing n level.

(b)   **Given:** $n = 1 \rightarrow n = 2$ and $n = 2 \rightarrow n = 3$ **Find:** λ

Conceptual Plan: $n = 1, n = 2 \rightarrow \Delta E_{atom} \rightarrow \Delta E_{photon} \rightarrow \lambda$

$$\Delta E_{atom} = E_2 - E_1 \qquad \Delta E_{atom} \rightarrow \quad -\Delta E_{photon} \quad E = \frac{hc}{\lambda}$$

Solution: Using the energies calculated in part a

$E_2 - E_1 = (1.00 \times 10^{-17} \text{ J} - 2.51 \times 10^{-18} \text{ J}) = 7.49 \times 10^{-18} \text{ J}$

$$\lambda = \frac{(6.626 \times 10^{-34} \text{ J} \cdot \text{s})(3.00 \times 10^{8.} \text{ m/s})}{7.49 \times 10^{-18} \text{ J}} = 2.65 \times 10^{-8} \text{ m} = 26.5 \text{ nm}$$

$E_3 - E_2 = (2.26 \times 10^{-17} \text{ J} - 1.00 \times 10^{-17} \text{ J}) = 1.26 \times 10^{-17} \text{ J}$

$$\lambda = \frac{(6.626 \times 10^{-34} \text{ J} \cdot \text{s})(3.00 \times 10^{8.} \text{ m/s})}{1.26 \times 10^{-17} \text{ J}} = 1.58 \times 10^{-8} \text{ m} = 15.8 \text{ nm}$$

These wavelengths would lie in the UV region.

Check: The units of the answers, m, are correct. The magnitude of the answers is reasonable based on the energies obtained for the levels.

7.97   For the 1s orbital in the Excel spreadsheet, call column A: r; and column B: $\Psi(1s)$. Make the values for r column A: 0–200. In column B, put the equation for the wave function written as follows: =(POWER(1/3.1415,1/2))*(1/POWER(53,3/2))*(EXP(-A2/53)). Go to make chart, choose xy scatter.

e.g., sample values

r	Ψ (1s)
0	7.000146224
1	7.000143491
2	7.000140809
3	7.000138177
4	7.000135594
5	7.00013306
6	7.000130573

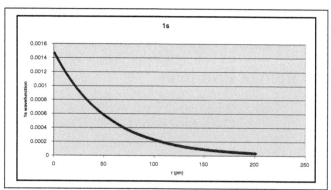

For the 2s orbital in the same Excel spreadsheet, call column A: r; and column C: $\Psi(2s)$. Use the same values for r in column A: 0–200. In column C, put the equation for the wave function written as follows: =(POWER(1/((32)*(3.1415)),1/2))*(1/POWER(53,3/2))*(2-(A2/53))*(EXP(-A2/53)). Go to make chart, choose xy scatter.

e.g., sample values

r	Ψ (2s)
0	7.0000516979
1	7.000050253
2	7.0000488441
3	7.0000474702
4	7.0000461307
5	7.0000448247
6	7.0000435513

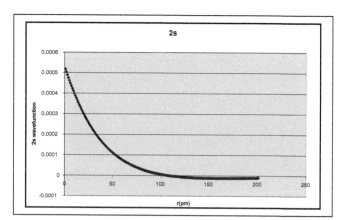

Note: The plot for the 2s orbital extends below the x axis. The x-intercept represents the radial node of the orbital.

7.99 **Given:** threshold frequency $= 2.25 \times 10^{14}\,s^{-1}$; $\lambda = 5.00 \times 10^{-7}\,m$ **Find:** v of electron

Conceptual Plan: v $\rightarrow$ **Φ and then λ** $\rightarrow$ **E and then** $\rightarrow$ **KE** $\rightarrow$ **v**

$$\Phi = h\nu \qquad\qquad E = \frac{hc}{\lambda} \qquad KE = E - \Phi \quad KE = 1/2\,mv^2$$

Solution:

$$\Phi = (6.626 \times 10^{-34}\,J\cdot s)(2.25 \times 10^{14}\,s^{-1}) = 1.49\underline{1} \times 10^{-19}\,J \quad E = \frac{(6.626 \times 10^{-34}\,J\cdot s)(3.00 \times 10^{8}\,m/s)}{5.00 \times 10^{-7}\,m} = 3.9\underline{7}6 \times 10^{-19}\,J$$

$$KE = 3.9\underline{7}6 \times 10^{-19}\,J - 1.4\underline{9}1 \times 10^{-19}\,J = 2.485 \times 10^{-19}\,J \quad v^2 = \frac{2.485 \times 10^{-19}\,\dfrac{kg\cdot m^2}{s^2}}{\dfrac{1}{2}\,(9.11 \times 10^{-31}\,kg)} = 5.455 \times 10^{11}\,\dfrac{m^2}{s^2}$$

$v = 7.39 \times 10^{5}\,m/s$

Check: The units of the answer, m/s, are correct. The magnitude of the answer is reasonable for the speed of an electron.

7.101 **Given:** $t = 5.0\,fs$, $\lambda_{low} = 722\,nm$ **Find:** ΔE, and λ_{high}

Conceptual Plan: t $\rightarrow$ **ΔE and then λ_{low}** $\rightarrow$ **E_{high}** $\rightarrow$ **E_{low}** $\rightarrow$ **λ_{high}**

$$\Delta t \times \Delta E \geq \frac{h}{4\pi} \qquad\qquad E = \frac{hc}{\lambda} \qquad E - \Delta E \qquad \lambda = \frac{hc}{E}$$

Solution: $\dfrac{6.626 \times 10^{-34}\,J\cdot s}{4(3.141)(5.0\,fs)\left(\dfrac{s}{1 \times 10^{15}\,fs}\right)} = 1.0\underline{5}5 \times 10^{-20}\,J$

$$E = \frac{(6.626 \times 10^{-34}\,J\cdot s)(3.00 \times 10^{8}\,m/s)}{722\,nm\left(\dfrac{m}{10^{9}\,nm}\right)} = 2.7\underline{5} \times 10^{-19}\,J$$

$2.75 \times 10^{-19}\,J - 1.06 \times 10^{-20}\,J = 2.6\underline{4} \times 10^{-19}\,J$

$$\frac{(6.626 \times 10^{-34}\,J\cdot s)(3.00 \times 10^{8}\,m/s)\left(\dfrac{10^{9}\,nm}{m}\right)}{(2.64 \times 10^{-19}\,J)} = 751.8\,nm = 7.5 \times 10^{2}\,nm$$

Check: The units of the answer, nm, are correct. The magnitude of the answer is reasonable since it is a longer wavelength but it is close to the original wavelength.

7.103 **Given:** $r = 1.8\,m$ **Find:** λ

Conceptual Plan: r $\rightarrow$ **C**

$$C = 2\pi r$$

Solution: $(2)(3.141)(1.8\,m) = 1\underline{1}.3\,m =$ the circumference of the orbit. So the largest wavelength that would fit the orbit would be 11 m.

Check: The units of the answer, m, are correct. The magnitude of the wave is about the circumference of the orbit.

Conceptual Problems

7.105 In the Bohr model of the atom, the electron travels in a circular orbit around the nucleus. It is a 2-dimensional model. The electron is constrained to move only from one orbit to another orbit. But, the electron is treated as a particle that behaves according to the laws of classical physics. The quantum-mechanical model of the atom is 3-dimensional. In this model, we treat the electron, an absolutely small particle, differently than we treat particles with classical physics. The electron is in an orbital, which gives us the probability of finding the electron within a volume of space.

Because the electron in the Bohr model is constrained to a circular orbit, it would theoretically be possible to know both the position and the velocity of the electron simultaneously. This contradicts the Heisenberg uncertainty principle, which states that position and velocity are complementary terms that cannot both be known with precision.

7.107   (a)   Since the interference pattern is caused by single electrons interfering with themselves, the pattern

minute. It will simply take longer for the full pattern to develop.

(b)   When a light is placed behind the slits, it flashes to indicate which hole the electron passed through, but the interference pattern is now absent. With the laser on, the electrons hit positions directly behind each slit, as if they were ordinary particles.

(c)   Diffraction occurs when a wave encounters an obstacle of a slit that is comparable in size to its wavelength. The wave bends around the slit. The diffraction of light through two slits separated by a distance comparable to the wavelength of the light results in an interference pattern. Each slit acts as a new wave source, and the two new waves interfere with each other, which results in a pattern of bright and dark lines.

(d)   Since the mass of the bullets and their particle size are not absolutely small, the bullets will not produce an interference pattern when they pass through the slits. The de Broglie wavelength produced by the bullets will not be sufficiently large enough to interfere with the bullet trajectory and no interference pattern will be observed.

8 Periodic Properties of the Elements

Review Questions

8.1   A periodic property is one that is predictable based on the element's position within the periodic table.

8.3   The first attempt to organize the elements according to similarities in their properties was made by the German chemist Johann Dobereiner. He grouped elements into triads; three elements with similar properties. A more complex approach was attempted by the English chemist John Newlands. He organized elements into octaves, analogous to musical notes. When arranged this way, the properties of every eighth element were similar.

8.5   Meyer proposed an organization of the known elements based on some periodic properties. Moseley listed elements according to the atomic number rather than atomic mass. This resolved the problems in Mendeleev's table where an increase in atomic mass did not correlate with similar properties.

8.7   Electron spin is a fundamental property of electrons. It is more correctly expressed as saying the electron has inherent angular momentum. The value m_s is the spin quantum number. An electron with $m_s = +1/2$ has a spin opposite of an electron with $m_s = -1/2$.

8.9   An electron configuration shows the particular orbitals that are occupied by electrons in an atom. Some examples are $H = 1s^1$, $He = 1s^2$, and $Li = 1s^2 2s^1$.

8.11   Shielding or screening occurs when one electron is blocked from the full effects of the nuclear charge so that the electron experiences only a part of the nuclear charge. It is the inner (core) electrons that shield the outer electrons from the full nuclear charge.

8.13   The sublevels within a principle level split in multielectron atoms because of penetration of the outer electrons into the region of the core electrons. The sublevels in hydrogen are not split because they are empty in the ground state.

8.15   The Pauli exclusion principle states the following: No two electrons in an atom can have the same four quantum numbers.

        Since two electrons occupying the same orbital have three identical quantum numbers (n, l, m_l), they must have different spin quantum numbers. The Pauli exclusion principle implies that each orbital can have a maximum of only two electrons, with opposing spins.

8.17   In order of increasing energy the orbitals are $1s < 2s < 2p < 3s < 3p < 4s < 3d < 4p < 5s$. The 4s orbital fills before the 3d and the 5s fills before the 4d. They are lower in energy because of greater penetration of the 4s and 5s orbitals.

8.19

8.21   The rows in the periodic table grow progressively longer because you are adding sublevels as the n level increases.

8.23   The row number of a main-group element is equal to the highest principal quantum number of that element. However, the principal quantum number of the d orbital being filled across each row in the transition series is equal to the row number minus one. For the inner transition elements, the principal quantum number of the f orbital being filled across each row is the row number minus two.

8.25   To use the periodic table to write the electron configuration find the noble gas that precedes the element. The element has the inner electron configuration of that noble gas. Place the symbol for the noble gas in [ ]. Obtain the outer electron configuration by tracing the element across the period and assigning electrons in the appropriate orbitals.

8.27   (a)   The alkali metals (group 1A) have 1 valence electron, are among the most reactive metals because their outer electron configuration (ns^1) is one electron beyond a noble gas configuration. They react to lose the ns^1 electron, obtaining a noble gas configuration. This is why the group 1A metals tend to form 1+ cations.

        (b)   The alkaline earth metals (group 2A) have 2 valence electrons, have an outer electron configuration of ns^2, and also tend to be reactive metals. They lose their ns^2 electrons to form 2+ cations.

        (c)   The halogens (group 7A) have 7 valence electrons and have an outer electron configuration of ns^2np^5. They are among the most reactive nonmetals. They are only one electron short of a noble gas configuration and tend to react to gain that one electron, forming 1– anions.

        (d)   The oxygen family (group 6A) has 6 valence electrons and has an outer electron configuration of ns^2np^4. They are 2 electrons short of a noble gas configuration and tend to react to gain those two electrons, forming 2– anions.

8.29   The effective nuclear charge (Z_{eff}) is the average or net charge from the nucleus experienced by the electrons in the outermost levels. Shielding is the blocking of nuclear charge from the outermost electrons. The shielding is primarily due to the inner (core) electrons although there is some interaction and shielding from the electron repulsions of the outer electrons with each other.

8.31   (a)   The radii of transition elements stay roughly constant across each row instead of decreasing in size as in the main group elements. The difference is that, across a row of transition elements, the number of electrons in the outermost principal energy level is nearly constant. As another proton is added to the nucleus with each successive element, another electron is added as well, but the electron goes into an

$n_{highest} - 1$ orbital. The number of outermost electrons stays constant and they experience a roughly constant effective nuclear charge, keeping the radius approximately constant.

(b)   As you go down the first two rows of a column within the transition metals, the elements follow the same general trend in atomic radii and the main-group elements; i.e., the radii get larger because you are adding outermost electrons into higher n levels.

8.33   An important exception to simply subtracting the number of electrons occurs for transition metal cations. When writing the electron configuration of a transition metal cation, remove the electrons in the highest n-value orbitals first, even if this does not correspond to the reverse order of filling. Normally, even though the d orbital electrons add after the s orbital electrons, the s orbital electrons are lost first. This is because 1) the ns and $(n - 1)$d orbitals are extremely close in energy and depending on the exact configuration can vary in relative energy ordering; and 2) as the $(n - 1)$d orbitals begin to fill in the first transition series, the increasing nuclear charge stabilizes the $(n - 1)$d orbitals relative to the ns orbitals. This happens because the $(n - 1)$d orbitals are not outermost orbitals and are therefore not effectively shielded from the increasing nuclear charge by the ns orbitals.

8.35   The ionization energy (IE) of an atom or ion is the energy required to remove an electron from the atom or ion in the gaseous state. The ionization energy is always positive because removing an electron always takes energy. The energy required to remove the first electron is called the first ionization energy (IE_1). The energy required to remove the second electron is called the second ionization energy (IE_2). The second IE is always greater than the first IE.

8.37   Exceptions occur with elements Be, Mg, and Ca in group 2A having a higher first ionization energy than elements B, Al, and Ga in group 3A. This exception is caused by the change in going from the s block to the p block. The result is that the electrons in the s orbital shield the electron in the p orbital from nuclear charge making it easier to remove.

Another exception occurs with N, P, and As in group 5A having a higher first ionization energy than O, S, and Se in group 6A. This exception is caused by the repulsion between electrons when they must occupy the same orbital. Group 5A has 3 p electrons while group 6A has 4 p electrons. In the group 5A elements the p orbitals are half-filled, which makes the configuration particularly stable. The fourth group 6A electron must pair with another electron making it easier to remove.

8.39   The electron affinity (EA) of an atom or ion is the energy change associated with the gaining of an electron by the atom in the gaseous state. The electron affinity is usually—though not always—negative because an atom or ion usually releases energy when it gains an electron. The trends in electron affinity are not as regular as trends in other properties. For main-group elements, electron affinity generally becomes more negative as you move to the right across a row in the periodic table. There is not a corresponding trend in electron affinity going down a column.

8.41   (a)   The reactions of the alkali metals with halogens result in the formation of metal halides.
$$2\,M(s) + X_2 \rightarrow 2\,MX(s)$$

(b)   Alkali metals react with water to form the dissolved alkali metal ion, the hydroxide ion, and hydrogen gas.
$$2\,M(s) + 2\,H_2O(l) \rightarrow 2\,M^+(aq) + 2\,OH^-(aq) + H_2(g)$$

Problems by Topic

Electron Configurations

8.43   (a)   Si   Silicon has 14 electrons. Distribute two of these into the 1s orbital, two into the 2s orbital, six into the 2p orbital, two into the 3s orbital, and two into the 3p orbital. $1s^2 2s^2 2p^6 3s^2 3p^2$

(b)   O   Oxygen has 8 electrons. Distribute two of these into the 1s orbital, two into the 2s orbital, and four into the 2p orbital. $1s^2 2s^2 2p^4$

(c) K Potassium has 19 electrons. Distribute two of these into the 1s orbital, two into the 2s orbital, six into the 2p orbital, two into the 3s orbital, six into the 3p orbital, and one into the 4s orbital. $1s^2 2s^2 2p^6 3s^2 3p^6 4s^1$

(d) Ne Neon has 10 electrons. Distribute two of these into the 1s orbital, two into the 2s orbital, and six into the 2p orbital. $1s^2 2s^2 2p^6$

8.45 (a) N Nitrogen has 7 electrons and has the electron configuration $1s^2 2s^2 2p^3$. Draw a box for each orbital, putting the lowest energy orbital (1s) on the far left and proceeding to orbitals of higher energy to the right. Distribute the 7 electrons into the boxes representing the orbitals, allowing a maximum of two electrons per orbital and remembering Hund's rule. You can see from the diagram that nitrogen has 3 unpaired electrons.

$$\boxed{\downarrow\uparrow} \quad \boxed{\downarrow\uparrow} \quad \boxed{\uparrow\,|\,\uparrow\,|\,\uparrow}$$
$$1s \qquad\quad 2s \qquad\quad 2p$$

(b) F Fluorine has 9 electrons and has the electron configuration $1s^2 2s^2 2p^5$. Draw a box for each orbital, putting the lowest energy orbital (1s) on the far left and proceeding to orbitals of higher energy to the right. Distribute the 9 electrons into the boxes representing the orbitals, allowing a maximum of two electrons per orbital and remembering Hund's rule. You can see from the diagram that fluorine has 1 unpaired electron.

$$\boxed{\downarrow\uparrow} \quad \boxed{\downarrow\uparrow} \quad \boxed{\downarrow\uparrow\,|\,\downarrow\uparrow\,|\,\uparrow}$$
$$1s \qquad\quad 2s \qquad\quad 2p$$

(c) Mg Magnesium has 12 electrons and has the electron configuration $1s^2 2s^2 2p^6 3s^2$. Draw a box for each orbital, putting the lowest energy orbital (1s) on the far left and proceeding to orbitals of higher energy to the right. Distribute the 12 electrons into the boxes representing the orbitals, allowing a maximum of two electrons per orbital and remembering Hund's rule. You can see from the diagram that magnesium has no unpaired electrons.

$$\boxed{\downarrow\uparrow} \quad \boxed{\downarrow\uparrow} \quad \boxed{\downarrow\uparrow\,|\,\downarrow\uparrow\,|\,\downarrow\uparrow} \quad \boxed{\downarrow\uparrow}$$
$$1s \qquad\quad 2s \qquad\quad 2p \qquad\quad 3s$$

(d) Al Aluminum has 13 electrons and has the electron configuration $1s^2 2s^2 2p^6 3s^2 3p^1$. Draw a box for each orbital, putting the lowest energy orbital (1s) on the far left and proceeding to orbitals of higher energy to the right. Distribute the 13 electrons into the boxes representing the orbitals, allowing a maximum of two electrons per orbital and remembering Hund's rule. You can see from the diagram that aluminum has 1 unpaired electron.

$$\boxed{\downarrow\uparrow} \quad \boxed{\downarrow\uparrow} \quad \boxed{\downarrow\uparrow\,|\,\downarrow\uparrow\,|\,\downarrow\uparrow} \quad \boxed{\downarrow\uparrow} \quad \boxed{\uparrow\,|\,\,|\,}$$
$$1s \qquad\quad 2s \qquad\quad 2p \qquad\quad 3s \qquad\quad 3p$$

8.47 (a) P The atomic number of P is 15. The noble gas that precedes P in the periodic table is neon, so the inner electron configuration is [Ne]. Obtain the outer electron configuration by tracing the elements between Ne and P and assigning electrons to the appropriate orbitals. Begin with [Ne]. Because P is in row 3, add two 3s electrons. Next add three 3p electrons as you trace across the p block to P, which is in the third column of the p block.

P $[Ne]3s^2 3p^3$

(b) Ge The atomic number of Ge is 32. The noble gas that precedes Ge in the periodic table is argon, so the inner electron configuration is [Ar]. Obtain the outer electron configuration by tracing the elements between Ar and Ge and assigning electrons to the appropriate orbitals. Begin with [Ar]. Because Ge is in row 4, add two 4s electrons. Next, add ten 3d electrons as you trace across the d block. Finally add two 4p electrons as you trace across the p block to Ge, which is in the second column of the p block.

Ge $[Ar]4s^2 3d^{10} 4p^2$

(c) Zr The atomic number of Zr is 40. The noble gas that precedes Zr in the periodic table is krypton, so the inner electron configuration is [Kr]. Obtain the outer electron configuration by tracing the elements between Kr and Zr and assigning electrons to the appropriate orbitals.

Begin with [Kr]. Because Zr is in row 5, add two 5s electrons. Next, add two 4d electrons as you trace across the d block to Zr, which is in the second column.

$$Zr\ [Kr]5s^2 4d^2$$

(d) I   The atomic number of I is 53. The noble gas that precedes I in the periodic table is krypton, so the inner electron configuration is [Kr]. Obtain the outer electron configuration by tracing the elements between Kr and I and assigning electrons to the appropriate orbitals. Begin with [Kr]. Because I is in row 5, add two 5s electrons. Next, add ten 4d electrons as you trace across the d block. Finally add five 5p electrons as you trace across the p block to I which is in the fifth column of the p block.

$$I\ [Kr]5s^2 4d^{10} 5p^5$$

8.49   (a)   Li is in period 2, and the first column in the s block so Li has one 2s electron.

(b)   Cu is in period 4, and the ninth column in the d block (n − 1) so Cu should have nine 3d electrons, however, it is one of our exceptions, so it has ten 3d electrons.

(c)   Br is in period 4, and the fifth column of the p block, so Br has five 4p electrons.

(d)   Zr is in period 5, and the second column of the d block (n − 1), so Zr has two 4d electrons.

8.51   (a)   In period 4, an element with five valence electrons could be V or As.

(b)   In period 4, an element with four 4p electrons would be in the fourth column of the p block, and is Se.

(c)   In period 4, an element with three 3d electrons would be in the third column of the d block (n − 1) and is V.

(d)   In period 4, an element with a complete outer shell would be in the sixth column of the p block and is Kr.

Valence Electrons and Simple Chemical Behavior form the Periodic Table

8.53   (a)   Ba is in column 2A, so it has two valence electrons.

(b)   Cs is in column 1A, so it has one valence electron.

(c)   Ni is in column 8 of the d block, so it has 10 valence electrons (8 from the d block and 2 from the s block).

(d)   S is in column 6A, so it has six valence electrons.

8.55   (a)   The outer electron configuration ns^2 would belong to a reactive metal in the alkaline earth family.

(b)   The outer electron configuration $ns^2 np^6$ would belong to an unreactive nonmetal in the noble gas family.

(c)   The outer electron configuration $ns^2 np^5$ would belong to a reactive nonmetal in the halogen family.

(d)   The outer electron configuration $ns^2 np^2$ would belong to an element in the carbon family. If $n = 2$, the element is a nonmetal, if n $n = 5$ or 6, the element is a metal.

Effective Nuclear Charge and Atomic Radius

8.57   The valence electrons in nitrogen would experience a greater effective nuclear charge. Be has four protons and N has seven protons. Both atoms have two core electrons that predominately contribute to the shielding, while the valence electrons will contribute a slight shielding effect. So, Be has an effective nuclear charge of slightly more than 2+ and N has an effective nuclear charge of slightly more than 5+.

8.59   (a)   K(19) [Ar]$4s^1$ $Z_{eff} = Z -$ core electrons $= 19 - 18 = 1+$

(b)   Ca(20) [Ar]$4s^2$ $Z_{eff} = Z -$ core electrons $= 20 - 18 = 2+$

(c)   O(8) [He]$2s^2 2p^4$ Z_{eff} = Z – core electrons = 8 – 2 = 6+

(d)   C(6) [He]$2s^2 2p^2$ Z_{eff} = Z – core electrons = 6 – 2 = 4+

8.61   (a)   Al or In   In atoms are larger than Al atoms because as you trace the path between Al and In on the periodic table you move down a column. Atomic size increases as you move down a column because the outermost electrons occupy orbitals with a higher principal quantum number that are therefore larger, resulting in a larger atom.

        (b)   Si or N   Si atoms are larger than N atoms because as you trace the path between N and Si on the periodic table you move down a column (atomic size increases) and then to the left across a period (atomic size increases). These effects add together for an overall increase.

        (c)   P or Pb   Pb atoms are larger than P atoms because as you trace the path between P and Pb on the periodic table you move down a column (atomic size increases) and then to the left across a period (atomic size increases). These effects add together for an overall increase.

        (d)   C or F   C atoms are larger than F atoms because as you trace the path between C and F on the periodic table you move to the right within the same period. As you move to the right across a period, the effective nuclear charge experienced by the outermost electrons increase, which results in a smaller size.

8.63   Ca, Rb, S, Si, Ge, F   F is above and to the right of the other elements, so we start with F as the smallest atom. As you trace a path from F to S you move to the left (size increases) and down (size increases), next you move left from S to Si (size increases), then down to Ge (size increases), next move to the left to Ca (size increases), and then to the left and down to Rb (size increases). So, in order of increasing atomic radii F < S < Si < Ge < Ca < Rb.

Ionic Electron Configurations, Ionic Radii, Magnetic Properties, and Ionization Energy

8.65   (a) O^{2-} Begin by writing the electron configuration of the neutral atom.
                O $1s^2 2s^2 2p^4$
                Since this ion has a 2 – charge, add two electrons to write the electron configuration of the ion.
                O^{2-} $1s^2 2s^2 2p^6$ This is isoelectronic with Ar.

        (b) Br^- Begin by writing the electron configuration of the neutral atom.
                Br   [Ar]$4s^2 3d^{10} 4p^5$
                Since this ion has a 1 – charge, add one electron to write the electron configuration of the ion.
                Br^- [Ar]$4s^2 3d^{10} 4p^6$ This is isoelectronic with Kr.

        (c) Sr^{2+} Begin by writing the electron configuration of the neutral atom.
                Sr   [Kr]$5s^2$
                Since this ion has a 2+ charge, remove two electrons to write the electron configuration of the ion.
                Sr^{2+} [Kr]

        (d) Co^{3+} Begin by writing the electron configuration of the neutral atom.
                Co   [Ar]$4s^2 3d^7$
                Since this ion has a 3+ charge, remove three electrons to write the electron configuration of the ion. Since it is a transition metal, remove the electrons from the 4s orbital before removing electrons from the 3d orbitals.
                Co^{3+} [Ar]$4s^0 3d^6$

        (e) Cu^{2+} Begin by writing the electron configuration of the neutral atom. Remember, Cu is one of our exceptions.
                Cu   [Ar]$4s^1 3d^{10}$

Since this ion has a 2+ charge, remove two electrons to write the electron configuration of the ion. Since it is a transition metal, remove the electrons from the $4s$ orbital before removing electrons from the $3d$ orbitals.
Cu^{2+} $[Ar]4s^03d^9$

8.67   (a) V^{5+} Begin by writing the electron configuration of the neutral atom.
V $[Ar]4s^23d^3$
Since this ion has a 5+ charge, remove five electrons to write the electron configuration of the ion. Since it is a transition metal, remove the electrons from the $4s$ orbital before removing electrons from the $3d$ orbitals.
V^{5+} $[Ar]4s^03d^0 = [Ne]3s^23p^6$
[Ne]   ↓↑   ↓↑ ↓↑ ↓↑
3            $3p$
V^{5+} is diamagnetic.

(b) Cr^{3+} Begin by writing the electron configuration of the neutral atom. Remember, Cr is one of our exceptions.
Cr $[Ar]4s^13d^5$
Since this ion has a 3+ charge, remove three electrons to write the electron configuration of the ion. Since it is a transition metal, remove the electrons from the $4s$ orbital before removing electrons from the $3d$ orbitals.
Cr^{3+} $[Ar]4s^03d^3$
[Ar]   ☐   ↑ ↑ ↑ ☐ ☐
4s   3d
Cr^{3+} is paramagnetic.

(c) Ni^{2+} Begin by writing the electron configuration of the neutral atom.
Ni $[Ar]4s^23d^8$
Since this ion has a 2+ charge, remove two electrons to write the electron configuration of the ion. Since it is a transition metal, remove the electrons from the $4s$ orbital before removing electrons from the $3d$ orbitals.
Ni^{2+} $[Ar]4s^03d^8$
[Ar]   ☐   ↓↑ ↓↑ ↓↑ ↑ ↑
4s   3d
Ni^{2+} is paramagnetic.

(d) Fe^{3+} Begin by writing the electron configuration of the neutral atom.
Fe $[Ar]4s^23d^6$
Since this ion has a 3+ charge, remove three electrons to write the electron configuration of the ion. Since it is a transition metal, remove the electrons from the 4s orbital before removing electrons from the 3d orbitals.
Fe^{3+} $[Ar]4s^03d^5$
[Ar]   ☐   ↑ ↑ ↑ ↑ ↑
4s   3d
Fe^{3+} is paramagnetic.

8.69   (a)   Li or Li^+ A Li atom is larger than Li^+ because cations are smaller than the atoms from which they are formed.

(b) I^- or Cs^+ An I^- ion is larger than a Cs^+ ion because, although they are isoelectronic, I^- has two fewer protons than Cs^+, resulting in a lesser pull on the electrons and therefore a larger radius.

(c)   Cr or Cr^{3+} A Cr atom is larger than Cr^{3+} because cations are smaller than the atoms from which they are formed.

(d)   O or O^{2-} An O^{2-} ion is larger than an O atom because anions are larger than the atoms from which they are formed.

8.71   Since all the species are isoelectronic, the radius will depend on the number of protons in each species. The fewer the protons the larger the radius.
F: Z = 9; Ne: Z = 10; O: Z = 8; Mg: Z = 12; Na: Z = 11
So: $O^{2-} > F^- > Ne > Na^+ > Mg^{2+}$

8.73   (a)   Br or Bi   Br has a higher ionization energy than Bi because, as you trace the path between Br and Bi on the periodic table, you move down a column (ionization energy decreases) and then to the left across a period (ionization energy decreases). These effects sum together for an overall decrease.

        (b)   Na or Rb   Na has a higher ionization energy than Rb because, as you trace a path between Na and Rb on the periodic table, you move down a column. Ionization energy decreases as you go down a column because of the increasing size of orbitals with increasing n.

        (c)   As or At   Based on periodic trends alone, it is impossible to tell which has a higher ionization energy because as you trace the path between As and At you go to the right across a period (ionization energy increases) and then down a column (ionization energy decreases). These effects tend to oppose each other, and it is not obvious which will dominate.

        (d)   P or Sn   P has a higher ionization energy than Sn because as you trace the path between P and Sn on the periodic table you move down a column (ionization energy decreases) and then to the left across a period (ionization energy decreases). These effects sum together for an overall decrease.

8.75   Since ionization energy increases as you move to the right across a period and increases as you move up a column, the element with the smallest first ionization energy would be the element farthest to the left and lowest down on the periodic table. So, In has the smallest ionization energy; as you trace a path to the right and up on the periodic table, the next element reached is Si; continuing up and to the right you reach N; and then continuing to the right you reach F. So, in the order of increasing first ionization energy the elements are In < Si < N < F.

8.77   The jump in ionization energy occurs when you change from removing a valence electron to removing a core electron. To determine where this jump occurs you need to look at the electron configuration of the atom.

        (a)   Be $1s^2 2s^2$ The first and second ionization energies involve removing $2s$ electrons, while the third ionization energy removes a core electron, so the jump will occur between the second and third ionization energies.

        (b)   N $1s^2 2s^2 2p^3$ The first five ionization energies involve removing the $2p$ and $2s$ electrons, while the sixth ionization energy removes a core electron, so the jump will occur between the fifth and sixth ionization energies.

        (c)   O $1s^2 2s^2 2p^4$ The first six ionization energies involve removing the $2p$ and $2s$ electrons, while the seventh ionization energy removes a core electron, so the jump will occur between the sixth and seventh ionization energies.

        (d)   Li $1s^2 2s^1$ The first ionization energy involves removing a $2s$ electron, while the second ionization energy removes a core electron, so the jump will occur between the first and second ionization energies.

Electron Affinities and Metallic Character

8.79   (a)   Na or Rb   Na has a more negative electron affinity than Rb. In column 1A electron affinity becomes less negative as you go down the column.

        (b)   B or S   S has a more negative electron affinity than B. As you trace from B to S in the periodic table you move to the right, which shows the value of the electron affinity becoming more negative. Also, as you move from period 2 to period 3 the value of the electron

affinity becomes more negative. Both of these trends sum together for the value of the electron affinity to become more negative.

(c)   C or N   C has the more negative electron affinity. As you trace from C to N across the periodic table you would normally expect N to have the more negative electron affinity. However, N has a half-filled p sublevel, which lends it extra stability, therefore it is harder to add an electron.

(d)   Li or F   F has the more negative electron affinity. As you trace from Li to F on the periodic table you move to the right in the period. As you go to the right across a period the value of the electron affinity generally becomes more negative.

8.81   (a)   Sr or Sb   Sr is more metallic than Sb because as we trace the path between Sr and Sb on the periodic table we move to the right within the same period. Metallic character decreases as you go to the right.

(b)   As or Bi   Bi is more metallic because as we trace a path between As and Bi on the periodic table we move down a column in the same family (metallic character increases).

(c)   Cl or O   Based on periodic trends alone, we cannot tell which is more metallic because as we trace the path between O and Cl we go to the right across a period (metallic character decreases) and then down a column (metallic character increases). These effects tend to oppose each other and it is not easy to tell which will predominate.

(d)   S or As   As is more metallic than S because as we trace the path between S and As on the periodic table we move down a column (metallic character increases) and then to the left across a period (metallic character increases). These effects add together for an overall increase.

8.83   The order of increasing metallic character is S < Se < Sb < In < Ba < Fr.
Metallic character decreases as you move left to right across a period and decreases as you move up a column, therefore, the element with the least metallic character will be to the top right of the periodic table. So, of these elements, S has the least metallic character. As you move down the column the next element is Se; as you continue down and then to the right you reach Sb; continuing to the right goes to In; going down the column and then to the right comes to Ba; and then down the column and to the right is Fr.

8.85   Alkaline earth metals react with halogens to form metal halides. Write the formulas for the reactants and the metal halide product.
$$Sr(s) + I_2(g) \rightarrow SrI_2(s)$$

8.87   Alkali metals react with water to form the dissolved metal ion, the hydroxide ion, and hydrogen gas. Write the skeletal equation including each of these and then balance it.
$$Li(s) + H_2O(l) \rightarrow Li^+(aq) + OH^-(aq) + H_2(g)$$
$$2\,Li(s) + 2\,H_2O(l) \rightarrow 2\,Li^+(aq) + 2\,OH^-(aq) + H_2(g)$$

8.89   The halogens react with hydrogen to form hydrogen halides. Write the skeletal reaction with each of the halogen and hydrogen as the reactants and the hydrogen halide compound as the product and balance the equation.
$$H_2(g) + Br_2(g) \rightarrow HBr(g)$$
$$H_2(g) + Br_2(g) \rightarrow 2\,HBr(g)$$

Cumulative Problems

8.91   Br: $1s^2 2s^2 2p^6 3s^2 3p^6 4s^2 3d^{10} 4p^5$
Kr: $1s^2 2s^2 2p^6 3s^2 3p^6 4s^2 3d^{10} 4p^6$
Krypton has a completely filled p sublevel giving it chemical stability. Bromine needs one electron to achieve a completely filled p sublevel and therefore has a highly negative electron affinity. It therefore easily takes on an electron and is reduced to the bromide ion, giving it the added stability of the filled p sublevel.

8.93   Write the electron configuration of vanadium.
        V: [Ar] $4s^2 3d^3$
        Since this ion has a 3+ charge, remove three electrons to write the electron configuration of the ion. Since it is a transition metal, remove the electrons from the $4s$ orbital before removing electrons from the $3d$ orbitals.
        V^{3+}: [Ar] $4s^0 3d^2$
        Both vanadium and the V^{3+} ion have unpaired electrons and are paramagnetic.

8.95   Since K^+ has a 1+ charge you would need a cation with a similar size and a 1+ charge. Looking at the ions in the same family, Na^+ would be too small and Rb^+ would be too large. If we then consider Ar^+ and Ca^+ we would have ions of similar size and charge. Between these two Ca^+ would be the easier to achieve because the first ionization energy of Ca is similar to that of K, while the first ionization energy of Ar is much larger. However, the second ionization energy of Ca is relatively low, making it easy to lose the second electron.

8.97   C has an outer shell electron configuration of $ns^2 np^2$; based on this you would expect Si and Ge, which are in the same family, to be most like carbon. Ionization energies for both Si and Ge are similar and tend to be slightly lower than C, but all are intermediate in the range of first ionization energies. The electron affinities of Si and Ge are close to that of C.

8.99   (a)   N: [He]$2s^2 2p^3$ Mg: [Ne]$3s^2$ O: [He]$2s^2 2p^4$
               F: [He]$2s^2 2p^5$ Al: [Ne]$3s\ 3p^1$

        (b)   Mg > Al > N > O > F

        (c)   Al < Mg < O < N < F   (from the table)

        (d)   Mg and Al would have the largest radius because they are in period $n = 3$; Al is smaller than Mg because radius decreases as you move to the right across the period. F is smaller than O, and O is smaller than N because as you move to the right across the period radius decreases.

               The first ionization energy of Al is smaller than the first ionization energy of Mg because Al loses the electron from the $3p$ orbital, which is shielded by the electrons in the $3s$ orbital; while Mg loses the electron from the filled $3s$
               energy of O is lower than the first ionization energy of N because N has a half-filled $2p$ orbitals, which adds extra stability, thus making it harder to remove the electron. The fourth electron in the O $2p$ orbitals experiences added electron-electron repulsion because it must pair with another electron in the same $2p$ orbital, thus making it easier to remove.

8.101   As you move to the right across a row in the periodic table for the main-group elements the effective nuclear charge (Z_{eff}) experienced by the electrons in the outermost principal energy level increases, resulting in a stronger attraction between the outermost electrons and the nucleus, and therefore a smaller atomic radii.

        Across the row of transition elements the number of electrons in the outermost principal energy level (highest n value) is nearly constant. As another proton is added to the nucleus with each successive element, another electron is added, but that electron goes into an $n_{highest} - 1$ orbital (a core level). The number of outermost electrons stays constant and they experience a roughly constant effective nuclear charge, keeping the radius approximately constant after the first couple of elements in the series.

8.103   The noble gases all have a filled outer quantum level, very high first ionization energies, and positive values for the electron affinity and are thus particularly unreactive. The lighter noble gases will not form any compounds because the ionization energies of He and Ne are both over 2000 kJ/mol. Since ionization energy decreases as you move down a column we find that the heavier noble gases, Ar, Kr, and Xe do form some compounds. They have ionization energies that are close to the ionization energy of H and can thus be forced to lose an electron.

8.105   Group 6A: ns^2np^4 Group 7A: ns^2np^5

The electron affinity of the group 7A elements are more negative than the group 6A elements in the same period because group 7A requires only one electron to achieve the noble gas configuration ns^2np^6, while the group 6A elements require two electrons. Adding one electron to the group 6A element will not give them any added stability and leads to extra electron-electron repulsions, so the value of the electron affinity is less negative than that for group 7A.

8.107 $35 = Br = [Ar]4s^23d^{10}4p^5$ $53 = I = [Kr]5s^24d^{10}5p^5$

Br and I are both halogens with an outermost electron configuration of ns^2np^5; the next element with the same outermost electron configuration is 85, At.

8.109   (a) $10 - 2 = 8 \rightarrow$ O; $12 - 2 = 10 \rightarrow$ Ne; $58 - 5 = 53 \rightarrow$ I; $11 - 2 = 9 \rightarrow$ F; $7 - 2 = 5 \rightarrow$ B; $44 - 5 = 39 \rightarrow$ Y; $63 - 6 = 57 \rightarrow$ La; $66 - 6 = 60 \rightarrow$ Nd   One If by Land

(b) $9 - 2 = 7 \rightarrow$ N; $99 - 7 = 92 \rightarrow$ U; $30 - 4 = 26 \rightarrow$ Fe; $95 - 7 = 88 \rightarrow$ Ra; $19 - 3 = 16 \rightarrow$ S $47 - 5 = 42 \rightarrow$ Mo; $79 - 6 = 73 \rightarrow$ Ta   (backwards) Atoms Are Fun

8.111   **Given:** r = 100.00 pm, q_{proton} = 1.60218×10^{-19} C, $q_{electron}$ = $- 1.60218 \times 10^{-19}$ C

Find: IE in kJ/mol and λ of ionization

Conceptual Plan: r, q_{proton}, $q_{electron}$, $\rightarrow$ E_{atom} $\rightarrow$ E_{mol} and then E_{atom} $\rightarrow$ λ

$$E = \frac{1}{4\pi\epsilon_0}\frac{q_p q_e}{r} \quad \frac{1000 J}{kJ} \quad \frac{6.022 \times 0^{23} atom}{mol} \qquad \lambda = \frac{hc}{E}$$

Solution: $E = \dfrac{1}{(4)(3.141)\left(8.85 \times 10^{-12} \frac{C^2}{J\,m}\right)} \times \dfrac{(1.602 \times 10^{-19} C)(- 1.602 \times 10^{-19} C)}{(100.00\,pm)\left(\frac{1\,m}{1 \times 10^{12}\,pm}\right)} = -2.308 \times 10^{-18}$ J/atom

-2.308×10^{-18} J/ atom $\times \dfrac{6.022 \times 10\ atom}{mol} \times \dfrac{kJ}{(1000 J)} = -1.39 \times 10^3$ kJ/ mol

IE = $0 - (-1.39 \times 10^3$ kJ/mol$) = 1.39 \times 10^3$ kJ/mol

$$\lambda = \frac{(6.626 \times 10^{-34} J\,s)(3.00 \times 10^8\,m/s)\left(\frac{1 \times 10^9\,nm}{m}\right)}{(2.308 \times 10^{-18}\,J)} = 86.1\ nm$$

Check: The units of the answer (kJ/mol) are correct. The magnitude of the answer is reasonable since the value is positive and energy must be added to the atom to remove the electron. The units of the wavelength (nm) are correct and the magnitude is reasonable based on the ionization energy.

Challenge Problems

8.113   (a)   Using Excel, make a table of radius, atomic number, and density. Using xy scatter, make a chart of radius vs. density. With an exponential trendline, estimate the density of argon and xenon. Also, make a chart of atomic number vs. density. With a linear trendline, estimate the density of argon and xenon.

element	radius(pm)	atomic number	density
He	32	2	0.18
Ne	70	10	0.90
Ar	98	18	
Kr	112	36	3.75
Xe	130	54	
Rn		86	9.73
		118	

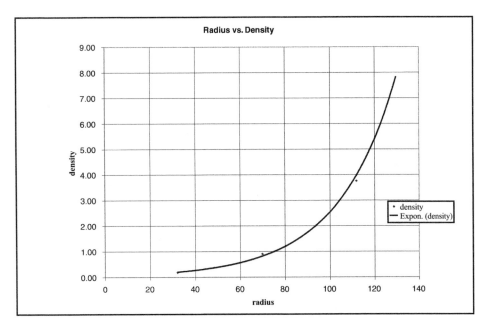

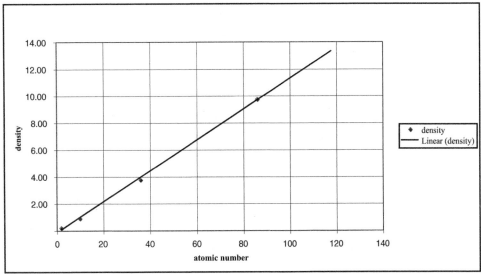

From the radius vs. density chart Ar has a density of ~ 2 g/L and Xe has a density of ~ 7.7 g/L. From the atomic number vs. density chart Ar has a density of ~1.8 g/L and Xe has a density of ~6 g/L.

(b)   Using the chart of atomic number vs. density, element 118 would be predicted to have a density of ~ 13 g/L.

(c)   **Given:** Ne: M = 20.18 g/mol; r = 70 pm   **Find:** mass of neon; d neon
        Conceptual Plan: M $\rightarrow$ m_{atom} and then r $\rightarrow$ vol_{atom} and then $\rightarrow$ d

$$\frac{6.022 \times 10^{23} \text{atoms}}{\text{mol}} \qquad V = \frac{4}{3}\pi r^3 \qquad d = \frac{\text{mass}}{\text{vol}}$$

Solution: $\dfrac{20.18 \text{ g}}{\cancel{\text{mol}}} \times \dfrac{\cancel{\text{mol}}}{6.022 \times 10^{23} \text{ atoms}} = 3.35 \times 10^{-23} \text{ g/atom}$

$V = \dfrac{4}{3} \times 3.14 \times (70 \cancel{\text{ pm}})^3 \times \left(\dfrac{\cancel{\text{m}}}{10^{12} \cancel{\text{ pm}}}\right)^3 \times \dfrac{\text{L}}{0.0010 \cancel{\text{ m}^3}} = 1.\underline{4}4 \times 10^{-27} \text{ L}$

$d = \dfrac{3.35 \times 10^{-23} \text{ g}}{1.\underline{4}4 \times 10^{-27} \text{ L}} = 2.\underline{3}3 \times 10^4 = 2.3 \times 10^4 \text{ g/L}$

Check: The units of the answer (g/L) are correct. This density is significantly larger than the actual density of neon gas. This suggests that a L of neon is composed of primarily empty space.

(d)   **Given:** Ne: M = 20.18 g/ mol, d = 0.90 g/L; Kr: M = 83.30 g/ mol, d = 3.75 g/L; Ar: M = 39.95 g/ mol
Find: d of argon in g/L
Conceptual Plan: d $\rightarrow$ mol/L $\rightarrow$ atoms/L for Kr and Ne and then atoms/L $\rightarrow$ mol/L $\rightarrow$ d for Ar

$$\text{mol} = \frac{\text{mass}}{\text{molar mass}} \quad \frac{6.022 \times 10^{23} \text{atoms}}{\text{mol}} \qquad\qquad \frac{\text{mol}}{6.022 \times 10^{23} \text{atoms}} \quad \frac{39.95 \text{ g}}{\text{mol}}$$

Solution: for Ne: $\dfrac{0.90 \text{ g}}{\text{L}} \times \dfrac{\text{mol}}{20.18 \text{ g}} \times \dfrac{6.022 \times 10^{23} \text{ atoms}}{\text{mol}} = 2.69 \times 10^{22} \text{ atoms/ L}$

for Kr: $\dfrac{3.75 \text{ g}}{\text{L}} \times \dfrac{\text{mol}}{83.80 \text{ g}} \times \dfrac{6.022 \times 10^{23} \text{ atoms}}{\text{mol}} = 2.69 \times 10^{22} \text{ atoms/ L}$

for Ar: $\dfrac{2.69 \times 10^{22} \text{ atoms}}{\text{L}} \times \dfrac{\text{mol}}{6.022 \times 10^{23} \text{ atoms}} \times \dfrac{39.95 \text{ g}}{\text{mol}} = 1.78 \text{ g/ L}$

This value is similar to the value calculated in part a. The value of the density calculated from the radius was 2 g/L and the value of the density calculated from the atomic number was 1.8 g/L.
Check: The units of the answer (g/L) are correct. The value of the answer agrees with published value.

8.115   The density increases as you move to the right across the first transition series. For the first transition series, the mass increases as you move to the right across the periodic table. However, the radius of the transition series elements stays nearly constant as you move to the right across the periodic table, thus the volume will remain nearly constant. Since density is mass/volume the density of the elements increases.

8.117   The longest wavelength would be associated with the lowest energy state next to the ground state of carbon, which has two unpaired electrons:
Ground state of carbon:

Longest wavelength: One of the p electrons flipped in its orbital, which requires the least amount of energy.

The next wavelength would be associated with the pairing of the two p electrons in the same orbital because this requires energy and raises the energy.

The next wavelength would be associated with the energy needed to promote one of the s electrons to a p orbital.

8.119   The element that would fill the $8s$ and $8p$ orbitals would have atomic number 168. The element is in the noble gas family and would have the properties of noble gases. It would have the electron configuration of $[118]8s^2 5g^{18} 6f^{14} 7d^{10} 8p^6$. The outer shell electron (highest n level) configuration would be $8s^2 8p^6$. The element would be relatively inert, have a first ionization energy less than 1037 kJ/mol (the first ionization energy of Rn), and have a positive electron affinity. It would be difficult to form compounds with most elements but would be able to form compounds with fluorine.

8.121   When you move down the column from Al to Ga, the size of the atom actually decreases because not much shielding is contributed by the 3d electrons in the Ga atom, while there is a large increase in the nuclear charge; therefore, the effective nuclear charge is greater for Ga than for Al, so the ionization energy does not decrease. As you go from In to Tl, the ionization energy actually increases because the 4f electrons do not contribute to the shielding of the outermost electrons and there is a large increase in the effective nuclear charge.

8.123   The second electron is added to an ion with a 1 – charge, so there is a large repulsive force that has to be overcome to add the second electron. Thus, it will require energy to add the second electron and the second electron affinity will have a positive value.

8.125   **Given:** Ra, Z = 88   **Find:** Z for next two alkaline earth metals

    Solution: The next element would lie in period 8, column 2A. The largest currently known element is 116 in period 7, column 6A. To reach period 8 column 2A you need to add 4 protons, and would have Z = 120.

    The alkaline earth metal following 120, would lie in period 9 column 2A. To reach this column, you need to add 18 g-block element protons, 10 d block element protons, 14 f block element protons, 6 p block element protons, and then 2 s block element protons. This would give Z = 170.

8.127   Francium would have an electron configuration of $[Rn]7s^1$; the atomic radius would be > 265 pm (atomic radius of Cs); the first ionization energy would be less than 376 kJ/mol; the density would be greater than 1.879 g/cm^3; and the melting would be less than 29°C.

    (a) $Fr + H_2O \rightarrow Fr^+(aq) + OH^-(aq) + H_2(g)$

    (b) $Fr + O_2(g) \rightarrow Fr_2O(s)$

    (c) $2Fr + Cl_2(g) \rightarrow FrCl(s)$

Conceptual Problems

8.129   If six electrons rather than eight electrons led to a stable configuration, the electron configuration of the stable configuration would be ns^2np^4.

    (a)   A noble gas would have the electron configuration ns^2np^4. This could correspond to the O atom.

    (b)   A reactive nonmetal would have one less electron than the stable configuration. This would have the electron configuration ns^2np^3. This could correspond to the N atom.

    (c)   A reactive metal would have one have one more electron than the stable configuration. This would have the electron configuration of ^{1}. This could correspond to the Li atom.

8.131   (a)   True: An electron in a 3s orbital is more shielded than an electron in a 2s orbital. This is true since there are more core electrons below a 3s orbital.

    (b)   True: An electron in a 3s orbital penetrates into the region occupied by the core electrons more than electrons in a 3p orbital. Examine Figure 8.5, the radial distribution functions for the 3s, 3p, and 3d orbitals. You will see that the 3s electrons penetrate more deeply than the 3p electrons and more than the 3d electrons.

    (c)   False: An electron in an orbital that penetrates closer to the nucleus will experience <u>less</u> shielding than an electron in an orbital that does not penetrate as far.

    (d)   True: An electron in an orbital that penetrates close to the nucleus will tend to experience a higher effective nuclear charge than one that does not. Since the orbital penetrates closer to the nucleus, the electron will experience less shielding and, therefore, a higher effective nuclear charge.

8.133   The 4s electrons in calcium have relatively low ionization energies (IE_1 = 590 kJ/mol; IE_2 = 1145 kJ/mol) because they are valence electrons. The energetic cost for calcium to lose a third electron is extraordinarily high because the next electron to be lost is a core electron. Similarly, the electron affinity of fluorine to gain one electron (- 328 kJ/mol) is highly exothermic because the added electron completes fluoride's valence shell. The gain of a second electron by the negatively charged fluoride anion would not be favorable. Therefore, we would expect calcium and fluoride to combine in a 1:2 ratio.

9   Chemical Bonding I: Lewis Theory

Review Questions

9.1   Bonding theories are central to chemistry because they explain how atoms bond together to form molecules. Bonding theories explain why some combinations of atoms are stable and others are not.

9.3   The three types of bonds are ionic bonds, which occur between metals and nonmetals and are characterized by the transfer of electrons; covalent bonds, which occur between nonmetals and are characterized by the sharing of electrons; and metallic bonds, which occur between metals and are characterized by electrons being pooled.

9.5   Bonds are formed when atoms attain a stable electron configuration. Since the stable configuration usually has eight electrons in the outermost shell; this is known as the octet rule.

9.7   In Lewis theory, we represent ionic bonding by moving electron dots from the metal to the nonmetal and then allowing the resultant ions to form a crystalline lattice composed of alternating cations and anions. The cation loses its valence electron(s) and is left with an octet in the previous principal energy level; the anion gains electron(s) to form an octet. The Lewis structure of the anion is usually written within brackets with the charge in the upper right-hand corner, outside the brackets. The positive and negative charges attract one another, resulting in the compound.

9.9   Lattice energy is the energy associated with forming a crystalline lattice of alternating cations and anions from the gaseous ions. Since the cations are positively charged and the anions are negatively charged there is a lowering of potential—as described by Coulomb's law—when the ions come together to form a lattice. That energy is emitted as heat when the lattice forms.

9.11   The Born–Haber cycle is a hypothetical series of steps that represents the formation of an ionic compound from its constituent elements. The steps are chosen so that the change in enthalpy of each step is known except for the last one, which is the lattice energy. In terms of the formation of NaCl, the steps are as follows:
Step 1: The formation of gaseous sodium from solid sodium (heat of sublimation of sodium)
Step 2: The formation of a chlorine atom from a chlorine molecule (bond energy of chlorine)
Step 3: The ionization of gaseous sodium (ionization energy of sodium)
Step 4: The addition of an electron to gaseous chlorine (the electron affinity of chlorine)
Step 5: The formation of the crystalline solid from the gaseous ions (the lattice energy)

The overall reaction is the formation of NaCl(s), so we can use Hess's law to determine the lattice energy.
$$\Delta H^{\circ}_f = \Delta H_{step\ 1} + \Delta H_{step\ 2} + \Delta H_{step\ 3} + \ H_{step\ 4} + \Delta H_{step\ 5}$$
$$\Delta H^{\circ}_f = \text{heat of sublimation} + \tfrac{1}{2} \text{ bond energy} + \text{ionization energy} + \text{electron affinity} + \text{lattice energy}$$
Since all the terms are known except the lattice energy, we can calculate the lattice energy.

9.13   We modeled ionic solids as a lattice of individual ions held together by coulombic forces, which are equal in all directions. To melt the solid, these forces must be overcome, which requires a significant amount of heat. Therefore, the model accounts for the high melting points of ionic solids.

9.15   A pair of electrons that is shared between two atoms is called a bonding pair, while a pair of electrons that is associated with only one atom—and therefore, not involved in bonding—is called a lone pair.

9.17   Generally, combinations of atoms that can satisfy the octet rule on each atom are stable, while those combinations that do not satisfy the octet rule are not stable.

9.19   Electronegativity is the ability of an atom to attract electrons to itself in a chemical bond. This results in a polar bond. Electronegativity generally increases across a period in the periodic table. And, electronegativity generally decreases down a column (group) in the periodic table. The most electronegative element is fluorine.

9.21   Percent ionic character is defined as the ratio of a bond's actual dipole moment to the dipole moment it would have if the electron were completely transferred from one atom to the other, multiplied by 100.

        A bond in which an electron is completely transferred from one atom to another would have 100% ionic character. However, no bond is 100% ionic. Percent ionic character generally increases as the electronegativity difference increases. In general, bonds with greater than 50% ionic character are referred to as ionic bonds.

9.23   To calculate the dipole moment we use $\mu = qr$:

$$\text{For 100 pm: } \mu = 1.6 \times 10^{-19}\ \cancel{C} \quad \diagdown \times \frac{\cancel{m}}{10^{12}\ \cancel{pm}} \times \frac{D}{3.34 \times 10^{-30}\ \cancel{C} \cdot m} = 4.8\ D$$

$$\text{For 200 pm: } \mu = 1.6 \times 10^{-19}\ \cancel{C} \times 200\ \cancel{pm} \times \frac{\cancel{m}}{10^{12}\ \cancel{pm}} \times \frac{D}{3.34 \times 10^{-30}\ \cancel{C} \cdot m} = 9.6\ D$$

9.25   The total number of electrons for a Lewis structure of a molecule is the sum of the valence electrons of each atom in the molecule.

        The total number of electrons for the Lewis structure of an ion is found by summing the number of valence electrons for each atom and then subtracting 1 electron for each positive charge or adding 1 electron for each negative charge.

9.27   In some cases we can write resonance structures that are not equivalent. One possible resonance structure may be somewhat better than another. In such cases the true structure may still be represented as an average of the resonance structures, but with the better resonance structure contributing more to the true structure. Multiple nonequivalent resonance structures may be weighted differently in their contributions to the true overall structure of a molecule.

9.29   The octet rule has some exceptions because not all atoms always have eight electrons surrounding them. The three major categories are 1) odd octets—electron species, molecules, or ions with an odd number of electron, for example, NO; 2) incomplete octets—molecules or ions with fewer than eight electrons around an atom, for example, BF_3; and 3) expanded octets—molecules or ions with more than eight electrons around an atom, for example, AsF_5.

9.31   The bond energy of a chemical bond is the energy required to break 1 mole of the bond in the gas phase. Since breaking bonds is endothermic and forming bonds is exothermic we can calculate the overall enthalpy change as a sum of the enthalpy changes associated with breaking the required bonds in the reactants and forming the required bonds in the products.

9.33   When metal atoms bond together to form a solid, each metal atom donates one or more electrons to an electron sea.

Problems by Topic

Valence Electrons and Dot Structures

9.35   N : $1s^2 2s^2 2p^3$ The electrons included in the Lewis structure are $2s^2 2p^3$.

9.37   (a)   Al: $1s^22s^22p^63s^23p^1$

$$\cdot\ Al\ \cdot$$

(b) Na^+: $1s^22s^22p^6$

$$Na^+$$

(c)   Cl: $1s^22s^22p^63s^23p^5$

$$\vdots\ Cl\ \cdot$$

(d) Cl^-: $1s^22s^22p^63s^23p^6$

$$\vdots\ Cl\ \vdots$$

Ionic Lewis Structures and Lattice Energy

9.39   (a)   NaF: Draw the Lewis structures for Na and F based on their valence electrons. Na: $3s^1$ F: $2s^22p^5$

$$Na\ \cdot\ \ \ \ \vdots\ F\ \cdot$$

Sodium must lose one electron and be left with the octet from the previous shell, while fluorine needs to gain one electron to get an octet.

$$Na^+\ \left[\ \vdots\ F\ \vdots\ \right]^-$$

(b)   CaO: Draw the Lewis structures for Ca and O based on their valence electrons. Ca: $4s^2$ O: $2s^22p^4$

$$Ca\vdots\ \ \ \ \vdots\ O\ \cdot$$

Calcium must lose two electrons and be left with two 1s electrons from the previous shell, while oxygen needs to gain two electrons to get an octet.

$$Ca^{2+}\ \left[\ \vdots\ O\ \vdots\ \right]^{2-}$$

(c) $SrBr_2$:   Draw the Lewis structures for Sr and Br based on their valence electrons. Sr: $5s^2$ Br: $4s^24p^5$

$$Sr\vdots\ \ \ \ \vdots\ Br\ \cdot$$

Strontium must lose two electrons and be left with the octet from the previous shell, while bromine needs to gain one electron to get an octet.

$$Sr^{2+}\ 2\left[\ \vdots\ Br\ \vdots\ \right]^-$$

(d) K_2O: Draw the Lewis structures for K and O based on their valence electrons. K: $4s^1$ O: $2s^22p^4$

$$K\ \cdot\ \ \ \ \vdots\ O\ \cdot$$

Potassium must lose one electron and be left with the octet from the previous shell, while oxygen needs to gain two electrons to get an octet.

$$2K^{+} \quad \left[:\overset{\bullet\bullet}{\underset{\bullet\bullet}{O}}: \right]^{2-}$$

9.41   (a)   Sr and Se: Draw the Lewis structures for Sr and Se based on their valence electrons.

Sr: $5s^2$ Se: $4s^2 4p^4$

$$Sr\,\vdots \quad :\overset{\bullet\bullet}{\underset{\bullet}{Se}}\, \bullet$$

Strontium must lose two electrons and be left with the octet from the previous shell, while selenium needs to gain two electrons to get an octet.

$$Sr^{2+} \quad \left[:\overset{\bullet\bullet}{\underset{\bullet\bullet}{Se}}: \right]^{2-}$$

Thus, we need one Sr^{2+} and one Se^{2-}. Write the formula with subscripts (if necessary) to indicate the number of atoms.

SrSe

(b)   Ba and Cl: Draw the Lewis structures for Ba and Cl based on their valence electrons.

Ba: $6s^2$ Cl: $3s^2 3p^5$

$$Ba\,\vdots \quad :\overset{\bullet\bullet}{\underset{\bullet\bullet}{Cl}}\, \bullet$$

Barium must lose two electrons and be left with the octet from the previous shell, while chlorine needs to gain one electron to get an octet.

$$Ba^{2+} \quad 2\left[:\overset{\bullet\bullet}{\underset{\bullet\bullet}{Cl}}: \right]^{-}$$

Thus, we need one Ba^{2+} and two Cl^{-}. Write the formula with subscripts (if necessary) to indicate the number of atoms.

$BaCl_2$

(c)   Na and S: Draw the Lewis structures for Na and S based on their valence electrons.

Na: $3s^1$ S: $3s^2 3p^4$

$$Na\, \bullet \quad :\overset{\bullet\bullet}{\underset{\bullet}{S}}\, \bullet$$

Sodium must lose one electron and be left with the octet from the previous shell, while sulfur needs to gain two electrons to get an octet.

$$2\,Na^{+} \quad \left[:\overset{\bullet\bullet}{\underset{\bullet\bullet}{S}}: \right]^{2-}$$

Thus, we need two Na^{+} and one S^{2-}. Write the formula with subscripts (if necessary) to indicate the number of atoms.

Na_2S

(d)   Al and O: Draw the Lewis structures for Al and O based on their valence electrons.

Al: $3s^2 3p^1$ O: $2s^2 2p^4$

$$\ddot{Al} \bullet \quad \vdots \ddot{O} \bullet$$

Aluminum must lose three electrons and be left with the octet from the previous shell, while oxygen needs to gain two electrons to get an octet.

$$2 \; Al^{3+} \quad 3 \left[\vdots \ddot{\underset{\displaystyle \cdot\cdot}{O}} \vdots \right]^{2-}$$

Thus, we need two Al^{3+} and three O^{2-} in order to lose and gain the same number of electrons. Write the formula with subscripts (if necessary) to indicate the number of atoms.

Al_2O_3

9.43   As the size of the alkaline metal ions increases down the column, so does the distance between the metal cation and the oxide anion. Therefore, the magnitude of the lattice energy of the oxides decreases, making the formation of the oxides less exothermic and the compounds less stable. Since the ions cannot get as close to each other, they therefore do not release as much energy.

9.45   Cesium is slightly larger than barium, but oxygen is slightly larger than fluorine, so we cannot use size to explain the difference in the lattice energy. However, the charge on cesium ion is 1+ and the charge on fluoride ion is 1−, while the charge on barium ion is 2+ and the charge on oxide ion is 2−. The coulombic equation states that the magnitude of the potential also depends on the product of the charges. Since the product of the charges for CsF = 1−, and the product of the charges for BaO = 4−, the stabilization for BaO relative to CsF should be about four times greater, which is what we see in its much more exothermic lattice energy.

9.47   **Given:** $\Delta H_f^\circ KCl = -436.5$ kJ/mol; $IE_1(K) = 419$ kJ/mol; $\Delta H_{sub}(K) = 89.0$ kJ/mol; $Cl_2(g)$ bond energy = 243 kJ/mol; EA(Cl) = − 349 kJ/mol **Find:** lattice energy

Conceptual Plan:

$$K(s)+1/2Cl_2(g) \xrightarrow{\Delta H_{sub}} K(g)+1/2Cl_2(g) \xrightarrow{IE_1} K^+(g)+1/2Cl_2(g) \xrightarrow{\text{bond energy}} K^+(g)+Cl(g) \xrightarrow{EA} K^+(g)+Cl^-(g) \xrightarrow{\text{lattice energy}} KCl(s)$$

$$\xrightarrow{\Delta H_f^\circ}$$

Solution: $\Delta H_f^\circ = \Delta H_{sub} + IE_1 + 1/2$ **bond energy** + EA + **lattice energy**

$$-436.5 \, \frac{kJ}{mol} = +89.0 \, \frac{kJ}{mol} + 419 \, \frac{kJ}{mol} + \frac{1}{2}(243) \, \frac{kJ}{mol} + (-349) \, \frac{kJ}{mol} + \text{lattice energy}$$

lattice energy = − 717 kJ/mol

Simple Covalent Lewis Structures, Electronegativity, and Bond Polarity

9.49   (a)   Hydrogen: Write the Lewis structure of each atom based on the number of valence electrons.

$$H \bullet \quad \bullet H$$

When the two hydrogen atoms share their electrons, they each get a duet, which is a stable configuration for hydrogen.

$$H \longrightarrow H$$

(b)   The halogens: Write the Lewis structure of each atom based on the number of valence electrons.

$$\vdots \ddot{X} \bullet \quad \bullet \ddot{X} \vdots$$

If the two halogens pair together they can each achieve an octet, which is a stable configuration. So, the halogens are predicted to exist as diatomic molecules.

$$\vdots \ddot{X} \longrightarrow \ddot{X} \vdots$$

(c)   Oxygen: Write the Lewis structure of each atom based on the number of valence electrons.

$$:\ddot{O}\cdot\ \cdot\ddot{O}:$$

In order to achieve a stable octet on each oxygen, the oxygen atoms will need to share two electron pairs. So, oxygen is predicted to exist as a diatomic molecule with a double bond.

$$:\ddot{O}=\ddot{O}:$$

(d)   Nitrogen: Write the Lewis structure of each atom based on the number of valence electrons.

$$\cdot\ddot{N}\cdot\ \ \cdot\ddot{N}\cdot$$

In order to achieve a stable octet on each nitrogen, the nitrogen atoms will need to share three electron pairs. So, nitrogen is predicted to exist as a diatomic molecule with a triple bond.

$$\overset{\bullet\bullet}{N}\equiv\overset{\bullet\bullet}{N}$$

9.51   (a)   PH$_3$:   Write the Lewis structure for each atom based on the number of valence electrons.

$$\cdot\overset{\bullet\bullet}{\underset{\bullet}{P}}\cdot\ \ \cdot H$$

Phosphorus will share an electron pair with each hydrogen in order to achieve a stable octet.

$$H-\overset{\bullet\bullet}{\underset{|}{P}}-H$$
$$H$$

(b)   SCl$_2$:   Write the Lewis structure for each atom based on the number of valence electrons.

$$:\overset{\bullet\bullet}{\underset{\bullet}{S}}\cdot\ \ :\overset{\bullet\bullet}{\underset{\bullet\bullet}{Cl}}\cdot$$

The sulfur will share an electron pair with each chlorine in order to achieve a stable octet.

$$:\overset{\bullet\bullet}{S}-\overset{\bullet\bullet}{\underset{\bullet\bullet}{Cl}}:$$
$$:\overset{}{\underset{\bullet\bullet}{Cl}}:$$

(c)   HI: Write the Lewis structure for each atom based on the number of valence electrons.

$$H\cdot\ \ \cdot\overset{\bullet\bullet}{\underset{\bullet\bullet}{I}}:$$

The iodine will share an electron pair with hydrogen in order to achieve a stable octet.

$$H-\overset{\bullet\bullet}{\underset{\bullet\bullet}{I}}:$$

(d)   CH$_4$:   Write the Lewis structure for each atom based on the number of valence electrons.

$$\cdot\overset{\bullet\bullet}{C}\cdot\ \ H\cdot$$

The carbon will share an electron pair with each hydrogen in order to achieve a stable octet.

9.53   (a)   SF$_2$:   Write the Lewis structure for each atom based on the number of valence electrons.

The sulfur will share an electron pair with each fluorine in order to achieve a stable octet.

(b)   SiH$_4$:   Write the Lewis structure for each atom based on the number of valence electrons.

The silicon will share an electron pair with each hydrogen in order to achieve a stable octet.

(c)   HCOOH Write the Lewis structure for each atom based on the number of valence electrons.

The carbon with share an electron pair with hydrogen, an electron pair with the interior oxygen and 2 electron pair with the terminal oxygen in order to achieve a stable octet. The terminal oxygen will share two electron pairs with carbon in order to achieve a stable octet. The interior oxygen with share an electron pair with carbon and an electron pair with hydrogen in order to achieve a stable octet.

(d)   CH$_3$SH Write the Lewis structure for each atom based on the number of valence electrons.

The carbon with share an electron pair with each hydrogen and an electron pair with sulfur in order to achieve a stable octet. The sulfur will share an electron pair with carbon and an electron pair with hydrogen in order to achieve a stable octet.

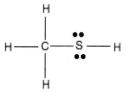

9.55   (a)   Br and Br: pure covalent   From Figure 9.8 we find the electronegativity of Br is 2.5. Since both atoms are the same, the electronegativity difference (ΔEN) = 0, and using Table 9.1 we classify this bond as pure covalent.

         (b)   C and Cl: polar covalent   From Figure 9.8 we find the electronegativity of C is 2.5 and Cl is 3.0. The electronegativity difference (ΔEN) is ΔEN = 3.0 – 2.5 = 0.5. Using Table 9.1 we classify this bond as polar covalent.

         (c)   C and S: pure covalent   From Figure 9.8 we find the electronegativity of C is 2.5 and S is 2.5. The electronegativity difference (ΔEN) is ΔEN = 2.5 – 2.5 = 0. Using Table 9.1 we classify this bond as pure covalent.

         (d)   Sr and O: ionic   From Figure 9.8 we find the electronegativity of Sr is 1.0 and O is 3.5. The electronegativity difference (ΔEN) is ΔEN = 3.5 – 1.0 = 2.5. Using Table 9.1 we classify this bond as ionic.

9.57   CO: Write the Lewis structure for each atom based on the number of valence electrons.

The carbon will share three electron pairs with oxygen in order to achieve a stable octet.
The oxygen atom is more electronegative than the carbon atom, so the oxygen will have a partial negative charge and the carbon will have a partial positive charge.

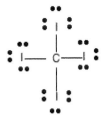

To estimate the percent ionic character, determine the difference in electronegativity between carbon and oxygen.
From Figure 9.8 we find the electronegativity of C is 2.5 and O is 3.5. The electronegativity difference (ΔEN) is ΔEN = 3.5 – 2.5 = 1.0.
From Figure 9.10, we can estimate a percent ionic character of 25%.

Covalent Lewis Structures, Resonance, and Formal Charge

9.59   (a)   CI₄: Write the correct skeletal structure for the molecule.

                          I
                          |
                    I—— C——I
                          |
                          I

                 Calculate the total number of electrons for the Lewis structure by summing the number of valence electrons of each atom in the molecule.
                     (number of valence e⁻ for C) + 4(number of valence e⁻ for I) = 4 + 4(7) = 32
                 Distribute the electrons among the atoms, giving octets to as many atoms as possible. Begin with the bonding electrons, then proceed to lone pairs on terminal atoms and finally to lone pairs on the central atom.

                 All 32 valence electrons are used.
                 If any atom lacks an octet, form double or triple bonds as necessary to give them octets.
                 All atoms have octets; the structure is complete.

(b)   N₂O: Write the correct skeletal structure for the molecule.
N is the less electronegative, so it is central.

$$N\!\!-\!\!\!-\!\! N\ \!\!-\!\!\!-\!\!O$$

Calculate the total number of electrons for the Lewis structure by summing the number of valence electrons of each atom in the molecule.

2(number of valence e^- for N) + (number of valence e^- for O) = 2(5) + 6 = 16

Distribute the electrons among the atoms, giving octets to as many atoms as possible. Begin with the bonding electrons, then proceed to lone pairs on terminal atoms and finally to lone pairs on the central atom.

All 16 valence electrons are used.
If any atom lacks an octet, form double or triple bonds as necessary.

All atoms have octets; the structure is complete.

(c)   SiH₄: Write the correct skeletal structure for the molecule.
H is always terminal, so Si is the central atom.

$$
\begin{array}{c}
\text{H}\\
|\\
\text{H}\!\!-\!\!\!-\!\text{Si}\ \!\!-\!\!\!-\!\text{H}\\
|\\
\text{H}
\end{array}
$$

Calculate the total number of electrons for the Lewis structure by summing the number of valence electrons of each atom in the molecule.

(number of valence e^- for Si) + 4(number of valence e^- for H) = 4 + 4(1) = 8

Distribute the electrons among the atoms, giving octets (or duets for H) to as many atoms as possible. Begin with the bonding electrons, then proceed to lone pairs on terminal atoms and finally to lone pairs on the central atom.

$$
\begin{array}{c}
\text{H}\\
|\\
\text{H}\!\!-\!\!\!-\!\text{Si}\ \!\!-\!\!\!-\!\text{H}\\
|\\
\text{H}
\end{array}
$$

All 8 valence electrons are used.
If any atom lacks an octet, form double or triple bonds as necessary to give them octets.
All atoms have octets; the structure is complete.

(d)   Cl₂CO: Write the correct skeletal structure for the molecule.
C is the least electronegative, so it is the central atom.

$$
\begin{array}{c}
\text{O}\\
\|\\
\text{Cl}\!\!-\!\!\!-\!\text{C}\ \!\!-\!\!\!-\!\text{Cl}
\end{array}
$$

Calculate the total number of electrons for the Lewis structure by summing the number of valence electrons of each atom in the molecule.

(number of valence e^- for C) + 2(number of valence e^- for Cl) + (number of valence e^- for O) = 4 + 2(7) + 6 = 24

Distribute the electrons among the atoms, giving octets to as many atoms as possible. Begin with the bonding electrons, then proceed to lone pairs on terminal atoms and finally to lone pairs on the central atom.

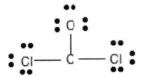

All 24 valence electrons are used.
If any atom lacks an octet, form double or triple bonds as necessary.

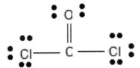

All atoms have octets; the structure is complete.

9.61   (a) N_2H_2:   Write the correct skeletal structure for the molecule.

$$H — N — N — H$$

Calculate the total number of electrons for the Lewis structure by summing the number of valence electrons of each atom in the molecule.

2(number of valence e^- for N) + 2(number of valence e^- for H) = 2(5) + 2(1) = 12

Distribute the electrons among the atoms, giving octets (or duets for H) to as many atoms as possible. Begin with the bonding electrons, then proceed to lone pairs on terminal atoms and finally to lone pairs on the central atom.

$$H — \overset{\bullet\bullet}{N} — \underset{\bullet\bullet}{\overset{\bullet\bullet}{N}} — H$$

All 12 valence electrons are used.
If any atom lacks an octet, form double or triple bonds as necessary.

$$H — \overset{\bullet\bullet}{N} = \overset{\bullet\bullet}{N} — H$$

All atoms have octets (duets for H); the structure is complete.

(b) N_2H_4:   Write the correct skeletal structure for the molecule.

$$
\begin{array}{ccc}
H & & H \\
\diagdown & & \diagup \\
& N — N & \\
\diagup & & \diagdown \\
H & & H
\end{array}
$$

Calculate the total number of electrons for the Lewis structure by summing the valence electrons of each atom in the molecule.

2(number of valence e^- for N) + 4(number of valence e^- for H) = 2(5) + 4(1) = 14

Distribute the electrons among the atoms, giving octets (or duets for H) to as many atoms as possible. Begin with the bonding electrons, then proceed to lone pairs on terminal atoms and finally to lone pairs on the central atom.

$$
\begin{array}{ccc}
H & & H \\
\diagdown & \overset{\bullet\bullet}{}\;\overset{\bullet\bullet}{} & \diagup \\
& N — N & \\
\diagup & & \diagdown \\
H & & H
\end{array}
$$

All 14 valence electrons are used.

If any atom lacks an octet, form double or triple bonds as necessary to give them octets. All atoms have octets (duets for H) structure is complete.

(c) C_2H_2:   Write the correct skeletal structure for the molecule.

$$H \longrightarrow C \longrightarrow C \longrightarrow H$$

Calculate the total number of electrons for the Lewis structure by summing the number of valence electrons of each atom in the molecule.

2(number of valence e⁻ for C) + 2(number of valence e⁻ for H) = 2(4) + 2(1) = 10

Distribute the electrons among the atoms, giving octets (or duets for H) to as many atoms as possible. Begin with the bonding electrons, then proceed to lone pairs on terminal atoms and finally to lone pairs on the central atom.

$$H \longrightarrow C \longrightarrow \overset{\bullet\bullet}{\underset{\bullet\bullet}{C}} \longrightarrow H$$

All 10 valence electrons are used.
If any atom lacks an octet, form double or triple bonds as necessary.

$$H \longrightarrow C \equiv C \longrightarrow H$$

All atoms have octets (duets for H); the structure is complete.

(d) C_2H_4:   Write the correct skeletal structure for the molecule.

Calculate the total number of electrons for the Lewis structure by summing the number of valence electrons of each atom in the molecule.

2(number of valence e⁻ for C) + 4(number of valence e⁻ for H) = 2(4) + 4(1) = 12

Distribute the electrons among the atoms, giving octets (or duets for H) to as many atoms as possible. Begin with the bonding electrons, then proceed to lone pairs on terminal atoms and finally to lone pairs on the central atom.

All 12 valence electrons are used.
If any atom lacks an octet, form double or triple bonds as necessary.

All atoms have octets (duets for H) structure is complete.

9.63   (a) SeO_2:   Write the correct skeletal structure for the molecule.
             Se is the less electronegative, so it is central.

$$O \longrightarrow Se \longrightarrow O$$

Calculate the total number of electrons for the Lewis structure by summing the number of valence electrons of each atom in the molecule.

(number of valence e⁻ for Se) + 2(number of valence e⁻ for O) = 6 + 2(6) = 18

Distribute the electrons among the atoms, giving octets to as many atoms as possible. Begin with the bonding electrons, then proceed to lone pairs on terminal atoms and finally to lone pairs on the central atom.

All 18 valence electrons are used.
If any atom lacks an octet, form double or triple bonds as necessary.

All atoms have octets; the structure is complete. However, the double bond can form from either oxygen atom, so there are two resonance forms.

Calculate the formal charge on each atom by finding the number of valence electrons and subtracting the number of lone pair electrons and one-half the number of bonding electrons.

number of valence electrons	6	6	6	6	6	6
- number of lone pair electrons	6	2	4	4	2	6
- 1/2(number of bonding electrons)	1	3	2	2	3	1
Formal charge	−1	+1	0	0	+1	−1

(b) CO_3^{2-}:   Write the correct skeletal structure for the ion.

Calculate the total number of electrons for the Lewis structure by summing the number of valence electrons of each atom in the ion and adding 2 for the 2 – charge.

  3(number of valence e⁻ for O) + (number of valence e⁻ for C) + 2 = 3(6) + 4 + 2 = 24

Distribute the electrons among the atoms, giving octets to as many atoms as possible. Begin with the bonding electrons, then proceed to lone pairs on terminal atoms and finally to lone pairs on the central atom.

All 24 valence electrons are used.
If any atom lack an octet, form double or triple bonds as necessary.

Lastly, write the Lewis structure in brackets with the charge of the ion in the upper right-hand corner.

All atoms have octets; the structure is complete. However, the double bond can form from any oxygen atom, so there are three resonance forms.

Calculate the formal charge on each atom by finding the number of valence electrons and subtracting the number of lone pair electrons and one-half the number of bonding electrons.

	O_{left}	O_{top}	O_{right}	C
number of valence electrons	6	6	6	4
- number of lone pair electrons	6	6	4	0
- 1/2(number of bonding electrons)	1	1	2	4
Formal charge	−1	−1	0	0

The sum of the formal charges is − 2, which is the overall charge of the ion. The other resonance forms would have the same values for the single and double bonded oxygen atoms.

(c) ClO^-:   Write the correct skeletal structure for the ion.

Cl —— O

Calculate the total number of electrons for the Lewis structure by summing the number of valence electrons of each atom in the ion and adding 1 for the 1 − charge.

(number of valence e^- for O) + (number of valence e^- for Cl) + 1 = 6 + 7 + 1 = 14

Distribute the electrons among the atoms, giving octets to as many atoms as possible. Begin with the bonding electrons, then proceed to lone pairs on terminal atoms and finally to lone pairs on the central atom.

All 14 valence electrons are used.

If any atom lacks an octet, form double or triple bonds as necessary to give them octets. Lastly, write the Lewis structure in brackets with the charge of the ion in the upper right-hand corner.

All atoms have octets; the structure is complete.

Calculate the formal charge on each atom by finding the number of valence electrons and subtracting the number of lone pair electrons and one-half the number of bonding electrons.

	Cl	O
number of valence electrons	7	6
- number of lone pair electrons	6	6
- 1/2(number of bonding electrons)	1	1
Formal charge	0	−1

The sum of the formal charges is − 1, which is the overall charge of the ion.

(d) NO_2^-:   Write the correct skeletal structure for the ion.

$$O \!-\! N \!-\! O$$

Calculate the total number of electrons for the Lewis structure by summing the number of valence electrons of each atom in the ion and adding 1 for the 1 − charge.

     2(number of valence e⁻ for O) + (number of valence e⁻ for N) + 1 = 2(6) + 5 + 1 = 18

Distribute the electrons among the atoms, giving octets to as many atoms as possible. Begin with the bonding electrons, then proceed to lone pairs on terminal atoms and finally to lone pairs on the central atom.

All 14 valence electrons are used.
If any atom lacks an octet, form double or triple bonds as necessary.

Lastly, write the Lewis structure in brackets with the charge of the ion in the upper right-hand corner.

All atoms have octets; the structure is complete. However, the double bond can form from either oxygen atom, so there are two resonance forms.

Calculate the formal charge on each atom by finding the number of valence electrons and subtracting the number of lone pair electrons and one-half the number of bonding electrons. Using the left side structure:

	O	N	O
number of valence electrons	6	5	6
- number of lone pair electrons	4	2	6
- 1/2(number of bonding electrons)	2	3	1
Formal charge	0	0	−1

The sum of the formal charges is − 1, which is the overall charge of the ion.

9.65

Calculate the formal charge on each atom in structure I by finding the number of valence electrons and subtracting the number of lone pair electrons and one-half the number of bonding electrons.

	H_{left}	H_{top}	C	S
number of valence electrons	1	1	4	6
- number of lone pair electrons	0	0	0	4
- 1/2(number of bonding electrons)	1	1	4	2
Formal charge	0	0	0	0

The sum of the formal charges is 0, which is the overall charge of the molecule.
Calculate the formal charge on each atom in structure II by finding the number of valence electrons and subtracting the number of lone pair electrons and one-half the number of bonding electrons.

	H_{left}	H_{top}	S	C
number of valence electrons	1	1	6	4
- number of lone pair electrons	0	0	0	4
- 1/2(number of bonding electrons)	1	1	4	2
Formal charge	0	0	+2	-2

The sum of the formal charges is 0, which is the overall charge of the molecule.
Structure I is the better Lewis structure because it has the least amount of formal charge on each atom.

9.67   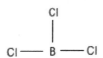   does not provide a significant contribution to the resonance hybrid as it has a +1 formal charge on a very electronegative oxygen.

	O_{left}	O_{right}	C
number of valence electrons	6	6	4
- number of lone pair electrons	2	6	0
- 1/2(number of bonding electrons)	3	1	4
Formal charge	+1	-1	0

Odd – Electron Species, Incomplete Octets, and Expanded Octets

9.69   (a) BCl_3:   Write the correct skeletal structure for the molecule.
B is the less electronegative, so it is central.

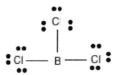

Calculate the total number of electrons for the Lewis structure by summing the number of valence electrons of each atom in the molecule.

(number of valence e$^-$ for B) + 3(number of valence e$^-$ for Cl) = 3 + 3(7) = 24

Distribute the electrons among the atoms, giving octets to as many atoms as possible. Begin with the bonding electrons, and then proceed to lone pairs on terminal atoms finally to lone pairs on the central atom.

All 24 valence electrons are used.
B has an incomplete octet. If we complete the octet, there is a formal charge of – 1 on the B, which is less electronegative than Cl.

(b) NO_2:   Write the correct skeletal structure for the molecule.
N is the less electronegative, so it is central.

O —— N —— O

Calculate the total number of electrons for the Lewis structure by summing the number of valence electrons of each atom in the molecule.

(number of valence e⁻ for N) + 2(number of valence e⁻ for O) = 5 +2(6) = 17

Distribute the electrons among the atoms, giving octets to as many atoms as possible. Begin with the bonding electrons, then proceed to lone pairs on terminal atoms and finally to lone pairs on the central atom.

All 17 valence electrons are used.

N has an incomplete octet. It has 7 electrons because we have an odd number of valence electrons.

(c)   BH₃: Write the correct skeletal structure for the molecule.
B is the less electronegative, so it is central.

Calculate the total number of electrons for the Lewis structure by summing the number of valence electrons of each atom in the molecule.

(number of valence e⁻ for B) + 3(number of valence e⁻ for H) = 3 +3(1) = 6

Distribute the electrons among the atoms, giving octets (or duets for H) to as many atoms as possible. Begin with the bonding electrons, then proceed to lone pairs on terminal atoms and finally to lone pairs on the central atom.

All 6 valence electrons are used.

B has an incomplete octet. H cannot double bond, so it is not possible to complete the octet on B with a double bond.

9.71   (a) PO_4^{3-}: Write the correct skeletal structure for the ion.

Calculate the total number of electrons for the Lewis structure by summing the number of valence electrons of each atom in the ion and adding 3 for the 3 – charge.

4(number of valence e⁻ for O) + (number of valence e⁻ for P) + 3 = 4(6) + 5 + 3 = 32

Distribute the electrons among the atoms, giving octets to as many atoms as possible. Begin with the bonding electrons, then proceed to lone pairs on terminal atoms and finally to lone pairs on the central atom.

All 32 valence electrons are used.

Lastly, write the Lewis structure in brackets with the charge of the ion in the upper right-hand corner.

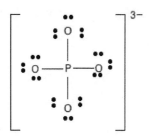

All atoms have octets (duets for H); the structure is complete.
Calculate the formal charge on each atom by finding the number of valence electrons and subtracting the number of lone pair electrons and one-half the number of bonding electrons.

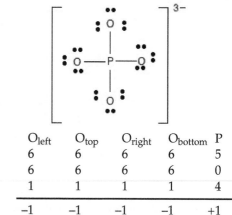

	O_{left}	O_{top}	O_{right}	O_{bottom}	P
number of valence electrons	6	6	6	6	5
- number of lone pair electrons	6	6	6	6	0
- 1/2(number of bonding electrons)	1	1	1	1	4
Formal charge	−1	−1	−1	−1	+1

The sum of the formal charges is −3, which is the overall charge of the ion. However, we can write a resonance structure with a double bond to an oxygen because P can expand its octet. This leads to lower formal charges on P and O.

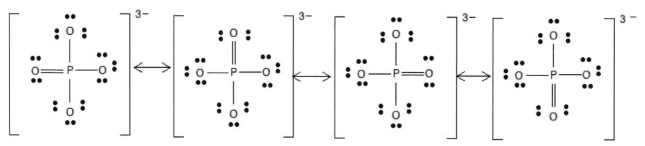

Using the leftmost structure, calculate the formal charge on each atom by finding the number of valence electrons and subtracting the number of lone pair electrons and one-half the number of bonding electrons.

	O_{left}	O_{top}	O_{right}	O_{bottom}	P
number of valence electrons	6	6	6	6	5
- number of lone pair electrons	4	6	6	6	0
- 1/2(number of bonding electrons)	2	1	1	1	5
Formal charge	0	−1	−1	−1	0

The sum of the formal charges is −3, which is the overall charge of the ion. These resonance forms would all have the lower formal charges associated with the double bonded O and P.

(b) CN^-:   Write the correct skeletal structure for the ion.

C ——— N

Calculate the total number of electrons for the Lewis structure by summing the number of valence electrons of each atom in the ion and adding 1 for the 1 − charge.

(number of valence e^- for C) + (number of valence e^- for N) + 1 = 4 + 5 + 1 = 10

Distribute the electrons among the atoms, giving octets \ to as many atoms as possible. Begin with the bonding electrons, then proceed to lone pairs on terminal atoms, and finally to lone pairs on the central atom.

$$:C \overset{\bullet\bullet}{\underset{\bullet\bullet}{-N}}:$$

All 10 valence electrons are used.
If any atom lacks an octet, form double or triple bonds as necessary.

$$:C \equiv N:$$

Lastly, write the Lewis structure in brackets with the charge of the ion in the upper right-hand corner.

$$\left[:C \equiv N: \right]^{-}$$

All atoms have octets; the structure is complete.
Calculate the formal charge on each atom by finding the number of valence electrons and subtracting the number of lone pair electrons and one-half the number of bonding electrons.

$$\left[:C \equiv N: \right]^{-}$$

	C	N
number of valence electrons	4	5
- number of lone pair electrons	2	2
- 1/2(number of bonding electrons)	3	3
Formal charge	−1	0

The sum of the formal charges is − 1, which is the overall charge of the ion.

(c) SO_3^{2-}: Write the correct skeletal structure for the ion.

$$O$$
$$|$$
$$O-S-O$$

Calculate the total number of electrons for the Lewis structure by summing the valence electrons of each atom in the ion and adding 2 for the 2 – charge.

3(number of valence e^- for O) + (number of valence e^- for S) + 2 = 3(6) + 6 + 2 = 26

Distribute the electrons among the atoms, giving octets to as many atoms as possible. Begin with the bonding electrons, then proceed to lone pairs on terminal atoms and finally to lone pairs on the central atom.

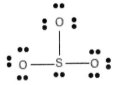

All 26 valence electrons are used.
Lastly, write the Lewis structure in brackets with the charge of the ion in the upper right-hand corner.

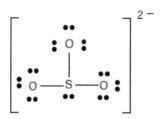

Calculate the formal charge on each atom by finding the number of valence electrons and subtracting the number of lone pair electrons and one-half the number of bonding electrons.

	O_{left}	O_{top}	O_{right}	S
number of valence electrons	6	6	6	6
- number of lone pair electrons	6	6	6	2
- 1/2(number of bonding electrons)	1	1	1	3
Formal charge	−1	−1	−1	+1

The sum of the formal charges is –2, which is the overall charge of the ion. However, we can write a resonance structure with a double bond to an oxygen because S can expand its octet. This leads to a lower formal charge.

Using the leftmost resonance form, calculate the formal charge on each atom by finding the number of valence electrons and subtracting the number of lone pair electrons and one-half the number of bonding electrons.

	O_{left}	O_{top}	O_{right}	S
number of valence electrons	6	6	6	6
- number of lone pair electrons	4	6	6	2
- 1/2(number of bonding electrons)	2	1	1	4
Formal charge	0	−1	−1	0

The sum of the formal charges is –2, which is the overall charge of the ion. These resonance forms would all have the lower formal charge on the double bonded O and S.

(d) ClO_2^-:   Write the correct skeletal structure for the ion.

O —— Cl —— O

Calculate the total number of electrons for the Lewis structure by summing the number of valence electrons of each atom in the ion and adding 1 for the 1 – charge.

2(number of valence e⁻ for O) + (number of valence e⁻ for Cl) + 1 = 2(6) + 7 + 1 = 20

Distribute the electrons among the atoms, giving octets (or duets for H) to as many atoms as possible. Begin with the bonding electrons, then proceed to lone pairs on terminal atoms and finally to lone pairs on the central atom.

All 20 valence electrons are used.

Lastly, write the Lewis structure in brackets with the charge of the ion in the upper right-hand corner.

All atoms have octets; the structure is complete.

Calculate the formal charge on each atom by finding the number of valence electrons and subtracting the number of lone pair electrons and one-half the number of bonding electrons.

	O_{left}	O_{right}	Cl
number of valence electrons	6	6	7
- number of lone pair electrons	6	6	4
- 1/2(number of bonding electrons)	1	1	2
Formal charge	−1	−1	+1

The sum of the formal charges is −1, which is the overall charge of the ion. However, we can write a resonance structure with a double bond to an oxygen because Cl can expand its octet. This leads to a lower formal charge

Using the leftmost resonance form, calculate the formal charge on each atom by finding the number of valence electrons and subtracting the number of lone pair electrons and one-half the number of bonding electrons.

	O_{left}	O_{right}	Cl
number of valence electrons	6	6	7
- number of lone pair electrons	4	6	4
- 1/2(number of bonding electrons)	2	1	3
Formal charge	0	−1	0

The sum of the formal charges is −1, which is the overall charge of the ion. These

O and Cl.

9.73 (a) PF_5: Write the correct skeletal structure for the molecule.

Calculate the total number of electrons for the Lewis structure by summing the number of valence electrons of each atom in the molecule.

(number of valence e⁻ for P) + 5(number of valence e⁻ for F) = 5 +5(7) = 40

Distribute the electrons among the atoms, giving octets to as many atoms as possible. Begin with the bonding electrons, then proceed to lone pairs on terminal atoms and finally to lone

pairs on the central atom. Arrange additional electrons around the central atom, giving it an expanded octet of up to 12 electrons.

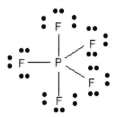

(b) I_3^- :   Write the correct skeletal structure for the ion.

I ⸺ I ⸺ I

Calculate the total number of electrons for the Lewis structure by summing the number of valence electrons of each atom in the ion and adding 1 for the 1 – charge.

3(number of valence e⁻ for I) + 1 = 3(7) + 1 = 22

Distribute the electrons among the atoms, giving octets to as many atoms as possible. Begin with the bonding electrons, then proceed to lone pairs on terminal atoms and finally to lone pairs on the central atom. Arrange additional electrons around the central atom, giving it an expanded octet of up to 12 electrons.

Lastly, write the Lewis structure in brackets with the charge of the ion in the upper right-hand corner.

(c) SF_4:   Write the correct skeletal structure for the molecule.

Calculate the total number of electrons for the Lewis structure by summing the number of valence electrons of each atom in the molecule.

(number of valence e⁻ for S) + 4(number of valence e⁻ for F) = 6 + 4(7) = 34

Distribute the electrons among the atoms, giving octets (or duets for H) to as many atoms as possible. Begin with the bonding electrons, and then proceed to lone pairs on terminal atoms and finally to lone pairs on the central atom. Arrange additional electrons around the central atom, giving it an expanded octet of up to 12 electrons.

(d) GeF$_4$: Write the correct skeletal structure for the molecule.

$$
\begin{array}{c}
\text{F} \\
| \\
\text{F} - \text{Ge} - \text{F} \\
| \\
\text{F}
\end{array}
$$

Calculate the total number of electrons for the Lewis structure by summing the number of valence electrons of each atom in the molecule.

(number of valence e⁻ for Ge) + 4(number of valence e⁻ for F) = 4 + 4(7) = 32

Distribute the electrons among the atoms, giving octets to as many atoms as possible. Begin with the bonding electrons, then proceed to lone pairs on terminal atoms and finally to lone pairs on the central atom.

$$
\begin{array}{c}
\ddot{\overset{\textstyle\cdot\cdot}{\text{F}}} \\
| \\
\ddot{\text{F}} - \text{Ge} - \ddot{\text{F}} \\
| \\
\ddot{\overset{\textstyle\cdot\cdot}{\text{F}}}
\end{array}
$$

Bond Energies and Bond Lengths

9.75   Bond strength: H$_3$CCH$_3$ < H$_2$CCH$_2$ < HCCH
Bond length: H$_3$CCH$_3$ > H$_2$CCH$_2$ > HCCH
Write the Lewis structures for the three compounds. Compare the C – C bonds. Triple bonds are stronger than double bonds, which are stronger than single bonds. Also, single bonds are longer than double bonds are longer than triple bonds.

HCCH (10 e⁻)   H$_2$CCH$_2$ (12 e⁻)   H$_3$CCH$_3$(14 e⁻)

$$
\text{H} - \text{C} \equiv \text{C} - \text{H}
$$

$$
\begin{array}{c}
\text{H} \qquad\qquad \text{H} \\
 \diagdown \qquad \diagup \\
\text{C} = \text{C} \\
\diagup \qquad \diagdown \\
\text{H} \qquad\qquad \text{H}
\end{array}
$$

$$
\begin{array}{c}
\text{H} \qquad \text{H} \\
| \qquad | \\
\text{H} - \text{C} - \text{C} - \text{H} \\
| \qquad | \\
\text{H} \qquad \text{H}
\end{array}
$$

9.77   Rewrite the reaction using the Lewis structures of the molecules involved.

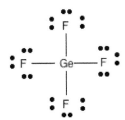

$$
+ \quad \text{H} - \text{H} \quad \longrightarrow \quad
\begin{array}{c}
\text{H} \qquad \text{H} \\
| \qquad | \\
\text{H} - \text{C} - \text{C} - \text{H} \\
| \qquad | \\
\text{H} \qquad \text{H}
\end{array}
$$

Determine which bonds are broken in the reaction and sum the bond energies of the following:

Σ(ΔH's bonds broken)
= 4mol(C – H) + 1mol(C = C) + 1mol(H – H)
= 4mol(414 kJ/mol) + 1mol(611 kJ/mol) + 1mol(436 kJ/mol)
= 2703 kJ/mol

Determine which bonds are formed in the reaction and sum the negatives of the bond energies of the following:

Σ(-ΔH's bonds formed)
= – 6mol(C – H) – 1mol(C – C)
= – 6mol(414 kJ/mol) –1mol (347 kJ/mol)
= –2831 kJ/mol

Find ΔH_{rxn} by summing the results of the two steps.

$$\Delta H_{rxn} = \Sigma(\Delta H's \text{ bonds broken}) + \Sigma(-\Delta H's \text{ bonds formed})$$
$$= 2703 \text{ kJ/mol} - 2831 \text{ kJ/mol}$$
$$= -128 \text{ kJ/mol}$$

9.79   Rewrite the reaction using the Lewis structures of the molecules involved.

Determine which bonds are broken in the reaction and sum the bond energies of the following:

$\Sigma(\Delta H's \text{ bonds broken})$

$= 4(O-H)$

$= 4(464 \text{ kJ/mol})$

$= 1856 \text{ kJ/mol}$

Determine which bonds are formed in the reaction and sum the negatives of the bond energies of the following:

$\Sigma(-\Delta H's \text{ bonds formed})$

$= -2(C=O) - 2(H-H)$

$= -2(799 \text{ kJ/mol}) - 2(436 \text{ kJ/mol})$

$= -2470 \text{ kJ/mol}$

Find ΔH_{rxn} by summing the results of the two steps.

$$\Delta H_{rxn} = \Sigma(\Delta H's \text{ bonds broken}) + \Sigma(-\Delta H's \text{ bonds formed})$$
$$= 1856 \text{ kJ/mol} - 2470 \text{ kJ/mol}$$
$$= -614 \text{ kJ/mol}$$

Cumulative Problems

9.81   (a) BI_3: This is a covalent compound between two nonmetals.
        Write the correct skeletal structure for the molecule.

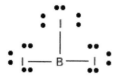

Calculate the total number of electrons for the Lewis structure by summing the number of valence electrons of each atom in the molecule.

(number of valence e⁻ for B) + (number of valence e⁻ for I) = 3 + 3(7) = 24

Distribute the electrons among the atoms, giving octets to as many atoms as possible. Begin with the bonding electrons, then proceed to lone pairs on terminal atoms and finally to lone pairs on the central atom.

(b) K_2S: This is an ionic compound between a metal and nonmetal.
        Draw the Lewis structures for K and S based on their valence electrons.   K: $4s^1$ S: $3s^2 3p^4$

to gain two electrons to get an octet.

(c)   HCFO: This is a covalent compound between nonmetals.
Write the correct skeletal structure for the molecule.

Calculate the total number of electrons for the Lewis structure by summing the number of valence electrons of each atom in the molecule.

(number of valence e⁻ for H)+(number of valence e⁻ for C)+(number of valence e⁻ for F)+(number of valence e⁻ for O) = 1 + 4 + 7 +6 = 18

Distribute the electrons among the atoms, giving octets to as many atoms as possible. Begin with the bonding electrons, then proceed to lone pairs on terminal atoms and finally to lone pairs on the central atom.

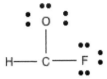

If any atom lacks an octet, form double or triple bonds as necessary to give them octets.

(d)   PBr₃: This is a covalent compound between two nonmetals.
Write the correct skeletal structure for the molecule.

Calculate the total number of electrons for the Lewis structure by summing the number of valence electrons of each atom in the molecule.

(number of valence e⁻ for P) + 3(number of valence e⁻ for Br) = 5 + 3(7) = 26.

Distribute the electrons among the atoms, giving octets to as many atoms as possible. Begin with the bonding electrons, and then proceed to lone pairs on terminal atoms and finally to lone pairs on the central atom.

9.83   (a)   BaCO₃: Ba²⁺

Determine the cation and anion.
Ba²⁺   CO₃²⁻

Write the Lewis structure for the barium cation based on the valence electrons.

Ba $5s^2$ Ba^{2+} $5s^0$

Ba : Ba^{2+}

Ba must lose two electrons and be left with the octet from the previous shell.

Write the Lewis structure for the covalent anion.

Write the correct skeletal structure for the ion.

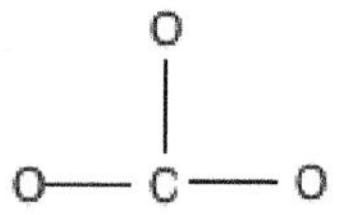

O
|
O — C — O

Calculate the total number of electrons for the Lewis structure by summing the number of valence electrons of each atom in the ion and adding two for the 2 – charge.

(number of valence e^- for C) + 3(number of valence e^- for O) = 4 + 3(6) + 2 = 24

Distribute the electrons among the atoms, giving octets to as many atoms as possible. Begin with the bonding electrons, then proceed to lone pairs on terminal atoms and finally to lone pairs on the central atom.

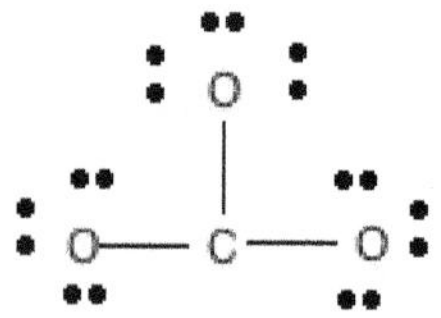

If any atom lacks an octet, form double or triple bonds as necessary.

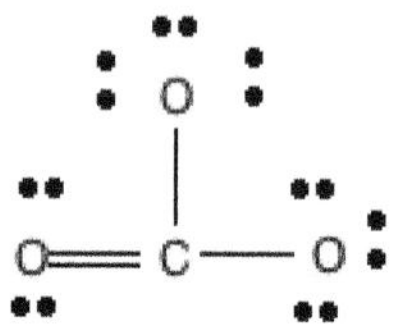

Lastly, write the Lewis structure in brackets with the charge of the ion in the upper right-hand corner.

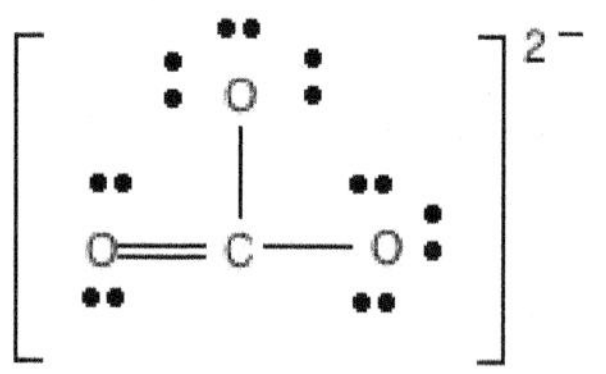

The double bond can be between the C and any of the oxygen atoms, so there are resonance structures.

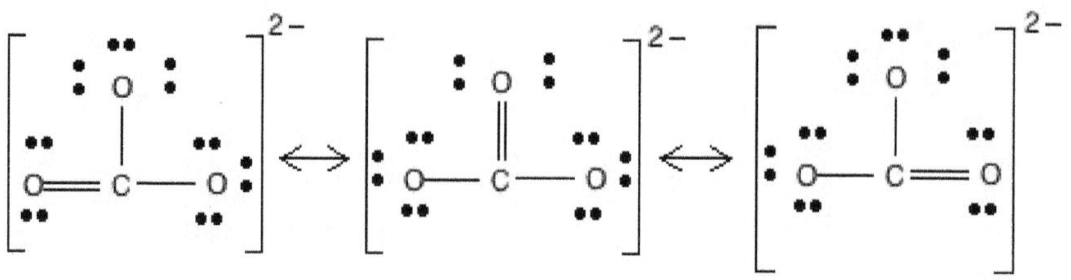

(b) $Ca(OH)_2$: Ca^{2+}

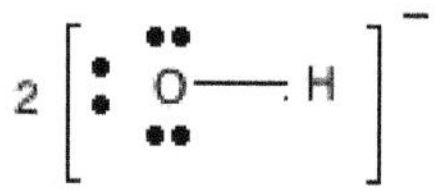

Determine the cation and anion.

Ca^{2+} OH^-

Write the Lewis structure for the calcium cation based on the valence electrons.
    Ca $4s^2$ Ca^{2+} $4s^0$

    Ca $\vdots$ Ca^{2+}

Ca must lose two electrons and be left with the octet from the previous shell.
Write the Lewis structure for the covalent anion.
Write the correct skeletal structure for the ion.

        O——H

Calculate the total number of electrons for the Lewis structure by summing the valence electrons of each atom in the ion and adding one for the 1 – charge.
        (number of valence e^- for H) + (number of valence e^- for O) +1 = 1 + 6 +1 = 8
Distribute the electrons among the atoms, giving octets (or duets for H) to as many atoms as possible. Begin with the bonding electrons, and then proceed to lone pairs on terminal atoms and finally to lone pairs of the central atom.

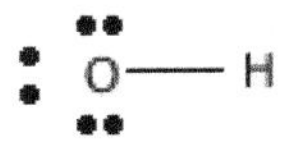

        $\vdots \ddot{O}$——H

Lastly, write the Lewis structure in brackets with the charge of the ion in the upper right-hand corner.

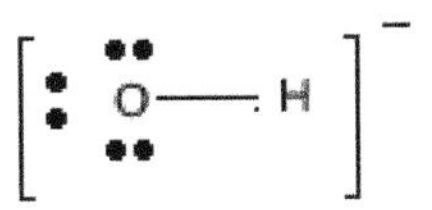

        $\left[\vdots \ddot{O}——\ddot{} H \right]^-$

(c) KNO_3: K^+

        $\left[\begin{array}{c} \vdots \ddot{O} \vdots \\ | \\ \ddot{O}{=}N——\ddot{O} \vdots \end{array} \right]^-$

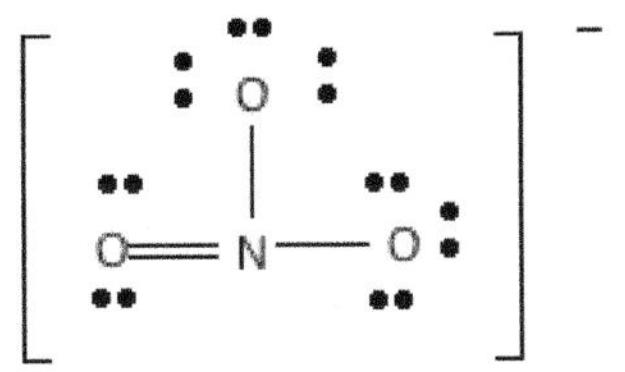

Determine the cation and anion.
        K^+ NO_3^-
Write the Lewis structure for the potassium cation based on the valence electrons.
        K $4s^1$ K^+ $4s^0$

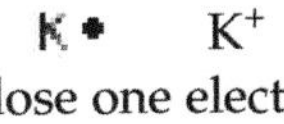

        K $\bullet$ K^+
K must lose one electron and be left with the octet from the previous shell.
Write the Lewis structure for the covalent anion.
Write the correct skeletal structure for the ion.

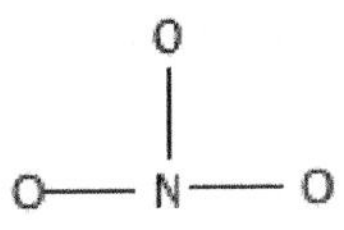

            O
            |
        O——N——O

Calculate the total number of electrons for the Lewis structure by summing the valence electrons of each atom in the ion and adding one for the 1 – charge.
        (number of valence e^- for N) + (number of valence e^- for O) = 5 + 3(6) +1 = 24
Distribute the electrons among the atoms, giving octets to as many atoms as possible. Begin with the bonding electrons, then proceed to lone pairs on terminal atoms and finally to lone pairs on the central atom.

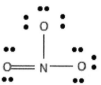

If any atom lacks an octet, form double or triple bonds as necessary.

Lastly, write the Lewis structure in brackets with the charge of the ion in the upper right-hand corner.

The double bond can be between the N and any of the oxygen atoms, so there are resonance structures.

(d)   LiIO: Li$^+$

Determine the cation and anion.

         Li$^+$ IO$^-$

Write the Lewis structure for the lithium cation based on the valence electrons.

         Li 2s^1 Li$^+$ 2s^0

         Li•   Li$^+$

Li must lose one electron and be left with the octet from the previous shell.
Write the Lewis structure for the covalent anion.
Write the correct skeletal structure for the ion.

         I —— O

Calculate the total number of electron for the Lewis structure by summing the number of valence electrons of each atom in the ion and adding one for the 1 – charge.

         (number of valence e$^-$ for I) + (number of valence e$^-$ for O) = 7 +6 + 1 = 14

Distribute the electrons among the atoms, giving octets to as many atoms as possible. Begin with the bonding electrons, then proceed to lone pairs on terminal atoms and finally to lone pairs on the central atom.

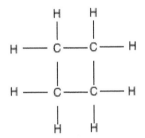

Lastly, write the Lewis structure in brackets with the charge of the ion in the upper right-hand corner.

9.85   (a) C_4H_8: Write the correct skeletal structure for the molecule.

Calculate the total number of electrons for the Lewis structure by summing the number of valence electrons of each atom in the molecule.

4 (number of valence e⁻ for C) + 8(number of valence e⁻ for H) = 4(4) + 8(1) = 24

Distribute the electrons among the atoms, giving octets (or duets for H) to as many atoms as possible.

All atoms have octets or duets for H.

(b) C_4H_4:   Write the correct skeletal structure for the molecule.

Calculate the total number of electrons for the Lewis structure by summing the number of valence electrons of each atom in the molecule.

4 (number of valence e⁻ for C) + 4(number of valence e⁻ for H) = 4(4) + 4(1) = 20

Distribute the electrons among the atoms, giving octets (or duets for H) to as many atoms as possible.

Complete octets by forming double bonds on alternating carbons; draw resonance structures.

(c) C_6H_{12}:   Write the correct skeletal structure for the molecule.

Calculate the total number of electrons for the Lewis structure by summing the valence electrons of each atom in the molecule.

6 (number of valence e⁻ for C) + 12(number of valence e⁻ for H) = 6(4) + 12(1) = 36

Distribute the electrons among the atoms, giving octets (or duets for H) to as many atoms as possible. Begin with the bonding.

All 36 electrons are used and all atoms have octets or duets for H.

(d) C_6H_6:   Write the correct skeletal structure for the molecule.

Calculate the total number of electrons for the Lewis structure by summing the number of valence electrons of each atom in the molecule.

6 (number of valence e⁻ for C) + 6(number of valence e⁻ for H) = 6(4) + 6(1) = 30

Distribute the electrons among the atoms, giving octets (or duets for H) to as many atoms as possible.

Complete octets by forming double bonds on alternating carbons; draw resonance structures.

9.87 **Given:** 26.01% C; 4.38 % H; 69.52 % O; molar mass = 46.02 g/mol
Find: molecular formula and Lewis structure
Conceptual Plan: convert mass to mol of each element → **pseudoformula** → **empirical formula**

$$\frac{1 \text{ mol C}}{12.01 \text{ g C}} \qquad \frac{1 \text{ mol H}}{1.008 \text{ g H}} \qquad \frac{1 \text{ mol O}}{16.00 \text{ g O}} \qquad\qquad \text{divide by smallest number}$$

→ **molecular formula** → **Lewis structure**

empirical formula x n

Solution:
$$26.01 \text{ g C} \times \frac{1 \text{ mol C}}{12.01 \text{ g C}} = 2.166 \text{ mol C}$$

$$4.38 \text{ g H} \times \frac{1 \text{ mol H}}{1.008 \text{ g H}} = 4.345 \text{ mol H}$$

$$69.52 \text{ g O} \times \frac{1 \text{ mol O}}{16.00 \text{ g O}} = 4.345 \text{ mol O}$$

$$C_{2.166}H_{4.345}O_{4.345}$$
$$C_{\frac{2.166}{2.166}}H_{\frac{4.345}{2.166}}O_{\frac{4.345}{2.166}} \rightarrow CH_2O_2$$

The correct empirical formula is CH_2O_2.
empirical formula mass = (12.01 g/mol) + 2(1.008 g/mol) + 2(16.00 g/mol) = 46.03 g/mol
$$n = \frac{\text{molar mass}}{\text{formula molar mass}} = \frac{46.02 \text{ g/mol}}{46.03 \text{ g/mol}} = 1$$
molecular formula $\quad = CH_2O_2 \times 1$
$\qquad\qquad\qquad\quad = CH_2O_2$

Write the correct skeletal structure for the molecule.

Calculate the total number of electrons for the Lewis structure by summing the number of valence electrons of each atom in the molecule.

(number of valence e^- for C) + 2(number of valence e^- for O) + 2(number of valence e^- for H) = 4 + 2(6) + 2(1) = 18

Distribute the electrons among the atoms, giving octets (or duets for H) to as many atoms as possible. Begin with the bonding electrons, and then proceed to lone pairs on terminal atoms and finally to lone pairs on the central atoms.

Complete the octet on C by forming a double bond.

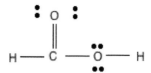

9.89   To determine the values of the lattice energy, it is necessary to look them up online. The lattice energy of Al_2O_3 is –15,916 kJ/mol, the value for Fe_2O_3 is - 14,774 kJ/mol. The thermite reaction is exothermic due to the energy released when the Al_2O_3 lattice forms. The lattice energy of Al_2O_3 is more negative than the lattice energy of Fe_2O_3.

9.91 HNO_3 Write the correct skeletal structure for the molecule.

O
|
H —— O —— N —— O

Calculate the total number of electrons for the Lewis structure by summing the number of valence electrons of each atom in the molecule.
   3(number of valence e for O) + (number of valence e⁻ for N) + (number of valence e⁻ for H) = 3(6) + 5 +1 = 24

Distribute the electrons among the atoms, giving octets (or duets for H) to as many atoms as possible. Begin with the bonding electrons, then proceed to lone pairs on terminal atoms and finally to lone pairs on the central atom.

All 24 valence electrons are used.
If any atoms lack an octet, form double or triple bonds as necessary. The double bond can be formed to any of the three oxygen atoms, so there are three resonance forms.

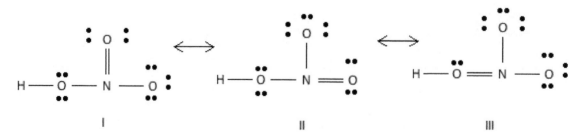

I   II   III

All atoms have octets (duets for H); the structure is complete.
To determine which resonance hybrid(s) is most important, calculate the formal charge on each atom in each structure by finding the number of valence electrons and subtracting the number of lone pair electrons and one-half the number of bonding electrons.

	Structure I					Structure II				
	O_{left}	O_{top}	O_{right}	N	H	O_{left}	O_{top}	O_{right}	N	H
number of valence electrons	6	6	6	5	1	6	6	6	5	1
- number of lone pair electrons	4	4	6	0	0	4	6	4	0	0
- 1/2(number of bonding electrons)	2	2	1	4	1	2	1	2	4	1
Formal charge	0	0	–1	+1	0	0	–1	0	+1	0

	Structure III				
	O_{left}	O_{top}	O_{right}	N	H
number of valence electrons	6	6	6	5	1
- 1/2(number of bonding electrons)	3	1	1	4	1
Formal charge	+1	−1	−1	+1	0

The sum of the formal charges is 0 for each structure, which is the overall charge of the molecule. However, in structures I and II the individual formal charges are lower. These two forms would contribute equally to the structure of HNO_3. Structure III would be less important since the individual formal charges are higher.

9.93 CNO^- Write the skeletal structure:

         C – N – O

Determine the number of valence electrons.

         (valence e^- from C) + (valence e^- from N) + (valence e^- from O) +1(from the negative charge)
         4 + 5 + 6 + 1 = 16

Distribute the electrons to complete octets if possible.

Determine the formal charge on each atom for each structure.

	Structure I			Structure II		
	C	N	O	C	N	O
number of valence electrons	4	5	6	4	5	6
- number of lone pair electrons	4	0	4	2	0	6
- 1/2(number of bonding electrons)	2	4	2	3	4	1
Formal charge	−2	+1	0	−1	+1	−1

	Structure III		
	C	N	O
number of valence electrons	4	5	6
- number of lone pair electrons	6	0	2
- 1/2(number of bonding electrons)	1	4	3
Formal charge	−3	+1	+1

Structures I, II, and III all follow the octet rule but have varying degrees of negative formal charge on carbon, which is the least electronegative atom. Also the amount of formal charge is very high in all three resonance forms. Although structure II is the best of the resonance forms, none of these resonance forms contribute strongly to the stability of the fulminate ion and the ion is not very stable.

9.95 $HCSNH_2$: Write the correct skeletal structure for the molecule.

Calculate the total number of electrons for the Lewis structure by summing the number of valence electrons of each atom in the molecule.

(number of valence e⁻ for N) + (number of valence e⁻ for S) + (number of valence e⁻ for C) + 3(number of valence e⁻ for H) = 5 + 6 + 4 + 3(1) = 18

Distribute the electrons among the atoms, giving octets (or duets for H) to as many atoms as possible. Begin with the bonding electrons, and then proceed to lone pairs on terminal atoms and finally to lone pairs on the central atoms.

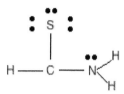

Complete the octet on C by forming a double bond.

9.97   (a) O_2^-:   Write the correct skeletal structure for the radical.

O —— O

Calculate the total number of electrons for the Lewis structure by summing the number of valence electrons of each atom in the radical and adding 1 for the 1 – charge.

2(number of valence e⁻ for O) + 1 = 2(6) + 1 = 13

Distribute the electrons among the atoms, giving octets to as many atoms as possible. Begin with the bonding electrons, then proceed to lone pairs on terminal atoms and finally to lone pairs on the central atom.

All 13 valence electrons are used.

O has an incomplete octet. It has 7 electrons because we have an odd number of valence electrons.

(b) O^-:   Write the Lewis structure based on the valence electrons $2s^2 2p^5$

(c)   OH: Write the correct skeletal structure for the molecule.

H —— O

Calculate the total number of electrons for the Lewis structure by summing the number of valence electrons of each atom in the molecule.

(number of valence e⁻ for O) + (number of valence e⁻ for H) = 6 + 1 = 7

Distribute the electrons among the atoms, giving octets (or duets for H) to as many atoms as possible. Begin with the bonding electrons, then proceed to lone pairs on terminal atoms and finally to lone pairs on the central atom.

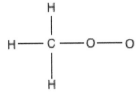

All 7 valence electrons are used.

O has an incomplete octet. It has 7 electrons because we have an odd number of valence electrons.

(d)   CH₃OO: Write the correct skeletal structure for the radical.
C is the least electronegative atom, so it is central.

$$H - C - O - O$$

Calculate the total number of electrons for the Lewis structure by summing the number of valence electrons of each atom in the molecule.

3(number of valence e⁻ for H) + (number of valence e⁻ for C) + 2(number of valence e⁻ for O) = 3(1) + 4 +2(6) = 19

Distribute the electrons among the atoms, giving octets (or duets for H) to as many atoms as possible. Begin with the bonding electrons, and then proceed to lone pairs on terminal atoms and finally to lone pairs on the central atoms.

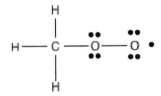

All 19 valence electrons are used.

O has an incomplete octet. It has 7 electrons because we have an odd number of valence electrons.

9.99   Rewrite the reaction using the Lewis structures of the molecules involved.

$$H - H\ (g)\ + 1/2\ O = O\ (g)\ \rightarrow\ H - O - H$$

Determine which bonds are broken in the reaction and sum the bond energies of the following:

Σ(ΔH's bonds broken)
= 1mol(H – H) + 1/2mol(O = O)
= 1mol(436 kJ/mol) + 1/2mol(498)
= 685 kJ/mol

Determine which bonds are formed in the reaction and sum the negatives of the bond energies of the following:

Σ(-ΔH's bonds formed)
= – 2mol(O – H)
= – 2mol(464 kJ/mol)
= –928 kJ/mol

Find ΔH_{rxn} by summing the results of the two steps.

ΔH_{rxn} = Σ(ΔH's bonds broken) + Σ(-ΔH's bonds formed)
= 685 kJ/mol – 928 kJ/mol
= – 243 kJ/mol

$CH_4(g) + 2O_2(g) \rightarrow CO_2(g) + 2H_2O(g)$

Rewrite the reaction using the Lewis structures of the molecules involved.

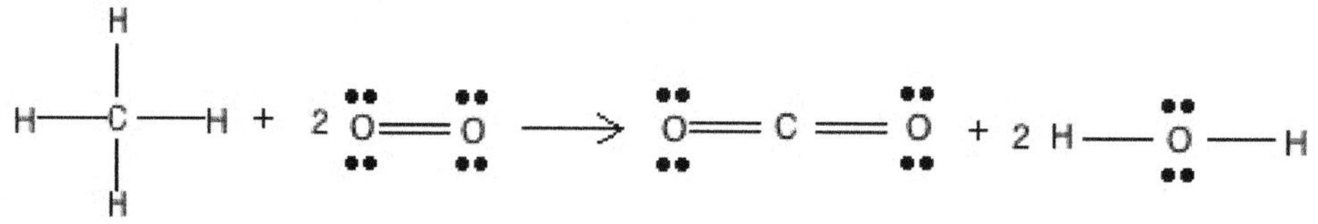

Determine which bonds are broken in the reaction and sum the bond energies of the following:

$\Sigma(\Delta H$'s bonds broken)

$= 4\text{mol}(C - H) + 2\text{mol}(O = O)$

$= 4\text{mol}(414 \text{ kJ/mol}) + 2\text{mol}(498)$

$= 2652 \text{ kJ/mol}$

Determine which bonds are formed in the reaction and sum the negatives of the bond energies of the following:

$\Sigma(-\Delta H$'s bonds formed)

$= - 2\text{mol}(C = O) - 4\text{mol}(O - H)$

$= - 2\text{mol}(799 \text{ kJ/mol}) - 4\text{mol}(464 \text{ kJ/mol})$

$= -3454 \text{ kJ/mol}$

Find ΔH_{rxn} by summing the results of the two steps.

$\Delta H_{rxn} \quad = \Sigma(\Delta H$'s bonds broken) $+ \Sigma(-\Delta H$'s bonds formed)

$= 2653 \text{ kJ/mol} - 3454 \text{ kJ/mol}$

$= - 802 \text{ kJ/mol}$

Compare the following:

	kJ/mol	kJ/g
H_2		−120
CH_4	−802	−50.1

So, methane yields more energy per mole but hydrogen yields more energy per gram.

9.101   (a) Cl_2O_7:   Write the correct skeletal structure for the molecule.

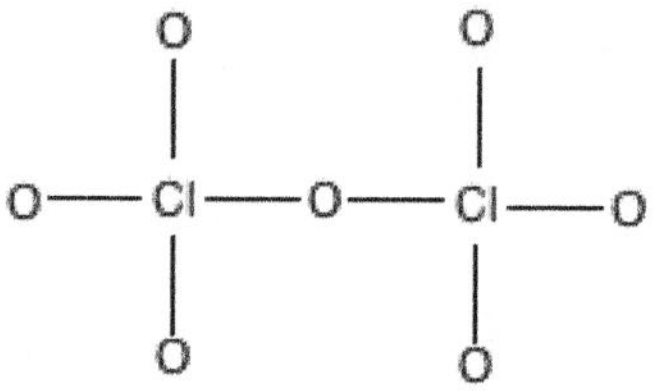

Calculate the total number of electrons for the Lewis structure by summing the valence electrons of each atom in the molecule.

2(number of valence e⁻ for Cl) + 7(number of valence e⁻

Distribute the electrons among the atoms, giving octets (or duets for H) to as many atoms as possible. Begin with the bonding electrons, and then proceed to lone pairs on terminal atoms and finally to lone pairs of the central atom.

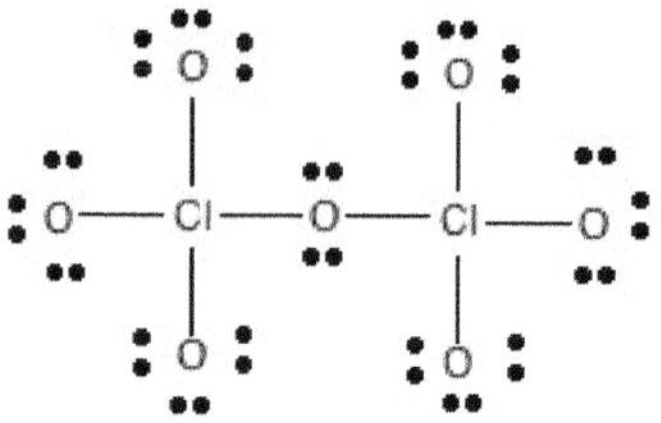

Form double bonds to minimize formal charge.

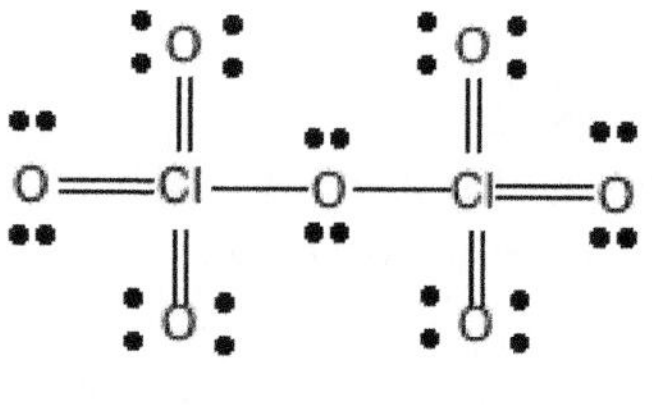

(b) H_3PO_3: Write the correct skeletal structure for the molecule.

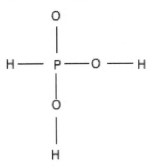

Calculate the total number of electrons for the Lewis structure by summing the valence electrons of each atom in the molecule.

(number of valence e⁻ for P) + 3(number of valence e⁻ for O) + 3(number of valence e⁻ for H) = 5 + 3(6) + 3(1) = 26

Distribute the electrons among the atoms, giving octets (or duets for H) to as many atoms as possible. Begin with the bonding electrons, and then proceed to lone pairs on terminal atoms and finally to lone pairs on central atoms.

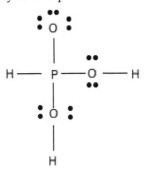

Form a double bond to minimize formal charge.

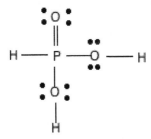

(c) H_3AsO_4: Write the correct skeletal structure for the molecule.

Calculate the total number of electrons for the Lewis structure by summing the valence electrons of each atom in the molecule.

(number of valence e⁻ for As) + 4(number of valence e⁻ for O) + 3(number of valence e⁻ for H) = 5 + 4(6) + 3(1) = 32

Distribute the electrons among the atoms, giving octets (or duets for H) to as many atoms as possible. Begin with the bonding electrons, and then proceed to lone pairs on terminal atoms and finally to lone pairs of the central atom.

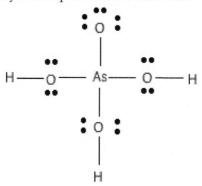

Form a double bond to minimize formal charge.

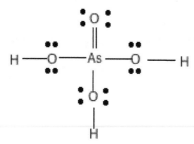

9.103 $Na^+F^- < Na^+O^{2-} < Mg^{2+}F^- < Mg^{2+}O^{2-} < Al^{3+}O^{2-}$
The lattice energy is proportional to the magnitude of the charge and inversely proportional to the distance between the atoms. Na^+F^- would have the smallest lattice energy because the magnitude of the charges on Na and F are the smallest. $Mg^{2+}F^-$ and Na^+O^{2-} both have the same magnitude formal charge, the O^{2-} is larger than F^- in size, and Na^+ is larger than Mg^{2+}, so Na^+O^{2-} should be less than Mg^{2+-}. The magnitude of the charge makes $Mg^{2+}O^{2-} < Al^{3+}O^{2-}$.

9.105   **Given:** heat atomization CH_4 = 1660 kJ/mol, CH_2Cl_2 = 1495 kJ/mol **Find:** bond energy C – Cl
Write the reaction using the Lewis structure.

$$H-\overset{\displaystyle H}{\underset{\displaystyle H}{\overset{|}{\underset{|}{C}}}}-H(g) \longrightarrow C(g) + 4H(g)$$

Determine the number and kinds of bonds broken and then ΔH atomization = Σ bonds broken.
ΔH atomization = Σ 4 (C – H) bonds broken
$$\frac{1660 \text{ kJ}}{1 \text{ mol } CH_4} \times \frac{1 \text{ mol } CH_4}{4 \text{ C} - \text{H bonds}} = 415 \text{ kJ/C} - \text{H bond}$$
Write the reaction using the Lewis structure.

$$:\!\ddot{C}l-\overset{\displaystyle H}{\underset{\displaystyle :\!\ddot{C}l\!:}{\overset{|}{\underset{|}{C}}}}-H(g) \longrightarrow 2C(g) + 2H(g) + 2Cl(g)$$

Determine the number and kinds of bonds broken and ΔH atomization = Σ bonds broken.
ΔH atomization = Σ 2 (C – H) bonds broken + 2(C – Cl) bonds broken
1495 kJ/mol = 2(415 kJ/ mol) + 2 (x)   x = 333 kJ/mol for the C – Cl bond energy
Check: The bond energy found (333 kJ/mol) is very close to the table value of 339 kJ/mol.

9.107   **Given:** 7.743% H **Find:** Lewis structure
            Conceptual Plan: %H $\rightarrow$ %C $\rightarrow$ mass C,H $\rightarrow$ mol C,H $\rightarrow$ pseudoformula $\rightarrow$ empirical formula

$$100\% - \%H \qquad \text{Assume 100 g sample} \qquad \frac{1\,\text{mol C}}{12.01\,\text{g}} \quad \frac{1\,\text{mol N}}{1.008\,\text{g}} \quad \text{divide by smallest number}$$

Solution: %C = 100% - 7.743% = 92.568% C
            In a 100.00 g sample; 7.743 g H, 92.568 g C

$$7.743\ \cancel{g\ H} \times \frac{1\,\text{mol H}}{1.008\ \cancel{g\ H}} \qquad 7.682\ \text{mol}$$

$$92.568\ \cancel{g\ C} \times \frac{1\,\text{mol C}}{12.011\ \cancel{g\ C}} = 7.7069\ \text{mol C}$$

$$C_{7.7068}H_{7.682}$$
$$C_{\frac{7.7068}{7.682}}H_{\frac{7.682}{7.682}} \rightarrow CH$$

The smallest molecular formula would be C_2H_2.
Write the correct skeletal structure for the molecule.

H —— C —— C —— H

Calculate the total number of electrons for the Lewis structure by summing the valence electrons of each atom in the molecule.
            2(number of valence e^- for C) + 2(number of valence e^- for H) = 2(4) + 2(1) = 10 e^-
Distribute the electrons among the atoms, giving octets (or duets for H) to as many atoms as possible. Begin with the bonding electrons, then proceed to lone pairs on terminal atoms and finally to lone pairs on the central atom.

H —— C —— C —— H

Complete the octet on C by forming a triple bond.

H —— C ≡≡≡ C —— H

9.109

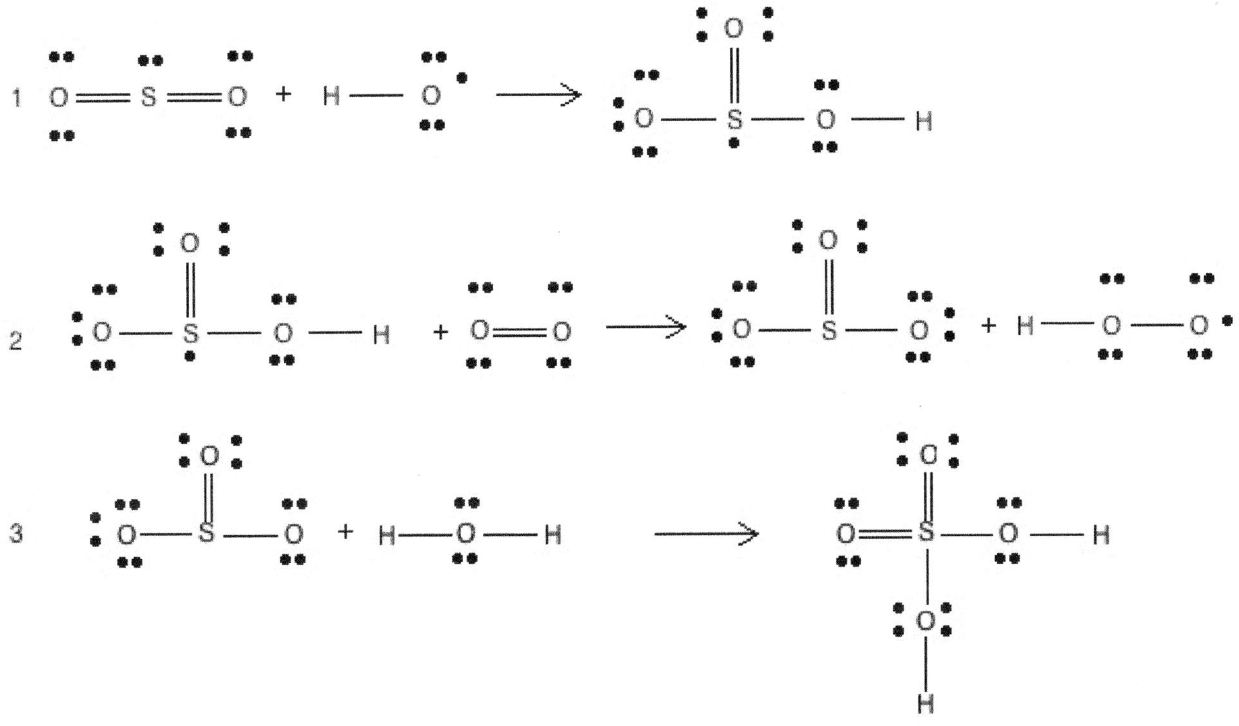

Step 1:

Bonds broken: 2mol(S = O) +1mol(H – O) = 2mol(523kJ/mol) + 1mol(464kJ/mol) = 1510 kJ/mol
Bonds formed: –2mol(S – O) –1mol(S = O) –1mol(O – H) =
–2mol(265 kJ/mol) –1mol(523 kJ/mol) –1mol(464 kJ/mol) = –1517 kJ/mol

$$\Delta H_{step} = -7 \text{ kJ/mol}$$

Step 2:

Bonds broken: 2mol(S – O) + 1mol(S = O) + 1mol(O – H) + 1mol(O = O) =
2mol(265 kJ/mol)+1mol(523 kJ/mol)+1mol(464 kJ/mol)+1mol(498 kJ/mol) =
2015 kJ/mol

Bonds formed: –2mol(S – O) –1mol(S = O) –1mol(O – H) –1mol(O – O) =
–2mol(265 kJ/mol) –1mol(523 kJ/mol) –1mol(464 kJ/mol) –1mol(142 kJ/mol)=
–1659 kJ/mol

$$\Delta H_{step}= +356 \text{ kJ/mol}$$

Step 3:

Bonds broken: 2mol(S – O) + 1mol(S = O) + 2mol(O – H) =
2mol(265 kJ/mol)+1mol(523 kJ/mol)+2mol(464 kJ/mol) = 1981 kJ/mol
Bonds formed: –2mol(S – O) – 2mol(S = O) – 2mol(O – H) =
–2mol(265 kJ/mol) + –2mol(523 kJ/mol) + –2mol(464 kJ/mol) = –2504 kJ/mol

$$\Delta H_{step}= - 523 \text{ kJ/mol}$$

Hess's law states that ΔH for the reaction is the sum of ΔH of the steps:
$\Delta H_{rxn} = (- 7 \text{ kJ/mol}) + (+356 \text{ kJ/mol}) + (- 523 \text{ kJ/mol}) = - 174 \text{ kJ/mol}$

9.111 **Given:** $\mu = 1.08$ D HCl, 20% ionic and $\mu = 1.82$ D HF, 45% ionic **Find:** r

Conceptual Plan: $\mu \rightarrow \mu_{calc} \rightarrow r$

$$\% \text{ ionic character} = \frac{\mu}{\mu_{calc}} \times 100$$

Solution: For HCl $\quad \mu_{calc} = \dfrac{1.08}{0.20} = 5.4 \text{ D}$

$$\dfrac{5.4 \cancel{D} \times \dfrac{3.34 \times 10^{-30} \cancel{C} \cdot \cancel{m}}{\cancel{D}} \times \dfrac{10^{12} \text{ pm}}{\cancel{m}}}{1.6 \times 10^{-19} \cancel{C}} = 113 \text{ pm}$$

For HF $\quad \mu_{calc} = \dfrac{1.82}{0.45} = 4.04 \text{ D}$

$$\dfrac{4.04 \cancel{D} \times \dfrac{3.34 \times 10^{-30} \cancel{C} \cdot \cancel{m}}{\cancel{D}} \times \dfrac{10^{12} \text{ pm}}{\cancel{m}}}{1.6 \times 10^{-19} \cancel{C}} = 84 \text{ pm}$$

From Table 9.4, the bond length of HCl = 127 pm, and HF = 92 pm. Both of these values are slightly higher than the calculated values.

9.113 In order for the four P atoms to be equivalent, they must all be in the same electronic environment. That is, they must all see the same number of bonds and lone pair electrons. The only way to achieve this is with a tetrahedral configuration where the P atoms are at the four points of the tetrahedron.

9.115 **Given:** $\Delta H_f^{\circ} PI_3(s) = -24.7 \text{kJ/mol}$; P – I = 184 kJ/mol; I – I = 151kJ/mol; $\Delta H_f^{\circ} P(g) = 334$ kJ/mol; $\Delta H_f^{\circ} I_2(g)$ = 62 kJ/mol **Find:** $\Delta H_{sub} PI_3(s)$

Conceptual Plan: $PI_3(s) \rightarrow PI_3(g)$; use Hess's law

Solution:

Reaction		$\Delta H(kJ/mol)$	
$PI_3(s)$	$\rightarrow P(s) + 3/2\ I_2(s)$	$+24.7$	(this is the reverse of the formation reaction)
$P(s)$	$\rightarrow P(g)$	$+334$	(formation of $P(g)$)
$3/2\ I_2(s)$	$\rightarrow 3/2\ I_2(g)$	$3/2(62)$	(formation of I (g))
$3/2\ I_2(g)$	$\rightarrow 3\ I(g)$	$3/2(151)$	(breaking I – I bond)
$P(g) + 3I(g)$	$\rightarrow\ PI_3(g)$	$-3(184)$	(forming P – I bond)
$PI_3(s) \rightarrow PI_3(g)$		$+126$	(sublimation of $PI_3(s)$)

9.117   **Given:** H_2S_4 linear **Find:** oxidation number of each S
Write the correct skeletal structure for the molecule.

$$H \text{---} S \text{---} S \text{---} S \text{---} S \text{---} H$$

Calculate the total number of electrons for the Lewis structure by summing the number of valence electrons of each atom in the molecule.
       4(number of valence e^- for S) + 2(number of valence e^- for H) = 4(6) + 2(1) = 26
Distribute the electrons among the atoms, giving octets (or duets for H) to as many atoms as possible.

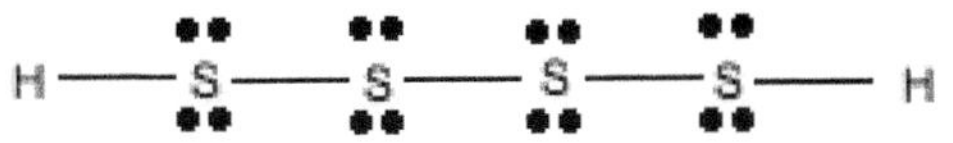

Determine oxidation number on each atom. EN(H) < EN(S), so the electrons in the H – S bond belong to the S atom, while the electrons in the S – S bonds split between the two S atoms.
       O. N. = valence electrons – electrons that belong to the atom

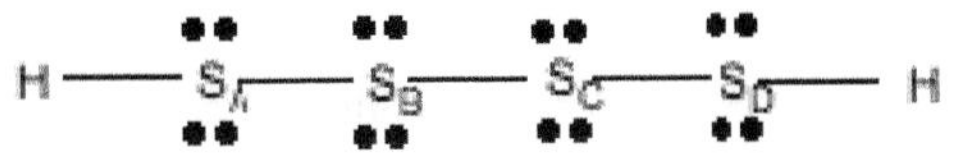

       H = 1 – 0 = +1 for each H
       S_A = 6 – 7 = –1
       S_B = 6 – 6 = 0
       S_C = 6 – 6 = 0
       S_D = 6 – 7 = –1

9.119   **Given:** $\Delta H_f\ SO_2$ = - 296.8 kJ/mol, S(g) = 277.2 kJ/mol, break O = O bond 498 kJ
Find: S = O bond energy
Conceptual Plan: Use ΔH_f for SO_2 and $S(g)$ and the bond energy of O_2 to determine heat of atomization of SO_2.

Reaction ΔH		(kJ/mol)
$SO_2(g)$	$\rightarrow$ ~~S(s, rhombic) + O₂(g)~~	$+296.8$
~~S(s, rhombic)~~	$\rightarrow S(g)$	$+277.2$
~~O=O(g)~~	$\rightarrow 2\ O(g)$	$+498$
$_2(g)$	$S(g) + 2\ O(g)$	$+1072$

Write the reaction using the Lewis structure.

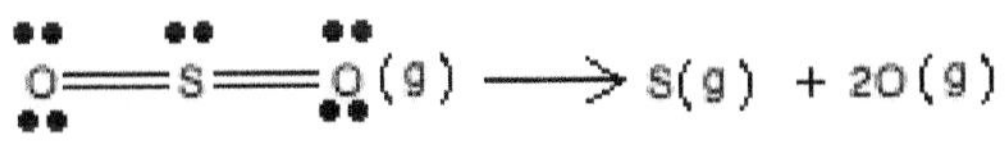

Determine the number and kinds of bonds broken and then ΔH atomization = bonds broken.
ΔH atomization = 2 Σ (S=O) bonds broken.
1072 kJ/mol = 2 (S=O) bonds broken.
S=O bond energy = 536 kJ /mol.
Check: The S=O bond energy is close to the table value of 523 kJ/mol.

Conceptual Problems

9.121   When we say that a compound is "energy rich" we mean that it gives off a great amount of energy when it reacts. It means that there is a lot of energy stored in the compound. This energy is released when the weak bonds in the compound break and much stronger bonds are formed in the product, thereby releasing energy.

9.123   Lewis theory is successful because it allows us to understand and predict many chemical observations. We can use it to determine the formulae of ionic compounds and to account for the low melting points and boiling points of molecular compounds compared to ionic compounds. Lewis theory allows us to predict what molecules or ions will be stable, which will be more reactive, and which will not exist. Lewis theory, however, does not really tell us anything about how the bonds in the molecules and ions form. It does not give us a way to account for the paramagnetism of oxygen. And, by itself, Lewis theory does not really tell us anything about the shape of the molecule or ion.

10 Chemical Bonding II: Molecular Shapes, Valence Bond Theory, and Molecular Orbital Theory

Review Questions

10.1   The properties of molecules are directly related to their shape. The sensation of taste, immune response, the sense of smell, and many types of drug action all depend on shape-specific interactions between molecules and proteins.

10.3   The five basic electron geometries are
   (1)   Linear, which has two electron groups.
   (2)   Trigonal planar, which has three electron groups.
   (3)   Tetrahedral, which has four electron groups.
   (4)   Trigonal bipyramid, which has five electron groups.
   (5)   Octahedral, which has six electron groups.
   An electron group is defined as a lone pair of electrons, a single bond, a multiple bond, or even a single electron.

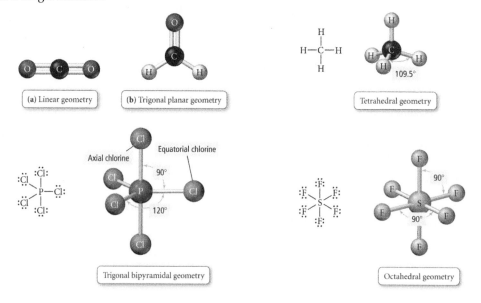

10.5   (a)   Four electron groups give tetrahedral electron geometry, while three bonding groups and one lone pair give a trigonal pyramidal molecular geometry.

       (b)   Four electron groups give a tetrahedral electron geometry, while two bonding groups and two lone pairs give a bent molecular geometry.

(c)   Five electron groups give a trigonal bipyramidal electron geometry, while four bonding groups and one lone pair give a seesaw molecular geometry.

(d)   Five electron groups give a trigonal bipyramidal electron geometry, while three bonding groups and two lone pairs give a T-shaped molecular geometry.

(e)   Five electron groups gives a trigonal bipyramidal electron geometry, while two bonding groups and three lone pair give a linear geometry.

(f)   Six electron groups give an octahedral electron geometry, while five bonding groups and one lone pair give a square pyramidal molecular geometry.

(g)   Six electron groups give an octahedral electron geometry, while four bonding groups and two lone pairs gives a square planar molecular geometry.

10.7   To determine if a molecule is polar, do the following:

1.   Draw the Lewis structure for the molecule and determine the molecular geometry.

2.   Determine whether the molecule contains polar bonds.

3.   Determine whether the polar bonds add together to form a net dipole moment.

Polarity is important because polar and nonpolar molecules have different properties. Polar molecules interact strongly with other polar molecules, but do not interact with nonpolar molecules, and vice versa.

10.9   According to valence bond theory, the shape of the molecule is determined by the geometry of the overlapping orbitals.

10.11   Hybridization is a mathematical procedure in which the standard atomic orbitals are combined to form new atomic orbitals called hybrid orbitals. Hybrid orbitals are still localized on individual atoms, but they have different shapes and energies from those of standard atomic orbitals. They are necessary in valence bond theory because they correspond more closely to the actual distribution of electrons in chemically-bonded atoms.

10.13   The number of standard atomic orbitals added together always equals the number of hybrid orbitals formed. The total number of orbitals is conserved.

10.15   The double bond in Lewis theory is simply two pairs of electrons that are shared between the same two atoms. However, in valence bond theory we see that the double bond is made up of two different kinds of bonds. The double bond in valence bond theory consists of one σ bond and one π bond. Valence bond theory shows us that rotation about a double bond is severely restricted. Because of the side-by-side overlap of the p orbitals, the π bond must essentially break for rotation to occur. The single bond consists of overlap that results in a σ bond. Since the overlap is linear, rotation is not restricted.

10.17   In molecular orbital theory, atoms will bond when the electrons in the atoms can lower their energy by occupying the molecular orbitals of the resultant molecule.

10.19   A bonding molecular orbital is lower in energy than the atomic orbitals from which it is formed. There is an increased electron density in the internuclear region.

10.21   The electrons in orbitals behave like waves. The bonding molecular orbital arises from the constructive interference between the atomic orbitals and is lower in energy than the atomic orbitals. The antibonding molecular orbital arises from the destructive interference between the atomic orbitals and is higher in energy than the atomic orbitals.

10.23   Molecular orbitals can be approximated by a linear combination of atomic orbitals (AOs). The total number of MOs formed from a particular set of AOs will always equal the number of AOs used.

10.25

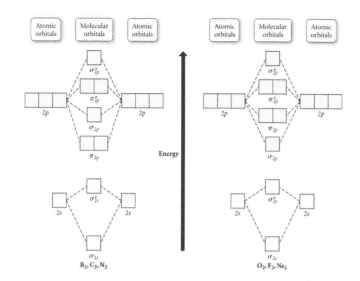

10.27   A paramagnetic species has unpaired electrons in molecular orbitals of equal energy. A paramagnetic species is attracted to a magnetic field. The magnetic property is a direct result of the unpaired electrons. The spin and angular momentum of the electrons generate tiny magnetic fields. A diamagnetic species has all of the electrons paired. The magnetic fields caused by the electron spin and orbital angular momentum tend to cancel each other. A diamagnetic species is not attracted to a magnetic field, and is, in fact, slightly repelled.

10.29   Nonbonding orbitals are atomic orbitals not involved in a bond and will remain localized on the atom.

Problems by Topic

VSEPR Theory and Molecular Geometry

10.31   Four electron groups: A trigonal pyramidal molecular geometry has three bonding groups and one lone pair of electrons, so there are four electron pairs on atom A.

10.33   (a)   4 total electron groups, 4 bonding groups, 0 lone pairs
               A tetrahedral molecular geometry has four bonding groups and no lone pairs. So, there are four total electron groups, four bonding groups, and pairs.

         (b)   5 total electron groups, 3 bonding groups, 2 lone pairs
               A T-shaped molecular geometry has three bonding groups and two lone pairs. So, there are five total electron groups, three bonding groups, and two lone pairs.

         (c)   6 total electron groups, 5 bonding groups, 1 lone pairs
               A square pyramidal molecular geometry has five bonding groups and one lone pair. So, there are six total electron groups, five bonding groups, and one lone pairs.

10.35   (a) PF_3:   Electron geometry–tetrahedral; molecular geometry–trigonal pyramidal; bond angle = 109.5°
               Because of the lone pair, the bond angle will be less than 109.5°.
               Draw a Lewis structure for the molecule:
               PF_3 has 26 valence electrons.

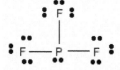

               Determine the total number of electron groups around the central atom:
               There are four electron groups on P.

Determine the number of bonding groups and the number of lone pairs around the central atom:
There are three bonding groups and one lone pair.
Use Table 10.1 to determine the electron geometry, molecular geometry, and bond angles:
Four electron groups give a tetrahedral electron geometry; three bonding groups and one lone pair give a trigonal pyramidal molecular geometry; the idealized bond angles for tetrahedral geometry are 109.5°. The lone pair will make the bond angle less than idealized.

(b) SBr_2:   Electron geometry–tetrahedral; molecular geometry–bent; bond angle = 109.5°
Because of the lone pairs, the bond angle will be less than 109.5°.
Draw a Lewis structure for the molecule:
SBr_2 has 20 valence electrons.

Determine the total number of electron groups around the central atom:
There are four electron groups on S.
Determine the number of bonding groups and the number of lone pairs around the central atom:
There are two bonding groups and two lone pairs.
Use Table 10.1 to determine the electron geometry, molecular geometry, and bond angles:
Four electron groups give a tetrahedral electron geometry; two bonding groups and two lone pair give a bent molecular geometry; the idealized bond angles for tetrahedral geometry are 109.5°. The lone pairs will make the bond angle less than idealized.

(c) $CHCl_3$:   Electron geometry–tetrahedral; molecular geometry–tetrahedral; bond angle = 109.5°
Because there are no lone pairs, the bond angle will be 109.5°.
Draw a Lewis structure for the molecule:
$CHCl_3$ has 26 valence electrons.

Determine the total number of electron groups around the central atom:
There are four electron groups on C.

There are four bonding groups and no lone pairs.
Use Table 10.1 to determine the electron geometry, molecular geometry, and bond angles:
Four electron groups give a tetrahedral electron geometry; four bonding groups and no lone pairs give a tetrahedral molecular geometry; the idealized bond angles for tetrahedral geometry are 109.5°; however, because the attached atoms have different electronegativities the bond angles are less than idealized.

(d) CS_2:   Electron geometry–linear; molecular geometry–linear; bond angle = 180°
Because there are no lone pairs, the bond angle will be 180°.
Draw a Lewis structure for the molecule:
CS_2 has 16 valence electrons.

Determine the total number of electron groups around the central atom:
There are two electron groups on C.
Determine the number of bonding groups and the number of lone pairs around the central atom:
There are two bonding groups and no lone pairs.

Use Table 10.1 to determine the electron geometry, molecular geometry, and bond angles:
Two electron groups give a linear geometry; two bonding groups and no lone pairs give a linear molecular geometry; the idealized bond angle is 180°. The molecule will not deviate from this.

10.37 H_2O will have the smaller bond angle because lone pair–lone pair repulsions are greater than lone pair–bonding pair repulsions.
Draw the Lewis structures for both structures:

H_3O^+ has eight valence electrons. H_2O has eight valence electrons.

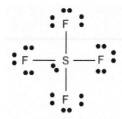

There are three bonding groups and   There are two bonding groups and
one lone pair.   two lone pairs.

Both have 4 electron groups, but the 2 lone pairs in H_2O will cause the bond angle to be smaller because of the lone pair–lone pair repulsions.

10.39   (a) SF_4 Draw a Lewis structure for the molecule:
SF_4 has 34 valence electrons.

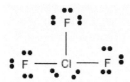

Determine the total number of electron groups around the central atom:
There are five electron groups on S.
Determine the number of bonding groups and the number of lone pairs around the central atom:
There are four bonding groups and one lone pair.
Use Table 10.1 to determine the electron geometry and molecular geometry:
The electron geometry is trigonal bipyramidal so the molecular geometry is seesaw.
Sketch the molecule:

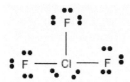

(b) ClF_3 Draw a Lewis structure for the molecule:
ClF_3 has 28 valence electrons.

Determine the total number of electron groups around the central atom:
There are five electron groups on Cl.
Determine the number of bonding groups and the number of lone pairs around the central atom:
There are three bonding groups and two lone pairs.
Use Table 10.1 to determine the electron geometry and molecular geometry:

The electron geometry is trigonal bipyramidal so the molecular geometry is T-shaped.
Sketch the molecule:

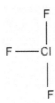

(c) IF_2^- Draw a Lewis structure for the ion:
IF_2^- has 22 valence electrons.

$$\left[\ :\!\ddot{F}\!\!-\!\!\overset{\bullet\bullet}{\underset{\bullet\bullet}{I}}\!\!-\!\!\ddot{F}\!: \ \right]^-$$

Determine the total number of electron groups around the central atom:
There are five electron groups on I.
Determine the number of bonding groups and the number of lone pairs around the central atom:
There are two bonding groups and three lone pairs.
Use Table 10.1 to determine the electron geometry and molecular geometry:
The electron geometry is trigonal bipyramidal so the molecular geometry is linear.
Sketch the ion:

$$[\,F \longrightarrow I \longrightarrow F\,]^-$$

(d) IBr_4^- Draw a Lewis structure for the ion:
IBr_4^- has 36 valence electrons.

$$\left[\begin{array}{c} :\!\ddot{Br}\!: \\ | \\ :\!\ddot{Br}\!\!-\!\!I\!\!-\!\!\ddot{Br}\!: \\ | \\ :\!\ddot{Br}\!: \end{array} \right]^-$$

Determine the total number of electron groups around the central atom:
There are six electron groups on I.
Determine the number of bonding groups and the number of lone pairs around the central atom:
There are four bonding groups and two lone pairs.
Use Table 10.1 to determine the electron geometry and molecular geometry:
The electron geometry is octahedral so the molecular geometry is square planar.
Sketch the ion:

$$\left[\begin{array}{ccc} Br & & Br \\ & \diagdown I \diagup & \\ Br & & Br \end{array} \right]^-$$

10.41   (a) C_2H_2 Draw the Lewis structure:

$$H - C \equiv C - H$$

Atom	Number of Electron Groups	Number of Lone Pairs	Molecular Geometry
Left C	2	0	Linear
Right C	2	0	Linear

Sketch the molecule:

$$H - C \equiv C - H$$

(b) C_2H_4 Draw the Lewis structure:

Atom	Number of Electron Groups	Number of Lone Pairs	Molecular Geometry
Left C	3	0	Trigonal planar
Right C	3	0	Trigonal planar

Sketch the molecule:

(c) $C_2{}_6$ Draw the Lewis structure:

Atom	Number of Electron Groups	Number of Lone Pairs	Molecular Geometry
Left C	4	0	Tetrahedral
Right C	4	0	Tetrahedral

Sketch the molecule:

10.43   (a)   Four pairs of electrons give a tetrahedral electron geometry. The lone pair would cause lone pair–bonded pair repulsions and would have a trigonal pyramidal molecular geometry.

         (b)   Five pairs of electrons give a trigonal bipyramidal electron geometry. The lone pair occupies an equatorial position in order to minimize lone pair–bonded pair repulsions and the molecule would have a seesaw molecular geometry.

         (c)   Six pairs of electrons give an octahedral electron geometry. The two lone pairs would occupy opposite positions in order to minimize lone pair–lone pair repulsions. The molecular geometry would be square planar.

10.45   (a) CH_3OH Draw the Lewis structure and determine the geometry about each interior atom:

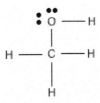

Atom	Number of Electron Groups	Number of Lone Pairs	Molecular Geometry
C	4	0	Tetrahedral
O	4	2	Bent

Sketch the molecule:

         (b) CH_3OCH_3 Draw the Lewis structure and determine the geometry about each interior atom:

Atom	Number of Electron Groups	Number of Lone Pairs	Molecular Geometry
C	4	0	Tetrahedral
O	4	2	Bent
C	4	0	Tetrahedral

Sketch the molecule:

(c) H_2O_2 Draw the Lewis structure and determine the geometry about each interior atom:

$$ H — \overset{\bullet\bullet}{\underset{\bullet\bullet}{O}} — \overset{\bullet\bullet}{\underset{\bullet\bullet}{O}} — H $$

Atom	Number of Electron Groups	Number of Lone Pairs	Molecular Geometry
O	4	2	Bent
O	4	2	Bent

Sketch the molecule:

$$ \overset{\displaystyle O—O}{\underset{\displaystyle H \qquad H}{} } $$

Molecular Shape and Polarity

10.47   Draw the Lewis structure for CO_2 and CCl_4 determine the molecular geometry and then the polarity.

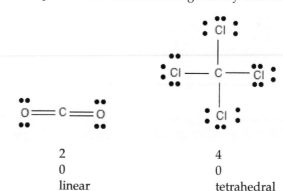

	CO_2	CCl_4
Number of electron groups on C	2	4
Number of lone pairs	0	0
Molecular geometry	linear	tetrahedral

Even though each molecule contains polar bonds, the sum of the bond dipoles gives a net dipole of zero for each molecule.

The linear molecular geometry of CO_2 will have bond vectors that are equal and opposite. $\longleftarrow \quad \longrightarrow$

The tetrahedral molecular geometry of CCl_4 will have bond vectors that are equal and have a net dipole of zero.

10.49   (a) PF_3 – polar

Draw the Lewis structure and determine the molecular geometry:
The molecular geometry from Exercise 35 is trigonal pyramidal.

Determine if the molecule contains polar bonds:
The electronegativities of P = 2.1 and F = 4. Therefore the bonds are polar.

Determine whether the polar bonds add together to form a net dipole:
Because the molecule is trigonal pyramidal, the three dipole moments sum to a nonzero net dipole moment. The molecule is polar. See Table 10.2 p. 415 in text to see how dipole moments add to determine polarity.

(b) SBr_2 – nonpolar

Draw the Lewis structure and determine the molecular geometry:
The molecular geometry from Exercise 35 is bent.

Determine if the molecule contains polar bonds:
The electronegativities of S = 2.5 and Br = 2.8. Therefore the bonds are nonpolar.

Even though the molecule is bent, since the bonds are nonpolar, the molecule is nonpolar.

(c) $CHCl_3$ – polar

Draw the Lewis structure and determine the molecular geometry:
The molecular geometry from Exercise 35 is tetrahedral.

Determine if the molecule contains polar bonds:
The electronegativities of C = 2.5, H = 2.1, and Cl = 3.0. Therefore the bonds are polar.

Determine whether the polar bonds add together to form a net dipole:
Because the bonds have different dipole moments due to the different atoms involved, the four dipole moments sum to a nonzero net dipole moment. The molecule is polar. See Table 10.2 p. 415 in text to see how dipole moments add to determine polarity.

(d) CS_2 – nonpolar

Draw the Lewis structure and determine the molecular geometry:
The molecular geometry from Exercise 35 is linear.

Determine if the molecule contains polar bonds:
The electronegativities of C = 2.5 and S = 2.5. Therefore the bonds are nonpolar. Also, the molecule is linear, which would result in a zero net dipole even if the bonds were polar.
The molecule is nonpolar. See Table 10.2 p. 415 in text to see how dipole moments add to determine polarity.

10.51   (a) ClO_3^- – polar

Draw the Lewis structure and determine the molecular geometry:

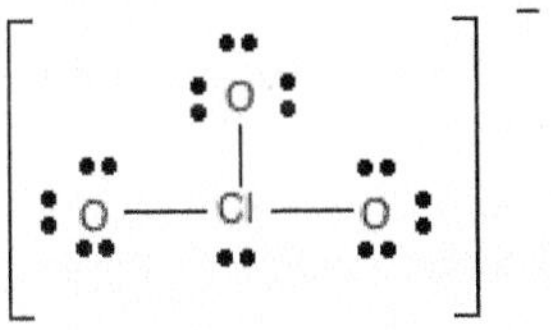

Four electron pairs, with one lone pair give a trigonal pyramidal molecular geometry.

Determine if the molecule contains polar bonds:
The electronegativities of Cl = 3.0 and O = 3.5. Therefore the bonds are polar.

Determine whether the polar bonds add together to form a net dipole:
Because the molecular geometry is trigonal pyramidal, the three dipole moments sum to a nonzero net dipole moment. The molecule is polar. See Table 10.2 p. 415 in text to see how dipole moments add to determine polarity.

(b) SCl_2 – polar

Draw the Lewis structure and determine the molecular geometry:

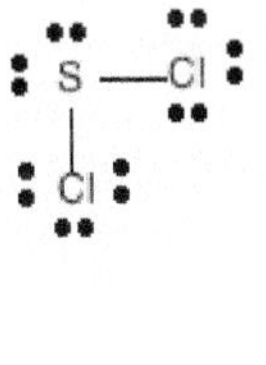

Four electron pairs with two lone pairs give a bent molecular geometry.

Determine if the molecule contains polar bonds:
The electronegativities of S = 2.5 and Cl = 3.0. Therefore the bonds are polar.

Determine whether the polar bonds add together to form a net dipole:
Because the molecular geometry is bent, the two dipole moments sum to a nonzero net dipole moment. The molecule is polar. See Table 10.2 p. 415 in text to see how dipole moments add to determine polarity.

(c) SCl_4 – polar
      Draw the Lewis structure and determine the molecular geometry:

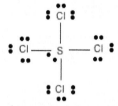

Five electron pairs with one lone pair give a seesaw molecular geometry.

Determine if the molecule contains polar bonds:
The electronegativities of S = 2.5 and Cl = 3.0. Therefore the bonds are polar.

Determine whether the polar bonds add together to form a net dipole:
Because the molecular geometry is seesaw, the four equal dipole moments sum to a nonzero net dipole moment. The molecule is polar.
The seesaw molecular geometry will not have offsetting bond vectors.

(d) $BrCl_5$ – nonpolar
      Draw the Lewis structure and determine the molecular geometry.

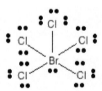

Six electron pairs with one lone pair gives square pyramidal molecular geometry.

Determine if the molecule contains polar bonds:
The electronegativity of Br = 2.8 and Cl = 3.0. The difference is only 0.2, therefore the bonds are nonpolar. Even though the molecular geometry is square pyramidal, the five bonds are nonpolar so there is no net dipole. The molecule is nonpolar.

Valence Bond Theory

10.53   (a)   Be $2s^2$ No bonds can form. Beryllium contains no unpaired electrons, so no bonds can form without hybridization.

        (b)   P $3s^2 3p^3$ Three bonds can form. Phosphorus contains three unpaired electrons, so three bonds can form without hybridization.

        (c)   F $2s^2 2p^5$ One bond can form. Fluorine contains one unpaired electron, so one bond can form without hybridization.

10.55 PH_3

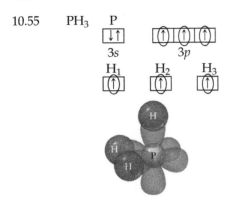

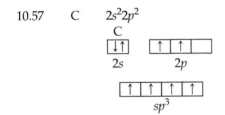

The unhybridized bond angles should be 90°. So, without hybridization, there is good agreement between valence bond theory and the actual bond angle of 93.3°.

10.57   C $2s^2 2p^2$

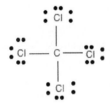

10.59 sp^2 Only sp^2 hybridization of this set of orbitals has a remaining p orbital to form a π bond.
sp^3 hybridization utilizes all 3 p orbitals.
$sp^3 d^2$ hybridization utilizes all 3 p orbitals and 2 d orbitals.

10.61   (a) CCl_4 Write the Lewis structure for the molecule:

$$\begin{array}{c}
: \overset{\displaystyle ..}{\underset{\displaystyle ..}{Cl}} : \\
| \\
: \overset{\displaystyle ..}{\underset{\displaystyle ..}{Cl}} \;—\; C \;—\; \overset{\displaystyle ..}{\underset{\displaystyle ..}{Cl}} : \\
| \\
: \overset{\displaystyle ..}{\underset{\displaystyle ..}{Cl}} :
\end{array}$$

Use VSEPR to predict the electron geometry:
Four electron groups around the central atom give a tetrahedral electron geometry.

Select the correct hybridization for the central atom based on the electron geometry:
Tetrahedral electron geometry has sp^3 hybridization.

Sketch the molecule and label the bonds:

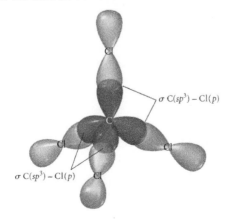

(b) NH_3 Write the Lewis structure for the molecule:

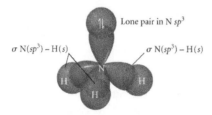

Use VSEPR to predict the electron geometry:
Four electron groups around the central atom give a tetrahedral electron geometry.

Select the correct hybridization for the central atom based on the electron geometry:
Tetrahedral electron geometry has sp^3 hybridization.

Sketch the molecule and label the bonds:

Lone pair in N sp^3

σ N(sp^3) – H(s) σ N(sp^3) – H(s)

(c) OF_2 Write the Lewis structure for the molecule:

$$:\!\overset{\displaystyle ..}{\underset{\displaystyle ..}{F}}\!-\!\overset{\displaystyle ..}{\underset{\displaystyle ..}{O}}\!-\!\overset{\displaystyle ..}{\underset{\displaystyle ..}{F}}\!:$$

Use VSEPR to predict the electron geometry:
Four electron groups around the central atom give a tetrahedral electron geometry.

Select the correct hybridization for the central atom based on the electron geometry:
Tetrahedral electron geometry has sp^3 hybridization.

Sketch the molecule and label the bonds:

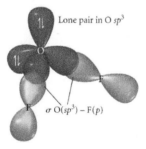

Lone pair in O sp^3

σ O(sp^3) – F(p)

(d)   CO   Write the Lewis structure for the molecule:

$$\overset{\displaystyle ..}{\underset{\displaystyle ..}{O}}\!=\!C\!=\!\overset{\displaystyle ..}{\underset{\displaystyle ..}{O}}$$

Use VSEPR to predict the electron geometry:
Two electron groups around the central atom give a linear electron geometry.

Select the correct hybridization for the central atom based on the electron geometry:
Linear electron geometry has   hybridization.

Sketch the molecule and label the bonds:

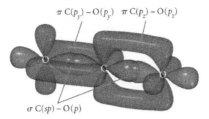

10.63   (a) $COCl_2$ Write the Lewis structure for the molecule:

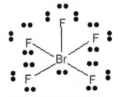

Use VSEPR to predict the electron geometry:
Three electron groups around the central atom give a trigonal planar electron geometry.

Select the correct hybridization for the central atom based on the electron geometry:
Trigonal planar electron geometry has sp^2 hybridization.

Sketch the molecule and label the bonds:

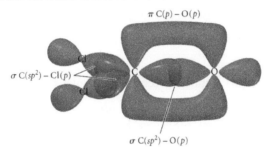

(b)   BrF   Write the Lewis structure for the molecule:

Use VSEPR to predict the electron geometry:
Six electron pairs around the central atoms gives an octahedral electron geometry.

Select the correct hybridization for the central atom based on the electron geometry:
Octahedral electron geometry has sp^3d^2 hybridization.

Sketch the molecule and label the bonds:

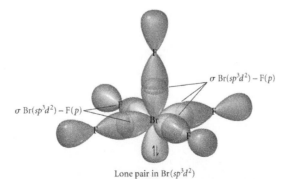

(c)   XeF₂   Write the Lewis structure for the molecule:

$$\overset{\bullet\bullet}{\underset{\bullet\bullet}{F}} \text{—} \overset{\bullet\bullet}{Xe} \text{—} \overset{\bullet\bullet}{\underset{\bullet\bullet}{F}}$$

Use VSEPR to predict the electron geometry:
Five electron groups around the central atom give a trigonal bipyramidal geometry.

Select the correct hybridization for the central atom based on the electron geometry:
Trigonal bipyramidal geometry has sp^3d hybridization.

Sketch the molecule and label the bonds:

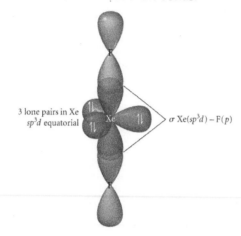

3 lone pairs in Xe
sp^3d equatorial

σ Xe(sp^3d) – F(p)

(d)   I₃⁻   Write the Lewis structure for the molecule:

$$\left[\;\overset{\bullet\bullet}{\underset{\bullet\bullet}{I}} \text{—} \overset{\bullet\bullet}{\underset{\bullet\bullet}{I}} \text{—} \overset{\bullet\bullet}{\underset{\bullet\bullet}{I}}\;\right]^{-}$$

Use VSEPR to predict the electron geometry:
Five electron groups around the central atom give a trigonal bipyramidal geometry.

Select the correct hybridization for the central atom based on the electron geometry:
Trigonal bipyramidal geometry has sp^3d hybridization.

Sketch the molecule and label the bonds:

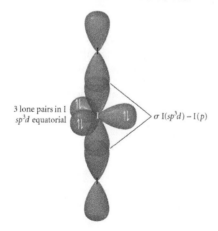

3 lone pairs in I
sp^3d equatorial

σ I(sp^3d) – I(p)

10.65   (a)   N₂H₂   Write the Lewis structure for the molecule:

$$H \text{—} \overset{\bullet\bullet}{N} \text{=} \overset{\bullet\bullet}{N} \text{—} H$$

Use VSEPR to predict the electron geometry:
Three electron groups around each interior atom give a trigonal planar electron geometry.

Select the correct hybridization for the central atoms based on the electron geometry:
Trigonal planar electron geometry has sp^2 hybridization.

Sketch the molecule and label the bonds:

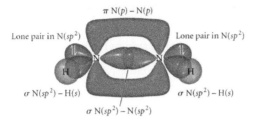

(b) N_2H_4 Write the Lewis structure for the molecule:

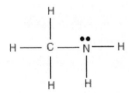

Use VSEPR to predict the electron geometry:
Four electron groups around each interior atom gives tetrahedral electron geometry.

Select the correct hybridization for the central atoms based on the electron geometry:
Tetrahedral electron geometry has sp^3 hybridization.

Sketch the molecule and label the bonds:

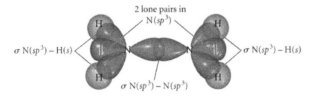

(c) CH_3NH_2 Write the Lewis structure for the molecule:

$$\begin{array}{c} H \\ | \\ H - C - \overset{\bullet\bullet}{N} - H \\ | \quad\; | \\ H \quad H \end{array}$$

Use VSEPR to predict the electron geometry:
Four electron groups around the C give a tetrahedral electron geometry around the C atom, and four electron groups around the N give a tetrahedral geometry around the N atom.

Select the correct hybridization for the central atoms based on the electron geometry:
Tetrahedral electron geometry has sp^3 hybridization of both C and N.

Sketch the molecule and label the bonds:

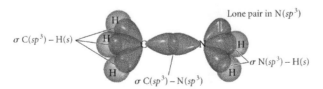

10.67

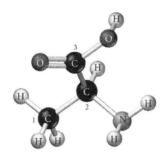

C – 1 and C – 2 each have four electron pairs around the atom, which is tetrahedral electron pair geometry. Tetrahedral electron pair geometry is sp^3 hybridization.

C – 3 has three electron groups around the atom, which is trigonal planar electron pair geometry. Trigonal planar electron pair geometry is sp^2 hybridization.

O has four electron pairs around the atom, which is tetrahedral electron pair geometry. Tetrahedral electron pair geometry is sp^3 hybridization.

N has four electron pairs around the atom, which is tetrahedral electron pair geometry. Tetrahedral electron pair geometry is sp^3 hybridization.

Molecular Orbital Theory

10.69 $1s + 1s$ constructive interference results in a bonding orbital:

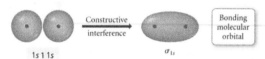

10.71 Be_2^+ has seven electrons. Be_2^- has nine electrons.

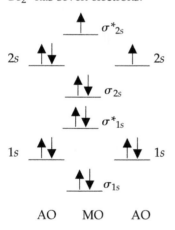

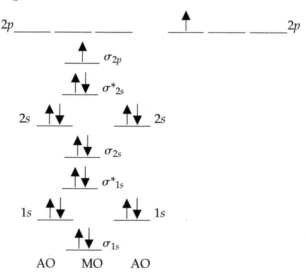

AO = Atomic Orbital; MO = Molecular Orbital

Bond order = $\dfrac{4-3}{2} = \dfrac{1}{2}$ stable   Bond order = $\dfrac{5-4}{2} = \dfrac{1}{2}$ stable

10.73   The bonding and antibonding molecular orbitals from the combination of p_x and p_x atomic orbitals lie along the internuclear axis.

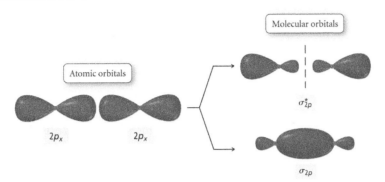

10.75   (a) 4 valence electrons   (b) 6 valence electrons   (c) 8 valence electrons   (d) 9 valence electrons

(a) Bond order $= \dfrac{2-2}{2} = 0$ diamagnetic

(b) Bond order $= \dfrac{4-2}{2} = 1$ paramagnetic

(c) Bond order $= \dfrac{6-2}{2} = 2$ diamagnetic

(d) Bond order $= \dfrac{7-2}{2} = 2.5$ paramagnetic

10.77   (a)   Write an energy level diagram for the molecular orbitals in H_2^{2-}. The ion has four valence electrons. Assign the electrons to the molecular orbitals beginning with the lowest energy orbitals and following Hund's rule.

         Bond order $= \dfrac{2-2}{2} = 0$.   With a bond order of 0, the ion will not exist.

       (b)   Write an energy level diagram for the molecular orbitals in Ne_2. The molecule has 16 valence electrons. Assign the electrons to the molecular orbitals beginning with the lowest energy orbitals and following Hund's rule.

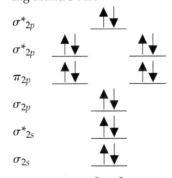

         Bond order $= \dfrac{8-8}{2} = 0$. With a bond order of 0, the molecule will not exist.

(c) Write an energy level diagram for the molecular orbitals in He_2^{2+}. The ion has two valence electrons. Assign the electrons to the molecular orbitals beginning with the lowest energy orbitals and following Hund's rule.

σ^*_{1s} _____

σ_{1s} ⤉

Bond order $= \dfrac{2-0}{2} = 1$. With a bond order of 1, the ion will exist.

(d) Write an energy level diagram for the molecular orbitals in F_2^{2-}. The molecule has 16 valence electrons. Assign the electrons to the molecular orbitals beginning with the lowest energy orbitals and following Hund's rule.

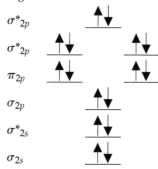

σ^*_{2p}

σ^*_{2p}

π_{2p}

σ_{2p}

σ^*_{2s}

σ_{2s}

Bond order $= \dfrac{8-8}{2} = 0$. With a bond order of 0, the ion will not exist.

10.79 C_2^- has the highest bond order, the highest bond energy, and the shortest bond.
Write an energy level diagram for the molecular orbitals in each of the C_2 species.
Assign the electrons to the molecular orbitals beginning with the lowest energy orbitals and following Hund's rule for each of the species.
C_2 (8 valence electrons); C_2^+ (7 valence electrons): C_2^- (9 valence electrons)

	C_2	C_2^+	C_2^-

σ^*_{2p}

σ^*_{2p}

σ_{2p}

π_{2p}

σ^*_{2s}

σ_{2s}

Bond order $= \dfrac{6-2}{2} = 2$ Bond order $= \dfrac{5-2}{2} = 1.5$ Bond order $= \dfrac{7-2}{2} = 2.5$

C_2^- has the highest bond order at 2.5. Bond order is directly related to bond energy, so C_2^- has the largest bond energy and bond order is inversely related to bond length, so C_2^- has the shortest bond length.

10.81 Write an energy level diagram for the molecular orbitals in CO using O_2 energy ordering.
Assign the electrons to the molecular orbitals beginning with the lowest energy orbitals and following Hund's rule.

CO has 10 valence electrons.

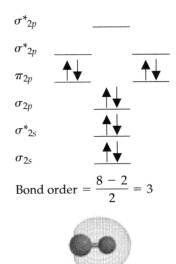

Bond order $= \dfrac{8-2}{2} = 3$

The electron density is toward the O atom since it is more electronegative.

Cumulative Problems

10.83   **(a)** COF_2 Write the Lewis structure for the molecule:

Use VSEPR to predict the electron geometry:
Three electron groups around the central atom give a trigonal planar electron geometry. Three bonding pairs of electrons give a trigonal planar molecular geometry.

Determine if the molecule contains polar bonds:
The electronegativities of C = 2.5, O = 3.5, and F = 4.0 Therefore the bonds are polar.

Determine whether the polar bonds add together to form a net dipole:
Even though a trigonal planar molecular geometry normally is nonpolar, because the bonds have different dipole moments, the sum of the dipole moments is not zero. The molecule is polar. See Table 10.2 p. 415 in text to see how dipole moments add to determine polarity.

Select the correct hybridization for the central atom based on the electron geometry:
Trigonal planar geometry has sp^2 hybridization.

Sketch the molecule and label the bonds:

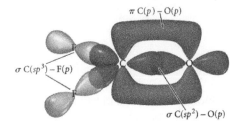

(b) S_2Cl_2 Write the Lewis structure for the molecule:

Use VSEPR to predict the electron geometry:
Four electron groups around the central atom give a tetrahedral electron geometry. Two bonding pairs and two lone pairs of electrons give a bent molecular geometry.

Determine if the molecule contains polar bonds:
The electronegativities of S = 2.5 and Cl = 3.0. Therefore the bonds are polar.

Determine whether the polar bonds add together to form a net dipole:
In a bent molecular geometry the sum of the dipole moments is not zero. The molecule is polar. See Table 10.2 p. 415 in text to see how dipole moments add to determine polarity.

Select the correct hybridization for the central atom based on the electron geometry:
Tetrahedral geometry has sp^3 hybridization.

Sketch the molecule and label the bonds:

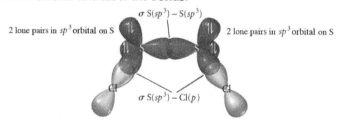

(c) SF_4 Write the Lewis structure for the molecule:

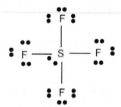

Use VSEPR to predict the electron geometry:
Five electron groups around the central atom give a trigonal bipyramidal electron geometry. Four bonding pairs and one lone pair of electrons give a seesaw molecular geometry.

Determine if the molecule contains polar bonds:
The electronegativities of S = 2.5 and F = 4.0. Therefore the bonds are polar.

Determine whether the polar bonds add together to form a net dipole:
In a seesaw molecular geometry the sum of the dipole moments is not zero. The molecule is polar. See Table 10.2 p. 415 in text to see how dipole moments add to determine polarity.

Select the correct hybridization for the central atom based on the electron geometry:
Trigonal bipyramidal electron geometry has sp^3d hybridization.

Sketch the molecule and label the bonds:

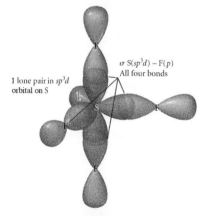

10.85   (a)   serine

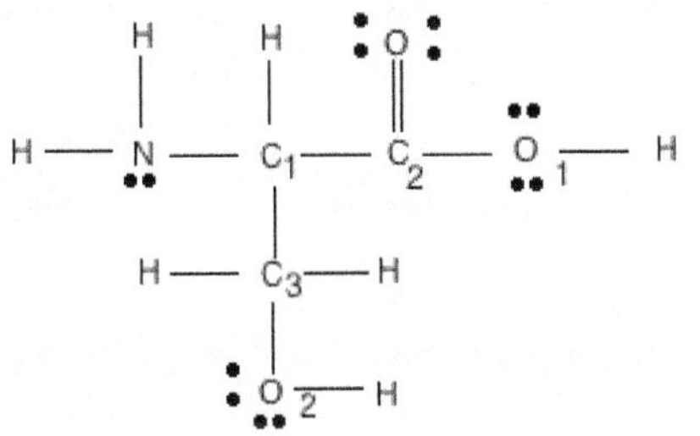

C – 1 and C – 3 each have four electron groups around the atom. Four electron pairs give a tetrahedral electron geometry; tetrahedral electron geometry has sp^3 hybridization. Four bonding pairs and zero lone pairs give a tetrahedral molecular geometry.

C – 2 has three electron groups around the atom. Three electron pairs give a trigonal planar geometry; trigonal planar geometry has sp^2 hybridization. Three bonding pairs and zero lone pairs give a trigonal planar molecular geometry.

N has four electron groups around the atom. Four electron pairs give a tetrahedral electron geometry; tetrahedral electron geometry has sp^3 hybridization. Three bonding pairs and one lone pair give a trigonal pyramidal molecular geometry.

O – 1 and O – 2 each have four electron groups around the atom. Four electron pairs give a tetrahedral electron geometry; tetrahedral electron geometry has sp^3 hybridization. Two bonding pairs and two lone pairs give a bent molecular geometry.

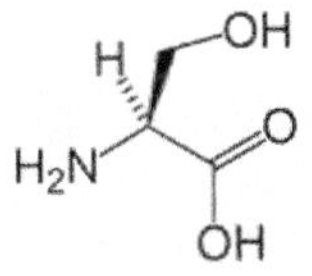

(b)   asparagine

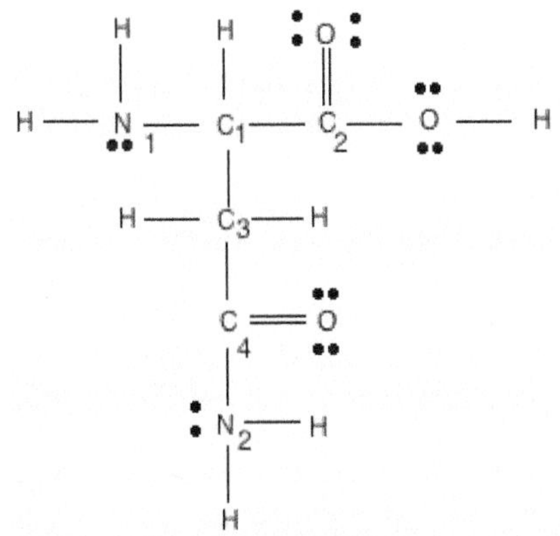

C – 1 and C – 3 each have four electron groups around the atom. Four electron groups give a tetrahedral electron geometry; tetrahedral electron geometry has sp^3 hybridization. Four bonding groups and zero lone pairs give a tetrahedral molecular geometry.

C – 2 and C – 4 each have three electron groups around the atom. Three electron groups give a trigonal planar geometry; trigonal planar geometry has sp^2 hybridization. Three bonding pairs and zero lone groups give a trigonal planar molecular geometry.

N – 1 and N – 2 each have four electron groups around the atom. Four electron groups give a tetrahedral electron geometry; tetrahedral electron geometry has sp^3 hybridization. Three bonding groups and one lone pair give a trigonal pyramidal molecular geometry.

O has four electron groups around the atom. Four electron groups give a tetrahedral electron geometry; tetrahedral electron geometry has sp^3 hybridization. Two bonding groups and two lone pairs give a bent molecular geometry.

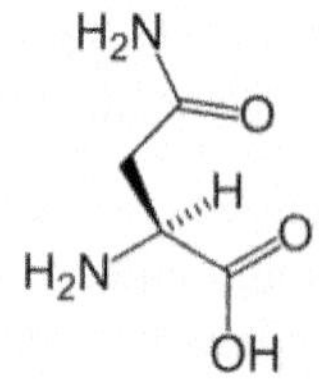

(c)   cysteine

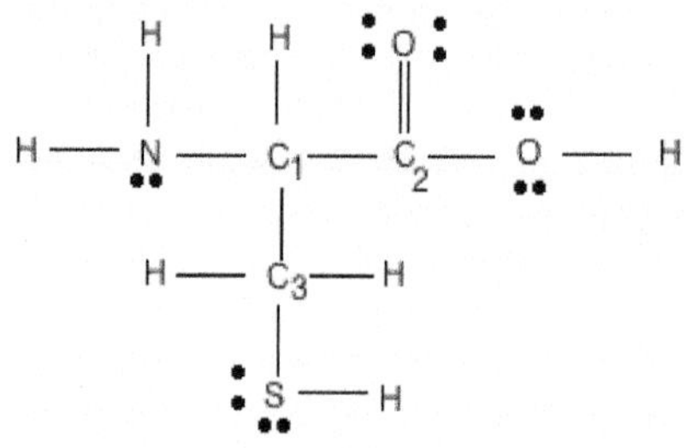

C – 1 and C – 3 each have four electron groups around the atom. Four electron pairs give a tetrahedral electron geometry; tetrahedral electron geometry has sp^3 hybridization. Four bonding pairs and zero lone pairs give a tetrahedral molecular geometry.

C – 2 has three electron groups around the atom. Three electron groups give a trigonal planar geometry; trigonal planar geometry has sp^2 hybridization. Three bonding groups and zero lone pairs give a trigonal planar molecular geometry.

N has four electron groups around the atom. Four electron groups give a tetrahedral electron geometry; tetrahedral electron geometry has sp^3 hybridization. Three bonding groups and one lone pair give a trigonal pyramidal molecular geometry.

O and S have four electron groups around the atom. Four electron groups give a tetrahedral electron geometry; tetrahedral electron geometry has sp^3 hybridization. Two bonding groups and two lone pairs gives bent molecular geometry.

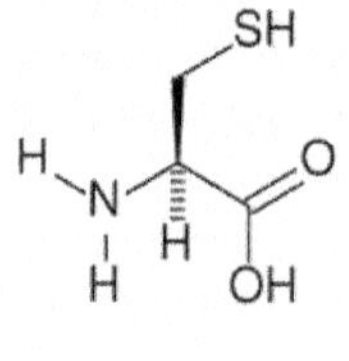

10.87   4 π bonds; 25 σ bonds; the lone pair on the Os and N – 2 occupy sp^2 orbitals; the lone pairs on N – 1, N – 3, and N – 4 occupy sp^3 orbitals.

caffeine

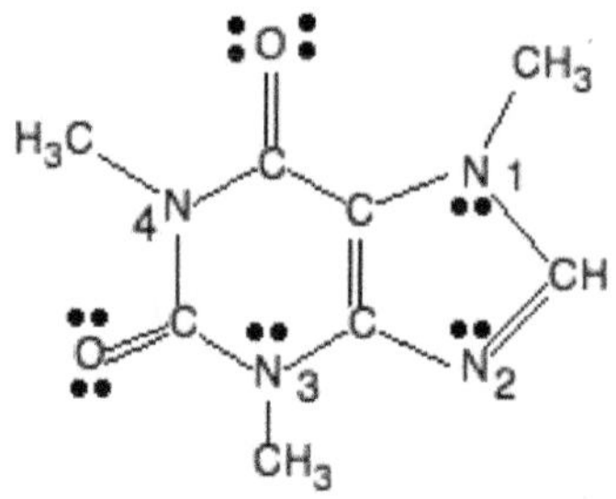

10.89   (a)   Water soluble: The 4 C – OH bonds, the C = O bond, and the C – O bonds in the ring, make the molecule polar. Because of the large electronegativity difference between the C and O, each of the bonds will have a dipole moment. The sum of the dipole moments does NOT give a net zero dipole moment, so the molecule is polar. Since it is polar, it will be water soluble.

(b)   Fat soluble: There is only one C – O bond in the molecule. The dipole moment from this bond is not enough to make the molecule polar because of all of the nonpolar components of the molecule. The C – H bonds in the structure lead to a net dipole of zero for most of the sites in the molecule. Since the molecule is nonpolar, it is fat soluble.

(c)   Water soluble: The carboxylic acid function (COOH group) along with the N atom in the ring make the molecule polar. Because of the electronegativity difference between the C and O and the C and N atoms, the bonds will have a dipole moment and the net dipole moment of the molecule is NOT zero, so the molecule is polar. Since the molecule is polar, it is water soluble.

(d)   Fat soluble: The two O atoms in the structure contribute a very small amount to the net dipole moment of this molecule. The majority of the molecule is nonpolar because there is no net dipole moment at the interior C atoms. Because the molecule is nonpolar it is fat soluble.

10.91   ClF has 14 valence electrons. Assign the electrons to the lowest energy MOs first and then follow Hund's rule. The MOs are formed from the $2s$ and $2p$ orbitals on F and the $3s$ and $3p$ orbitals on Cl.

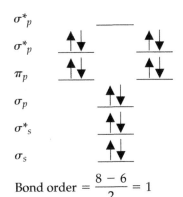

Bond order $= \dfrac{8-6}{2} = 1$

10.93   BrF (14 valence electrons)

$$:\!\overset{\textstyle ..}{\underset{\textstyle ..}{Br}}\!-\!\overset{\textstyle ..}{\underset{\textstyle ..}{F}}\!:$$

no central atom, no hybridization, no electron structure

BrF_2^- (22 valence electrons)

$$\left[\,:\!\overset{\textstyle ..}{\underset{\textstyle ..}{F}}\!-\!\overset{\textstyle ..}{\underset{\textstyle ..}{Br}}\!-\!\overset{\textstyle ..}{\underset{\textstyle ..}{F}}\!:\,\right]^-$$

There are five electron pairs on the central atom so the electron geometry is trigonal bipyramidal. The two bonding pairs and three lone pairs give a linear molecular geometry. An electron geometry of trigonal bipyramidal has sp^3d hybridization.

BrF_3 (28 valence electrons)

$$\overset{\displaystyle :\!\overset{..}{F}\!:}{\underset{\displaystyle :\!\overset{..}{\underset{..}{F}}\!-\!\overset{..}{\underset{..}{Br}}\!-\!\overset{..}{\underset{..}{F}}\!:}{\big|}}$$

There are five electron pairs on the central atom so the electron geometry is trigonal bipyramidal. The three bonding pairs and two lone pairs give a T-shaped molecular geometry. An electron geometry of trigonal bipyramidal has sp^3d hybridization.

BrF_4^- (36 valence electrons)

There are six electron pairs on the central atom so the electron geometry is octahedral. The four bonding pairs and two lone pairs give a square planar molecular geometry. An electron geometry of octahedral has d^2 hybridization.

BrF_5 (42 valence electrons)

There are six electron pairs on the central atom so the electron geometry is octahedral. The five bonding pairs and one lone pair give a square pyramidal molecular geometry. An electron geometry of octahedral has sp^3d^2 hybridization.

10.95   Draw the Lewis structure: $C_4H_6Cl_2$ (36 valence electrons)

Even though the C –Cl bonds are polar, the net dipole will since the C – Cl bonds and the C – CH$_3$ bonds are on opposite sides of the double bond. This will result in bond vectors that cancel each other.

10.97   (a)   N O$_5$ Draw the Lewis structure: (40 valence electrons)

Each N has a trigonal planar electron geometry so there are 3 sp^2 hybrid orbitals on each N. The central O has tetrahedral electron geometry, so there are 4 sp^3 hybrid orbitals. There are a total of 10 hybrid orbitals.

(b) C_2H_5NO Draw the Lewis structure: (24 valence electrons)

C_A has a trigonal planar electron geometry, so there are 3 sp^2 hybrid orbitals.
N has a trigonal planar electron geometry, so there are 3 sp^2 hybrid orbitals.

C_B has a tetrahedral electron geometry, so there are 4 sp^3 hybrid orbitals.
O has a tetrahedral electron geometry, so there are 4 sp^3 hybrid orbitals.
There are a total of 14 hybrid orbitals.

(c)   BrCN   Draw the Lewis structure: (16 valence electrons)

$$:\!\ddot{Br}\!-\!C\!\equiv\!N:$$

The C has linear electron geometry, so there are 2 sp hybrid orbitals.

10.99   According to valence bond theory, CH_4, NH_3, and H_2O are all sp^3 hybridized. This hybridization results in
a tetrahedral electron group configuration with a 109.5° bond angle. NH_3 and H_2O deviate from this idealized bond angle because their lone electron pairs exist in their own sp^3 orbitals. The presence of lone pairs
lowers the tendency for the central atom's orbitals to hybridize. As a result, as lone pairs are added, the bond
angle moves from the 109.5° hybrid angle toward the 90° unhybridized angle.

10.101   Using the MO diagram for NH_3 assign the eight valence electrons to the molecular orbitals. Start with the

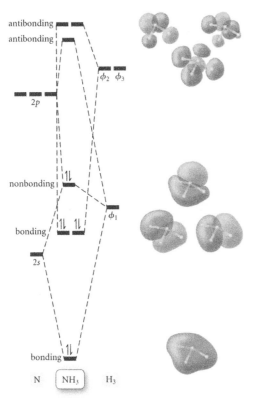

Bond order $= \dfrac{6-}{2} = 3.$

With a bond order of 3, the molecule is stable.

10.103   For each write the Lewis structure.
          Determine electron pair geometry around each central atom.
          Determine the molecular geometry, determine idealized bond angles, and predict actual bond angles.

NO_2

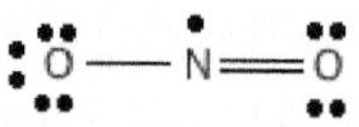

Two bonding groups and a lone electron give a trigonal planar electron geometry; the molecular geometry will be bent. Trigonal planar electron geometry has idealized bond angles of 120°. The bond angle is expected to be slightly less than 120° because of the lone electron occupying the third sp^2 orbital.

NO_2^+

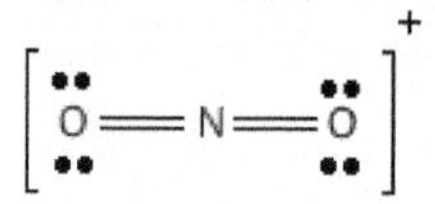

Two bonding groups of electrons and no lone pairs give a linear electron geometry and molecular geometry. Linear electron geometry has a bond angle of 180°.

NO_2^-

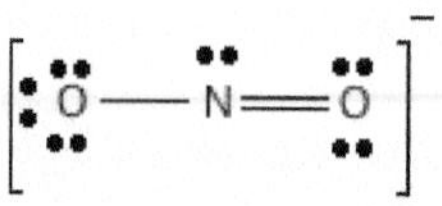

Two bonding groups of electrons and one lone pair give a trigonal planar electron geometry; the molecular geometry will be bent.
Trigonal planar electron geometry has idealized bond angles of 120°. The bond angle is expected to be less than 120° because of the lone pair electrons occupying the third sp^2 orbital. Further, the bond angle should be less than the bond angle in NO_2 because the presence of lone pairs lowers the tendency for the central atom's orbitals to hybridize. As a result, as lone pairs are added, the bond angle moves further from the 120° hybrid angle to the 90° unhybridized angle and the two electrons will increase this tendency.

10.105 CH_5^+ Draw the Lewis structure: (nine valence electrons)

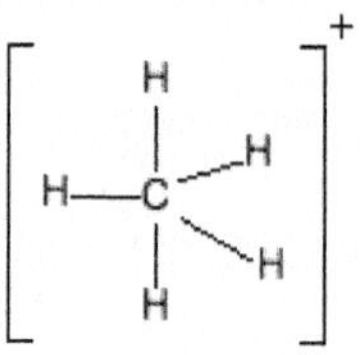

To accommodate the five σ bonds, you need five equal energy hybrid orbitals. So you need to combine five atomic orbitals. The valence electrons on C are in the 2s and 2p orbitals, so you can combine the s and 3 p orbitals, but this would only give you four hybrid orbitals. The next lowest energy orbital available on C is the 3s, so this would be the next atomic orbital added in. This gives a hybridization of s^2p^3. VSEPR theory would predict that the geometry would be trigonal bipyramid to accommodate the five bonds.

Conceptual Problems

10.107   Statement a is the best statement.
          Statement b neglects the lowering of potential energy that arises from the interaction of the lone pair electrons with the bonding electrons.
          Statement c neglects the interaction of the electrons altogether. The molecular geometries are determined by the number and types of electron groups around the central atom.

10.109   In Lewis theory, a covalent bond comes from the sharing of electrons.

A single bond shares two electrons (one pair).

A double bond shares four electrons (two pairs).

A triple bond shares six electrons (three pairs).

In valence bond theory, a covalent bond forms when orbitals overlap. The orbitals can be unhybridized or hybridized orbitals.

A single bond forms when a σ bond is formed from the overlap of an s orbital with an s orbital, an s orbital with a p orbital, or a p orbital and a p orbital overlapping end to end. A σ can also form from the overlap of a hybridized orbital on the central atom with an s orbital or with a p orbital overlapping end to end.

A double bond is a combination of a σ bond and a π bond. The π bond forms from the sideways overlap of a p orbital on each of the atoms involved in the bond. The p orbitals must have the same orientation.

A triple bond is a combination of a σ bond and 2π bonds. The π bonds form from the sideways overlap of a p orbital on each of the atoms involved in the bond. The p orbitals must have the same orientation so each π bond is formed from a different set of p orbitals.

In molecular orbital theory, molecular orbitals form. These are combinations of the atomic orbitals of the atoms involved in the bond. The bonds form when the valence electrons occupy more bonding molecular orbitals than antibonding molecular orbitals. This is calculated by the bond order.

A single bond has a bond order of 1.

A double bond has a bond order of 2.

A triple bond has a bond order of 3.

All three models show the formation of bonds between two atoms. All three models show the formation of the same number of bonds between the atoms involved. Lewis theory tells us only about the number of bonds formed and combined with VSEPR theory allows us to predict the shape of the molecule. It does not, however, tell us anything about how the bonds are formed. Valence bond theory addresses the formation of the different types of bonds, sigma and pi. In valence bond theory the bonds form from the overlap of atomic orbitals on the individual atoms involved in the bonds and the atoms are localized between the two atoms involved in the bond. Molecular orbital theory approaches the formation of bonds by looking at the entire molecule. The electrons are not restricted to any two individual atoms, but treated as belonging to the whole molecule. The electrons reside in molecular orbitals that are part of the entire molecule rather than being restricted to individual atoms. Each model gives us information about the molecule. The amount and type of information that we need determines the model that we choose to use.

11 Liquids, Solids, and Intermolecular Forces

Review Questions

11.1 The key to the gecko's sticky feet lies in the millions of microhairs, called setae, that line its toes. Each seta is between 30 and 130 μm long and branches out to end in several hundred flattened tips called spatulae. This unique structure allows the gecko's toes to have unusually close contact with the surfaces it climbs. The close contact allows intermolecular forces—which are significant only at short distances—to hold the gecko to the wall.

11.3 The main properties of liquids are that liquids have much higher densities in comparison to gases and generally have lower densities in comparison to solids; liquids have an indefinite shape and assume the shape of their container; liquids have a definite volume; and liquids are not easily compressed.

11.5 Solids may be crystalline, in which case the atoms or molecules that compose them are arranged in a well-ordered three-dimensional array, or they may be amorphous, in which case the atoms or molecules that compose them have no long-range order.

11.7 Since there is the most molecular motion in the gas phase and the least molecular motion in the solid phase (atoms are pushed closer together), a substance will be converted from a solid then to a liquid and finally to a gas as the temperature increases. The strength of the intermolecular interactions is least in the gas phase, since there are large distances between particles and they are moving very fast. Intermolecular forces are stronger in liquids and solids, where molecules are "touching" one another. The strength of the interactions in the condensed phases will determine at what temperature the substance will melt and boil.

11.9 Intermolecular forces, even the strongest ones, are generally much weaker than bonding forces. The reason for the relative weakness of intermolecular forces compared to bonding forces is related to Coulomb's law $\left(E = \dfrac{1}{4\pi\epsilon_o} \dfrac{q_1 q_2}{r} \right)$. Bonding forces are the result of large charges (the charges on protons and electrons, q_1 and q_2) interacting at very close distances (r). Intermolecular forces are the result of smaller charges (as we shall see in the following discussion) interacting at greater distances.

11.11 The dipole–dipole force exists in all molecules that are polar. Polar molecules have permanent dipoles that interact with the permanent dipoles of neighboring molecules. The positive end of one permanent dipole is attracted to the negative end of another; this attraction is the dipole–dipole force.

11.13 The hydrogen bond is a sort of super dipole–dipole force. Polar molecules containing hydrogen atoms bonded directly to fluorine, oxygen, or nitrogen exhibit an intermolecular force called hydrogen bonding. The large electronegativity difference between hydrogen and these electronegative elements means that the H atoms will have fairly large partial positive charges ($\delta+$), while the F, O, or N atoms will have fairly large partial negative charges ($\delta-$). In addition, since these atoms are all quite small, they can approach one another very closely. The result is a strong attraction between the hydrogen in each of these molecules and the F, O, or N on its neighbors, an attraction called a hydrogen bond.

11.15   Surface tension is the tendency of liquids to minimize their surface area. Molecules at the surface have relatively fewer neighbors with which to interact, because there are no molecules above the surface. Consequently, molecules at the surface are inherently less stable—they have higher potential energy—than those in the interior. In order to increase the surface area of the liquid, some molecules from the interior have to be moved to the surface, a process requiring energy. The surface tension of a liquid is the energy required to increase the surface area by a unit amount. Surface tension decreases with decreasing intermolecular forces.

11.17   Capillary action is the ability of a liquid to flow against gravity up a narrow tube. Capillary action results from a combination of two forces: the attraction between molecules in a liquid, called cohesive forces, and the attraction between these molecules and the surface of the tube, called adhesive forces. The adhesive forces cause the liquid to spread out over the surface of the tube, while the cohesive forces cause the liquid to stay together. If the adhesive forces are greater than the cohesive forces (as is the case for water in a glass tube), the attraction to the surface draws the liquid up the tube while the cohesive forces pull along those molecules not in direct contact with the tube walls. The liquid rises up the tube until the force of gravity balances the capillary action—the thinner the tube, the higher the rise. If the adhesive forces are smaller than the cohesive forces (as is the case for liquid mercury), the liquid does not rise up the tube at all (and in fact will drop to a level below the level of the surrounding liquid).

11.19   The molecules that leave the liquid are the ones at the high end of the energy curve—the most energetic. If no additional heat enters the liquid, the average energy of the entire collection of molecules goes down—much as the class average on an exam goes down if you eliminate the highest-scoring students. So vaporization is an endothermic process; it takes energy to vaporize the molecules in a liquid. Also, vaporization requires overcoming the intermolecular forces that hold liquids together. Since energy must be absorbed to pull the molecules apart, the process is endothermic. Condensation is the opposite process, so it must be

          that condense, adding energy to the liquid.

11.21   The heat of vaporization (ΔH_{vap}) is the amount of heat required to vaporize one mole of a liquid to a gas. The heat of vaporization of a liquid can be used to calculate the amount of heat energy required to vaporize a given mass of the liquid (or the amount of heat given off by the condensation of a given mass of liquid), and can be used to compare the volatility of two substances.

11.23   When a system in dynamic equilibrium is disturbed, the system responds so as to minimize the disturbance and return to a state of equilibrium.

11.25   The boiling point of a liquid is the temperature at which its vapor pressure equals the external pressure. The normal boiling point of a liquid is the temperature at which its vapor pressure equals 1 atm.

11.27   As the temperature rises, more liquid vaporizes and the pressure within the container increases. As more and more gas is forced into the same amount of space, the density of the gas becomes higher and higher. At the same time, the increasing temperature causes the density of the liquid to become lower and lower. At the critical temperature, the meniscus between the liquid and gas disappears and the gas and liquid phases commingle to form a supercritical fluid.

11.29   Fusion, or melting, is the phase transition from solid to liquid. The term fusion is used for melting because, if you heat several crystals of a solid, they will fuse into a continuous liquid upon melting. Fusion is endothermic because solids have less kinetic energy than liquids, so energy must be added to a solid to get it to melt.

11.31   There are two horizontal lines (i.e. heat is added, but the temperature stays constant) in the heating curve because there are two endothermic phase changes. The heat that is added is used to change the phase from solid to liquid or liquid to gas.

11.33   A phase diagram is simply a map of the phase of a substance as a function of pressure (on the y-axis) and temperature (on the x-axis).

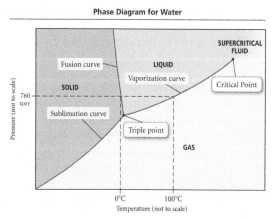

Phase Diagram for Water

11.35   Water has a low molar mass (18.01 g/mol), yet it is a liquid at room temperature. Water's high boiling point for its molar mass can be understood by examining the structure of the water molecule. The bent geometry of the water molecule and the highly polar nature of the O–H bonds result in a molecule with a significant dipole moment. Water's two O–H bonds (hydrogen directly bonded to oxygen) allow a water molecule to form strong hydrogen bonds with four other water molecules, resulting in a relatively high boiling point. Water's high polarity also allows it to dissolve many other polar and ionic compounds, and even a number of nonpolar gases such as oxygen and carbon dioxide (by inducing a dipole moment in their molecules). Water has an exceptionally high specific heat capacity. One significant difference between the phase diagram of water and that of other substances is that the fusion curve for water has a negative slope. The fusion curve within the phase diagrams for most substances has a positive slope because increasing pressure favors the denser phase, which for most substances is the solid phase. This negative slope means that ice is less dense than liquid water and so ice floats. The solid phase sinks in the liquid of most other substances.

11.37   A crystalline lattice is the regular arrangements of atoms within a crystalline solid. The crystalline lattice can be represented by a small collection of atoms, ions, or molecules—a fundamental building block called the unit cell. When the unit cell is repeated over and over—like tiles in a floor or the pattern in a wallpaper

11.39   Atoms in a simple cubic cell structure have a coordination number of 6, an edge length of $2r$, and 1 atom in the unit cell. Atoms in a body-centered cubic cell structure have a coordination number of 8, an edge length of $4r/\sqrt{3}$, and 2 atoms in the unit cell. Atoms in a face-centered cubic cell structure have a coordination number of 12, an edge length of $2\sqrt{2}r$, and 4 atoms in the unit cell.

11.41   The three types of solids are molecular solids, ionic solids and atomic solids. Molecular solids are those solids whose composite units are molecules. The lattice sites in a crystalline molecular solid are therefore occupied by molecules. Ice (solid H_2O) and dry ice (solid CO_2) are examples of molecular solids. Molecular solids are held together by the kinds of intermolecular forces—dispersion forces, dipole–dipole forces, and hydrogen bonding. Ionic solids are those solids whose composite units are ions. Table salt (NaCl) and calcium fluoride (CaF_2) are good examples of ionic solids. Ionic solids are held together by the coulombic interactions that occur between the cations and anions occupying the lattice sites in the crystal, which is an ionic bond. Atomic solids are those solids whose composite units are individual atoms. Atomic solids can themselves be divided into three categories—nonbonding atomic solids, metallic atomic solids, and network covalent atomic solids—each held together by a different kind of force. Nonbonding atomic solids, which include only the noble gases in their solid form, are held together by relatively weak dispersion forces. Metallic atomic solids, such as iron or gold, are held together by metallic bonds, which in the simplest model are represented by the interaction of metal cations with a sea of electrons that surround them. Network covalent atomic solids, such as diamond, graphite, and silicon dioxide, are held together by covalent bonds.

11.43   Cesium chloride (CsCl) is a good example of an ionic compound containing cations and anions of similar size (Cs$^+$ radius = 167 pm; Cl$^-$ radius = 181 pm). In the cesium chloride structure, the chloride ions occupy the lattice sites of a simple cubic cell and one cesium ion lies in the very center of the cell, as shown in Figure 11.51. Notice that the cesium chloride unit cell contains one chloride anion (8 x 1/8 = 1) and one cesium cation (the cesium ion in the middle belongs entirely to the unit cell) for a ratio of Cs to Cl of 1:1, just as in the formula for the compound.

The crystal structure of sodium chloride must accommodate the more disproportionate sizes of Na$^+$ (radius = 97 pm) and Cl$^-$ (radius = 181 pm). The larger chloride anion could theoretically fit many of the smaller sodium cations around it, but charge neutrality requires that each sodium cation be surrounded by an equal number of chloride anions. The structure that minimizes the energy is shown in Figure 11.52 and has a coordination number of 6 (each chloride anion is surrounded by six sodium cations and vice versa). You can visualize this structure, called the rock salt structure, as chloride anions occupying the lattice sites of a face-centered cubic structure with the smaller sodium cations occupying the holes between the anions. (Alternatively, you can visualize this structure as the sodium cations occupying the lattice sites of a face-centered cubic structure with the larger chloride anions occupying the spaces between the cations.) Each unit cell contains four chloride anions ([8 x 1/8] + [6 x $\frac{1}{2}$] = 4) and four sodium cations (12 x $\frac{1}{4}$) resulting in a ratio of 1:1, just as in the formula of the compound.

You can visualize this structure (shown in Figure 11.53), called the zinc blende structure, as sulfide anions occupying the lattice sites of a face-centered cubic structure with the smaller zinc cations occupying four of the eight tetrahedral holes located directly beneath each corner atom. A tetrahedral hole is the empty space

([8 x 1/8] + [6 x $\frac{1}{2}$] = 4) and four zinc cations (each of the four zinc cations is completely contained within the unit cell), resulting in a ratio of 1:1, just as in the formula of the compound.

11.45   Atomic solids can themselves be divided into three categories—nonbonding atomic solids, metallic atomic solids, and network covalent atomic solids. Nonbonding atomic solids, which include only the noble gases in their solid form, are held together by relatively weak dispersion forces. Metallic atomic solids, such as iron or gold, are held together by metallic bonds, which in the simplest model are represented by the interaction of metal cations with a sea of electrons that surround them. Network covalent atomic solids, such as diamond, graphite, and silicon dioxide, are held together by covalent bonds.

11.47   The band gap is an energy gap that exists between the valence band and conduction band. In metals, the valence band and conduction band are always energetically continuous—the energy difference between the top of the valence band and the bottom of the conduction band is infinitesimally small. In semiconductors, the band gap is small, allowing some electrons to be promoted at ordinary temperatures resulting in limited conductivity. In insulators, the band gap is large, and electrons are not promoted into the conduction band at ordinary temperatures, resulting in no electrical conductivity.

Intermolecular Forces

11.49   (a)   dispersion forces

(b)   dispersion forces, dipole–dipole forces, and hydrogen bonding

(c)   dispersion forces and dipole–dipole forces

(d)   dispersion forces

11.51   (a)   dispersion forces and dipole–dipole forces

(b)   dispersion forces, dipole–dipole forces, and hydrogen bonding

(c)   dispersion forces

(d)   dispersion forces

11.53   (a) CH_4 < (b) CH_3CH_3 < (c) CH_3CH_2Cl < (d) CH_3CH_2OH. The first two molecules only exhibit dispersion forces, so the boiling point increases with increasing molar mass. The third molecule also exhibits dipole–dipole forces, which are stronger than dispersion forces. The last molecule exhibits hydrogen bonding. Since these are by far the strongest intermolecular forces in this group, the last molecule has the highest boiling point.

11.55   (a) CH_3OH has the higher boiling point since it exhibits hydrogen bonding.

(b) CH_3CH_2OH has the higher boiling point since it exhibits hydrogen bonding.

(c) CH_3CH_3 has the higher boiling point since it has the larger molar mass.

11.57   (a) Br_2 has the higher vapor pressure since it has the smaller molar mass.

(b) H_2S has the higher vapor pressure since it does not exhibit hydrogen bonding.

(c) PH_3 has the higher vapor pressure since it does not exhibit hydrogen bonding.

11.59   (a)   This will not form a homogeneous solution, since one is polar and one is nonpolar.

(b)   This will form a homogeneous solution. There will be ion–dipole interactions between the K^+ and Cl^- ions and the water molecules. There will also be dispersion forces, dipole–dipole forces, and hydrogen bonding between the water molecules.

(c)   This will form a homogeneous solution. There will be dispersion forces present among all of the molecules.

(d)   This will form a homogeneous solution. There will be dispersion forces, dipole–dipole forces, and hydrogen bonding among all of the molecules.

Surface Tension, Viscosity, and Capillary Action

11.61   Water will have the higher surface tension since it exhibits hydrogen bonding, a strong intermolecular force. Acetone cannot form hydrogen bonds.

11.63   Compound A will have the higher viscosity since it can interact with other molecules along the entire molecule. The more branched isomer has a smaller surface area allowing for fewer interactions. Also the molecule is very flexible and the molecules can get tangled with each other.

11.65   In a clean glass tube the water can generate strong adhesive interactions with the glass (due to the dipoles at the surface of the glass). Water experiences adhesive forces with glass that are stronger than its cohesive forces, causing it to climb the surface of a glass tube. When grease or oil coats the glass this interferes with the formation of these adhesive interactions with the glass, since oils are nonpolar and cannot interact strongly with the dipoles in the water. Without experiencing these strong intermolecular forces with oil, the water's cohesive forces will be greater and it will be drawn away from the surface of the tube.

Vaporization and Vapor Pressure

11.67   The water in the 12 cm diameter beaker will evaporate more quickly because there is more surface area for the molecules to evaporate from. The vapor pressure will be the same in the two containers because the vapor pressure is the pressure of the gas when it is in dynamic equilibrium with the liquid (evaporation rate = condensation rate). The vapor pressure is dependent only on the substance and the temperature. The 12 cm diameter container will reach this dynamic equilibrium faster.

11.69   The boiling point and higher heat of vaporization of oil are much higher than that of water, so it will not vaporize as quickly as the water. The evaporation of water cools your skin because evaporation is an endothermic process.

11.71   **Given:** 915 kJ from candy bar, water $d = 1.00$ g/ml   **Find:** L(H_2O) vaporized at 100.0 °C
Other: $\Delta_{vap}^\circ = 40.7$ kJ/mol
Conceptual Plan: $q \rightarrow$ mol $H_2O \rightarrow$ g $H_2O \rightarrow$ mL $H_2O \rightarrow$ L H_2O

$$\frac{1 \text{ mol}}{40.7 \text{ kJ}} \qquad \frac{18.01 \text{ g}}{1 \text{ mol}} \qquad \frac{1.00 \text{ mL}}{1.00 \text{ g}} \qquad \frac{1 \text{ L}}{1000 \text{ mL}}$$

Solution: $915 \text{ kJ} \times \dfrac{1 \text{ mol}}{40.7 \text{ kJ}} \times \dfrac{18.02 \text{ g}}{1 \text{ mol}} \times \dfrac{1.00 \text{ mL}}{1 \text{ g}} \times \dfrac{1 \text{ L}}{1000 \text{ mL}} = 0.405$ L H_2O

Check: The units (L) are correct. The magnitude of the answer (< 1 L) makes physical sense because we are vaporizing about 22 moles of water.

11.73   **Given:** 0.95 g water condenses on iron block 75.0 g at $T_i = 22$ °C   **Find:** T_f (iron block)
Other: $\Delta H_{vap}^\circ = 44.0$ kJ/mol; $C_{Fe} = 0.449$ J/g $\cdot$ °C from text
Conceptual Plan: g $H_2O \rightarrow$ mol $H_2O \rightarrow q_{H_2O}$ (kJ) $\rightarrow q_{H_2O}$ (J) then $q_{Fe}, m_{Fe}, T_i \rightarrow T_f$

$$\frac{1 \text{ mol}}{18.01 \text{ g}} \qquad \frac{-44.0 \text{ kJ}}{1 \text{ mol}} \qquad \frac{1000 \text{ J}}{1 \text{ kJ}} \qquad -q_{H_2O} = q_{Fe} \qquad q = mC_s(T_f - T_i)$$

Solution: $0.95 \text{ g} \times \dfrac{1 \text{ mol}}{18.02 \text{ g}} \times \dfrac{-44.0 \text{ kJ}}{1 \text{ mol}} \times \dfrac{1000 \text{ J}}{1 \text{ kJ}} = -2319.64$ J then $-q_{H_2O} = q_{Fe} = 2319.64$ J then

$q = m\,C_s(T_f - T_i)$. Rearrange to solve for T_f.

$$T_f = \frac{m\,C_s\,T_i + q}{m\,C_s} = \frac{\left(75.0 \text{ g} \times 0.449 \dfrac{\text{J}}{\text{g} \cdot °\text{C}} \times 22 °\text{C}\right) + 2319.64 \text{ J}}{75.0 \text{ g} \times 0.449 \dfrac{\text{J}}{\text{g} \cdot °\text{C}}} = 91 °\text{C}.$$

Check: The units (°C) are correct. The temperature rose, which is consistent with heat being added to the block. The magnitude of the answer (91 °C) makes physical sense because even though we have $\sim \frac{1}{20}$ of a mole, the energy involved in condensation is very large.

11.75   **Given:**

Temperature (K)	apor Pressure (torr)
200	65.3
210	134.3
220	255.7
230	456.0
235	597.0

Find: ΔH_{vap}° (NH_3) and normal boiling point

Conceptual Plan: To find the heat of vaporization, use Excel or similar software to make a plot of the natural log of vapor pressure (ln P) as a function of the inverse of the temperature in K (1/T). Then fit the points to a line and determine the slope of the line. Since the slope = $-\Delta H_{vap}/R$, we find the heat of vaporization as follows:
slope = $-\Delta H_{vap}/R \rightarrow \Delta H_{vap} = -$ slope $\times R$ then J $\rightarrow$ kJ.

$$\frac{1 \text{ kJ}}{1000 \text{ J}}$$

For the normal boiling point, use the equation of the best fit line, substitute 760 torr for the pressure and calculate the temperature.
Solution: Data was plotted in Excel.
The slope of the best fitting line is $-$ 2969.9 K.

$$\Delta H_{vap} = -\text{ slope} \times R = -(-2969.9 \text{ K}) \times \frac{8.314 \text{ J}}{\text{K mol}} = \frac{2.46917 \times 10^4 \text{ J}}{\text{mol}} \times \frac{1 \text{ kJ}}{1000 \text{ J}} = 24.7 \frac{\text{kJ}}{\text{mol}}$$

$$\ln P = -2969.9 \text{ K}\left(\frac{1}{T}\right) + 19.036 \rightarrow$$

$$\ln 760 = -2969.9 \text{ K}\left(\frac{1}{T}\right) + 19.036 \rightarrow$$

$$2969.9 \text{ K}\left(\frac{1}{T}\right) = 19.036 - 6.63332 \rightarrow$$

$$T = \frac{2969.9 \text{ K}}{12.40268} = 239 \text{ K}$$

Check: The units (kJ/mol) are correct. The magnitude of the answer (25) is consistent with other values in the text.

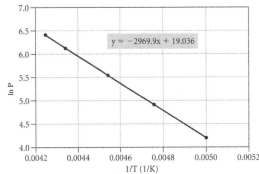

11.77 **Given:** ethanol, $\Delta H^\circ_{vap} = 38.56$ kJ/mol; normal boiling point $= 78.4\ °C$ **Find:** $P_{Ethanol}$ at $15\ °C$

Conceptual Plan: $°C \rightarrow K$ and $kJ \rightarrow J$ then $\Delta H^\circ_{vap},\ T_1,\ P_1,\ T_2 \rightarrow P_2$

$$K = °C + 273.15 \qquad \frac{1000\ J}{1\ kJ} \qquad \ln\frac{P_2}{P_1} = \frac{-\Delta H_{vap}}{R}\left(\frac{1}{T_2} - \frac{1}{T_1}\right)$$

Solution: $T_1 = 78.4\ °C + 273.15 = 351.6$ K; $\quad T_2 = 15\ °C + 273.15 = 288$ K;

$$\frac{38.56\ \cancel{kJ}}{mol} \times \frac{1000\ J}{1\ \cancel{kJ}} = 3.856 \times 10^4\ \frac{J}{mol} \quad P_1 = 760\ torr \quad \ln\frac{P_2}{P_1} = \frac{-\Delta H_{vap}}{R}\left(\frac{1}{T_2} - \frac{1}{T_1}\right).\ \text{Substitute values in}$$

equation. $\ln\dfrac{P_2}{760\ torr} = \dfrac{-3.856 \times 10^4\ \frac{\cancel{J}}{\cancel{mol}}}{8.314\ \frac{\cancel{J}}{K\cdot\cancel{mol}}}\left(\dfrac{1}{288\ K} - \dfrac{1}{351.6\ K}\right) = -2.9\underline{1}302 \rightarrow$

$\dfrac{P_2}{760\ torr} = e^{-2.9\underline{1}302} = 0.05\underline{4}311 \rightarrow P_2 = 0.05\underline{4}311 \times 760\ torr = 41\ torr.$

Check: The units (torr) are correct. Since $15\ °C$ is significantly below the boiling point, we expect the answer to be much less than 760 torr.

Sublimation and Fusion

11.79 **Given:** 65.8 g water freezes **Find:** energy released **Other:** $\Delta H^\circ_{fus} = 6.02$ kJ/mol from text

Conceptual Plan: $g\ H_2O \rightarrow mol\ H_2O \rightarrow q_{H_2O}\ (kJ) \rightarrow q_{H_2O}\ (J)$

$$\frac{1\ mol}{18.01\ g} \qquad \frac{-6.02\ kJ}{1\ mol} \qquad \frac{1000\ J}{1\ kJ}$$

Solution: $65.8\ \cancel{g} \times \dfrac{1\ \cancel{mol}}{18.02\ \cancel{g}} \times \dfrac{-6.02\ \cancel{kJ}}{1\ \cancel{mol}} \times \dfrac{1000\ J}{1\ \cancel{kJ}} = -2198\underline{2}\ J = 2.20 \times 10^4\ J$ or 2.20×10^4 J released

or 22.0 kJ released

Check: The units (J) are correct. The magnitude (22000 J) makes sense since we are freezing about 3 moles of water. Freezing is exothermic, so heat is released.

11.81 **Given:** 8.5 g ice; 255 g water **Find:** ΔT of water

Other: $\Delta H^\circ_{fus} = 6.0$ kJ/mol; $C_{H_2O} = 4.18$ J/g $\cdot$ °C from text

Conceptual Plan: The first step is to calculate how much heat is removed from the water to melt the ice.

$q_{ice} = -q_{water}$ so $g\ (ice) \rightarrow mol\ (ice) \rightarrow q_{fus}(kJ) \rightarrow q_{fus}\ (J) \rightarrow q_{water}\ (J)$ then $q,\ m,\ C_s \rightarrow \Delta T_1$

$$\frac{1\ mol}{18.01\ g} \qquad \frac{6.0\ kJ}{1\ mol} \qquad \frac{1000\ J}{1\ kJ} \qquad q_{water} = -q_{ice} \qquad q = mC_s\Delta T_1$$

Now we have slightly cooled water (at a temperature of T_1) in contact with 0.0 °C water, and we can calculate a second temperature drop of the water due to mixing of the water that was ice with the initially room temperature water, so $q_{ice} = -q_{water}$ with $m,\ C_s \rightarrow \Delta T_2$ with $\Delta T_1\ \Delta T_2 \rightarrow \Delta T_{Total}$.

$$q = m\ C_s\Delta T_2\ \text{then set}\ q_{ice} = -q_{water}\quad \Delta T_{Total} = \Delta T_1 + \Delta T_2$$

Solution: $8.5\ \cancel{g} \times \dfrac{1\ \cancel{mol}}{18.01\ \cancel{g}} \times \dfrac{6.0\ \cancel{kJ}}{1\ \cancel{mol}} \times \dfrac{1000\ J}{1\ \cancel{kJ}} = 2.83176 \times 10^3\ J,\ q_{water} = -q_{ice} = -2.\underline{8}3176 \times 10^3\ J$

$q = mC_s\Delta T$. Rearrange to solve for ΔT. $\Delta T_1 = \dfrac{q}{mC_s} = \dfrac{-2.\underline{8}3176 \times 10^3\ \cancel{J}}{255\ \cancel{g} \times 4.18\ \frac{\cancel{J}}{\cancel{g}\cdot °C}} = -2.\underline{6}567\ °C.$

$q = mC_s\Delta T$ substitute in values and set $q_{ice} = -q_{H_2O}$.

$q_{ice} = m_{ice}\ C_{ice}\left(T_f - T_{icei}\right) = 8.5\ \cancel{g} \times 4.18\ \dfrac{J}{g\cdot °C} \times \left(T_f - 0.0\ °C\right) =$

$-q_{water} = -m_{water}C_{water}\Delta T_{water2} = -255\ \cancel{g} \times 4.18\ \dfrac{J}{g\cdot °C} \times \Delta T_{water2} \rightarrow$

$8.5\ T_f = -255\Delta T_{water2} = -255(T_f - T_{f1})$. Rearrange to solve for T_f. $8.5\ T_f + 255\ T_f = 255\ T_{f1} \rightarrow$

$263.5\ T_f = 255\ T_{f1} \rightarrow T_f = 0.96\underline{7}74\ T_{f1}$ but $\Delta T_1 = (T_{f1} - T_{i1}) = -2.\underline{6}567\ °C$ which says that

$T_{f1} = T_{i1} - 2.\underline{6}567\ °C$ and $\Delta T_{Total} = (T_f - T_{i1})$ so

$\Delta T_{Total} = 0.96\underline{7}74\ T_{f1} - T_{i1} = 0.96\underline{7}74(T_{i1} - 2.\underline{6}567\ °C) - T_{i1} = -2.\underline{6}567\ °C - 0.03\underline{2}26\ T_{i1}.$

This implies that the larger the initial temperature of the water, the larger the temperature drop. If the initial temperature was 90 °C, the temperature drop would be 5.6 °C. If the initial temperature was 25 °C, the temperature drop would be 3.5 °C. If the initial temperature was 5 °C, the temperature drop would be 2.8 °C. This makes physical sense because the lower the initial temperature of the water, the less kinetic energy it initially has and the smaller the heat transfer from the water to the melted ice will be.

Check: The units (°C) are correct. The temperature drop from the melting of the ice is only 2.7 °C because the mass of the water is so much larger than the ice.

11.83   **Given:** 10.0 g ice $T_i = -10.0$ °C to steam at $T_f = 110.0$ °C   **Find:** heat required (kJ)
Other: $\Delta H^\circ_{fus} = 6.02$ kJ/mol; $\Delta H^\circ_{vap} = 40.7$ kJ/mol; $C_{ice} = 2.09$ J/g · °C; $C_{water} = 4.18$ J/g · °C; $C_{steam} = 2.01$ J/g · °C

Conceptual Plan: Follow the heating curve in Figure 11.36. $q = q_1 + q_2 + q_3 + q_4 + q_5$ where $q_1, q_3,$ and q_5 are heating of a single phase then J $\rightarrow$ kJ and q_2 and q_4 are phase transitions.

$$q = mC_S(T_f - T_i) \qquad \frac{1\text{ kJ}}{1000\text{ J}} \qquad q = m \times \frac{1\text{ mol}}{18.01\text{ g}} \times \frac{\Delta H}{1\text{ mol}}$$

Solution:

$$q_1 = m_{ice}C_{ice}(T_{icef} - T_{icei}) = 10.0\text{ g} \times 2.09\,\frac{\text{J}}{\text{g} \cdot \text{°C}} \times (0.0\text{ °C} - (-10.0\text{ °C})) = 209\text{ J} \times \frac{1\text{ kJ}}{1000\text{ J}} = 0.209\text{ kJ},$$

$$q_2 = m \times \frac{1\text{ mol}}{18.01\text{ g}} \times \frac{\Delta H_{fus}}{1\text{ mol}} = 10.0\text{ g} \times \frac{1\text{ mol}}{18.01\text{ g}} \times \frac{6.02\text{ kJ}}{1\text{ mol}} = 3.3\underline{4}3\text{ kJ},$$

$$q_3 = m_{water}C_{water}(T_{waterf} - T_{wateri}) = 10.0\text{ g} \times 4.18\,\frac{\text{J}}{\text{g} \cdot \text{°C}} \times (100.0\text{ °C} - 0.0\text{ °C}) = 4180\text{ J} \times \frac{1\text{ kJ}}{1000\text{ J}} = 4.18\text{ kJ},$$

$$q_4 = m \times \frac{1\text{ mol}}{18.01\text{ g}} \times \frac{\Delta H_{vap}}{1\text{ mol}} = 10.0\text{ g} \times \frac{1\text{ mol}}{18.01\text{ g}} \times \frac{40.7\text{ kJ}}{1\text{ mol}} = 22.5\underline{9}9\text{ kJ},$$

$$q_5 = m_{steam}C_{steam}(T_{steamf} - T_{steami}) = 10.0\text{ g} \times 2.01\,\frac{\text{J}}{\text{g} \cdot \text{°C}} \times (110.0\text{ °C} - 100.0\text{ °C})$$

$$= 201\text{ J} \times \frac{1\text{ kJ}}{1000\text{ J}} = 0.201\text{ kJ}.$$

$q_{Total} = q_1 + q_2 + q_3 + q_4 + q_5 = 0.209$ kJ $+ 3.3\underline{4}3$ kJ $+ 4.18$ kJ $+ 22.5\underline{9}9$ kJ $+ 0.201$ kJ $= 30.5$ kJ

Check: The units (kJ) are correct. The total amount of heat is dominated by the vaporization step. Since we have less than 1 mole we expect less than 41 kJ.

Phase Diagrams

11.85   (a)   solid

(b)   liquid

(c)   gas

(d)   supercritical fluid

(e)   solid/liquid equilibrium

(f)   liquid/gas equilibrium

(g)   solid/liquid/gas equilibrium

11.87   **Given:** nitrogen, normal boiling point = 77.3 K, normal melting point = 63.1 K, critical temperature = 126.2 K, critical pressure = 2.55 x 10^4 torr, triple point at 63.1 K and 94.0 torr

Find: Sketch phase diagram. Does nitrogen have a stable liquid phase at 1 atm?

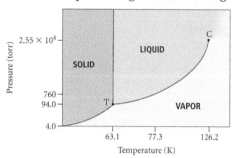

Nitrogen has a stable liquid phase at 1 atm.
Note that the axes are not to scale.

11.89   (a)   0.027 mmHg, the higher of the two triple points

       (b)   The rhombic phase is denser because if we start in the monoclinic phase at 100 °C and increase the pressure, we will cross into the rhombic phase.

The Uniqueness of Water

11.91   Water has a low molar mass (18.01 g/mol), yet it is a liquid at room temperature. Water's high boiling point for its molar mass can be understood by examining the structure of the water molecule. The bent geometry of the water molecule and the highly polar nature of the O–H bonds result in a molecule with a significant dipole moment. Water's two O–H bonds (hydrogen directly bonded to oxygen) allow a water molecule to form very strong hydrogen bonds with four other water molecules, resulting in a relatively high boiling point.

11.93   Water has an exceptionally high specific heat capacity, which has a moderating effect on the climate of coastal cities. Also, its high ΔH_{vap} causes water evaporation and condensation to have a strong effect on temperature. A tremendous amount of heat can be stored in large bodies of water. Heat will be absorbed or released from large bodies of water preferentially over land around it. In some cities, such as San Francisco, for example, the daily fluctuation in temperature can be less than 10 °C. This same moderating effect occurs over the entire planet, two-thirds of which is covered by water. In other words, without water, the daily temperature fluctuations on our planet might be more like those on Mars, where temperature fluctuations of 63 °C (113 °F) have been measured between early morning and midday.

Types of Solids and Their Structures

11.95   **Given:** X-ray with $\lambda = 154$ pm, maximum reflection angle of $\theta = 28.3°$, assume $n = 1$
       Find: distance between layers
       Conceptual Plan: $\lambda, \theta, n \rightarrow d$
$$n\lambda = 2\,d\,\sin\theta$$
       Solution: $n\lambda = 2\,d\,\sin\theta$. Rearrange to solve for d. $d = \dfrac{n\,\lambda}{2\,\sin\theta} = \dfrac{1 \times 154\text{ pm}}{2\,\sin 28.3°} = 162$ pm.
       Check: The units (pm) are correct. The magnitude (164 pm) makes sense since n = 1 and the *sin* is always < 1. The number is consistent with interatomic distances.

11.97   (a)   8 corner atoms x (1/8 atom / unit cell) = 1 atom / unit cell

       (b)   8 corner atoms x (1/8 atom / unit cell) + 1 atom in center = (1 + 1) atoms / unit cell = 2 atoms / unit cell

       (c)   8 corner atoms x (1/8 atom / unit cell) + 6 face-centered atoms x (1/2 atom / unit cell) = (1 + 3) atoms / unit cell = 4 atoms / unit cell

11.99   **Given:** platinum, face-centered cubic structure, $r = 139$ pm   **Find:** edge length of unit cell and density (g/cm³)
       Conceptual Plan: $r \rightarrow l$ and $l \rightarrow V(\text{pm}^3) \rightarrow V(\text{cm}^3)$ and $\mathcal{M}$, FCC structure $\rightarrow m$ then $m, V \rightarrow d$
$$l = 2\sqrt{2}\,r \qquad V = l^3 \qquad \frac{(1\text{ cm})^3}{(10^{10}\text{ pm})^3} \qquad m = \frac{4\text{ atoms}}{\text{unit cell}} \times \frac{\mathcal{M}}{N_A} \qquad d = m/V$$

Solution: $l = 2\sqrt{2}\,r = 2\sqrt{2} \times 139$ pm $= 393.\underline{1}51$ pm $= 393$ pm and

$$V = l^3 = (393.\underline{1}51 \;\cancel{pm})^3 \times \frac{(1 \text{ cm})^3}{(10^{10} \;\cancel{pm})^3} = 6.0\underline{7}682 \times 10^{-23} \text{ cm}^3 \text{ and}$$

$$m = \frac{4 \text{ atoms}}{\text{unit cell}} \times \frac{\mathcal{M}}{N_A} = \frac{4 \;\cancel{atoms}}{\text{unit cell}} \times \frac{195.09 \text{ g}}{1 \;\cancel{mol}} \times \frac{1 \;\cancel{mol}}{6.022 \times 10^{23} \;\cancel{atoms}} = 1.29\underline{5}848 \times 10^{-21} \;\frac{g}{\text{unit cell}} \text{ then}$$

$$d = \frac{m}{V} = \frac{1.29\underline{5}848 \times 10^{-21} \;\dfrac{g}{\cancel{unit\;cell}}}{6.0\underline{7}682 \times 10^{-23} \;\dfrac{cm^3}{\cancel{unit\;cell}}} = 21.3 \;\frac{g}{cm^3}$$

Check: The units (pm and g/cm^3) are correct. The magnitude (393 pm) makes sense because it must be larger than the radius of an atom. The magnitude (21 g/ cm^3) is consistent for Pt from Chapter 1.

11.101   **Given:** rhodium, face-centered cubic structure, $d = 12.41$ g/cm^3 **Find:** r (Rh)
         Conceptual Plan: $\mathcal{M}$, FCC structure $\rightarrow m$ then $m, V \rightarrow d$ then $V(\text{cm}^3) \rightarrow l$ (cm) $\rightarrow l$ (pm) then $l \rightarrow r$

$$m = \frac{4 \text{ atoms}}{\text{unit cell}} \times \frac{\mathcal{M}}{N_A} \qquad d = m/V \qquad V = l^3 \qquad \frac{10^{10} \text{ pm}}{1 \text{ cm}} \qquad l = 2\sqrt{2}\,r$$

Solution: $m = \dfrac{4 \text{ atoms}}{\text{unit cell}} \times \dfrac{\mathcal{M}}{N_A} = \dfrac{4 \;\cancel{atoms}}{\text{unit cell}} \times \dfrac{102.905 \text{ g}}{1 \;\cancel{mol}} \times \dfrac{1 \;\cancel{mol}}{6.022 \times 10^{23} \;\cancel{atoms}} = 6.83\underline{5}271 \times 10^{-22} \;\dfrac{g}{\text{unit cell}}$

then $d = \dfrac{m}{V}$. Rearrange to solve for V. $V = \dfrac{m}{d} = \dfrac{6.83\underline{5}271 \times 10^{-22} \;\dfrac{\cancel{g}}{\text{unit cell}}}{12.41 \;\dfrac{\cancel{g}}{cm^3}} = 5.50\underline{7}873 \times 10^{-23} \;\dfrac{cm^3}{\text{unit cell}}$

then $V = l^3$. Rearrange to solve for l.

$$l = \sqrt[3]{V} = \sqrt[3]{5.50\underline{7}873 \times 10^{-23} \text{ cm}^3} = 3.80\underline{4}831 \times 10^{-8} \text{ cm} \times \frac{10^{10} \text{ pm}}{1 \text{ cm}} = 380.\underline{4}831 \text{ pm then } l = 2\sqrt{2}r.$$

Rearrange to solve for r. $r = \dfrac{l}{2\sqrt{2}} = \dfrac{380.\underline{4}831 \text{ pm}}{2\sqrt{2}} = 134.5 \text{ pm}.$

Check: The units (pm) are correct. The magnitude (135 pm) is consistent with an atomic diameter.

11.103   **Given:** polonium, simple cubic structure, $d = 9.3$ g/cm ; $r = 167$ pm; $\mathcal{M} = 209$ g/mol **Find:** estimate N_A
         Conceptual Plan: $r \rightarrow l$ and $l \rightarrow V(\text{pm}^3) \rightarrow V(\text{cm}^3)$ then $d, V \rightarrow m$ then $\mathcal{M}$, SC structure $\rightarrow m$

$$l = 2r \qquad V = l^3 \qquad \frac{(1 \text{ cm})^3}{(10^{10} \text{ pm})^3} \qquad d = m/V \qquad m = \frac{1 \text{ atom}}{\text{unit cell}} \times \frac{\mathcal{M}}{N_A}$$

Solution: $l = 2r = 2 \times 167$ pm $= 334$ pm and $V = l^3 = (334 \;\cancel{pm})^3 \times \dfrac{(1 \text{ cm})^3}{(10^{10} \;\cancel{pm})^3} = 3.7\underline{2}597 \times 10^{-23} \text{ cm}^3$ then

$d = \dfrac{m}{V}$. Rearrange to solve for m. $m = dV = 9.3 \;\dfrac{g}{\cancel{cm^3}} \times \dfrac{3.7\underline{2}597 \times 10^{-23} \;\cancel{cm^3}}{\text{unit cell}} = 3.4\underline{6}515 \times 10^{-22} \;\dfrac{g}{\text{unit cell}}$

then $m = \dfrac{1 \text{ atom}}{\text{unit cell}} \times \dfrac{\mathcal{M}}{N_A}$. Rearrange to solve for N_A.

$N_A = \dfrac{1 \text{ atom}}{\text{unit cell}} \times \dfrac{\mathcal{M}}{m} = \dfrac{1 \text{ atom}}{\cancel{unit\;cell}} \times \dfrac{209 \;\cancel{g}}{1 \text{ mol}} \times \dfrac{1 \;\cancel{unit\;cell}}{3.4\underline{6}515 \times 10^{-22} \;\cancel{g}} = 6.0 \times 10^{23} \;\dfrac{\text{atom}}{\text{mol}}.$

Check: The units (atoms/mol) are correct. The magnitude (6 x 10^{23}) is consistent with Avogadro's number.

11.105   (a)   atomic, since Ar is an atom

         (b)   molecular, since water is a molecule

         (c)   ionic, since K$_2$O is an ionic solid

         (d)   atomic, since iron is an atom

11.107   LiCl has the highest melting point since it is the only ionic solid in the group. The other three solids are held together by intermolecular forces, while LiCl is held together by stronger coulombic interactions between the cations and anions of the crystal lattice.

11.109   (a) TiO_2 because it is an ionic solid

      (b) $SiCl_4$ because it has a higher molar mass and therefore has stronger dispersion forces

      (c)   Xe because it has a higher molar mass and therefore has stronger dispersion forces

      (d)   CaO because the ions have greater charge and therefore stronger dipole–dipole interactions

11.111   The Ti atoms occupy the corner positions and the center of the unit cell: 8 corner atoms x (1/8 atom / unit cell) + 1 atom in center = (1 + 1) Ti atoms / unit cell = 2 Ti atoms / unit cell. The O atoms occupy four positions on the top and bottom faces and two positions inside the unit cell: 4 face-centered atoms x (1/2 atom / unit cell) + 2 atoms in the interior = (2 + 2) O atoms / unit cell = 4 O atoms / unit cell. Therefore there are 2 Ti atoms / unit cell and 4 O atoms / unit cell, so the ratio Ti:O is 2:4 or 1:2. The formula for the compound is TiO_2.

11.113   In CsCl: The Cs atoms occupy the center of the unit cell: 1 atom in center = 1 Cs atom / unit cell. The Cl atoms occupy corner positions of the unit cell: 8 corner atoms x (1/8 atom / unit cell) = 1 Cl atom / unit cell. Therefore there are 1 Cl atom / unit cell and 1 Cl atom / unit cell, so the ratio Cs:Cl is 1:1. The formula for the compound is CsCl, as expected.

      In $BaCl_2$: The Ba atoms occupy the corner positions and the face-centered positions of the unit cell: 8 corner atoms x (1/8 atom / unit cell) + 6 face-centered atoms x (1/2 atom / unit cell) = (1 + 3) Ba atoms / unit cell = 4 Ba atoms / unit cell. The Cl atoms occupy eight positions inside the unit cell: 8 Cl atoms / unit cell. Therefore there are 4 Ba atoms / unit cell and 8 Cl atoms / unit cell, so the ratio Ba:Cl is 4:8 or 1:2. The formula for the compound is $BaCl_2$, as expected.

Band Theory

11.115   (a)   Zn should have little or no band gap because it is the only metal in the group.

11.117   (a)   p-type semiconductor: Ge is Group 4A and Ga is Group 3A, so the Ga will generate electron "holes."

      (b)   n-type semiconductor: Si is Group 4A and As is Group 5A, so the As will add electrons to the conduction band.

Cumulative Problems

11.119   The general trend is that melting point increases with increasing molar mass. This is due to the fact that the electrons of the larger molecules are held more loosely and a stronger dipole moment can be induced more easily. HF is the exception to the rule. It has a relatively high melting point due to strong intermolecular forces due to hydrogen bonding.

11.121   **Given:** P_{H_2O} = 23.76 torr at 25 °C; 1.25 g water in 1.5 L container   **Find:** m (H_2O) as liquid

      Conceptual Plan: °C $\rightarrow$ K and torr $\rightarrow$ atm then $P, V, T \rightarrow$ mol $(g) \rightarrow$ g (g) then g (g), g $(l)_i \rightarrow$ g $(l)_f$

$$K = °C + 273.15 \qquad \frac{1\ atm}{760\ torr} \qquad PV = nRT \qquad \frac{18.01\ g}{1\ mol} \qquad g\ (l)_f = g\ (l)_i - g\ (g)$$

      Solution: T = 25 °C + 273.15 = 298 K, 23.76 torr x $\dfrac{1\ atm}{760\ torr}$ = 0.0312632 atm then $PV = nRT$.

      Rearrange to solve for n. $n = \dfrac{PV}{RT} = \dfrac{0.0312632\ atm \times 1.5\ L}{0.08206\ \dfrac{L \cdot atm}{K \cdot mol} \times 298\ K}$ = 0.00191768 mol in the gas phase then

0.00191768 mol x $\dfrac{18.01\ g}{1\ mol}$ = 0.0345375 g in gas phase then

g $(l)_f$ = g $(l)_i$ − g (g) = 1.25 g − 0.0345375 g = 1.22 g remaining as liquid. Yes, there is 1.22 g of liquid.

      Check: The units (g) are correct. The magnitude (1.2 g) is expected since very little material is expected to be in the gas phase.

11.123   Since we are starting at a temperature that is higher and a pressure that is lower than the triple point, the phase transitions will be gas $\rightarrow$ liquid $\rightarrow$ solid, or condensation followed by freezing.

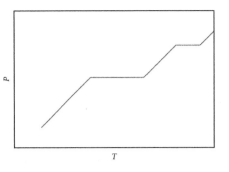

11.125   Ice: $T_1 = 0$ °C exactly, $m = 53.5$ g; Water: $T_1 = 75$ °C, $m = 115$ g   **Find:** $_f$
Other: $\Delta H^\circ_{fus} = 6.0$ kJ/mol; $C_{water} = 4.18$ J/g · °C
Conceptual Plan: $q_{ice} = -q_{water}$ so g (ice) $\rightarrow$ mol (ice) $\rightarrow$ q_{fus}(kJ) $\rightarrow$ q_{fus} (J) $\rightarrow$ q_{water} (J) then

$$\frac{1 \text{ mol}}{18.01 \text{ g}} \qquad \frac{6.02 \text{ kJ}}{1 \text{ mol}} \qquad \frac{1000 \text{ J}}{1 \text{ kJ}} \qquad q_{water} = -q_{ice}$$

$q, m, C_s \rightarrow \Delta T$ then T_i , $\Delta T \rightarrow T_2$ now we have slightly cooled water in contact with 0.0 °C water
$\quad q = m C_s \Delta T \qquad\qquad \Delta T = T_2 - T_i$
so $q_{ice} = -q_{water}$ with $m, C_s, T_i \rightarrow T_f$
$\qquad\qquad q = mC_s(T_f - T_i) \text{ then set } q_{ice} = -q_{water}$

Solution: $53.5 \text{ g} \times \dfrac{1 \text{ mol}}{18.01 \text{ g}} \times \dfrac{6.02 \text{ kJ}}{1 \text{ mol}} \times \dfrac{1000 \text{ J}}{1 \text{ kJ}} = 1.78828 \times 10^4$ J, $q_{water} = -q_{ice} = -1.78828 \times 10^4$ J

$q = mC_s\Delta T$. Rearrange to solve for ΔT. $\Delta T = \dfrac{q}{mC_s} = \dfrac{-1.78828 \times 10^4 \text{ J}}{115 \text{ g} \times 4.18 \dfrac{\text{J}}{\text{g} \cdot °\text{C}}} = -37.\underline{2}017$ °C then

$\Delta T = T_2 - T_i \qquad\qquad T_2. \; T_2 = \Delta T + T_i = -37.\underline{2}017 °\text{C} + 75 °\text{C} = 37.\underline{7}98 °\text{C}$

$q = m\,C_s(T_f - T_i)$ substitute in values and set $q_{ice} = -q_{water}$.

$q_{ice} = m_{ice}C_{ice}(T_f - T_{icei}) = 53.5 \text{ g} \times 4.18 \dfrac{\text{J}}{\text{g} \cdot °\text{C}} \times (T_f - 0.0 °\text{C}) =$

$- q_{water} = -m_{water}C_{water}(T_f - T_{water2}) = -115 \text{ g} \times 4.18 \dfrac{\text{J}}{\text{g} \cdot °\text{C}} \times (T_f - 37.\underline{7}98 °\text{C}).$

Rearrange to solve for T_f.
$53.5T_f = -115(T_f - 37.\underline{7}98 °\text{C}) \rightarrow 53.5\,T_f = -115\,T_f + 4346.8 °\text{C} \rightarrow -4346.8 °\text{C} = -168.5\,T_f$

$\rightarrow T_f = \dfrac{-4346.8 °\text{C}}{-168.5} = 25.\underline{8} °\text{C} = 26 °\text{C}.$

Check: The units (°C) are correct. The temperature is between the two initial temperatures. Since the ice mass is about half the water mass, we are not surprised that the temperature is closer to the original ice temperature.

11.127   **Given:** Home: 6.0 m x 10.0 m x 2.2 m; $T = 30$ °C, $P_{H_2O} = 85$ % of $P^\circ_{H_2O}$ **Find:** m (H_2O) removed
Other: $P^\circ_{H_2O} = 31.86$ mmHg from text
$\qquad\qquad$ **Conceptual Plan:** $l, w, h \rightarrow V$ (m³) $\rightarrow$ V (cm³) $\rightarrow$ V (L) and $P^\circ_{H_2O} \rightarrow P_{H_2O}$ (mmHg) $\rightarrow P_{H_2O}$
(atm) and

$$V = l\,w\,h \qquad \frac{(100 \text{ cm})^3}{(1 \text{ m})^3} \qquad \frac{1 \text{ L}}{1000 \text{ cm}^3} \qquad\qquad P_{H2O} = 0.85\,P^\circ_{H_2O} \qquad \frac{1 \text{ atm}}{760 \text{ mmHg}}$$

°C $\rightarrow$ K then P $V, T \rightarrow$ mol (H_2O) $\rightarrow$ g (H_2O)

$$\text{K} = °\text{C} + 273.15 \qquad\qquad PV = nRT \qquad \frac{18.01 \text{ g}}{1 \text{ mol}}$$

Solution: $V = l\,w\,h = 6.0 \text{ m} \times 10.0 \text{ m} \times 2.2 \text{ m} = 132 \text{ m}^3 \times \dfrac{(100 \text{ cm})^3}{(1 \text{ m})^3} \times \dfrac{1 \text{ L}}{1000 \text{ cm}^3} = 1.32 \times 10^5 \text{ L},$

$P_{H_2O} = 0.85\,P^\circ_{H_2O} = 0.85 \times 31.86 \text{ mmHg} \times \dfrac{1 \text{ atm}}{760 \text{ mmHg}} = 0.035633 \text{ atm}, \; T = 30 °\text{C} + 273.15 = 3\underline{0}3 \text{ K},$

then $PV = nRT$. Rearrange to solve for n.

$$n = \frac{PV}{RT} = \frac{0.035633 \text{ atm} \times 1.32 \times 10^5 \text{ L}}{0.08206 \frac{\text{L} \cdot \text{atm}}{\text{K} \cdot \text{mol}} \times 303 \text{ K}} = 189.17 \text{ mol then } 189.17 \text{ mol} \times \frac{18.01 \text{ g}}{1 \text{ mol}} = 3400 \text{ g to remove.}$$

Check: The units (g) are correct. The magnitude of the answer (3400 g) makes sense since the volume of the house is so large. We are removing almost 200 moles of water.

11.129   CsCl has a higher melting point than AgI because of its higher coordination number. In CsCl, one anion bonds to eight cations (and vice versa), while in AgI, one anion bonds only to four cations.

11.131   (a)   Atoms are connected across the face diagonal (c), so $c = 4r$.

(b)   From the Pythagorean Theorem $c^2 = a^2 + b^2$, from part (a) $c = 4r$, and for a cubic structure $a = l, b = l$ so
$(4r)^2 = l^2 + l^2 \rightarrow 16r^2 = 2l^2 \rightarrow 8r^2 = l^2 \rightarrow l = \sqrt{8r^2} \rightarrow l = 2\sqrt{2}r.$

11.133   **Given:** diamond, V (unit cell) $= 0.0454$ nm^3; $d = 3.52$ g/cm^3 **Find:** number of carbon atoms / unit cell
Conceptual Plan: $V(\text{nm}^3) \rightarrow V(\text{cm}^3)$ then $d, V \rightarrow m \rightarrow \text{mol} \rightarrow \text{atoms}$

$$\frac{(1 \text{ cm})^3}{(10^7 \text{ nm})^3} \qquad d = m/V \quad \frac{1 \text{ mol}}{12.01 \text{ g}} \quad \frac{6.022 \times 10^{23} \text{ atoms}}{1 \text{ mol}}$$

Solution: $0.0454 \text{ nm}^3 \times \frac{(1 \text{ cm})^3}{(10^7 \text{ nm})^3} = 4.54 \times 10^{-23} \text{ cm}^3$ then $d = \frac{m}{V}$. Rearrange to solve for m.

$m = dV = 3.52 \frac{\text{g}}{\text{cm}^3} \times 4.54 \times 10^{-23} \text{ cm}^3 = 1.59808 \times 10^{-22} \text{ g then}$

$$\frac{1.59808 \times 10^{-22} \text{ g}}{\text{unit cell}} \times \frac{1 \text{ mol}}{12.01 \text{ g}} \times \frac{6.022 \times 10^{23} \text{ atoms}}{1 \text{ mol}} = 8.01 \frac{\text{C atoms}}{\text{unit cell}} = 8 \frac{\text{C atoms}}{\text{unit cell}}$$

Check: The units (atoms) are correct. The magnitude (8) makes sense because it is a fairly small number and our answer is within calculation error of an integer.

11.135   (a) CO_2 (s) $\rightarrow$ CO_2 (g) at 194.7 K

(b) CO_2 (s) $\rightarrow$ triple point at 216.5 K $\rightarrow$ CO_2 (g) just above 216.5 K

(c) CO_2 (s) $\rightarrow$ CO_2 (l) at somewhat above 216 K $\rightarrow$ CO_2 (g) at around 250 K

(d) CO_2 (s) $\rightarrow$ CO_2 above the critical point where there is no distinction between liquid and gas. This change occurs at about 300 K.

11.137   **Given:** metal, $d = 7.8748$ g/cm^3; $l = 0.28664$ nm, body-centered cubic lattice **Find:** $\mathcal{M}$
Conceptual Plan: $l \rightarrow V(\text{nm}^3) \rightarrow V(\text{cm}^3)$ then $d, V \rightarrow m$ then m, FCC structure $\rightarrow \mathcal{M}$

$$V = l^3 \qquad \frac{(1 \text{ cm})^3}{(10^7 \text{ nm})^3} \qquad d = m/V \qquad m = \frac{2 \text{ atoms}}{\text{unit cell}} \times \frac{\mathcal{M}}{N_A}$$

Solution: $V = l^3 = (0.28664 \text{ nm})^3 = 0.02355105602 \text{ nm}^3 \times \frac{(1 \text{ cm})^3}{(10^7 \text{ nm})^3} = 2.355105602 \times 10^{-23} \text{ cm}^3$ then $d = \frac{m}{V}$.

Rearrange to solve for m. $m = dV = 7.8748 \frac{\text{g}}{\text{cm}^3} \times 2.355105602 \times 10^{-23} \text{ cm}^3 = 1.854598559 \times 10^{-22} \text{ g}$

then $m = \frac{2 \text{ atoms}}{\text{unit cell}} \times \frac{\mathcal{M}}{N_A}$. Rearrange to solve for $\mathcal{M}$.

$$\mathcal{M} = \frac{\text{unit cell}}{2 \text{ atoms}} \times N_A \times m = \frac{\text{unit cell}}{2 \text{ atoms}} \times \frac{6.022 \times 10^{23} \text{ atoms}}{1 \text{ mol}} \times \frac{1.854598559 \times 10^{-22} \text{ g}}{\text{unit cell}} = 55.842 \frac{\text{g}}{\text{mol}}$$

$= 55.84 \frac{\text{g}}{\text{mol}}$ iron.

Check: The units (g/mol) are correct. The magnitude (55.8) makes sense because it is a reasonable atomic mass for a metal and it is close to iron.

Challenge Problems

11.139   **Given:** KCl, rock salt structure **Find:** density (g/cm^3) **Other:** $r(K^+) = 133$ pm; $r(Cl^-) = 181$ pm from Chapter 8
Conceptual Plan: Rock salt structure is a face-centered cubic structure with anions at the lattice points and cations in the holes between lattice sites $\rightarrow$ assume $r = r(Cl^-)$, but $\mathcal{M} = \mathcal{M}(KCl)$
$r(K^+), r(Cl^-) \rightarrow l$ and $l \rightarrow V(pm^3) \rightarrow V(cm^3)$ and, FCC structure $\rightarrow m$ then $m, V \rightarrow d$.

$$\text{from Figure 11.52} \quad l = 2r(Cl^-) + 2r(K^+) \quad V = l^3 \quad \frac{(1cm)^3}{(10^{10}pm)^3} \quad m = \frac{4 \text{ formula units}}{\text{unit cell}} \times \frac{\mathcal{M}}{N_A} \quad d = m/V$$

Solution: $l = 2r(Cl^-) + 2r(K^+) = 2(181 \text{ pm}) + 2(133 \text{ pm}) = 628 \text{ pm}$ and

$$V = l^3 = (628 \text{ pm})^3 \times \frac{(1 \text{ cm})^3}{(10^{10} \text{ pm})^3} = 2.47673 \times 10^{-22} \text{ cm}^3 \text{ and}$$

$$m = \frac{4 \text{ formula units}}{\text{unit cell}} \times \frac{\mathcal{M}}{N_A} = \frac{4 \text{ formula units}}{\text{unit cell}} \times \frac{74.55 \text{ g}}{1 \text{ mol}} \times \frac{1 \text{ mol}}{6.022 \times 10^{23} \text{ formula units}}$$

$$= 4.951976 \times 10^{-22} \frac{\text{g}}{\text{unit cell}}$$

$$\text{then } d = \frac{m}{V} = \frac{4.951976 \times 10^{-22} \dfrac{\text{g}}{\text{unit cell}}}{2.47673 \times 10^{-22} \dfrac{\text{cm}^3}{\text{unit cell}}} = 1.99940 \frac{\text{g}}{\text{cm}^3} = 2.00 \frac{\text{g}}{\text{cm}^3}$$

Check: The units (g/cm^3) are correct. The magnitude (2 g/cm^3) is reasonable for a salt density. The published value is 1.98 g/cm^3. This method of estimating the density gives a value that is close to the experimentally measured density.

11.141   Decreasing the pressure will decrease the temperature of liquid nitrogen. Because the nitrogen is boiling, its temperature must be constant at a given pressure. As the pressure decreases, the boiling point decreases, and therefore so does the temperature. Remember that vaporization is an endothermic process, so as the nitrogen vaporizes it will remove heat from the liquid, dropping its temperature. If the pressure drops below the pressure of the triple point, the phase change will shift from vaporization to sublimation and the liquid nitrogen will become solid.

11.143   **Given:** cubic closest packing structure = cube with touching spheres of radius = r on alternating corners of a cube **Find:** body diagonal of cube and radius of tetrahedral hole
Solution: The cell edge length = l and $l^2 + l^2 = (2r)^2 \rightarrow 2l^2 = 4r^2 \rightarrow l^2 = 2r^2$. Since body diagonal = BD is the hypotenuse of the right triangle formed by the face diagonal and the cell edge we have $(BD)^2 = l^2 + (2r)^2 = 2r^2 + 4r^2 = 6r^2 \rightarrow BD = \sqrt{6}r$. The radius of the tetrahedral hole = r_T is half the body diagonal minus the radius of the sphere or

$$r_T = \frac{BD}{2} - r = \frac{\sqrt{6}r}{2} - r = \left(\frac{\sqrt{6}}{2} - 1\right)r = \left(\frac{\sqrt{6} - 2}{2}\right)r = \left(\frac{\sqrt{3}\sqrt{2} - \sqrt{2}\sqrt{2}}{\sqrt{2}\sqrt{2}}\right)r$$

$$= \left(\frac{\sqrt{3} - \sqrt{2}}{\sqrt{2}}\right)r \approx 0.22474r.$$

11.145   **Given:** 1.00 L water, $T_i = 298$ K, $T_f = 373$ K - vapor; $P_{CH_4} = 1.00$ atm **Find:** V (CH_4)
Other: $\Delta H^\circ_{comb} (CH_4) = 890.4$ kJ/mol; $C_{water} = 75.2$ J/mol·K; $\Delta H^\circ_{vap} (H_2O) = 40.7$ kJ/mol, $d = 1.00$ g/mL
Conceptual Plan: L $\rightarrow$ mL $\rightarrow$ g $\rightarrow$ mol then heat liquid water: $n, C_s, T_i, T_f \rightarrow q_{1water}$ (J)

$$\frac{1000 \text{ mL}}{1 \text{ L}} \quad \frac{1.00 \text{ g}}{1.00 \text{ mL}} \quad \frac{1 \text{ mol}}{18.01 \text{ g}} \qquad\qquad q = mC_s(T_f - T_i)$$

vaporize water: $n_{water}, \Delta H^\circ_{vap} \rightarrow q_{2water}$ (J) then calculate total heat $q_{1water}, q_{2water} \rightarrow q_{water}$ (J) then

$$q = n\Delta H \qquad\qquad q_{1water} + q_{2water} = q_{water}$$

q_{water}(J) $\rightarrow -q_{CH_4 comb}$ (J) $\rightarrow n_{CH_4}$ finally $n_{CH_4}, P, T \rightarrow V$

$$q_{water} = -q_{CH_4 comb} \qquad q = n\Delta H \qquad\qquad PV = nRT$$

Solution: $1.00 \text{ L} \times \dfrac{1000 \text{ mL}}{1 \text{ L}} \times \dfrac{1.00 \text{ g}}{1.00 \text{ mL}} \times \dfrac{1 \text{ mol}}{18.01 \text{ g}} = 55.\underline{5}247 \text{ mol } H_2O$

$q_{1water} = n_{water}C_{water}(T_f - T_i) = 55.\underline{5}247 \text{ mol} \times 75.2 \dfrac{J}{\text{mol} \cdot K} \times (373 \text{ K} - 298 \text{ K}) = 3.1\underline{3}15936 \times 10^5 \text{ J}$

$= 31\underline{3}.15936 \text{ kJ},$

$q_{2water} = n\Delta H = 55.\underline{5}247 \text{ mol} \times 40.7 \dfrac{kJ}{\text{mol}} = 2.2\underline{5}9855 \times 10^3 \text{ kJ}$

$q_{1water} + q_{2water} = q_{water} = 31\underline{3}.15936 \text{ kJ} + 2.2\underline{5}9855 \times 10^3 \text{ kJ} = 2.5\underline{7}301465 \times 10^3 \text{ kJ}$

$q_{water} = -q_{CH_4comb} = 2.5\underline{7}301465 \times 10^3 \text{ kJ}$ then $q_{CH_4comb} = n\Delta H$. Rearrange to solve for n.

$n_{CH_4} = \dfrac{q_{CH_4}}{\Delta H_{CH_4comb}} = \dfrac{-2.5\underline{7}301465 \times 10^3 \text{ kJ}}{-890.4 \dfrac{kJ}{\text{mol}}} = 2.8\underline{8}97289 \text{ mol}$ then $PV = nRT$.

Rearrange to solve for V. $V = \dfrac{nRT}{P} = \dfrac{2.8\underline{8}97289 \text{ mol} \times 0.08206 \dfrac{L \cdot atm}{\text{mol} \cdot K} \times 298 \text{ K}}{1.00 \text{ atm}} = 70.\underline{6}65085 \text{ L} = 70.7 \text{ L}.$

Check: The units (L) are correct. The volume (71 L) is reasonable since we are using about 3 moles of methane.

11.147　　$P_{Total} = P_{N_2} + P_{H_2O} + P_{ethanol}$

P_{N_2}: Use Boyle's law to calculate $P_1V_1 = P_2V_2$. Rearrange to solve for P_2.

$P_2 = P_1\dfrac{V_1}{V_2} = 1.0 \text{ atm} \times \dfrac{1.0 \text{ L}}{3.0 \text{ L}} \times \dfrac{760 \text{ mmHg}}{1 \text{ atm}} = 25\underline{3}.333 \text{ mmHg}.$

For water and ethanol, we need to calculate the pressure if all of the liquid were to vaporize in the 3.0 L apparatus. $PV = nRT$. Rearrange to solve for P.

$P = \dfrac{nRT}{V} = \dfrac{2.0 \text{ g} \times \dfrac{1 \text{ mol}}{18.01 \text{ g}} \times 0.08206 \dfrac{L \cdot atm}{\text{mol} \cdot K} \times \dfrac{760 \text{ mmHg}}{1 \text{ atm}} \times 308 \text{ K}}{3.00 \text{ L}} = 7\underline{1}.103 \text{ mmHg } H_2O.$ Since this

pressure is greater than the vapor pressure of water at this temperature, then $P_{H_2O} = 42 \text{ mmHg}$.

$P = \dfrac{nRT}{V} = \dfrac{0.50 \text{ g} \times \dfrac{1 \text{ mol}}{46.07 \text{ g}} \times 0.08206 \dfrac{L \cdot atm}{\text{mol} \cdot K} \times \dfrac{760 \text{ mmHg}}{1 \text{ atm}} \times 308 \text{ K}}{3.00 \text{ L}} = 6\underline{9}.4937 \text{ mmHg ethanol}.$ Since this

pressure is less than the vapor pressure of ethanol at this temperature (102 mmHg), all of the liquid will vaporize and $P_{ethanol} = 6\underline{9}.4937 \text{ mmHg}$.

Finally, the total pressure is

$P_{Total} = P_{N_2} + P_{H_2O} + P_{ethanol} = 25\underline{3}.333 \text{ mmHg} + 42 \text{ mmHg} + 6\underline{9}.4937 \text{ mmHg} = 36\underline{4}.827 \text{ mmHg}$
$= 360 \text{ mmHg}.$

Conceptual Problems

11.149　　The water, a container with a larger surface area will evaporate more quickly because there is more surface area for the molecules to evaporate from. Vapor pressure is the pressure of the gas when it is in dynamic equilibrium with the liquid (evaporation rate = condensation rate). The vapor pressure is dependent only on the substance and the temperature. The larger the surface area, the more quickly it will reach this equilibrium state.

11.151　　The triple point will be at a lower temperature since the fusion equilibrium line has a positive slope. This means that we will be increasing both temperature and pressure as we travel from the triple point to the normal melting point.

11.153   The liquid segment will have the least steep slope because it takes the most kJ/mol to raise the temperature of the phase.

11.155   The heat of fusion of a substance is always smaller than the heat of vaporization because the number of interactions between particles that are broken is less in fusion than in vaporization. When we melt a solid, the particles have increased mobility, but are still strongly interacting with other liquid particles. In vaporization, all of the interactions between particles must be broken (gas particles have essentially no intermolecular interactions) and the particles must absorb enough energy to move much more rapidly.

12 Solutions

Review Questions

12.1   As seawater moves through the intestine, it flows past cells that line the digestive tract, which consist of largely fluid interiors surrounded by membranes. Although cellular fluids themselves contain dissolved ions, including sodium and chloride, the fluids are more dilute than seawater. Nature's tendency towards mixing (which tends to produce solutions of uniform concentration), together with the selective permeability of the cell membranes (which allow water to flow in and out, but restrict the flow of dissolved solids), cause a flow of solvent out of the body's cells and into the seawater.

12.3   A substance is soluble in another substance if they can form a homogeneous mixture. The solubility of a substance is the amount of the substance that will dissolve in a given amount of solvent. Many different units can be used to express solubility, including grams of solute per 100 grams of solvent, grams of solute per liter of solvent, moles of solute per liter of solution, and moles of solute per kilogram of solvent.

12.5   Entropy is a measure of energy randomization or energy dispersal in a system. When two substances mix to form a solution there is an increase in randomness, due to the fact that the components are no longer segregated to separate regions. This makes the formation of a solution energetically favorable, even when it is endothermic.

12.7   A solution always forms if the solvent–solute interactions are comparable to, or stronger than, the solvent–solvent interactions and the solute–solute interactions.

12.9   Step 1: Separate the solute into its constituent particles. This step is always endothermic (positive ΔH) because energy is required to overcome the forces that hold the solute together.

Step 2: Separate the solvent particles from each other to make room for the solute particles. This step is also endothermic because energy is required to overcome the intermolecular forces among the solvent particles.

Step 3: Mix the solute particles with the solvent particles. This step is exothermic because energy is released as the solute particles interact with the solvent particles through the various types of intermolecular forces.

12.11   In any solution formation, the initial rate of dissolution far exceeds the rate of deposition. But as the concentration of dissolved solute increases, the rate of deposition also increases. Eventually the rate of dissolution and deposition become equal—dynamic equilibrium has been reached.

A saturated solution is a solution in which the dissolved solute is in dynamic equilibrium with the solid (or undissolved) solute. If you add additional solute to a saturated solution, it will not dissolve.

An unsaturated solution is a solution containing less than the equilibrium amount of solute. If you add additional solute to an unsaturated solution, it will dissolve.

A supersaturated solution is a solution containing more than the equilibrium amount of solute. Such solutions are unstable and the excess solute normally precipitates out of the solution. However, in some cases, if left undisturbed, a supersaturated solution can exist for an extended period of time.

12.13   The solubility of gases in liquids decreases with increasing temperature. The decreasing solubility of gases with increasing temperature results in a lower oxygen concentration available for fish and other aquatic life in warm waters.

12.15   Henry's law quantifies the solubility of gases with increasing pressure as follows: $S_{gas} = k_H P_{gas}$, where S_{gas} is the solubility of the gas; k_H is a constant of proportionality (called the Henry's law constant) that depends on the specific solute, solvent, and temperature; and P_{gas} is the partial pressure of the gas. The equation simply shows that the solubility of a gas in a liquid is directly proportional to the pressure of the gas above the liquid. If the solubility of a gas is known at a certain temperature, the solubility at another pressure at this temperature can be calculated.

12.17   Parts by mass and parts by volume are ratios of masses and volume, respectively. A parts by mass concentration is the ratio of the mass of the solute to the mass of the solution, all multiplied by a multiplication factor, where percent by mass (%) is the desired unit, the factor = 100; where parts per million by mass (ppm) is the desired unit, the factor = 10^6; and for parts per billion by mass (ppb), the factor = 10^9. The size of the multiplication factor depends on the concentration of the solution. For example, in percent by mass, the

multiplication factor is 100 %, so percent by mass $= \dfrac{\text{mass solute}}{\text{mass solution}} \times 100\ \%$. A solution with a concentration of 28 % by mass contains 28 g of solute per 100 g of solution.

12.19   Raoult's law quantifies the relationship between the vapor pressure of a solution and its concentration as $P_{solution} = \chi_{solvent} P^{\circ}_{solvent}$, where $P_{solution}$ is the vapor pressure of the solution, $\chi_{solvent}$ is the mole fraction of the solvent, and $P^{\circ}_{solvent}$ is the vapor pressure of the pure solvent. This equation allows you to calculate the vapor pressure of a solution or to calculate the concentration of a solution, given the vapor pressure of the solution.

12.21   If the solute–solvent interactions are particularly strong (stronger than solvent–solvent interactions), then the solute tends to prevent the solvent from vaporizing as easily as it would otherwise and the vapor pressure of the solution will be less than that predicted by Raoult's law. If the solute–solvent interactions are particularly weak (weaker than solvent-solvent interactions), then the solute tends to allow more vaporization than would occur with just the solvent and the vapor pressure of the solution will be greater than predicted by Raoult's law.

12.23   Colligative properties are properties that depend on the amount of solute and not the type of solute. Examples of colligative properties are vapor pressure lowering, freezing point depression, boiling point elevation, and osmotic pressure.

12.25   The van't Hoff factor (i) is the ratio of moles of particles in solution to moles of formula units dissolved: $i = \dfrac{\text{moles of particles}}{\text{moles of formula units dissolved}}$. The van't Hoff factor often does not match its theoretical value, due to the fact that the ionic solute is not completely dissolved into the expected number of ions, leaving ion pairs in solution. The result is that the number of particles in the solution is not as high as theoretically expected.

12.27   The Tyndall effect is the scattering of light by a colloidal dispersion. The Tyndall effect is often used as a test to determine whether a mixture is a solution or a colloid, since solutions contain completely dissolved solute molecules that are too small to scatter light.

Solubility

12.29   (a)   hexane, toluene, or CCl_4; dispersion forces

         (b)   water, methanol, acetone; dispersion, dipole–dipole, hydrogen bonding

(c)   hexane, toluene, or CCl_4; dispersion forces

(d)   water, acetone, methanol, ethanol; dispersion, ion–dipole

12.31 $HOCH_2CH_2CH_2OH$ would be more soluble in water because it has –OH groups on both ends of the molecule, so it can hydrogen bond on both ends.

12.33   (a)   water; dispersion, dipole–dipole, hydrogen bonding

(b)   hexane; dispersion forces

(c)   water; dispersion, dipole–dipole

(d)   water; dispersion, dipole–dipole, hydrogen bonding

Energetics of Solution Formation

12.35   (a)   endothermic

(b)   The lattice energy is greater in magnitude than the heat of hydration.

(c)

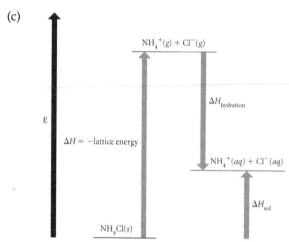

(d) The solution forms because chemical systems tend towards greater entropy.

12.37   **Given:** $AgNO_3$ ΔH_{soln} = + 22.6 kJ/mol   **Find:** $\Delta H_{hydration}$
Conceptual Plan: Lattice Energy, ΔH_{soln} $\rightarrow$ $\Delta H_{hydration}$
$$\Delta H_{soln} = \Delta H_{solute} + \Delta H_{hydration} \ where \ \Delta H_{solute} = -\Delta H_{lattice}$$
Solution: ΔH_{soln} = ΔH_{solute} + $\Delta H_{hydration}$ where $\Delta H_{solute} = -\Delta H_{lattice}$ so $\Delta H_{hydration}$ = ΔH_{soln} + $\Delta H_{lattice}$
$\Delta H_{hydration}$ = 22.6kJ/mol − 820.kJ/mol = − 797kJ/mol
Check: The units (kJ/mol) are correct. The magnitude of the answer (– 800) makes physical sense because the lattice energy is so negative, and thus it dominates the calculation.

12.39   **Given:** LiI: Lattice Energy = − 7.3 x 10^2 kJ/mol, $\Delta H_{hydration}$ = − 793 kJ/mol; 15.0 g LiI
Find: ΔH_{soln} and heat evolved
Conceptual Plan: Lattice Energy, $\Delta H_{hydration}$ $\rightarrow$ ΔH_{soln} **and g** $\rightarrow$ **mol then mol,** ΔH_{soln} $\rightarrow$ q
$$\Delta H_{soln} = \Delta H_{solute} + \Delta H_{hydration} \ where \ \Delta H_{solute} = -\Delta H_{lattice} \qquad \frac{1 \ mol}{133.843 \ g} \qquad q = n \ \Delta H_{soln}$$
Solution: ΔH_{soln} = ΔH_{solute} + $\Delta H_{hydration}$ where $\Delta H_{solute} = -\Delta H_{lattice}$ so ΔH_{soln} = $\Delta H_{hydration}$ − $\Delta H_{lattice}$
ΔH_{soln} = − 793 kJ/mol − (−730 kJ/mol) = − 63 kJ/mol = − 6.3 x 10^1 kJ/mol and

$15.0 \ g \ x \dfrac{1 \ mol}{133.843 \ g}$ = 0.112072 mol then

$q = n\Delta H_{soln}$ = 0.112072 mol x − 6.3 x $10^1 \dfrac{kJ}{mol}$ = −7.0 kJ or 7 kJ released

Check: The units (kJ/mol and kJ) are correct. The magnitude of the answer (– 60) makes physical sense because the lattice energy and the heat of hydration are about the same. The magnitude of the heat (7) makes physical sense since 15 g is much less than a mole, and thus the amount of heat released is going to be small.

Solution Equilibrium and Factors Affecting Solubility

12.41   The solution is unsaturated since we are dissolving 25 g of NaCl per 100 g of water and the solubility from the figure is ~ 35 g NaCl per 100 g of water at 25° C.

12.43   At 40 °C the solution has 45 g of KNO_3 per 100 g of water and it can contain up to 63 g of KNO_3 per 100 g of water. At 0 °C the solubility from the figure is ~ 14 g KNO_3 per 100 g of water, so ~ 31 g KNO_3 per 100 g of water will precipitate out of solution.

12.45   Since the solubility of gases decreases as the temperature increases boiling will cause dissolved oxygen to be removed from the solution.

12.47   Henry's law says that as pressure increases, nitrogen will more easily dissolve in blood. To reverse this process, divers should ascend to lower pressures.

12.49   **Given:** room temperature, 80.0 L aquarium, $P_{Total} = 1.0$ atm; $\chi_{N_2} = 0.78$ **Find:** m (N_2)
Other: $k_H(N_2) = 6.1 \times 10^{-4}$ M/L at 25 °C
Conceptual Plan: $P_{Total}, \chi_{N_2} \rightarrow P_{N_2}$ then $P_{N_2}, k_H(N_2) \rightarrow S_{N_2}$ then $L \rightarrow$ mol $\rightarrow$ g

$$P_{N_2} = \chi_{N_2}P_{Total} \qquad S_{N_2} = k_H(N_2)P_{N_2} \quad M = \frac{\text{amount solute (moles)}}{\text{volume solution (L)}} \frac{28.01 \text{ g } N_2}{1 \text{ mol } N_2}$$

Solution: $P_{N_2} = \chi_{N_2} P_{Total} = 0.78 \times 1.0$ atm $= 0.78$ atm then

$S_{N_2} = k_H(N_2)P_{N_2} = 6.1 \times 10^{-4} \dfrac{M}{\text{atm}} \times 0.78 \text{ atm} = 4.758 \times 10^{-4}$ M then

$80.0 \text{ L} \times 4.758 \times 10^{-4} \dfrac{\text{mol}}{\text{L}} \times \dfrac{28.01 \text{ g}}{1 \text{ mol}} = 1.1 \text{ g}$

Check: The units (g) are correct. The magnitude of the answer (1) seems reasonable since we have 80 L of water and expect much less than a mole of nitrogen.

Concentrations of Solutions

12.51   **Given:** NaCl and water; 112 g NaCl in 1.00 L solution **Find:** M, m, and mass percent
Other: $d = 1.08$ g/mL
Conceptual Plan: $g_{NaCl} \rightarrow$ mol and $L \rightarrow$ mL $\rightarrow g_{soln}$ and $g_{soln} \, g_{NaCl} \rightarrow g_{H_2O} \rightarrow kg_{H_2O}$ then

$$\frac{1 \text{ mol NaCl}}{58.44 \text{ g NaCl}} \qquad \frac{1000 \text{ mL}}{1 \text{ L}} \quad \frac{1.08 \text{ g}}{1 \text{ mL}} \qquad g_{H_2O} = g_{soln} - g_{NaCl} \qquad \frac{1 \text{ kg}}{1000 \text{ g}}$$

mol, $V \rightarrow$ M and mol, $kg_{H_2O} \rightarrow m$ and $g_{soln} \, g_{NaCl} \rightarrow$ mass percent

$$M = \frac{\text{amount solute (moles)}}{\text{volume solution (L)}} \quad m = \frac{\text{amount solute (moles)}}{\text{mass solvent (kg)}} \quad \text{mass percent} = \frac{\text{mass solute}}{\text{mass solution}} \times 100\%$$

Solution: $112 \text{ g NaCl} \times \dfrac{1 \text{ mol NaCl}}{58.44 \text{ g NaCl}} = 1.9164956$ mol NaCl and

$1.00 \text{ L} \times \dfrac{1000 \text{ mL}}{1 \text{ L}} \times \dfrac{1.08 \text{ g}}{1 \text{ mL}} = 1080$ g soln and

$g_{H_2O} = g_{soln} - g_{NaCl} = 1080 \text{ g} - 112 \text{ g} = 968 \text{ g } H_2O \times \dfrac{1 \text{ kg}}{1000 \text{ g}} = 0.968 \text{ kg } H_2O$ then

$M = \dfrac{\text{amount solute (moles)}}{\text{volume solution (L)}} = \dfrac{1.9164956 \text{ mol NaCl}}{1.00 \text{ L soln}} = 1.92$ M and

$m = \dfrac{\text{amount solute (moles)}}{\text{mass solvent (kg)}} = \dfrac{1.9164956 \text{ mol NaCl}}{0.968 \text{ kg } H_2O} = 2.0 \, m$ and

$\text{mass percent} = \dfrac{\text{mass solute}}{\text{mass solution}} \times 100\% = \dfrac{112 \text{ g NaCl}}{1080 \text{ g soln}} \times 100\% = 10.4\%$ by mass.

Check: The units (M, m, and percent by mass) are correct. The magnitude of the answer (2 M) seems reasonable since we have 112 g NaCl, which is a couple of moles and we have 1 L. The magnitude of the answer (2 m) seems reasonable since it is a little higher than the molarity, which we expect since we only use the solvent weight in the denominator. The magnitude of the answer (10%) seems reasonable since we have 112 g NaCl and just over 1000 g of solution.

12.53 **Given:** initial solution: 50.0 mL of 5.00 M KI; final solution contains: 3.05 g KI in 25.0 mL
Find: final volume to dilute initial solution to
Conceptual Plan: final solution: $g_{KI} \rightarrow$ $\rightarrow$ $V \rightarrow M_2$ then $M_1, V_1, M_2 \rightarrow V_2$

$$\frac{1 \text{ mol KI}}{166.006 \text{ g KI}} \qquad \frac{1 \text{ L}}{1000 \text{ mL}} \qquad M = \frac{\text{amount solute (moles)}}{\text{volume solution (L)}} \qquad M_1 V_1 = M_2 V_2$$

Solution: $3.05 \text{ g KI} \times \dfrac{1 \text{ mol KI}}{166.006 \text{ g KI}} = 0.01837283 \text{ mol KI}$ and $25.0 \text{ mL} \times \dfrac{1 \text{ L}}{1000 \text{ mL}} = 0.0250 \text{ mL}$

then $M = \dfrac{\text{amount solute (moles)}}{\text{volume solution (L)}} = \dfrac{0.01837283 \text{ mol KI}}{0.0250 \text{ L soln}} = 0.7349132 \text{ M}$ then $M_1 V_1 = M_2 V_2$.

Rearrange to solve for V_2. $V_2 = \dfrac{M_1}{M_2} \times V_1 = \dfrac{5.00 \text{ M}}{0.7349132 \text{ M}} \times 50.0 \text{ mL} = 340. \text{ mL diluted volume.}$

Check: The units (mL) are correct. The magnitude of the answer (340 mL) seems reasonable since we are starting with a concentration of 5 M and ending with a concentration of less than 1 M.

12.55 **Given:** $AgNO_3$ and water; 3.4% Ag by mass, 4.8 L solution **Find:** m (Ag) **Other:** $d = 1.01$ g/mL
Conceptual Plan: L $\rightarrow$ **mL** $\rightarrow$ $g_{soln} \rightarrow g_{Ag}$

$$\frac{1000 \text{ mL}}{1 \text{ L}} \qquad \frac{1.01 \text{ g}}{1 \text{ mL}} \qquad \frac{3.4 \text{ g Ag}}{100 \text{ g soln}}$$

Solution: $4.8 \text{ L} \times \dfrac{1000 \text{ mL}}{1 \text{ L}} \times \dfrac{1.01 \text{ g}}{1 \text{ mL}} = 4848 \text{ g soln}$ then

$4848 \text{ g soln} \times \dfrac{3.4 \text{ g Ag}}{100 \text{ g soln}} = 160 \text{ g Ag} = 1.6 \times 10^2 \text{ g Ag.}$

Check: The units (g) are correct. The magnitude of the answer (160 g) seems reasonable since we have almost 5000 g solution.

12.57 **Given:** Ca^{2+} and water; 0.0085% Ca^{2+} by mass, 1.2 g Ca **Find:** m (water)
Conceptual Plan: $g_{Ca} \rightarrow g_{soln} \rightarrow g_{H_2O}$

$$\frac{100 \text{ g soln}}{0.0085 \text{ g Ca}} \qquad g_{H_2O} = g_{soln} - g_{Ca}$$

Solution: $1.2 \text{ g Ca} \times \dfrac{100 \text{ g soln}}{0.0085 \text{ g Ca}} = 14118 \text{ g soln}$ then

Check: The units (g) are correct. The magnitude of the answer (10^4 g) seems reasonable since we have such a low concentration of Ca.

12.59 **Given:** concentrated HNO_3: 70.3% HNO_3 by mass, $d = 1.41$ g/mL; final solution: 1.15 L of 0.100 M HNO_3
Find: describe final solution preparation
Conceptual Plan: $M_2, V_2 \rightarrow mol_{HNO_3} \rightarrow g_{HNO_3} \rightarrow g_{conc\ acid} \rightarrow mL_{conc\ acid}$ **then describe method**

$$mol = MV \qquad \frac{63.02 \text{ g } HNO_3}{1 \text{ mol } HNO_3} \quad \frac{100 \text{ g conc acid}}{70.3 \text{ g } HNO_3} \quad \frac{1 \text{ mL}}{1.41 \text{ g}}$$

Solution: $mol = MV = 0.100 \dfrac{\text{mol } HNO_3}{1 \text{ L soln}} \times 1.15 \text{ L soln} = 0.115 \text{ mol } HNO_3$ then

$0.115 \text{ mol } HNO_3 \times \dfrac{63.02 \text{ g } HNO_3}{1 \text{ mol } HNO_3} \times \dfrac{100 \text{ g conc acid}}{70.3 \text{ g } HNO_3} \times \dfrac{1 \text{ mL conc acid}}{1.41 \text{ g conc acid}} = 7.31 \text{ mL conc acid.}$

Prepare the solution by putting about 1.00 L of distilled water in a container. Carefully pour in the 7.31 mL of the concentrated acid, mix the solution, and allow it to cool. Finally add enough water to generate the total volume of solution (1.15 L). It is important to add acid to water, and not the reverse, since there is such a large amount of heat released upon mixing.

Check: The units (mL) are correct. The magnitude of the answer (7 g) seems reasonable since we are starting with such a very concentrated solution and diluting it to a low concentration.

12.61   (a)   **Given:** 1.00×10^2 mL of 0.500 M KCl   **Find:** describe final solution preparation

Conceptual Plan: mL $\rightarrow$ L then $M, V \rightarrow$ mol$_{KCl} \rightarrow$ g$_{KCl}$ then describe method

$$\frac{1\ L}{1000\ mL} \qquad\qquad mol = M\,V \qquad\qquad \frac{74.56\ g\ KCl}{1\ mol\ KCl}$$

Solution: 1.00×10^2 mL $\times \dfrac{1\ L}{1000\ mL} = 0.100$ L

$mol = M\,V = 0.500\ \dfrac{mol\ KCl}{1\ L\ soln} \times 0.100$ L soln $= 0.0500$ mol KCl

then 0.0500 mol KCl $\times \dfrac{74.56\ g\ KCl}{1\ mol\ KCl} = 3.73$ g KCl.

Prepare the solution by carefully adding 3.73 g KCl to a 100 mL volumetric flask. Add ~ 75 mL of distilled water and agitate the solution until the salt dissolves completely. Finally add enough water to generate a total volume of solution (add water to the mark on the flask).

Check: The units (g) are correct. The magnitude of the answer (4 g) seems reasonable since we are making a small volume of solution and the formula weight of KCl is ~ 75 g/mol.

   (b)   **Given:** 1.00×10^2 g of 0.500 m KCl   **Find:** describe final solution preparation

Conceptual Plan:

$m \rightarrow$ mol$_{KCl}$ /1 kg solvent $\rightarrow$ g$_{KCl}$/1 kg solvent then g$_{KCl}$/1 kg solvent, g$_{soln} \rightarrow$ g$_{KCl}$, g$_{H_2O}$

$$m = \frac{amount\ solute\ (moles)}{mass\ solvent\ (kg)} \qquad \frac{74.56\ g\ KCl}{1\ mol\ KCl} \qquad\qquad g_{soln} = g_{KCl} + g_{H_2O}$$

then describe method

Solution: $m = \dfrac{amount\ solute\ (moles)}{mass\ solvent\ (kg)}$ so $0.500\ m = \dfrac{0.500\ mol\ KCl}{1\ kg\ H_2O}$ so

$\dfrac{0.500\ mol\ KCl}{1\ kg\ H_2O} \times \dfrac{74.56\ g\ KCl}{1\ mol\ KCl} = \dfrac{37.28\ g\ KCl}{1000\ g\ H_2O}$ $g_{soln} = g_{KCl} + g_{H_2O}$ so $g_{soln} - g_{KCl} = g_{H_2O}$

substitute into ratio $\dfrac{37.28\ g\ KCl}{1037.28\ g\ solution} = \dfrac{x\ g\ KCl}{500\ g\ solution}$.   Cross multiply, and solve for grams KCl.

$0.03728(100\ g\ soln - x\ g\ KCl) = x\ g\ KCl \rightarrow 3.728 - 0.03728\ (x\ g\ KCl) = x\ g\ KCl \rightarrow$

$3.728 = 1.03728\ (x\ g\ KCl) \rightarrow \dfrac{3.728}{1.03728} = x\ g\ KCl = 3.59$ g KCl then

$g_{H_2O} = g_{soln} - g_{KCl} = 100.\ g - 3.59\ g = 96.41$ g H_2O.

Prepare the solution by carefully adding 3.59 g KCl to a container with 96.41 g of distilled water and agitate the solution until the salt dissolves completely.

Check: The units (g) are correct. The magnitude of the answer (3.6 g) seems reasonable since we are making a small volume of solution and the formula weight of KCl is ~ 75 g/mol.

   (c)   **Given:** 1.00×10^2 g of 5.0 % KCl by mass   **Find:** describe final solution preparation

Conceptual Plan: g$_{soln} \rightarrow$ g$_{KCl}$ then g$_{KCl}$, g$_{soln} \rightarrow$ g$_{H_2O}$

$$\frac{5.0\ g\ KCl}{100\ g\ soln} \qquad\qquad g_{soln} = g_{KCl} + g_{H_2O}$$

then describe method

Solution: 1.00×10^2 g soln $\times \dfrac{5.0\ g\ KCl}{100\ g\ soln} = 5.0$ g KCl then $g_{soln} = g_{KCl} + g_{H_2O}$.

So $g_{H_2O} = g_{soln} - g_{KCl} = 100.\ g - 5.0\ g = 95$ g H_2O.

Prepare the solution by carefully adding 5.0 g KCl to a container with 95 g of distilled water and agitate the solution until the salt dissolves completely.

Check: The units (g) are correct. The magnitude of the answer (5 g) seems reasonable since we are making a small volume of solution and the solution is 5 % by mass KCl.

12.63   (a)   **Given:** 28.4 g of glucose ($C_6H_{12}O_6$) in 355 g water; final volume = 378 mL   **Find:** molarity

Conceptual Plan: mL $\rightarrow$ L and g $_{C_6H_{12}O_6} \rightarrow$ mol $_{C_6H_{12}O_6}$ then mol $_{C_6H_{12}O_6}$, $V \rightarrow$ M

$$\frac{1\ L}{1000\ mL} \qquad\qquad \frac{1\ mol\ C_6H_{12}O_6}{180.16\ g\ C_6H_{12}O_6} \qquad\qquad M = \frac{amount\ solute\ (moles)}{volume\ solution\ (L)}$$

Solution: $378 \text{ mL} \times \dfrac{1 \text{ L}}{1000 \text{ mL}} = 0.378 \text{ L}$ and

$28.4 \text{ g C}_6\text{H}_{12}\text{O}_6 \times \dfrac{1 \text{ mol C}_6\text{H}_{12}\text{O}_6}{180.16 \text{ g C}_6\text{H}_{12}\text{O}_6} = 0.15\underline{7}638 \text{ mol C}_6\text{H}_{12}\text{O}_6$

$M = \dfrac{\text{amount solute (moles)}}{\text{volume solution (L)}} = \dfrac{0.15\underline{7}638 \text{ mol C}_6\text{H}_{12}\text{O}_6}{0.378 \text{ L}} = 0.417 \text{ M}$

Check: The units (M) are correct. The magnitude of the answer (0.4 M) seems reasonable since we have 1/8 mole in about 1/3 L.

(b)   **Given:** 28.4 g of glucose ($C_6H_{12}O_6$) in 355 g water; final volume = 378 mL **Find:** molality

Conceptual Plan: $\text{g}_{\text{H}_2\text{O}} \rightarrow \text{kg}_{\text{H}_2\text{O}}$ and $\text{g}_{\text{C}_6\text{H}_{12}\text{O}_6} \rightarrow \text{mol}_{\text{C}_6\text{H}_{12}\text{O}_6}$ then $\text{mol}_{\text{C}_6\text{H}_{12}\text{O}_6}, \text{kg}_{\text{H}_2\text{O}} \rightarrow m$

$$\dfrac{1 \text{ kg}}{1000 \text{ g}} \qquad\qquad \dfrac{1 \text{ mol C}_6\text{H}_{12}\text{O}_6}{180.16 \text{ g C}_6\text{H}_{12}\text{O}_6} \qquad\qquad m = \dfrac{\text{amount solute (moles)}}{\text{mass solvent (kg)}}$$

Solution: $355 \text{ g} \times \dfrac{1 \text{ kg}}{1000 \text{ g}} = 0.355 \text{ kg}$ and

$28.4 \text{ g C}_6\text{H}_{12}\text{O}_6 \times \dfrac{1 \text{ mol C}_6\text{H}_{12}\text{O}_6}{180.16 \text{ g C}_6\text{H}_{12}\text{O}_6} = 0.15\underline{7}638 \text{ mol C}_6\text{H}_{12}\text{O}_6$

$m = \dfrac{\text{amount solute (moles)}}{\text{mass solvent (kg)}} = \dfrac{0.15\underline{7}638 \text{ mol C}_6\text{H}_{12}\text{O}_6}{0.355 \text{ kg}} = 0.444 \ m$

Check: The units (m) are correct. The magnitude of the answer (0.4 m) seems reasonable since we have 1/8 mole in about 1/3 kg.

(c)   **Given:** 28.4 g of glucose ($C_6H_{12}O_6$) in 355 g water; final volume = 378 mL **Find:** percent by mass

Conceptual Plan: $\text{g}_{\text{C}_6\text{H}_{12}\text{O}_6}, \text{g}_{\text{H}_2\text{O}} \rightarrow \text{g}_{\text{soln}}$ then $\text{g}_{\text{C}_6\text{H}_{12}\text{O}_6}, \text{g}_{\text{soln}} \rightarrow$ **percent by mass**

$$g_{\text{soln}} = g_{\text{C}_6\text{H}_{12}\text{O}_6} + g_{\text{H}_2\text{O}} \qquad\qquad \text{mass percent} = \dfrac{\text{mass solute}}{\text{mass solution}} \times 100\%$$

Solution: $g_{\text{soln}} = g_{\text{C}_6\text{H}_{12}\text{O}_6} + g_{\text{H}_2\text{O}} = 28.4 \text{ g} + 355 \text{ g} = 38\underline{3}.4 \text{ g soln}$ then

$\text{mass percent} = \dfrac{\text{mass solute}}{\text{mass solution}} \times 100\% = \dfrac{28.4 \text{ g C}_6\text{H}_{12}\text{O}_6}{38\underline{3}.4 \text{ g soln}} \times 100\% = 7.41 \text{ percent by mass.}$

Check: The units (percent by mass) are correct. The magnitude of the answer (7%) seems reasonable since we are dissolving 28 g in 355 g.

(d)   **Given:** 28.4 g of glucose ($C_6H_{12}O_6$) in 355 g water; final volume = 378 mL **Find:** mole fraction

Conceptual Plan:

$\text{g}_{\text{C}_6\text{H}_{12}\text{O}_6} \rightarrow \text{mol}_{\text{C}_6\text{H}_{12}\text{O}_6}$ and $\text{g}_{\text{H}_2\text{O}} \rightarrow \text{mol}_{\text{H}_2\text{O}}$ then $\text{mol}_{\text{C}_6\text{H}_{12}\text{O}_6}, \text{mol}_{\text{H}_2\text{O}} \rightarrow \chi_{\text{C}_6\text{H}_{12}\text{O}_6}$

$$\dfrac{1 \text{ mol C}_6\text{H}_{12}\text{O}_6}{180.16 \text{ g C}_6\text{H}_{12}\text{O}_6} \qquad\qquad \dfrac{1 \text{ mol H}_2\text{O}}{18.02 \text{ g H}_2\text{O}} \qquad\qquad \chi = \dfrac{\text{amount solute (in moles)}}{\text{total amount of solute and solvent (in moles)}}$$

Solution: $28.4 \text{ g C}_6\text{H}_{12}\text{O}_6 \times \dfrac{1 \text{ mol C}_6\text{H}_{12}\text{O}_6}{180.16 \text{ g C}_6\text{H}_{12}\text{O}_6} = 0.15\underline{7}638 \text{ mol C}_6\text{H}_{12}\text{O}_6$ and

$355 \text{ g H}_2\text{O} \times \dfrac{1 \text{ mol H}_2\text{O}}{18.02 \text{ g H}_2\text{O}} = 19.\underline{7}003 \text{ mol H}_2\text{O}$ then

$\chi = \dfrac{\text{amount solute (in moles)}}{\text{total amount of solute and solvent (in moles)}} = \dfrac{0.15\underline{7}638 \text{ mol}}{0.15\underline{7}638 \text{ mol} + 19.\underline{7}003 \text{ mol}} = 0.00794$

Check: The units (none) are correct. The magnitude of the answer (0.008) seems reasonable since we have many more grams of water and water has a much lower molecular weight.

(e)   **Given:** 28.4 g of glucose ($C_6H_{12}O_6$) in 355 g water; final volume = 378 mL **Find:** mole percent

Conceptual Plan: use answer from part d) then $\chi_{\text{C}_6\text{H}_{12}\text{O}_6} \rightarrow$ **mole percent**

$$\chi \times 100\%$$

Solution: $\text{mole percent} = \chi \times 100\% = 0.00794 \times 100\% = 0.794 \text{ mole percent}$

Check: The units (%) are correct. The magnitude of the answer (0.8) seems reasonable since we have many more grams of water, water has a much lower molecular weight, than glucose, and we are increasing the answer from part d) by a factor of 100.

Given: 3.0 % H_2O_2 by mass, d = 1.01 g/mL **Find:** molarity

Conceptual Plan:

Assume exactly 100 g of solution; $g_{solution} \rightarrow g_{H_2O_2} \rightarrow mol_{H_2O_2}$ **and** $g_{solution} \rightarrow mL_{solution} \rightarrow L_{solution}$

$$\frac{3.0 \text{ g } H_2O_2}{100 \text{ g solution}} \quad \frac{1 \text{ mol } H_2O_2}{34.02 \text{ g } H_2O_2} \qquad \qquad \frac{1 \text{ mL}}{1.01 \text{ g}} \quad \frac{1 \text{ L}}{1000 \text{ mL}}$$

then $mol_{H_2O_2}, L_{solution} \rightarrow \textbf{M}$

$$M = \frac{\text{amount solute (moles)}}{\text{volume solution (L)}}$$

Solution: $100 \; \overline{g \; solution} \times \dfrac{3.0 \; \overline{g \; H_2O_2}}{100 \; \overline{g \; solution}} \times \dfrac{1 \text{ mol } H_2O_2}{34.02 \; \overline{g \; H_2O_2}} = 0.0881834 \text{ mol } H_2O_2$ and

$100 \; \overline{g \; solution} \times \dfrac{1 \; \overline{mL \; solution}}{1.01 \; \overline{g \; solution}} \times \dfrac{1 \text{ L solution}}{1000 \; \overline{mL \; solution}} = 0.0990099 \text{ L solution then}$

$M = \dfrac{\text{amount solute (moles)}}{\text{volume solution (L)}} = \dfrac{0.0881834 \text{ mol } H_2O_2}{0.0990099 \text{ L solution}} = 0.89 \text{ M } H_2O_2.$

Check: The units (M) are correct. The magnitude of the answer (1) seems reasonable since we are starting with a low concentration solution and pure water is ~ 55.5 M.

12.67 **Given:** 36 % HCl by mass **Find:** molality and mole fraction

Conceptual Plan: Assume exactly 100 g of solution; $g_{solution} \rightarrow g_{HCl} \rightarrow mol_{HCl}$ **and** $g_{HCl}, g_{solution} \rightarrow$

$$\frac{36 \text{ g HCl}}{100 \text{ g solution}} \quad \frac{1 \text{ mol HCl}}{36.46 \text{ g HCl}} \qquad g_{soln} = g_{HCl} + g_{H_2O}$$

$g_{solvent} \rightarrow kg_{solvent}$ **then** $mol_{HCl}, kg_{solvent} \rightarrow m$ **and** $g_{solvent} \rightarrow mol_{solvent}$ **then** $mol_{HCl}, mol_{solvent} \rightarrow \chi_{HCl}$

$$\frac{1 \text{ kg}}{1000 \text{ g}} \qquad m = \frac{\text{amount solute (moles)}}{\text{mass solvent (kg)}} \quad \frac{1 \text{ mol } H_2O}{18.02 \text{ g } H_2O} \quad \chi = \frac{\text{amount solute (in moles)}}{\text{total amount of solute and solvent (in moles)}}$$

Solution: $100 \; \overline{g \; solution} \times \dfrac{36 \text{ g HCl}}{100 \; \overline{g \; solution}} = 36 \; \overline{g \; HCl} \times \dfrac{1 \text{ mol HCl}}{36.46 \; \overline{g \; HCl}} = 0.987383 \text{ mol HCl}$ and

$g_{soln} = g_{HCl} + g_{H_2O}.$ Rearrange to solve for $g_{solvent}.$ $g_{H_2O} = g_{soln} - g_{HCl} = 100 \text{ g} - 36 \text{ g} = 64 \text{ g } H_2O$

$64 \; \overline{g \; H_2O} \times \dfrac{1 \text{ kg } H_2O}{1000 \; \overline{g \; H_2O}} = 0.064 \text{ kg } H_2O$ then

$m = \dfrac{\text{amount solute (moles)}}{\text{mass solvent (kg)}} = \dfrac{0.987383 \text{ mol HCl}}{0.064 \text{ kg}} = 15 \; m \text{ HCl}$ and

$64 \; \overline{g \; H_2O} \times \dfrac{1 \text{ mol } H_2O}{18.02 \; \overline{g \; H_2O}} = 3.55161 \text{ mol } H_2O$ then

$\chi = \dfrac{\text{amount solvent (in moles)}}{\text{total amount of solute and solvent (in moles)}} = \dfrac{0.987383 \; \overline{mol}}{0.987383 \; \overline{mol} + 3.55161 \; \overline{mol}} = 0.22.$

Check: The units (m and unitless) are correct. The magnitudes of the answers (15 and 0.2) seem reasonable since we are starting with a high concentration solution and the molar mass of water is much less than that of HCl.

Vapor Pressure of Solutions

12.69 The level has decreased more in the beaker filled with pure water. The dissolved salt in the seawater decreases the vapor pressure and subsequently lowers the rate of vaporization.

12.71 **Given:** 24.5 g of glycerin ($C_3H_8O_3$) in 135 mL water at 30 °C; $P^{\circ}_{H_2O}$ = 31.8 torr **Find:** P_{H_2O}

Other: d (H_2O) = 1.00 g/mL; glycerin is not ionic solid

Conceptual Plan: $g_{C_3H_8O_3} \rightarrow mol_{C_3H_8O_3}$ **and** $mL_{H_2O} \rightarrow g_{H_2O} \rightarrow mol_{H_2O}$ **then** $mol_{C_3H_8O_3}, mol_{H_2O} \rightarrow \chi_{H_2O}$

$$\frac{1 \text{ mol } C_3H_8O_3}{92.09 \text{ g } C_3H_8O_3} \qquad \frac{1.00 \text{ g}}{1 \text{ mL}} \quad \frac{1 \text{ mol } H_2O}{18.01 \text{ g } H_2O} \quad \chi = \frac{\text{amount solute (in moles)}}{\text{total amount of solute and solvent (in moles)}}$$

then $\chi_{H_2O}, P^{\circ}_{H_2O} \rightarrow P_{H_2O}$

$$P_{solution} = \chi_{solvent} P^{\circ}_{solvent}$$

Solution: $24.5 \, \cancel{g \, C_3H_8O_3} \times \dfrac{1 \text{ mol } C_3H_8O_3}{92.09 \, \cancel{g \, C_3H_8O_3}} = 0.266\underline{0}441 \text{ mol } C_3H_8O_3$ and

$135 \, \cancel{mL} \times \dfrac{1.00 \, \cancel{g}}{1 \, \cancel{mL}} \times \dfrac{1 \text{ mol } H_2O}{18.01 \, \cancel{g \, H_2O}} = 7.495836 \text{ mol } H_2O$ then

$\chi = \dfrac{\text{amount solvent (in moles)}}{\text{total amount of solute and solvent (in moles)}} = \dfrac{7.495836 \, \cancel{mol}}{0.266\underline{0}441 \, \cancel{mol} + 7.495836 \, \cancel{mol}} = 0.965\underline{7}243$ then

$P_{\text{solution}} = \chi_{\text{solvent}} P_{\text{solvent}}^{\circ} = 0.965\underline{7}243 \times 31.8 \text{ torr} = 30.7 \text{ torr}$

Check: The units (torr) are correct. The magnitude of the answer (31 torr) seems reasonable since it is a drop from the pure vapor pressure. Very few moles of glycerin are added, so the pressure will not drop much.

12.73   **Given:** 50.0 g of heptane (C_7H_{16}) and 50.0 g of octane (C_8H_{18}) at 25 °C; $P_{C_7H_{16}}^{\circ} = 45.8$ torr; $P_{C_8H_{18}}^{\circ} = 10.9$ torr

(a)   **Find:** $P_{C_7H_{16}}, \, P_{C_8H_{18}}$

Conceptual Plan: g $C_7H_{16} \rightarrow$ mol C_7H_{16} and g $C_8H_{18} \rightarrow$ mol C_8H_{18} then mol C_7H_{16},

$$\dfrac{1 \text{ mol } C_7H_{16}}{100.20 \text{ g } C_7H_{16}} \qquad \dfrac{1 \text{ mol } C_8H_{18}}{114.22 \text{ g } C_8H_{18}} \qquad \chi_{C_7H_{16}} = \dfrac{\text{amount } C_7H_{16} \text{ (in moles)}}{\text{total amount (in moles)}}$$

mol $C_8H_{18} \rightarrow \chi\, C_7H_{16}, \, \chi\, C_8H_{18}$ then $\chi\, C_7H_{16}, \, P_{C_7H_{16}}^{\circ} \rightarrow P_{C_7H_{16}}$ and $\chi\, C_8H_{18}, \, P_{C_8H_{18}}^{\circ} \rightarrow P_{C_8H_{18}}$

$$\chi_{C_8H_{18}} = 1 - \chi_{C_7H_{16}} \qquad\qquad P_{C_7H_{16}} = \chi_{C_7H_{16}} P_{C_7H_{16}}^{\circ} \qquad\qquad P_{C_8H_{18}} = \chi_{C_8H_{18}} P_{C_8H_{18}}^{\circ}$$

Solution: $50.0 \, \cancel{g \, C_7H_{16}} \times \dfrac{1 \text{ mol } C_7H_{16}}{100.20 \, \cancel{g \, C_7H_{16}}} = 0.49\underline{9}002 \text{ mol } C_7H_{16}$ and

$50.0 \, \cancel{g \, C_8H_{18}} \times \dfrac{1 \text{ mol } C_8H_{18}}{114.22 \, \cancel{g \, C_8H_{18}}} = 0.43\underline{7}752 \text{ mol } C_8H_{18}$ then

$\chi_{C_7H_{16}} = \dfrac{\text{amount } C_7H_{16} \text{ (in moles)}}{\text{total amount (in moles)}} = \dfrac{0.49\underline{9}002 \, \cancel{mol}}{0.49\underline{9}002 \, \cancel{mol} + 0.43\underline{7}752 \, \cancel{mol}} = 0.53\underline{2}693$ and

$\chi_{C_8H_{18}} = 1 - \chi_{C7H16} = 1 - 0.53\underline{2}693 = 0.46\underline{7}307$ then

$P_{C_7H_{16}} = \chi_{C_7H_{16}} P_{C_7H_{16}}^{\circ} = 0.53\underline{2}693 \times 45.8 \text{ torr} = 24.4 \text{ torr}$ and

$P_{C_8H_{18}} = \chi_{C_8H_{18}} P_{C_8H_{18}}^{\circ} = 0.46\underline{7}307 \times 10.9 \text{ torr} = 5.09 \text{ torr}$

Check: The units (torr) are correct. The magnitude of the answer (24 and 5 torr) seems reasonable because we expect a drop in half from the pure vapor pressures since we have roughly a 50:50 mole ratio of the two components.

(b)   **Find:** P_{Total}

Conceptual Plan: $P_{C_7H_{16}}, \, P_{C_8H_{18}} \rightarrow P_{\text{Total}}$

$$P_{\text{Total}} = P_{C_7H_{16}} + P_{C_8H_{18}}$$

Solution: $P_{\text{Total}} = P_{C_7H_{16}} + P_{C_8H_{18}} = 24.4 \text{ torr} + 5.09 \text{ torr} = 29.5 \text{ torr}$

Check: The units (torr) are correct. The magnitude of the answer (30 torr) seems reasonable considering the two pressures.

(c)   **Find:** mass percent composition of the gas phase

Conceptual Plan: since $n \, \alpha \, P$ and we are calculating a mass percent, which is a ratio of masses, we can simply convert 1 torr to 1 mole so

$P_{C_7H_{16}}, \, P_{C_8H_{18}} \rightarrow n_{C_7H_{16}}, \, n_{C_8H_{18}}$ then mol$_{C_7H_{16}} \rightarrow$ g$_{C_7H_{16}}$ and mol $C_8H_{18} \rightarrow$ g C_8H_{18}

$$\dfrac{100.20 \text{ g } C_7H_{16}}{1 \text{ mol } C_7H_{16}} \qquad\qquad \dfrac{114.22 \text{ g } C_8H_{18}}{1 \text{ mol } C_8H_{18}}$$

then g$_{C_7H_{16}}$, g $C_8H_{18} \rightarrow$ mass percents

$$\text{mass percent} = \dfrac{\text{mass solute}}{\text{mass solution}} \times 100\%$$

Solution: so $n_{C_7H_{16}} = 24.4$ mol and $n_{C_8H_{18}} = 5.09$ mol then

$24.4 \, \cancel{mol \, C_7H_{16}} \times \dfrac{100.20 \text{ g } C_7H_{16}}{1 \, \cancel{mol \, C_7H_{16}}} = 244\underline{4}.88 \text{ g } C_7H_{16}$ and

$5.09 \, \cancel{mol \, C_8H_{18}} \times \dfrac{114.22 \text{ g } C_8H_{18}}{1 \, \cancel{mol \, C_8H_{18}}} = 58\underline{1}.380 \text{ g } C_8H_{18}$ then

$$\text{mass percent} = \frac{\text{mass solute}}{\text{mass solution}} \times 100\% = \frac{2444.88 \ \cancel{g \ C_7H_{16}}}{2444.88 \ \cancel{g \ C_7H_{16}} + 581.380 \ \cancel{g \ C_8H_{18}}} \times 100\% =$$

= 80.8 percent by mass C_7H_{16}

then 100% − 80.8% = 19.2 percent by mass C_8H_{18}

Check: The units (%) are correct. The magnitudes of the answers (81% and 19%) seem reasonable considering the two pressures.

(d)   The two mass percents are different because the vapor is richer in the more volatile component (the lighter molecule).

12.75   **Given:** 4.08 g of chloroform ($CHCl_3$) and 9.29 g of acetone (CH_3COCH_3); at 35 °C $P^{\circ}_{CHCl_3}$ = 295 torr; $P^{\circ}_{CH_3COCH_3}$ = 332 torr; assume ideal behavior; $P_{\text{Total measured}}$ = 312 torr

Find: P_{CHCl_3}, $P_{CH_3COCH_3}$, P_{Total}, and if the soln is ideal.

Conceptual Plan: $g_{CHCl_3} \rightarrow mol_{CHCl_3}$ and $g_{CH_3COCH_3} \rightarrow mol_{CH_3COCH_3}$ then

$$\frac{1 \ \text{mol } CHCl_3}{119.38 \ \text{g } CHCl_3} \qquad\qquad \frac{1 \ \text{mol } CH_3COCH_3}{58.08 \ \text{g } CH_3COCH_3}$$

mol_{CHCl_3}, $mol_{CH_3COCH_3} \rightarrow \chi_{CHCl_3}$, $\chi_{CH_3COCH_3}$ then χ_{CHCl_3}, $P^{\circ}_{CHCl_3} \rightarrow P_{CHCl_3}$ and

$$\chi_{CHCl_3} = \frac{\text{amount } CHCl_3 \ (\text{in moles})}{\text{total amount (in moles)}} \qquad \chi_{CH_3COCH_3} = 1 - \chi_{CHCl_3} \qquad P_{CHCl_3} = \chi_{CHCl_3}P^{\circ}_{CHCl_3}$$

$\chi_{CH_3COCH_3}$, $P^{\circ}_{CH_3COCH_3} \rightarrow P_{CH_3COCH_3}$ then P_{CHCl_3}, $P_{CH_3COCH_3} \rightarrow P_{Total}$ then compare values

$$P_{CH_3COCH_3} = \chi_{CH_3COCH_3}P^{\circ}_{CH_3COCH_3} \qquad\qquad \text{Total} = P_{CHCl_3} + P_{CH_3COCH_{33}}$$

Solution:

$$4.08 \ \cancel{g \ CHCl_3} \times \frac{1 \ \text{mol } CHCl_3}{119.38 \ \cancel{g \ CHCl_3}} = 0.0341766 \ \text{mol } CHCl_3 \text{ and}$$

$$9.29 \ \cancel{g \ CH_3COCH_3} \times \frac{1 \ \text{mol } CH_3COCH_3}{58.08 \ \cancel{g \ CH_3COCH_3}} = 0.159952 \ \text{mol } CH_3COCH_3 \text{ then}$$

$$\chi_{CHCl_3} = \frac{\text{amount } CHCl_3 \ (\text{in moles})}{\text{total amount (in moles)}} = \frac{0.0341766 \ \cancel{mol}}{0.0341766 \ \cancel{mol} + 0.159952 \ \cancel{mol}} = 0.176052 \text{ and}$$

$\chi_{CH_3COCH_3} = 1 - \chi_{CHCl_3} = 1 - 0.176052 = 0.823948$ then

$P_{CHCl_3} = \chi_{CHCl_3}P^{\circ}_{CHCl_3} = 0.176052 \times 295 \ \text{torr} = 51.9 \ \text{torr}$ and

$P_{CH_3COCH_3} = \chi_{CH_3COCH_3}P^{\circ}_{CH_3COCH_3} = 0.823948 \times 332 \ \text{torr} = 274 \ \text{torr}$ then

$P_{Total} = P_{CHCl_3} + P_{CH_3COCH_3} = 51.9 \ \text{torr} + 274 \ \text{torr} = 326 \ \text{torr}$.

Since 326 torr ≠ 312 torr, the solution is not behaving ideally. The chloroform–acetone interactions are stronger than the chloroform–chloroform and acetone–acetone interactions.

Check: The units (torr) are correct. The magnitude of the answer seems reasonable since each is a fraction of the pure vapor pressure. We are not surprised that the solution is not ideal, since the types of bonds in the two molecules are very different.

Freezing Point Depression, Boiling Point Elevation, and Osmosis

12.77   **Given:** 55.8 g of glucose ($C_6H_{12}O_6$) in 455 g water   **Find:** T_f and T_b **Other:** K_f = 1.86 °C/m; K_b = 0.512 °C/m;

Conceptual Plan: $g_{H_2O} \rightarrow kg_{H_2O}$ and $g_{C_6H_{12}O_6} \rightarrow mol_{C_6H_{12}O_6}$ then $mol_{C_6H_{12}O_6}$, $kg_{H_2O} \rightarrow m$

$$\frac{1 \ \text{kg}}{1000 \ \text{g}} \qquad\qquad \frac{1 \ \text{mol } C_6H_{12}O_6}{180.16 \ \text{g } C_6H_{12}O_6} \qquad\qquad m = \frac{\text{amount solute (moles)}}{\text{mass solvent (kg)}}$$

m, $K_f \rightarrow \Delta T_f \rightarrow T_f$ and m, $K_b \rightarrow \Delta T_b \rightarrow T_b$

$$\Delta T_f = K_f m \qquad T_f = T_f^{\circ} - \Delta T_f \qquad\qquad \Delta T_b = K_b m \quad \Delta T_b = T_b - T_b^{\circ}$$

Solution: $455 \ \cancel{g} \times \dfrac{1 \ \text{kg}}{1000 \ \cancel{g}} = 0.455 \ \text{kg}$ and $55.8 \ \cancel{g \ C_6H_{12}O_6} \times \dfrac{1 \ \text{mol } C_6H_{12}O_6}{180.16 \ \cancel{g \ C_6H_{12}O_6}} = 0.309725 \ \text{mol } C_6H_{12}O_6$ then

$$m = \frac{\text{amount solute (moles)}}{\text{mass solvent (kg)}} = \frac{0.309725 \ \text{mol } C_6H_{12}O_6}{0.455 \ \text{kg}} = 0.680714 \ m \text{ then}$$

$\Delta T_f = K_f m = 1.86 \ \dfrac{°C}{\cancel{m}} \times 0.680714 \ \cancel{m} = 1.27 \ °C$ then $T_f = T_f^{\circ} - \Delta T_f = 0.00 \ °C - 1.27 \ °C = -1.27 \ °C$ and

$\Delta T_b = K_b m = 0.512 \ \dfrac{°C}{\cancel{m}} \times 0.680714 \ \cancel{m} = 0.349 \ °C$ and $\Delta T_b = T_b - T_b^{\circ}$ so

$T_b = T_b^{\circ} + \Delta T_b = 100.000 \ °C + 0.349 \ °C = 100.349 \ °C$

Check: The units (°C) are correct. The magnitudes of the answers seem reasonable since the molality is ~ 2/3. The shift in boiling point is less than the shift in freezing point because the constant for boiling is smaller than the constant for freezing is smaller than the con.

12.79 **Given:** 17.5 g of unknown nonelectrolyte in 100.0 g water, $T_f = -1.8$ °C **Find:** $\mathcal{M}$
Other: $K_f = 1.86$ °C/m
Conceptual Plan: $g_{H_2O} \rightarrow kg_{H_2O}$ and $T_f \rightarrow \Delta T_f$ then $\Delta T_f, K_f \rightarrow m$ then $m, kg_{H_2O} \rightarrow mol_{Unk}$

$$\frac{1\ kg}{1000\ g} \qquad T_f = T_f^\circ - \Delta T_f \qquad \Delta T_f = K_f m \qquad m = \frac{\text{amount solute (moles)}}{\text{mass solvent (kg)}}$$

then $g_{Unk}, mol_{Unk} \rightarrow \mathcal{M}$

$$\mathcal{M} = \frac{g_{Unk}}{mol_{Unk}}$$

Solution: $100.0\ \cancel{g} \times \dfrac{1\ kg}{1000\ \cancel{g}} = 0.1000$ kg and $T_f = T_f^\circ - \Delta T_f$ so

$\Delta T_f = T_f^\circ - T_f = 0.00$ °C $- (-1.8$ °C$) = +1.8$ °C $\quad \Delta T_f = K_f m$. Rearrange to solve for m.

$$m = \frac{\Delta T_f}{K_f} = \frac{1.8\ \cancel{°C}}{1.86\ \dfrac{\cancel{°C}}{m}} = 0.9\underline{6}774\ m \text{ then } m = \frac{\text{amount solute (moles)}}{\text{mass solvent (kg)}} \text{ so}$$

$mol_{Unk} = m_{Unk} \times kg_{H_2O} = 0.9\underline{6}774\ \dfrac{\text{mol Unk}}{\cancel{kg}} \times 0.1000\ \cancel{kg} = 0.09\underline{6}774$ mol Unk then

$$\mathcal{M} = \frac{g_{Unk}}{mol_{Unk}} = \frac{17.5\ g}{0.09\underline{6}774\ mol} = 180\ \frac{g}{mol} = 1.8 \times 10^2\ \frac{g}{mol}.$$

Check: The units (g/mol) are correct. The magnitude of the answer (180 g/mol) seems reasonable since the molality is ~ 0.1 and we have ~18 g. It is a reasonable molecular weight for a solid or liquid.

12.81 **Given:** 24.6 g of glycerin ($C_3H_8O_3$) in 250.0 mL of solution at 298 K **Find:** Π
Conceptual Plan: mL $\rightarrow L_{soln}$ and $g\ C_3H_8O_3 \rightarrow mol\ C_3H_8O_3$ then $mol\ C_3H_8O_3, L_{soln} \rightarrow M$ then

$$\frac{1\ L}{1000\ mL} \qquad \frac{1\ mol\ C_3H_8O_3}{92.09\ g\ C_3H_8O_3} \qquad M = \frac{\text{amount solute (moles)}}{\text{volume solution (L)}}$$

$M, T \rightarrow \Pi$

$$\Pi = M\,RT$$

Solution:

$250.0\ \cancel{mL} \times \dfrac{1\ L}{1000\ \cancel{mL}} = 0.2500$ L and $24.6\ \cancel{g\ C_3H_8O_3} \times \dfrac{1\ mol\ C_3H_8O_3}{92.09\ \cancel{g\ C_3H_8O_3}} = 0.26\underline{7}130\ mol\ C_3H_8O_3$ then

$$M = \frac{\text{amount solute (moles)}}{\text{volume solution (L)}} = \frac{0.26\underline{7}130\ mol\ C_3H_8O_3}{0.2500\ L} = 1.0\underline{6}852\ M \text{ then}$$

$$\Pi = M\,RT = 1.0\underline{6}852\ \frac{mol}{\cancel{L}} \times 0.08206\ \frac{\cancel{L} \cdot atm}{K \cdot \cancel{mol}} \times 298\ \cancel{K} = 26.1\ atm$$

Check: The units (atm) are correct. The magnitude of the answer (26 atm) seems reasonable since the molarity is ~ 1.

12.83 **Given:** 27.55 mg unknown protein in 25.0 mL solution; $\Pi = 3.22$ torr at 25 °C **Find:** $\mathcal{M}_{\text{unknown protein}}$
Conceptual Plan: °C $\rightarrow$ K and torr $\rightarrow$ atm then $\Pi, T \rightarrow M$ then $mL_{soln} \rightarrow L_{soln}$ then

$$K = °C + 273.15 \qquad \frac{1\ atm}{760\ torr} \qquad \Pi = M\,RT \qquad \frac{1\ L}{1000\ mL}$$

$L_{soln}, M \rightarrow mol_{\text{unknown protein}}$ and $mg \rightarrow g$ then $g_{\text{unknown protein}}, mol_{\text{unknown protein}} \rightarrow \mathcal{M}_{\text{unknown protein}}$

$$M = \frac{\text{amount solute (moles)}}{\text{volume solution (L)}} \qquad \frac{1\ g}{1000\ mg} \qquad \mathcal{M} = \frac{g_{\text{unknown protein}}}{mol_{\text{unknown protein}}}$$

Solution: 25 °C $+ 273.15 = 298$ K and $3.22\ \cancel{torr} \times \dfrac{1\ atm}{760\ \cancel{torr}} = 0.004\underline{2}3684$ atm $\Pi = M\,RT$ for M.

$$M = \frac{\Pi}{RT} = \frac{0.004\underline{2}3684\ \cancel{atm}}{0.08206\ \dfrac{L \cdot \cancel{atm}}{K \cdot mol} \times 298\ \cancel{K}} = 1.7\underline{3}258 \times 10^{-4}\ \frac{mol}{L} \text{ then } 25.0\ \cancel{mL} \times \dfrac{1\ L}{1000\ \cancel{mL}} = 0.0250\ L \text{ then}$$

$M = \dfrac{\text{amount solute (moles)}}{\text{volume solution (L)}}$. Rearrange to solve for $\text{mol}_{\text{unknown protein}}$.

$\text{mol}_{\text{unknown protein}} = M \times L = 1.73258 \times 10^{-4}\,\dfrac{\text{mol}}{\text{L}} \times 0.0250\,\text{L} = 4.33146 \times 10^{-6}\,\text{mol}$

$27.55\,\text{mg} \times \dfrac{1\,\text{g}}{1000\,\text{mg}} = 0.02755\,\text{g}$ $\qquad M = \dfrac{g_{\text{unknown protein}}}{\text{mol}_{\text{unknown protein}}} = \dfrac{0.02755\,\text{g}}{4.33146 \times 10^{-6}\,\text{mol}} = 6.36 \times 10^3\,\dfrac{\text{g}}{\text{mol}}$

Check: The units (g/mol) are correct. The magnitude of the answer (6400 g/mol) seems reasonable for a large biological molecule. A small amount of material is put into 0.025 L, so the concentration is very small

12.85   (a)   **Given:** 0.100 m of K_2S, completely dissociated **Find:** T_f, T_b
Other: $K_f = 1.86\,°C/m$; $K_b = 0.512\,°C/m$;
Conceptual Plan: $m, i, K_f \rightarrow \Delta T_f$ then $\Delta T_f \rightarrow T_f$ and $m, i, K_b \rightarrow \Delta T_b$ then $\Delta T_b \rightarrow T_b$
$\qquad\qquad \Delta T_f = K_f\, i m_{i=3} \qquad T_f = T_f° - \Delta T_f \qquad \Delta T_b = K_b\, i m_{i=3} \qquad T_b = T_b° + \Delta T_b$
Solution: $\Delta T_f = K_f\, im = 1.86\,\dfrac{°C}{m} \times 3 \times 0.100\,m = 0.558\,°C$ then

$T_f = T_f° - \Delta T_f = 0.000\,°C - 0.558\,°C = -0.558\,°C$ and

$\Delta T_b = K_b\, im = 0.512\,\dfrac{°C}{m} \times 3 \times 0.100\,m = 0.154\,°C$ then

$T_b = T_b° - \Delta T_b = 100.000\,°C + 0.154\,°C = 100.154\,°C$.

Check: The units (°C) are correct. The magnitude of the answer (– 0.6 °C and 100.2 °C) seems reasonable since the molality of the particles is 0.3. The shift in boiling point is less than the shift in freezing point because the constant for boiling is larger than the constant for freezing.

(b)   **Given:** 21.5 g $CuCl_2$ in 4.50×10^2 g water, completely dissociated **Find:** T_f, T_b
Other: $K_f = 1.86\,°C/m$; $K_b = 0.512\,°C/m$;
Conceptual Plan: $g_{H_2O} \rightarrow kg_{H_2O}$ and $g\,_{CuCl_2} \rightarrow \text{mol}\,_{CuCl_2}$ then $\text{mol}\,_{CuCl_2},\,kg_{H_2O} \rightarrow m$
$\qquad\qquad\qquad \dfrac{1\,kg}{1000\,g} \qquad\qquad \dfrac{1\,\text{mol}\,CuCl_2}{134.46\,g\,CuCl_2} \qquad\qquad\qquad m = \dfrac{\text{amount solute (moles)}}{\text{mass solvent (kg)}}$
$m, i, K_f \rightarrow \Delta T_f \rightarrow T_f$ and $m, i, K_b \rightarrow \Delta T_b \rightarrow T_b$
$\quad \Delta T_f = K_f\, im_{i=3}\;\; T_f = T_f° - \Delta T_f \quad \Delta T_b = K_b\, im_{i=3}\;\; T_b = T_b° + \Delta T_b$
Solution:

$4.5 \times 10^2\,g \times \dfrac{1\,kg}{1000\,g} = 0.450\,kg$ and $21.5\,g\,CuCl_2 \times \dfrac{1\,\text{mol}\,CuCl_2}{134.46\,g\,CuCl_2} = 0.159904\,\text{mol}\,CuCl_2$ then

$m = \dfrac{\text{amount solute (moles)}}{\text{mass solvent (kg)}} = \dfrac{0.159904\,\text{mol}\,CuCl_2}{0.450\,kg} = 0.355341\,m$ then

$\Delta T_f = K_f\, im = 1.86\,\dfrac{°C}{m} \times 3 \times 0.355341\,m = 1.98\,°C$ then

$T_f = T_f° - \Delta T_f = 0.000\,°C - 1.98\,°C = -1.98\,°C$ and

$\Delta T_b = K_b\, im = 0.512\,\dfrac{°C}{m} \times 3 \times 0.355341\,m = 0.546\,°C$ then

$T_b = T_b° - \Delta T_b = 100.000\,°C + 0.546\,°C = 100.546\,°C$.

Check: The units (°C) are correct. The magnitude of the answer (– 2 °C and 100.5 °C) seems reasonable since the molality of the particles is ~ 1. The shift in boiling point is less than the shift in freezing point because the constant for boiling is larger than the constant for freezing.

(c)   **Given:** 5.5 % by mass $NaNO_3$, completely dissociated **Find:** T_f, T_b
Other: $K_f = 1.86\,°C/m$; $K_b = 0.512\,°C/m$;
Conceptual Plan: percent by mass $\rightarrow g_{NaNO_3},\,g_{H_2O}$ then $g_{H_2O} \rightarrow kg_{H_2O}$ and $g\,_{NaNO_3} \rightarrow \text{mol}\,_{NaNO_3}$
$\qquad\qquad\qquad \text{mass percent} = \dfrac{\text{mass solute}}{\text{mass solution}} \times 100\% \qquad \dfrac{1\,kg}{1000\,g} \qquad \dfrac{1\,\text{mol}\,NaNO_3}{84.99\,g\,NaNO_3}$
then $\text{mol}\,_{NaNO_3},\,kg_{H_2O} \rightarrow m$ then $m, i, K_f \rightarrow \Delta T_f \rightarrow T_f$ and $m, i, K_b \rightarrow \Delta T_b \rightarrow T_b$
$\qquad m = \dfrac{\text{amount solute (moles)}}{\text{mass solvent (kg)}} \quad \Delta T_f = K_f\, im_{i=2}\;\; T_f = T_f° - \Delta T_f \quad \Delta T_b = K_b\, im_{i=2}\;\; T_b = T_b° + \Delta T_b$

Solution: mass percent $= \dfrac{\text{mass solute}}{\text{mass solution}} \times 100\%$ so 5.5 % by mass $NaNO_3$ means 5.5 g $NaNO_3$ and

100.0 g – 5.5 g = 94.5 g water. Then $94.5 \text{ g} \times \dfrac{1 \text{ kg}}{1000 \text{ g}} = 0.0945$ kg and

$5.5 \text{ g } NaNO_3 \times \dfrac{1 \text{ mol } NaNO_3}{84.99 \text{ g } NaNO_3} = 0.064713 \text{ mol } NaNO_3$ then

$m = \dfrac{\text{amount solute (moles)}}{\text{mass solvent (kg)}} = \dfrac{0.064713 \text{ mol } NaNO_3}{0.0945 \text{ kg}} = 0.68480 \ m$ then

$\Delta T_f = K_f im = 1.86 \dfrac{^\circ C}{m} \times 2 \times 0.68480 \ m = 2.5 \ ^\circ C$ then

$T_f = T_f^\circ - \Delta T_f = 0.000 \ ^\circ C - 2.3 \ ^\circ C = -2.5 \ ^\circ C$ and

$\Delta T_b = K_b im = 0.512 \dfrac{^\circ C}{m} \times 2 \times 0.68480 \ m = 0.70 \ ^\circ C$ then

$T_b = T_b^\circ - \Delta T_b = 100.000 \ ^\circ C + 0.64 \ ^\circ C = 100.70 \ ^\circ C$.

Check: The units (°C) are correct. The magnitude of the answer (– 2.5 °C and 100.7 °C) seems reasonable since the molality of the particles is ~ 1. The shift in boiling point is less than the shift in freezing point because the constant for boiling is larger than the constant for freezing.

12.87   (a)   **Given:** 0.100 m of $FeCl_3$ **Find:** T_f **Other:** $K_f = 1.86 \ ^\circ C/m$; $i_{measured} = 3.4$

Conceptual Plan: $m, i, K_f \rightarrow \Delta T_f$ then $\Delta T_f \rightarrow T_f$

$$\Delta T_f = K_f im \qquad\qquad T_f = T_f^\circ - \Delta T_f$$

Solution: $\Delta T_f = K_f im = 1.86 \dfrac{^\circ C}{m} \times 3.4 \times 0.100 \ m = 0.632 \ ^\circ C$ then

$T_f = T_f^\circ - \Delta T_f = 0.000 \ ^\circ C - 0.632 \ ^\circ C = -0.632 \ ^\circ C$.

Check: The units (°C) are correct. The magnitude of the answer (– 0.6 °C) seems reasonable since the theoretical molality of the particles is 0.4.

(b)   **Given:** 0.085 M of K_2SO_4 at 298 K   **Find:** Π **Other:** $i_{measured} = 2.6$

Conceptual Plan: $M, i, T \rightarrow \Pi$

$$\Pi = iM \, RT$$

Solution: $\Pi = iM \, RT = 2.6 \times 0.085 \dfrac{\text{mol}}{L} \times 0.08206 \dfrac{L \cdot atm}{K \cdot mol} \times 298 \text{ K} = 5.4$ atm

Check: The units (atm) are correct. The magnitude of the answer (5 atm) seems reasonable since the molarity of particles is ~ 0.2 m.

(c)   **Given:** 1.22 % by mass $MgCl_2$ **Find:** T_b **Other:** $K_b = 0.512 \ ^\circ C/m$; $i_{measured} = 2.7$

Conceptual Plan: percent by mass $\rightarrow g_{MgCl_2}, g_{H_2O}$ then $g_{H_2O} \rightarrow kg_{H_2O}$ and $g_{MgCl_2} \rightarrow$ mol $_{MgCl_2}$ then

$$\text{mass percent} = \dfrac{\text{mass solute}}{\text{mass solution}} \times 100\% \qquad \dfrac{1 \text{ kg}}{1000 \text{ g}} \qquad \dfrac{1 \text{ mol } MgCl_2}{95.22 \text{ g } MgCl_2}$$

mol $_{MgCl_2}$, $kg_{H_2O} \rightarrow m$ then $m, i, K_b \rightarrow \Delta T_b \rightarrow T_b$

$$m = \dfrac{\text{amount solute (moles)}}{\text{mass solvent (kg)}} \qquad \Delta T_b = K_b im \quad T_b = T_b^\circ + \Delta T_b$$

Solution: mass percent $= \dfrac{\text{mass solute}}{\text{mass solution}} \times 100\%$ so 1.22 % by mass $MgCl_2$ means 1.22 g $MgCl_2$ and

100.00 g – 1.22 g = 98.78 g water. Then $98.78 \text{ g} \times \dfrac{1 \text{ kg}}{1000 \text{ g}} = 0.09878$ kg and

$1.22 \text{ g } MgCl_2 \times \dfrac{1 \text{ mol } MgCl_2}{95.23 \text{ g } MgCl_2} = 0.0128110 \text{ mol } MgCl_2$ then

$m = \dfrac{\text{amount solute (moles)}}{\text{mass solvent (kg)}} = \dfrac{0.0128110 \text{ mol } MgCl_2}{0.09878 \text{ kg}} = 0.129693 \ m$ then

$\Delta T_b = K_b im = 0.512 \dfrac{^\circ C}{m} \times 2.7 \times 0.129706 \ m = 0.18 \ ^\circ C$ then

$T_b = T_b^\circ - \Delta T_b = 100.000 \ ^\circ C + 0.18 \ ^\circ C = 100.18 \ ^\circ C$.

Check: The units (°C) are correct. The magnitude of the answer (100.2 °C) seems reasonable since the molality of the particles is ~ 1/3.

12.89   **Given:** 0.100 M of ionic solution, $\Pi = 8.3$ atm at 25 °C   **Find:** $i_{measured}$
     Conceptual Plan: °C $\rightarrow$ K then $\Pi, M, T \rightarrow i$

$$K = °C + 273.15 \qquad\qquad \Pi = iM\,RT$$

     Solution: 25 °C + 273.15 = 298 K then $\Pi = iM\,RT$. Rearrange to solve for i.

$$i = \frac{\Pi}{M\,RT} = \frac{8.3\ \cancel{atm}}{0.100\ \dfrac{\cancel{mol}}{\cancel{L}} \times 0.08206\ \dfrac{\cancel{L} \cdot \cancel{atm}}{K \cdot \cancel{mol}} \times 298\ K} = 3.4.$$

     Check: The units (none) are correct. The magnitude of the answer (3) seems reasonable for an ionic solution with a high osmotic pressure.

12.91   **Given:** 5.50 % NaCl by mass in water at 25 °C   **Find:** P_{H_2O} **Other:** $P^{\circ}_{H_2O} = 23.78$ torr
     Conceptual Plan: % NaCl by mass $\rightarrow$ g_{NaCl}, g_{H_2O} then g_{NaCl} $\rightarrow$ mol $_{NaCl}$ and

$$\frac{5.50\ g\ NaCl}{100\ g\ (NaCl + H_2O)} \qquad\qquad \frac{1\ mol\ NaCl}{58.44\ g\ NaCl}$$

     g_{H_2O} $\rightarrow$ mol $_{H_2O}$ then mol $_{NaCl}$, mol $_{H_2O}$ $\rightarrow$ χ_{H_2O} then χ_{H_2O}, $P^{\circ}_{H_2O}$ $\rightarrow$ P_{H_2O}

$$\frac{1\ mol\ H_2O}{18.01\ g\ H_2O} \qquad \chi = \frac{\text{amount solute (in moles)}}{\text{total amount of solute and solvent (in moles)}} \quad P_{solution} = \chi_{solvent}\,P^{\circ}_{solvent}$$

     Solution: $\dfrac{5.50\ g\ NaCl}{100\ g\ (NaCl + H_2O)}$ means 5.50 g NaCl and (100 g – 5.50 g) = 94.5 g H_2O then

$$5.50\ \cancel{g\ NaCl} \times \frac{1\ mol\ NaCl}{58.44\ \cancel{g\ NaCl}} = 0.094\underline{1}136\ mol\ NaCl \text{ and } 94.5\ \cancel{g\ H_2O} \times \frac{1\ mol\ H_2O}{18.01\ \cancel{g\ H_2O}} = 5.2\underline{4}708\ mol\ H_2O \text{ the}$$

     number of moles of solute = $i_{NaCl} \times n_{NaCl}$ so $\chi_{solv} = \dfrac{\text{amount solvent (in moles)}}{\text{total amount solute and solvent particles (in moles)}} =$

$$\frac{5.2\underline{4}708\ \cancel{mol}}{5.2\underline{4}708\ \cancel{mol} + 2(0.094\underline{1}136\ \cancel{mol})} = 0.96\underline{5}36 \text{ then } P_{soln} = \chi_{solv}\,P^{\circ}_{solv} = 0.96\underline{5}36 \times 23.78\ torr = 23.0\ torr$$

     Check: The units (torr) are correct. The magnitude of the answer (23 torr) seems reasonable since it is a drop from the pure vapor pressure. Only a fraction of a mole of NaCl is added, so the pressure will not drop much.

Cumulative Problems

12.93   Chloroform is polar and has stronger solute–solvent interactions than nonpolar carbon tetrachloride.

12.95   **Given:** $KClO_4$: lattice energy = – 599 kJ/mol, $\Delta H_{hydration}$ = – 548 kJ/mol; 10.0 g $KClO_4$ in 100.00 mL solution
     Find: ΔH_{soln} and ΔT **Other:** $C_s = 4.05$ J/g °C; $d = 1.05$ g/mL
     Conceptual Plan: lattice energy, $\Delta H_{hydration}$ $\rightarrow$ ΔH_{soln} and g $\rightarrow$ mol then mol, ΔH_{soln} $\rightarrow$ $q(kJ)$ $\rightarrow$ $q(J)$

$$\Delta H_{soln} = \Delta H_{solute} + \Delta H_{hydration} \ where\ \Delta H_{solute} = -\Delta H_{lattice} \qquad \frac{1\ mol}{138.56\ g} \qquad q = n\,\Delta H_{soln} \qquad \frac{1000\ J}{1\ kJ}$$

     then mL_{soln} $\rightarrow$ g_{soln} then q, g_{soln}, C_s $\rightarrow$ ΔT

$$\frac{1.05\ g}{1\ mL} \qquad\qquad q = m\,C_s\,\Delta T$$

     Solution: $\Delta H_{soln} = \Delta H_{solute} + \Delta H_{hydration}$ where $\Delta H_{solute} = -\Delta H_{lattice}$ so $\Delta H_{soln} = \Delta H_{hydration} - \Delta H_{lattice}$

$$\Delta H_{soln} = -548\ kJ/mol - (-599\ kJ/mol) = +51\ kJ/mol \text{ and } 10.0\ \cancel{g} \times \frac{1\ mol}{138.56\ \cancel{g}} = 0.072\underline{1}709\ mol \text{ then}$$

$$q = n\,\Delta H_{soln} = 0.072\underline{1}709\ \cancel{mol} \times 51\ \frac{kJ}{\cancel{mol}} = +3.\underline{6}807\ \cancel{kJ} \times \frac{1000\ J}{1\ \cancel{kJ}} = +3680.7\ J \text{ absorbed then}$$

$$100.0\ \cancel{mL} \times \frac{1.05\ g}{1\ \cancel{mL}} = 105\ g. \text{ Since heat is absorbed when } KClO_4 \text{ dissolves, the temperature will}$$

     drop or $q = -3\underline{6}80.7$ J and $q = m\,C_s\,\Delta T$. Rearrange to solve for ΔT.

$$\Delta T = \frac{q}{m\,C_s} = \frac{-3\underline{6}80.7\ \cancel{J}}{105\ \cancel{g} \times 4.05\ \dfrac{\cancel{J}}{\cancel{g} \cdot °C}} = -8.7\ °C.$$

     Check: The units (kJ/mol and °C) are correct. The magnitude of the answer (51 kJ/mol) makes physical sense because the lattice energy is larger than the heat of hydration. The magnitude of the temperature change (– 9 °C) makes physical sense since heat is absorbed and the heat of solution is fairly small.

12.97   **Given:** Argon, 0.0537 L; 25 °C, $P_{Ar} = 1.0$ atm to make 1.0 L saturated solution   **Find:** $k_H(Ar)$
Conceptual Plan: °C → K and P_{Ar}, V, T → mol_{Ar} then $mol_{Ar}, V_{soln}, P_{Ar}$ → $k_H(Ar)$

$$K = °C + 273.15 \qquad PV = nRT \qquad S_{Ar} = k_H(Ar)P_{Ar} \ with \ S_{Ar} = \frac{mol_{Ar}}{L_{soln}}$$

Solution: 25 °C + 273.15 = 298 K and $PV = nRT$. Rearrange to solve for n.

$$n = \frac{PV}{RT} = \frac{1.0 \ atm \times 0.0537 \ L}{0.08206 \ \frac{L \cdot atm}{K \cdot mol} \times 298 \ K} = 0.00219597 \ mol \ then \ S_{Ar} = k_H(Ar)P_{Ar} \ with \ S_{Ar} = \frac{mol_{Ar}}{L_{so \ ln}}.$$

Substitute in values and rearrange to solve for k_H.

$$k_H(Ar) = \frac{mol_{Ar}}{L_{soln} \quad Ar} = \frac{0.00219597 \ mol}{1.0 \ L_{soln} \times 1.0 \ atm} = 2.2 \times 10^{-3} \ \frac{M}{atm}.$$

Check: The units (M/atm) are correct. The magnitude of the answer (10^{-3}) seems reasonable since it is consistent with other values in the text.

12.99   **Given:** 0.0020 ppm by mass Hg = legal limit; 0.0040 ppm by mass Hg = contaminated water; 50.0 mg Hg ingested   **Find:** volume of contaminated water
Conceptual Plan: mg_{Hg} → g_{Hg} → g_{H_2O} → mL_{H_2O} → L_{H_2O}

$$\frac{1 \ g}{1000 \ mg} \quad \frac{10^6 \ g \ water}{0.0040 \ g \ Hg} \quad \frac{1 \ mL}{1.00 \ g} \quad \frac{1 \ L}{1000 \ mL}$$

Solution: $50.0 \ mg \ Hg \times \frac{1 \ g \ Hg}{1000 \ mg \ Hg} \times \frac{10^6 \ g \ water}{0.0040 \ g \ Hg} \times \frac{1 \ mL \ water}{1.00 \ g \ water} \times \frac{1 \ L \ water}{1000 \ mL \ water} = 1.3 \times 10^4 \ L$ water.

Check: The units (L) are correct. The magnitude of the answer (10^4 L) seems reasonable since the concentration is so low.

12.101   **Given:** 12.5% NaCl by mass in water at 55 °C; 2.5 L vapor   **Find:** $g \ H_2O$ in vapor
Other: $P°_{H_2O} = 118$ torr, $i_{NaCl} = 2.0$ (complete dissociation)
Conceptual Plan: % NaCl by mass → $g_{NaCl}, g \ H_2O$ then $g \ NaCl$ → $mol \ NaCl$ and $g \ H_2O$ → $mol \ H_2O$

$$\frac{12.5 \ g \ NaCl}{100 \ g \ (NaCl + H_2O)} \qquad \frac{1 \ mol \ NaCl}{58.44 \ g \ NaCl} \qquad \frac{1 \ mol \ H_2O}{18.01 \ g \ H_2O}$$

then $mol \ NaCl, mol \ H_2O$ → $\chi \ NaCl$ → $\chi \ H_2O$ then $\chi \ H_2O, P°_{H_2O}$ → P_{H_2O}

$$\chi = \frac{amount \ solute \ (in \ moles)}{total \ amount \ of \ solute \ and \ solvent \ (in \ moles)} \quad \chi_{H_2O} = 1 - i_{NaCl}\chi_{NaCl} \quad P_{solution} = \chi_{solvent}P°_{solvent}$$

then torr → atm and °C → K P, V, T → mol_{H_2O} → g_{H_2O}

$$\frac{1 \ atm}{760 \ torr} \qquad K = °C + 273.15 \qquad PV = nRT \qquad \frac{18.01 \ g \ H_2O}{1 \ mol \ H_2O}$$

Solution: $\frac{12.5 \ g \ NaCl}{100 \ g \ (NaCl + H_2O)}$ means 12.5 g NaCl and (100 g – 12.5 g) = 87.5 g H_2O then

$12.5 \ g \ NaCl \times \frac{1 \ mol \ NaCl}{58.44 \ g \ NaCl} = 0.213895 \ mol \ NaCl$ and $87.5 \ g \ H_2O \times \frac{1 \ mol \ H_2O}{18.01 \ g \ H_2O} = 4.85572 \ mol \ H_2O$

then $\chi = \frac{amount \ solute \ (in \ moles)}{total \ amount \ of \ solute \ and \ solvent \ (in \ moles)} = \frac{0.213895 \ mol}{0.213895 \ mol + 4.85572 \ mol} = 0.0421916$

then $\chi_{H_2O} = 1 - i_{NaCl}\chi_{NaCl} = 1 - (2.0 \times 0.0421916) \quad 0.915617$ then

$P_{solution} = \chi_{solvent}P°_{solvent} = 0.915617 \times 118$ torr $= 108.043$ torr H_2O then

$108.043 \ torr \ H_2O \times \frac{1 \ atm}{760 \ torr} = 0.142162$ atm

and 55 °C + 273.15 = 328 K then $PV = nRT$. Rearrange to solve for n.

$$n = \frac{PV}{RT} = \frac{0.142162 \ atm \times 2.5 \ L}{0.08206 \ \frac{L \cdot atm}{K \cdot mol} \times 328 \ K} = 0.013204 \ mol \ then$$

$0.013204 \ mol \ H_2O \times \frac{18.02 \ g \ H_2O}{1 \ mol \ H_2O} = 0.24$ g H_2O.

Check: The units (g) are correct. The magnitude of the answer (0.2 g) seems reasonable since there is very little mass in a vapor.

12.103   **Given:** $T_b = 106.5\ °C$ aqueous solution **Find:** T_f **Other:** $K_f = 1.86\ °C/m$; $K_b = 0.512\ °C/m$

Conceptual Plan: $T_b \rightarrow \Delta T_b$ then $\Delta T_b, K_b \rightarrow m$ then $m, K_f \rightarrow \Delta T_f \rightarrow T_f$

$$T_b = T_b° + \Delta T_b \qquad\qquad \Delta T_b = K_b m \qquad\qquad \Delta T_f = K_f m \qquad T_f = T_f° - \Delta T_f$$

Solution: $T_b = T_b° + \Delta T_b$ so $\Delta T_b = T_b - T_b° = 106.5\ °C - 100.0\ °C = 6.5\ °C$ then $\Delta T_b = K_b m$.

Rearrange to solve for m. $m = \dfrac{\Delta T_b}{K_b} = \dfrac{6.5\ \cancel{°C}}{0.512\ \dfrac{\cancel{°C}}{m}} = 12.\underline{6}95\ m$ then

$\Delta T_f = K_f m = 1.86\ \dfrac{°C}{\cancel{m}} \times 12.\underline{6}95\ \cancel{m} = 23.\underline{6}\ °C$ then $T_f = T_f° - \Delta T_f = 0.000\ °C - 23.\underline{6}\ °C\ °C = -24\ °C$.

Check: The units (°C) are correct. The magnitude of the answer (– 24 °C) seems reasonable since the shift in boiling point is less than the shift in freezing point because the constant for boiling is smaller than the constant for freezing.

12.105   **(a)**   **Given:** 0.90 % NaCl by mass per volume; isotonic aqueous solution at 25 °C; KCl; $i = 1.9$
   Find: % KCl by mass per volume
   Conceptual Plan: Isotonic solutions will have the same number of particles. Since i is the same,
$$\frac{1\ mol\ KCl}{1\ mol\ NaCl}$$
   the new % mass per volume will be the mass ratio of the two salts.
$$\text{percent by mass per volume} = \frac{\text{mass solute}}{V} \times 100\% \qquad \frac{1\ mol\ NaCl}{58.44\ g\ NaCl} \qquad \text{and}\ \frac{74.56\ g\ KCl}{1\ mol\ KCl}$$
   Solution: percent by mass per volume $= \dfrac{\text{mass solute}}{V} \times 100\% =$

$$= \frac{0.0090\ \cancel{g\ NaCl}}{V} \times \frac{1\ \cancel{mol\ NaCl}}{58.44\ \cancel{g\ NaCl}} \times \frac{1\ \cancel{mol\ KCl}}{1\ \cancel{mol\ NaCl}} \times \frac{74.56\ g\ KCl}{1\ \cancel{mol\ KCl}} \times 100\%$$

   $= 1.1\%$ KCl by mass per volume
   Check: The units (% KCl by mass per volume) are correct. The magnitude of the answer (1.1) seems reasonable since the molar mass of KCl is larger than the molar mass of NaCl.

   (b)   **Given:** 0.90 % NaCl by mass per volume; isotonic aqueous solution at 25 °C; NaBr; $i = 1.9$
   Find: % NaBr by mass per volume
   Conceptual Plan: Isotonic solutions will have the same number of particles. Since i is the same,
$$\frac{1\ mol\ NaBr}{1\ mol\ NaCl}$$
   the new % mass per volume will be the mass ratio of the two salts.
$$\text{percent by mass per volume} = \frac{\text{mass solute}}{V} \times 100\% \qquad \frac{1\ mol\ NaCl}{58.44\ g\ NaCl}\ \text{and}\ \frac{102.90\ g\ NaBr}{1\ mol\ NaBr}$$
   Solution: percent by mass per volume $= \dfrac{\text{mass solute}}{V} \times 100\% =$

$$= \frac{0.0090\ \cancel{g\ NaCl}}{V} \times \frac{1\ \cancel{mol\ NaCl}}{58.44\ \cancel{g\ NaCl}} \times \frac{1\ \cancel{mol\ NaBr}}{1\ \cancel{mol\ NaCl}} \times \frac{102.90\ g\ NaBr}{1\ \cancel{mol\ NaBr}} \times 100\%$$

   $= 1.6\%$ NaBr by mass per volume
   Check: The units (% NaBr by mass per volume) are correct. The magnitude of the answer (1.6) seems reasonable since the molar mass of NaBr is larger than the molar mass of NaCl.

   (c)   **Given:** 0.90 % NaCl by mass per volume; isotonic aqueous solution at 25 °C; glucose ($C_6H_{12}O_6$); $i = 1.9$ **Find:** % glucose by mass per volume
   Conceptual Plan: Isotonic solutions will have the same number of particles. Since glucose is a nonelectrolyte, the i is not the same, then use the mass ratio of the two compounds.
$$\frac{1.9\ mol\ C_6H_{12}O_6}{1\ mol\ NaCl}\ \text{percent by mass per volume} = \frac{\text{mass solute}}{V} \times 100\%\ \frac{1\ mol\ NaCl}{58.44\ g\ NaCl}\ \text{and}\ \frac{180.16\ g\ C_6H_{12}O_6}{1\ mol\ C_6H_{12}O_6}$$
   Solution: percent by mass per volume $= \dfrac{\text{mass solute}}{V} \times 100\% =$

$$= \frac{0.0090\ \cancel{g\ NaCl}}{V} \times \frac{1\ \cancel{mol\ NaCl}}{58.44\ \cancel{g\ NaCl}} \times \frac{1.9\ \cancel{mol\ C_6H_{12}O_6}}{1\ \cancel{mol\ NaCl}} \times \frac{180.16\ g\ C_6H_{12}O_6}{1\ \cancel{mol\ C_6H_{12}O_6}} \times 100\% =$$

   $= 5.3\%\ C_6H_{12}O_6$ by mass per volume
   Check: The units (% $C_6H_{12}O_6$ by mass per volume) are correct. The magnitude of the answer (1.6) seems reasonable since the molar mass of $C_6H_{12}O_6$ is larger than the molar mass of NaCl and we need more moles of $C_6H_{12}O_6$ since it is a nonelectrolyte.

12.107 **Given:** 4.5701 g of $MgCl_2$ and 43.238 g water, $P_{soln} = 0.3624$ atm, $P°_{soln} = 0.3804$ atm at 348.0 K **Find:** $i_{measured}$
Conceptual Plan: $g_{MgCl_2} \rightarrow mol_{MgCl_2}$ and $g_{H_2O} \rightarrow mol_{H_2O}$ then $P_{soln}, P°_{soln}, \rightarrow \chi_{MgCl_2}$

$$\frac{1 \text{ mol } MgCl_2}{95.218 \text{ g } MgCl_2} \qquad \frac{1 \text{ mol } H_2O}{18.015 \text{ g } H_2O} \qquad P_{Soln} = (1 - \chi_{MgCl_2})P°_{H_2O}$$

then $mol_{MgCl_2}, mol_{H_2O}, \chi_{MgCl_2} \rightarrow i$

$$\chi_{MgCl_2} = \frac{i \text{ (moles } MgCl_2)}{\text{moles } H_2O + i \text{ (moles } MgCl_2)}$$

Solution: $4.5701 \text{ g } MgCl_2 \times \dfrac{1 \text{ mol } MgCl_2}{95.218 \text{ g } MgCl_2} = 0.047996177$ mol $MgCl_2$ and

$43.238 \text{ g } H_2O \times \dfrac{1 \text{ mol } H_2O}{18.015 \text{ g } H_2O} = 2.4001110$ mol H_2O then $P_{soln} = (1 - \chi_{MgCl_2})P°_{H_2O}$ so

$\chi_{MgCl_2} = 1 - \dfrac{P_{soln}}{P°_{H_2O}} = 1 - \dfrac{0.3624 \text{ atm}}{0.3804 \text{ atm}} = 0.04731861$. Solve for i.

$i\,(0.047996177) = 0.04731861(2.4001110 + i\,(0.047996177)) \rightarrow$

$i\,(0.047996177 - 0.002271112) = 0.1135699 \rightarrow i = \dfrac{0.1135699}{0.04572506} = 2.484$.

Check: The units (none) are correct. The magnitude of the answer (2.5) seems reasonable for $MgCl_2$ since we expect i to be 3 if it completely dissociates. Since Mg is small and doubly charged, we expect a significant drop from 3.

12.109 **Given:** $T_b = 375.3$ K aqueous solution **Find:** P_{H_2O} **Other:** $P°_{H_2O} = 0.2467$ atm; $K_b = 0.512$ °C/m
Conceptual Plan: $T_b \rightarrow \Delta T_b$ then $\Delta T_b, K_b \rightarrow m$ assume 1 kg water kg $_{H_2O} \rightarrow mol_{H_2O}$ then

$$T_b = T°_b + \Delta T_b \qquad\qquad \Delta T_b = K_b m \qquad\qquad \frac{1 \text{ mol } H_2O}{18.01 \text{ g } H_2O}$$

$m \rightarrow mol_{Solute}$ then $mol_{H_2O}, mol_{Solute} \rightarrow \chi_{H_2O}$ then $\chi_{H_2O}, P°_{H_2O} \rightarrow P_{H_2O}$

$$m = \frac{\text{amount solute (moles)}}{\text{mass solvent (kg)}} \qquad \chi_{H_2O} = \frac{\text{moles } H_2O}{\text{moles } H_2O + \text{moles solute}} \qquad P_{H_2O} = \chi_{H_2O} P°_{H_2O}$$

Solution: $T_b = T°_b + \Delta T_b$ so $\Delta T_b = T_b - T°_b = 375.3 \text{ K} - 373.15 \text{ K} = 2.2 \text{ K} = 2.2 \text{ °C}$ then

$\Delta T_b = K_b m$. Rearrange to solve for m. $m = \dfrac{\Delta T_b}{K_b} = \dfrac{2.2 \text{ °C}}{0.512 \dfrac{\text{°C}}{m}} = 4.296875 \, m$ then

$1000 \text{ g } H_2O \times \dfrac{1 \text{ mol } H_2O}{18.01 \text{ g } H_2O} = 55.49390$ mol H_2O then

$m = \dfrac{\text{amount solute (moles)}}{\text{mass solvent (kg)}} = \dfrac{x \text{ mol}}{1 \text{ kg}} = 4.296875 \, m \qquad x = 4.296875$ mol

$\chi_{H_2O} = \dfrac{\text{moles } H_2O}{\text{moles } H_2O + \text{moles solute}} = \dfrac{55.49390 \text{ mol}}{55.49390 \text{ mol} + 4.296875 \text{ mol}} = 0.9281348$

then $P_{H_2O} = \chi_{H_2O} P°_{H_2O} = 0.9281348 \times 0.2467$ atm $= 0.229$ atm.
Check: The units (atm) are correct. The magnitude of the answer (0.229 atm) seems reasonable since the mole fraction is lowered by ~ 7%.

12.111 **Given:** equal masses of carbon tetrachloride (CCl_4) and chloroform ($CHCl_3$) at 316 K; $P°_{CCl_4} = 0.354$ atm; $P°_{CHCl_3} = 0.526$ atm **Find:** $\chi_{CCl_4}, \chi_{CHCl_3}$ in vapor; and P_{CHCl_3} in flask of condensed vapor
Conceptual Plan: assume 100 grams of each $g_{CCl_4} \rightarrow mol_{CCl_4}$ and $g_{CHCl_3} \rightarrow mol_{CHCl_3}$ then

$$\frac{1 \text{ mol } CCl_4}{153.82 \text{ g } CCl_4} \qquad\qquad \frac{1 \text{ mol } CHCl_3}{119.38 \text{ g } CHCl_3}$$

$mol_{CCl_4}, mol_{CHCl_3} \rightarrow \chi_{CCl_4}, \chi_{CHCl_3}$ then $\chi_{CCl_4}, P°_{CCl_4} \rightarrow P_{CCl_4}$ and $\chi_{CHCl_3}, P°_{CHCl_3} \rightarrow P_{CHCl_3}$ then

$$\chi_{CCl_4} = \frac{\text{amount } CCl_4 \text{ (in moles)}}{\text{total amount (in moles)}} \quad \chi_{CHCl_3} = 1 - \chi_{CCl_4} \qquad P_{CCl_4} = \chi_{CCl_4} P°_{CCl_4} \qquad P_{CHCl_3} = \chi_{CHCl_3} P°_{CHCl_3}$$

$P_{CCl_4}, P_{CHCl_3} \rightarrow P_{Total}$ then since $n \, \alpha \, P$ and we are calculating a mass percent, which is a ratio of masses,

$$P_{Total} = P_{CCl_4} + P_{CHCl_3}$$

we can simply convert 1 atm to 1 mole so $P_{CCl_4}, P_{CHCl_3} \rightarrow n_{CCl_4}, n_{CHCl_3}$ **then**

$$\chi_{CCl_4} = \frac{\text{amount } CCl_4 \text{ (in moles)}}{\text{total amount (in moles)}}$$

$\text{mol}_{CCl_4}, \text{mol}_{CHCl_3} \rightarrow \chi_{CCl_4}, \chi_{CHCl_3}$ then for the second vapor $\chi_{CHCl_3}, P^{\circ}_{CHCl_3} \rightarrow P_{CHCl_3}$

$$\chi_{CHCl_3} = 1 - \chi_{CCl_4}$$ $$P_{CHCl_3} = \chi_{CHCl_3} P^{\circ}_{CHCl_3}$$

Solution: $100.00 \text{ g CCl}_4 \times \dfrac{1 \text{ mol CCl}_4}{153.82 \text{ g CCl}_4} = 0.65011051 \text{ mol CCl}_4$ and

$100.00 \text{ g CHCl}_3 \times \dfrac{1 \text{ mol CHCl}_3}{119.38 \text{ g CHCl}_3} = 0.83766125 \text{ mol CHCl}_3$ then

$\chi_{CCl_4} = \dfrac{\text{amount CCl}_4 \text{ (in moles)}}{\text{total amount (in moles)}} = \dfrac{0.65011051 \text{ mol}}{0.65011051 \text{ mol} + 0.83766125 \text{ mol}} = 0.43696925$ and

$\chi_{CHCl_3} = 1 - \chi_{CCl_4} = 1 - 0.43696925 = 0.56303075$ then

$P_{CCl_4} = \chi_{CCl_4} P^{\circ}_{CCl_4} = 0.43696925 \times 0.354 \text{ atm} = 0.154687 \text{ atm}$ and

$P_{CHCl_3} = \chi_{CHCl_3} P^{\circ}_{CHCl_3} = 0.56303075 \times 0.526 \text{ atm} = 0.296154 \text{ atm}$ then

$P_{\text{Total}} = P_{CCl_4} + P_{CHCl_3} = 0.154687 \text{ atm} + 0.296154 \text{ atm} = 0.450841 \text{ atm}$ then

$\text{mol}_{CCl_4} = 0.154687 \text{ mol}$ and $\text{mol}_{CHCl_3} = 0.296154 \text{ mol}$ then

$\chi_{CCl_4} = \dfrac{\text{amount CCl}_4 \text{ (in moles)}}{\text{total amount (in moles)}} = \dfrac{0.154687 \text{ mol}}{0.154687 \text{ mol} + 0.296154 \text{ mol}} = 0.343108 = 0.343$ in the first vapor

and $\chi_{CHCl_3} = 1 - \chi_{CCl_4} = 1 - 0.343108 = 0.656892 = 0.657$ in the first vapor; then in the second vapor

$P_{CHCl_3} = \chi_{CHCl_3} P^{\circ}_{CHCl_3} = 0.656892 \times 0.526 \text{ atm} = 0.345525 \text{ atm} = 0.346 \text{ atm}$.

Check: The units (none and atm) are correct. The magnitudes of the answers seem reasonable since it we expect the lighter component to be found preferentially in the vapor phase. This effect is magnified in the second vapor.

12.113   **Given:** 49.0 % H_2SO_4 by mass, $d = 1.39 \text{ g/cm}^3$, 25.0 mL diluted to 99.8 cm^3 **Find:** molarity
Conceptual Plan: initial $\text{mL}_{\text{solution}} \rightarrow \text{g}_{\text{solution}} \rightarrow \text{g}_{H_2SO_4} \rightarrow \text{mol}_{H_2SO_4}$ and final $\text{mL}_{\text{solution}} \rightarrow L_{\text{solution}}$

$$\dfrac{1.39 \text{ g}}{1 \text{ mL}} \qquad \dfrac{49.0 \text{ g } H_2SO_4}{100 \text{ g solution}} \qquad \dfrac{1 \text{ mol } H_2SO_4}{98.09 \text{ g } H_2SO_4} \qquad\qquad \dfrac{1 \text{ L}}{1000 \text{ mL}}$$

then $\text{mol}_{H_2SO_4}, L_{\text{solution}} \rightarrow \mathbf{M}$

$$M = \dfrac{\text{amount solute (moles)}}{\text{volume solution (L)}}$$

Solution:

$25.0 \text{ mL solution} \times \dfrac{1.39 \text{ g solution}}{1 \text{ mL solution}} \times \dfrac{49.0 \text{ g } H_2SO_4}{100 \text{ g solution}} \times \dfrac{1 \text{ mol } H_2SO_4}{98.09 \text{ g } H_2SO_4} = 0.1735906 \text{ mol } H_2SO_4$ and

$99.8 \text{ mL solution} \times \dfrac{1 \text{ L solution}}{1000 \text{ mL solution}} = 0.0998 \text{ L solution}$ then

$M = \dfrac{\text{amount solute (moles)}}{\text{volume solution (L)}} = \dfrac{0.1735906 \text{ mol } H_2SO_4}{0.0998 \text{ L solution}} = 1.74 \text{ M } H_2SO_4$.

Check: The units (M) are correct. The magnitude of the answer (1.74 M) seems reasonable since the solutions is ~ 1/6 surfuric acid.

12.115   **Given:** 10.05 g of unknown compound in 50.0 g water, $T_f = -3.16 \text{ °C}$, mass percent composition of the compound is 60.97% C, 11.94% H, and the rest is O **Find:** molecular formula
Other: $K_f = 1.86 \text{ °C}/m$; $d = 1.00 \text{ g/mL}$
Conceptual Plan: $\text{g}_{H_2O} \rightarrow \text{kg}_{H_2O}$ and $T_f \rightarrow \Delta T_f$ then $\Delta T_f, K_f \rightarrow m$ then $m, \text{kg}_{H_2O} \rightarrow \text{mol}_{\text{Unk}}$

$$\dfrac{1 \text{ kg}}{1000 \text{ g}} \qquad\qquad T_f = T_f^{\circ} - \Delta T_f \qquad\qquad \Delta T_f = K_f m \qquad\qquad m = \dfrac{\text{amount solute (moles)}}{\text{mass solvent (kg)}}$$

then $\text{g}_{\text{Unk}}, \text{mol}_{\text{Unk}} \rightarrow \mathcal{M} \rightarrow \text{g}_C, \text{g}_H, \text{g}_O \rightarrow \text{mol}_C, \text{mol}_H, \text{mol}_O \rightarrow$ molecular formula

$$\mathcal{M} = \dfrac{g_{\text{Unk}}}{mol_{\text{Unk}}} \text{ mass percents} \qquad \dfrac{1 \text{ mol C}}{12.01 \text{ g C}} \dfrac{1 \text{ mol H}}{1.008 \text{ g H}} \dfrac{1 \text{ mol O}}{16.00 \text{ g O}}$$

Solution: $50.0 \text{ g} \times \dfrac{1 \text{ kg}}{1000 \text{ g}} = 0.0500 \text{ kg}$ and $T_f = T_f^{\circ} - \Delta T_f$ so

$\Delta T_f = T_f^{\circ} - T_f = 0.00 \text{ °C} - -3.16 \text{ °C} = +3.16 \text{ °C} \quad \Delta T_f = K_f m$. Rearrange to solve for m.

$$m = \frac{\Delta T_f}{K_f} = \frac{3.16 \,°C}{1.86 \,\frac{°C}{m}} = 1.69\underline{8}92 \, m \quad \text{then} \quad m = \frac{\text{amount solute (moles)}}{\text{mass solvent (kg)}} \quad \text{so}$$

$$mol_{Unk} = m_{Unk} \times kg_{H_2O} = 1.69\underline{8}92 \,\frac{\text{mol Unk}}{kg} \times 0.0500 \, kg = 0.08\underline{4}94624 \text{ mol Unk then}$$

$$\mathcal{M} = \frac{g_{Unk}}{mol_{Unk}} = \frac{10.05 \text{ g}}{0.08\underline{4}94624 \text{ mol}} = 118.\underline{3}101 \,\frac{g}{mol} \text{ then}$$

$$\frac{118.\underline{3}101 \text{ g Unk}}{1 \text{ mol Unk}} \times \frac{60.97 \text{ g C}}{100 \text{ g Unk}} \times \frac{1 \text{ mol C}}{12.01 \text{ g C}} = \frac{6.01 \text{ mol C}}{1 \text{ mol Unk}}$$

$$\frac{118.\underline{3}101 \text{ g Unk}}{1 \text{ mol Unk}} \times \frac{11.94 \text{ g H}}{100 \text{ g Unk}} \times \frac{1 \text{ mol H}}{1.008 \text{ g H}} = \frac{14.0 \text{ mol H}}{1 \text{ mol Unk}} \text{ and}$$

$$\frac{118.\underline{3}101 \text{ g Unk}}{1 \text{ mol Unk}} \times \frac{(100 - (60.97 + 11.94)) \text{ g O}}{100 \text{ g Unk}} \times \frac{1 \text{ mol O}}{16.00 \text{ g O}} = \frac{2.00 \text{ mol O}}{1 \text{ mol Unk}}.$$

So the molecular formula is $C_6H_{12}O_2$.

Check: The units (formula) are correct. The magnitude of the answer (formula with ~ 118 g/mol) seems reasonable since the molality is ~ 1.7 and we have ~10 g. It is a reasonable molecular weight for a solid or liquid. The formula does have the correct molar mass.

12.117   **Given:** 100.0 mL solution 13.5 % by mass NaCl, $d = 1.12$ g/mL; $T_b = 104.4 \,°C$ **Find:** g NaCl or water to add
Other: $K_b = 0.512 \,°C/m$; $i_{measured} = 1.8$
Conceptual Plan: $T_b \rightarrow \Delta T_b$ then $\Delta T_b, i, K_b \rightarrow m$ then $mL_{solution} \rightarrow g_{solution} \rightarrow g_{NaCl} \rightarrow mol_{NaCl}$ then

$$\Delta T_b = T_b - T_b^\circ \qquad\qquad \Delta T_b = K_b \, im \qquad\qquad \frac{1.12 \text{ g Solution}}{1 \text{ mL Solution}} \quad \frac{13.5 \text{ g NaCl}}{100 \text{ g Solution}} \quad \frac{1 \text{ mol NaCl}}{58.44 \text{ g NaCl}}$$

$m, mol_{NaCl} \rightarrow kg_{H_2O} \rightarrow g_{H_2O}$ and $g_{solution}, g_{NaCl} \rightarrow g_{H_2O}$ then **compare the initial and final** g_{H_2O} then

$$m = \frac{\text{amount solute (moles)}}{\text{mass solvent (kg)}} \quad \frac{1000 \text{ g}}{1 \text{ kg}} \qquad\qquad g_{solution} = g_{NaCl} + g_{H_2O}$$

calculate the total NaCl in final solution by scaling-up the amount from the initial solution. Then calculate the difference between the needed and starting amounts of NaCl.

Solution: $\Delta T_b = T_b - T_b^\circ = 104.4 \,°C - 100.0 \,°C = 4.4 \,°C$ then $\Delta T_b = K_b \, im$.

Rearrange to solve for m. $m = \dfrac{\Delta T_b}{K_b \, i} = \dfrac{4.4 \,°C}{0.512 \,\frac{°C}{m} \times 1.8} = 4.7\underline{7}4306 \, m$ NaCl then

$$100.0 \text{ mL solution} \times \frac{1.12 \text{ g solution}}{1 \text{ mL solution}} = 112 \text{ g solution} \times \frac{13.5 \text{ g NaCl}}{100 \text{ g solution}} = 15.1\underline{3} \text{ g NaCl} \times \frac{1 \text{ mol NaCl}}{58.44 \text{ g NaCl}}$$

$= 0.25\underline{8}7269$ mol NaCl

then $m = \dfrac{\text{amount solute (moles)}}{\text{mass solvent (kg)}}$. Rearrange to solve for kg_{H_2O}.

$$kg_{H_2O} = \frac{mol_{NaCl}}{m} = \frac{0.25\underline{8}7269 \text{ mol NaCl}}{4.7\underline{7}4306 \,\frac{\text{mol NaCl}}{1 \text{ kg}_{H_2O}}} = 0.05\underline{4}1915 \text{ kg}_{H_2O} \times \frac{1000 \text{ g}_{H_2O}}{1 \text{ kg}_{H_2O}} = 54.\underline{1}915 \text{ g}_{H_2O} \text{ in final solution}$$

then $g_{solution} = g_{NaCl} + g_{H_2O} = 112$ g solution $- 15.\underline{1}2$ g NaCl $= 96.88$ g H_2O in initial solution. Comparing the initial and final solutions, there is a lot more water in the initial solution so NaCl needs to be added.

In the solution with a boiling point of 104.4 °C, $\dfrac{15.\underline{1}2 \text{ g NaCl}}{54.\underline{1}915 \text{ g H}_2O} = \dfrac{x \text{ g NaCl}}{96.88 \text{ g H}_2O}$. Solve for x g NaCl.

x g NaCl $= \dfrac{15.\underline{1}2 \text{ g NaCl}}{54.\underline{1}915 \text{ g H}_2O} \times 96.88 \text{ g H}_2O = 27.\underline{0}31$ g NaCl so the amount to be added is

$27.\underline{0}31$ g NaCl $- 15.\underline{1}2$ g NaCl $= 11.\underline{9}11$ g NaCl $= 12$ g NaCl.

Check: The units (g) are correct. The magnitude of the answer (12 g) seems reasonable since there is approximately twice as much water as is desired in the initial solution, so the NaCl amount needs to be approximately doubled.

Challenge Problems

12.119   **Given:** N_2: $k_H(N_2) = 6.1 \times 10^{-4}$ M/L at 25 °C; 14.6 mg/L at 50 °C and 1.00 atm; $P_{N_2} = 0.78$ atm;
O_2: $k_H(O_2) = 1.3 \times 10^{-3}$ M/L at 25 °C; 27.8 mg/L at 50 °C and 1.00 atm; $P_{O_2} = 0.21$ atm; and 1.5 L water
Find: V (N_2) and V (O_2)

Conceptual Plan: at 25 °C: $P_{Total}, \chi_{N_2} \rightarrow P_{N_2}$ then $P_{N_2}, k_H(N_2) \rightarrow S_{N_2}$ then L $\rightarrow$ mol

$\qquad\qquad\qquad\qquad P_{N_2} = \chi_{N_2} P_{Total} \qquad\qquad S_{N_2} = k_H(N_2)P_{N_2} \qquad S_{N_2}$

at 50 °C: L $\rightarrow$ mL $\rightarrow$ mg $\rightarrow$ g $\rightarrow$ mol then $mol_{25 °C}$, $mol_{25 °C} \rightarrow mol_{removed}$ then °C $\rightarrow$ K

$\qquad\quad \dfrac{1000\ mL}{1\ L} \quad \dfrac{14.6\ mg}{1\ L} \quad \dfrac{1\ g}{1000\ mg}\ \dfrac{1\ mol}{28.01\ g} \qquad\qquad mol_{removed} = mol_{25 °C} - mol_{50 °C} \qquad K = °C + 273.15$

then $P, n, T \rightarrow V$

$\qquad\quad PV = nRT$

at 25 °C: $P_{Total}, \chi_{O_2} \rightarrow P_{O_2}$ then $P_{O_2}, k_H(O_2) \rightarrow S_{O_2}$ then L $\rightarrow$ mol

$\qquad\qquad\qquad\qquad P_{O_2} = \chi_{O_2} P_{Total} \qquad\qquad S_{O_2} = k_H(O_2)P_{O_2} \qquad S_{O_2}$

at 50 °C: L $\rightarrow$ mL $\rightarrow$ mg $\rightarrow$ g $\rightarrow$ mol then $mol_{25 °C}$, $mol_{25 °C} \rightarrow mol_{removed}$ then °C $\rightarrow$ K

$\qquad\quad \dfrac{1000\ mL}{1\ L} \quad \dfrac{27.8\ mg}{1\ L} \quad \dfrac{1\ g}{1000\ mg}\ \dfrac{1\ mol}{32.00\ g} \qquad\qquad mol_{removed} = mol_{25 °C} - mol_{50 °C} \qquad K = °C + 273.15$

then $P, n, T \rightarrow V$

$\qquad\quad PV = nRT$

Solution: at 25 °C: $P_{N_2} = \chi_{N_2} P_{Total} = 0.78 \times 1.0$ atm = 0.78 atm then

$S_{N_2} = k_H(N_2)P_{N_2} = 6.1 \times 10^{-4} \dfrac{M}{\cancel{atm}} \times 0.78\ \cancel{atm} = 4.\underline{7}58 \times 10^{-4}$ M then

$1.5\ \cancel{L} \times 4.\underline{7}58 \times 10^{-4} \dfrac{mol}{\cancel{L}} = 0.00071\underline{3}71$ mol

at 50 °C: $1.5\ \cancel{L} \times \dfrac{14.6\ \cancel{mg}}{1\ \cancel{L} \cdot \cancel{atm}} \times 0.78\ \cancel{atm} \times \dfrac{1\ \cancel{g}}{1000\ \cancel{mg}} \times \dfrac{1\ mol}{28.01\ \cancel{g}} = 0.000609\underline{8}5$ mol then

$mol_{removed} = mol_{25 °C} - mol_{50 °C} = 0.00071\underline{3}71$ mol $- 0.000609\underline{8}5$ mol $= 1.\underline{0}39 \times 10^{-4}$ mol N_2

then 50 °C + 273.15 = 323 K then $PV = nRT$. Rearrange to solve for V.

$$V = \dfrac{nRT}{P} = \dfrac{1.\underline{0}39 \times 10^{-4}\ \cancel{mol} \times 0.08206\ \dfrac{L \cdot \cancel{atm}}{\cancel{K} \cdot \cancel{mol}} \times 323\ \cancel{K}}{1.00\ \cancel{atm}} = 0.002\underline{7}539\ L\ N_2$$

at 25 °C: $P_{O_2} = \chi_{O_2} P_{Total} = 0.21 \times 1.0$ atm = 0.21 atm then

$S_{O_2} = k_H(O_2)P_{O_2} = 1.3 \times 10^{-3} \dfrac{M}{\cancel{atm}} \times 0.21\ \cancel{atm} = 2.\underline{7}3 \times 10^{-4}$ M then

$1.5\ \cancel{L} \times 2.\underline{7}3 \times 10^{-4} \dfrac{mol}{\cancel{L}} = 0.0004\underline{0}95$ mol

at 50 °C: $1.5\ \cancel{L} \times \dfrac{27.8\ \cancel{mg}}{1\ \cancel{L} \cdot \cancel{atm}} \times 0.21\ \cancel{atm} \times \dfrac{1\ \cancel{g}}{1000\ \cancel{mg}} \times \dfrac{1\ mol}{32.00\ \cancel{g}} = 0.000273\underline{6}6$ mol then

$mol_{removed} = mol_{25 °C} - mol_{50 °C} = 0.0004\underline{0}95$ mol $- 0.000273\underline{6}6$ mol $= 1.\underline{3}58 \times 10^{-4}$ mol O_2

then 50 °C + 273.15 = 323 K then $PV = nRT$. Rearrange to solve for V.

$$V = \dfrac{nRT}{P} = \dfrac{1.\underline{3}58 \times 10^{-4}\ \cancel{mol} \times 0.08206\ \dfrac{L \cdot \cancel{atm}}{\cancel{K} \cdot \cancel{mol}} \times 323\ \cancel{K}}{1.00\ \cancel{atm}} = 0.003\underline{5}994\ L\ O_2\ \text{finally}$$

$V_{Total} = V_{N_2} + V_{O_2} = 0.002\underline{7}526$ L $+ 0.003\underline{5}994$ L $= 0.0064$ L.

Check: The units (L) are correct. The magnitude of the answer (0.006 L) seems reasonable since we have so little dissolved gas at room temperature and most is still soluble at 50 °C.

12.121   **Given:** 1.10 g glucose ($C_6H_{12}O_6$) and sucrose ($C_{12}H_{22}O_{11}$) mixture in 25.0 mL solution and $\Pi = 3.78$ atm at 298 K **Find:** percent composition of mixture

Conceptual Plan: $\Pi, T \rightarrow M$ then $mL_{soln} \rightarrow L_{soln}$ then $L_{soln}, M \rightarrow mol_{mixture}$ then

$\qquad\qquad\qquad\qquad \Pi = MRT \qquad\qquad \dfrac{1\ L}{1000\ mL} \qquad M = \dfrac{\text{amount solute (moles)}}{\text{volume solution (L)}}$

$mol_{mixture}, g_{mixture} \rightarrow mol_{C_6H_{12}O_6}, mol_{C_{12}H_{22}O_{11}}$ then

$g_{mixture} = mol\ C_6H_{12}O_6 \times \dfrac{180.16\ g\ C_6H_{12}O_6}{1\ mol\ C_6H_{12}O_6} + mol\ C_{12}H_{22}O_{11} \times \dfrac{342.30\ g\ C_{12}H_{22}O_{11}}{1\ mol\ C_{12}H_{22}O_{11}}$ *with* $mol_{mixture} = mol_{C_6H_{12}O_6} + mol_{C_{12}H_{22}O_{11}}$

$mol_{C_6H_{12}O_6} \rightarrow g\ C_6H_{12}O_6$ and $mol_{C_{12}H_{22}O_{11}} \rightarrow g_{C_{12}H_{22}O_{11}}$ and $g\ C_6H_{12}O_6$, $g_{C_{12}H_{22}O_{11}} \rightarrow$ **mass percents**

$\dfrac{180.16\ g\ C_6H_{12}O_6}{1\ mol\ C_6H_{12}O_6}$ $\dfrac{342.30\ g\ C_{12}H_{22}O_{11}}{1\ mol\ C_{12}H_{22}O_{11}}$ mass percent $= \dfrac{\text{mass solute}}{\text{mass solution}} \times 100\%$

Solution: $\Pi = MRT$. Rearrange to solve for M.

$$M = \frac{\Pi}{RT} = \frac{3.78\ \text{atm}}{0.08206\ \dfrac{\text{L} \cdot \text{atm}}{\text{K} \cdot \text{mol}} \times 298\ \text{K}} = 0.154577\ \frac{\text{mol mixture}}{\text{L}} \quad \text{then}\ 25.0\ \text{mL} \times \frac{1\ \text{L}}{1000\ \text{mL}} = 0.0250\ \text{L}$$

then $M = \dfrac{\text{amount solute (moles)}}{\text{volume solution (L)}}$ so

$mol_{\text{mixture}} = M \times L_{\text{soln}} = 0.154577\ \dfrac{\text{mol mixture}}{\text{L}} \times 0.0250\ \text{L} = 0.00386442$ mol mixture then

$g_{\text{mixture}} = \text{mol } C_6H_{12}O_6 \times \dfrac{180.16\ g\ C_6H_{12}O_6}{1\ \text{mol } C_6H_{12}O_6} + \text{mol } C_{12}H_{22}O_{11} \times \dfrac{342.30\ g\ C_{12}H_{22}O_{11}}{1\ \text{mol } C_{12}H_{22}O_{11}}$ with

$mol_{\text{mixture}} = mol\ C_6H_{12}O_6 + mol\ C_{12}H_{22}O_{11}$ so

$1.10\ g = mol\ C_6H_{12}O_6 \times \dfrac{180.16\ g\ C_6H_{12}O_6}{1\ mol\ C_6H_{12}O_6} + (0.00386442\ \text{mol} - mol\ C_6H_{12}O_6) \times \dfrac{342.30\ g\ C_{12}H_{22}O_{11}}{1\ mol\ C_{12}H_{22}O_{11}} \rightarrow$

$1.10 = 180.16 \times mol\ C_6H_{12}O_6 + 1.32228 - 342.30 \times mol\ C_6H_{12}O_6 \rightarrow 162.14\ x\ mol\ C_6H_{12}O_6 = 0.22228 \rightarrow$

$x\ mol\ C_6H_{12}O_6 = \dfrac{0.22228}{162.14} = 0.00137091\ mol\ C_6H_{12}O_6$ then

$mol_{C_{12}H_{22}O_{11}} = mol_{\text{mixture}} - mol_{C_6H_{12}O_6} = 0.00386442\ \text{mol} - 0.00137091\ \text{mol}$

$= 0.0024935\ mol\ C_{12}H_{22}O_{11}$ then

$0.00137091\ \text{mol } C_6H_{12}O_6 \times \dfrac{180.16\ g\ C_6H_{12}O_6}{1\ \text{mol } C_6H_{12}O_6} = 0.24698\ g\ C_6H_{12}O_6$ and

$0.0024935\ \text{mol } C_{12}H_{22}O_{11} \times \dfrac{342.30\ g\ C_{12}H_{22}O_{11}}{1\ \text{mol } C_{12}H_{22}O_{11}} = 0.85353\ g\ C_{12}H_{22}O_{11}$ and finally

mass percent $= \dfrac{\text{mass solute}}{\text{mass solution}} \times 100\% = \dfrac{0.24698\ g\ C_6H_{12}O_6}{0.24698\ g\ C_6H_{12}O_6 + 0.85353\ g\ C_{12}H_{22}O_{11}} \times 100\%$

$= 22.44\%\ C_6H_{12}O_6$ by mass and $100.00\% - 22.44\% = 77.56\%\ C_{12}H_{22}O_{11}$ by mass.

Check: The units (% by mass) are correct. We expect the percent by $C_6H_{12}O_6$ to be larger than that for $C_{12}H_{22}O_{11}$ since the $g_{\text{mixture}}/mol_{\text{mixture}} = 285\ g/mol$, which is closer to $C_{12}H_{22}O_{11}$ than $C_6H_{12}O_6$ and the molar mass of $C_{12}H_{22}O_{11}$ is larger than the molar mass of $C_6H_{12}O_6$. In addition, and most definitively, the masses obtained for sucrose and glucose sum to 1.1g, the initial amount of solid dissolved.

12.123   **Given:** isopropyl alcohol $((CH_3)_2CHOH)$ and propyl alcohol $(CH_3CH_2CH_2OH)$ at 313 K; solution 2/3 by mass isopropyl alcohol $P_{2/3} = 0.110$ atm; solution 1/3 by mass isopropyl alcohol $P_{1/3} = 0.089$ atm;
Find: P°_{iso} and P°_{pro} and explain why they are different
Conceptual Plan: since these are isomers, they have the same molar mass and so the fraction by mass is the same as the mole fraction so mole fractions, P_{soln}s $\rightarrow$ P°s

$\chi_{\text{iso}} = \dfrac{\text{amount iso (in moles)}}{\text{total amount (in moles)}}$ $\chi_{\text{pro}} = 1 - \chi_{\text{iso}}$ $P_{\text{iso}} = \chi_{\text{iso}}P^{\circ}_{\text{iso}}$ $P_{\text{pro}} = \chi_{\text{pro}}P^{\circ}_{\text{pro}}$ and $P_{\text{soln}} = P_{\text{iso}} + P_{\text{pro}}$

Solution:
Solution 1: $\chi_{\text{iso}} = 2/3$ and $\chi_{\text{iso}} = 1/3$ $P_{\text{soln}} = P_{\text{iso}} + P_{\text{pro}}$ so 0.110 atm $= 2/3 P^{\circ}_{\text{iso}} + 1/3 P^{\circ}_{\text{pro}}$.

Solution 2: $\chi_{\text{iso}} = 1/3$ and $\chi_{\text{iso}} = 2/3$ $P_{\text{soln}} = P_{\text{iso}} + P_{\text{pro}}$ so 0.089 atm $= 1/3 P^{\circ}_{\text{iso}} + 2/3 P^{\circ}_{\text{pro}}$. We now have

two equations and two unknowns and a number of ways to solve this. One way is to rearrange the first equation for P°_{iso} and then substitute into the other equation. Thus, $P^{\circ}_{\text{iso}} = 3/2(0.110\ \text{atm} - 1/3P^{\circ}_{\text{pro}})$ and

0.089 atm $= \dfrac{1}{3}\dfrac{3}{2}(0.110\ \text{atm} - 1/3\ P^{\circ}_{\text{pro}}) + \dfrac{2}{3}P^{\circ}_{\text{pro}} \rightarrow 0.089$ atm $= 0.0550$ atm $- \dfrac{1}{6}P^{\circ}_{\text{pro}} + \dfrac{2}{3}P^{\circ}_{\text{pro}} \rightarrow$

$\dfrac{1}{2}P^{\circ}_{\text{pro}} = 0.0340$ atm $\rightarrow P^{\circ}_{\text{pro}} = 0.0680$ atm $= 0.068$ atm and then

$P^{\circ}_{\text{iso}} = 3/2(0.110\ \text{atm} - 1/3P^{\circ}_{\text{pro}}) = 3/2(0.110\ \text{atm} - 1/3(0.0680\ \text{atm})) = 0.131$ atm.

The major intermolecular attractions are between the OH groups. The OH group at the end of the chain in propyl alcohol is more accessible than the one in the middle of the chain in isopropyl alcohol. In addition, the molecular shape of propyl alcohol is a straight chain of carbon atoms, while that of isopropyl alcohol has a branched chain and is more like a ball. The contact area between two ball-like objects is smaller than that

of two chain-like objects. The smaller contact area in isopropyl alcohol means the molecules do not attract each other as strongly as do those of propyl alcohol. As a result of both of these factors, the vapor pressure of isopropyl alcohol is higher.

Check: The units (atm) are correct. The magnitude of the answers seems reasonable since the solution partial pressures are both ~0.1 atm.

12.125 **Given:** 0.1000 m H_2SO_4 solution; complete dissociation to H^+ and HSO_4^-; limited dissociation to SO_4^{2-}; $T_f = 272.76$ K **Find:** $m (SO_4^{2-})$ **Other:** $K_f = 1.86$ K/m

Conceptual Plan: $T_f \rightarrow \Delta T_f$ then $m, \Delta T_f, K_f \rightarrow i \rightarrow m (SO_4^{2-})$

$$T_f = T_f^\circ - \Delta T_f \qquad \Delta T_f = K_f im \quad m (SO_4^{2-}) = m \, H_2SO_4 \, (i - 2.0)/2$$

Solution: $T_f = T_f^\circ - \Delta T_f$. Rearrange to solve for ΔT_f. So

$\Delta T_f = T_f^\circ - T_f = 273.15$ K $- 272.76$ K $= -0.39$ K then $\Delta T_f = K_f im$. Rearrange to solve for i.

$$i = \frac{\Delta T_f}{K_f m} = \frac{0.39 \text{ K}}{1.86 \dfrac{\text{K}}{m} \times 0.1000 \, m} = 2.0968.$$

Remember that when H_2SO_4 completely dissociates, two particles are formed (H^+ and HSO_4^-), so $i = 2$. When HSO_4^- dissociates two particles are generated (SO_4^{2-} and H^+).

$$m(SO_4^{2-}) = m \, H_2SO_4 \frac{i-2}{2} = (0.1000 \, m) \frac{2.0968 - 2}{2} = 0.04839 \, m = 0.4 \, m \, SO_4^{2-}.$$

Check: The units (m) are correct. The magnitude of the answer (0.4 m) seems reasonable since not much of the HSO_4^- dissociates.

12.127 **Given:** $Na_2CO_3 + NaHCO_3 = 11.60$ g in 1.00 L; treat 300.0 cm³ of solution with HNO_3 and collect 0.940 L CO_2 at 298 K and 0.972 atm **Find:** $M(Na_2CO_3)$ and $M(NaHCO_3)$

Conceptual Plan: $P, V, T \rightarrow n$ in 300.0 cm³ then n in 300.0 cm³ $\rightarrow n$ in 1.00 L then

$$PV = nRT \qquad\qquad \text{take ratio of volumes}$$

set up equations for the total mass and the total moles and solve. Then calculate concentrations.

$$g_{Na_2CO_3} + g_{NaHCO_3} = 11.60 \text{ g} \quad \frac{105.99 \text{ g Na}_2\text{CO}_3}{1 \text{ mol Na}_2\text{CO}_3} \quad \frac{84.01 \text{ g NaHCO}_3}{1 \text{ mol NaHCO}_3} \quad n_{Na_2CO_3} + n_{NaHCO_3} = n.$$

Solution: $PV = nRT$. Rearrange to solve for n. $n = \dfrac{PV}{RT}$

$$n_{CO_2} = \frac{0.972 \text{ atm} \times 0.940 \text{ L}}{0.08206 \dfrac{\text{L} \cdot \text{atm}}{\text{mol} \cdot \text{K}} \times 298 \text{ K}} = 0.03736340 \text{ mol } CO_2 \text{ in } 300.0 \text{ cm}^3 \text{ then take ratio of moles to volume to}$$

get the moles in 1.00 L

$$\frac{0.03736340 \text{ mol } CO_2}{300.0 \text{ cm}^3} \times 1000 \text{ cm}^3 = 0.1245447 \text{ mol } CO_2 \text{ in } 1.00 \text{ L since one mole of } CO_2 \text{ is generated for each}$$

mole of carbonate. So $n = n_{Na_2CO_3} + n_{NaHCO_3} = 0.1245447$ mol and $g_{Na_2CO_3} + g_{NaHCO_3} = 11.60$ g or $g_{Na_2CO_3} = 11.60$ g $- g_{NaHCO_3}$ using molar masses and substituting

$$n_{Na_2CO_3} + n_{NaHCO_3} = 0.1245447 \text{mol} = g_{Na_2CO_3} \times \frac{1 \text{ mol Na}_2\text{CO}_3}{105.99 \text{ g Na}_2\text{CO}_3} + g_{NaHCO_3} \times \frac{1 \text{ mol NaHCO}_3}{84.01 \text{ g NaHCO}_3} =$$

$$(11.60 \text{ g} - g_{NaHCO_3}) \times \frac{1 \text{ mol Na}_2\text{CO}_3}{105.99 \text{ g Na}_2\text{CO}_3} + g_{NaHCO_3} \times \frac{1 \text{ mol NaHCO}_3}{84.01 \text{ g NaHCO}_3}$$

$$\rightarrow 0.1245447 \text{ mol} = 0.10944429 \text{ mol} - g_{NaHCO_3} \times 0.009434852 \frac{\text{mol}}{\text{g}} + g_{NaHCO_3} \, 0.011903345 \frac{\text{mol}}{\text{g}}$$

$$\rightarrow 0.01510041 \text{ mol} = g_{NaHCO_3} \times 0.002468493 \frac{\text{mol}}{\text{g}} \rightarrow$$

$$g_{NaHCO_3} = \frac{0.01510041 \text{ mol}}{0.002468493 \dfrac{\text{mol}}{\text{g}}} = 6.117259 \text{ g NaHCO}_3 = 6.1 \text{ g NaHCO}_3 \text{ and then } g_{Na_2CO_3} =$$

$11.60 \text{ g} - g_{\text{NaHCO}_3} = 11.60 \text{ g} - 6.\underline{1}17259 \text{ g NaHCO}_3 = 5.\underline{4}8274 \text{ g Na}_2\text{CO}_3 = 5.5 \text{ g Na}_2\text{CO}_3$ then M = mol/L

$$\frac{6.\underline{1}17259 \text{ g NaHCO}_3 \times \dfrac{1 \text{ mol NaHCO}_3}{84.01 \text{ g NaHCO}_3}}{1.00 \text{ L}} = 0.073 \text{ M NaHCO}_3 \text{ and}$$

$$\frac{5.\underline{4}8274 \text{ g Na}_2\text{CO}_3 \times \dfrac{1 \text{ mol Na}_2\text{CO}_3}{105.99 \text{ g Na}_2\text{CO}_3}}{1.00 \text{ L}} = 0.052 \text{ M Na}_2\text{CO}_3.$$

Check: The units (M and M) are correct. The magnitude of the answer (0.052 M and 0.073 M) makes sense because the number of moles of CO_2 is small (0.12 M). The balance of the two components make sense because if it were all Na_2CO_3 the number of moles would have been 0.109 moles (11.6/105.99) and if it were all $NaHCO_3$ the number of moles would have been 0.138 moles (11.6/84.01)—the actual number of moles is roughly in the middle of these two values.

Conceptual Problems

12.129   The warm coolant water should not be put directly into the river without cooling, because it will raise the temperature of the water. When water is warmed, there is less dissolved oxygen in the water and this will be detrimental to aquatic life that depends on this dissolved oxygen.

12.131   b) NaCl. If all of the substances have the same cost per kilogram, we need to determine which substance will generate the largest number of particles per kilogram (or gram). $HOCH_2CH_2OH$ generates 1 mol particle / 62.07 g; NaCl generates 2 mol particles / 58.44 g; KCl generates 2 mol particles / 74.56 g; $MgCl_2$ generates 3 mol particles / 95.22 g; and $SrCl_2$ generates 3 particles / 158.53 g. So NaCl will generate 1 mole of particles for each 29 g.

Glossary

accuracy A term that refers to how close a measured value is to the actual value. (1.7)

acid A molecular compound that is able to donate an H^+ ion (proton) when dissolved in water, thereby increasing the concentration of H^+. (3.6)

acid ionization constant (K_a) The equilibrium constant for the ionization reaction of a weak acid; used to compare the relative strengths of weak acids. (15.4)

acid–base reaction (neutralization reaction) A reaction in which an acid reacts with a base and the two neutralize each other, producing water. (4.8)

acid–base titration A laboratory procedure in which a basic (or acidic) solution of unknown concentration is reacted with an acidic (or basic) solution of known concentration, in order to determine the concentration of the unknown. (16.4)

acidic solution A solution containing an acid that creates additional H_3O^+ ions, causing $[H_3O^+]$ to increase. (15.4)

activated carbon Very fine carbon particles with high surface area. (22.5)

activated complex (transition state) A high-energy intermediate state between reactant and product. (13.5)

activation energy An energy barrier in a chemical reaction that must be overcome for the reactants to be converted into products. (13.5)

active site The specific area of an enzyme at which catalysis occurs. (13.7)

actual yield The amount of product actually produced by a chemical reaction. (4.3)

addition polymer A polymer in which the monomers simply link together without the elimination of any atoms. (20.14)

addition reaction A type of organic reaction in which two substituents are added across a double bond. (20.10)

alcohol A member of the family of organic compounds that contain a hydroxyl functional group (—OH). (3.11, 20.9)

aldehyde A member of the family of organic compounds that contain a carbonyl functional group (C=O) bonded to two R groups, one of which is a hydrogen atom. (20.10)

aldose A sugar that is an aldehyde. (21.3)

aliphatic hydrocarbons Organic compounds in which carbon atoms are joined in straight or branched chains. (20.3)

alkali metals Highly reactive metals in group 1A of the periodic table. (2.7)

alkaline battery A dry-cell battery that employs slightly different half-reactions in a basic medium. (18.7)

alkaline earth metals Fairly reactive metals in group 2A of the periodic table. (2.7)

alkaloid Organic bases found in plants; they are often poisonous. (15.2)

alkane A hydrocarbon containing only single bonds. (3.11)

alkene A hydrocarbon containing one or more carbon–carbon double bonds. (3.11)

alkyne A hydrocarbon containing one or more carbon–carbon triple bonds. (3.11)

alloy A metallic material that contains more than one element. (23.4)

alpha (α) decay The form of radioactive decay that occurs when an unstable nucleus emits a particle composed of two protons and two neutrons. (19.3)

alpha (α) particle A low-energy particle released during alpha decay; equivalent to a He-4 nucleus. (19.3)

α-helix A pattern in the secondary structure of a protein that occurs when the amino acid chain is wrapped tightly in a coil with the side chains extending outward. (21.5)

aluminosilicates Members of a family of compounds in which aluminum atoms substitute for silicon atoms in some of the silicon lattice sites of the silica structure. (22.3)

amino acids Organic compounds that contain a carbon atom, called the α-carbon, bonded to four different groups: an amine group, an R group, a carboxylic acid group, and a hydrogen atom. (21.4)

ammonia NH_3, the strong smelling compound in which nitrogen displays its lowest oxidation state (-3). (22.6)

amorphous solid A solid in which atoms or molecules do not have any long-range order. (1.3, 11.2)

ampere (A) The SI unit for electrical current; $1\ A = 1\ C/s$. (18.3)

amphoteric Able to act as either an acid or a base. (15.3)

amplitude The vertical height of a crest (or depth of a trough) of a wave; a measure of wave intensity. (7.2)

angular momentum quantum number (l) An integer that determines the shape of an orbital. (7.5)

anion A negatively charged ion. (2.6)

anode The electrode in an electrochemical cell where oxidation occurs; electrons flow away from the anode. (18.3)

antibonding orbital A molecular orbital that is higher in energy than any of the atomic orbitals from which it was formed. (10.8)

aqueous solution A solution in which water acts as the solvent. (4.4, 12.2)

arachno-boranes Boranes with the formula B_nH_{n+6}, consisting of a cage of boron atoms that is missing two or three corners. (22.4)

arc-melting A method in which the solid metal is melted with an arc from a high-voltage electric source in a controlled atmosphere to prevent oxidation. (23.5)

Arrhenius definitions (of acids and bases) The definitions of an acid as a substance that produces H^+ ions in aqueous solution and a base as a substance that produces OH^- ions in aqueous solution. (4.8, 15.3)

Arrhenius equation An equation which relates the rate constant of a reaction to the temperature, the activation energy, and the frequency factor; $k = Ae^{\frac{-E_a}{RT}}$. (13.5)

Arrhenius plot A plot of the natural log of the rate constant ($\ln k$) versus the inverse of the temperature in kelvins ($1/T$) that yields a straight line with a slope of $-E_a/R$ and a y-intercept of $\ln A$. (13.5)

atmosphere (atm) A unit of pressure based on the average pressure of air at sea level; $1\ atm = 101{,}325\ Pa$. (5.2)

atom A submicroscopic particle that constitutes the fundamental building block of ordinary matter; the smallest identifiable unit of an element. (1.1)

G-1

atomic element   Those elements that exist in nature with single atoms as their basic units. (3.4)

atomic mass (atomic weight)   The average mass in amu of the atoms of a particular element based on the relative abundance of the various isotopes; it is numerically equivalent to the mass in grams of one mole of the element. (2.8)

atomic mass unit (amu)   A unit used to express the masses of atoms and subatomic particles, defined as $1/12^{th}$ the mass of a carbon atom containing six protons and six neutrons. (2.6)

atomic number (Z)   The number of protons in an atom; the atomic number defines the element. (2.6)

atomic solids   Solids whose composite units are atoms; they include nonbonding atomic solids, metallic atomic solids, and network covalent solids. (11.12)

atomic theory   The theory that each element is composed of tiny indestructible particles called atoms, that all atoms of a given element have the same mass and other properties, and that atoms combine in simple, whole-number ratios to form compounds. (1.2, 2.3)

aufbau principle   The principle that indicates the pattern of orbital filling in an atom. (8.3)

autoionization   The process by which water acts as an acid and a base with itself. (15.4)

Avogadro's law   The law that states that the volume of a gas is directly proportional to its amount in moles ($V \propto n$). (5.3)

Avogadro's number   The number of ^{12}C atoms in exactly 12 g of ^{12}C; equal to 6.0221421×10^{23}. (2.9)

balanced   see *chemical equation* (3.10)

ball and stick model   A representation of the arrangement of atoms in a molecule that shows how the atoms are bonded to each other and the overall shape of the molecule. (3.3)

band gap   An energy gap that exists between the valence band and conduction band of semiconductors and insulators. (11.13)

band theory   A model for bonding in atomic solids that comes from molecular orbital theory in which atomic orbitals combine and become delocalized over the entire crystal. (11.13)

barometer   An instrument used to measure atmospheric pressure. (5.2)

base ionization constant (K_b)   The equilibrium constant for the ionization reaction of a weak base; used to compare the relative strengths of weak bases. (15.7)

basic solution   A solution containing a base that creates additional OH^- ions, causing the $[OH^-]$ to increase. (15.4)

beta (β) decay   The form of radioactive decay that occurs when an unstable nucleus emits an electron. (19.3)

beta (β) particle   A medium-energy particle released during beta decay; equivalent to an electron. (19.3)

β-pleated sheet   A pattern in the secondary structure of a protein that occurs when the amino acid chain is extended and forms a zigzag pattern. (21.5)

bidentate   Describes ligands that donate two electron pairs to the central metal. (24.3)

bimolecular   An elementary step in a reaction that involves two particles, either the same species or different, that collide and go on to form products. (13.6)

binary acid   An acid composed of hydrogen and a nonmetal. (3.6)

binary compound   A compound that contains only two different elements. (3.5)

biochemistry   The study of the chemistry occurring in living organisms. (21.1)

biological effectiveness factor (RBE)   A correction factor multiplied by the dose of radiation exposure in rad to obtain the dose rem. (19.11)

black phosphorus   An allotrope of phosphorus with a structure similar to that of graphite; the most thermodynamically stable form. (22.6)

body-centered cubic   A unit cell that consists of a cube with one atom at each corner and one atom at the center of the cube. (11.11)

boiling point   The temperature at which the vapor pressure of a liquid equals the external pressure. (11.5)

boiling point elevation   The effect of a solute that causes a solution to have a higher boiling point than the pure solvent. (12.6)

bomb calorimeter   A piece of equipment designed to measure ΔE_{rxn} for combustion reactions at constant volume. (6.5)

bond energy   The energy required to break 1 mol of the bond in the gas phase. (9.10)

bond length   The average length of a bond between two particular atoms in a variety of compounds. (9.10)

bond order   For a molecule, the number of electrons in bonding orbitals minus the number of electrons in nonbonding orbitals divided by two; a positive bond order implies that the molecule is stable. (10.8)

bonding orbital   A molecular orbital that is lower in energy than any of the atomic orbitals from which it was formed. (10.8)

bonding pair   A pair of electrons shared between two atoms. (9.5)

boranes   Compounds composed of boron and hydrogen. (22.4)

Born–Haber cycle   A hypothetical series of steps based on Hess's law that represents the formation of an ionic compound from its constituent elements. (9.4)

Boyle's law   The law that states that volume of a gas is inversely proportional to its pressure $\left(V \propto \dfrac{1}{P} \right)$. (5.3)

brass   A widely used alloy that contains copper and zinc. (23.5)

Brønsted-Lowry definitions (of acids and bases)   The definitions of an acid as a proton (H^+ ion) donor and a base as a proton acceptor. (15.3)

bronze   An alloy of copper and tin that has been used for thousands of years. (23.5)

buffer   A solution containing significant amounts of both a weak acid and its conjugate base (or a weak base and its conjugate acid) that resists pH change by neutralizing added acid or added base. (16.2)

buffer capacity   The amount of acid or base that can be added to a buffer without destroying its effectiveness. (16.3)

calcination   The heating of an ore in order to decompose it and drive off a volatile product. (23.3)

calorie (cal)   A unit of energy defined as the amount of energy required to raise one gram of water 1 °C; equal to 4.184 J. (6.2)

Calorie (Cal)   Shorthand notation for the kilocalorie (kcal), or 1000 calories; also called the nutritional calorie, the unit of energy used on nutritional labels. (6.2)

calorimetry   The experimental procedure used to measure the heat evolved in a chemical reaction. (6.5)

capillary action   The ability of a liquid to flow against gravity up a narrow tube due to adhesive and cohesive forces. (11.4)

carbohydrate   A polyhydroxyl aldehyde or ketone. (21.3)

carbon black   A fine powdered form of carbon. (22.5)

carbonyl group A functional group consisting of a carbon atom double-bonded to an oxygen atom (C=O). (20.10)

carboxylic acid An organic acid containing the functional group —COOH. (15.2, 20.11)

catalyst A substance that is not consumed in a chemical reaction, but increases the rate of the reaction by providing an alternate mechanism in with the rate-determining step has a smaller activation energy. (13.7)

cathode The electrode in an electrochemical cell where reduction occurs; electrons flow toward the cathode. (18.3)

cathode rays A stream of electrons produced when a high electrical voltage is applied between two electrodes within a partially evacuated tube. (2.4)

cation A positively charged ion. (2.6)

cell potential (cell emf) (E_{cell}) The potential difference between the cathode and the anode in an electrochemical cell. (18.3)

cellulose A polysaccharide that consists of glucose units bonded together by β-glycosidic linkages; the main structural component of plants, and the most abundant organic substance on earth. (21.3)

Celsius (°C) scale The temperature scale most often used by scientists (and by most countries other than the United States), on which pure water freezes at 0 °C and boils at 100 °C (at atmospheric pressure). (1.6)

chain reaction A series of reactions in which previous reactions cause future ones; in a fission bomb, neutrons produced by the fission of one uranium nucleus induce fission in other uranium nuclei. (19.7)

charcoal A fuel similar to coal made by heating wood in the absence of air. (22.5)

Charles's law The law that states that the volume of a gas is directly proportional to its temperature ($V \propto T$). (5.3)

chelate A complex ion that contains either a bi- or polydentate ligand. (24.3)

chelating agent The coordinating ligand of a chelate. (24.3)

chemical bond The sharing or transfer of electrons to attain stable electron configurations for the bonding atoms. (9.3)

chemical change A change that alters the molecular composition of a substance; see also *chemical reaction*. (1.4)

chemical energy The energy associated with the relative positions of electrons and nuclei in atoms and molecules (6.2)

chemical equation A symbolic representation of a chemical reaction; a balanced equation contains equal numbers of the atoms of each element on both sides of the equation. (3.10)

chemical formula A symbolic representation of a compound which indicates the elements present in the compound and the relative number of atoms of each. (3.3)

chemical property A property that a substance displays only by changing its composition via a chemical change. (1.4)

chemical reaction A process by which one or more substances are converted to one or more different substances; see also *chemical change*. (3.10)

chemical symbol A one- or two-letter abbreviation for an element that is listed directly below its atomic number on the periodic table. (2.6)

chemistry The science that seeks to understand the behavior of matter by studying the behavior of atoms and molecules. (1.1)

chiral molecule A molecule that is not superimposable on its mirror image, and thus exhibits optical isomerism. (20.3)

chromosome The DNA-containing structures that occur in the nuclei of living cells. (21.6)

cis-trans isomerism Another term for geometric isomerism; cis-isomers have the same functional group on the same side of a bond and trans-isomers have the same functional group on opposite sides of a bond. (20.5)

Claus process An industrial process for obtaining sulfur through the oxidation of hydrogen sulfide. (22.8)

Clausius–Clapeyron equation An equation that displays the exponential relationship between vapor pressure and temperature;

$$\ln(P_{vap}) = \frac{-\Delta H_{vap}}{R}\left(\frac{1}{T}\right) + \ln \beta \quad (11.5)$$

***closo*-boranes** Boranes that have the formula $B_{12}H_{12}^{2-}$ and form the full icosahedral shape. (22.4)

coal A solid, black fuel with high carbon content, the product of the decomposition of ancient plant material. (22.5)

codon A sequence of three bases in a nucleic acid that codes for one amino acid. (21.6)

coffee-cup calorimeter A piece of equipment designed to measure ΔH_{rxn} for reactions at constant pressure. (6.6)

coke A solid formed by heating coal in the absence of air that consists primarily of carbon and ash. (22.5)

colligative property A property that depends on the amount of a solute but not on the type. (12.6)

collision model A model of chemical reactions in which a reaction occurs after a sufficiently energetic collision between two reactant molecules. (13.5)

colloidal dispersion (colloid) A mixture in which a dispersed substance is finely divided but not truly dissolved in a dispersing medium. (12.8)

combustion analysis A method of obtaining empirical formulas for unknown compounds, especially those containing carbon and hydrogen, by burning a sample of the compound in pure oxygen and analyzing the products of the combustion reaction. (3.9)

combustion reaction A type of chemical reaction in which a substance combines with oxygen to form one or more oxygen-containing compounds; the reaction often causes the evolution of heat and light in the form of a flame. (3.10)

common ion effect The tendency for a common ion to decrease the solubility of an ionic compound or to decrease the ionization of a weak acid or weak base. (16.2)

common name A traditional name of a compound that gives little or no information about its chemical structure; for example, the common name of $NaHCO_3$ is "baking soda." (3.5)

complementary Capable of precise pairing; in particular, the bases of nucleic acids. (21.6)

complementary properties Those properties that exclude one another, i.e., the more you know about one, the less you know about the other. For example, the wave nature and particle nature of the electron are complementary. (7.4)

complete ionic equation An equation which lists individually all of the ions present as either reactants or products in a chemical reaction. (4.7)

complex carbohydrate Another term for a polysaccharide based on the fact that it is made up of many simple sugars. (21.3)

complex ion An ion that contains a central metal ion bound to one or more ligands. (16.8, 24.3)

compound A substance composed of two or more elements in fixed, definite proportions. (1.3)

concentrated solution A solution that contains a large amount of solute relative to the amount of solvent. (4.4, 12.5)

condensation   The phase transition from gas to liquid. (11.5)

condensation polymer   A polymer formed by elimination of an atom or small group of atoms (usually water) between pairs of monomers during polymerization. (20.14)

condensation reaction   A reaction in which two or more organic compounds are joined, often with the loss of water or some other small molecule. (20.11)

conjugate acid   Any base to which a proton has been added. (15.3)

conjugate acid–base pair   Two substances related to each other by the transfer of a proton. (15.3)

conjugate base   Any acid from which a proton has been removed. (15.3)

constructive interference   The interaction of waves from two sources that align with overlapping crests, resulting in a wave of greater amplitude. (7.2)

contact process   An industrial method for the production of sulfuric acid. (22.8)

conversion factor   A factor used to convert between two different units; a conversion factor can be constructed from any two quantities known to be equivalent. (1.8)

coordinate covalent bond   The bond formed when a ligand donates electrons to an empty orbital of a metal in a complex ion. (24.3)

coordination compound   A neutral compound made when a complex ion combines with one or more counterions. (24.3)

coordination isomers   Isomers of complex ions that occur when a coordinated ligand exchanges places with the uncoordinated counterion. (24.4)

coordination number (secondary valence)   The number of molecules or ions directly bound to the metal atom in a complex ion. (24.3)

coordination number   The number of atoms with which each atom in a crystal lattice is in direct contact. (11.11)

core electrons   Those electrons in a complete principal energy level and those in complete d and f sublevels. (8.4)

corrosion   The gradual, nearly always undesired oxidation of metals that occurs when they are exposed to oxidizing agents in the environment. (18.9)

Coulomb's law   The potential energy of two charged particles is directly proportional to the product of their charges (q_1 and q_2) and distance between them (r). $E = \dfrac{1}{4\pi\varepsilon_0}\dfrac{q_1 q_2}{r}$ (8.3)

covalent bond   A chemical bond in which two atoms share electrons that interact with the nuclei of both atoms, lowering the potential energy of each through electrostatic interactions. (3.2, 9.2)

covalent carbides   Binary compounds composed of carbon combined with low-electronegativity nonmetals or metalloids. (22.5)

covalent radius (bonding atomic radius)   Defined in nonmetals as one-half the distance between two atoms bonded together, and in metals as one-half the distance between two adjacent atoms in a crystal of the metal. (8.6)

critical mass   The necessary amount of a radioactive isotope required to produce a self-sustaining fission reaction. (19.7)

critical point   The temperature and pressure above which a supercritical fluid exists. (11.8)

critical pressure   The pressure required to bring about a transition to a liquid at the critical temperature. (11.5)

critical temperature   The temperature above which a liquid cannot exist, regardless of pressure. (11.5)

crystalline lattice   The regular arrangement of atoms in a crystalline solid. (11.11)

crystalline solid (crystal)   A solid in which atoms, molecules, or ions are arranged in patterns with long-range, repeating order. (1.3, 11.2)

cubic closest packing   A closest-packed arrangement in which the third layer of atoms is offset from the first; the same structure as the face-centered cubic. (11.11)

cyclotron   A particle accelerator in which a charged particle is accelerated in an evacuated ring-shaped tube by an alternating voltage applied to each semi-circular half of the ring. (19.10)

Dalton's law of partial pressures   The law stating that the sum of the partial pressures of the components in a gas mixture must equal the total pressure. (5.6)

de Broglie relation   The observation that the wavelength of a particle is inversely proportional to its momentum $\lambda = \dfrac{h}{mv}$ (7.4)

decanting   A method of separating immiscible liquids by pouring the top layer into another container. (1.3)

degenerate   A term describing two or more electron orbitals with the same value of n that have the same energy. (8.3)

density (d)   The ratio of an object's mass to its volume. (1.6)

deposition   The phase transition from gas to solid. (11.6)

derived unit   A unit that is a combination of other base units. For example, the SI unit for speed is meters per second (m/s), a derived unit. (1.6)

destructive interference   The interaction of waves from two sources aligned so that the crest of one overlaps the trough of the other, resulting in cancellation. (7.2)

deterministic   A characteristic of the classical laws of motion, which imply that present circumstances determine future events. (7.4)

dextrorotatory   Capable of rotating the plane of polarization of light clockwise. (20.3)

diamagnetic   The state of an atom or ion that contains only paired electrons and is, therefore, slightly repelled by an external magnetic field. (10.8)

diamond   An elemental form of carbon with a crystal structure that consists of carbon atoms connected to four other carbon atoms at the corners of a tetrahedron, creating a strong network covalent solid. (22.5)

diffraction   The phenomena by which a wave emerging from an aperture spreads out to form a new wave front. (7.2)

diffusion   The process by which a gas spreads through a space occupied by another gas. (5.9)

dilute solution   A solution that contains a very small amount of solute relative to the amount of solvent. (4.4, 12.5)

dimensional analysis   The use of units as a guide to solving problems. (1.8)

dimer   The product that forms from the reaction of two monomers. (20.14)

diode   A device that allows the flow of electrical current in only one direction. (11.13)

dipeptide   Two amino acids linked together. (21.4)

dipole moment   A measure of the separation of positive and negative charge in a molecule. (9.6)

dipole–dipole force   An intermolecular force exhibited by polar molecules that results from the uneven charge distribution. (11.3)

diprotic acid   An acid that contains two ionizable protons. (4.8, 15.4)

disaccharide   A carbohydrate composed of two monosaccharides. (21.3)

dispersion force (London force) An intermolecular force exhibited by all atoms and molecules that results from fluctuations in the electron distribution. (11.3)

distillation The process by which mixtures of miscible liquids are separated by heating the mixture to boil off the more volatile liquid. The vaporized component is then recondensed and collected in a separate flask. (1.3)

disubstituted benzene A benzene in which two hydrogen atoms have been replaced by other atoms. (20.7)

double bond The bond that forms when two electrons are shared between two atoms. (9.5)

dry-cell battery A battery that does not contain a large amount of liquid water, often using the oxidation of zinc and the reduction of MnO_2 to provide the electrical current. (18.7)

duet A Lewis structure with two dots, signifying a filled outer electron shell for the elements H and He. (9.3)

dynamic equilibrium The point at which the rate of the reverse reaction or process equals the rate of the forward reaction or process. (11.5, 12.4, 14.2)

effective nuclear charge (Z_{eff}) The actual nuclear charge experienced by an electron, defined as the charge of the nucleus plus the charge of the shielding electrons. (8.3)

effusion The process by which a gas escapes from a container into a vacuum through a small hole. (5.9)

electrical charge A fundamental property of certain particles that causes them to experience a force in the presence of electric fields. (2.4)

electrical current The flow of electric charge. (18.3)

electrochemical cell A device in which a chemical reaction either produces or is carried out by an electrical current. (18.3)

electrode A conductive surface through which electrons can enter or leave a half-cell. (18.3)

electrolysis The process by which electrical current is used to drive an otherwise nonspontaneous redox reaction. (18.8)

electrolyte A substance that dissolves in water to form solutions that conduct electricity. (4.5)

electrolytic cell An electrochemical cell which uses electrical current to drive a nonspontaneous chemical reaction. (18.3)

electromagnetic radiation A form of energy embodied in oscillating electric and magnetic fields. (7.2)

electromagnetic spectrum The range of the wavelengths of all possible electromagnetic radiation. (7.2)

electrometallurgy The use of electrolysis to produce metals from their compounds. (23.3)

electromotive force (emf) The force that results in the motion of electrons due to a difference in potential. (18.3)

electron A negatively charged, low mass particle found outside the nucleus of all atoms that occupies most of the atom's volume but contributes almost none of its mass. (2.4)

electron affinity (EA) The energy change associated with the gaining of an electron by an atom in its gaseous state. (8.7)

electron capture The form of radioactive decay that occurs when a nucleus assimilates an electron from an inner orbital. (19.3)

electron configuration A notation that shows the particular orbitals that are occupied by electrons in an atom. (8.3)

electron geometry The geometrical arrangement of electron groups in a molecule. (10.3)

electron groups A general term for lone pairs, single bonds, multiple bonds, or lone electrons in a molecule. (10.2)

electron spin A fundamental property of electrons; spin can have a value of $\pm^1/_2$. (8.3)

electronegativity The ability of an atom to attract electrons to itself in a covalent bond. (9.6)

element A substance that cannot be chemically broken down into simpler substances. (1.3)

elementary step An individual step in a reaction mechanism. (13.6)

emission spectrum The range of wavelengths emitted by a particular element; used to identify the element. (7.3)

empirical formula A chemical formula that shows the simplest whole number ratio of atoms in the compound. (3.3)

empirical formula molar mass The sum of the masses of all the atoms in an empirical formula. (3.9)

enantiomers (optical isomers) Two molecules that are nonsuperimposable mirror images of one another. (20.3, 24.4)

endothermic reaction A chemical reaction that absorbs heat from its surroundings; for an endothermic reaction, $\Delta H > 0$. (6.6)

endpoint The point of pH change where an indicator changes color. (16.4)

energy The capacity to do work. (1.5, 6.2)

English system The system of units used in the United States and various other countries in which the inch is the unit of length, the pound is the unit of force, and the ounce is the unit of mass. (1.6)

enthalpy (H) The sum of the internal energy of a system and the product of its pressure and volume; the energy associated with the breaking and forming of bonds in a chemical reaction. (6.6)

enthalpy of solution The overall enthalpy change upon solution formation

$$\Delta H_{soln} = \Delta H_{solute} + \Delta H_{solvent} + \Delta H_{mix}$$
$$\text{endothermic (+) endothermic (+) exothermic (−)} \quad (12.3)$$

entropy A thermodynamic function that is proportional to the number of energetically equivalent ways to arrange the components of a system to achieve a particular state; a measure of the energy randomization or energy dispersal in a system. (12.2, 17.3)

enzyme A biochemical catalyst made of protein that increases the rates of biochemical reactions. (13.7, 21.4)

equilibrium constant (K) The ratio, at equilibrium, of the concentrations of the products of a reaction raised to their stoichiometric coefficients to the concentrations of the reactants raised to their stoichiometric coefficients. (14.3)

equivalence point The point in a titration at which the added solute completely reacts with the solute present in the solution; for acid–base titrations, the point at which the amount of acid is stoichiometrically equal to the amount of base in solution. (4.8, 16.4)

ester A family of organic compounds with the general structure R—COO—R. (20.11)

ester linkage The bonds that form between a carboxylic acid and an alcohol to form an ester, such as those in triglycerides. (21.2)

ether A member of the family of organic compounds of the form R—O—R′. (20.12)

exact numbers Numbers that have no uncertainty and thus do not limit the number of significant figures in any calculation. (1.7)

exothermic reaction A chemical reaction that releases heat to its surroundings; for an exothermic reaction, $\Delta H < 0$. (6.6)

experiment A highly controlled procedure designed to generate observations that may support a hypothesis or prove it wrong. (1.2)

exponential factor A number between 0 and 1 that represents the fraction of molecules that have enough energy to make it over the activation barrier on a given approach. (13.5)

extensive property   A property that depends on the amount of a given substance, such as mass. (1.6)

extractive metallurgy   The process by which an elemental metal must be extracted from the compounds in which it is found. (23.3)

face-centered cubic   A crystal structure whose unit cell consists of a cube with one atom at each corner and one atom in the center of every face. (11.11)

Fahrenheit (°F) scale   The temperature scale that is most familiar in the United States, on which pure water freezes at 32 °F and boils at 212 °F. (1.6)

family   A group of organic compounds with the same functional group. (3.11)

family (group)   Columns within the main group elements in the periodic table that contain elements that exhibit similar chemical properties. (2.7)

Faraday's constant (F)   The charge in coulombs of 1 mol of electrons: $F = \dfrac{96,485 \text{ C}}{\text{mol e}^-}$. (18.5)

fatty acid   A carboxylic acid with a long hydrocarbon tail. (21.2)

ferromagnetic   The state of an atom or ion that is very strongly attracted by an external magnetic field. (23.5)

fertilizer   A material containing large amounts of nitrogen or phosphorus that is used to increase plant growth. (22.6)

fibrous protein   A protein with a relatively linear structure; fibrous proteins tend to be insoluble in aqueous solutions. (21.5)

film-badge dosimeter   A device for monitoring exposure to radiation consisting of photographic film held in a small case that is pinned to clothing. (19.5)

filtration   A procedure used to separate a mixture composed of an insoluble solid and a liquid by pouring it through filter paper or some other porous membrane or layer. (1.3)

first law of thermodynamics   The law stating that the total energy of the universe is constant. (6.3)

flux   In pyrometallurgy, material that will react with the gangue to form a substance with a low melting point. (23.3)

formal charge   The charge that an atom in a Lewis structure would have if all the bonding electrons were shared equally between the bonded atoms. (9.8)

formation constant (K_f)   The equilibrium constant associated with reactions for the formation of complex ions. (16.8)

formula mass   The average mass of a molecule of a compound in amu. (3.7)

formula unit   The smallest, electrically neutral collection of ions in an ionic compound. (3.4)

Frasch process   An industrial process for the recovery of sulfur that uses superheated water to liquefy sulfur deposits in Earth's crust and bring the molten sulfur to the surface. (22.8)

free energy of formation (ΔG_f°)   The change in free energy when 1 mol of a compound forms from its constituent elements in their standard states. (17.7)

free radical   A molecule or ion with an odd number of electrons in its Lewis structure. (9.9)

freezing   The phase transition from liquid to solid. (11.6)

freezing point depression   The effect of a solute that causes a solution to have a lower melting point than the pure solvent. (12.6)

frequency (ν)   For waves, the number of cycles (or complete wavelengths) that pass through a stationary point in one second. (7.2)

frequency factor   The number of times that reactants approach the activation energy per unit time. (13.5)

fuel cell   A voltaic cell that uses the oxidation of hydrogen and the reduction of oxygen, forming water, to provide electrical current. (18.7)

fullerenes   Carbon clusters, such as C_{60}, bonded in roughly spherical shapes containing from 36 to over 100 carbon atoms. (22.5)

functional group   A characteristic atom or group of atoms that imparts certain chemical properties to an organic compound. (3.11)

gamma (γ) rays   The form of electromagnetic radiation with the shortest wavelength and highest energy. (7.2, 19.3)

gamma (γ) ray emission   The form of radioactive decay that occurs when an unstable nucleus emits extremely high frequency electromagnetic radiation. (19.3)

gangue   The undesirable minerals that are separated from specific ores. (23.3)

gas   A state of matter in which atoms or molecules have a great deal of space between them and are free to move relative to one another; lacking a definite shape or volume, a gas conforms to those of its container. (1.3)

gas-evolution reaction   A reaction in which two aqueous solutions are mixed and a gas forms, resulting in bubbling. (4.8)

Geiger-Müller counter   A device used to detect radioactivity that uses argon atoms that become ionized in the presence of energetic particles to produce an electrical signal. (19.5)

gene   A sequence of codons within a DNA molecule that codes for a single protein. (21.6)

geometric isomerism   A form of stereoisomerism involving the orientation of functional groups in a molecule that contains bonds incapable of rotating. (20.5)

geometric isomers   For complex ions, isomers that result when the ligands bonded to the metal have a different spatial arrangement. (24.4)

Gibbs free energy (G)   A thermodynamic state function related to enthalpy and entropy by the equation $G = H - TS$; chemical systems tend towards lower Gibbs free energy, also called the *chemical potential*. (17.5)

globular protein   A protein that folds into a roughly spherical shape so that its polar side chains are oriented outward and its nonpolar side chains toward the interior; globular proteins tend to be soluble in water. (21.5)

glycogen   A highly branched form of starch. (21.3)

glycolipid   A triglyceride composed of a fatty acid, a hydrocarbon chain, and a sugar molecule as the polar section. (21.2)

glycosidic linkage   A bond between carbohydrates that results from a dehydration reaction. (21.3)

graphite   An elemental form of carbon consisting of flat sheets of carbon atoms, bonded together as interconnected hexagonal rings held together by intermolecular forces, that can easily slide past each other. (22.5)

Haber-Bosch process   The industrial process for producing ammonia from nitrogen gas and hydrogen gas. (22.6)

half-cell   One half of an electrochemical cell where either oxidation or reduction occurs. (18.3)

half-life ($t_{1/2}$)   The time required for the concentration of a reactant or the amount of a radioactive isotope to fall to one-half of its initial value. (13.4)

halogens   Highly reactive nonmetals in group 7A of the periodic table. (2.7)

heat (q)   The flow of energy caused by a temperature difference. (6.2)

heat capacity (*C*) The quantity of heat required to change a system's temperature by 1 °C. (6.4)

heat of fusion (ΔH_{fus}) The amount of heat required to melt 1 mole of a solid. (11.6)

heat of hydration ($\Delta H_{hydration}$) The enthalpy change that occurs when 1 mole of gaseous solute ions are dissolved in water. (12.3)

heat of reaction (ΔH_{rxn}) The enthalpy change for a chemical reaction. (6.6)

heat of vaporization (ΔH_{vap}) The amount of heat required to vaporize one mole of a liquid to a gas. (11.5)

Heisenberg's uncertainty principle The principle stating that due to the wave-particle duality, it is fundamentally impossible to precisely determine both the position and velocity of a particle at a given moment in time. (7.4)

Henderson–Hasselbalch equation An equation used to easily calculate the pH of a buffer solution from the initial concentrations of the buffer components, assuming that the "*x is small*" approximation is valid: $\text{pH} = \text{p}K_a + \log\dfrac{[\text{base}]}{[\text{acid}]}$ (16.2)

Henry's law An equation that expresses the relationship between solubility of a gas and pressure: $S_{gas} = k_H P_{gas}$ (12.4)

Hess's law The law stating that if a chemical equation can be expressed as the sum of a series of steps, then ΔH_{rxn} for the overall equation is the sum of the heats of reactions for each step. (6.8)

heterogeneous catalysis Catalysis in which the catalyst and the reactants exist in different phases. (13.7)

heterogeneous mixture A mixture in which the composition varies from one region to another. (1.3)

hexagonal closest packing A closest packed arrangement in which the atoms of the third layer align exactly over those in the first layer. (11.11)

hexose A six-carbon sugar. (21.3)

high-spin complex A complex ion with weak field ligands that have the same number of unpaired electrons as the free metal ion. (24.5)

homogeneous catalysis Catalysis in which the catalyst exists in the same phase as the reactants. (13.7)

homogeneous mixture A mixture with the same composition throughout. (1.3)

Hund's rule The principle stating that when electrons fill degenerate orbitals they first fill them singly with parallel spins. (8.3)

hybrid orbitals Orbitals formed from the combination of standard atomic orbitals that correspond more closely to the actual distribution of electrons in a chemically bonded atom. (10.7)

hybridization A mathematical procedure in which standard atomic orbitals are combined to form new, hybrid orbitals. (10.7)

hydrate An ionic compound that contains a specific number of water molecules associated with each formula unit. (3.5)

hydrazine N_2H_4, a nitrogen and hydrogen compound in which nitrogen has a negative oxidation state (-2). (22.6)

hydrocarbon An organic compound that contains only carbon and hydrogen. (3.11)

hydrogen azide A nitrogen and hydrogen compound with a higher hydrogen-to-nitrogen ratio than ammonia or hydrazine. (22.6)

hydrogen bond A strong dipole–dipole attractive force between a hydrogen bonded to O, N, or F and one of these electronegative atoms on a neighboring molecule. (11.3)

hydrogenation The catalyzed addition of hydrogen to alkene double bonds to make single bonds. (13.7)

hydrolysis The splitting of a chemical bond with water, resulting in the addition of H and OH to the products. (21.3)

hydrometallurgy The use of an aqueous solution to extract metals from their ores. (23.3)

hydronium ion H_3O^+, the ion formed from the association of a water molecule with an H^+ ion donated by an acid. (4.8, 15.3)

hypothesis A tentative interpretation or explanation of an observation. A good hypothesis is *falsifiable*. (1.2)

hypoxia A physiological condition caused by low levels of oxygen, marked by dizziness, headache, and shortness of breath and eventually unconsciousness or even death in severe cases. (5.6)

ideal gas A gas that exactly follows the ideal gas law. (5.4)

ideal gas constant The proportionality constant of the ideal gas law, *R*, equal to 8.314 J/mol·K or 0.08206 L·atm/mol·K. (5.4)

ideal gas law The law that combines the relationships of Boyle's, Charles's, and Avogadro's laws into one comprehensive equation of state with the proportionality constant *R* in the form $PV = nRT$. (5.4)

ideal solution A solution that follows Raoult's law at all concentrations for both solute and solvent. (12.6)

indeterminacy The principle that present circumstances do not necessarily determine future events in the quantum-mechanical realm. (7.4)

indicator A dye whose color depends on the pH of the solution it is dissolved in; often used to detect the endpoint of a titration. (4.8, 16.4)

infrared (IR) radiation Electromagnetic radiation emitted from warm objects, with wavelengths slightly larger than those of visible light. (7.2)

insoluble Incapable of dissolving in water or being extremely difficult of solution. (4.5)

integrated rate law A relationship between the concentrations of the reactants in a chemical reaction and time. (13.4)

intensive property A property such as density that is independent of the amount of a given substance. (1.6)

interference The superposition of two or more waves overlapping in space, resulting in either an increase in amplitude (constructive interference) or a decrease in amplitude (destructive interfence). (7.2)

interhalogen compounds A class of covalent compounds that contain two different halogens. (22.9)

internal energy (*E*) The sum of the kinetic and potential energies of all of the particles that compose a system. (6.3)

International System of Units (SI) The standard unit system used by scientists, based on the metric system. (1.6)

interstitial alloy An alloy in which small, usually nonmetallic atoms fit between the metallic atoms of a crystal. (23.4)

ion An atom or molecule with a net charge caused by the loss or gain of electrons. (2.6)

ion product constant for water (K_w) The equilibrium constant for the autoionization of water. (15.5)

ion–dipole force An intermolecular force between an ion and the oppositely charged end of a polar molecule. (11.3)

ionic bond A chemical bond formed between two oppositely charged ions, generally a metallic cation and a nonmetallic anion, that are attracted to one another by electrostatic forces. (3.2, 9.2)

ionic carbides Binary compounds composed of carbon combined with low-electronegativity metals. (22.5)

ionic compound A compound composed of cations and anions bound together by electrostatic attraction. (3.4)

ionic solids Solids whose composite units are ions; they generally have high melting points. (11.12)

ionization energy (IE) The energy required to remove an electron from an atom or ion in its gaseous state. (8.7)

ionizing power The ability of radiation to ionize other molecules and atoms. (19.3)

irreversible reaction A reaction that does not achieve the theoretical limit of available free energy. (17.7)

isotopes Atoms of the same element with the same number of protons but different numbers of neutrons and consequently different masses. (2.6)

joule (J) The SI unit for energy: equal to $1 \text{ kg} \cdot \text{m}^2/\text{s}^2$. (6.2)

kelvin (K) The SI standard unit of temperature. (1.6)

Kelvin scale The temperature scale that assigns 0 K (-273 °C or -459 °F) to the coldest temperature possible, absolute zero, the temperature at which molecular motion virtually stops. 1 K = 1 °C. (1.6)

ketone A member of the family of organic compounds that contain a carbonyl functional group ($C{=}O$) bonded to two R groups, neither of which is a hydrogen atom. (20.10)

ketose A sugar that is a ketone. (21.3)

kilogram (kg) The SI standard unit of mass defined as the mass of a block of metal kept at the International Bureau of Weights and Measures at Sèvres, France. (1.6)

kilowatt-hour (kWh) An energy unit used primarily to express large amounts of energy produced by the flow of electricity; equal to 3.60×10^6 J. (6.2)

kinetic energy The energy associated with motion of an object. (1.5, 6.2)

kinetic molecular theory A model of an ideal gas as a collection of point particles in constant motion undergoing completely elastic collisions. (5.8)

lanthanide contraction The trend toward leveling off in size of the atoms in the third and fourth transition rows due to the ineffective shielding of the f sublevel electrons. (24.2)

lattice energy The energy associated with forming a crystalline lattice from gaseous ions. (9.4)

law see *scientific law*

law of conservation of energy A law stating that energy can neither be created nor destroyed, only converted from one form to another. (1.5, 6.2)

law of conservation of mass A law stating that matter is neither created nor destroyed in a chemical reaction. (1.2)

law of definite proportions A law stating that all samples of a given compound have the same proportions of their constituent elements. (2.3)

law of mass action The relationship between the balanced chemical equation and the expression of the equilibrium constant. (14.3)

law of multiple proportions A law stating that when two elements (A and B) form two different compounds, the masses of element B that combine with one gram of element A can be expressed as a ratio of small whole numbers. (2.3)

Le Châtelier's principle The principle stating that when a chemical system at equilibrium is disturbed, the system shifts in a direction that minimizes the disturbance. (14.9)

leaching The process by which a metal is separated out of a mixture by selectively dissolving it into solution. (23.3)

lead–acid storage battery A battery that uses the oxidation of lead and the reduction of lead(IV) oxide in sulfuric acid to provide electrical current. (18.7)

lever rule The rule that states that in a two-phase region, whichever phase is closest to the composition of the alloy is the more abundant phase. (23.4)

levorotatory Capable of rotating the polarization of light counterclockwise. (20.3)

Lewis acid An atom, ion, or molecule that is an electron pair acceptor. (15.11)

Lewis base An atom, ion, or molecule that is an electron pair donor. (15.11)

Lewis electron-dot structures (Lewis structures) A drawing that represents chemical bonds between atoms as shared or transferred electrons; the valence electrons of atoms are represented as dots. (9.1)

Lewis theory A simple model of chemical bonding using diagrams that represent bonds between atoms as lines or pairs of dots. In this theory, atoms bond together to obtain stable octets (8 valence electrons). (9.1)

ligand A neutral molecule or an ion that acts as a Lewis base with the central metal ion in a complex ion. (16.8, 24.3)

limiting reactant The reactant that has the smallest stoichiometric amount in a reactant mixture and consequently limits the amount of product in a chemical reaction. (4.3)

linear accelerator A particle accelerator in which a charged particle is accelerated in an evacuated tube by a potential difference between the ends of the tube or by alternating charges in sections of the tube. (19.10)

linear geometry The molecular geometry of three atoms with a 180° bond angle due to the repulsion of two electron groups. (10.2)

linkage isomers Isomers of complex ions that occur when some ligands coordinate to the metal in different ways. (24.4)

lipid A member of the class of biochemical compounds that are insoluble in water but soluble in nonpolar solvents; include fatty acids, triglycerides, and steroids. (21.2)

lipid bilayer A double-layered structure made of phospholipids or glycolipids, in which the polar heads of the molecules interact with the environment and the nonpolar tails interact with each other; a component of many cellular membranes. (21.2)

liquid A state of matter in which atoms or molecules pack about as closely as they do in solid matter but are free to move relative to each other, giving a fixed volume but not a fixed shape. (1.3)

liter (L) A unit of volume equal to 1000 cm^3 or 1.057 qt. (1.6)

lithium-ion battery A battery that produces electrical current in the form of motion of lithium ions from the anode to the cathode. (18.7)

lone pair A pair of electrons associated with only one atom. (9.5)

low-spin complex A complex ion with strong field ligands that have fewer unpaired electrons than the free metal ion. (24.5)

magic numbers Certain numbers of nucleons (N or Z = 2, 8, 20, 28, 50, 82, and N = 126) that confer unique stability. (19.4)

magnetic quantum number (m_l) An integer that specifies the orientation of an orbital. (7.5)

main-group elements Those elements found in the s or p blocks of the periodic table, whose properties tend to be predictable based on their position in the table. (2.7, 22.2)

manometer An instrument used to determine the pressure of a gaseous sample, consisting of a liquid-filled U-shaped tube with one

end exposed to the ambient pressure and the other end connected to the sample. (5.2)

mass A measure of the quantity of matter making up an object. (1.6)

mass defect The difference in mass between the nucleus of an atom and the sum of the separated particles that make up that nucleus. (19.8)

mass number (A) The sum of the number of protons and neutrons in an atom. (2.6)

mass percent composition (mass percent) An element's percentage of the total mass of a compound containing the element. (3.8)

mass spectrometry An experimental method of determining the precise mass and relative abundance of isotopes in a given sample using an instrument called a *mass spectrometer*. (2.8)

matter Anything that occupies space and has mass. (1.3)

mean free path The average distance that a molecule in a gas travels between collisions. (5.9)

melting (fusion) The phase transition from solid to liquid. (11.6)

melting point The temperature at which the molecules of a solid have enough thermal energy to overcome intermolecular forces and become a liquid. (11.6)

metals A large class of elements that are generally good conductors of heat and electricity, malleable, ductile, lustrous, and tend to lose electrons during chemical changes. (2.7)

metallic atomic solids Atomic solids held together by metallic bonds; they have variable melting points. (11.12)

metallic bonding The type of bonding that occurs in metal crystals, in which metal atoms donate their electrons to an electron sea, delocalized over the entire crystal lattice. (9.2)

metallic carbides Binary compounds composed of carbon combined with metals that have a metallic lattice with holes small enough to fit carbon atoms. (22.5)

metalloids A category of elements found on the boundary between the metals and nonmetals of the periodic table, with properties intermediate between those of both groups; also called *semimetals*. (2.7)

metallurgy The part of chemistry that includes all the processes associated with mining, separating, and refining metals and the subsequent production of pure metals and mixtures of metals called alloys. (23.1)

meter (m) The SI standard unit of length; equivalent to 39.37 inches. (1.6)

metric system The system of measurements used in most countries in which the meter is the unit of length, the kilogram is the unit of mass, and the second is the unit of time. (1.6)

microwaves Electromagnetic radiation with wavelengths slightly longer than those of infrared radiation; used for radar and in microwave ovens. (7.2)

milliliter (mL) A unit of volume equal to 10^{-3} L or 1 cm^3. (1.6)

millimeter of mercury (mmHg) A common unit of pressure referring to the air pressure required to push a column of mercury to a height of 1 mm in a barometer; 760 mmHg = 1 atm. (5.2)

minerals Homogenous, naturally occurring, crystalline inorganic solids. (23.2)

miscibility The ability to mix without separating into two phases. (11.3)

miscible The ability of two or more substances to be soluble in each other in all proportions. (12.2)

mixture A substance composed of two or more different types of atoms or molecules that can be combined in variable proportions. (1.3)

molality (m) A means of expressing solution concentration as the number of moles of solute per kilogram of solvent. (12.5)

molar heat capacity The amount of heat required to raise the temperature of one mole of a substance by 1 °C. (6.4)

molar mass The mass in grams of one mole of atoms of an element; numerically equivalent to the atomic mass of the element in amu. (2.9)

molar solubility The solubility of a compound in units of moles per liter. (16.5)

molar volume The volume occupied by one mole of a substance. (5.5)

molarity (M) A means of expressing solution concentration as the number of moles of solute per liter of solution. (4.4, 12.5)

mole (mol) A unit defined as the amount of material containing 6.0221421×10^{23} (Avogadro's number) particles. (2.9)

mole fraction (χ_A) The number of moles of a component in a mixture divided by the total number of moles in the mixture. (5.6)

mole fraction (χ_{solute}) A means of expressing solution concentration as the number of moles of solute per moles of solution. (12.5)

mole percent A means of expressing solution concentration as the mole fraction multiplied by 100%. (12.5)

molecular compound Compounds composed of two or more covalently bonded nonmetals. (3.4)

molecular element Those elements that exist in nature with diatomic or polyatomic molecules as their basic unit. (3.4)

molecular equation An equation showing the complete neutral formula for each compound in a reaction. (4.7)

molecular formula A chemical formula that shows the actual number of atoms of each element in a molecule of a compound. (3.3)

molecular geometry The geometrical arrangement of atoms in a molecule. (10.3)

molecular orbital theory An advanced model of chemical bonding in which electrons reside in molecular orbitals delocalized over the entire molecule. In the simplest version, the molecular orbitals are simply linear combinations of atomic orbitals. (10.8)

molecular solids Solids whose composite units are molecules; they generally have low melting points. (11.12)

molecularity The number of reactant particles involved in an elementary step. (13.6)

molecule Two or more atoms joined chemically in a specific geometrical arrangement. (1.1)

monodentate Describes ligands that donate only one electron pair to the central metal. (24.3)

monomer The individual unit repeated in a chain to form a polymer. (20.14)

monoprotic acid An acid that contains only one ionizable proton. (15.4)

monosaccharide The simplest carbohydrates, with 3 to 8 carbon atoms and only one aldehyde or ketone group. (21.3)

nanotubes Long, tubular structures consisting of interconnected C$_6$ rings. (22.5)

natural abundance The relative percentage of a particular isotope in a naturally occurring sample with respect to other isotopes of the same element. (2.6)

Nernst equation The equation relating the cell potential of an electrochemical cell to the standard cell potential and the reaction quotient;

$$E_{\text{cell}} = E_{\text{cell}}^{\circ} - \frac{0.0592\text{ V}}{n}\log Q. \quad (18.6)$$

net ionic equation An equation that shows only the species that actually change during the reaction. (4.7)

network covalent atomic solids Atomic solids held together by covalent bonds; they have high melting points. (11.12)

neutral The state of a solution where the concentrations of H_3O^+ and OH^- are equal. (15.4)

neutron An electrically neutral subatomic particle found in the nucleus of an atom, with a mass almost equal to that of a proton. (2.5)

nickel–cadmium (NiCad) battery A battery that consists of an anode composed of solid cadmium and a cathode composed of $NiO(OH)(s)$ in a KOH solution. (18.7)

nickel–metal hydride (NiMH) battery A battery that uses the same cathode reaction as the NiCad battery but a different anode reaction, the oxidation of hydrogens in a metal alloy. (18.7)

***nido*-boranes** Boranes that have the formula B_nH_{n+4} and consist of a cage of boron atoms missing one corner. (22.4)

nitrogen narcosis A physiological condition caused by an increased partial pressure of nitrogen, resulting in symptoms similar to those of intoxication. (5.6)

noble gases The group 8A elements, which are largely unreactive (inert) due to their stable filled p orbitals. (2.7)

node A point where the wave function (ψ), and therefore the probability density (ψ^2) and radial distribution function, all go through zero. (7.6)

nonbonding atomic solids Atomic solids held together by dispersion forces; they have low melting points. (11.12)

nonbonding electrons The electrons in a Lewis structure that are not in a chemical bond. Also called lone pair electrons.

nonbonding orbital An orbital whose electrons remain localized on an atom. (10.8)

nonelectrolyte A compound that does not dissociate into ions when dissolved in water. (4.5)

nonmetal A class of elements that tend to be poor conductors of heat and electricity and usually gain electrons during chemical reactions. (2.7)

nonvolatile Not easily vaporized. (11.5)

normal boiling point The temperature at which the vapor pressure of a liquid equals 1 atm. (11.5)

n-type semiconductor A semiconductor that employs negatively charged electrons in the conduction band as the charge carriers. (11.13)

nuclear binding energy The amount of energy that would be required to break apart the nucleus into its component nucleons. (19.8)

nuclear equation An equation that represents nuclear processes such as radioactivity. (19.3)

nuclear fission The splitting of the nucleus of an atom, resulting in a tremendous release of energy. (19.7)

nuclear fusion The combination of two light nuclei to form a heavier one. (19.9)

nuclear theory The theory that most of the atom's mass and all of its positive charge is contained in a small, dense nucleus. (2.5)

nucleotides The individual units composing nucleic acids; each consists of a phosphate group, a sugar, and a nitrogenous base. (21.6)

nucleus The very small, dense core of the atom that contains most of the atom's mass and all of its positive charge; it is composed of protons and neutrons. (2.5)

nuclide A particular isotope of an atom. (19.3)

octahedral arrangement The molecular geometry of seven atoms with 90° bond angles. (10.2)

octahedral hole A space that exists in the middle of six atoms on two adjacent close-packed sheets of atoms in a crystal lattice. (23.4)

octet A Lewis structure with eight dots, signifying a filled outer electron shell for s and p block elements. (9.3)

octet rule The tendency for most bonded atoms to possess or share eight electrons in their outer shell to obtain stable electron configurations and lower their potential energy. (9.3)

optical isomers Two molecules that are nonsuperimposable mirror images of one another. (20.3, 24.4)

orbital A probability distribution map, based on the quantum mechanical model of the atom, used to describe the likely position of an electron in an atom; also an allowed energy state for an electron. (7.5)

orbital diagram A diagram which gives information similar to an electron configuration, but symbolizes an electron as an arrow in a box representing an orbital, with the arrow's direction denoting the electron's spin. (8.3)

ore A rock that contains a high concentration of a specific mineral. (23.2)

organic chemistry The study of carbon-based compounds. (20.1)

organic molecule A molecule containing carbon combined with several other elements including hydrogen, nitrogen, oxygen, or sulfur. (20.1)

orthosilicates Silicates in which tetrahedral SO_4^{4-} ions stand alone. (22.3)

osmosis The flow of solvent from a solution of lower solute concentration to one of higher solute concentration. (12.6)

osmotic pressure The pressure required to stop osmotic flow. (12.6)

Ostwald process An industrial process used for commercial preparation of nitric acid. (22.6)

overall order The sum of the orders of all reactants in a chemical reaction. (13.3)

oxidation The loss of one or more electrons; also the gaining of oxygen or the loss of hydrogen. (4.9)

oxidation state (oxidation number) A positive or negative whole number that represents the "charge" an atom in a compound would have if all shared electrons were assigned to the atom with a greater attraction for those electrons. (4.9)

oxidation–reduction (redox) reaction Reactions in which electrons are transferred from one reactant to another and the oxidation states of certain atoms are changed. (4.9)

oxidizing agent A substance that causes the oxidation of another substance; an oxidizing agent gains electrons and is reduced. (4.9)

oxyacid An acid composed of hydrogen and an oxyanion. (3.6)

oxyanion A polyatomic anion containing a nonmetal covalently bonded to one or more oxygen atoms. (3.5)

oxygen toxicity A physiological condition caused by an increased level of oxygen in the blood, resulting in muscle twitching, tunnel vision, and convulsions. (5.6)

ozone O_3, an allotrope of oxygen that is a toxic blue diamagnetic gas with a strong odor. (22.7)

packing efficiency The percentage of volume of a unit cell occupied by the atoms, assumed to be spherical. (11.11)

paramagnetic The state of an atom or ion that contains unpaired electrons and is, therefore, attracted by an external magnetic field. (10.8)

partial pressure (P_n) The pressure due to any individual component in a gas mixture. (5.6)

parts by mass A unit for expressing solution concentration as the mass of the solute divided by the mass of the solution multiplied by a multiplication factor. (12.5)

parts by volume A unit for expressing solution concentration as the volume of the solute divided by the volume of the solution multiplied by a multiplication factor. (12.5)

parts per billion (ppb) A unit for expressing solution concentration in parts by mass where the multiplication factor is 10^9. (12.5)

parts per million (ppm) A unit for expressing solution concentration in parts by mass where the multiplication factor is 10^6. (12.5)

pascal (Pa) The SI unit of pressure, defined as 1 N/m^2. (5.2)

Pauli exclusion principle The principle that no two electrons in an atom can have the same four quantum numbers. (8.3)

penetrating power The ability of radiation to penetrate matter. (19.3)

penetration The phenomenon of some higher-level atomic orbitals having significant amounts of probability within the space occupied by orbitals of lower energy level. For example, the $2s$ orbital penetrates into the $1s$ orbital. (8.3)

peptide bond The bond that forms between the amine end of one amino acid and the carboxylic end of another. (21.4)

percent by mass A unit for expressing solution concentration in parts by mass with a multiplication factor of 100%. (12.5)

percent ionic character The ratio of a bond's actual dipole moment to the dipole moment it would have if the electron were transferred completely from one atom to the other, multiplied by 100%. (9.6)

percent ionization The concentration of ionized acid in a solution divided by the initial concentration of acid multiplied by 100%. (15.6)

percent yield The percentage of the theoretical yield of a chemical reaction that is actually produced; the ratio of the actual yield to the theoretical yield multiplied by 100%. (4.3)

periodic law A law based on the observation that when the elements are arranged in order of increasing mass, certain sets of properties recur periodically. (2.7)

periodic property A property of an element that is predictable based on an element's position in the periodic table. (8.1)

permanent dipole A permanent separation of charge; a molecule with a permanent dipole always has a slightly negative charge at one end and a slightly positive charge at the other. (11.3)

pH The negative log of the concentration of H_3O^+ in a solution; the pH scale is a compact way to specify the acidity of a solution. (15.4)

phase The sign of the amplitude of a wave; can be positive or negative. (7.6)

phase diagram A map of the phase of a substance as a function of pressure and temperature. (11.8)

phenyl group A benzene ring treated as a substituent. (20.7)

phosphine PH_3, a colorless, poisonous gas that smells like decaying fish and has an oxidation state of -3 for phosphorus. (22.6)

phospholipid Compound similar in structure to a triglyceride but with one fatty acid replaced by a phosphate group. (21.2)

phosphorescence The long-lived emission of light that sometimes follows the absorption of light by certain atoms and molecules. (19.2)

photoelectric effect The observation that many metals emit electrons when light falls upon them. (7.2)

photon (quantum) The smallest possible packet of electromagnetic radiation with an energy equal to $h\nu$. (7.2)

physical change A change that alters only the state or appearance of a substance but not its chemical composition. (1.4)

physical property A property that a substance displays without changing its chemical composition. (1.4)

pi (π) bond The bond that forms between two p orbitals that overlap side to side. (10.7)

p–n junctions Tiny areas in electronic circuits that have p-type semiconductors on one side and n-type on the other. (11.13)

polar covalent bond A covalent bond between two atoms with significantly different electronegativities, resulting in an uneven distribution of electron density. (9.6)

polyatomic ion An ion composed of two or more atoms. (3.5)

polydentate Describes ligands that donate more than one electron pair to the central metal. (24.3)

polymer A long chainlike molecule composed of repeating units called monomers. (20.14)

polypeptide A chain of amino acids joined together by peptide bonds. (21.4)

polyprotic acid An acid that contains more than one ionizable proton and releases them sequentially. (4.8, 15.9)

polysaccharide A long, chainlike molecule composed of many monosaccharide units bonded together. (21.3)

positron The particle released in positron emission; equal in mass to an electron but opposite in charge. (19.3)

positron emission The form of radioactive decay that occurs when an unstable nucleus emits a positron. (19.3)

positron emission tomography (PET) A specialized imaging technique that employs positron-emitting nuclides, such as fluorine-18, as a radiotracer. (19.12)

potential difference A measure of the difference in potential energy (usually in joules) per unit of charge (coulombs). (18.3)

potential energy The energy associated with the position or composition of an object. (1.5, 6.2)

powder metallurgy A process by which metallic components are made from powdered metal. (23.3)

precipitate A solid, insoluble ionic compound that forms in, and separates from, a solution. (4.6)

precipitation reaction A reaction in which a solid, insoluble product forms upon mixing two solutions. (4.6)

precision A term that refers to how close a series of measurements are to one another or how reproducible they are. (1.7)

prefix multipliers Multipliers that change the value of the unit by powers of 10. (1.6)

pressure A measure of force exerted per unit area; in chemistry, most commonly the force exerted by gas molecules as they strike the surfaces around them. (5.1)

pressure–volume work The work that occurs when a volume change takes place against an external pressure. (6.4)

primary structure The sequence of amino acids in a protein chain. (21.5)

primary valence The oxidation state on the central metal atom in a complex ion. (24.3)

principal level (shell) The group of orbitals with the same value of n. (7.5)

principal quantum number (n) An integer that specifies the overall size and energy of an orbital. The higher the quantum number n, the greater the average distance between the electron and the nucleus and the higher its energy. (7.5)

probability density The probability (per unit volume) of finding the electron at a point in space as expressed by a three-dimensional plot of the wave function squared (ψ^2). (7.6)

products The substances produced in a chemical reaction; they appear on the right-hand side of a chemical equation. (3.10)

proton A positively charged subatomic particle found in the nucleus of an atom. (2.5)

p-type semiconductor A semiconductor that employs positively charged "holes" in the valence band as the charge carriers. (11.13)

pure substance A substance composed of only one type of atom or molecule. (1.3)

pyrometallurgy A technique of extractive metallurgy in which heat is used to extract a metal from its mineral. (23.3)

pyrosilicates Silicates in which two SO_4^{4-} tetrahedral ions share a corner. (22.3)

pyroxenes Silicates in which SO_4^{4-} tetrahedral ions bond together to form chains. (22.3)

qualitative analysis A systematic way to determine the ions present in an unknown solution. (16.7)

quantitative analysis A systematic way to determine the amounts of substances in a solution or mixture. (16.7)

quantum number One of four interrelated numbers that determine the shape and energy of orbitals, as specified by a solution of the Schrödinger equation. (7.5)

quantum-mechanical model A model that explains the behavior of absolutely small particles such as electrons and photons. (7.1)

quartz A silicate crystal which has a formula unit of SiO_2. (22.3)

quaternary structure The way that subunits fit together in a multimeric protein. (21.5)

racemic mixture An equimolar mixture of two optical isomers that does not rotate the plane of polarization of light at all. (20.3)

radial distribution function A function that represents the total probability of finding an electron within a thin spherical shell at a distance r from the nucleus. (7.6)

radio waves The form of electromagnetic radiation with the longest wavelengths and smallest energy. (7.2)

radioactive The state of those unstable atoms that emit subatomic particles or high-energy electromagnetic radiation. (19.1)

radioactivity The emission of subatomic particles or high-energy electromagnetic radiation by the unstable nuclei of certain atoms. (2.5, 19.1)

radiocarbon dating A form of radiometric dating based on the C-14 isotope. (19.6)

radiometric dating A technique used to estimate the age of rocks, fossils, or artifacts that depends on the presence of radioactive isotopes and their predictable decay with time. (19.6)

radiotracer A radioactive nuclide that has been attached to a compound or introduced into a mixture in order to track the movement of the compound or mixture within the body. (19.12)

random coils Sections of a protein's secondary structure that have less regular patterns than α-helixes or β-pleated sheets. (21.5)

random error Error that has equal probability of being too high or too low. (1.7)

Raoult's law An equation used to determine the vapor pressure of a solution; $P_{soln} = X_{solv}P^\circ_{solv}$. (12.6)

rate constant (k) A constant of proportionality in the rate law. (13.3)

rate law A relationship between the rate of a reaction and the concentration of the reactants. (13.3)

rate-determining step The step in a reaction mechanism that occurs much more slowly than any of the other steps. (13.6)

reactants The starting substances of a chemical reaction; they appear on the left-hand side of a chemical equation. (3.10)

reaction intermediates Species that are formed in one step of a reaction mechanism and consumed in another. (13.6)

reaction mechanism A series of individual chemical steps by which an overall chemical reaction occurs. (13.6)

reaction order (n) A value in the rate law that determines how the rate depends on the concentration of the reactants. (13.3)

reaction quotient (Q_c) The ratio, at any point in the reaction, of the concentrations of the products of a reaction raised to their stoichiometric coefficients to the concentrations of the reactants raised to their stoichiometric coefficients. (14.7)

recrystallization A technique used to purify solids in which the solid is put into hot solvent until the solution is saturated; when the solution cools, the purified solute comes out of solution. (12.4)

red phosphorus An allotrope of phosphorus similar in structure to white phosphorus but with one of the bonds between two phosphorus atoms in the tetrahedron broken; red phosphorus is more stable than white. (22.6)

reducing agent A substance that causes the reduction of another substance; a reducing agent loses electrons and is oxidized. (4.9)

reduction The gaining of one or more electrons; also the gaining of hydrogen or the loss of oxygen. (4.9)

refine To purify, particularly a metal. (23.3)

refining A process in which the crude material is purified. (23.3)

rem A unit of the dose of radiation exposure that stands for roentgen equivalent man, where a roentgen is defined as the amount of radiation that produces 2.58×10^{-4} C of charge per kg of air. (19.11)

resonance hybrid The actual structure of a molecule that is intermediate between two or more resonance structures. (9.8)

resonance structures Two or more valid Lewis structures that are shown with double-headed arrows between them to indicate that the actual structure of the molecule is intermediate between them. (9.8)

reversible As applied to a reaction, the ability to proceed in either the forward or the reverse direction. (14.2)

reversible reaction A reaction that achieves the theoretical limit with respect to free energy and will change direction upon an infinitesimally small change in a variable (such as temperature or pressure) related to the reaction. (17.7)

roasting Heating that causes a chemical reaction between a furnace atmosphere and a mineral in order to process ores. (23.3)

salt An ionic compound formed in a neutralization reaction by the replacement of an H^+ ion from the acid with a cation from the base. (4.8)

salt bridge An inverted, U-shaped tube containing a strong electrolyte such as KNO_3 that connects the two half-cells, allowing a flow of ions that neutralizes the charge buildup. (18.3)

saturated fat A triglyceride with no double bonds in the hydrocarbon chain; saturated fats tend to be solid at room temperature. (21.2)

saturated hydrocarbon A hydrocarbon containing no double bonds in the carbon chain. (20.4)

saturated solution A solution in which the dissolved solute is in dynamic equilibrium with any undissolved solute; any added solute will not dissolve. (12.4)

scientific law A brief statement or equation that summarizes past observations and predicts future ones. (1.2)

scientific method An approach to acquiring knowledge about the natural world that begins with observations and leads to the formation of testable hypotheses. (1.2)

scintillation counter A device for the detection of radioactivity using a material that emits ultraviolet or visible light in response to excitation by energetic particles. (19.5)

second (s) The SI standard unit of time, defined as the duration of 9,192,631,770 periods of the radiation emitted from a certain transition in a cesium-133 atom. (1.6)

second law of thermodynamics A law stating that for any spontaneous process, the entropy of the universe increases ($\Delta S_{univ} > 0$). (17.3)

secondary structure The regular periodic or repeating patterns in the arrangement of protein chains. (21.5)

secondary valence The number of molecules or ions directly bound to the metal atom in a complex ion; also called the *coordination number*. (24.3)

seesaw The molecular geometry of a molecule with trigonal bipyramidal electron geometry and one lone pair in an axial position. (10.3)

selective precipitation A process involving the addition of a reagent to a solution that forms a precipitate with one of the dissolved ions but not the others. (16.6)

semiconductor A material with intermediate electrical conductivity that can be changed and controlled. (2.7)

semipermeable membrane A membrane that selectively allows some substances to pass through but not others. (12.6)

shielding The effect on an electron of repulsion by electrons in lower-energy orbitals that screen it from the full effects of nuclear charge. (8.3)

sigma (σ) bond The resulting bond that forms between a combination of any two *s*, *p*, or hybridized orbitals that overlap end to end. (10.7)

significant figures (significant digits) In any reported measurement, the non-place-holding digits that indicate the precision of the measured quantity. (1.7)

silica A silicate crystal which has a formula unit of SiO_2, also called *quartz*. (22.3)

silicates Covalent atomic solids that contain silicon, oxygen, and various metal atoms. (22.3)

simple cubic A unit cell that consists of a cube with one atom at each corner. (11.11)

slag In pyrometallurgy, the waste liquid solution that is formed between the flux and gangue; usually a silicate material. (23.3)

smelting A form of roasting in which the product is liquefied, which aids in the separation. (23.3)

solid A state of matter in which atoms or molecules are packed close to one another in fixed locations with definite volume. (1.3)

solubility The amount of a substance that will dissolve in a given amount of solvent. (12.2)

solubility product constant (K_{sp}) The equilibrium expression for a chemical equation representing the dissolution of a slightly to moderately soluble ionic compound. (16.5)

soluble Able to dissolve to a significant extent, usually in water. (4.5)

solute The minority component of a solution. (4.4, 12.1)

solution A homogenous mixture of two substances. (4.4, 12.1)

solvent The majority component of a solution. (4.4, 12.1)

space-filling molecular model A representation of a molecule that shows how the atoms fill the space between them. (3.3)

specific heat capacity (C_s) The amount of heat required to raise the temperature of 1 g of a substance by 1 °C. (6.4)

spectator ion Ions in a complete ionic equation that do not participate in the reaction and therefore remain in solution. (4.7)

spin quantum number, m_s The fourth quantum number, which denotes the electron's spin as either $^1/_2$ (up arrow) or $-^1/_2$ (down arrow). (8.3)

spontaneous process A process that occurs without ongoing outside intervention. (17.2)

square planar The molecular geometry of a molecule with octahedral electron geometry and two lone pairs. (10.3)

square pyramidal The molecular geometry of a molecule with octahedral electron geometry and one lone pair. (10.3)

standard cell potential (standard emf) (E°_{cell}) The cell potential for a system in standard states (solute concentration of 1 M and gaseous reactant partial pressure of 1 atm). (18.3)

standard change in free energy (ΔG°_{rxn}) The change in free energy for a process when all reactants and products are in their standard states. (17.7)

standard electrode potential The potential of an electrode in a half-cell. (18.4)

standard enthalpy change (ΔH°) The change in enthalpy for a process when all reactants and products are in their standard states. (6.9)

standard enthalpy of formation (ΔH°_f) The change in enthalpy when 1 mol of a compound forms from its constituent elements in their standard states. (6.9)

standard entropy change (ΔS_{rxn}) The change in entropy for a process when all reactants and products are in their standard states. (17.6)

standard entropy change for a reaction (ΔS°_{rxn}) The change in entropy for a process in which all reactants and products are in their standard states. (17.6)

standard heat of formation The change in enthalpy when 1 mol of a compound forms from its constituent elements in their standard states. (6.9)

standard hydrogen electrode (SHE) The half-cell consisting of an inert platinum electrode immersed in 1 M HCl with hydrogen gas at 1 atm bubbling through the solution; used as the standard of a cell potential of zero. (18.4)

standard molar entropy (S°) A measure of the energy dispersed into one mole of a substance at a particular temperature. (17.6)

standard state For a gas the standard state is the pure gas at a pressure of exactly 1 atm; for a liquid or solid the standard state is the pure substance in its most stable form at a pressure of 1 atm and the temperature of interest (often taken to be 25 °C); for a substance in solution the standard state is a concentration of exactly 1 M. (6.9)

standard temperature and pressure (STP) The conditions of $T = 0$ °C (273 K) and $P = 1$ atm; used primarily in reference to a gas, also known as standard conditions. (5.5)

starch A polysaccharide that consists of glucose units bonded together by α-glycosidic linkages; the main energy storage medium for plants. (21.3)

state A classification of the form of matter as a solid, liquid, or gas. (1.3)

state function A function whose value depends only on the state of the system, not on how the system got to that state. (6.3)

stereoisomers Molecules in which the atoms are bonded in the same order, but have a different spatial arrangement. (20.3, 24.4)

steroid A lipid composed of four fused hydrocarbon rings. (21.2)

stock solution A highly concentrated form of a solution used in laboratories to make less concentrated solutions via dilution. (4.4)

stoichiometery The numerical relationships between amounts of reactants and products in a balanced chemical equation. (4.2)

strong acid An acid that completely ionizes in solution. (4.5, 15.4)

strong base A base that completely dissociates in solution. (15.7)

strong electrolyte A substance that completely dissociates into ions when dissolved in water. (4.5)

strong force Of the four fundamental forces of physics, the one that is the strongest but acts over the shortest distance; the strong force is responsible for holding the protons and neutrons together in the nucleus of an atom. (19.4)

strong-field complex A complex ion in which the crystal field splitting is large. (24.5)

structural formula A molecular formula that shows how the atoms in a molecule are connected or bonded to each other. (3.3, 20.3)

structural isomers Molecules with the same molecular formula but different structures. (20.3, 24.4)

sublevel (subshell) Those orbitals in the same principal level with the same value of n and l. (7.5)

sublimation The phase transition from solid to gas. (11.6)

substitutional alloy An alloy in which one metal atom substitutes for another in the crystal structure. (23.4)

substrate The reactant molecule of a biochemical reaction that binds to an enzyme at the active site. (13.7)

supersaturated solution An unstable solution in which more than the equilibrium amount of solute is dissolved. (12.4)

surface tension The energy required to increase the surface area of a liquid by a unit amount; responsible for the tendency of liquids to minimize their surface area, giving rise to a membrane-like surface. (11.4)

surroundings In thermodynamics, everything in the universe which exists outside the system under investigation. (6.2)

system In thermodynamics, the portion of the universe which is singled out for investigation. (6.1)

systematic error Error that tends towards being consistently either too high or too low. (1.7)

systematic name An official name for a compound, based on well-established rules, that can be determined by examining its chemical structure. (3.5)

temperature A measure of the average kinetic energy of the atoms or molecules that compose a sample of matter. (1.6)

termolecular An elementary step of a reaction in which three particles collide and go on to form products. (13.6)

tertiary structure The large-scale bends and folds produced by interactions between the R groups of amino acids that are separated by large distances in the linear sequence of a protein chain. (21.5)

tetrahedral geometry The molecular geometry of five atoms with 109.5° bond angles. (10.2)

tetrahedral hole A space that exists directly above the center point of three closest packed metal atoms in one plane, and a fourth metal located directly above the center point in the adjacent plane in a crystal lattice. (23.4)

theoretical yield The greatest possible amount of product that can be made in a chemical reaction based on the amount of limiting reactant. (4.3)

theory A proposed explanation for observations and laws based on well-established and tested hypotheses, that presents a model of the way nature works and predicts behavior beyond the observations and laws on which it was based. (1.2)

thermal energy A type of kinetic energy associated with the temperature of an object, arising from the motion of individual atoms or molecules in the object; see also *heat*. (1.5, 6.2)

thermal equilibrium The point at which there is no additional net transfer of heat between a system and its surroundings. (6.4)

thermochemistry The study of the relationship between chemistry and energy. (6.1)

thermodynamics The general study of energy and its interconversions. (6.3)

third law of thermodynamics The law stating that the entropy of a perfect crystal at absolute zero (0 K) is zero. (17.6)

titration A laboratory procedure in which a substance in a solution of known concentration is reacted with another substance in a solution of unknown concentration in order to determine the unknown concentration; see also *acid–base titration*. (4.8)

transition elements (transition metals) Those elements found in the d block of the periodic table whose properties tend to be less predictable based simply on their position in the table. (2.7)

transmutation The transformation of one element into another as a result of nuclear reactions. (19.10)

triglyceride Triesters composed of glycerol with three fatty acids attached. (21.2)

trigonal bipyramidal The molecular geometry of six atoms with 120° bond angles between the three equatorial electron groups and 90° bond angles between the two axial electron groups and the trigonal plane. (10.2)

trigonal planar geometry The molecular geometry of four atoms with 120° bond angles in a plane. (10.2)

trigonal pyramidal The molecular geometry of a molecule with tetrahedral electron geometry and one lone pair. (10.3)

triple bond The bond that forms when three electron pairs are shared between two atoms. (9.5)

triple point The unique set of conditions at which all three phases of a substance are equally stable and in equilibrium. (11.8)

triprotic acid An acid that contains three ionizable protons. (15.4)

T-shaped The molecular geometry of a molecule with trigonal bipyramidal electron geometry and two lone pairs in axial positions. (10.3)

two-phase region The region between the two phases in a metal alloy phase diagram, where the amount of each phase depends upon the composition of the alloy. (23.4)

Tyndall effect The scattering of light by a colloidal dispersion. (12.8)

ultraviolet (UV) radiation Electromagnetic radiation with slightly smaller wavelengths than visible light. (7.2)

unimolecular Describes a reaction that involves only one particle that goes on to form products. (13.6)

unit cell The smallest divisible unit of a crystal that, when repeated in three dimensions, reproduces the entire crystal lattice. (11.11)

units Standard quantities used to specify measurements. (1.6)

unsaturated fat A triglyceride with one or more double bonds in the hydrocarbon chain; unsaturated fats tend to be liquid at room temperature. (21.2)

unsaturated hydrocarbon A hydrocarbon that includes one or more double or triple bonds. (20.5)

unsaturated solution A solution containing less than the equilibrium amount of solute; any added solute will dissolve until equilibrium is reached. (12.4)

valence bond theory An advanced model of chemical bonding in which electrons reside in quantum-mechanical orbitals localized on individual atoms that are a hybridized blend of standard atomic orbitals; chemical bonds result from an overlap of these orbitals. (10.6)

valence electrons Those electrons that are important in chemical bonding. For main-group elements, the valence electrons are those in the outermost principal energy level. (8.4)

valence shell electron pair repulsion (VSEPR) theory A theory that allows prediction of the shapes of molecules based on the idea that electrons—either as lone pairs or as bonding pairs—repel one another. (10.2)

van der Waals equation The extrapolation of the ideal gas law that considers the effects of intermolecular forces and particle volume in a nonideal gas: $P + a\left(\dfrac{n}{V}\right)^2 \times (V - nb) = nRT$ (5.9)

van der Waals radius (nonbonding atomic radius) Defined as one-half the distance between the centers of adjacent, nonbonding atoms in a crystal. (8.6)

van't Hoff factor (i) The ratio of moles of particles in a solution to moles of formula units dissolved. (12.7)

vapor pressure The partial pressure of a vapor in dynamic equilibrium with its liquid. (5.6, 11.5)

vapor pressure lowering (ΔP) The difference in vapor pressure between a pure solvent and a solution of the solvent $\Delta P = P^\circ_{solvent} - P_{solution}$ (12.6)

vaporization The phase transition from liquid to gas. (11.5)

viscosity A measure of the resistance of a liquid to flow. (11.4)

visible light Those frequencies of electromagnetic radiation that can be detected by the human eye. (7.2)

volatile Tending to vaporize easily. (1.3, 11.5)

voltaic (galvanic) cell An electrochemical cell which produces electrical current from a spontaneous chemical reaction. (18.3)

volume (V) A measure of space. Any unit of length, when cubed (raised to the third power), becomes a unit of volume. (1.6)

washing soda The hydrated crystal of sodium carbonate, $Na_2CO_3 \cdot 10\ H_2O$. (22.5)

wave function (ψ) A mathematical function that describes the wavelike nature of the electron. (7.5)

wavelength (λ) The distance between adjacent crests of a wave. (7.2)

weak acid An acid that does not completely ionize in water. (4.5, 15.4)

weak base A base that only partially ionizes in water. (15.7)

weak electrolyte A substance that does not completely ionize in water and only weakly conducts electricity in solution. (4.5)

weak-field complex A complex ion in which the crystal field splitting is small. (24.5)

white phosphorus An unstable allotrope of phosphorus consisting of P_4 molecules in a tetrahedral shape, with the phosphorus atoms at the corners of the tetrahedron. (22.6)

work (w) The result of a force acting through a distance. (1.5, 6.2)

X-rays Electromagnetic radiation with wavelengths slightly longer than those of gamma rays; used to image bones and internal organs. (7.2)

X-ray diffraction A powerful laboratory technique that allows for the determination of the arrangement of atoms in a crystal and the measuring of the distance between them. (11.10)

Photo Credits

Chapter 1 Page 2 top left: Ed Reschke/Peter Arnold, Inc. Page 2 top center: Ken Eward/BioGrafx. Page 3 top: Jacques Louis David French, 1748–1825. "Antoine-Laurent Lavoisier 1743–1794 and His Wife Marie-Anne-Pierrette Paulze, 1758–1836", 1788, oil on canvas, H. 102-1/4 in. W. 76-5/8 in. 259.7 × 194.6 cm. The Metropolitan Museum of Art, Purchase, Mr. and Mrs. Charles Wrightsman Gift, in honor of Everett Fahy, 1977. 1977.10 Image copyright © The Metropolitan Museum of Art/Art Resource, NY. Page 6 top left: Fotolia. Page 7 left: The Goodyear Tire & Rubber Company. Page 7 center left: Fotolia. Page 7 center right: Istockphoto. Page 7 right: TH Foto-Werbung/Phototake NYC. Page 9 bottom right: Michael Dalton/Fundamental Photographs, NYC. Page 9 bottom left: Getty Images. Page 10 top: Yoav Levy/Phototake NYC. Page 10 center: Renn Sminkey/Pearson Science. Page 10 bottom: Lon C. Diehl/PhotoEdit Inc. Page 13 bottom: NASA Earth Observing System. Page 14 top left: Dorling Kindersley Media Library. Page 14 center left: Getty Images. Page 14 bottom: Richard Megna/Fundamental Photographs, NYC. Page 16 left: Getty Images. Page 16 center: Istockphoto. Page 16 right: Shutterstock. Page 20 left: Michael Klein/Peter Arnold, Inc. Page 20 right: ISM/Phototake NYC. Page 21: Richard Megna/Fundamental Photographs, NYC. Page 37 top right and left: Richard Megna/Fundamental Photographs, NYC. Page 37 bottom: Istockphoto. Page 38 top: Warren Rosenberg/Fundamental Photographs, NYC. Page 38 bottom left: Richard Megna/Fundamental Photographs, NYC. Page 38 bottom center & right: Warren Rosenberg/Fundamental Photographs, NYC. Page 40: NASA. Chapter 2 Page 44 left: Veeco Instruments, Inc. Page 44 right: IBM Research, Almaden Research Center Unauthorized use is prohibited. Page 46 left: Charles D. Winters/Photo Researchers. Page 46 center: Charles D. Winters/Photo Researchers. Page 46 right: Shutterstock. Page 49: Richard Megna/Fundamental Photographs, NYC. Page 53: Richard Megna/Fundamental Photographs, NYC. Page 54 top: Getty Images. Page 54 bottom left: Getty Images. Page 54 bottom right: Pearson Education/Modern Curriculum Press. Page 55: Library of Congress. Page 58: NASA. Page 60 top: Stamp from the private collection of Professor C. M. Lang, photography by Gary J. Shulfer, University of Wisconsin, Stevens Point. "Russia: #3607 1969"; Scott Standard Postage Stamp Catalogue, Scott Pub. Co., Sidney, Ohio. Page 60, 1st image from left: Courtesy of Wikimedia Commons. Page 60, 2nd from left: Charles D. Winters/Photo Researchers. Page 60, 3rd from left: Shutterstock. Page 60, 4th from left: Clive Streeter/Dorling Kindersley Media Library. Page 60, 5th from left: Tom Bochsler/Pearson Education/PH College. Page 60, 6th from left: Wikipedia, The Free Encyclopedia. Page 60, 7th from left: Harry Taylor/Dorling Kindersley Media Library. Page 60, 8th from left: Mark A. Schneider/Photo Researchers. Page 60, 9th from left: Istockphoto. Page 60, 10th from left: Charles D. Winters/Photo Researchers. Page 60, 11th from left: Perennou Nuridsany/Photo Researchers. Page 61 top: Richard Megna/Fundamental Photographs, NYC. Page 61 bottom: Martyn F. Chillmaid/Photo Researchers. Page 62 top: Charles D. Winters/Photo Researchers. Page 62 bottom: Charles D. Winters/Photo Researchers. Page 66 top: Richard Megna/Fundamental Photographs, NYC. Page 66 bottom: Dorling Kindersley Media Library. Page 76: IBM Research, Almaden Research Center. Chapter 3 Page 80 top: Istockphoto. Page 81 left: Richard Megna/Fundamental Photographs, NYC. Page 81 center: Charles Falco/Photo Researchers. Page 81 right: Charles D. Winters/Photo Researchers. Page 85: Charles D. Winters/Photo Researchers. Page 86 top right: Charles Falco/Photo Researchers, Inc. Page 86: Michael Dalton/Fundamental Photographs, NYC. Page 87 left: Sindey Moulds/Photo Researchers. Page 87 right: Basement Stock/Alamy. Page 88 top left: Renn Sminkey/Pearson Science. Page 88 top right: CDV LLC/Pearson Science. Page 92: Yoav Levy/Phototake, NYC. Page 94: Shutterstock. Page 95: Richard Megna/Fundamental Photographs, NYC. Page 96 bottom: Oliver Strewe/Getty Images. Page 96 center: Vanessa Miles/Environmental Images. Page 100: NASA/Goddard Space Flight Center. Page 103 top: Richard Megna/Fundamental Photographs, NYC. Page 105: David R. Frazier Photolibrary, Inc./Alamy. Page 115 top: David Young-Wolff/PhotoEdit Inc. Page 116: CDV LLC/Pearson Science. Chapter 4 Page 139: Robert W. Ginn/PhotoEdit. Page 148: Richard Megna/Fundamental Photographs, NYC. Page 149: Richard Megna/Fundamental Photographs, NYC. Page 150: Martyn F. Chillmaid/Photo Researchers. Page 151: Dorling Kindersley Media Library. Page 152: Richard Megna/Fundamental Photographs, NYC. Page 155: Chip Clark. Page 156: Richard Megna/Fundamental Photographs, NYC. Page 157–161: Richard Megna/Fundamental Photographs, NYC. Page 162 left: Tom Bochsler/Pearson Education/PH College. Page 162 right: Charles D. Winters/Photo Researchers, Inc. Page 163: Richard Megna/Fundamental Photographs, NYC. Page 168: Corbis. Chapter 5 Page 183: Patrick Watson/Pearson Education. Page 188 top: Shutterstock. Page 188 bottom: Dorling Kindersley Media Library. Page 191: CDV LLC/Pearson Science. Page 220: NASA. Page 227: Tom Bochsler/Pearson Education/PH College. Chapter 6 Page 235: Image taken from the Historical and Interpretive Collections of The Franklin Institute Science Museum, Philadelphia, PA. Page 241: Getty Images. Page 250 left: Tom Bochsler/Pearson Education/PH College. Page 250 right: Royalty-Free/Corbis RF. Page 261: Richard Megna/Fundamental Photographs, NYC. Page 266 bottom left: National Geophysical Data Center. Page 266 bottom center: Sandia National Laboratories. Page 266 bottom right: Jacobs Stock Photography/Getty Images. Page 266 top right: Courtesy of Honda. Page 266 center: Getty Images. Page 272: Istockphoto. Page 273: Charles D. Winters/Photo Researchers. Chapter 7 Page 279: Yegor Piaskovsky/Istockphoto. Page 280 left: Comstock/Sub. Page 280 right: Shutterstock. Page 282 top left: Rob Crandall/ Stock Connection. Page 282 top right: David Collier/Getty Images. Page 282 center: Yoav Levy/Phototake NYC. Page 282 bottom: Istockphoto. Page 283 top: Bob Richards/ Sierra Pacific Innovations Corporation. Page 283 bottom: Shutterstock. Page 288 top: Shutterstock. Page 288 bottom: Tom Bochsler/Pearson Education. Page 289 center: Wabash Instrument Corp/Fundamental Photographs, NYC. Page 290 top: mjs1973/ Istockphoto. Page 290 bottom: American National Standards Institute. Page 291 top: Jerry Mason/Photo Researchers. Page 291 bottom: American National Standards Institute. Page 295: Segre Collection/Photo Researchers. Page 296 top: Stephen Dunn/ Getty Images. Page 296 bottom: Associated Press. Chapter 8 Page 316: University of Pennsylvania, Van Pelt Library. Page 317 left: Charles D. Winters/Photo Researchers. Page 317 right: Richard Megna/Fundamental Photographs, NYC. Page 345, 1 from left: Courtesy of Wikipedia. Page 345, 2 from left: Richard Megna/Fundamental Photographs, NYC. Page 345, 3 from left: Charles D. Winters/Photo Researchers. Page 345, 4 from left: Wikipedia, The Free Encyclopedia - was Heilman. Page 345, 5 from left: Charles D. Winters/Photo Researchers. Page 345, 6 from left: Steve Gorton/Dorling Kindersley Media Library. Page 345, 7 from left: Charles D. Winters/Photo Researchers. Page 345, 8 from left: Edward Kinsman/Photo Researchers. Page 345, 9 from left: Shutterstock. Page 345, 10 from left: Dorling Kindersley Media Library. Page 345, 11 from left: Charles D. Winters/Photo Researchers. Page 345, 12 from left: Dorling Kindersley Media Library. Page 348 top: Andrew Lambert Photography/SPL/Photo Researchers. Page 348 bottom: Richard Megna/Fundamental Photographs, NYC. Page 349: Richard Megna/ Fundamental Photographs, NYC. Page 350: Barbara Galati/Phototake NYC. Page 351: Dan McCoy/Rainbow Image Library. Chapter 9 Page 360: Call Number 13:596. Courtesy of The Bancroft Library, University of California, Berkeley. Page 361 top left: Richard M. Busch. Page 361 top right: Getty Images. Page 361 bottom: Dorling Kindersley Media Library. Page 368: Richard Megna/Fundamental Photographs, NYC. Page 369: Shutterstock. Page 383 top: Jorge Uzon/Getty Images. Page 383 bottom: Michael Newman/PhotoEdit. Page 391: Istockphoto. Chapter 10 Page 402, 403: CDV LLC/Pearson Science. Page 416 left: Kip Peticolas/Fundamental Photographs, NYC. Page 416 right: Richard Megna/Fundamental Photographs, NYC. Page 416 bottom: Istockphoto. Page 441: Richard Megna/Fundamental Photographs, NYC. Chapter 11 Page 455 bottom: Andrew Syred/Photo Researchers. Page 468 top: stammphoto.com LLC. Page 468 bottom: Richard Megna/Fundamental Photographs, NYC. Page 469 top: NASA/Johnson Space Center. Page 469 bottom: Renn Sminkey/Pearson Science. Page 470 top: Photos of StatSpin products provided by StatSpin Inc., a wholly owned subsidiary of IRIS, Chatsworth, CA. Page 470 center: Ken Kay/Fundamental Photographs, NYC. Page 470 bottom: Sinclair Stammers/Photo Researchers. Page 472: Istockphoto. Page 475: Michael Dalton/Fundamental Photographs, NYC. Page 479: Dr. P.A. Hamley, University of Nottingham. Page 480: Alamy. Page 481: Charles D. Winters/Photo Researchers. Page 482 left: CDV LLC/Pearson Science. Page 482 center & right: Shutterstock. Page 487: NASA/Jet Propulsion Laboratory. Page 488 top: CDV LLC/Pearson Science. Page 488 bottom: Shehzad Noorani/Peter Arnold, Inc. Page 489 top: Shutterstock. Page 489 bottom: Ted Kinsman/Photo Researchers. Page 491: CSHL Archives/Peter Arnold, Inc. Page 497, 1 from left: Photos.com. Page 497, 2 from left: Andrew Syred/Photo Researchers. Page 497, 3 from left: Dr. Mark J. Winter. Page 497, 4 & 5 from left: Shutterstock. Page 499 left: Charles D. Winters/Photo Researchers. Page 499 right: Astrid & Hanns-Frieder Michler/Science Photo Library/Photo Researchers. Page 500 left: Dorling Kindersley Media Library. Page 500 right: Wikipedia, The Free Encyclopedia. Page 506 left: Dorling Kindersley Media Library. Page 506 right: Professor Nivaldo Jose Tro. Chapter 12 Page 514 top: Shutterstock. Page 514 bottom: Charles D. Winters/Photo Researchers Inc. Page 524–525: Richard Megna/Fundamental Photographs, NYC. Page 528 top: T. Orban/Corbis. Page 528 bottom: "Nyos degassing system conceived, designed and manufactured by a French Company, Data Environment and the University of Savoie, France" Courtesy J. C. Sabroux. Page 532 top: Robert Brook/Alamy. Page 532 bottom: Paul A. Souders/Corbis. Page 535 top: Associated Press. Page 542: Lon C. Diehl/PhotEdit Inc. Page 545: Shutterstock. Page 549: Sam Singer. Page 550 left: FURGOLLE/Corbis. Page 550 right: Scott Camazine/Alamy. Page 550 bottom: Richard Megna/Fundamental Photographs, NYC. Page 551, 1 from top: Istockphoto. Page 551, 2 from top: Shutterstock. Page 551, 3, 4, 5 from top: Istockphoto. Page 552 left: Image created using the LightWorks rendering engine, Copyright LightWork Design, www.lightworkdesign.com. Page 552 right: Kip Peticolas/ Fundamental Photographs, NYC. Chapter 13 Page 595: NASA/John F. Kennedy Space Center. Page 596: The Ozone Hole Inc. Page 599: Ken Eward/BioGrafx. Chapter 14 Page 614: Ken Eward/BioGrafx. Page 620: Eye of Science/Photo Researchers. Page 647: Fundamental Photographs, NYC. Chapter 15 Page 661 top: Dorling Kindersley Media Library. Page 661 bottom left: Istockphoto. Page 661 bottom right: Getty Images. Page 662: Richard Megna/Fundamental Photographs, NYC. Page 672: CNRI/Photo Researchers. Page 686: Richard Megna/Fundamental Photographs, NYC. Page 702 left: Adam Hart-Davis/Photo Researchers. Page 702 right: Ken Sherman/Phototake NYC. Page 709: Mark Edwards/Peter Arnold, Inc. Chapter 16 Page 716: Richard Megna/ Fundamental Photographs, NYC. Page 728: Steve Dunwell/Getty Images. Page 729: Richard Megna/Fundamental Photographs, NYC. Page 741, 742: Tom Bochsler/ Pearson Education. Page 745 left: Bernhard Edmaier/Photo Researchers. Page 745 right: Sheila Terry/Photo Researchers. Page 748: David Muench/Corbis. Page 749 top: Richard

Megna/Fundamental Photographs, NYC. Page 749 bottom: Charles D. Winters/Photo Researchers. Page 754 top: Charles D. Winters/Photo Researchers. Page 754 bottom: Jerry Mason/Photo Researchers. Page 757: Richard Megna/Fundamental Photographs, NYC. **Chapter 17** Page 770 top: Eryrie/Alamy Images. Page 770 bottom: Fotolia. Page 771 top row: Getty Images. Page 771 center row left: James King-Holmes/Photo Researchers. Page 771 center row center: Getty Images. Page 771 center row right: Istockphoto. Page 771 bottom row left: Courtesy of Siemans. Page 771 bottom row right: Getty Images. Page 771 bottom left: Dorling Kindersley Media Library. Page 771 bottom right: Corbis. Page 772 left: Istockphoto. Page 772 right: Courtesy of Wikipedia. Page 773: Getty Images. Page 774 top: John Lamb/Getty Images. Page 774 bottom: Richard Megna/Fundamental Photographs, NYC. Page 775: Frantisek Zboray. Page 779: Fotolia. Page 799: Getty Images. **Chapter 18** Page 816 top: Carla Browning/University of Alaska Fairbanks. Page 816 bottom: Couresty of Honda. Page 820: Richard Megna/Fundamental Photographs, NYC. Page 821: Alejandro Diaz Diez/age fotostock. Page 831: Richard Megna/Fundamental Photographs, NYC. Page 841: Dorling Kindersley Media Library. Page 842: CDV LLC/Pearson Science. Page 844: China Images/Getty Images. Page 848: Charles D. Winters/Photo Researchers. Page 853 top: John Mead/Photo Researchers. Page 853 center: Donovan Reese/Getty Images. Page 853 bottom: Getty Images. Page 854 top: Istockphoto. Page 854 bottom: Renn Sminkey/Pearson Science. **Chapter 19** Page 866 top: Istockphoto. Page 866 bottom: Photo Researchers. Page 867 top: Getty Images. Page 867 bottom: Klaus Guldbrandsen/Photo Researchers. Page 874: Yoav Levy/Phototake NYC. Page 875: Hank Morgan/Photo Researchers. Page 879 top: R Sheridan/The Ancient Art & Architecture Collection Ltd. Page 879 bottom: Istockphoto. Page 881: Associated Press. Page 883: "Otto Hahn, A Scientific Autobiography", Charles Scribner's Sons, New York, 1966, courtesy AIP Emilio Segre Visual Archives. Page 884: Getty Images. Page 885 top: Franklin D. Roosevelt Library. Page 885 bottom: Istockphoto. Page 886: Associated Press. Page 889: General Atomics MS 15–124. Page 890: Hulton Archives/Getty Images. Page 891 top: David Parker/Photo Researchers. Page 891 bottom: Fermilab Visual Media Services. Page 894: CNRI/

Phototake, NYC. Page 895 top: Wellcome Dept. of Cognitive Neurology/Science Photo Library/Photo Researchers. Page 895 center: Centre Oscar Lambret/Photo Researchers. Page 895 bottom: Cordelia Molloy/Photo Researchers. Page 901: Barbara Galati/Phototake, NYC. **Chapter 20** Page 904: CDV LLC/Pearson Science. Page 905: Photos.com. Page 916: Istockphoto. Page 917: Fotolia. Page 922: maxwell-artandphoto.com. Page 931: Shutterstock. Page 932: Dorling Kindersley Media Library. Page 934 top: Istockphoto. Page 934 bottom: Shutterstock. Page 937 left: Marco Polo/Phototake, NYC. Page 937 right: Jupiter Images. Page 939: Second Chance Armor. **Chapter 21** Page 956 top: maxwellartandphoto.com. Page 956 bottom: Dorling Kindersley Media Library. Page 957: maxwellartandphoto.com. Page 967: Food Features/Alamy Images. Page 969: Oliver Meckes & Nicole Ottawa/Photo Researchers. Page 974: Adrian T. Sumner/Getty Images. Page 975: National Cancer Institute. Page 977: Istockphoto. **Chapter 22** Page 992 top: SciMAT/Photo Researchers. Page 992 bottom: Chip Clark. Page 998 top: Chris Sorensen/Corbis. Page 998 bottom: Shutterstock. Page 999: Y. Shirai/Rice University Office of News and Media Relations. Page 1000: From Metals Handbook, 9th Edition, Volume 9: Metallurgy and Microstructures, American Society for Metals, Metals Park, Ohio, 1985. Page 1001: Veer. Page 1008: Dudley Foster/Woods Hole Oceanographic Institution. Page 1011 top: Chris Eisenger. Page 1011 center & bottom: Richard Megna/Fundamental Photographs, NYC. Page 1013: Martyn F. Chillmaid/Photo Researchers. **Chapter 23** Page 1026: © 2007 Theodore Gray www.periodictable.com. Page 1027 left: Corbis. Page 1027 right: Robert Harding Picture Library Ltd/Alamy. Page 1030: Photo courtesy of Metal Powder Industries Federation. Page 1037: Richard Megna/Fundamental Photographs, NYC. Page 1038: Joseph P. Sinnot/Fundamental Photographs, NYC. Page 1039: Chip Simons/Getty Images. Page 1040 top: Dorling Kindersley Media Library. Page 1040 center: Lester Lefkowitz/Corbis. Page 1040 bottom: Ken Davies/Masterfile. Page 1041: Heatbath Corporation. **Chapter 24** Page 1048 top: Dorling Kindersley Media Library. Page 1048 center row, 1st, 2nd, and 3rd from left: Dorling Kindersley Media Library. Page 1048 center row, 4th from left: Shutterstock. Pages 1058, 1063, 1064, 1067: Richard Megna/Fundamental Photographs, NYC.

Index

Conversion Factors and Relationships

Length
SI unit: meter (m)

1 m	= 1.0936 yd
1 cm	= 0.39370 in
1 in	= 2.54 cm (exactly)
1 km	= 0.62137 mi
1 mi	= 5280 ft
	= 1.6093 km
1 Å	= 10^{-10} m

Temperature
SI unit: kelvin (K)

$$0\,K = -273.15\,°C$$
$$= -459.67\,°F$$
$$K = °C + 273.15$$
$$°C = \frac{(°F - 32)}{1.8}$$
$$°F = 1.8\,(°C) + 32$$

Energy (derived)
SI unit: joule (J)

1 J	= 1 kg·m^2/s^2
	= 0.23901 cal
	= 1 C·V
	= 9.4781×10^{-4} Btu
1 cal	= 4.184 J
1 eV	= 1.6022×10^{-19} J

Pressure (derived)
SI unit: pascal (Pa)

1 Pa	= 1 N/m^2
	= 1 kg/(m·s^2)
1 atm	= 101,325 Pa
	= 760 torr
	= 14.70 lb/in^2
1 bar	= 10^5 Pa
1 torr	= 1 mmHg

Volume (derived)
SI unit: cubic meter (m^3)

1 L	= 10^{-3} m^3
	= 1 dm^3
	= 10^3 cm^3
	= 1.0567 qt
1 gal	= 4 qt
	= 3.7854 L
1 cm^3	= 1 mL
1 in^3	= 16.39 cm^3
1 qt	= 32 fluid oz

Mass
SI unit: kilogram (kg)

1 kg	= 2.2046 lb
1 lb	= 453.59 g
	= 16 oz
1 amu	= $1.66053873 \times 10^{-27}$ kg
1 ton	= 2000 lb
	= 907.185 kg
1 metric ton	= 1000 kg
	= 2204.6 lb

Geometric Relationships

π	= 3.14159 ...
Circumference of a circle	= $2\pi r$
Area of a circle	= πr^2
Surface area of a sphere	= $4\pi r^2$
Volume of a sphere	= $\frac{4}{3}\pi r^3$
Volume of a cylinder	= $\pi r^2 h$

Fundamental Constants

Atomic mass unit	1 amu 1 g	= $1.66053873 \times 10^{-27}$ kg = $6.02214199 \times 10^{23}$ amu
Avogadro's number	N_A	= $6.02214179 \times 10^{23}$/mol
Bohr radius	a_0	= $5.29177211 \times 10^{-11}$ m
Boltzmann's constant	k	= $1.38065052 \times 10^{-23}$ J/K
Electron charge	e	= $1.60217653 \times 10^{-19}$ C
Faraday's constant	F	= 9.64853383×10^4 C/mol
Gas constant	R	= 0.08205821 (L·atm/(mol·K) = 8.31447215 J/(mol·K)
Mass of an electron	m_e	= $5.48579909 \times 10^{-4}$ amu = $9.10938262 \times 10^{-31}$ kg
Mass of a neutron	m_n	= 1.00866492 amu = $1.67492728 \times 10^{-27}$ kg
Mass of a proton	m_p	= 1.00727647 amu = $1.67262171 \times 10^{-27}$ kg
Planck's constant	h	= $6.62606931 \times 10^{-34}$ J·s
Speed of light in vacuum	c	= 2.99792458×10^8 m/s (exactly)

SI Unit Prefixes

a	f	p	n	μ	m	c	d	k	M	G	T	P	E
atto	femto	pico	nano	micro	milli	centi	deci	kilo	mega	giga	tera	peta	exa
10^{-18}	10^{-15}	10^{-12}	10^{-9}	10^{-6}	10^{-3}	10^{-2}	10^{-1}	10^3	10^6	10^9	10^{12}	10^{15}	10^{18}

3

Molecules, Compounds, and Chemical Equations   78

4

Chemical Quantities and Aqueous Reactions   126

Contents

Brief Contents

To Michael, Ali, Kyle, and Kaden

About the Author

Nivaldo Tro is a Professor of Chemistry at Westmont College in Santa Barbara, California, where he has been a faculty member since 1990. He received his Ph.D. in chemistry from Stanford University for work on developing and using optical techniques to study the adsorption and desorption of molecules to and from surfaces in ultrahigh vacuum. He then went on to the University of California at Berkeley, where he did postdoctoral research on ultrafast reaction dynamics in solution. Since coming to Westmont, Professor Tro has been awarded grants from the American Chemical Society Petroleum Research Fund, from Research Corporation, and from the National Science Foundation to study the dynamics of various processes occurring in thin adlayer films adsorbed on dielectric surfaces. He has been honored as Westmont's outstanding teacher of the year three times and has also received the college's outstanding researcher of the year award. Professor Tro lives in Santa Barbara with his wife, Ann, and their four children, Michael, Ali, Kyle, and Kaden. In his leisure time, Professor Tro enjoys mountain biking, surfing, reading to his children, and being outdoors with his family.

Dear Student:

In this course you will be using MasteringChemistry®, an online tutorial and homework program that accompanies your textbook. *If you have joined a MasteringChemistry course before and can still log in*: Save time by following the guide for joining another course (available from www.masteringchemistry.com > Tours & Training > Getting Started) instead of this page.

What You Need:

- ✓ **A valid email address**
- ✓ **A student access code**
  (Comes in the Student Access Code Card/Kit that may have been packaged with your new textbook or that may be available separately in your school's bookstore. Otherwise, you can purchase access online at www.masteringchemistry.com.)
- ✓ **The ZIP or other postal code for your school:** **95823**
- ✓ **A Course ID:** _____ (Provided by your instructor)

1. Register

- Go to www.masteringchemistry.com and click **Students** under **Register**.
- To register using the student access code inside the MasteringChemistry Student Access Code Card/Kit, select **Yes, I have an access code**. Click **Continue**.

  –OR– *Purchase access online*: Select **No, I need to purchase access online now**. Select your textbook, whether you want access to the eText, and click **Continue**. Follow the on-screen instructions to purchase access using a credit card. The purchase path includes registration, but the process is a bit different from the steps printed here.

- **License Agreement and Privacy Policy:** Click **I Accept** to indicate that you have read and agree to the license agreement and privacy policy.
- Select the appropriate option under "Do you have a Pearson Education account?" Continue to give the requested information until you complete the process. The **Confirmation & Summary** page confirms your registration. This information will also be emailed to you for your records. You can either click **Log In Now** or return to www.masteringchemistry.com later.

2. Log In

- Go to www.masteringchemistry.com.
- Enter your Login Name and Password that you specified during registration and click **Log In**.

3. Join Your Instructor's Online Course and/or Open Self-Study Resources

Upon first login, you'll be asked to do one or more of the following:

- **Join a Course** by entering the **MasteringChemistry Course ID** provided by your instructor. If you don't have a Course ID now, you can return to join the MasteringChemistry course later. When you join a course, you may also be asked for a Student ID (follow on-screen instructions).
- **Explore the Study Area** or **Launch Your eText**, if these resources are available for your textbook.

To Access MasteringChemistry Again Later

Simply go to www.masteringchemistry.com, enter your Login Name and Password, and click **Log In**.

After you have joined a course: You can open any assignments from the **Assignments Due Soon** area or from the **Assignments** page. For self-study, click **eText** or **Study Area**, if these options are available.

Support

Access Customer Support at http://www.masteringchemistry.com/support, where you will find:

- System Requirements
- Answers to Frequently Asked Questions
- Registration Tips & Tricks video
- Additional contact information for Customer Support, including Live Chat

ALWAYS LEARNING   PEARSON